ESSCIRC 2008

Proceedings of the
34th European Solid-State Circuits Conference

Edinburgh International Conference Centre
Edinburgh, Scotland, UK

15-19 September 2008

Organised by

IOP Institute of Physics

IOP Institute of Physics

Proceedings sponsored by CSR

Edited by

William Redman-White
Anthony Walton

PROCEEDINGS
OF
ESSDERC
(38th European Solid-State Device Research Conference)
and
ESSCIRC
(34th European Solid-State Circuits Conference)

IEEE Catalog Number   CFP08542-PRT
ISBN: 978-1-4244-2361-3
ISSN: 1930-8833

Proceedings Contents

Foreword

The European Solid-State Circuits Conference (ESSCIRC) and the European Solid-State Device Research Conference (ESSDERC) are recognised as the premier events in the European microelectronics calendar, with long established traditions of high quality presentations covering major aspects of solid-state systems and circuits down to technology and devices. Since 2002, the ESSCIRC and ESSDERC conferences have been organised jointly in recognition of the benefits arising from interaction between the two communities and from the opportunities to participate in presentations from the partner community. Specialists from both communities are able to share perspectives in creating high complexity and high precision systems and circuits within the opportunities and constraints of the latest technological advances

270 high quality submissions were received for the 34th ESSCIRC conference, from contributors in industry and academia in 27 countries. The global impact of the conference is clearly evident with 144 papers coming from Europe, 90 from the Asia-Pacific region, and 34 from the Americas. About 25% of the submissions came from industry, although with a higher success rate in the reviews.

The difficult task of selecting papers for presentation at the conference was the responsibility of the Technical Programme Committee (TPC), made up of 85 experts from industry and academia around the world. After a rigorous review and voting procedure, the TPC selected 111 papers for oral presentation. Papers are organised in three parallel tracks with the aim of maximising choice for delegates between specialist areas, with three sessions held jointly with the ESSDERC programme.

In addition to the contributed papers, the programme has a number of invited plenary papers from internationally recognised technical leaders, addressing subjects of topical interest and debate. Six plenary talks are on wide range of subjects important to both the circuit design and device research communities. The plenary presentations cover technology interfacing for fables design companies, research for the 22nm node, the European position beyond Moore's law, along with flexible electronics, 3D integration and energy scavenging. A further three plenary papers deal with subjects specific to the ESSCIRC community, covering ultra low power biomedical design, the state of the art in audio integration, and SOI design for high performance processors.

In addition to the main conference presentations, there is a comprehensive tutorial programme on the day before, with advanced material for the RF specialist and more broad and accessible coverage of PLLs and filters for the working engineer. At the end of the conference we also have several workshops dealing in depth with issues of technology and design.

The printed proceedings contain full length papers of the invited presentations, followed by the full set of ESSCIRC contributed papers, grouped by technical session. The papers are also available in PDF format together with the papers from ESSDERC on a USB Rom. All the contributed ESSCIRC and ESSDERC papers will shortly become accessible on the IEEE Explore website.

We would like to acknowledge the efforts of all who have contributed to the excellent scientific programme for ESSCIRC 2008. Firstly, thanks go to all the authors for submitting their research. Secondly, we would like to express our gratitude to the members of the TPC for their dedication and commitment in undertaking the reviews and making the final selection that determines the success of the conference. Particular thanks go to the conference secretariat for handling all aspects of this complex event with great competence and efficiency, and for their tireless efforts and dedication.

We look forward to seeing colleagues old and new at the conference this year. We wish all a successful and rewarding time in the excellent scientific programme, and encourage all to join in the opportunities to develop new contacts as well as renew old ones in the many social activities while staying with us in the beautiful and ancient city of Edinburgh

William Redman-White
ESSCIRC 2008
Technical Programme
Committee Chair

Anthony Walton
ESSCIRC 2008
General Chair

Organising Committee
- **Conference Chair**
  Anthony Walton, University of Edinburgh
  Deputy Chair - Peter Ashburn, University of
  Southampton

- **ESSCIRC TPC**
  Chair: William Redman-White, NXP
  Semiconductors/University of Southampton
  Deputy Chair: Robert Henderson, University of
  Edinburgh
  Vice Chair: Yannis Papanaos, NTU Athens

- **ESSDERC TPC**
  Chair: Steve Hall, University of Liverpool
  Deputy Chair: Asen Asenov, University of Glasgow
  Vice Chair: A Dimoulas, IMEL/NCSR Demokritos

Tutorial Chairs
- **ESSCIRC**
  Peter Mole, Intersil

- **ESSDERC**
  Anthony O'Neil, Newcastle University

- **Workshop Chair**
  Anthony O'Neil, Newcastle University

- **ESS-Fringe Poster Chairs**
  A J Snell, University of Edinburgh
  J T M Stevenson, University of Edinburgh

- **Local Chair**
  Les Haworth, University of Edinburgh

Local Organising Committee
Scott Roy, *University of Glasgow*
Rebecca Cheung, *University of Edinburgh*
Tom Stevenson, *University of Edinburgh*
Stewart Smith, *University of Edinburgh*
Jon Terry, *University of Edinburgh*

Steering Committee
Peter Ashburn, *University of Southampton*
Roberto Bez, *ST Microelectronics*
Ralf Brederlow, *Texas Instruments*
Cor Clareys *(Permanet Secretary), IMEC*
Sorin Cristploveanu, *ENSERG-IMEP*
Franz Dielacher, *Infineon*
Christian Enz, *CSEM*
Gaudenzio Meneghesso, *University of Padova*
Hervé Mingam, *ST Microelectronics*
Erneston Perea, *ST Microelectronics*
Hans-Jörg Pfleiderer, *University of Ulm*
William Redman-White, *(Vice Chair) NXP/University of
Southampton*

Doris Schmitt-Landsiedel, *Technical University Munich*
Hannu Tenhunen, *KTH, Stockholm*
Roland Thewes, *Qimonda AG*
Reinout Woltjer *(Chair), NXP*

ESSCIRC Technical Programme Committee
Pietro Andreani, *TU Denmark*
Andrea Baschirotto, *Univ Lecce*
Eric Belhaire, *IEF CNRS Uni Paris*
Didier Belot, *ST*
Marco Berkhout, *NXP*
Alexis Birbas, *Uni Patras*
Ralf Brederlow, *TI*
Werner Brockherde, *Fraunhofer IMS*
Dominique Brunel, *NXP*
Erik Bruun, *TU Denmark*
Klaas Bult, *Broadcom*
Rinaldo Castello, *Uni Pavia*
Andreia Cathelin, *ST*
Sudipo Chakraborty, *TI*
Anantha Chandrakasan, *MIT*
Jan Craninckx, *IMEC*
Jan Crols, *Ansem*
Ian Dedic, *Fujitsu Microelectronics*
Wim Dehaene, *K Uni Leuven*
Andreas Demosthenous, *UCL*
Yann Deval, *IXL Uni Bordeaux*
Christian Enz, *CSEM*
Tobias Gemmeke, *IBM Boeblingen*
Friedel Gerfers, *Acquantia*
Giuseppe Gramegna, *CSR*
Christoph Hagleitner, *IBM Zurich*
Kari Halonen, *Helsinki Uni Tech*
Ralph Hasholzner, *Infineon*
Markus Helfenstein, *NXP Zurich*
Robert Henderson, *Uni Edinburgh*
Luis Hernandez, *Uni Carlos III Madrid*
Qiuting Huang, *ETH Zurich*
Jos Huisken, *Silicon Hive*
Jed Hurwitz, *Gigle Semi, Edinburh*
David Johns, *U Toronto*
Andreas Kaiser, *ISEN Lille*
Maher Kayal, *EPFL*
Peter Kennedy, *University of Cork*
Peter Kinget, *Columbia Uni*
Heinrich Klar, *TU Berlin*
Rudolf Koch, *Infineon*
Masaru Kokubo, *Hitachi*
Per Larsson-Edefors, *Chalmers Uni Technol*
Domine Leenaerts, *NXP Research*
John Long, *TU Delft*
Colin Lyden, *ADI*
Kofi Makinwa, *TU Delft*
Piero Malcovati, *Uni Pavia*
Yiannos Manoli, *Microelectronics, Ini Freiburg*
Hans Juergen Mattausch, *Hiroshima Uni*

Sven Mattisson, *Ericsson*
Peter Mole, *Intersil*
Dominique Morche, *CEA/LETI*
Miki Moyal, *Intel*
Paul Muller, *Marvell*
Bram Nauta, *U Twente*
Tobias Noll, *RWTH Aachen*
Yannis Papananos, *Nat TU Athens*
John Pennock, *Wolfson*
Ian Phillips, *ARM*
Christian Piguet, *CSEM*
Wolfgang Pribyl, *TU Graz*
Patrick Quinn, *Xilinx Dublin*
Bill Redman-White, *NXP*
Angel Rodriguez-Vazquez, *CNEM Seville*
Albrecht Rothermel, *Uni Ulm*
Stefan Rusu, *Intel*
Takayasu Sakurai, *Uni Tokyo*
Willy Sansen, *KU Leuven*
Doris Scmitt-Landsiedel, *TU Munich*
Tadashi Shibata, *Univ Tokyo*
Michiel Steyaert, *KU Leuven*
Jon Strange, *Mediatek*
Hannu Tenhunen, *Royal Inst Technol*
Albert Theuwissen, *Harvest Imaging/Delft University*
Marc Tiebout, *Infieon*
Janez Trontelj, *Uni Lubljana*
Pascal Urard, *ST*
Harry Veendrick, *NXP Research*
Andrei Vladimirescu, *UC Berkeley*
Arthur van Roermund, *TU Eindhoven*
Piet Wambacq, *IMEC*
Hubert Watzinger, *NXP Gratkorn*
Changsik Yoo, *Hanyang Uni*
Horst Zimmermann, *TU Vienna*

Joint Plenary Talks
Nanotechnology for Future High-Speed and Energy-Efficient CMOS Applications
R Chau, *Intel Corporation, USA*

Technology Interfacing for Fabless Semiconductor Companies
V Manian, *Broadcom, USA*

Solving Issues of Integrated Circuits by 3D-Stacking
T Sakurai, *University of Tokyo, Japan*

Printed Electronics for Low-Cost Electronic Systems: Technology Status and Application Development
V Subramanian, *University of California, USA*

More than Moore and More Moore in Europe
M Thompson, *ST Microelectronics, France*

Micropower Energy Scavenging
C van Hoof, *IMEC, Belgium*
ESSCIRC Plenary Talks
Information, Energy, and Entropy: Design Principles for Adaptive, Therapeutic Modulation of Neural Circuits
T Demisen, *Medtronic, USA*

Audio at Low and High Power
M Berkhout, *NXP, NL*

SOI Design for the CELL Processor and Beyond
Y Hagihara, *AIPS/AINS Consortium (formerly with Sony), Japan*

ESSDERC Plenary Talks
The Future of High-Performance CMOS: Trends and Requirements
D Antoniadis, *MIT, USA*

Overview and Future Challenges of Floating Body RAM (FBRAM) Technology for 32nm Technology node and Beyond
T Hamamoto, *Toshiba, Japan*

High Mobility Ge and III-V Materials and Novel Device Structures for High Performance Nanoscale MOSFETS
T Krishnamohan, *Stanford University, USA*

Sponsors

ESSCIRC Table of Contents

A3L-D   RF Building Block

Time: Tuesday, September 16, 2008, 11:20 - 12:50
Place   Tinto
Chair   Marc Tiebout, *Infineon Technologies*

A3L-E   Unconventional Image Sensors and Circuits

Time: Tuesday, September 16, 2008, 11:20 - 12:50
Place   Moorfoot
Chair   Jed Hurwitz, *Gigle Semiconductor*

A3L-F   On-chip digital monitors and regulators

Time: Tuesday, September 16, 2008, 11:20 - 12:50
Place   Kilsyth
Chair   Per Larsson-Edefors, *Chalmers University of Technology*

B3L-D   Oversampled Data Converters

Time: Wednesday, September 17, 2008, 10:40 - 12:20
Place   Tinto
Chair   Piero Malcovati, *University of Pavia*

B3L-E   Memory Design Techniques

Time: Wednesday, September 17, 2008, 10:40 - 12:20
Place   Moorfoot
Chair   Wim Dehaene, *KU Leuven-ESAT*

B5L-E Low Power SRAM

Time: Wednesday, September 17, 2008, 14:40 - 16:00
Place Moorfoot
Chair Tobias Noll, *RWTH Aachen University*

B5L-F Circuit Techniques for UWB

Time: Wednesday, September 17, 2008, 14:40 - 16:00
Place Kilsyth
Chair Jan Craninckx, *IMEC*

B6L-D Amplifiers

Time: Wednesday, September 17, 2008, 16:30 - 17:50
Place Tinto
Chair Marco Berkhout, *NXP*

C2L-F   Impulse UWB Recievers

Time:	Thursday, September 18, 2008, 09:30 - 10:50
Place	Kilsyth
Chair	Kari Halonen, *Helsinki University of Technology*

C3L-D   Low-Power Analogue

Time:	Thursday, September 18, 2008, 11:20 - 12:40
Place	Tinto
Chair	Ralf Brederlow, *Texas instruments Deutschland GmbH*

C3L-E   Multi-Standard RF

Time:	Thursday, September 18, 2008, 11:20 - 12:40
Place	Moorfoot
Chair	Peter Kennedy, *University College Cork*

C3L-F   Short Range Low Data Rate Wireless Communications

Time:	**Thursday, September 18, 2008, 11:20 - 12:40**
Place	**Kilsyth**
Chair	**Christian Enz, *CSEM***

C6L-D   Sensor Interface Circuits

Time:	**Thursday, September 18, 2008, 16:10 - 17:50**
Place	**Tinto**
Chair	**Kofi Makinwa, *Delft University of Technology***

C6L-E High-Speed Digital Circuits and Systems

Time: Thursday, September 18, 2008, 16:10 - 17:50
Place Moorfoot
Chair Hannu Tenhunen, *KTH-Stockholm*

C6L-F RF Power Amplifiers and Radar

Time: Thursday, September 18, 2008, 16:10 - 17:50
Place Kilsyth
Chair Braum Nauta, *University of Twente*

Notes

Emerging Device Nanotechnology for Future High-Speed and Energy-Efficient VLSI: Challenges and Opportunities

Robert S. Chau

Components Research, Technology and Manufacturing Group
Intel Corporation
Mailstop: RA3-252, 5200 N.E. Elam Young Parkway, Hillsboro, OR 97124, USA
robert.s.chau@intel.com

Abstract—**Emerging device nanotechnologies as well as their integration on large silicon wafers present both challenges and opportunities for future high-speed and energy-efficient digital VLSI applications.**

Since the early 2000's, the silicon industry has been exploring many new electronic materials and incorporating them into silicon CMOS transistors to boost their device performance and enhance their energy efficiency. For instance, since the 90nm technology node, silicon germanium has been used to replace silicon to form the source and drain regions of the PMOS transistor in order to induce uni-axial compressive strain in the silicon channel, thereby increasing hole mobility and improving device performance [1]. In the current 45nm technology node, which started volume production in late 2007, hafnium-based high-K gate dielectric and dual band-edge work-function metal gate electrodes are used to replace SiO_2/polysilicon as the gate stacks of CMOS transistors to increase device performance while reducing gate leakage significantly [2]. This change in the gate stack materials has been considered as the biggest change to the silicon transistor in 40 years [3]. Going forward, it is expected that this trend of incorporating more new materials into CMOS transistors will continue, and that more non-silicon materials will be integrated onto the silicon substrate in future technology nodes.

Recently there has been much interest generated and good progress made in the research of non-silicon materials to replace silicon as the future transistor channel material, and their integration onto the silicon platform. Among the materials studied are Ge [4], low band-gap III-V compound semiconductors [5-8], carbon nanotubes [9], graphene [10], semiconductor nanowires [11] and so on. These materials, in general, have significantly higher intrinsic (p or n) mobility

compared to silicon, thus they have the potential for enabling future high speed transistors for digital applications at very low supply voltages. For example, the p-channel single-walled CNT field-effect transistors have exhibited some interesting and useful characteristics, as shown in Figure 1 [12]. However, like other "bottom-up" chemically synthesized materials, CNTs are currently suffering from the fundamental placement problem as there is no practical way to precisely align and position them. This problem needs to be solved before CNTs find many practical applications in VLSI nanelectronics. Graphene transistors, on the other hand, can be formed and patterned using "top-down" techniques. However simulation results show that graphene has significantly lower mobility compared to CNT at matched bandgap, and that it requires a narrow device width to open up its bandgap for low power transistor applications (e.g. <4nm widths are required to achieve bandgaps >0.2eV) [13].

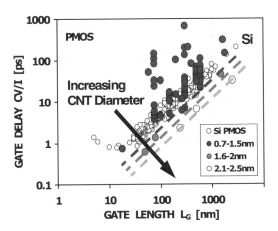

Figure 1. Intrinsic gate delay of the p-channel CNT transistors compared with standard silicon p-ch MOSFETs. Electrical characteristics of CNT are related to its tube diameter which in turn is related to its bandgap [ref. 12].

Of all these non-Si materials, Ge and III-V compound semiconductors are the most studied, with the later having been used in commercial communication and optoelectronic products for a long time. Among the III-V systems of interest, InSb quantum well has the highest electron mobility of 20,000-30,000 $cm^2V^{-1}s^{-1}$ at sheet carrier density of 1.3 x 10^{12} cm^{-2}, while InGaAs quantum well has electron mobility of 10,000 $cm^2V^{-1}s^{-1}$ at sheet carrier density of 3.5 x 10^{12} cm^{-2}. Both InSb and InGaAs quantum-well field effect transistors (QWFETs) show significantly improved transistor energy-delay product, which is related to the energy efficiency of the transistor, over standard silicon n-channel MOSFETs, as shown in Figure 2 [14].

N Channel
ENERGYxDELAY/WIDTH [Js/m]
10^-17
10^-19
10^-21
10^-23
10
100
1000
10000
GATE LENGTH [nm]
Si MOSFETs
InGaAs/InAlAs
InSb/InAlSb

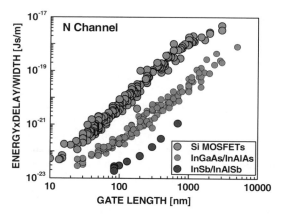

Figure 2. Normalized energy-delay product of n-channel InSb and InGaAs quantum-well transistors compared with that of standard silicon MOSFETs [ref. 14]

For III-V compound semiconductors to become applicable for future high-speed and low-power digital applications, they will need to be integrated onto large silicon wafers. A seamless, robust heterogeneous integration scheme of III-V on silicon will allow high-speed, low-voltage III-V based transistors to couple with the mainstream Si CMOS platform, while avoiding the need for developing large diameter ($\geq$ 300mm) III-V substrates. Besides transistor applications, successful integration of III-V on silicon can open up opportunities for integrating new functionalities and features on silicon, such as integrating logic, optoelectronic and communication platforms on the same silicon wafer. However, heterogeneous integration of III-V on silicon imposes many significant technical challenges because of the large lattice mismatch between the two materials. A metamorphic composite buffer layer with graded III-V compositions, such as the one shown in Figure 3 [8], will need to be inserted between the silicon substrate and the final III-V quantum-well device layer as an effective filter for containing defects without degrading the quantum-well device properties such as carrier mobility. The roles of this composite buffer include minimizing anti-phase domains, bridging the lattice constants, relaxing strain energy and gliding dislocations, eliminating parallel conduction, providing large conduction band-edge discontinuity and inducing strain to the quantum-well device layer. It also needs to be sufficiently thin for cost reduction and ease of integration with Si CMOS transistors on the same silicon wafer.

n++-In0.53Ga0.47As contact : 20 nm
InP etch stop : 6 nm
In0.52Al0.48As top barrier : 8 nm
Si delta-doped layer
In0.52Al0.48As spacer layer : 5 nm
In0.7Ga0.3As channel : 13 nm
In0.52Al0.48As bottom barrier : 100 nm
InxAl1-xAs graded buffer (x=0-0.52): 0.7-1.1 µm
GaAs nucleation and buffer layer: 0.5-2.0 µm
4°(100) Offcut p-type Si substrate
Metamorphic buffer

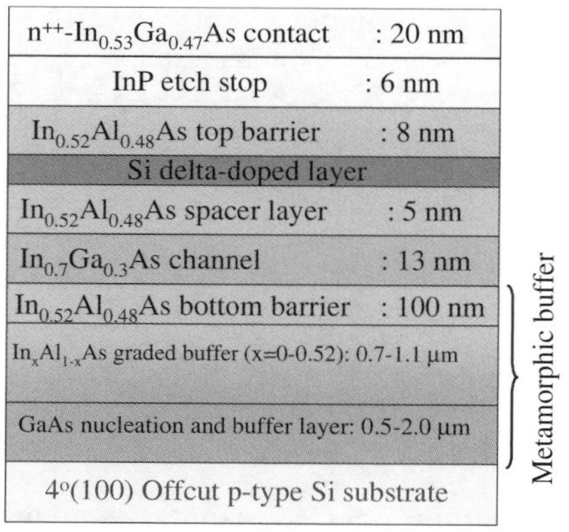

Figure 3. Heterogeneous integration of the InGaAs QWFET device layer on silicon substrate using metamorphic composite buffer architecture [ref. 8].

Recently $In_{0.7}Ga_{0.3}As$ quantum-well device structures have been successfully integrated onto silicon using the above composite metamorphic buffer architecture with total buffer thickness scaled down to 1.3μm, resulting in high-performance 80nm enhancement-mode $In_{0.7}Ga_{0.3}As$ QWFETs on silicon with transistor characteristics shown in Figure 4 [8]. Compared to the silicon n-channel MOSFET reference, the 80nm enhancement-mode $In_{0.7}Ga_{0.3}As$ QWFET on Si exhibits more than 10X reduction in DC power dissipation for the same speed performance, or more than 2X gain in speed performance for the same power, as shown in Figure 5 [8, 14].

While III-V QWFETs have shown some very attractive and tangible merits, many technical challenges need to be overcome before they will become practical for future high-speed and low-power digital applications. For instance, due to the lack of a stable gate dielectric, currently all of these quantum-well devices use a direct Schottky metal gate, which results in a large parasitic gate leakage. A gate dielectric stack which is compatible with III-V materials will be needed to solve this problem. Also, the formation of an unpinned dielectric/semiconductor interface has been particularly challenging for III-V materials and it is critical towards achieving III-V devices with correct transistor threshold voltages. Another challenge is the low hole mobility in III-V and the lack of a viable p-channel device strategy for the CMOS configuration, which is required for low power applications. One proposed solution involves improving hole mobility in III-V by incorporating bi-axial strain [15] and/or uni-axial strain in the device quantum-well channel. Another alternative is to explore the use of other materials with high hole mobility, such as Ge quantum-well systems [16], for the p-channel transistor. Yet another challenge is the scalability of III-V devices. Like silicon CMOS transistors, the III-V transistor may also need a non-planar device structure to improve its electrostatics with scaling [17,18].

In summary, emerging device nanotechnologies (e.g. carbon nanotubes, nanowires, graphene, III-V quantum-well devices and so on) and their integration onto silicon present both challenges and opportunities for future high-speed and energy-efficient digital VLSI applications.

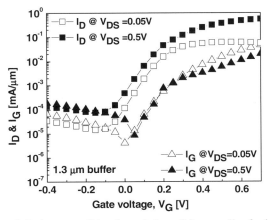

Figure 4. Drain current (I_D) and gate leakage (I_G) versus V_G of enhancement-mode L_G=80nm $In_{0.7}Ga_{0.3}As$ QWFET on Si with 1.3μm composite buffer at room temperature [ref. 8].

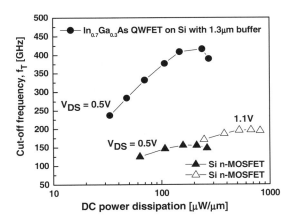

Figure 5. Cut-off frequency versus DC power dissipation for the enhancement-mode L_G=80nm $In_{0.7}Ga_{0.3}As$ QWFET on Si with 1.3μm composite buffer at V_{DS}=0.5V, versus standard Si n-MOSFET with L_G = 60nm at V_{DS}=0.5V and 1.1V [refs. 8, 14].

REFERENCES

[1] T. Ghani et al., "A 90nm High Volume Manufacturing Logic Technology Featuring Novel 45nm Gate Length Strained Silicon CMOS Transistors," International Electron Devices Meeting (IEDM) Technical Digest, 2003, pp. 978-980.

[2] K. Mistry et al., "A 45nm Logic Technology with High-K+Metal Gate Transistors, Strained Silicon, 9 Cu Interconnect Layers, 193nm Dry Patterning, and 100% Pb-free Packaging," International Electron Devices Meeting (IEDM) Technical Digest, 2007, pp. 247-250.

[3] M.T. Bohr et al., "The High-k Solution," IEEE Spectrum, Oct 2007, pp. 29-35.

[4] Y. Kamata, "High-k/Ge MOSFETs for future nanoelectronics," Materials Today, Vol. 11, No. 1-2, Jan-Feb 2008, pp. 30-38.

[5] S. Datta et al., "85nm Gate Length Enhancement and Depletion mode InSb Quantum Well Transistors for Ultra High Speed and very Low Power Digital Logic Applications," International Electron Devices Meeting (IEDM) Technical Digest, 2005, pp. 783-786.

[6] T. Ashley et al., "Heterogeneous InSb quantum well transistors on silicon for ultra-high speed, low power logic applications," Electronics Letters, Vol. 43, No. 14, July 2007.

[7] D-H. Kim and J. del Alamo, "Logic Performance of 40nm InAs HEMTs," International Electron Devices Meeting (IEDM) Technical Digest, 2007, pp. 629-632.

[8] M.K. Hudait et al., "Heterogeneous Integration of Enhancement Mode $In_{0.7}Ga_{0.3}As$ Quantum Well Transistor on Silicon Substrate using Thin ($\leq$ 2um) Composite Buffer Architecture for High-Speed and Low-Voltage (0.5V) Logic Applications," International Electron Devices Meeting (IEDM) Technical Digest, 2007, pp. 625-628.

[9] S.J. Wind et al., "Vertical Scaling of Carbon Nanotube Field-Effect Transistors Using Top Gate Electrodes," Appl. Phys. Lett., Vol. 80, 2002, pp.3817-3819.

[10] W. A. de Heer et al., " Pionics: the Emerging Science and Technology of Graphene-based Nanoelectronics," International Electron Devices Meeting (IEDM) Technical Digest, 2007, pp. 199-202.

[11] M. Lieber, "Nanowires as Building Blocks for Nanoelectronics and Nanophotonics," International Electron Devices Meeting (IEDM) Technical Digest, 2003, pp. 300-302.

[12] R. Chau et al., "Integrated nanoelectronics for the future," Nature Materials, Vol. 6, Nov 2007, pp. 810-812.

[13] B. Obradovic, R. Kotlyar, F. Heinz, P. Matagne, T. Rakshit, M.D. Giles, M.A. Stettler, D.E. Nikonov, "Analysis of graphene nanoribbons as a channel material for field-effect transistors," Applied Physics Letters, Vol. 88, 2006, 142102.

[14] R. Chau, " III-V on Silicon for Future High-Speed and Ultra-Low Power Digital Applications: Challenges and Opportunities," Digest of papers, Compound Semiconductor Mantech, 2008, pp. 15-18.

[15] J.B. Boos et al., "High mobility p-channel HFETs using strained Sb-based materials," Electronics Letters, Vol. 43 No. 15, July 2007.

[16] M. Myronov et al., "Observation of two-dimensional hole gas with mobility and carrier density exceeding those of two-dimensional electron gas at room temperature in the SiGe heterostructures," Applied Physics Letters, Vol. 91, 2007, 082108.

[17] R. Chau et al., "Advanced depleted-substrate transistors: single-gate, double-gate and tri-gate," Ext. Abst. 2002 Int. Conf. Solid State Devices & Materials, Nagoya, Japan, pp. 68-69.

[18] J. Kavalieros et al., "Tri-Gate Transistor Architecture with High-k Gate Dielectrics, Metal Gates and Strain Engineering," VLSI Tech. Dig., 2006, pp. 62-63.

Micropower Energy Scavenging

P. Fiorini, I. Doms, C. Van Hoof
Integrated Systems, IPSI Department
IMEC
Leuven, Belgium

R. Vullers
WATS Division
IMEC-NL, Holst Centre
Eindhoven, the Netherlands

Abstract—**More than a decade of research in the field of thermal, motion, and vibrational energy scavenging has yielded increasing power output and smaller embodiments. Power management circuits for rectification and DC-DC conversion are becoming able to efficiently convert the power from these energy scavengers. This paper summarizes recent energy scavenging results and their power management circuits.**

I. INTRODUCTION

The low power consumption of silicon-based electronics combined with the significant power densities of modern primary or rechargeable batteries has enabled a broad variety of battery-powered handheld, wearable and even implantable devices. A range of devices powered by batteries and spanning six orders of magnitude power consumption are shown in Table 1, with their typical power consumption and their energy autonomy. All these devices need a compact, low-cost and lightweight energy source, which enables the desired portability and achieves a certain level of energy autonomy. In the 100uW range power consumption, wearable wireless sensor nodes are situated.

Emerging wireless sensors are finding growing application in body area networks and health monitoring of machine, industrial and civil structures. This paper focuses on emerging methods for power generation and power management of these wireless autonomous transducers systems that can enable energy autonomy over the entire lifetime of the device. Particularly for wireless applications, this is essential as battery replacement or remote charging is unpractical or simply not feasible. Simply increasing the size of the battery to ensure energy autonomy during the lifetime of the system would increase system size and cost beyond what is tolerable. As a consequence, there is a clear need for alternative methods for powering these sensor nodes, as a major increase in the energy density of batteries is not expected. One possible solution is harvesting energy from the ambient by using for example vibrational energy, thermal energy or light. In Fig. 1 a comparison is made for several battery systems and how energy harvesting could improve the autonomy. A battery volume of 1cm³ is assumed.

TABLE I. SELECTED BATTERY-OPERATED SYSTEMS

	Device Type	
	Power Consumption	*Energy Autonomy*
Smartphone	1W	5 hours
MP3 player	50mW	15 hours
Hearing Aid	1mW	5 days
Wearable Sensor Node	100uW	Lifetime
Cardiac Pacemaker	50uW	7 years
Quartz watch	5uW	5 years

If the power consumption of the system is approximately 100µW, the lifetime of a primary battery is only a few months. The combination of a rechargeable battery and an energy harvester with a power generation of 100µW is shown for comparison. In such case, the harvester ensures power for the whole lifetime of the system and could be combined with thin-film rechargeable battery or a super capacitor. The energy density of batteries has increased a factor of 3 over the past 15 years, and dramatic improvements are not expected in the coming years.

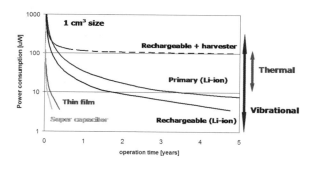

Figure 1. Effect of energy harvesters on the operational lifetime of battery-powered systems.

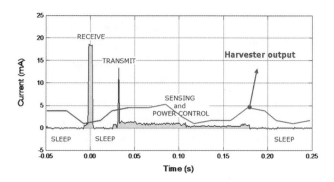

Figure 2. A typical scenario for the power consumption of a sensor node. Since the consumption does not equally match the harvester output, an energy buffer (energy storage system) and power management IC in between is necessary.

Abolishing the battery altogether is not an option in most cases. In practice, a wireless sensor node needs a wireless transceiver. The peak currents needed during transmit and receive operation go beyond what is achievable using the scavenger alone (see Fig. 2). Furthermore, buffering is also needed to ensure continuous operation during times without power generation. Depending on the application, the energy storage system can be a battery or a supercapacitor.

Table II summarizes the output power that could be obtained from environmental sources when using optimized devices built with the currently available transducer technology. While industrial environments seem to have energy to spare, around the body energy is far more limited. In the following the different harvesting devices are discussed in more details and examples from the literature are given.

TABLE II.   CHARACTERISTICS OF VARIOUS ENERGY SOURCES AVAILABLE IN THE AMBIENT AND HARVESTED POWER

Source	Device Type	
	Source Characteristics	*Harvested Power*
Photovoltaic		
Indoor	0.1mW/cm2	10 µW/cm2
Outdoor	100mW/cm2	10mW/cm2
Vibration/motion		
Human	0.5m@1Hz 1m/s2@50Hz	4 µW/cm2
Industrial	1m@5Hz 10m/s2@1kHz	100 µW/cm2
Thermal Energy		
Human	20mW/cm2	30µW/cm2
Industrial	100 mW/cm2	1-10mW/cm2
RF		
Cell phone	0.3 µW/cm2	0.1 µW /cm2

II. ENERGY SCAVENGING APPROACHES

A.   Harvesting Energy from Motion and Vibrations

For converting motion or vibration, the established transduction mechanisms are electrostatic, piezoelectric or electromagnetic and their working principles are as follows. In electrostatic transducers, the distance or overlap of two electrodes of a polarized capacitor changes due to the movement or of the vibration of one movable electrode. This motion causes a voltage change across the capacitor and results in a current flow in an external circuit. In piezoelectric transducers, vibrations or movement cause the deformation of a piezoelectric capacitor thereby generating a voltage. In electromagnetic transducers, the relative motion of a magnetic mass with respect to a coil causes a change in the magnetic flux. This generates an AC voltage across the coil.

If the energy source is a slow, long-stroke movement, it may be possible to anchor one of the two parts of the transducer to a fixed reference and the other to the source of movement [1]. In most cases however this is not possible and the principle of inertia has to be used: one part of the transducer is fixed to a frame and the other is inserted inside the frame and can move inside it. The frame is attached to the moving or vibrating object and relative motion of the parts of the transducer is controlled by the law of inertia. This approach is the most widely used for harvesting energy from vibrations [2]; in most cases the system is made resonant by means of suspending the moveable part to a spring. It can also be used for motion energy harvesters [3,4] in which case no spring is used and a non-resonant system is the result.

Resonant vibration harvesters are by far the most widely investigated harvesting devices in the literature. Fine-machined versions are the earliest emerging commercial energy harvesting devices while micromachined versions on the other hand are far less mature. Their power levels need to be raised, reliability needs to be achieved, and cost-effective production has to be established.

In a first and rather crude approximation, resonant harvesters can be treated as a mass spring system. It has been shown [2] that in this case the maximum power P is obtained at the resonance frequency f and is given by (1) where Y is the amplitude of the external vibrations and z_{max} the maximum possible displacement inside the frame.

$$P = 4\pi^3 m f^3 Y z_{max} \qquad (1)$$

It is also shown that the same maximum power can be obtained from non-resonant systems having the same physical characteristics [5]. In principle this optimum power can be achieved with any type of transducer [6], but, depending on the transducer type it is delivered at different voltages. With typically available vibrations, the output voltage tends to be too low in the case of electromagnetic transducers and too high for electrostatic transducers.

Let us first consider micromachined harvesters. From a process perspective, the electrostatic and piezoelectric harvesters are easy to fabricate and devices with lateral sizes between 1mm and 10mm have been reported in literature. Most electromagnetic harvesters on the other hand have been fabricated using a combination of micromachining and mechanical tooling techniques because the creation of coils with sufficient windings is not compatible with planar microfabrication. As a consequence the electromagnetic energy harvesting devices are large and therefore also generate more power.

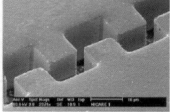

Figure 3.   Example electrostatic energy harvesters from [9] and [10].

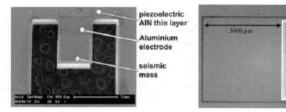

Figure 4.   Example piezoelectric energy harvesters from [12] and [13].

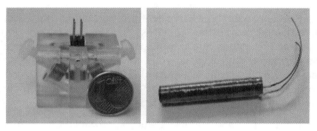

Figure 5.   Example electromagnetic energy harvesters from [16] and [3].

A completely micromachined electromagnetic energy harvester has been presented in [7], but generated only 150nW produced by an acceleration of 0.4g at 8 kHz. It is beyond the scope of this review to describe all devices reported in literature. Representative results are summarized in Fig. 3, Fig. 4 and Fig. 5 for electrostatic, piezoelectric and electro-magnetic energy harvesters respectively and results can be found in [8-16]. Electrostatic harvesters evolved from the initially reported 12nW for a 2mm³ device [8], to 2.4 µW for a 3cm² device [9] and more recently 12 µW for a 1cm² device [10]. Piezoelectric harvesters results achieved 2µW [12], 3µW [11] and 40 µW [13]. A comparison is not obvious as the sizes, resonance frequencies and vibration conditions are different. Macroscopic electromagnetic harvesters achieved 300µW for 3-5cm² devices [3, 16].

B.   Harvesting energy from temperature differences

Thermal energy harvesters are based on the Seebeck effect. Their core element is a thermopile, formed by a large number of thermocouples placed between a hot and a cold plate. The thermocouples are thermally connected in parallel and electrically in series. The generator may include a radiator

for efficient dissipation of heat in the ambient and specific structures aimed to increase thermal isolation between the hot and cold plate.

If α is the Seebeck coefficient of the thermocouples and n is their number, the voltage developed is given by (2).

$$\Delta V = n \, \alpha \, \Delta T \qquad (2)$$

In (2) ΔT is the temperature difference between the hot and cold plate. The efficiency of a thermoelectric device is determined by the material properties which are combined in a figure of merit ZT given by (3).

$$ZT = \alpha^2 T \sigma / \kappa \qquad (3)$$

In (3) T is the absolute temperature, σ is the electrical conductivity and κ the thermal conductivity.

The most widely used material for the fabrication of thermoelectric generators operating at room temperature is BiTe, which exhibits a ZT of 1. PolySiGe (ZT=0.12) has also been used, especially for micromachined thermoelectric generators [17, 18]. Research on nanostructured materials and multilayers is ongoing worldwide in order to optimize thermoelectric properties and ZT values as large as 3.5 have been reported [19]. These encouraging results may replace BiTe in the long term. Apart from improving the material properties, miniaturization using micromachining is ongoing [17, 18, 20] and the main challenges of micromachined energy harvesters are listed in [21]. Selected device results reported in literature [17-25] are shown in Fig. 6. The reported power levels however cannot be directly compared, as output values are often calculated using a well-defined temperature drop across the thermopile (i.e. the temperatures of both plates have been fixed). In real applications the temperature drop across the thermopile is lower than the one between the hot plate and the ambient, and therefore the extrapolated results are too optimistic. It has been shown that the most challenging task in designing an efficient thermoelectric converter consists in maximizing this temperature drop across the thermopiles [22].

Figure 6.   Example thermoelectric energy harvesters from [20] and [25].

C.   Photovoltaic harvesting

Photovoltaic cells convert incoming photons into electricity. Outdoor they are an obvious energy source for self-powered systems. Efficiencies range from 5% to 30%, depending on the material used. Indoor the illumination levels are much lower (100 to 1000µW/cm²) and photovoltaic cells generate a surface power density similar or slightly larger than that of the harvesters described above. As photovoltaic technology is well developed it will not be discussed here. The indoor use requires a fine-tuning of the cell design to the different spectral composition of the light and the lower level of illumination.

D. RF energy harvesting

It is in principle possible to use existing electromagnetic radiation, like the one generated by cell phones, radio transmitters, WiFi equipment, but this solution is not viable except in specific locations. First the available energy density is low (typically $\mu W/cm^2$), and second it is not always desirable, or even legally allowed, to block radiation (e.g. for emergency calls).

A second possibility consists in using a dedicated broadcasting device, which can power sensors in its proximity. A point of concern is the maximum power that is allowed to be transmitted into the environment, which is typically 1W. This solution has been able to power wireless sensor networks in some cases, but it is more a wireless energy distribution system than a harvesting device and it will therefore also not be discussed further in this paper.

III. MICROPOWER POWER MANAGEMENT

A. General concepts

The output of an energy scavenger is not directly suited as power supply for circuits because of variations in its power and voltage over time, and a power management circuit is required. This power management unit should be able to handle very low feeding power and be able to adapt its input to the energy scavenger and its output to the load. It should also be self-starting, which is not trivial. If the power generated is of the order of milliWatts, an efficient power management system is easy to construct. In the $100\mu W$ range however it is highly non-trivial to construct an efficient system.

Scavengers can be categorized in two groups. Thermoelectric generators and solar cells generate a variable DC-output voltage. They require a DC-DC-converter with a variable conversion factor and a controller to provide the battery or the electronics with the correct bias. Vibration and RF energy scavengers on the other hand produce an AC-output voltage. These scavengers require first a rectifying AC-DC-converter stage.

Furthermore, each energy scavenger has an operation point where the extracted electrical energy is maximum. This maximum power point depends on the individual properties of the energy scavenger. Maximum power is achieved by adapting the input impedance to the maximum power point of the scavenger. A controller is required to do this. Finally, when the scavenger generates less energy than the energy used by the controller and the converters, the power management system has to shut down and ensure that it does not discharge

the output. When there is again sufficient power available, the power management system has to start up again autonomously. Finally, a battery management circuit can be needed to ensure safe operating conditions when a battery is charged at the output.

The figure of merit of a DC-DC converter is its efficiency, which is the fraction of the input power that is available at the output. DC-DC converters can be boost converters or charge pumps. Boost converters have a high efficiency and a flexible conversion factor. Most DC-DC-converters use an external inductor for a high efficiency. Boost converters with integrated inductors have a lower efficiency because large value inductors cannot be realized monolithically. An alternative solution is the use of charge pumps [27] with switched capacitors. This allows obtaining efficient DC-DC-conversion for very low power in a small volume.

Different configurations for DC-DC-conversion with switching capacitors exist, for example the voltage doubler, the Dickson charge pump [26], the ring converter and the Fibonacci type converter. The conversion factor of a charge pump is less flexible than the one of a boost converter with inductors. Furthermore, charging and discharging of the switching capacitors results in a circuit that cannot be totally lossless, even when using ideal components. A Dickson charge pump with n stages where the clock amplitude equals V_{in} is studied in [28].

B. Power Management methods

1) Thermal power management circuits

This section summarizes selected discrete and integrated power management circuits reported in literature.

Our earliest autonomous systems were powered by thermoelectric generators and featured discrete components. The system consists of two stages. The first stage, the charging circuit, is an ideal diode that has no voltage drop and consists of a MOS-switch with a comparator across it. This 'diode' is followed by a boost converter with a high efficiency. The control circuit consumes 16 μW, and the circuit is designed to work with a 100 μW at the input [29].

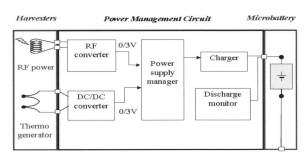

Figure 7. Schematic power management circuit capable of handling RF energy and thermal energy [31].

As some thermal harvesters generate very low voltages, associated power management [30] focused on low-voltage startup. The reported circuit can start working from an input voltage of 0.13V and is designed to transfer approximately 2mW. The control power is as high as 0.4mW, but in view of the milliWatts generated this is manageable. A power management circuit for two sources of power was presented by [31] and is shown schematically in Fig. 7. It is able to convert thermally harvested power and RF power. For thermal power management, an integrated boost converter with an external inductor was used. The circuit consumes 70μW and can transfer approximately 1mW. In 2008, a power management circuit for very low power application was demonstrated [32]. It is shown in Fig. 8 and it is self-starting above 0.76V and a charge pump is used as DC-DC converter. As no external passives are needed, this circuit can be monolithic. The controller consumes only 2.1 μW which makes this circuit suitable for ultra-low power energy systems.

2) *Vibrational power management*

When using vibrational energy, an AC voltage is generated. Therefore, the input voltage of the power management system can also be negative. As most types of load cannot handle negative voltages, the circuit has to perform rectification and also an adjustment of the DC-level of the voltage. In the seminal work by Shenck and Paradiso [1] a complete power management system was presented. Rectification is performed by a regular diode bridge which was suitable given the high voltages generated. A linear regulator was used for voltage regulation which leads to a low efficiency for the DC-DC-converter. The control circuit consumes only 15μA.

The power output can be further optimized by doing a joint mechanical and electrical system optimization. In [33] a piezoelectric power management system reverses the potential across the piezoelectric cantilever when it is at its maximum. This way more mechanical power needs to be delivered during the next cycle which leads to a higher output power and a higher output voltage. This system increases the harvested power by 150%. This demonstrates that joint electro-mechanical optimization is needed to optimize the power output from energy harvesters.

Resonant piezoelectric power management circuits that achieve a peak efficiency of 70% are presented in [34]. Control power is only 0.6μW.

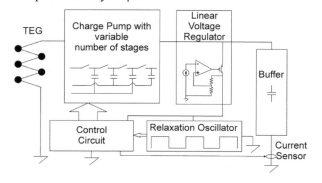

Figure 8. Block diagram of the capacitive charge pump based power management circuit for converting thermoelectric power [32].

As most AC-DC-converters use diodes, the voltage drop across them introduces losses. To achieve a higher efficiency, rectification based on switches has been proposed. The switches have a lower voltage drop because transistors substitute diodes. A discrete embodiment was reported by [29] and an integrated circuit power management system by [35]. Overall, this circuit shows an efficiency that can be higher than 90%. For a specific multi-phase piezoelectric energy harvester [36], an integrated full-wave rectifier reported peak efficiency as high as 98%.

3) *RF power management*

The overall design of a power management circuits for RF [31] and vibration scavenger are similar. The main difference is that reduction of the power losses due to the voltage drop across the diodes cannot be avoided by using switches. Due to the high frequency, the comparators have to switch very fast, thus increasing switching losses.

IV. CONCLUSIONS

This paper summarized energy harvesting components and their associated power management circuits. A decade of research has increased power levels and first industrially viable systems are emerging. Progress in micromachined embodiments is clearly visible but these systems still need to demonstrate reliability and cost-effective production. Power management circuits for these micropower sources have received comparatively little attention. A summary of recent circuits is given.

This report summarizes contributions to a document on energy harvesting for autonomous systems made in the framework of the MEDEA+ working group on Energy Autonomous Systems (WG-EAS).

BIBLIOGRAPHY

[1] N.S. Shenck J.A. Paradiso, "Energy Scavenging with Shoe-Mounted Piezoelectrics", *IEEE Micro* **21** 30-42, 2001.

[2] P.D. Mitcheson T.C. Green, E.M. Yeatman and A.S Holmes, "Architectures for Vibration-driven Micropower", *Journal of MEMS* **13**, IEEE/ASME, pp. 429-440, 2004.

[3] M. Renaud, P. Fiorini and C. Van Hoof, "Optimization of a piezoelectric unimorph for shock and impact energy harvesting", Smart Mater. Struct. 16 1125-1135,2007.

[4] T. Sterken, P. Fiorini, R. Puers, "Motion-based generators for industrial applications", Proceedings of the International Conference on Design, Test, Integration and Packaging of MEMS/MOEMS – DTIP 26-04-2006 Stresa (Italy) pp. 328-331.

[5] M. Renaud, T. Sterken, P. Fiorini, R. Puers, K. Baert, C. Van Hoof, "Scavenging energy from human-body: design of a piezoelectric transducer", in Proceedings of the 13th Int. Conf. On Solid-State Sensors, Actuators and Microsystems – Transducers 2005, 5-9 june 2005 Seoul(Korea) pp. 784,787.

[6] T. Sterken, K. Baert, C. Van Hoof, R. Puers, G. Borghs, P. Fiorini, "Comparative modeling for vibration scavengers", Proceedings of IEEE Sensors Conference Vienna (Austria) 24 -26 Oct. 2004 pp. 1249-1252.

[7] S. Kulkarni, E. Koukharenko, J. Tudor, S. Beeby, T. O'Donnell, S. Roy, "Fabrication and Test of Integrated Micro-Scale Vibration Based Electromagnetic Generator", Int.   Conf. on Solid-State Sensors,

Actuators and Microsystems, 2007. TRANSDUCERS 2007. 10-14 June 2007, pp. 879 – 882.

[8] T. Sterken, P. Fiorini, K. Baert, R. Puers, G. Borghs, "An electret-based electrostatic micro-generator", in Proceedings of the 12th Int. Conf. On Solid-State Sensors, Actuators and Microsystems – Transducers 2003 08-12 June 2003 Boston(USA), pp. 1291-1294.

[9] P. Miao, P. D. Mitcheson, A. S. Holmes, E. M. Yeatman, T. C. Green, B. H. Stark, "MEMS inertial power generators for biomedical applications" Microsyst Technol (2006) 12, pp. 1079–1083.

[10] G. Despesse, J.J. Chaillout, T. Jager, F. Cardot, A. Hoogerwerf, "Innovative Structure for Mechanical Energy Scavenging", Int. Conf. on Solid-State Sensors, Actuators and Microsystems, TRANSDUCERS 2007. 10-14 June 2007, pp. 895 – 898.

[11] P. Glynne-Jones, S.P. Beeby, E.P. James , N.M. White, "The Modelling of a Piezoelectric Vibration Powered Generator for Microsystems", Int. Conf. On Solid-State Sensors, Actuators and Microsystems, 2001. TRANSDUCERS 2001. 10-14 June 2001.

[12] M. Marzencki, Y. Ammar, S. Basrour, "Integrated Power Harvesting System Including a MEMS Generator and a Power Management Circuit", Int. Conf. on Solid-State Sensors, Actuators and Microsystems, 2007. TRANSDUCERS 2007, 10-14 June 2007, pp. 887 – 890.

[13] M. Renaud, T. Sterken, A. Schmitz, P. Fiorini, C. Van Hoof, R. Puers, "Piezoelectric Harvesters and MEMS Technology: Fabrication, Modeling and Measurements", Int. Conf. On Solid-State Sensors, Actuators and Microsystems, 2007. TRANSDUCERS 2007. 10-14 June 2007, pp. 891 – 894.

[14] Neil N. H. Ching, H. Y. Wong2, Wen J. Li, Philip H. W. Leong, and Zhiyu Wen, "A Laser- micromachined Vibrational to Electrical Power Transducer for Wireless Sensing Systems", Int. Conf. On Solid-State Sensors, Actuators and Microsystems, 2001. TRANSDUCERS 2001. 10-14 June 2001.

[15] http://www.perpetuum.co.uk

[16] D. Spreemann, Y. Manoli, B. Folkmer, D. Mintenbeck, " Non- resonant vibration conversion", Journal of Micromechanics and Microengineering Vol.16, pp. S169-73, 2006.

[17] V. Leonov, P. Fiorini, S. Sedky, T. Torfs, C. Van Hoof, "Thermoelectric MEMS generators as a power supply for a body area network", Proceedings of the 13th Int. Conf. On Solid-State Sensors, Actuators and Microsystems – Transducers 2005 05-06-2005 Seoul(Korea), pp. 291-294.

[18] M. Strasser, R. Aigner, C. Lauterbach, T. F. Sturm, M. Franosch and G. Wachutka, "Micromachined CMOS Thermoelectric Generator As On-chip Power Supply", *Sensors and Actuators A*, Vol.114, pp.362-370, 2004.

[19] G. Snyder and E. Toberer, "Complex Thermoelectric Materials", Nature materials Vol **7**(2), February 2008, pp 105-114.

[20] V. Leonov, unpublished. See also: Z. Wang, V. Leonov, P. Fiorini, C. Van Hoof, "Micromachined thermopiles for energy scavenging on

human body", Int. Conf. On Solid-State Sensors, Actuators and Microsystems TRANSDUCERS 2007. 10-14 June 2007, pp. 911-914.

[21] V. Leonov, T. Torfs, P. Fiorini, C. Van Hoof, "Thermoelectric converters of human warmth for self-powered wireless sensor nodes", IEEE Sensors Journal, pp. 650 – 657, 2007.

[22] V. Leonov and P. Fiorini, "Thermal matching of a thermoelectric energy scavenger with the ambient", Proceedings 5th European Conference on Thermoelectrics, 10-12 September 2007 Odessa (Ukraine), pp. 129-133.

[23] http://www.poweredbythermolife.com/thermolife.htm

[24] http://www.nextreme.com/

[25] http://www.micropelt.com/

[26] J.F. Dickson, "On-chip high-voltage generation in MNOS integrated circuits using an improved voltage multiplier technique", IEEE Journal of Solid-State Circuits, vol. 11(3), pp. 374-378, June 1976.

[27] I. Doms, P. Merken, C. Van Hoof, "Comparison of DC-DC-converter Architectures of Power Management Circuits for Thermoelectric Generators", Proceedings of 2007 European Conference on Power Electronics and Applications, pp. 1-5.

[28] H. Shao, C-Y. Tsui, W-H. Ki; "An Inductor-less Micro Solar Power Management System Design for Energy Harvesting Applications", Proceedings of ISCAS 2007, pp. 1353-1356.

[29] T. Torfs, V. Leonov, C. Van Hoof, B. Gyselinckx, "Body-Heat Powered Autonomous Pulse Oximeter", Proceedings of IEEE Sensors 2006, pp. 427-430.

[30] L. Mateu, M. Pollak and P. Spies, "Power management for energy harvesting applications", presented at PowerMEMS 2007.

[31] H. Lhermet, C. Condemine, M. Plissonnier, R. Salot, P. Audebert, M. Rosset, "Efficient Power Management Circuit: From Thermal Energy Harvesting to Above-IC Microbattery Energy Storage", Journal of Solid-State Circuits, Vol. 43(1) 2008, pp. 246-255.

[32] I. Doms, P. Merken, R. Mertens, C. Van Hoof, "A Capacitive Power-Management Circuit for Micropower Thermoelectric Generators with a 2.1μW Controller", Presented at ISSCC 2008.

[33] D. Guyomar, A. Badel, E. Lefeuvre, C. Richard, IEEE Trans. on UFFC, 52 (2005), 584-595.

[34] S. Xu, K. Ngo, T. Nishida, G. Chung, A. Sharma, "Low Frequency Pulsed Resonant Converter for Energy Harvesting," IEEE Trans. Power Electronics, Vol. 22, pp. 63 – 68, January 2007.

[35] J. Han, A. von Jouanne, T. Le, l. Mayaram, T.S. Fiez, "Novel Power Conditioning Circuits for Piezoelectric Micro Power Generators", 19th annual IEEE Applied Power Electronics Conference and Exposition, vol. 3, pp. 1541-1546, 2004.

[36] N. J. Guilar, R. Amirtharajah, P. J. Hurst, "A Full-Wave Rectifier for Interfacing with Multi-Phase Piezoelectric Energy Harvesters", ISSCC2008, pp. 302-303.

Solving Issues of Integrated Circuits by 3D-Stacking
Meeting with the era of power, integrity attackers and NRE explosion and a bit of future

Takayasu Sakurai

Institute of Industrial Science, The University of Tokyo, Tokyo, Japan
tsakurai@iis.u-tokyo.ac.jp, http://lowpower.iis.u-tokyo.ac.jp/

Abstract— In the foreseeable future, VLSI design will meet a couple of explosions: explosion of power, explosion of integrity attackers including power integrity and signal integrity and explosion of NRE (non-recurring engineering cost). A remedy for power explosion and explosion of integrity attackers lies in "voltage engineering". A remedy for the NRE explosion is to reduce the number of developments and sell tens of millions of chips with a fixed design. 3D-stacked LSI approach may embody such possibility. The talk will cover example of the solutions based on 3D-stacking. Several new circuit technologies for voltage engineering, including distributed DC-DC converters and proximity interfaces are described to enable 3-D stacking of chips to build high-performance yet low-power electronics systems. On the other extreme of the silicon VLSI's which stay as small as a centimeter square, a new domain of electronics called large-area integrated circuit as large as meters is waiting to open up a new continent of applications in the era of ubiquitous electronics. One of the implementations of the large-area electronics is based on organic transistors. The talk will provide perspectives of the organic circuit design taking E-skin, sheet-type scanner, Braille display and wireless power transmission and communication sheet as examples.

I. INTRODUCTION

As scaling continues, the following three crises become eminent in Si VLSI designsas shown in Fig.1.

Explosion of power
Explosion of integrity attackers
Explosion of complexity (explosion of NRE)

Three-dimensional stacking of chips can reduce the power consumption due to the inherently reduced distance of communication (Figs.2-4). Added to this property, the 3D-stacked System-in-a-Package (SiP) can provide a platform to realize efficient DC-DC converters possibly distributed on a chip by high-Q inductors on an interposer (Figs.5-9). This helps to reduce the system power and increase the power integrity. The high efficiency come from the fact that the efficiency, η, of the converter can be expressed as the following formula.

$$\eta = \frac{1}{1 + \alpha \left(L / R_S \right)^{-1/3}}.$$

Here, α is a function of performance of switching transistors and voltage conversion ratio, and is a constant when CMOS technology is fixed. L and Rs signify inductance and resistance of a coil (Ref.1-2). By building DC-DC converters on a chip, it is possible to achieve a quicker supply voltage transition by aid of "aim-high" concept (Figs. 10-14).

3D-stacking can also reduce development cost by providing a way of best "mix and match" of VLSI's without designing new chips (Figgs.15-16). Realizing 3D-stacking may need Through-Silicon-Via (TSV) technology but a circuit solution of proximity wireless communication may provide another way without technology cost overhead (Figs.17-27). This proximity wireless communication may also provide a way to solve Known-Good-Die problem.

On the other extreme of the silicon VLSI's, 3D-stacking of organic sheets will provide solutions for large-area electronics, which is valuable in the forthcoming ubiquitous electronics era. The new integrated circuit designs are discussed based on organic transistors and 3D-stacking of organic sheets (Figs.28-48, Ref.1). This approach may open up a new continent of electronics applications.

ACKNOWLEDGMENT

Fruitful discussions with Prof. T. Kuroda from Keio University and Prof. M. Takamiya and lab. members from the University of Tokyo are to be acknowledged.

REFERENCES

[1] K. Onizuka, K. Inagaki, H. Kawaguchi, M. Takamiya, and T. Sakurai, "Stacked-Chip Implementation of On-Chip Buck Converter for Distributed Power Supply System in SiPs," IEEE JSSC, Vol.42, No.11, pp.2404-2410, Nov. 2007.

[2] K.Onizuka and T.Sakurai, "VDD-Hopping Accelerator for On-Chip Power Supplies Achieving Nano-Second Order Transient Time," A-SSCC'05, Paper#6.1, Nov. 2005.

[3] T.Sakurai, "Organic-transistor circuit design (tutorial)," invited, T8, ISSCC'07, Feb. 2007

Gate
Drain
Source
0.2micron
Size 1/2

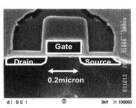

Favorable effects	
Size	x1/2
Voltage	x1/2
Electric Field	x1
Speed	x3
Cost	x1/4

Unfavorable effects	
Power density	x1.6
RC delay/Tr. delay	x3.2
Current density	x1.6
Voltage noise	x3.2
Design complexity	x4

Fig.1 Moore's law continues as a backbone but…

1/100
Leakage
x1.4 / 3 years
x1.1 / 3 years
x4 / 3 years
ITRS requirement
Power per chip [W]
10000
1000
100
10
1
0.1
0.01
1980 1985 1990 1995 2000 2005 2010 2015
MPU
DSP
Processors published in ISSCC

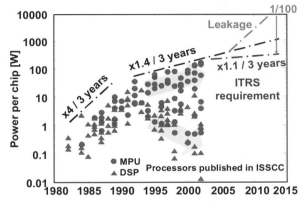

Fig.2 Deep submicron on fire

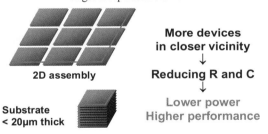

2D assembly
Substrate < 20µm thick
3-D SiP
8 times more devices in 1mm distance
More devices in closer vicinity
Reducing R and C
Lower power
Higher performance

Fig.3 D achieves low power and high performance

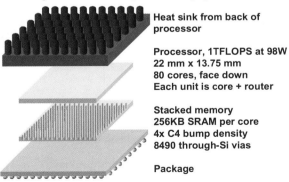

Heat sink from back of processor
Processor, 1TFLOPS at 98W
22 mm x 13.75 mm
80 cores, face down
Each unit is core + router
Stacked memory
256KB SRAM per core
4x C4 bump density
8490 through-Si vias
Package

Fig.4 Stacked processor & cache by processor

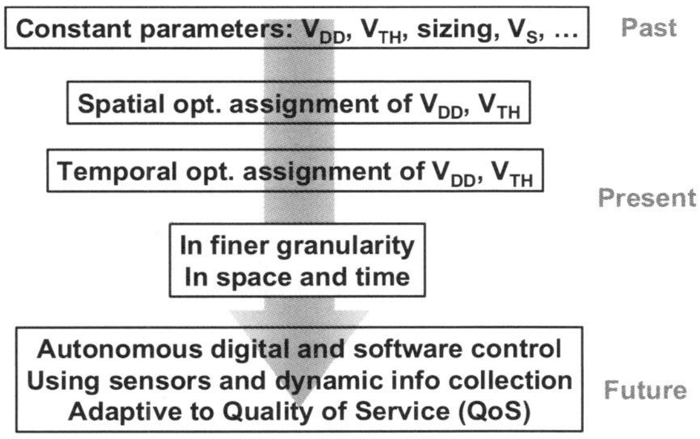

Constant parameters: V_{DD}, V_{TH}, sizing, V_S, …
Past
Spatial opt. assignment of V_{DD}, V_{TH}
Temporal opt. assignment of V_{DD}, V_{TH}
Present
In finer granularity
In space and time
Autonomous digital and software control
Using sensors and dynamic info collection
Adaptive to Quality of Service (QoS)
Future

Fig.5 Trend in adaptive control for low-power

Stacked memories
Power control proc.
Proc. unit
Power unit
Specialized blocks
Sensors and information collecting circuits
Stacked analog/RF, HV, sensors, MEMS…
HV Power grid
T. Sakurai, "Low Power Digital Circuit Design (Keynote)," ESSCIRC'04, pp.11-18, Sept. 2004.
T.Sakurai, "Moore's Law Plus (Keynote)" VMIC, Oct. 2005.

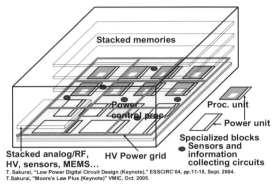

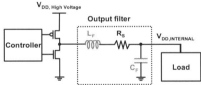

Fig.6 Future power-awareness by 3D stacking

$V_{DD, High Voltage}$
Output filter
Controller
L_F
R_S
C_F
$V_{DD,INTERNAL}$
Load
Chopping frequency > 300MHz
Need good low-resistive L & high-capacitive C.
They are also needed for low-power RF circuits.
➔ Si with L and C
K. Onizuka, K.Inagaki, H. Kawaguchi, M. Takamiya, and T. Sakurai, "Stacked-Chip Implementation of On-Chip Buck Converter for Distributed Power Supply SYstem in SiPs," IEEE JSSC, Vol.42, No.11, Nov. 2007.

Fig.7 On-chip distributed DC-DC converter

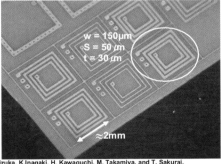

w = 150µm
S = 50µm
t = 30µm
≈2mm
K. Onizuka, K.Inagaki, H. Kawaguchi, M. Takamiya, and T. Sakurai, "Stacked-Chip Implementation of On-Chip Buck Converter for Distributed Power Supply SYstem in SiPs," IEEE JSSC, Vol.42, No.11, Nov. 2007.

Fig.8 Inductor made on FR-4

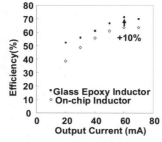

Efficiency Improvement of 10%
Simply by using thicker inductor.

Fig.9 Measurement Setup and Results

Measurement

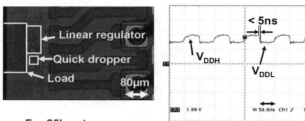

For 25k-gates
equivalent load
@ 0.18μm CMOS

Transition time smaller than 5ns

K.Onizuka and T.Sakurai, "VDD-Hopping Accelerator for On-Chip Power Supplies Achieving
Nano-Second Order Transient Time," A-SSCC'05, Paper#6.1, Nov. 2005.

Fig.10 5ns transition on-chip power supply

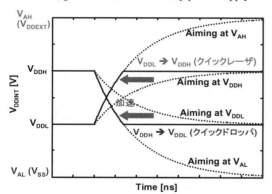

Fig11 "Aim-high"

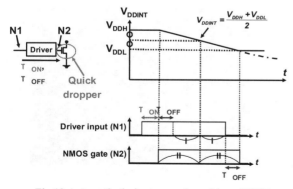

Fig.12 Automatic timing generation without VREF

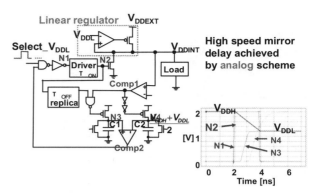

High speed mirror
delay achieved
by analog scheme

Fig.13 Circuit implementation

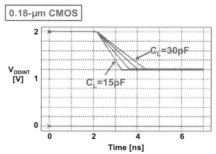

0.18-μm CMOS

Feasibility of timing control without V_{REF} is
demonstrated for C_L = 15 ~ 30 pF (not indefinite)

Fig.14 Simulation results

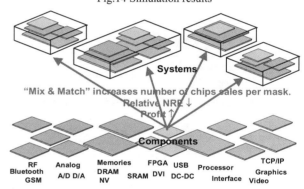

"Mix & Match" increases number of chips sales per mask.
Relative NRE ↓
Profit ↑

Fig.15 SiP reduces NRE

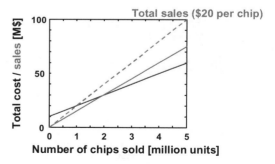

● **More SoC profit with SiP/SoC hybrid business model**

Fig.16 Mixed business model for profitability

12

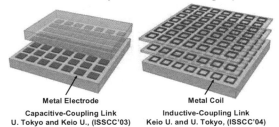

Capacitive and inductive-coupling links
Wireless data links between stacked chips
No need for additional wafer process = low cost
No need for ESD protection circuit = high speed
Metal Electrode
Metal Coil
Capacitive-Coupling Link
U. Tokyo and Keio U., (ISSCC'03)
Inductive-Coupling Link
Keio U. and U. Tokyo, (ISSCC'04)

Fig.17 Don't forget wireless connect

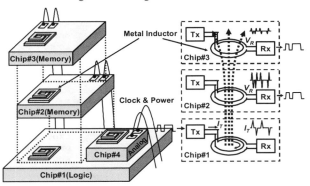

Metal Inductor
Chip#3(Memory)
Chip#2(Memory)
Clock & Power
Chip#4
Analog
Chip#1(Logic)
Tx
Rx
Chip#3
Chip#2
Chip#1

Fig.18 Inductive Wireless Superconnect

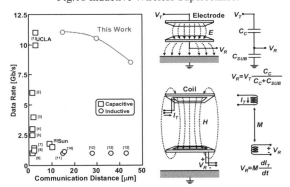

This Work
[1]UCLA
[6]Sun
Capacitive
Inductive
Data Rate [Gb/s]
Communication Distance [μm]
Electrode
Coil
$V_R=V_T\frac{C_C}{C_C+C_{SUB}}$
$V_R=M\frac{dI_T}{dt}$

Fig.19 How were we and how are we?

Txdata
Rxdata
Receiver
I_T [mA]
V_R [mV]
Rxdata [V]
Time [ns]

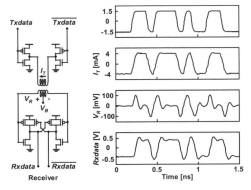

Fig.20 High-Speed Inductive-Coupling Link

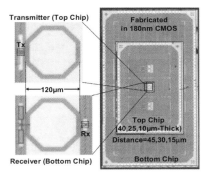

Transmitter (Top Chip)
Receiver (Bottom Chip)
120μm
Tx
Rx
Fabricated in 180nm CMOS
Top Chip (40,25,10μm-Thick)
Distance=45,30,15μm
Bottom Chip
Voltage supply by bonding does not increase power nor decrease speed.

Fig.21 120μm coils couple over stacked chips

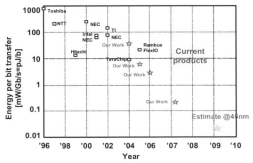

Energy per bit transfer [mW/Gb/s=pJ/b]
Year
Toshiba
NTT
NEC
TI
Intel
Hitachi
Rambus
FlexIO
TeraChip
Our Work
Current products
Estimate @45nm
Drastically lowering power consumption of I/O's
N.Miura, H.Ishikuro, T.Sakurai, T.Kuroda, "A 0.14pJ/b Inductive-Coupling Inter-Chip Data Transceiver with Digitally-Controlled Precise Pulse Shaping," Paper#20.2, ISSCC, Feb.2007.

Fig.22 L-coupled link: lower power contender

- **KGD (Known Good Die)**
  At-speed testing of wafer, Wafer burn-in, Huge pin counts
- **Heat removal and inspection of contacts**
  Heat estimate, Testing by X-ray and ultrasonic
- **Interposer**
  Secure power distribution circuits, RLC testing
- **Design environments**
  EMC, Noise, Heat, 3D modeling, Simulation
- **Standardization**
  Protocol, Electrical, Physical, Testing, Logistics, Legal issues, 3D data handling

Fig.23 It's not paradise: remaining issues for 3D SiP

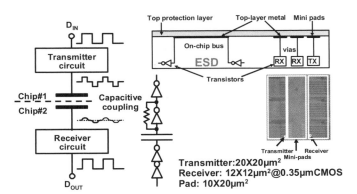

D_{IN}
Transmitter circuit
Chip#1
Chip#2
Capacitive coupling
Receiver circuit
D_{OUT}
Top protection layer
Top-layer metal
Mini pads
On-chip bus
vias
ESD
RX
TX
Transistors
Transmitter
Receiver
Mini-pads
Transmitter:20X20μm²
Receiver: 12X12μm²@0.35μmCMOS
Pad: 10X20μm²

Fig.24 KDG by L- or C- coupling links?

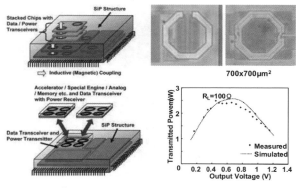

Fig.25 Even wireless power transmission

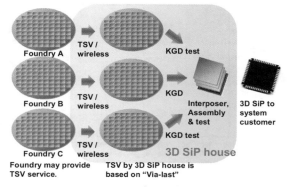

Foundry A
Foundry B
Foundry C

TSV / wireless

KGD test
KGD
KGD test

Interposer, Assembly & test

3D SiP to system customer

3D SiP house

Foundry may provide TSV service.

TSV by 3D SiP house is based on "Via-last"

Fig.26 3D SiP house

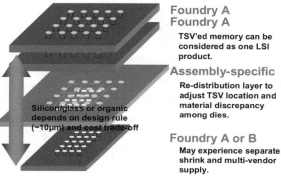

Foundry A
Foundry A

TSV'ed memory can be considered as one LSI product.

Assembly-specific

Re-distribution layer to adjust TSV location and material discrepancy among dies.

Foundry A or B

May experience separate shrink and multi-vendor supply.

Silicon/glass or organic depends on design rule (~10μm) and cost trade-off

Fig.27 Interposer to ensure design freedom

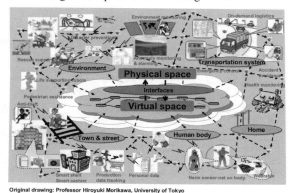

Original drawing: Professor Hiroyuki Morikawa, University of Tokyo

Fig.28 New electronics targets physical space

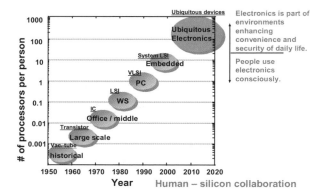

Fig.29 Increasing penetration into people's life

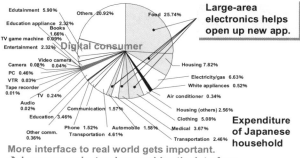

Large-area electronics helps open up new app.

Expenditure of Japanese household

More interface to real world gets important.
→ Large-area electronics provides the interface
→ More VLSI usage

Fig.30 Expenditure of Japanese household

Huge number of devices
→ Extremely low power (3D SiP)
→ Low cost (3D SiP)

Everywhere
→ Very short distance communication (L & C stacked)
→ Ubiquitous energy source (Large-area electronics)

Interfaces to real-world
→ Sensors & actuators (Large-area electronics)
→ Heterogeneous systems (Heterogeneous ICs stack)

New sets of electronics is needed.

Fig.31 Required innovations for ubiquitous electronics

Fig.32 Unique manufacturing process:
Printing large-area organic transistor array

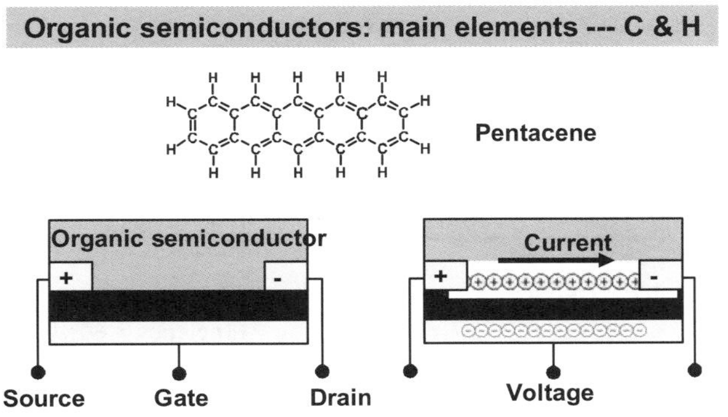

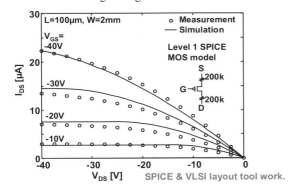

Organic semiconductors: main elements --- C & H

Pentacene

Organic semiconductor

Source   Gate   Drain

Current

Voltage

Fig.33 Organic transistors

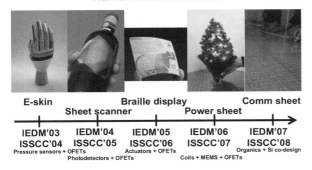

$L=100\mu m$, $W=2mm$

○ Measurement
— Simulation

$V_{GS}=$
-40V

Level 1 SPICE
MOS model

-30V

-20V

-10V

I_{DS} [μA]

V_{DS} [V]

SPICE & VLSI layout tool work.

Fig.34 Modeling by SPICE level1

Human-scale interfaces

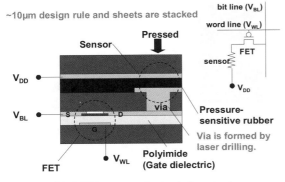

E-skin   Braille display   Comm sheet
Sheet scanner   Power sheet

IEDM'03   IEDM'04   IEDM'05   IEDM'06   IEDM'07
ISSCC'04   ISSCC'05   ISSCC'06   ISSCC'07   ISSCC'08
Pressure sensors + OFETs   Actuators + OFETs   Organics + Si co-design
Photodetectors + OFETs   Coils + MEMS + OFETs

Fig.35 Large-area electronics

~10μm design rule and sheets are stacked

Sensor   Pressed
bit line (V_{BL})
word line (V_{WL})
FET
sensor
V_{DD}
V_{DD}
V_{BL} via
Pressure-sensitive rubber
Via is formed by laser drilling.
V_{WL}
FET   Polyimide (Gate dielectric)

Fig.36 Via connect in plastic is an issue

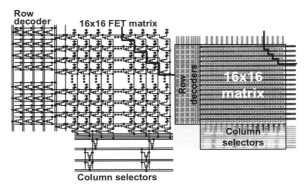

Row decoder   16x16 FET matrix   16x16 matrix
Row decoders
Column selectors
Column selectors

Fig.37 Cut-and-paste feature (16x16 sencels)

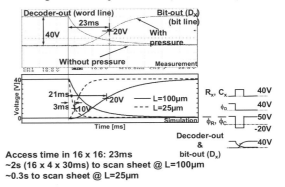

Decoder-out (word line)   Bit-out (D_x)
23ms   (bit line)
40V   -20V   With pressure
Without pressure   Measurement

Voltage [V]
21ms   -20V $L=100\mu m$
3ms   -10V $L=25\mu m$
Time [ms]   Simulation

R_x, C_x 40V
ϕ_D 40V
ϕ_R, ϕ_C -50V   -20V
Decoder-out & bit-out (D_x)   -40V

Access time in 16 x 16: 23ms
~2s (16 x 4 x 30ms) to scan sheet @ L=100μm
~0.3s to scan sheet @ L=25μm

Fig.38 Access time measurement

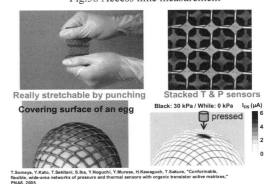

Really stretchable by punching   Stacked T & P sensors

Black: 30 kPa / While: 0 kPa I_{DS} (μA)
Covering surface of an egg   pressed

T.Someya, Y.Kato, T.Sekitani, S.Iba, Y.Noguchi, Y.Murase, H.Kawaguch, T.Sakura, "Conformable, flexible, wide-area networks of pressure and thermal sensors with organic transistor active matrixes," PNAS, 2005.

Fig.39 Advanced e-skin (pressure and temperature)

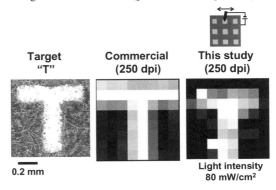

Target "T"   Commercial (250 dpi)   This study (250 dpi)

0.2 mm   Light intensity 80 mW/cm²

Fig.40 Scanned image by sheet-type scanner

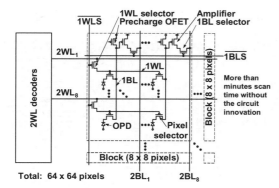

Total: 64 x 64 pixels

Fig.41 Double WL & BL to reduce time

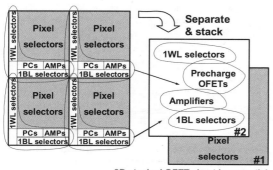

3D stacked OFET sheet is essential.

Fig.42 Scanner layout

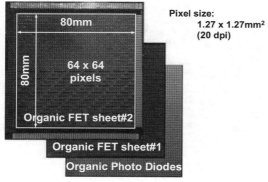

Pixel size:
1.27 x 1.27mm²
(20 dpi)

Fig.43 Three stacked sheets implementation

Cycle time
Single WL/BL: WL 17ms + BL 18ms + recovery 4ms = 39ms
Double WL/BL: WL 3ms + BL 3ms + recovery 1ms = 7ms

	Single WL/BL	Double WL/BL	
Cycle time	39ms	7ms	39ms
		5x faster	
Total power	2.5mW	900µW	350µW
		7x less	

Fig.44 Speed and power improvement by 3D

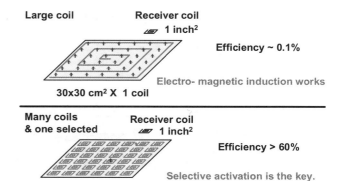

Fig.45 Large-area & high efficiency

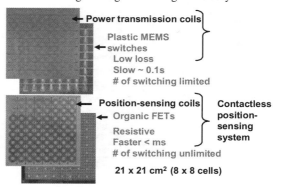

Fig.46 Combination of MEMS and OFET

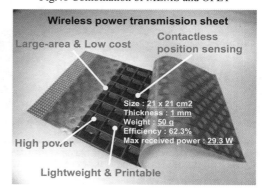

Fig.47 Wireless power transmission sheet

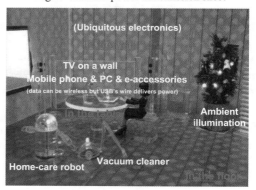

Fig.48 Demonstration of power transmission

Printed Electronics For Low-Cost Electronic Systems: Technology Status and Application Development

Vivek Subramanian, Josephine B. Chang, Alejandro de la Fuente Vornbrock, Daniel C. Huang, Lakshmi Jagannathan, Frank Liao, Brian Mattis, Steven Molesa, David R. Redinger, Daniel Soltman, Steven K. Volkman, Qintao Zhang

Department of Electrical Engineering and Computer Sciences
University of California, Berkeley
Berkeley, CA 94720, USA
viveks@eecs.berkeley.edu

Abstract☐ In recent years, printing has received substantial interest as a technique for realizing low cost, large area electronic systems. Printing allows the use of purely additive processing, thus lowering process complexity and material usage. Coupled with the use of low-cost substrates such as plastic, metal foils, etc., it is expected that printed electronics will enable the realization of a wide range of easily deployable electronic systems, including displays, sensors, and RFID tags. We review our work on the development of technologies and applications for printed electronics. By combining synthetically derived inorganic nanoparticles and organic materials, we have realized a range of printable electronic ☐inks☐, and used these to demonstrate printed passive components, multilayer interconnection, diodes, transistors, memories, batteries, and various types of gas and biosensors. By exploiting the ability of printing to cheaply allow for the integration of diverse functionalities and materials onto the same substrate, therefore, it is possible to realize printed systems that exploit the advantages of printing while working around the disadvantages of the same.

I. INTRODUCTION

In recent years, there has been a significant level of interest in the use of printing as a technique for the realization of low-cost, large area electronic systems. Printing is expected to allow for the realization of electronics on flexible, relatively low-cost, substrates such as plastic and metal foils. An analysis of the costs and capabilities of printing-based microelectronics fabrication suggests that printing can potentially enable the realization of electronic systems on plastic at costs that are substantially lower than conventional lithography-based fabrication, per unit area. On the other hand, cost per function is expected to be higher, based on the worse resolution of printed electronics. As a consequence, various potential applications for printed electronics have been proposed, including displays [1, 2], various types of sensors [3, 4, 5], and RFID [6, 7, 8, 9]. To realize these systems, it is necessary, of course, to develop the requisite "inks" that can be printed to realize the required inductors, capacitors, batteries, interconnects, resistors, transistor, diodes, memories, and sensing and display elements. Additionally, development

of appropriate printing techniques, including techniques for achieving requisite film uniformity, line-edge control, and layer-to-layer registration, is also required. Therefore, in this work, we analyze the state of the art and outlook for printed electronics. First, the viability of printing as a technique for realizing printed electronics is studied. Next, we review classes of printable materials that we have developed for us in printed electronics. Finally, we examine the state of the art in printed electronic devices and estimate the needs for realizing viable applications for printed electronics.

II. PRINTING TECHNOLOGY FOR ELECTRONICS

The interest in printing as a means of realizing electronic systems is traditionally primarily driven by the fact that printing is expected to be a low-cost technique for realization of electronic systems. To validate this claim, it is worthwhile to compare printing-based fabrication to traditional microelectronic fabrication techniques at a high level. First, printing has been claimed to be cheaper than lithography-based fabrication due to a lower capital expenditure. In fact, this is not accurate for linewidths > 1μm, since highly depreciated lithographic tooling is available in this regime; additionally, to realize high up-time, low defectivity printing tooling will necessitate the development of new equipment for printed electronics, adding to capital expenditure for the same. Therefore, it isn't clear that printing will reduce capital expenditure on a per-tool basis. Second, printing is expected to reduce overall process complexity, since it can enable the use of entirely additive processing, rather than necessitating the use of lithography+etch based subtractive processing. This is a tremendous advantage, since it reduces overall step count, raw material costs, and overall tooling cost, therefore reducing capital expenditure and increasing throughput across the entire flow. Third, printing can potentially enable low-cost substrate handling and factory automation, since it allows the use of low-cost roll-to-roll or sheet-feed processing techniques. While this is likely true in the long run, the development of high registration accuracy tooling for such handling is still pending, and, as a result, the final outcome is still unclear. By using material costs, substrate costs, capital expenditure estimates, and throughput estimates, it is possible

Portions of this work were funded by the Defense Advanced Research Projects Agency, the Semiconductor Research Corporation, The National Science Foundation, the Environmental Protection Agency, The University of California Discovery Program, Agilent Technologies, Eastman Kodak Company, National Starch, Inc., Soligie, Inc., and Delta Electronics.

to draw a broad conclusion regarding the economic viability of printed electronics. This analysis suggests that printing should potentially be cheaper per unit area than conventional electronics; the actual cost advantages depend on the specific process flows used, but cost advantages of >10X per unit area appear quite feasible. On the other hand, the cost per transistor in printed electronics is several orders of magnitude higher than the cost per transistor in silicon, due to the much worse linewidth (the best achievable linewidth in high-speed printing techniques today is worse than 10μm). As a consequence, the economic comparison can be summarized very simply – printed electronics is likely economically advantageous in applications that are area-constrained, while it is likely economically unviable in applications that are functional density-constrained.

Various printing techniques are available to be used in the fabrication of electronics. It is therefore worthwhile to summarize the advantages and disadvantages of each of the broad classes of printing techniques. The printing techniques that will broadly be included here are screen printing, inkjet printing, stamping / nanoimprinting, and gravure printing. Other printing techniques do exist, but have generally not been applied to printed electronics fabrication.

Screen printing is arguably the most mature technique for fabrication of printed electronics. Screen printing has been applied to the fabrication of printed circuit boards for decades. In screen printing, a viscous ink is "pressed" through a patterned screen using a squeegee. The pattern on the screen is typically generated using a photosensitive screen coating. Screen printing is in wide-spread use in electronics, since it is used to pattern conductor traces (typically using silver pastes), resistors (using carbon films), capacitors (using polyimide dielectrics), etc., for printed circuit boards. The resolution of commercial high-speed screen printing tools is typically worse than 50μm, though, in research, screen technology has been applied to realize prints in the range of <10μm. The main disadvantage of screen printing relates to the viscosity of the ink. Since the ink is forced through a screen and is therefore freestanding when it lands on the substrate, inks with relatively high viscosity (typically >1000cP) are required to prevent excessive spreading and bleedout. This is problematic for some materials in printed electronics. High viscosity inks are typically realized by adding polymer binders to the ink. While this isn't a problem for graphic arts, it can be a serious problem for printed electronics, since such binders can destroy the functionality of semiconductors, introduce excessive leakage and dissipation in dielectrics, or degrade the conductivity of conductors. As a result, the use of screen printing is typically limited to applications where binders can be added without unacceptable loss of performance. For example, binder-laden silver pastes are commonly screen printed. While the conductivity is degraded relatively to pure thin film silver, it is still acceptable for the target applications (e.g., thin film membrane switches, automotive keypads, etc.). Screen printing has been used in some limited applications for printed electronics such as printing interconnection, etc. [10].

The most widely used technique for printing active electronic circuits today is inkjet printing. Inkjet printing allows the use of low viscosity inks (1-20cP); this is extremely important, since it allows for the formulation of inks that only contain active material and solvents without the need for binders. Coupled with digital input, which allows for on-the-fly design changes, inkjet printing dominates research into printed transistors, etc. On the other hand, the manufacturing viability of inkjet printing is still unclear. First, inkjet printing, being a drop-by-drop technique, is probe to severe pixilation-related issues, where the complex drying phenomena associated with droplets can produce widely variant printed patterns. This will be discussed further below. Second, inkjet printing tends to be slow, and high throughput is only achieved by using large numbers of heads in parallel. This in turn introduced yield concerns related to the misfiring of individual heads during printing of a pattern. Third, there is a cone of uncertainty associated with the ejection angle of drops from a nozzle; this typically results in a ±3σ variance in placement of the drop of up to 10μm. This in turn introduces line edge roughness and places limits on design rule scaling.

The drying phenomena associated with inkjet printing are particularly important, since smooth, thin films with low line edge roughness are typically very important for the realization of printed devices. Inherent to the drying of drops is the so-called "coffee ring effect". In this effect, as drops dry, there is strong migration of material from the center of the drop towards the edges of the drop due to strong convective forces associated with solvent evaporation from the drop. Depending on the relatively evaporative and convective fluxes, as the drop dries, it is possible for a donut shaped final film to result, as shown in figure 1. This is obviously a serious concern for printed electronics, since the large thickness variation, inherent presence of pinholes, and sharp ridges all contribute to unacceptable film formation. The impact of drying on line formation is clearly visible by referring to figure 2, which shows the variation in line morphology as a function of drop-spacing in a printed line. All other parameters are held the same. Clearly, simply by changing one parameter, there is a large impact on printed line morphology [11], again due to the strong convective forces associated with droplet drying.

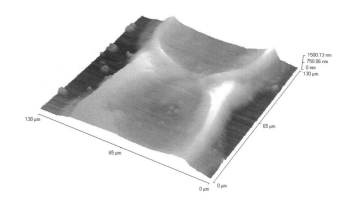

Figure 1.   Atomic force micrograph of a inkjetted pattern, showing formation of the "coffee ring" in the dried film.

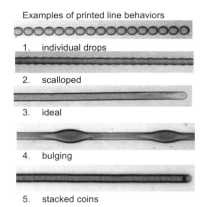

Examples of printed line behaviors

1. individual drops

2. scalloped

3. ideal

4. bulging

5. stacked coins

Figure 2.   Effect of droplet spacing on final printed line morphology

The origin of the printed line variations above is easily understood by considering the convective forces associated with drying (Figure 3). As a drop is appended to the end of an already formed line, convective forces cause the fluid within the drop to flow towards the connection point to the line. If the drop-spacing is too wide, then this connection is too small to support the flow, resulting in the drop drying before a continuous line is formed (Figure 2.1). If the spacing is slightly closer, then some material flows into the line, but the narrow connection constricts flow, resulting in the drop drying / gelling before a smooth sidewall is formed, resulting in scalloped lines (Figure 2.2). If the drop spacing is reduced further, then smooth continuous lines can in fact be formed (Figure 2.3). However, should the drop spacing be reduced further still, then the connection point between the drop and the line gets too large, and excessive material from the drop flows into the line. The line is unable to support this flow, and therefore, the line pools up, producing a bulge. The increased cross-section of the bulge allows further absorption of fluid and thus the bulge necks back down again, only to increase when the impedance to fluid flow builds back up again. This results in the formation of periodic bulges in the line (Figure 2.4). It is clear, therefore, that line morphology control is complicated, and the manufacturability of the same is therefore challenging. A brute force solution that is commonly adopted by numerous authors involves "flash drying" the line such that drops dry very rapidly upon hitting the substrate. This forms lines composed of overlapping individually dried drops (Figure 2.5). Unfortunately, such lines suffer from poor thickness uniformity, limiting film and feature scalability.

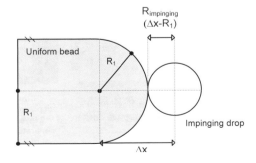

Figure 3.   Schematic representation of a drop impinging on the end of a line; the neck diameter strongly impacts final film morphology.

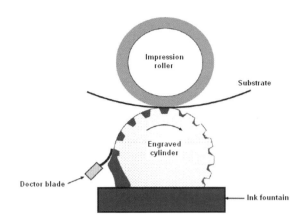

Figure 4.   Schematic representation of gravure printing process.

The pixilated nature of inkjet printing and its low throughput and manufacturing challenges have driven interest in alternative printing technologies. The big concern, of course, is viscosity; the next lowest printing technique in terms of viscosity requirements is gravure printing, and indeed, there has been substantial interest in gravure printing for printed electronics in recent years [12, 13]. In gravure printing, a drum with features (cells) etched into it is inked and wiped with a doctor blade to remove ink from field regions [14]. This drum is then rolled over the substrate to be printed. Some fraction of the ink in the wells transfers to the substrate, resulting in printed patterns. The advantage of gravure printing is that it is very high speed, and is scalable to produce patterns below 20μm with excellent pattern fidelity, including good film uniformity and low line edge roughness. The disadvantages of gravure include the fact that it is a contact technique, and therefore has significant defectivity challenges, and that it requires higher viscosity inks (typically 40cP-2000cP). As a result, it is relatively unstudied for printed electronics, but has gained attention in recent years.

As will inkjet printing, the stringent line edge morphology and surface roughness requirements of printed electronics have implications on the use of gravure printing. Since gravure printing involves the inking and subsequent de-inking of the wells on the gravure cylinder, the optimization of these processes must be considered very carefully. For example, during de-inking, there are strong lateral shear forces, and improper optimization of the process can result in pickout, in which ink is "pulled" off the printed pattern (Figure 5).

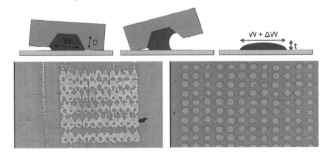

Figure 5.   Pickout effect in gravure printing (left). The strong shear forces (top) can cause significant deviation from the desired ink transfer (right) if improper optimization is not performed.

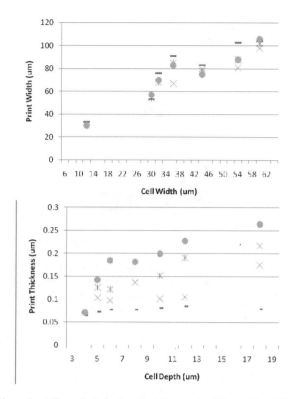

Figure 6. Effect of cell depth and width on printed linewidth and line thicknesss for different ink mass-loadings

In gravure, the printed pattern depends strongly on the cell structure. By varying the cell height and width it is therefore possible to tune the printed feature size. Gravure has the advantage of allowing printing of films with a wide range of thicknesses, from 50nm-5μm, while also allowing good scalability of linewidth, to below 20μm.

The final printing techniques that are being pursued are stamping and nanoimprinting. These are similar to gravure printing, in that a patterned master is used to transfer a pattern onto a substrate. In stamping, the master is inked and pressed on the substrate, while in nanoimprinting, the substrate is inked and the master is pressed into it. Both techniques have shown good results in research [15, 16], though it is too early to comment on their manufacturability.

Overall, it is likely that printed electronics will ultimately make use of many of the above. For different layers, different printing techniques will be optimal, based on pattern requirements and material compatibility. Therefore, a mix-and-match approach will be used, with the goal of maximizing process throughput for a given capital expenditure.

III. MATERIALS AND DEVICES

Printed wiring boards are typically made using inks based on metallic flakes for conductors, carbon films for resistors, and polymers for dielectrics. With the emphasis on printing active devices, the scope of materials being developed as inks for printed electronics has increased dramatically. Within the scope of our work, we focus on three main classes of materials – nanoparticles, soluble oligomers, and soluble polymers.

One of the major recent trends in printed electronics is the use of nanoparticles. Nanoparticles are promising for two main reasons. First, the can be easily solubilized in printable solvents to form stable, printable inks. In many cases, the choice of solvent can be tuned to match the needs of the specific printing technique and application. Second, because of the increased surface area to volume ratio in such small particles (diameter <10nm), nanoparticles show a dramatic reduction in effective melting point. This allows printed nanoparticle films to be heated, causing fusing of the particles at low temperatures (<250°C, even below 150°C in many cases). The fused films then have properties very close to those of thin films deposited by more conventional techniques.

We synthesize nanoparticles using wet chemical techniques to produce particles with well-controlled diameter [17]. The particles are encapsulated with organic ligands. The ligands serve two functions. First, they allow for the synthesis of particles with controlled diameters, and second, they stabilize the particles by preventing agglomeration and allow them to be solubilized. We have realized processes for synthesizing a range of particles, including Au, Ag, Cu, ZnO, ZrO_2, Al_2O_3, CuInS, Co, etc [18, 19]. All are printable and sinter at low temperatures. By printing these particles, we are able to realize a wide range of printed structures, including inductors, capacitors, multilevel interconnection, etc [20]. The particles may be sintered at <150°C, making them compatible with low cost polyester substrates.

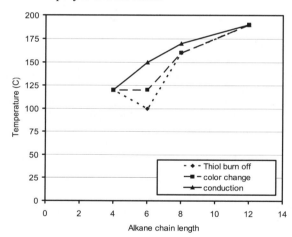

Figure 7. Effect of encapsulant on sintering temperature for 3nm Au particles. By tuning the particle size and choice of encapsulant, it is possible to realize particles that sinter at plastic-compatible temperatures.

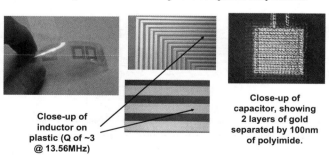

Close-up of inductor on plastic (Q of ~3 @ 13.56MHz)

Close-up of capacitor, showing 2 layers of gold separated by 100nm of polyimide.

Figure 8. Photos of passive components printed using nanoparticles.

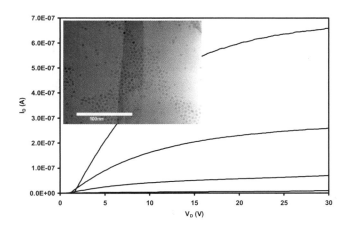

Figure 9. Output characteristics (top) of transistors formed using sintered ZnO nanoparticles (inset) as the channel

The nanoparticles may be used on their own, or in combination with organic materials, to form active devices such as transistors. We typically use a bottom-gated transistor process flow, since this ensures that the organic semiconductor is printed last, and is therefore not subjected to the thermal budgets associated with nanoparticle annealing. By optimizing the various processes, it is possible to realize transistors with mobility approaching that of amorphous silicon TFTs. Of course, printed linewidth and layer-to-layer registration limit channel length to >20µm. Additionally, there is a fair mount of overlap capacitance due to the need to account for registration runout in printing the various layers.

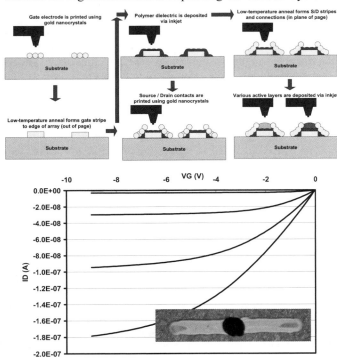

Figure 10. (top) process flow used to printed transistors. Transistors with mobility >0.2cm^2/V-s and V$_{DD}$ <10V have been realized on plastic.

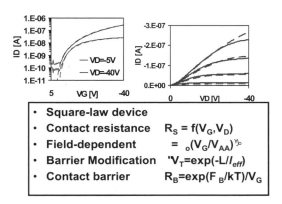

Figure 11. Modeling of printed organic transistors

An important requirement to use printed electronics in circuits is, of course, to have robust models for printed transistors. We have developed compact models that account for all the major observed phenomena affecting such devices, and have implemented a behavioral model in Verilog-A. This is then used for circuit design and simulation.

IV. APPLICATIONS OF PRINTED ELECTRONICS

By examining the devices and economic considerations above, it is possible to draw certain conclusion regarding the best uses of printed electronics:

First, printed electronics is economically attractive in applications that are area-constrained, rather than functional density constrained. Displays are therefore an obvious application. Other applications include some types of sensors (the functional density of a sensor is often dominated by the size and form-factor of the sensing element) and RFID tags operating at relatively low frequencies, such that the size of the antenna and passive components dominate the overall size of the tag.

Second, printing in general and inkjet printing in particular allows for the relatively easy integration of mutually incompatible and diverse materials on the same substrate. Therefore, applications that require diverse materials functionality are often attractive for printed electronics. Again, various types of sensors are obvious candidates, as are tags incorporating a range of functions including communication, sensing, visualization, etc.

Third, the performance of printed electronic devices will generally be relatively poor, particularly for electronics on plastic. Due to the low-temperature processes, lack of self-alignment, poor film quality, large linewidth, and low-performance materials used, transistors fabricated for printed electronics will typically operate at frequencies below 1MHz, and will be relatively large. This limits the use of printed electronics to applications that don't require large numbers of transistors or high performance. Again, obvious examples are displays, some simple sensing circuits, and perhaps some simple electronic barcodes.

At this point, therefore, it is appropriate to review some of the major applications of printed electronics on a case-by-case basis, identified the advantages and tradeoffs therein.

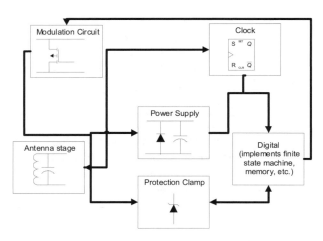

Figure 12. Block diagram of a 13.56MHz RFID tag

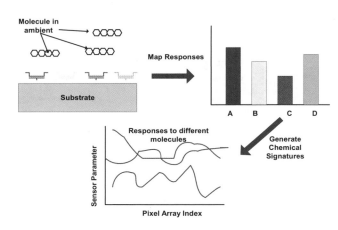

Figure 13. Conceptual basis for an arrayed sensor

A. Printed RFID tags

In recent years, there has been a lot of interest in printed RFID. The fundamental issue is one of cost; printed RFID attempts to compete with silicon-based RFID by providing a low cost alternative. A block diagram of a 13.56MHz RFID tag is shown above. All the transistor functionality in a silicon-based RFID tag is implemented in a small chip, typically <0.5mm on a side. The large inductor and tuning capacitor are implemented off-chip, on a plastic or paper inlay to save space. The chip is attached to this inlay, either directly, or via an interposer. Given the small chip size, the silicon is virtually free. The antenna cost is typically a couple of cents, as is the attach cost. Printed electronics attempts to reduce the cost by eliminating the expensive chip attach. It is believed that this should enable the realization of low-cost RFID, though at this point, the outcome isn't entirely clear.

There are consequences of choosing to implement an RFID tag using printed electronics. First, since transistor size is large, functionality will be limited to minimize chip area. Depending on the process used, the crossover point at which silicon is cheaper than a printed tag may range from a few hundred transistors to a few thousand transistors. As a result, printed RFID will be limited to simple read-only barcodes in the near term. Second, since the performance of printed electronics will limit switching to <1MHz, the derivation of the clock signal becomes an issue. In conventional RFID tags, the clock is divided from the incoming carrier signal. Obviously, this is a significant challenge for printed RFID. The consequence is that the clock will likely be generated locally in such tags. Given that LC oscillators take too much space at such low frequencies, it will be necessary to use RC-based oscillators. Since the frequency stability of these is poor, this will necessitate the use of more sophisticated reader systems, in addition to developing a new standard.

Overall, therefore, printed RFID is a challenging application for printed electronics; given that it is fundamentally a cost play, it isn't clear that this is a good first application; costs of incumbent technology will typically be lower. On the other hand, the high volumes make this a very attractive proposition for high-speed printing, and as a result, numerous groups are pursuing this very actively.

B. Printed arrayed sensors

From the previous section, it is apparent that the performance tradeoffs associated with printed electronics can be substantial. On the other hand, printing does offer a tremendous advantage with respect to integration of disparate materials on the same substrate. Inkjet printing, for example, allows the printing of multiple different semiconductor inks on the same substrate, thus allowing for the realization of arrays of different transistors in a very economical and efficient manner. This has naturally led to an interest in printed sensor arrays based on printed organic transistor sensors.

Many organic semiconductors show a strong performance response to materials in their ambient. The mechanisms for this behavior are diverse, and include swelling of the semiconductor upon absorption of the analyte, doping of the semiconductor by the analyte, distortion of grain boundaries due to accumulation of the analyte, and various steric effects within the semiconductor upon analyte exposure. By fabricating organic transistors with exposed channels, numerous authors have established that organic transistors are usable as sensing elements. Unfortunately, the specificity of these sensors is typically poor, since the above response mechanisms are clearly not unique. Therefore, to achieve specificity, electronic noses are typically implemented.

In an electronic nose, arrays of individually non-specific sensing elements are connected in an array, and pattern matching is performed across the array to achieve specificity. This is therefore an excellent fit for printed electronics. As discussed above, printed transistors may be printed with exposed channels. By using inkjet printing, it is straightforward to print transistors with different channel materials. These may be used in an electronic nose system.

While it is theoretically possible to construct sophisticated noses to detect a wide range of materials, this ends up being difficult to implement due to the limited accuracy of pattern matching. Therefore, we have implemented two modifications; first, we do not attempt to develop a true nose; rather, we use arrays as a means of discriminating specific false positives. Second, we use synthetic chemistry to improve specificity of each sensing element.

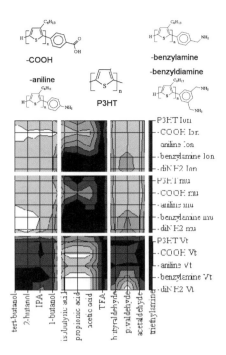

Figure 14. A library of synthetically modified polythiophene derivatives (top) showing differential responses to a range of analytes (bottom).

We synthesize end-functionalized polythiophenes and use them as active materials. These provide discrimination ability between specific analytes; while these are not usable as general noses, they are very effective for detecting specific analytes; for example, we have successfully implemented sensors that detect wine spoilage using this technique [21].

Most printed devices show a fair amount of drift in electrical performance while under bias. This causes two problems. First, the drift in the sensing element itself complicates detection. We solve this by implementing a differential architecture, where identical sensors are connected in a bridge circuit. One side is protected using an overlayer, while the second side is exposed. By looking at the bridge response, we are able to correct for drift in the sensor.

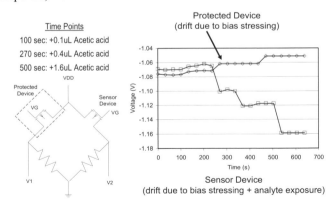

Figure 15. Use of differential architectures to correct for drift in electronic nose sensing elements.

The second problem is related to the pattern-matching circuitry. Printed reference circuits typically make use of the V_T of a MOSFET; unfortunately, this tends to drift with bias stress, leading to inaccuracy in A/D conversion, for example. Since matching in devices is also poor in printed electronics, this is a problem for implementation of integrated arrayed sensors in printed electronics. Our sensors above are implemented with silicon-based processing. In the long term, it is clear that improvements in stability are required.

In addition to detecting gases, it is also possible to detect biomolecules. We have recently demonstrated the detection of DNA [22, 23]. DNA, being charged, causes local increase in hole concentration in organic semiconductors. Single- and double-strand DNA shows a difference in response, for reasons that are not entirely obvious at this time. We are therefore able to implement DNA sequencing with electrical output provided by the organic transistors. Organic transistor arrays are implemented with different known DNA single-strands at different array points. An unknown DNA strand is brought in and hybridized using pulse-enhanced hybridization. By looking at the on-current of the transistors before and after hybridization, it is therefore possible to determine the location with which the unknown DNA matched, thereby allowing sequence of the strand. While the results are preliminary, and linearity studies, etc, are underway, such a system is clearly an attractive application for printed electronics, since it may allow for the field deployment of low-cost, disposable strips of sensors on plastic connected to a silicon-based readout system.

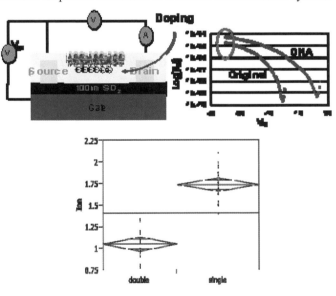

Figure 16. Organic transistor-based DNA sensing. Doping by DNA causing a shift in the transistor characteristics (top). The shift is different for single- and double-straned DNA, thus allowing for hybridization detection (bottom).

C. Displays

Since printed electronics has economic advantages with respect to cost per area, it is natural that the most obvious and most actively pursued application of printed electronics is as a means of realizing displays, including OLEDs [24], LCDs [25], and various types of bistable displays [26]. It is appropriate to discuss some of the shortcomings of printed displays. First, since the eye is extremely adept at noticing nonuniformity and defects, the manufacturing requirements for printed displays can be substantial. This has led to most printed display makers focusing on electronic signage or low-resolution displays [27]. To realize higher quality displays, it will also be necessary to realize a compatible backplane technology. There are several challenges with regard to realizing printed backplanes. First, for LCD and many bistable displays, it is necessary to have low leakage to ensure a high quality black. Unfortunately, this is a problem; most printed transistors suffer from relatively poor on-off ratio. Second, for good refresh rate or drivability, it is necessary to realize relatively high drive currents and/or relatively short channel lengths. This is problematic for printed electronics, since printing does not achieve linewidths commensurate with those used in modern display backplanes, and also, the performance of most printed materials today is at best on par or only slightly better than amorphous silicon.

We have been focused on addressing this latter problem by using transparent transistors. By printing transistors based on transparent semiconductor nanoparticles such as ZnO, it is possible to fabricate display pixels with very wide transistors, covering a substantial portion of the pixel. These therefore provide enhanced drivability without requiring the use of short channel lengths. While we are still in the relatively early stages of transparent electronics, it is likely that the combination of printing and transparent electronics will offer a tremendous opportunity in the future, since transparency can be used to overcome some of the disadvantages of printing.

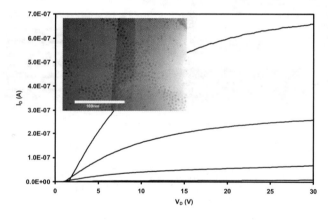

Figure 17. Output characteristics of a transistor formed using ZnO nanoparticles. Mobility is 0.2cm^2/V-s, and transparency is >90%.

V. CONCLUSIONS

Printed electronics is an attractive technology for realizing electronic systems on flexible substrates. Economic considerations suggest that printed electronics may be advantageous for systems requiring large areas or low functional densities, such as displays, sensors, and some RFID tags. While the performance of printed transistors is generally poor, it is improving rapidly, and is already at a point at which it merits serious consideration as a candidate technology for low-resolution displays, various types of sensors, and perhaps some simple electronic barcodes. By exploiting the advantages of printing, it is likely that viable applications of printed electronics will become prevalent in the near future.

REFERENCES

[1] H. Sirringhaus, N. Tessler, and R. H. Friend, "Integrated Optoelectronic Devices Based on Conjugated Polymers", Science, 280, 1741, 1998.

[2] http://www.polymervision.com

[3] B. Crone et al, "Electronic sensing of vapors with organic transistors", Appl. Phys. Lett. 78, 2229, 2001.

[4] F. Liao, C. Chen, V. Subramanian, "Organic TFTs as gas sensors for electronic nose applications", Sensors and Actuators B, 107, 849, 2005.

[5] T. Someya et al, "A large-area, flexible pressure sensor matrix with organic field-effect transistors for artificial skin applications", Proc. Nat. Acad. Sci., 101, pp. 9966-9970, 2004.

[6] W. Clemens, W. Fix, J. Ficker, A. Knobloch, A. Ullmann, "From polymer transistors toward printed electronics", 19, pp. 1963, 2004.

[7] V. Subramanian et al, "Progress towards development of all-printed RFID tags", Proc. IEEE, 93, 1330, 2005.

[8] Y. J. Chan, C. P. Kung, and Z. Pei, "Printed RFID: technology and application", 2005 IEEE International Workshop on Radio-Frequency Integration Technology, pp. 139- 141, 2005.

[9] S. Steudel et al, "Comparison of organic diode structures regarding high-frequency rectification behavior in radio-frequency identification tags", J. Appl. Phys. 99, 114519, 2006.

[10] Y. Noguchi, T. Sekitani, and T. Someya, "Printed shadow masks for organic transistors", Applied Physics Letters 91, 133502 (2007).

[11] D. Soltman et al, "Inkjet-Printed Line Morphologies and Temperature Control of the Coffee Ring Effect"., Langmuir, 24, 2224, 2008.

[12] T. Kololuoma et al, "Towards roll-to-roll fabrication of electronics, optics, and optoelectronics for smart and intelligent packaging", Proceedings of SPIE -- Volume 5363, June 2004, pp. 77-85

[13] T. Makela et al, "Continuous roll to roll nanoimprinting of inherently conducting polyaniline", Microelectronic Eng., 84, pp. 877-879, 2007

[14] X. Yin and S. Kumar, "Flow visualization of the liquid-emptying process in scaled-up gravure grooves and cells." Chemical Engineering Science, 61:4:1146-1156, 2005.

[15] K. S. Lee et al, "Direct patterning of conductive water-soluble polyaniline for thin-film organic electronics", Appl. Phys. Lett. 86, 074102, 2005.

[16] I. Park et al, "Nanoscale Patterning and Electronics on Flexible Substrate by Direct Nanoimprinting of Metallic Nanoparticles", Advanced Materials, 20, pp. 489 – 496, 2008.

[17] D. Huang et al, "Plastic-compatible low-resistance printable gold nanoparticle conductors for flexible electronics", J. electrochem. Soc., 150, pp. 412, 2003

[18] S. K. Volkman et al, "Ink-Jetted Silver/Copper Conductors for Printed RFID Applications", Mater. Res. Soc. Symp. Proc. 814, I7.8, 2004.

[19] S. K. Volkman et al, "A novel transparent air-stable printable n-type semiconductor technology using ZnO nanoparticles", IEEE International Electron Device meeting Technical Digest, pp. 769, 2004.

[20] D. Redinger et al, "An ink-jet-deposited passive component process for RFID", IEEE Trans. Electron Dev., 51, pp. 1978, 2004.

[21] V. Subramanian, J. Lee, V. Liu, S. Molesa, "Printed Electronic Nose Vapor Sensors for Consumer Product Monitoring", IEEE International Solid State Circuits Conference, Paper 15.3, February, 2006.

[22] Q. Zhang and V. Subramanian, "Label-free low-cost disposable DNA hybridization detection systems using organic TFTs", IEEE International Electron Device Meeting, 2007.

[23] Q. Zhang and V. Subramanian, "DNA hybridization detection with organic thin film transistors: Toward fast and disposable DNA microarray chips", Biosensors and Bioelectronics, 22, pp. 3182, 2007.

[24] N. C. van der Vaart et al, "Towards large-area full-color active-matrix printed polymer OLED television", J. Soc. Inf. Display , 13, 9, 2005.

[25] I. Shiyanovskaya et al, "Rugged and drapable cholesteric liquid crystal displays", Proceedings of the SPIE, vol.5801, pp. 204-12, 2005.

[26] B. Comiskey et al, "An electrophoretic ink for all-printed reflective electronic displays", Nature 394, 253 - 255 (1998).

[27] http://www.add-vision.com

SOI Design in Cell Processor and Beyond

Yoshiaki Daimon Hagihara

Chairman and CEO , AIPS/AINS Consortium

(Ex-Sony Fellow, Semiconductor Strategic Planning)

Hagihara-Yoshiaki@aiplab.com

Abstract—**A brief historical overview of the microelectronics of the present home entertainment LSI chips with regard to the product specifications and performance aspects of the home entertainment LSI chip sets, such as for digital cameras, home robotics and games are given in order to explore the possible killer applications as our driving force for our future semiconductor and electrical and electronic industries. SOI design in Cell Processor is one good example. But some further technology break-through may be needed for our future potential real-time AIPS/AINS applications. Here, AIPS stands for Artificial Intelligent Partner Systems and AINS stands for Artificial Intelligent Nursery Systems.**

I. INTRODUCTION

This talk is actually a continuation or the second part of the presentation delivered by the author at the ESSCIRC2001, which was held in Vilach Austria in September 18-20 2001 [1] Due to events of 11 September, the author could not attend in person, but his presentation via a conference connection was exemplary and well received.

At that presentation, a brief historical overview of a first home entertainment consumer electronic gadget, called a portable transistor radio was given, and then some introductory comments on the basic semiconductor device concepts were explained. They were strongly related to the microelectronics of the present home entertainment LSI chips with regard to the product specifications and performance aspects of the home entertainment LSI chip sets, such as for digital cameras, mobiles, and games.

Seven years have passed since then and surely these evolving modern electronic gadgets surely have changed our life and style drastically, but the consumers are demanding always, still better performance and quality. The semiconductor and electrical and electronic industries have drastically transformed their status for the customers' needs in their surviving games.

There were many merging and immerging companies in order to provide swiftly for the consumers better products with better performance and quality. It is very important to find out what the consumers really want, and much more important to supply what

they really want as soon as possible or at least in time. Yes, sometimes, it is very hard to predict what the consumers really want.

Too early introduction to the consumer market may cause some critical damage or discouragements for the future product planning and development. However, it is worth trying ASAP to challenge to see the feasibility of a new methodology or a choice of technology to realize the desired product specifications and performance aspects of a new revolutionizing home entertainment gadget.

Bipolar Transistor Technology is one example that accelerated the portable radio consumer market in 1950s. CCD Technology is another example that accelerated the portable video and digital cameras in 1980s. SOI Design in Cell Processor [2] could be considered as another challenge to revolutionize the consumer semiconductor technology that has been proved to be successfully adopted for the mass-production just in time for customers' needs.

The Bipolar technology, the CCD technology and the SOI technology will surely contribute for the future consumers' specific high-class products for many, many years to come, and the real profit may lie in these devices enjoyed by a limited number of semiconductor vendors who have accumulated many year's production experience and know-how while the CMOS Logic LSI Chips Technology, the CMOS Imager Technology, and the CMOS Bulk Technology for future Multi-core processors may be well standardized and utilized for low-cost and low-profit products, but serving for a huge consumer market segment.

Our future is not ours to see. Whatever will be will be, but some insight and future prospective may be possible if the future killer application can be clear in picture with well-defined product specifications and performance aspects of a new revolutionizing home entertainment gadget for our future mass-production consumer business enhancement.

Some further technology breakthrough may be needed for our future potential real-time AIPS/AINS applications. Here, AIPS stands for Artificial Intelligent Partner Systems and AINS stands for Artificial Intelligent Nursery Systems.

II. BIPOLAR AND MOS DESIGNS

A small portable radio called TR-1 in Regency brand was being sold in Liberty Music Store in New York City for the price of $49.95 during the December Christmas holiday season in 1954. It was seven years after the invention of the bipolar transistor in December 1947.

The radio is made of four n-p-n grown-type Bipolar Transistors with the 22.5 volt stacked type 015N battery being used in US Army. The picture of the TR-1 Regency brand Radio and its Circuit Diagram are shown in Fig.1a and Fig1b. below .

Figure 1 a   Regency TR-1 Radio

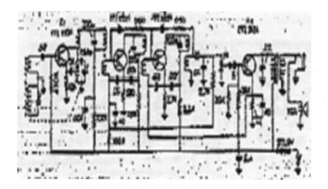

Figure 1b   Circuits Diagram of Regency TR-1 Radio

However only ten thousand units were produced due to the poor reliability and high cost. The problem is that the transistor has a very low internal impedance and it needs a high by-pass capacitor of a few micro-farads. The transistor itself had a very low yield these days.

A small venture company in the far east conquered these problems and introduced the world most reliable and compact consumer TR-55 portable radio with 6 volt supply voltage in Aug 20, 1955.

More than fifty years have passed, but many innovative RF and Wireless papers with integrated capacitors and inductors are still high lighted in the international technical conferences and being implemented in real consumer products.

Though we see the transition from Bipolar to CMOS in many applications such as the one shown in Figure 2 below, the analog , wireless and RF circuits are still holding important roles in our semiconductor industry.

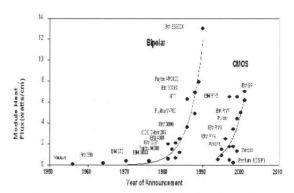

Figure 2   Transition from Bipolar to CMOS

III. CCD AND CMOS IMAGER DESIGNS.

The basic pinned-diode structures adopted for the sensor elements both in CCD imagers and CMOS imagers are identical. The original structure was proposed by the author in 1975 and now it is a free patent[3][4][6]. The original idea came from the floating and lightly-doped base n-region utilized as the photo-electrons dynamic storage area in a conventional but slightly modified p-n-p bipolar junction transistor embedded in the n-substrate. This structure was the basic of the most of the universally adopted sensor elements in CCD and CMOS solid-state imagers now a day. Figure 3 below shows the structure

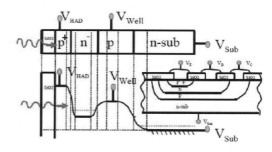

Figure 3   p-n-p-n Sensor Structure for CCD&CMOS Imagers

The relatively highly-doped emitter region quenched the undesired electric field at the Silicon SiO2 interface, and very low dark current and defect free image sensing element was realized. More over even though this is very similar to the p-n-p bipolar transistor structure with n-type substrate, the p-n-p transistor operates dynamically with the base storage junction capacitor region floating. With this structure one single photo detection may be possible when the lightly doped floating base is depleted completed. The same floating lightly doped base BJT sensor elements can be utilized both in the CCD imager in Figure 4a and in the MOS imager case as seen in Figure 4b below.

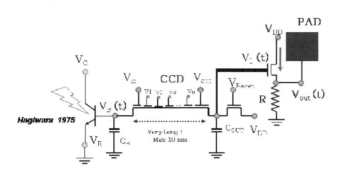

Figure 4a CCD Imager with Floating-Base BJT Sensors with Vertical and Horizontal CCD Shift Registers

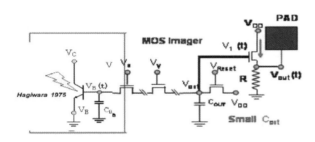

Figure 4b The Same Floating-Base BJT Sensor with CMOS X and Y Transfer lines in CMOS Imager

Here we observe that even in CCD Imagers the output circuits are made of the CMOS source-follower circuits. And even in the CMOS imager case, the basic sensor element is the basic BJT sensor structure. Even a pinned diode, it is a p-n-p structure. A variety of technologies are all incorporated and utilized to achieve the best device performance.

IV. CMOS BULK AND SOI DESIGNS

Ten years has passed after the introduction of SOI into a product. Was SOI considered as a competitor to bulk CMOS then ? Now we see both technologies continue to co-exit in some of the application domains, such as microprocessors and gaming.

However, we also see the exclusive use of bulk CMOS in main stream SOC. It was thought 10 years ago that SOI has a performance advantage over bulk, and the cost would be its barrier for wide application. In this speculatives no one was sure about what were the applications. There were no clear pictures of the killer applications except PC and game processors in the huge consumer markets.

Figure 5 Two Technologies Overview

Osamu Takahashi ISSCC2008 Technology		65nm SOI CMOS Technology on p-SOI Substrate	45nm SOI CMOS Technology on p-SOI Substrate	Scaling
Used Device Type	Thin Ox Hvt	yes	yes	
	Thin Ox Rvt	yes	yes	
	Thick Ox Rvt	yes	yes	
Thin Ox Tox		1.12 nm	1.16 nm	
Thick Ox Tox		2.35 nm	2.50 nm	
Nominal Supply (Thin Ox)		1.0 V	0.9-1.0 V	
Nominal Supply (Thick Ox)		1.5 V	1.5-1.8 V	
M1 Minimum Width		0.1* um	0.076* um	0.76
M1 Minimum Spacing		0.1* um	0.076* um	0.76
Metal Layers		10	10	
SRAM Cell Area		0.700 um²	0.404 um²	(0.76)²

* Cell/B.E. design specific. Not technology specific

Since most of the circuits engineers are working on bulk-CMOS chips, before comparing or discussing about the features of BulK and SOI CMOS, the basics of SOI needs to be understand.

Figures 5 thru 7 give some good insights of SOI performance. Obviously, there are specific performance requirements from graphics/games processors. Some specifics of the technology used in the CELL processor must be understood.

It would be of general interest to learn about new design and library techniques - challenges faced, new solutions, how technology features are exploited and what has been achieved. Then we can really discuss on why do it, and about the key issues.

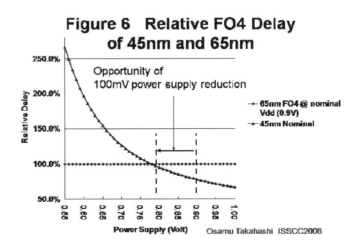

Figure 6 Relative FO4 Delay of 45nm and 65nm

V. CELL PROCESSOR

Ken Kutaragi[5] in his plenary talk "The future of computing for real-time entertainment", at ISSCC2006, February 2006 started with a short review of computing and computer games, from Eniac, through microprocessors and text-based games, to Pong, and now approaching real-time computer generated graphics.

Figure 7 Simulated Relative Power of Cell/B.E. with Three Technologies

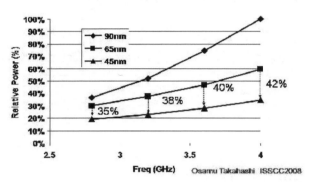

This trend is continuing, expanding the market from homes and fixed-location gaming, to the mobile space. This trend will increase IC content and push the limits of the semiconductor processes. In the early games, the game platforms used mature technologies like TTL, so the internal silicon was always one or two generations back from the leading edge. The gaming market was fairly small and most games were just advanced toys. Designs were integrated into ASICs to reduce costs and size, but there was no effort to push the technology.

Figure 8 45nm Cell/B.E. Die Photo

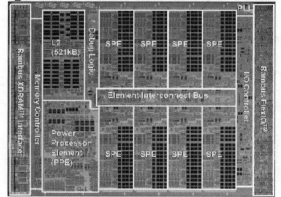

Osamu Takahashi ISSCC2008

By 1994, the games were just starting to move to 0.5-micron processes, while the leading process was 0.35 micron. Eventually over time, the game chips migrated to smaller processes to increase integration and reduce costs. Now games

are a big business, Over 700 million gaming platforms are in players' hands, and the industry consumes 70,000 8-inch wafers per month for logic and memory – with demand increasing in 2007 to over 120,000 8-and 12-inch wafers per month. The latest games are multi-core SoC devices that push the state of the art in semiconductors.

The PlayStation became one of the first gaming systems to push the technology. It is similar in architecture to a PC, except for its MIPS processor and dedicated geometry transfer engine. Due to the 5-stage pipeline in the graphics chip, the latency approached 100 msec – a speed that humans discern as discontinuous and definitely not real time.

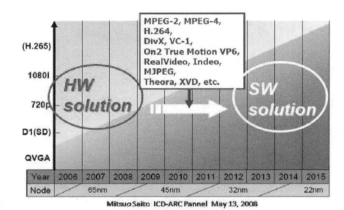

Figure 9 Trend of HW Solution to SW Solution

To address the latency issue, the emotion engine was developed in 1998. This groundbreaking graphics chip needed the latest technologies to achieve its performance and level of integration. By reducing the number of pipeline stages and increasing integration – with 10.5 million transistor and a 128-bit dual vector processor – the Playstation pushed all of the existing limits of the 250-nanometer process.

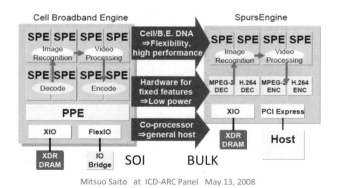

Mitsuo Saito at ICD-ARC Panel May 13, 2008

Figure 10 Cell/B.E. and Toshiba SpursEngine

In 1999, the design was ported to a 4-metal, 180-nanometer process to reduce size and increase performance. The following year, it was ported to a 130-nanometer process. The 2-chip set was reduced to a single chip in a 90-nanometer process in 2004.

Also in 2004, the portable PSP platform was introduced. This gaming system uses a 9-metal, 90-nanometer process and has 18 million transistors in a multi-core architecture. The advent of real-time response in games changed the entire experience. Just as computers changed lives by bringing new compute capabilities to the office – first through spreadsheets, then communications and publishing, and finally to the rest of the high-technology lifestyle through video and music – the new games brought other changes.

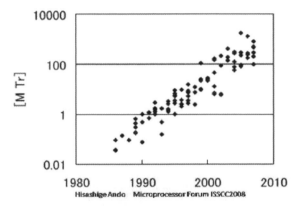

Figure 11   # of Transistors on a MPU chip

Real-time response now allows the user to interact more closely with the games. The absence of any noticeable lag immerses the user in the action. The need for more computing and massive I/O capabilities is acknowledged in any real-time situation.

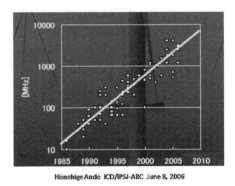

Figure 12   Trend of Processor in ISSCC papers

For example, a Formula 1 car has over 200 sensors and needs a supercomputer to process the data in the time available. Other real-time applications have similar requirements. The

real-time environment forces the computer designer to change from a storage-centric to a processing centric model, with low latency and high throughput as essential design characteristics.

The Cell chip is a very highly parallel, multi-core processor with massive bandwidth for memory and I/O. Among the new capabilities in the chip are internal hardware security functions and an architecture geared for high scalability. Figure 8 shows the current 45 nm Cell Processor .

The Cell chip represents the convergence of supercomputers and computer entertainment in massively parallel systems with real-time response, quickly approaching the prospect of a super artificial intelligence that includes vision systems, intelligence – and even curiosity, as we saw in HAL in the film 2001.

The weight on the software developments efforts will be much heavier and heavier in near future. See Figure 9 above. We also see now SOI and Bulk co-exist in variety of different unique applications. See Figure 10.

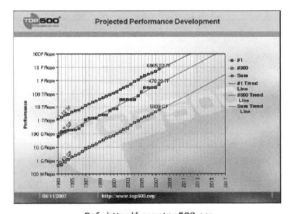

Ref: http://www.top500.org
Figure 13   Projected Performance Development

Next-generation systems will include not only the supercomputers as explained in Figures 11 thru 13, but also vast number of sensors of all types to change the way humans and computers interact. Game machines have gone from trailing-edge components to leading-edge SoC devices over the past 30 years. But Game machines are not the only real-time applications. There must be more potential applications of real real-time machines in order to meet our human needs.

The future of real-time computing will include massive assemblies of parallel processors over mesh-connected networks to execute the vast amounts of computation that recognize and react to the real world with many types of sensors and interface and networking connections.

The enhanced capabilities of the supercomputer-class devices will change user experiences and expectations in ways we are not fully aware of and not able to define, at least for now. Face recognition and real-time cosmetic face simulation can be realized with dedicated processors. SpursEngine by Toshiba is one good example. See Figure 10 above.

But the real killer application may be just waiting at the corner to appear in front of us suddenly soon. Since the need is the mother of inventions, all we need to look for is just what we really wish to have in our daily life at home and outdoors.

VI. AIPS/AINS-ROBOT Applications

The author believes the key lies in the human friendly AIPS and AINS-Robot Applications. A robot is a product of many technology achievements including material science, mechanical engineering, electrical engineering and a huge amount of supporting software environments with real-time supercomputers and communication wire-line and wireless networking.

If the robot application is dedicated for the daily care of old and disabled people at home, the dedicated AIPS/AINS system also needs to consider the barrier free house design efforts and for the natural friendly human-robot interface, the human-friendly robot appearance and cloths are desired.

The convergence of supercomputers and computer entertainment in massively parallel systems with real-time response, quickly approaching the prospect of a super artificial intelligence that includes vision systems, intelligence – and even curiosity, as we saw in HAL in the film 2001.

Next-generation systems will include vast number of sensors of all types to change the way humans and computers interact.

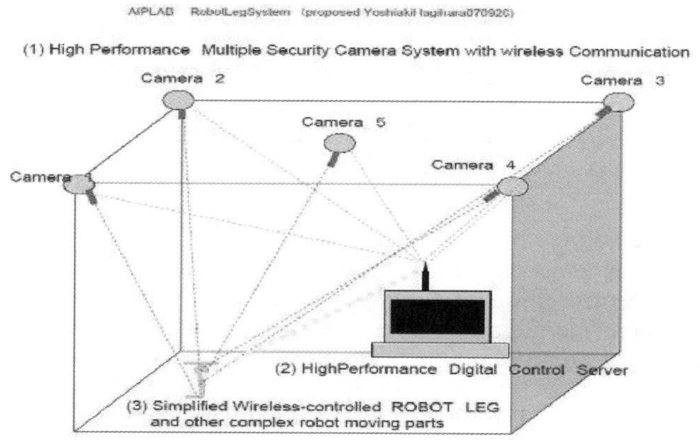

Figure 14   AIPS–ROBOT   Application at Home

At home, every room has many, many sensing video cameras and audio sound pick-up systems wired together in the home network system with the super computers processing the voice and image pattern recognitions in real time, and the advanced AIPS/AINS Software will control the robust mechanical robot arms, legs and moving wheels to

respond in real time to the requirements and requests given by the old and disabled people at home.

Current humanoid robots are being designed to be mobile and portability-oriented design with many constraints in power management and body-space limitations.

But by sharing a variety of functions with in- door furniture-type TV display super computer terminal, internet remote control intelligent services, toy-type sensors, the mechanical robot body itself can be designed and dedicated to achieve fully- reliable and accurate human-like gentle and strong movements.

What we really needs is the total computer controlled robot system that can really control in real-time the complicated mechanical system such as the One-legged Ghost Umbrella Toy or the Classical Japanese Johruri Doll Play.

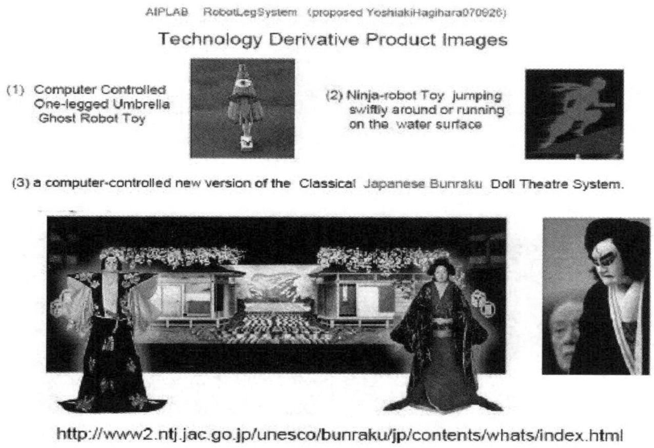

Figure 15   Another AIPS/AINS-ROBOT Application Images

These systems can be achieved with the real-time feedback systems with many video camera and audio pick-up interfaces.

The entire system may be connected to the established security service company or privately connected to their children and wives outside home by mobile phone and wireless real-time communication system so that the old and disabled people need not be cared and confined in the remote hospital away from their family and friends. With the dedicated their own private AIPS/AINS-Robot services, the old people's daily care nursery home may not be important for them.. They can stay at home with their children, grandchildren and friends and family for the rest of their lives happy after.

While the person is still active and clear in mind, the AIPS-Robot serves as the real partner friend to them. They can teach or program the AIPS-Robot as they wish with many dedicated hours for their own dedicated requirements.

When the people gets old, forgettable, and disabled, the AIPS-Robot can work continuously now as the AINS-Robot as a friend to the old and disabled man. These applications can be realized with the super-computing processors, video camera and audio sound sensing systems all connected effectively with wire-line and wireless real-time communication channels , also with the comfortable display screen and audio-sound track systems built-in at home. Since the day-care home service system for the old and disabled people can be defined quite accurately, the system requirements and specifications can be well defined. The entire system can be also achieved in a much larger scale in outdoors. Maybe what we need is only one supercomputer or one big network of supercomputers all connected in one to act as one entity in super real-time. All the AIPS/AINS-robots can be assisted to perform natural way serve people.

VII. CONCLUSION

In ISSCC2006, Ken Kutaragi talked his vision on the future of computing for real-time entertainment in details. Almost three years have passed since then. And now the PS3 game consoles with blue-ray disk and SOI-CELL Processor are now in the hands of the consumer market in the stage of the full enjoyment of mass production. Time is now ready for us to see the real real-time applications, more functions with the full supports of the game machine capability, supporting the virtual-world entertainment applications. We now look for more than the simple real real-world applications such as the game-robots and the Robo-Cups. The real killer application is what the mass consumer market is waiting for.

The author believes that the target application is the completely human-friendly AIPS/AINS-robot total service system solution at home. To achieve this, goal, the semiconductor engineers, electrical and electronic engineers, software engineers , mechanical engineers, house-designers, even the garments fashion-clothes designers and art designers must work together hands in hands.

ACKNOWLEDMENTS

The author expresses his sincere appreciations and gratitude to Osamu Takahashi, IBM Austin, Mitsuo Saito, Toshiba Japan, Hisashige Ando, Fujitsu Japan and Michinori Nishihara, IBM Japan for supporting and providing me their precious presentation materials with kind advice and suggestions. Also special thanks go to many friends of Sony-Toshiba-IBM Projects, PS2 and PS1 including colleagues of the newly formed the AIPS/AINS Consortium:

AIPS =Artificial Intelligent Partner Systems.

AINS= Artificial Intelligent Nursery Systems.

See http://www.aiplab.com/

REFERENCES

[1] Yoshiaki Hagiwara, "Microelectronics for home entertainment." An Invited Talk at The European Solid-State Circuits Conference (ESSCIRC 2001) 18-20 September,2001 , in Villach, Austria.

[2] Osamu Takahashi, et al, "Migration of Cell Broadband " from 65 nm SOI to 45 nm SOI", pp.86-87, and p.597, Paper 4.3, Digest of Technical Papers, ISSCC2008, February 4, 2008, San Francisco California

[3] JP1215101, a Japanese Patent#58-46905, invented and filed by Yoshiaki Hagiwara, Nov 10, 1975.

[4] Yoshiaki Daimon-Hagiwara, Motoaki Abe1 and Chikao Okada,"A 380H × 488V CCD Imager with Narrow Channel Transfer Gates"10th Conf. Solid State Devices, Tokyo, 1978 Japanese Journal of Applied Physics Vol. 18 (1979) Suppl. 18-1, pp. 335-340

[5] Ken Kutaragi, "The future of computing for real-time entertainment", a plenary talk at ISSCC2006, February 2006 in San Francisco, California

Information, Energy, and Entropy: Design Principles for Adaptive, Therapeutic Modulation of Neural Circuits

S Jensen, G Molnar, J Giftakis, W Santa, R Jensen, D Carlson, M Lent and T Denison

Medtronic Neuromodulation Research and Technology
Medtronic LN240
Fridley, MN 55421

Abstract –This paper discusses the challenges and opportunities designing technology for deep brain stimulation (DBS). DBS is currently approved for the treatment of movement disorders such as Parkinson Disease, essential tremor and dystonia, and a number of studies are underway to determine its clinical efficacy for the treatment of epilepsy, treatment resistant depression, and obsessive compulsive disorder (OCD). Designing a DBS system is a complex system engineering problem, drawing on such diverse fields as applied physics, circuit design, algorithms and biology. But fundamental to device design is the neurophysiology of the 'brain circuits' affected by the disease, and how they can be modulated for therapeutic affect. Recent activities are drawing on information theory to help better understand the operation of brain circuits. From that understanding, we hope to clarify the mechanisms by which existing DBS therapy works. In addition, considerations from information theory, and the relationships between concepts like entropy, energy and information flow, can help guide the design of more advanced therapy systems. We briefly review these concepts as applied to brain circuits and disease. We then describe our recent work in designing research tools that allow for exploration of adaptive circuit modulation based on measured *electrical* biomarkers, which are believed to represent compromised information processing in the brain. Future opportunities are discussed to highlight that electrical engineering, from MEMS to circuits to signal processing, is crucial to enabling the next generation of neurological therapies.

I. OVERVIEW OF DEEP BRAIN STIMULATION: ENTROPY MODULATION IN THE BRAIN?

Deep Brain Stimulation (DBS) refers to the extracellular electrical stimulation of brain tissue via the delivery of relatively high frequency current pulses, and is an effective and approved therapy for a number of pathologies of the human nervous system. The major components of DBS are shown in Fig 1. An implantable pulse generator (IPG) is placed into the pectoral region of the chest. The IPG contains the energy for stimulation within its battery, as well as the circuitry to provide stimulation pulses. The IPG interfaces to neural tissue through a series of electrodes placed in a specific physiological target in the brain (e.g. Subthalamic Nucleus for Parkinsons). Stimulation pulses from the IPG are localized to the vicinity of the electrodes, providing targeted modulation of the firing pattern in a specific neural circuit. DBS is currently approved for the treatment of movement disorders such as Parkinson disease, essential tremor and dystonia, and a number of studies are underway exploring new therapy opportunities.

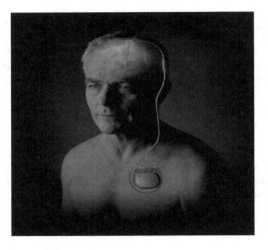

Figure 1: Elements of a deep brain stimulator. The battery and circuitry form the IPG, which is implanted in the chest. The electrodes are placed into a specific neural circuit into the brain.

Although DBS produces dramatic therapeutic clinical effects, the precise mechanism(s) of action remains unclear. For the purpose of understanding how to improve therapies, researchers have proposed that deep brain stimulation might be viewed in terms of how it affects the information processing characteristics of brain tissue.

We can broadly consider the primary role of the brain in terms of its functional capacity as an information processor. Information about the current state of the 'system', as well as the world in which it is acting, is provided to the central nervous system through various afferent sensory signals, where it is then transformed, or 'processed', in some way. The transformed information effects action through efferent pathways connected to musculature, hormone regulating organs and other bio-physical and bio-chemical mechanisms. The input/output transformation can be viewed as an information transformation with the mutual information providing a measure of the capacity of that system.

Exactly how information is represented in the brain is still a matter of some controversy. Individual neurons are connected in complex networks and appear to communicate primarily through the conduction of digital 'spikes' in membrane voltage. Many theories of how these spikes might encode information abound, including spike-*rate* theories in which information is encoded in the rate at which spikes are generated, and spike-*timing* theories that take into account the inter-spike intervals and their timing relationships with those generated from other interconnected cells. It is also not clear if information is encoded by individual neurons, or populations of neurons acting in concert. In all likelihood, each of these methods is probably used to some degree in various combinations throughout the central nervous system of complex organisms.

Pathological dysfunction of brain systems can take a number of forms, and in accordance with the information processing framework, can be viewed as an information processing failure. Information might be corrupted due to noise or the intermittent loss of signal, or it can be lost entirely due to a transmission failure or lesion of central elements as occurs with infarction due to stroke. The information transfer functions can be corrupted due to many factors including the loss of individual neurons throughout the brain or the failure of various biochemical reactions affecting cellular processes.

A particular form of information processing failure is increasingly being investigated as a causal agent in numerous brain pathologies such as epilepsy, Parkinson's disease, bipolar disorders and obsessive compulsive disorders. This failure occurs when the largely uncorrelated firing of individual neurons throughout a region of brain tissue devolves into a coherently organized synchronous oscillation. In this state, the normal, transiently correlated behavior of individual elements throughout the network is forced into a phase-locked firing pattern that significantly reduces the mutual information between afferent/efferent signals and completely disrupts the information processing capacity of the system as a whole.

An interesting property of this disease model is that correlated firing makes it feasible to design sensing systems to detect and monitor the presence of an information processing pathology. The 'biomarker,' or clinical signature, of this type of pathology is often represented as electrical oscillation that appears within a discrete frequency band in a specific anatomical location. Using spectral analysis, we can decipher the coding of the network close to the sensing electrodes and make deductions on the state of the neural circuit. Unlike the spike recordings often discussed for motor prosthesis systems [1], these ensemble cell firings result in diffuse field potentials that are amenable to chronic measurement from electrodes already approved for DBS therapy [2]. A system engineering challenge is to map the field fluctuations to a specific disease state, and to devise a stimulation strategy that can provide therapeutic benefits when the pathological state is detected.

As an example, epilepsy is characterized by the abnormal emergence of highly coherent, periodic synchronous firing of large populations of neurons. If we consider the phase of individual neurons firing in a population, the total phase coherence across the population can be loosely considered as a probability measure over phase. In the case of oscillatory dysfunctions, as phase coherence increases the entropy measure--defined as the information capacity in a channel--over the phase distribution decreases. This entropy decrease

negatively impacts the information capacity of the system as a whole. In a seizure, this phase-locked behavior becomes extreme, yielding a nearly total information processing failure and a strong increase of energy diffused across the alpha (8-12 Hz) and beta (12–40 Hz) spectral bands. Research is actively exploring neuromodulation to eliminate seizures by breaking reentrant information pathways [3]. Recent work is also suggesting that subdural electrodes, with an electrode below the protective dura and proximal to cortical tissue, can detect high frequency oscillations at hundreds of Hz. These higher oscillations, denoted 'fast ripples,' are hypothesized to signal that circuit conditions are biased towards a higher probability of seizure state, and might serve as a pre-seizure indicator [4].

Another example is Parkinson's disease. The functional mechanisms of Parkinson disease are presently unknown; however, recent research has demonstrated a strong correlation between patient symptoms and highly coherent Beta band (15-30Hz) oscillations in spike firing intervals within certain motor-control populations of neurons [5,20]. The result of this synchronized firing could be a reduction in the uncorrelated (high information capacity) state space or, alternatively, increased power in a correlated noise source. In either case, the information processing capacity of the system is degraded.

As briefly stated earlier, the precise mechanism(s) of action of stimulation in deep brain tissue remains controversial. However, there are several ways in which the mutual information between input/output of firing neurons might be affected by applying high frequency electrical pulses to disrupted systems. In one case, it is postulated that DBS actually induces an 'information lesion' [6] in which portions of dysfunctional brain structures are effectively disabled, allowing other, redundant, systems to communicate without error. From an information theory point of view, the rapid stimulation rate reduces the entropy of the neural circuit by greatly restricting its available states and thereby its ability to carry information. From a therapeutic standpoint, the benefit of suppressing the pathological information content within the circuit is posited to provide similar benefits as a lesion [6]. Another hypothesis [7] is that high frequency DBS is acting to desynchronize overly coherent oscillation, which, in turn, increases the information capacity of the dysfunctional region.

Are we adding information capacity to the circuit, or taking it away, or a combination of both? How do we answer these questions?

A major difficulty in deciphering neural dynamics is the barrier to extracting information from the brain circuit. Scientific tools that monitor neural dynamics are needed to uncover the basic principles of function, the therapeutic effects of stimulation, and to provide the observability needed for adaptive neuromodulation. Systems for accomplishing these tasks are becoming practical, as we learn enough about brain coding to architect devices for practical sensing and stimulation.

II. CIRCUIT ARCHITECTURES FOR NEUROMODULATION: CONVERTING ENERGY TO INFORMATION

A. Information and Energy Flow in Neuromodulators

The previous section discussed recent ideas on how constant stimulation can impact the information content of a neural circuit. Using this model as a conceptual guide, the core functionality of a neuromodulator can be thought of as the translation of energy from a battery into information embedded within the nervous system. Fig 2 represents the model of the DBS system from this perspective, where the IC stimulation engine draws energy off the battery and converts it to the current pulses that stimulate excitable cells. The goal is to control this flow of energy, from battery to information modulation in the tissue, in a useful way.

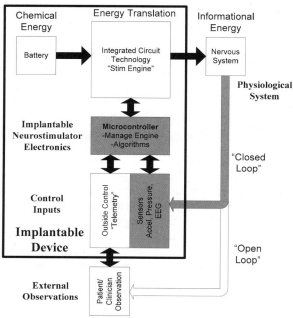

Figure 2: Signal flow model for a neurostimulator illustrating the modes of energy translation from the battery to the tissue, and opportunities for adaptive modulation.

Approved DBS systems operate in an "open-loop" mode, meaning the device has no inherent sensing capability and adjustments require external intervention through a telemetry system. In reality, the system is never truly open-loop, since adjustments are made based on observations of a patient's response to therapy. These observations, however, must be made in the presence of a clinician and titration of stimulation is made manually through an external programmer.

Adding sensing technology to a stimulator could provide several benefits. The scientific benefit is driven by the need for better understanding basic network dynamics, information flow, and mechanisms of action for DBS therapies. From a clinical standpoint, there is interest in using sensing of neurological activity to help provide "closed-loop" therapy based on therapeutically relevant biomarkers. The goals of closed-loop therapy, aka adaptive modulation, are to improve therapeutic outcomes and potentially increase device longevity by entering low-energy states when stimulation is not required. The addition of sensing can also provide quantitative diagnostics to aid in therapy titration in "open" and closed loop modes. The addition of sensing, however, requires thoughtful engineering to be practical, effective, and safe.

The hurdles to designing closed-loop systems include the practical, chronic measurement of neurological information and creating algorithms for closed-loop titration of therapy actuation. Although a *gross oversimplification* of the real neurological system, for the purposes of discussion, we can frame the proposed closed loop neuromodulation architecture within the context of classical state equations:

$$\dot{\mathbf{x}}(t) = \mathbf{A}(t)\mathbf{x}(t) + \mathbf{B}(t)u(t)$$
$$\mathbf{y}(t) = \mathbf{C}(t)\mathbf{x}(t) + \mathbf{D}(t)u(t) \tag{1}$$

where we will define the vector $\mathbf{x}(t)$ as the neural circuit's 'state,' $u(t)$ is the input to the neural circuit, which can include sensory input, drugs or electrical stimulation, and $\mathbf{y}(t)$ is the output of interest such as tremor or another representative biomarker. The neural circuit dynamics and therapeutic transfer functions are then represented by the four transfer-function matrices: $\mathbf{A}(t)$, representing neural circuit dynamics, $\mathbf{B}(t)$, defining the effect of stimulation on the neural state, $\mathbf{C}(t)$, representing how the neural state is mapped to observable therapeutic biomarkers, and $\mathbf{D}(t)$, representing the feed-forward path from stimulation to biomarker. Per our model of stimulation as an informational modulator, stimulation almost certainly impacts $\mathbf{A}(t)$ as well.

Our goal is to control a *therapeutically-relevant* variable $\mathbf{y}(t)$, denoted as the biomarker, through modulation of the stimulation parameter $u(t)$. This is done by creating a net feedback path to the stimulation of the network,

$$\dot{\mathbf{x}}(t) = \mathbf{A}(t, y(t))\mathbf{x}(t) + \mathbf{B}(t)\mathbf{K}(y,t)y(t) + \mathbf{B}_s(t)u_s(t)$$
$$\mathbf{y}(t) = \mathbf{C}(t)\mathbf{x}(t) + \mathbf{D}(t)\mathbf{K}(y,t)y(t) \tag{2}$$

through the control matrix $\mathbf{K}(y,t)$; note that we have partitioned a separate $u_s(t)$ to represent sources like sensory inputs which are not part of the stimulator's controller.

Consideration of these state equations illustrates our main design hurdles for adaptive therapy modulation. First, we need to identify the biomarker $\mathbf{y}(t)$ which is closely correlated to the therapeutic outcome of interest. Second, we need to create a control algorithm to implement $\mathbf{K}(y,t)$ which is flexible, time dependent and potentially non-linear, but requires minimal power to implement. Third, we need to minimize feedforward corruption of our biomarker through stimulation coupling represented by $\mathbf{D}(t)$.

In addition to these sense and control issues, we have practical constraints that must be considered. A typical DBS stimulation requires roughly 250µW of power to be delivered to the tissue to provide therapeutic benefit. For a sensing and algorithm control to be useful, we need to keep the feedback controller to the order of 25µW to avoid undermining device longevity. In addition, the knowledge of neural circuit dynamics, therapeutically-relevant biomarkers, and closed-loop neuromodulation algorithms is rapidly evolving but very incomplete. This motivates the architecture be highly flexible and programmable to allow for fine-tuning of the neuromodulation controller with minimal hardware effort.

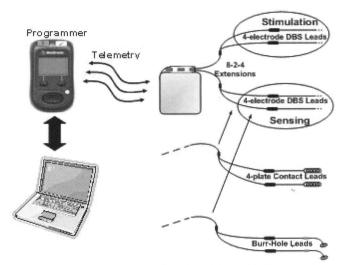

Figure 3: Prototype system for closed-loop DBS research.

To try to address these issues, we are building a flexible research tool to help explore practical sensing and control strategies applied to neural circuit dynamics. This device attempts to address the practical requirements such as power, while providing the flexibility and technical solutions to address the fundamental issues of sensing, diagnostics and adaptive therapy control developed from Eqn 2. Fig 3 shows the elements of the complete research system. The implantable device has a connector block that enables various leads to be attached. These leads are strategically placed into sense and stimulation targets within the brain. The implanted device communicates with a programmer through a wireless telemetry link. The programmer is in turn connected to a computer that can be used to program the device for algorithm and sensing adjustments, issue commands, uplink recorded loop data and provide analysis. Drawing on similar themes to the discussion of brain dynamics, the system is designed to address the high-level engineering challenges of managing "information, energy, and entropy."

B. **Information***: How is the Brain's State Coded?*

The first task in constructing the device is to establish a biomarker of therapeutic interest: *How is the information representing network dynamics encoded*? The choice of sensing paradigm drives the sensing and control architecture, so care must be taken to choose an appropriate signal. Since we already have electrodes available in the brain for therapy, and the diseases we are interested in treating are hypothesized to be ensemble circuit issues, our primary focus is on chronically measuring electrical behavior of neural circuits. Neuronal activity, however, can be measured with a number of techniques, ranging in resolution from single cell recording to the measurement of gross cortical activity with the

electroencephalogram (EEG). Each technique has its advantages and disadvantages--the choice of a particular measurement approach is a balance of several system constraints including the measurement electrode's spatial resolution, the desired neurophysiological information content, and the available power for sensing, algorithm, control and telemetry. Balancing technical trade-offs is the key to designing practical neuroprosthesis systems.

Local field potentials (LFPs) represent a good compromise for chronic closed-loop neuromodulation. Because LFPs represent the ensemble activity of thousands to millions of cells in an *in vivo* neural population, their recording can often avoid chronic recording issues like tissue encapsulation and micromotion encountered in single-unit recording [2]. In addition, the large geometry of stimulation electrodes, on the order of a few mm², takes a spatial average of neuronal activity that is by default representative of the LFP activity. Perhaps most importantly, the model of the disease states as synchronously coherent oscillations results in biomarkers which are often encoded robustly as field potential spectral fluctuations.

But how is information encoded within LFPs? Similar to amplitude modulation in radio communications, the spectral power fluctuations of LFPs within discrete frequency bands provide useful markers for discriminating brain states. In many cases, pathological states can be differentiated by such biomarkers, and even nominal brain activity can be tracked using spectral analysis. Spectral LFP biomarkers are ubiquitous and span a broad frequency spectrum, from <1 Hz oscillations in deep sleep to > 500 Hz "fast ripples" in the hippocampus, and show "Q" variations [for an excellent review, see 9]. As an example of typical LFP coding, the spectrogram of Fig 4 shows the band power fluctuations within the premotor cortex indicating the *intent* to move. The ability of a primate to modulate this band has motivated its use as the control input for a prosthetic actuator [8], and it might likewise be useful for modulating stimulation for movement disorders patients.

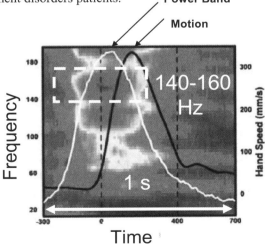

Figure 4: An example of LFP spectral band fluctuations in the motor cortex preceeding motion; the power envelope (white) leads the actual motion (black), providing a mechanism for feedforward control of a prosthetic. Reprinted with permission from [8].

Other examples of high-frequency spectral activity include fast ripples at several hundred Hz, which is being explored for seizure prediction [4], and gamma frequency processing that is indicative of processing of smells in the olfactory bulb [10]. Interest in the information coding of LFPs is continuing to grow, as its role as an indicator of processing state expands into more applications. Recent reviews suggest LFPs offer certain practical advantages over spike-based systems, in particular providing contextual information and better chronic recording capability [11].

C. *Energy: Flexible Micropower Processing by Architecting a System that "Speaks the Neural Code"*

Field potentials are attractive biomarkers since they both encode ensemble neural activity and are practical to measure chronically. By taking advantage of the neural coding of field potentials, we can also design a flexible architecture for low power signal processing and control. The spectral encoding of LFP information coding motivates a processing strategy that directly extracts energy at key neuronal bands and tracks the relatively slow power fluctuations--*much as an AM radio extracts the audio signal from a high-frequency carrier signal.*

The architectural goal of the LFP analyzer is to play to the relative strengths of analog and digital processing in order to minimize power while maintaining acceptable flexibility and robustness. Referring to the feedback state equations in Eqn 2, we partitioned our signal chain to extract the low-frequency bandpower in a physiological band as the therapeutic signal y(t) using analog preprocessing. The analog spectral processing decreases the bandwidth and dynamic range requirements prior to transitioning to digital processing. After digitization, the control kernel represented by K(y,t) is implemented in software using a standard microprocessor. The processor provides the mechanism for flexible algorithmic control, but now with the ability to run at reduced bandwidth so that the net system power requirements are reduced to a practical level of tens of microwatts. Another advantage of this partition is that adjustments to the control kernel can be made through telemetry download, based on observations and learning made during research.

With the partitioning defined, we can add sensing and control functionality to an existing neurostimulator. Fig 5 shows the system architecture with the sense/control extension interconnected to the existing neurostimulator's circuits and electrodes. The extension has three key blocks: an analog spectral processor that connects to the electrodes and conditions field potentials, a microprocessor for performing algorithms on the features from the field potentials, and a memory unit for recording events and general data-logging. Command and control between the sensing extension and the existing stimulator is made through an interrupt vector and I2C interface. The digital communication port allows for the extension to send commands for adaptive titration based on the algorithm output. Connections between the extension and the electrodes are made through a protection network that isolates the sense IC from stimulation and blocks dc currents.

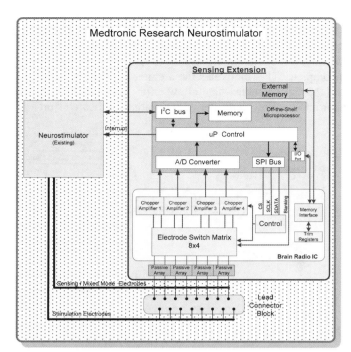

Figure 5: Architecture for a neurostimulator feasibility research tool with an extension for exploring diagnostics and adaptive algorithms.

The heart of the research neurostimulator is the analog preprocessing IC, which we dub the 'brain radio." The IC's function is to extract the key biomarker information from the neural field potential prior to digitization by the microprocessor. As shown in the block diagram, we designed the IC to have four independent channels of spectral processing, and also included custom digital circuitry for managing the loop recorder SRAM to save system power.

The mathematics of spectral analysis, specifically the short-term Fourier transform, helped to motivate the brain radio's circuit architecture. The spectral density of the signal is derived from the conjugate product of the Fourier transform including a window function 'w(t)' reflecting the bandwidth of interest,

$$\phi(f) = \frac{X(f)^* X(f)}{2\pi}, X(f) = \int_{-\infty}^{\infty} x(t)w(t)e^{-j2\pi ft}dt . \quad (3)$$

Expanding out the spectral power φ(f) using Euler's identity, we see that the net energy can be measured by the superposition of two orthogonal signal sources representing an 'in-phase' and 'quadrature' signal,

$$\phi(f) = \left| \int_{-\infty}^{\infty} x(t)w(t)\left[\cos(2\pi ft)\right]dt \right|^2$$
$$+ \left| \int_{-\infty}^{\infty} x(t)w(t)\left[\sin(2\pi ft)\right]dt \right|^2 \quad (4)$$

Both terms must be considered since the phase relationship between the neural circuit in the brain and the analog processing IC are not correlated; this is identical to the phase matching required in any AM communication system.

To implement the short-time Fourier transform in Eqn 4 for our application, we adapted a chopper stabilized amplifier to provide band extraction. Chopper stabilization is being explored as an efficient architecture for amplifying low-frequency neural signals in micropower applications [12,13]. The novel design change for spectral analysis was to displace the clocks within the chopper amplifier to translate the frequency domain of the signal and allow for spectral extraction. Using separate up- and down-modulation frequencies with the non-linear frequency properties of chopper stabilization merges heterodyning radio principles with low-noise amplification. As described in [14], this allows us to broadly tune into a range of spectral biomarkers while drawing roughly 5μW/channel and resolving 1μVrms signals. Fig 6 shows the die shot of our complete IC.

To summarize, our sensing and control approach for the research tool was architected around the coding properties of LFPs. This architecture allows for robust adaptive titration and diagnostics for neuromodulation while drawing only microwatts of power.

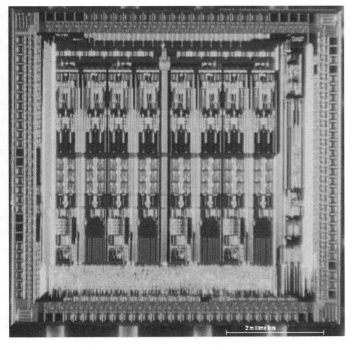

Figure 6: Die photograph of the analog preprocessing IC. Note the four independent channels of spectral processing, each with two paths (in-phase and quadrature) per channel. The digital loop controller is on the bottom, partitioned from the sensitive analog.

D. *Entropy*: Keeping the Information Channel Clear

To monitor the information flow in the brain and be able to detect pathological states, we need to insure that we maintain access to the biomarkers of interest. A significant challenge of measuring neural biomarkers is avoiding contamination of the biomarker with stimulation feed-through. The signals we are interested in sensing are on the order of microvolts, while the signals we are injecting (the stimulation) are on the order of volts. The extraction of a biomarker that is six orders of

magnitude lower poses a challenge. Several therapies involve delivering stimulation continuously, or at least a significant portion of the time, so shutting down sensing, or 'blanking,' during this time is not really a desirable option.

The information coding of LFPs and our spectral analysis strategy can help to improve the robustness of the sensing chain, but the problem needs to be handled in stages. The first issue is to manage the analog headroom by minimizing the coupling between stimulation and sensing vectors. The goal is to prevent the amplifier from saturating. In addition to the simple physical separation of the leads, careful vector orientation of the leads and sense/stim configuration can take advantage of the reciprocity theorem of electromagnetism, using a physical constraint shown in Fig 7. Stated mathematically, we try to arrange the electrode dipoles such that

$$\phi_B - \phi_A = \frac{\vec{E}_{AB} \bullet I\vec{d}}{I_{AB}} \to 0 \qquad (5)$$

where $A \leftrightarrow B$ represents the sensing dipole, and $C \leftrightarrow D$ represents the stimulation dipole. The dot product relationship of Eqn 5 indicates minimum coupling when the measurement vector is orthogonal to the stimulation current flow. Intuitively, we can think of this mathematical relationship imposing a symmetry constraint on the sense-stim electrode system. Figure 7 shows one example where the sensing dipole $(A \leftrightarrow B)$ is placed symmetrically about a unipolar stimulation electrode $(C \leftrightarrow D)$ with far-field return. Note that the dipole from therapy stimulation is then orthogonal to the biomarker sensing vector and our chances for extracting a signal are greatly increased.

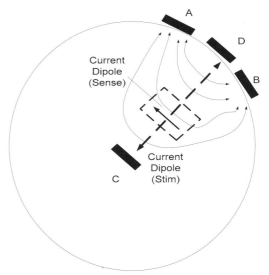

Figure 7: Diagram of lead placement exploiting reciprocity relationship; orthogonality minimizes cross-coupling.

Electrode orthoganality provides a first level of stimulation noise rejection, but practical systems will require additional techniques to further mitigate coupling. We can use the coding properties of LFPs to further suppress feed-through contamination. One potential method exploits the spectral separation between the LFP biomarker and the therapeutic band excited by neurostimulation. With this approach, if we can select the stimulation frequency to be outside the sensitive band of the biomarker, then we can use the spectral processing characteristics of the sensing IC to reject stimulation artifacts with techniques similar to those described in [15]. The sharp attenuation of out of band signals with the heterodyning spectral processor can often reject stimulation coupling adequately to extract biomarker fluctuations, at least at the level of major pathological activity. The constraint that the stimulation frequency and LFP biomarker be separated in the frequency domain is not overly restrictive, since the stimulation frequency can often be set over a broad frequency distribution and still maintain efficacy.

III. INFORMATION, ENERGY, ENTROPY: PUTTING THE CONCEPTS TOGETHER FOR ADAPTIVE CONTROL

With the system design constraints addressed and the sensing IC reduced to silicon, we are prepared to prototype a neurostimulator that can utilize adaptive control. Revisiting our analytical model of adaptive neuromodulation, the concept is to adjust the information flow in a neural circuit, essentially dynamic entropy control, based on a measured biomarker representing that the neural circuit is in a pathological state. For the adaptive controller, we programmed the algorithm to initiate stimulation upon detection of a burst of LFP energy in the 'β band' (15-40 Hz). As discussed in the first section, the β band is often an indicator of a pathological information pattern flowing through the neural circuit. Referencing Fig 8, a recorded signal from a human subject was fed into a saline tank. This signal was then extracted by the input electrodes placed across the appropriate sensing vector representing a cortical input, while the stimulation electrodes were placed within 1cm of the sensing electrode using a return provided with an indifferent far-field electrode. This electrode placement achieves the dipole relationship motivated by Eqn 5, to first order. The saline conductivity and signal drive strength was adjusted to mimic the electrical properties and signal levels of brain tissue, respectively.

Adaptive therapy modulation is demonstrated by responding to the presence of a pathological signal. After amplification and bandpower extraction with the sensing IC, the microprocessor of Fig 5 sampled the signal at 5 Hz and ran an algorithm comparing the mean energy in the last two seconds to the median energy of the last thirty minutes, using techniques similar to those in [16]. When the ratio exceeded a preset threshold for a preset time duration, indicative of a true pathological event, a detection flag was passed to the neurostimulator stimulation controller over the I2C bus. This initiated stimulation at 140 Hz, as shown in Fig 9. Stimulation proceeded over the duration of the elevated β energy. The frequency separation between stimulation and the LFP band allowed us to maintain sensitivity to the biomarker even in the presence of stimulation from an electrode 1cm away.

This system demonstration illustrates that the research tool can address the major challenges of implementing an adaptive neuromodulation system. The system is designed around the electrical biomarker of LFP band fluctuations. The processing partition extracts the signal with a total current draw of roughly 25uW/channel (sense, control), which is practical for implementing within a battery-powered implantable neuromodulation system. This approach of using analog preprocessing for power efficient computation is similar in strategy to recent work, including cochlear prosthesis [17].

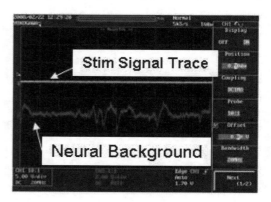

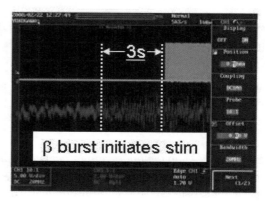

Figure 9: Prototype waveforms for an adaptive neurostimulator responding to a burst of energy in the β band. In both screenshots, the top trace is the stimulation monitor, and the bottom trace is the recorded neurological activity driven through the tank (100μV/div, 1s/div).

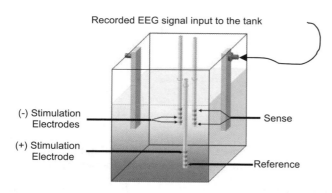

3 Medtronic 3387 DBS Leads

Figure 8: Diagram of the saline tank model for evaluating the closed-loop neurostimulator prototype.

IV. TECHNICAL OPPORTUNITIES

This research tool is by no means the end of the road for neural engineering in DBS applications, and many technical opportunities await further development (see [18] for review). As a brief summary of a few key opportunities, we highlight:

- **Information**: Many systems described in IC papers are focused on the measurement of neural spikes. Neural circuits can convey information in a variety of physical modes, however. These include field potentials, inertial measurement and biochemical markers of activity. The practical challenge for all of these measurements is making them chronic, but they could provide key auxiliary data to the algorithm.

- **Energy**: Improving the reservoir of available energy could allow for increased device longevity, and/or improved features in the device. This paper described doing "more with less" by prototyping a micropower controller to adaptively titrate therapy intelligently. A parallel path can be found in advanced energy sources, like energy scavengers and fuel cells.

- **Entropy**: We are only beginning to understand the mechanisms of action for DBS—aka how stimulation provides therapeutic benefit. Increased modeling, science and data provided by tools, like that described in this paper, should help advance stimulation patterns by managing information flow more intelligently [19].

V. CONCLUSION

This paper discussed several key design principles for adaptive, therapeutic modulation of neural circuits. These general principles of modeling and measuring information content in neural circuits, managing energy usage, and titrating the information capacity of a neural processing channel, are foundations that we can use to understand how today's therapies work, as well as to potentially extend device longevity and therapy efficacy.

One particularly attractive area for exploration is "closing the loop" on stimulation based on measured biomarkers. The technology of adaptive modulation was explored in detail, including a design concept for a feasibility research tool that we are exploring. The design focuses on efficiently extracting neuronal biomarkers using analog preprocessing prior to digitization and algorithms, taking advantage of the information coding found in LFPs. LFPs are a robust biomarker that represents the ensemble processing activity of a neural circuit; early research is indicating LFPs provide information on a variety of disease states. Since the field of fundamental brain science and DBS is rapidly evolving, the architecture provides broad 'tuning' capability and robustness, as well as the ability to run flexible control algorithms for titration of therapy and/or monitoring of diagnostics.

With this research tool, our goal is to enable researchers to explore advanced neuromodulation therapy strategies based on therapeutically relevant biomarkers, as well as establish the fundamental mechanisms of neuromodulation.

VI. ACKNOWLEDGEMENTS

The authors would like to thank Drs William Marks, Apostolos Georgopoulos, Dan Moran and Reid Harrison for helpful discussions related to brain sensing circuits and strategies.

REFERENCES

[1] R. R. Harrison, et. al., "A Low-Power Integrated Circuit for a Wireless 100-Electrode Neural Recording System" JSSC, Vol. 42, pp 123-133.
[2] Schwartz, A.B., et. al., "Brain-Controlled Interfaces: Movement Restoration with Neural Prosthetics," Neuron, vol. 52, pp.205-220.
[3] Kossoff EH, Ritzl EK, Politsky JM, Murro AM, Smith JR, Duckrow RB, Spencer DD, Bergey GK, "Effect of an external responsive neurostimulator on seizures and electrographic discharges during subdural electrode monitoring." Epilepsia. 2004 Dec;45(12):1560-7.
[4] Worrell, G, et. al., "High-frequency oscillations in human temporal lobe: simultaneous microwire and clinical macroelectrode recordings," Brain, Advance Access, Feb 7, 2008.
[5] Levy, R., Hutchinson, W., Lozano, A., Dostrovsky, J., 2002. "Synchronized neuronal discharge in the basal ganglia of parkinsonian patients is limited to oscillatory activity" . J. Neuroscience; 22: 2855– 2861
[6] Grill WM, Snyder AN, Miocinovic S. "Deep brain stimulation creates an informational lesion of the stimulated nucleus." Neuroreport. 2004 May 19;15(7):1137-40.
[7] Wingeier B, Tcheng T, Miller Koop M, Hill B, Heit G, Bronte-Stewart H. "Intra-operative STN DBS attenuates the prominent beta rhythm in the STN in Parkinson's disease". Experimental Neurology 2005
[8] D.A. Heldman et.al., "Local field potential spectral tuning in motor cortex during reaching," IEEE Trans. Neural Systems and Rehad. Eng., vol 14, no 2.
[9] Buszaki, G, Rhythms of the Brain, Oxford University Press, 2006.
[10] Beshel, J, Kopell, N, Kay, LM, "Olfactory bulb gamma oscillations are enhanced with task demands," J Neuroscience, 27(31) pp 8358-8365, 2007.
[11] Andersen RA, Musallam S, Pesaran B, "Selecting the signals for a brain-machine interface," Current Opinion in Neurobiology, 14:720-726, 2004.
[12] Denison et al. "A 2,2uW 94nV/Hz, Chopper-Stabilized Instrumentation Amplifier for EEG Detection in Chronic Implants," JSSC, vol 42, No 12, .Page(s):2934-2945.
[13] R.F. Yazicioglu, P. Merken, R. Puers, and C. Van Hoof, "A 60uW 60nV/rtHz Readout Front-End for Portable Biopotential Acquisition Systems," IEEE JSSC, vol. 42, no. 5, pp 1100-1110.
[14] Denison et. at., "An 8uW heterodyning chopper amplifier for direct extraction of 2uVrms brain biomarkers," ISSCC 2008, paper 8.1.
[15] Rossi, L, et.al., "An electronic device for artifact suppression in human local field potentials during deep brain stimulation," Journal of Neural Engineering, 4, pp 96-106, 2007.
[16] Osorio et. al, "Real-time automated detection and quantitative analysis of seizures and short-term prediction of clinical onset," Epilepsia, 39(6):615-627, 1998
[17] Sarpeshkar, R, "Borrowing from biology makes for low-power computing," IEEE Spectrum, pp 24-29, May 2006.
[18] Loeb, G. and Wills, J., "General Purpose Technology for a General Purpose Nervous System," ISCAS 2008, pp 340-343, May 2008.
[19] Garcia L, D'Alessandro G, Bioulac B, Hammond C, "High-frequency stimulation in Parkinson's disease: More or less?" Trends Neurosci, 13: 2758-2771, 2005.
[20] Brown P and Williams D. "Basal ganglia local field potential activity: Character and functional significance in the human". Clinical Neurophysiology pp 116:2510-2519, 2005.

Audio at Low and High Power

Marco Berkhout
NXP Semiconductors
Nijmegen, The Netherlands
Marco.Berkhout@nxp.com

Lucien Breems
NXP Research
Eindhoven, The Netherlands
Lucien.Breems@nxp.com

Ed van Tuijl
Axiom IC
Enschede, The Netherlands
Ed.van.Tuijl@axiom-ic.com

Abstract An overview is presented of recent developments in the analog boundaries of the audio chain. The main focus is on class-D amplifiers that are by now almost standard in consumer applications and emerging in automotive and mobile applications as well. Further, an overview of the state-of-the-art in A/D and D/A conversion is given.

I. INTRODUCTION

The acquisition and reproduction of audio signals was among the first applications of electronic circuits. Nowadays, audio electronics are ubiquitous and can be found in television and hifi-stereo sets, car audio systems and more recently in cellular phones and many other portable applications. The vast majority of these electronics is in the form of integrated circuits. A generic audio chain is shown in figure 1. Nowadays, almost all audio sources are digital with the exception of microphone and line inputs. In case of an analog input it is desirable to convert to the digital domain as soon as possible using an analog-to-digital converter (ADC). A programmable gain amplifier (PGA) adjusts the input signal level to maximize the dynamic range of the ADC.

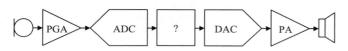

Figure 1. Generic audio processing chain.

At the end of the chain the signal is converted back to analog by a digital-to-analog converter (DAC) and amplified by a power amplifier (PA) before it is delivered to the load. This load can be a loudspeaker, a headphone or a line load. The digital connection between the analog boundaries can be anything ranging from digital signal processing, wired and/or wireless communication links (telephone) to storage and playback systems (CD-player). A system containing a plurality of all these elements in the audio chain is called an *audio codec*. However partitioning of the audio chain is possible in many different ways. The PA is often realized in a dedicated technology allowing for higher voltages and more power. Also ADCs and DACs are available as stand alone parts. The emergence of battery fed applications such as cellular phones and MP3 players has driven the need for reduced power consumption. The current trend is to make the audio chain configurable so that power can be exchanged for performance. On the PA side a gradual but definite shift has taken place from linear class-AB to high efficiency class-D amplifiers.

II. ANALOG TO DIGITAL CONVERSION

The use of ΣΔ modulators in audio ADCs and DACs has already been popular since the 1980's. This is due to the fact that the high-resolution, high-linearity and low-bandwidth audio requirements naturally fit to the characteristics of a one-bit ΣΔ modulator. Today, the ΣΔ modulator has become a versatile solution for many different standards, ranging from sensor applications, audio, AM/FM radio, cellular to connectivity with signal bandwidths in the range from a few Hertz to several tens of MegaHertz. Numerous techniques such as higher-order filters, multi-bit quantizers, cascaded (or MASH) topologies, continuous-time and switched-capacitor filter implementations, data-weighted averaging algorithms, etc. have been pushing the ΣΔ modulator performance to new state-of-the-art data points in terms of bandwidth, resolution, power and figure-of-merit. Many of these techniques also find their entry in audio ΣΔ modulators, as modern technologies put new challenges and constraints on the design of ΣΔ modulators and require different solutions than the traditional one-bit ΣΔ modulator architecture.

A. Switched-capacitor versus switched-current design

The main requirements for audio ΣΔ modulators are: low-voltage, low power, medium to high accuracy and low-cost. High-end audio ADCs have distortion figures better than 95dB and a dynamic range of 100dB. The decreasing feature size of newer technologies, accompanied by a lower supply voltage imposes new challenges for ΣΔ designs. Traditionally, switched-capacitor (SC) implementations of audio ΣΔ modulators are favored over switched-current continuous-time (CT) designs. Switched-capacitor ΣΔ modulators are known for their clock jitter tolerance, precise filter coefficients (defined by capacitor ratios), and high linearity. Moreover, as flicker noise is one of the dominant noise sources in audio ΣΔ modulators, the employment of chopper stabilization techniques is relatively simple in SC designs [1]. Another practical aspect of SC ΣΔ modulators is that they can be scaled with the sampling frequency. A SC ΣΔ modulator can be utilized at different sampling rates without the need for changing the filter coefficients. This way, the bandwidth of the modulator or the audio data rate can be easily scaled. Continuous-time ΣΔ modulators are less clock jitter tolerant, are not scaled easily with the sampling frequency, and compared to SC designs, incorporation of choppers in CT implementations is less common practice.

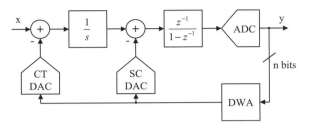

Figure 2.   Combined CT/SC ΣΔ architecture [1]

Continuous-time ΣΔ modulators offer different advantages that have become more and more attractive recently. A CT ΣΔ modulator does not need sampling switches at the input. As the supply voltage lowers for each new technology node, it has become increasingly more difficult to design a high linearity switch. Techniques like voltage boosting and bootstrapping increase the switch performance, but come with a power and area penalty. A CT ΣΔ modulator does not suffer from the switch problem. Another implication of a lowering supply voltage is the reduction of the maximum input signal swing. The lower the input signal amplitude becomes, the lower the circuit noise has to be designed in order to achieve the required resolution. This results in higher power consumption. Utilizing the maximum possible input signal amplitude is therefore from utmost importance, but is difficult to interface to a SC ΣΔ modulator because of the earlier mentioned sampling switch non-linearity. This is one of the main reasons why several recently published audio ΣΔ modulators utilize CT input stages [1,2] as shown in figure 2. Also, CT ΣΔ modulators have been shown to be very power efficient, which is attractive for battery-operated products like portable MP3 players, mobile phones, etc. As the input stage of a CT ΣΔ modulator is resistive, it does not introduce EMI radiation to the input pins of the ADC, which is an issue with SC modulators as a result of clock feed-through of the input sampling stage [2]. Furthermore, a continuous-time ΣΔ modulator has inherent anti-alias suppression, which results in better noise immunity.

B. Audio ΣΔ modulator architectures

To achieve the low quantization noise levels that are needed for high-resolution audio ΣΔ modulators, different architectures can be used, ranging from higher-order one-bit topologies to multi-bit modulators with low-order loopfilters, all with their specific pros and cons. Single-bit ΣΔ modulators have the advantage of superior linearity over multi-bit modulators due to the employment of an inherently linear one-bit DAC. However, one-bit converters suffer from idle in-band tones and require high slew rate, fast settling opamps due to the large error step size [3]. Multi-bit ΣΔ modulators can

achieve similar quantization noise suppression as one-bit converters at a lower sampling frequency and/or filter order [1]. Moreover, multi-bit ΣΔ modulators suffer much less from idle channel tones and have more relaxed opamp requirements due to the smaller error step size. On the other hand, a multi-bit DAC introduces mismatch induced non-linearity in the ΣΔ modulator that puts a limit to the maximum achievable harmonic distortion. Mismatch-shaping algorithms like data-weighted averaging (DWA) with first-order [4,1,2] and second-order [5] spectral shaping of static DAC errors overcome the harmonic distortion limitation and enable the use of multi-bit DACs in high-performance low-distortion audio converters (Figure 2).

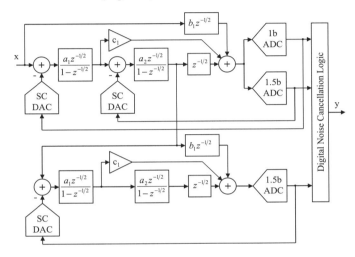

Figure 3.   MASH ΣΔ architecture [6]

Employing a cascaded or MASH (multi-stage noise shaping) ΣΔ modulator topology is a way to achieve high resolution at a much lower oversampling factor compared to single-loop converters. A MASH type ΣΔ modulator incorporates multiple cascaded ΣΔ modulators that process the quantization error of the previous stage. Figure 3 shows a 2-2 MASH ΣΔ architecture for an audio ADC [6]. The lower loop digitizes the quantization error of the upper loop. With digital noise cancellation logic, the quantization noise of the upper loop is highly suppressed. Besides quantization noise, idle tones are also suppressed by the noise cancellation logic. As a result, the architecture proposed in figure 3 combines the excellent linearity of a one-bit feedback DAC in the first ΣΔ loop without the idle tone problems of a single loop one-bit modulator.

III.   CLASS-D POWER AMPLIFIERS

The most important feature of class-D amplifiers is high efficiency that typically is higher than 90% at full output power. This efficiency allows very high output power with modest heat sinking. Output powers well over 100W per channel are no exception [7,8]. Integrated class-D amplifiers typically have distortion better than 70dB and a dynamic range of 100dB.

A basic class-D amplifier is shown in figure 4. At the heart of a class-D amplifier are two low-ohmic switches that alternately connect the output node to the positive or negative supply rail. Usually, some form of Pulse Width Modulation (PWM) is used to encode the audio signal. The audio signal is subsequently retrieved by means of an external LC lowpass filter connected between the class-D output stage and the load.

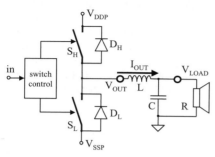

Figure 4.   Basic class-D amplifier.

The simplest form of PWM is so-called natural sampling PWM or NPWM [9]. A NPWM signal can easily be constructed by comparing the audio signal to a triangular reference as shown in figure 5. The fundamental frequency of the triangular reference is usually much higher than the highest audio frequency, e.g. around 350kHz or 8*44.1kHz, and is called the carrier frequency.

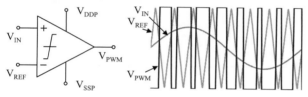

Figure 5.   Natural sampling PWM.

The *modulation depth M* is defined between +1 and –1 and is related to the duty-cycle D of the PWM signal as:

$$M = 2 \cdot D - 1 \qquad (1)$$

Although the generation of NPWM involves a highly nonlinear comparator the frequency spectrum of a NPWM does not contain harmonics of the input signal but only intermodulation products of the carrier and the input signal, i.e., NPWM is free from harmonic distortion. Assuming that the triangular reference has a sufficiently high frequency, the intermodulation products do not fold back to the audio frequency band and are filtered out by the LC lowpass filter. In a practical implementation it is not possible to reproduce the PWM pulses at the output with mathematical precision because the switching output stage introduces timing and amplitude errors that result in distortion.

A class-D output stage can be either single-ended (SE) or differential, yielding a so-called bridge-tied-load (BTL) configuration as shown in figure 6. In a BTL amplifier both sides of the loudspeaker load are driven in opposite (audio) phase. This enables operation from a single supply while doubling the voltage swing across the load, yielding four times more output power than a SE amplifier. Furthermore, the balanced operation cancels out even order distortion. On the

downside, a BTL amplifier needs twice the number of power switches and inductors making it relatively expensive.

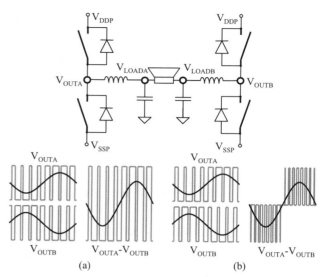

Figure 6.   BTL configuration with (a) AD modulation (b) BD modulation.

In a BTL class-D amplifier the phase of the carriers of both bridge halves can be chosen independently. When the carriers are in opposite phase, as shown in figure 6(a), this is called AD-modulation. The main advantage of AD-modulation is that the output signal has zero common-mode since the bridge halves always switch simultaneously in opposite directions. Conversely, when the carriers are in-phase carriers, as shown in figure 6(b), this is called BD-modulation. Compared to AD-modulation, BD-modulation is much less sensitive to clock jitter. [10]. In practice both modulation types are being used.

IV.   CLASS-D AMPLIFIER ARCHITECTURE

Many Class-D amplifier architectures exist. A coarse division can be made in *open loop* and *closed loop* architectures.

A.   Open Loop Architectures

In open loop class-D amplifiers the PWM signal is generated in the digital domain and directly drives a class-D output stage. In this architecture the class-D output stage itself serves as DAC. Because the PWM signal is generated in the digital domain the effects of *sampling* and *quantization* have to be dealt with.

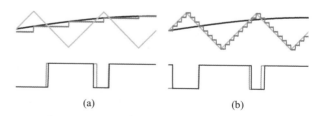

Figure 7.   Digital PWM (a) sampling (b) quantization.

A sampled input signal intersects the reference triangle at different moment than the original modulating signal as illustrated in figure 7(a). The resulting shift of the PWM signal edges cause distortion. In a digital PWM modulator the edges are synchronized to a high-frequency bit-clock, e.g. $256f_s$. Consequently, the pulse widths are quantized to a limited number of discrete values as illustrated in figure 7(b) causing quantization noise.

Sampling and quantization effects can be handled separately or integrally. In a separated approach as shown in figure 8(a) first the distortion caused by sampling is corrected by either approximating NPWM using linear or higher order interpolation [9] or applying pre-correction based on a digital PWM distortion model [11]. Secondly, the quantization noise is shaped out-of-band by a $\Sigma\Delta$ modulator before converting to digital PWM.

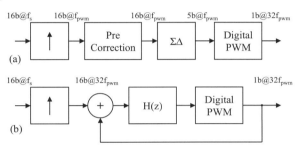

Figure 8.   Digital PWM (a) precorrection (b) PWM-$\Sigma\Delta$.

In an integral approach the digital PWM generator is used as quantizer in a $\Sigma\Delta$ loop yielding a PWM-$\Sigma\Delta$ loop as shown in figure 8(b). A disadvantage of this approach is that the entire loop needs to run at the high bit-clock frequency.

Essentially, with both approaches any required SNR and THD can be achieved at the expense of higher clock rates as long as the signal remains in the digital domain. Actually, even without correction of output stage errors open loop class-D amplifiers can have very good performance [8,12] provided that an accurate regulated power supply is used. Because of the lack off power supply rejection open loop class-D amplifiers are invariably BTL such that at small modulation depths supply variations largely cancel out.

Some attempts have been made to improve power supply rejection by sensing the supply voltage with a DAC and using feed forward correction of the digital PWM signal, but these designs only yield a moderate improvement in power supply rejection [13,14]. Open loop class-D amplifiers can be found mainly in consumer electronics such as television sets and home-theatre systems.

B.   Closed Loop Architectures

An evident way to improve power supply rejection is to apply feedback. Since the output signal of a class-D amplifier is essentially analog most feedback class-D amplifiers require an analog input signal. Closed loop class-D amplifiers can be either *self-oscillating* or *fixed-carrier* based.

1)   Delay Based

A basic self-oscillating class-D feedback loop is the delay based loop shown in figure 9. The oscillating frequency f_{PWM} of the loop is expressed as:

$$f_{PWM} = \frac{1 - M^2}{4 \cdot T_D} \qquad (2)$$

where T_D is the delay time and M is the modulation depth. From (2) can be seen that the switching frequency drops to zero at large modulation depth.

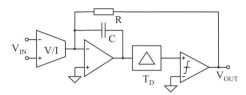

Figure 9.   Delay based self-oscillating class-D feedback loop.

An elegant variation on this topology is described in [15] where the demodulation filter is incorporated in the feedback loop. A delay based self-oscillating class-D amplifier is always stable. The loop transfer is expressed as.

$$A\beta(f) = \frac{2}{\pi} \frac{f_{PWM}}{f} \qquad (3)$$

From (3) it can be seen that the unity-gain frequency of the feedback loop is coupled to the PWM switching frequency f_{PWM}. This is a common characteristic of class-D feedback loops. Because self-oscillating loops have a variable switching frequency it is not straightforward to increase the order of the feedback loop to achieve higher loopgain.

2)   Hysteretic

In a hysteretic class-D feedback loop as shown in figure 10 the output of the loop integrator is constrained within a hysteresis window. The oscillating frequency f_{PWM} of the loop is expressed as:

$$f_{PWM} = \frac{1 - M^2}{4 \cdot h \cdot RC} \qquad (4)$$

where h is the ratio between the hysteresis window and the supply voltage, RC is the time constant of the integrator and M is again the modulation depth.

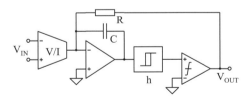

Figure 10.   Hysteretic self-oscillating class-D feedback loop.

At first glance the hysteretic loop appears similar to the delay based loop but they are actually very different when comparing both loop transfers. This is because the hysteresis forces the average value of the integrator output to zero creating a virtual ground for low frequencies. The result is a second order loop transfer:

$$A\beta(f) = \frac{12}{\pi^2} \left(\frac{f_{PWM}}{f} \right)^2 \qquad (5)$$

Note that the unity-gain frequency of this loop transfer is actually higher than the PWM switching frequency f_{PWM}. Unfortunately the loop transfer of hysteretic loops collapses when a delay is introduced in the loop. For large delays the loop transfer of the hysteretic loop converges to that of a delay based loop. Still for modest (realistic) delays the loop transfer of hysteretic loops is always higher than for any other feedback topology, especially at the higher audio frequencies. Very good performance has been reported on discrete hysteretic amplifiers aimed at high-end audio [16]. A hysteretic $\Delta\Sigma$ class-D amplifier with discrete-time PWM output with very impressive performance is presented in [17].

The main drawback of self-oscillating class-D amplifiers is the variable switching frequency. In multi-channel systems differences in switching frequency can cause audible inter-modulation products known as beat tones. Also when the switching frequencies of two channels are nearly equal they tend to lock onto each other, deteriorating the performance. The variable switching frequency is sometimes presented as an EMI advantage since it distributes energy over a range of frequencies [17] but in practice many equipment builders prefer the predictability of fixed carrier class-D amplifiers.

3) Fixed-Carrier

Figure 11(a) shows a fixed-carrier class-D feedback loop where a triangular reference wave V_{REF} is applied at the inverting input of the comparator creating an NPWM generator. The loop transfer of the fixed-carrier feedback loop is expressed as:

$$A\beta(f) = \frac{1}{\pi} \frac{f_{PWM}}{f} \qquad (6)$$

The unity gain frequency is lower than that of self-oscillating loops but because the carrier frequency is fixed it is rather straightforward to upgrade the feedback loop to second order for low frequencies as shown in figure 11(b). In this topology the second integrator both increases the loop order and facilitates generation of the reference triangle V_{REF} [7].

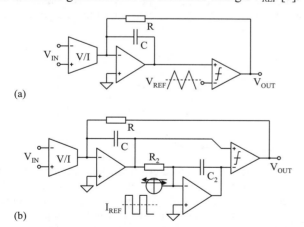

(a)

(b)

Figure 11. Fixed-Carrier class-D feedback loops (a) 1st order (b) 2nd order.

4) Direct Pulse Amplification

The feedback loops shown in figure 11 can be readily modified to accept a PWM instead of audio input signal by

deleting the reference signal. In [18] a class-D amplifier is presented where a feedback loop similar to the one shown in figure 11(b) is driven directly by a bitstream coming from a fifth order noise-shaper running at $64f_s$. Using a digitally generated PWM signal instead has the advantage that the average switching frequency is both reduced *and* constant.

For stability the closed loop gain g needs to be higher than unity to guarantee that the PWM input signal always dominates the feedback. Consequently the modulation depth of the PWM input signal is multiplied by a factor g at the output. The PWM input signal is effectively analog and needs to be well defined in both amplitude and timing. When the PWM source is digital this requires low-jitter re-sampling or, in other words, a high quality one-bit DAC.

V. POWER STAGE DESIGN

It is a common misconception that *dead time* is required to avoid the occurrence of shoot-through currents in class-D power stages. In [19] it is shown that a proper design of the gate driver circuits is both necessary and sufficient.

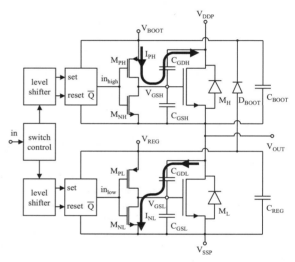

Figure 12. Typical class-D output stage configuration.

In figure 12 a typical class-D output stage is shown in more detail. Two very large DMOS power transistors M_L and M_H are used as switches. Usually n-type power transistors are preferred because they have a lower R_{on}Area product, requiring less area for a given on-resistance, but also complementary output stages are feasible [20]. The backgate diodes of the DMOS transistors serve as fly-back diodes. The lowside gate driver uses an externally decoupled supply V_{REG}. The highside gate driver is supplied from an external capacitor C_{BOOT} that is bootstrapped to V_{REG} with a diode D_{BOOT}. The switching of the output is controlled by a logic circuit *switch control* that communicates with the drivers through high-speed levelshifters [19,8,20]. As can be seen in figure 12, two (identical) inverters $M_{PH/NH}$ and $M_{PL/NL}$ drive the gates of the power transistors M_H and M_L. The dimensions of these inverters together with the parasitic capacitances of the power transistors determine the dynamic behavior of the class-D output stage.

Figure 13 shows some typical waveforms that occur during a rising transition at the output V_{OUT}. The top graphs show the gate-source voltages V_{GSL} and V_{GSH} of the power transistors M_L and M_H respectively. The bottom graph shows the output voltage V_{OUT} and the drain currents I_{DL} and I_{DH} of the power transistors M_L and M_H respectively. The inductor in the demodulation filter forces the output current I_{OUT} to remain nearly constant during output transitions. The output current I_{OUT} can be flowing either towards or from the output stage yielding two scenarios called *soft switching* and *hard switching*.

1) Soft Switching

In case the output transition is supported by the output current this is called soft switching. For a rising output transition this occurs when the output current I_{OUT} flows towards the class-D output stage as shown in figure 13(a). Initially, the lowside power transistor M_L is conducting. Three phases can be distinguished in the transition. Phase I starts when, simultaneously, the input signals in_{high} and in_{low} of both gate drivers change state turning on M_{PH} in the highside and M_{NL} in the lowside. Consequently, the gate of the lowside power transistor M_L is discharged with a current I_{NL} that is proportional to the size of M_{NL}. At the same time the gate of the highside transistor M_H is charged with a current I_{PH} that is proportional to the size of M_{PH}. As soon as V_{GSL} approaches the threshold voltage V_T, the output current I_{OUT} pulls the output node V_{OUT} up entering phase II. During the transition the gate-source voltage V_{GSL} stalls and the discharge current I_{NL} flows almost entirely through lowside gate-drain capacitance C_{GDL}. The slope of the output V_{OUT} is now approximately:

$$\frac{dV_{OUT}}{dt} \approx \frac{I_{NL}}{C_{GDL}} \qquad (7)$$

This slope imposes a current equal to I_{NL} through the highside gate-drain capacitance C_{GDH}. This pushes the gate-source voltage V_{GSH} down under the *mandatory* condition that I_{PH} is smaller than I_{NL}. After the transition phase III starts and the charging of the gate of the highside power transistor M_H is resumed. Remarkably, the currents I_{DL} and I_{DH} through the power transistors hardly change during the output transition but change very abruptly afterwards.

2) Hard Switching

In case the output current resists the output transition this is called hard switching. For a rising output transition this occurs when the output current I_{OUT} flows out of the class-D output stage as shown in figure 13(b).

The start of phase I is identical to the soft switching scenario. As V_{GSH} reaches the threshold level the drain current I_{DH} of highside power transistor M_H starts to build up while the drain current I_{DL} of the lowside power transistor M_L starts to decrease. The sum of these currents equals the output current I_{OUT}. The output node V_{OUT} sticks to the lowside while V_{GSH} increases further until the current I_{DH} through M_H matches the output current I_{OUT}. At this moment the current through the lowside power transistor M_L is zero and one would expect the output node V_{OUT} to start the transition immediately. However the drain current I_{DH} of the highside power transistor M_H keeps

increasing while the current through the lowside power transistor M_L reverses. This happens because there is still minority charge left in the backgate diode that needs to be flushed out. This mechanism, known as *reverse recovery* is probably the most important source of EMI in class-D amplifiers. When the backgate diode finally runs out of minority carriers the reverse recovery current stops abruptly causing the output transition to start at an accelerated pace.

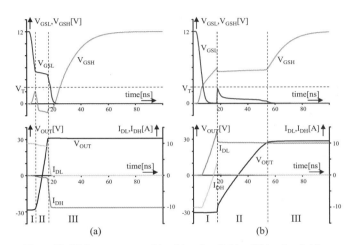

Figure 13. Rising output transition (a) soft switching (b) hard switching.

Subsequently, feedback through the gate-drain capacitance C_{GDH} causes V_{GSH} to be pushed down causing a characteristic 'overshoot' in V_{GSH}. Also the gate of the lowside power transistor M_L is pulled up which can lead to additional peak current if the threshold voltage V_T is exceeded. After this rapid start the transition continues at a more moderate pace during in phase II. During the transition the gate-source voltage V_{GSH} stalls and the charge current I_{PH} flows almost entirely through gate-drain capacitance C_{GDL}. The slope of the output node V_{OUT} is now approximately:

$$\frac{dV_{OUT}}{dt} \approx \frac{I_{PH}}{C_{GDH}} \qquad (8)$$

This slope imposes a current equal to I_{PH} through the lowside gate-drain capacitance C_{GDL} that attempts to pull up the gate of the lowside power transistor M_L. To prevent M_L from turning on discharge current I_{NL} needs to be sufficiently larger than I_{PH}. Because the charge current I_{PH} is smaller than the discharge current I_{NL} the slope of the hard switching transition is less steep than during soft switching. After the transition the charging of the gate of highside power transistor M_H is finalized in third phase III.

VI. DESIGN EXAMPLES

High power class-D amplifiers have become standard in many consumer electronic applications such as television sets and home-theatre systems. Currently, class-D is also making a cautious entrance into the automotive domain. The first integrated class-D audio amplifiers designed to operate directly from the car battery are now entering the market. A third domain where class-D is emerging is in mobile applications such as cellular phones and MP3 players. In these applications the output power is low, e.g. around 1W, so not heat production but extension of battery life is the driver behind class-D.

Class-D amplifiers for both consumer and automotive applications are typically made in dedicated high-voltage technologies [21]. For mobile applications standard CMOS technologies are preferred. Although conceptually similar, class-D amplifiers in the different application domains have to deal with rather different environments.

A. Consumer Electronics

The high volume consumer electronics market is very much cost driven. Moreover there is a tendency towards higher output power and more channels. A major concern with high power class-D amplifiers is robustness. Switching a current of 10A from a 60V supply rail is no trivial matter. During hard switching the peak dissipation in the power transistors easily exceeds 600W. Also, because of extremely high dI/dt's in the supply lines during soft switching the influence of parasitic inductances need to be taken into account. The voltage excursions that occur at the supply terminals can easily exceed the breakdown voltage of the power transistors causing permanent damage.

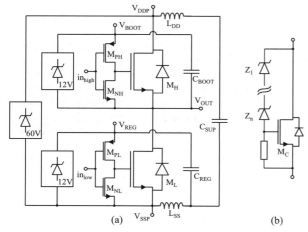

Figure 14. (a) parasitic inductances and voltage clamping (b) active clamp

However, the Achilles heel is the lowside driver because the external decoupling capacitor C_{REG} is in series with inductance L_{SS} as shown in figure 14(a). Consequently, the negative voltage excursions at the source of the lowside power transistor M_L appear directly across the lowside driver circuits that typically have a lower voltage rating. Creating headroom by raising the breakdown voltage would also increase the R_{on}Area product and consequently chip area.

An effective way to prevent damage to the circuits is the use of active voltage clamps as shown in figure 14(b) where a reasonably large transistor M_C is turned on when the voltage across the terminals exceeds a limit that is determined by the number of Zener diodes in the stack and can be tuned to match the breakdown voltage of power transistors. In this way power transistors can be used with a minimal overhead in breakdown voltage.

B. Automotive

Audio amplifiers aimed at automotive applications are very similar to those for consumer electronics but demands on robustness and EMI are more stringent. Automotive audio amplifiers are supplied directly from the 14.4V car battery and have a BTL configuration by default in order to get enough output power. However, open loop amplifiers are unacceptable since the battery voltage is rather noisy. In addition to supply noise the amplifier needs to deal with extreme supply voltage excursions. During *engine start* the battery voltage can drop from 14.4V to 6V while the amplifier needs to continue playing without causing audible artifacts. When the battery is disconnected while the engine is running *load dump* occurs causing the supply voltage to surge up to as high as 50V. Since the audio amplifier is supplied directly from the battery it needs to be capable of surviving this condition. This leads to a different clamping strategy to limit inductive voltage peaking compared to the high voltage designs in consumer applications. In terms of area it is more economical to use power transistors with a lower breakdown voltage and distribute the load dump voltage between them. In that case it is not possible anymore to use a central active clamp as shown previously. Instead a separate clamp is added parallel to each power transistor with an ignition voltage below the breakdown voltage of the power transistors as shown in figure 15.

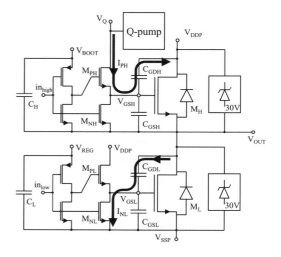

Figure 15. Automotive class-D output stage

As can be seen also the gate driver topology is different. This is because the preferred format for automotive amplifiers is the four-channel quad. When using external bootstrapping this adds up to eight external capacitors requiring eight pins. Therefore it makes sense to use a single externally decoupled charge-pump to generate the drive voltage for the highside power transistors. The voltage slope at the output during hard switching transitions is now controlled by the gate-drain capacitance $C_{GDL,GDH}$ of the power transistors and the g_m of the source followers $M_{PL/PH}$. The inverters driving the source followers $M_{PL/PH}$ can be decoupled with small on-chip capacitors $C_{L/H}$.

C. Mobile

The need for class-D amplifiers in mobile applications is driven by the demand for longer battery life and again more output power. Three product types can be seen where class-D is emerging.

Class-D amplifiers are being integrated in audio codecs that are part of large mixed-signal SoC's where GSM baseband and audio interfaces (ABB) are combined [22]. A block diagram of such an audio codec, shown in figure 16. contains multiple analog microphone and line inputs and analog speaker, headphone and line outputs. These complex systems are typically realized in advanced deep submicron CMOS technologies.

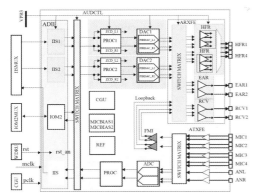

Figure 16. Audio codec in typical ABB system.

In direct competition with the ABB are power management units (PMU) that can be found in cellular phones but also many other portable applications such as PDA's and MP3 players. Such PMU chips are often made in dedicated CMOS technologies with high voltage capabilities that facilitate the realization of switch-mode DC/DC converters that are akin to class-D amplifiers. These technologies are generally better suited for the implementation of class-D amplifiers and a convergence of PMU with audio codecs is ongoing. Besides integration in ABB or PMU there is a significant market for stand-alone class-D amplifiers.

Output power for speaker drivers in mobile applications is typically in the range from 500mW to 1W. The output stage is preferably connected directly to the battery [23]. This battery voltage ranges between 2.5V and 4.5V and can even be as high as 5.5V during charging. A high power supply rejection is essential especially in cell phones because the battery voltage is polluted by the characteristic 217 Hz interval of the transmit power amplifier. Consequently, class-D amplifiers with feedback are preferred. A key feature in mobile class-D amplifiers is filterless operation. In a BTL amplifier that uses BD-modulation the amount of differential mode high frequency energy is reduced compared to AD-modulation. In this case the speaker itself can act as filtering element provided that the speaker is close to the amplifier output.

Class-D amplifiers in mobile applications are typically realized in standard CMOS technologies. The maximum allowed voltage between the device terminals is usually much lower than 5.5V. In this case cascodes can be used to distribute voltage between devices. A simplified cascoded class-D power stage is shown in figure 17.

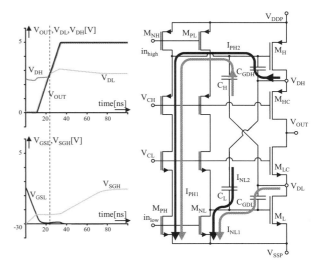

Figure 17. Cascoded class-D output stage for direct battery hookup.

The highside PMOS transistors do not require bootstrapping. The cascodes $M_{LC/HC}$ are biased such that when the corresponding power transistor is switched off the supply voltage is distributed evenly. To maintain slope control during the output transitions two capacitors $C_{L/H}$ are added that match the gate-drain capacitances $C_{GDL/GDH}$ of the power transistors $M_{L/H}$. During the first half of a rising edge transition the lowside cascade M_{LC} is in the linear region while the highside cascade M_{HC} is off. In this case the voltage V_{DL} at the drain of power transistor M_L follows the output voltage V_{OUT} and the voltage slope is determined by current I_{PH1} and capacitor C_H. During the second half M_{HC} is in the linear region and M_{LC} is off. In this case the voltage V_{DH} at the drain of the highside power transistor M_H follows the output voltage V_{OUT} and the voltage slope is determined by the current I_{PH2} and gate-drain capacitance C_{GDH}.

D. Headphone amplifiers

Headphone amplifiers are typically stereo SE with a common return line. Operation from a single supply rail is realized with AC-coupling as shown in figure 18(a). Typical output power ranges from 10mW to 100mW.

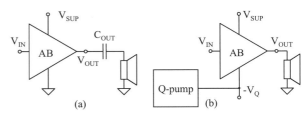

Figure 18. Headphone amplifiers (a) AC coupled (b) True ground

At such low output power there is not much to be gained by using class-D. Besides, the relatively long cable that is usually connects to the headphone excludes the possibility of filterless operation. Instead the current trend is class-AB with a negative supply rail to enable so-called true ground application as shown in figure 18(b) that eliminates the coupling capacitor C_{OUT}. Because of the modest power requirements the negative supply voltage can be generated with a charge-pump circuit.

VII. DIGITAL TO ANALOG CONVERSION

High-end audio DACs [24] have distortion figures better than 100 dB, a resolution of 16 bit or more and a dynamic range of more than 100 dB in the audioband. Older designs have 16 to 18 bit resolution, 2 to 4 times oversampling and binary weighted current sources to make the output signal. The high precision is realized by trimming or Dynamic Element Matching (DEM) techniques [25,26]. Later designs use high oversampling rates (128, 192, $256f_s$) and low resolution (1-5bits). The resulting quantization noise is suppressed in the audioband by aggressive noise shaping in the digital front-end of the ($\Sigma\Delta$) DAC. The out-of-band noise must be attenuated to a level lower than -60 dB by an analog low-pass filter or by Finite Impulse Response (FIR) filtering in the DAC output [27]. Both switched-current continuous-time (CT) and switched-capacitor (SC) outputs are used. The demands on the analog precision of the output circuit are high. In one-bit DACs the clock jitter must be extremely low and the symmetry of the rising and falling edges of the output signal must be near perfect to limit the effect of Inter Symbol Interference (ISI). In multi-bit DACs the accuracy of the DAC elements must be very high as it determines the linearity of the converter. DEM techniques like DWA are used to improve on this. The tolerance to clock jitter is better because the steps in the output signal are smaller.

A. D/A Conversion for closed-loop Class-D Amplifiers

Audio signal sources are dominantly digital while class-D (and class-AB) audio amplifiers are fundamentally analog. Although PWM signals can be generated in the digital domain it is not self-evident to maintain the signal quality in the power output stage of the class-D amplifier. This quality depends on the precision of the edges of the class-D output stage and the stability of the supply voltage. Therefore class-D amplifiers with analog feedback are preferred having better audio performance at lower cost. However, the input signal must be analog so a DAC is needed in front of the class-D amplifier. Most modern audio DAC solutions have an output signal that still contains considerable out-of-band noise. The combination of DAC with closed-loop class-D amplifiers requires dedicated architectures to avoid intermodulation of out-of-band quantization noise back into the audio band [28,29].

An attractive D/A architecture for combination with class-D amplifiers is a digital PWM modulator followed by a FIRDAC as shown in figure 19. A FIRDAC performs D/A conversion and lowpass filtering simultaneously. The advantage of using a digital PWM signal instead of a bitstream from a one-bit $\Sigma\Delta$ modulator is the transition rate is signal independent. Due to the fixed transition rate that is inherent to PWM signals, distortion caused by ISI is eliminated completely. Digital audio PCM signals have a high resolution ranging from 16 to 24 bits. To convert of a high resolution PCM signal to a digital PWM signal without degrading signal quality a number of digital signal processing steps is needed.

Starting from a 16-bit non-oversampled ($1f_s$) input signal, for example from a CD player, upsampling and interpolation is needed to get to a convenient PWM frequency. The first stage performs 8 times upsampling to $8f_s$ and is then lowpass filtered to remove the aliases.

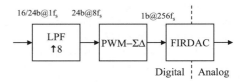

Figure 19. PWM $\Sigma\Delta$ FIRDAC

A 16 bit resolution in the pulse width would require a unpractical high clock frequency of 23 GHz. Therefore the signal is truncated to 4-bit PWM resolution in a PWM-$\Sigma\Delta$ noiseshaper resulting in a $256f_s$ PWM bitstream with a $16f_s$ transition rate. The PWM signal still contains a lot of out-of-band quantisation noise. This noise attenuated effectively by the FIRDAC structure.

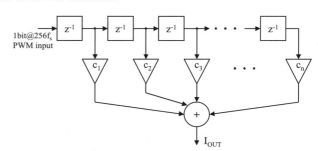

Figure 20. FIRDAC block diagram

A block diagram of the FIRDAC is shown in figure 20. It consists of a digital delayline for the PWM bitstream. Each delayline tap is connected to a one-bit DAC. Each one-bit DAC is a switchable differential current source. The value of the current is proportional to the coefficient value that is needed to get the intended filter characteristics. An important observation is that all separate one-bit DACs work in parallel. Since a one-bit converter with a PWM bitstream input produces no distortion, the summation of the independent output signals does not add any distortion by itself either. The filtering comes from the summation of delayed (and weighted) versions of the same output signal. Errors in the coefficient weight factors only influence the filter characteristic, mainly in the stopband. To attenuate the out-of-band noise to less than -60dB an averaging Hamming filter with 320 coefficients is used. The FIRDAC solution not only shows high attenuation of the out-of-band noise, it also produces an output signal with very small output steps. Because of these small steps the FIRDAC is quite insensitive to clock jitter. For 110dB SNR in the audioband the clock jitter can be as high as 6ns whereas a one-bit converter needs a clock jitter of a few picoseconds for the same SNR.

The chip area of a FIRDAC depends on the required coefficient accuracy that determines the stopband attenuation. The SNR increases with higher DAC output currents because the gate-source voltage of the current source transistors increases leading to a more optimal biasing for noise. Details about noise and filter optimization can be found in [30]. From this article it can be concluded that the FIRDAC area scales down considerably with improving lithography and thinner gate oxide. The PWM-ΣΔ FIRDAC is not only favorable in combination with class-D amplifiers. Besides being tolerant to jitter and ISI the PWM-ΣΔ FIRDAC is generally insensitive to signal dependent disturbances. This facilitates portability of design and makes the PWM-ΣΔ FIRDAC very attractive as general-purpose audio DAC.

VIII. CONCLUSION

Employing a continuous-time input filter in a traditionally favored switched-capacitor audio ΣΔ modulator overcomes the input sampling switch non-linearity that becomes more problematic at lower supply voltages. MASH ΣΔ converters and multi-bit A/D and D/A architectures incorporating data weighted averaging algorithms achieve excellent linearity and suffer much less from idle channel tones compared to a single-loop one-bit ΣΔ modulator.

Class-D amplifiers are largely replacing class-AB in most application areas. Fixed-carrier closed loop architectures are widely preferred mainly because they have good power supply rejection. Different application domains result in different topologies for the output stage but the switching dynamics remain essentially the same.

The PWM-ΣΔ FIRDAC is an attractive D/A architecture especially for combination with class-D amplifiers because it offers good out-of-band noise suppression and high linearity.

ACKNOWLEDGEMENTS

The authors would like to thank M. Helfenstein at NXP Semiconductors and D. Schinkel and W. Groothedde at Axiom-IC for their valuable contribution to the paper.

REFERENCES

[1] P. Morrow, *et al.*, "A 0.18μm 102dB-SNR Mixed CT SC Audio-Band ΔΣ ADC", *ISSCC Dig. Tech. Papers*, pp. 178-179, Feb. 2005.

[2] K. Nguyen, R. Adams, K. Sweetland, H. Chen, "A 106-dB SNR Hybrid Oversampling Analog-to-Digital Converter for Digital Audio", *IEEE J. Solid-State Circuits*, Vol. 40, No. 12, pp. 2408-2415, Dec. 2005.

[3] K. Nguyen, B. Adams, K. Sweetland, "A 105dB SNR Multibit ΣΔ ADC for Digital Audio Applications", *Proc. IEEE CICC*, pp. 27-30, May. 2001.

[4] M.J. Story, "Digital to analogue converter adapted to select input sources based on preselected algorithm once per cycle of a sampling signal", U.S. patent No. 5,138,317, Aug. 11, 1992.

[5] E. Fogleman, J. Welz, I. Galton, "An Audio ADC Delta-Sigma Modulator with 100dB SINAD and 102dB DR Using a Second-Order Mismatch-Shaping DAC", *Proc. IEEE CICC*, pp. 17-20, May. 2000.

[6] G. Ahn, *et al.*, "A 0.6V 82dB ΔΣ Audio ADC Using Switched-RC Integrators", *ISSCC Dig. Tech. Papers*, pp. 166-167, Feb. 2005.

[7] M. Berkhout, "An Integrated 200W Class-D Audio Amplifier", *IEEE J. Solid-State Circuits*, vol. 38, no. 7, pp 1198-1206, July 2003.

[8] F. Nyboe, C. Kaya, L. Risbo and P. Andreani., "A 240W Monolithic Class-D Audio Amplifier Output Stage", *ISSCC Dig. Tech Papers*, Feb. 2006.

[9] K. Nielsen, "A Review and Comparison of Pulse Width Modulation (PWM) Methods For Analog and Digital Input Switching Power Amplifiers", presented at the 102nd AES Convention, Munich, Germany, March 1997.

[10] M. Berkhout, "Clock Jitter in Class-D Audio Power Amplifiers", *Proc. ESSCIRC*, pp.444-447, Sept. 2007.

[11] L. Risbo and T. Mørch, "Performance of an all-digital power amplification system", presented at the 104th AES Convention, Amsterdam, The Netherlands, May 1998.

[12] C. Neesgaard, *et al.*, "Class D Digital Power Amp (PurePath Digital™) High Q Musical Content", *Proc. ISPSD*, pp.97-100, 2004.

[13] L. Zhang, J. Melanson, J. Gaboriau, M. Hagge and R. Boudreaux, "Real-time Power Supply Compensation for Noise-shaped Class D Amplifier", presented at the 117th AES Convention, San Fransisco, USA, October 2004.

[14] J. Tol, *et al.*, "A Digital Class-D Amplifier with Power Supply Correction", presented at the 121st AES Convention, San Fransisco, USA, October 2006.

[15] B. Putzeys, "Simple Self_oscillating Class D Amplifier with Full Output Filter Control", presented at the 118th AES Convention, Barcelona, Spain, May 2005.

[16] P. van der Hulst, A. Veltman and R. Groenenberg, "An Asynchronous Switching High-end Power Amplifier", presented at the 112th AES Convention, Munich, Germany, May 2002.

[17] E. Gaalaas, B.Y. Liu, N. Nishimura, R. Adams and K. Sweetland, "Integrated Stereo ΔΣ Class D Amplifier", *IEEE J. Solid-State Circuits*, vol. 40, no. 12, pp 2388-2397, December 2005.

[18] K. Philips, J. van den Homberg and C. Dijkmans, "PowerDAC: A single-chip audio DAC with a 70%-efficient power stage in 0.5 mm CMOS", *ISSCC Dig. Tech Papers*, pp. 154-155, Feb. 1999.

[19] M. Berkhout, "A Class-D Output Stage with Zero Dead Time", *ISSCC Dig. Tech Papers*, pp.134-135, Feb. 2003.

[20] P. Morrow, E. Gaalaas and O. McCarthy, "A 20-W Stereo Class-D Audio Output Power Stage in 0.6-mm BCDMOS Technology", *IEEE J. Solid-State Circuits*, vol. 39, no. 11, pp 1948-1958, November 2004.

[21] P. Wessels, *et al.* "Advanced BCD technology for automotive audio and power applications", *Solid-State Electronics*, no. 51, pp.195-211, 2007.

[22] B. Baggini, *et al.* "Baseband and Audio Mixed-Signal Front-End IC for GSM/EDGE Applications", *IEEE J. Solid-State Circuits*, vol. 41, no. 6, pp.1364-1379, June 2006.

[23] B. Forejt, V. Rentala, J.D. Arteaga and G. Burra, "A 700+mW Class D Design With Direct Battery Hookup in a 90-nm Process", *IEEE J. Solid-State Circuits*, vol. 40, no. 9, pp.1880-1887, September 2005.

[24] R. Adams, K. Nguyen and K. Sweetland, "A 113dB SNR Oversampling DAC with Segmented Noise- Shaped Scrambling," *ISSCC Dig. Tech. Papers*, pp.62-63, Feb. 1998.

[25] I. Fujimori, A. Nogi and T. Sugimoto, "A Multi-Bit ΣΔ Audio DAC with 120dB Dynamic Range", *ISSCC Dig. Tech. Papers*, pp. 152-153, Feb. 1999.

[26] E. van Tuijl, J. van den Homberg, D. Reefman, C. Bastiaansen and L. van der Dussen, "A 128fs Multi-Bit ΣΔ CMOS Audio DAC with Real-Time DEM and 115dB SFDR", *ISSCC Dig. Tech Papers*, pp.368-369, Feb. 2004.

[27] D.K. Su and B.A. Wooley, "A CMOS Oversampling D/A Converter with a Current-Mode Semidigital Reconstruction Filter", *IEEE J. Solid-State Circuits*, vol.28, no.12, pp.1224-1233, December 1993.

[28] A. Grosso, E. Botti, F. Stefani and M. Ghioni, "A 250W Audio Amplifier with Straightforward Digital Input – PWM Output Conversion", *Proc. ESSCIRC*, pp.225-228, Sept 2001.

[29] T. Ido, S. Ishizuka, L. Risbo, F. Aoyagi and T. Hamasaki, "A Digital Input Controller for Audio Class-D Amplifiers with 100W 0.004% THD+N and 113dB DR", *ISSCC Dig. Tech Papers*, pp.1366-1375, Feb. 2006.

[30] T. Doorn, *et al*, "An audio FIR-DAC in a BCD process for high power Class-D amplifiers" *Proc. ESSCIRC*, pp.459-462, Sept. 2005.

Experimental Assessment of Logic Circuit Performance Variability with Regular Fabrics at 90nm Technology Node

Sungdae Choi, Katsuyuki Ikeuchi, Hyunkyung Kim, Kenichi Inagaki, Masami Murakata*, Nobuyuki Nishiguchi*, Makoto Takamiya and Takayasu Sakurai

The University of Tokyo, Japan
* Semiconductor Technology Academic Research Center (STARC), Japan
(sungdae@iis.u-tokyo.ac.jp)

Abstract□ **Regular fabric structure is expected to reduce the process variations and increase the yield in sub-micron technology regime. Few experimental assessments, however, for the effectiveness of the regular structures has been carried out yet. In this paper, three kinds of circuit blocks are implemented with four kinds of layout styles with different regularity, and the effect of regularity on the circuit performance variations is evaluated. A test chip is fabricated with 90nm CMOS logic process and measured results show that the regular structure increases average delay, and the worst delay of the regular structure is not better than the worst delay of normal circuits with irregular standard cells.**

I. INTRODUCTION

Performance variations due to the device mismatches and random process parameters are crucial problems to reduce the chip cost as the technology scales down to deep submicron. Many researches find out the source of the variations [1, 2, 3], and regular fabric structure is expected to be one of the promising solutions [4, 5, 6] in the circuit design level. There are, however, few researches on how much regular structures are attractive from the variation and performance point of view, although layout is revealed to have huge impact on lithography-induced variability [7]. This work focuses on the effect of the layout regularity on the performance and variations of the chip.

II. TEST STRUCTURES WITH VARIOUS LAYOUT STYLES

3- and 11-stage ring oscillators (RO3, RO11) with four layout patterns, composition of regular and irregular MOSFET fabric structure and interconnections, are implemented. And the effects of the regularity on the circuit performance and variation are analyzed by measuring the oscillation frequency of each RO. The oscillation frequency is determined only by the devices which construct the RO chain. And the frequency is more robust to noise than voltage and current. Adders with best-effort clock operation are also implemented with various layout patterns to survey the performance and variations in practical logic which is more complicated than simple ROs. They are design to generate periodic signal as soon as they finish the calculation so that the measured frequency distributions represent the performance and variations. Each of RO and adder patterns has 128 and 64 samples, respectively, and the frequency is measured using

specially-cared frequency dividers (FD). Since the variation of each device is averaged out as the number of the oscillation stage increases [8], the oscillation frequencies of RO3, the shortest number of oscillation stage, maximize the effect of the local random variations. RO11s are measured in order to compare the effect of the number of the logic stage. 16-bit ripple-carry adders with best-effort clock operation show the results of practical circuit situations.

Fig. 1 shows the block diagram of RO3s and RO11s. ROs consist of static logic gates such as NAND, NOR and inverter. All ROs place neighbored to keep the layout regularity. And all edges of the regularity-considered area are filled with regular dummy patterns to prevent the systematic variations of edge-placed samples. In the peripheral area, each FD with minimum capacitive load is dedicated to a single RO to minimize the interconnection load and preserve the RO's characteristic frequency. Once the frequency is divided and buffered, it passes through the shared dividing path which consists of FD and XOR gates. External address activates only one RO at a time, and corresponding frequency passes through the shared dividing blocks. Shared dividing path of RO3, RO11 and adder has 10, 7 and 6 FDs, respectively, so that the generated frequencies show order of MHz range from the pad and are easy to measure with off-chip measurement.

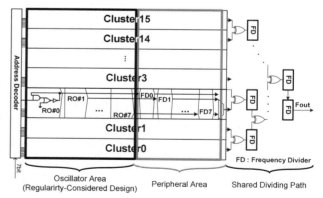

Fig. 1 Block diagram of ROs structure (16 clusters x 8 ROs)

The FD with minimum capacitive load shown in the Fig. 2 is required to catch the oscillation frequency of RO3 which generates order of gigahertz oscillation range. The simple D-Flip/Flop-based FD divides up to 8-GHz signal by two on the post-layout simulation. Due to its simplicity and the layout considering minimum parasitic capacitance, it consumes 0.14mW power with 4.7GHz input frequency. Measured data show that it successfully divides average 4.7GHz of RO3 oscillation frequency.

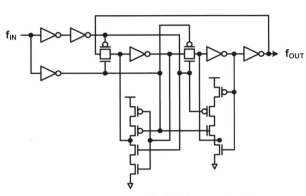

Fig. 2 Minimum capacitive load frequency divider

Fig. 3 shows the block diagram and operation flow of the best-effort clock operation adder. It executes two calculations, critical-path calculation and recovery calculation so that the MSB carry-out generates oscillatory signal.

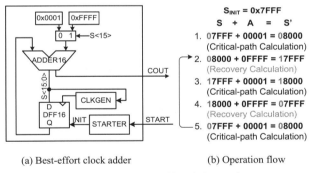

(a) Best-effort clock adder   (b) Operation flow

Fig. 3 Adder with best-effort clock operation

Each RO and adder block is implemented with four kinds of layout styles, namely regular transistor layout (RT) with regular interconnections (RI), RT with irregular interconnections (iRI), irregular transistor (iRT) with RI, and iRT with iRI. Fig. 4 shows the layout regularity of each style. RT is implemented with the Sea-of-Gates (SOG) design style using gate-isolation method as shown in the Fig. 4 (a) to keep the pattern of all MOSFETs equal, while iRT is implemented with normal standard cells. The cell

height of RT is 27% higher than that of iRT, as is found in other RT designs [5]. For regular interconnection, all the widths and spaces use minimum design rule regulations, and dummy metal bars are inserted in the empty area. For irregular interconnections, metals have various widths and no dummy bars are used.

Fig. 5 shows equivalent schematics of RO3 and RO11 with RT and iRT patterns. SOG using gate-isolation method causes redundant MOSFETs between logic gate separations as shown in the Fig. 5 (a) and (c). SOG using oxide-isolation eliminates such redundancy, but it doesn't guarantee the diffusion regularity. Size of all transistors is the same in all ROs, while size of transistors in adders varies. Core area overhead of RO3, RO11 and adder block with RT design style increases 25%, 28% and 85% compared with those of iRT implementations, respectively.

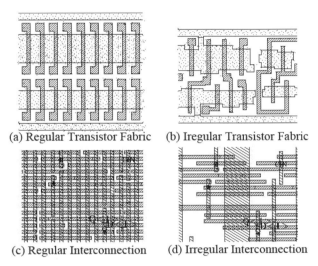

(a) Regular Transistor Fabric   (b) Iregular Transistor Fabric

(c) Regular Interconnection   (d) Irregular Interconnection

Fig. 4 Regular/Irregular Transistor/Interconnection layout

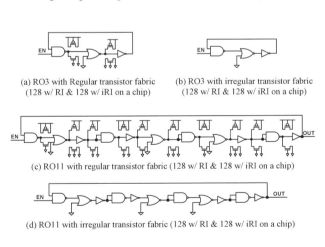

(a) RO3 with Regular transistor fabric
(128 w/ RI & 128 w/ iRI on a chip)

(b) RO3 with irregular transistor fabric
(128 w/ RI & 128 w/ iRI on a chip)

(c) RO11 with regular transistor fabric (128 w/ RI & 128 w/ iRI on a chip)

(d) RO11 with irregular transistor fabric (128 w/ RI & 128 w/ iRI on a chip)

Fig. 5 RO schematics with RT and iRT layouts

Fig. 6 shows the test chip implemented with 90nm CMOS logic process. 11 kinds of patterns are implemented in 1.6mm x 0.9mm core area. For ROs, each layout style has 128 samples and adder block has 64 samples for each style on a chip. Frequencies of 11 dies, 1216 samples for each die, are automatically measured using LabVIEW [9], and analyzed to figure out the performance variations.

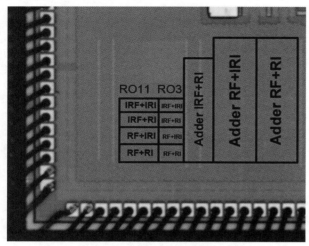

Fig. 6 Measured test chip

III. CYCLE TIME DISTRIBUTIONS

Fig. 7 distributes the average cycle time (μ) and its 3σ (standard deviation) of 11 test chips. For RO3 shown in Fig. 7 (a), composition of RT and RI shows the largest μ, and iRT+iRI shows the shortest μ among 4 different layout styles. With the same transistor layout style, that is, if RT or iRT is fixed, RI is 3% slower than iRI. And RT is 18% and 17% slower than iRT with the same RI and iRI, respectively. The 3σ range is similar to each other, regardless of the layout regularity. This is because the random dopant fluctuation dominates the variation, which can not be controlled by layout style.

In RO11 shown in Fig. 7 (b), average of RT is 23% and 24% slower than iRT in equal RI and iRI condition, respectively. And RI is 1% and 2% slower than iRI with RT and iRT condition, respectively. Again the random dopant fluctuation dominates the variation, which is independent from the layout styles. For all 11 test chips, worst cycle time of iRTs doesn't exceed that of best cycle time of RT, which means that the regular fabrics does not show any advantage over normal standard cell approach in both worst-case performance and area.

Since the blocks in adders run asynchronously to generate a clock, it happens to be very sensitive to glitch noise. This phenomenon unexpectedly acts as a performance variability magnifier. With the help of these magnifying effects, RT styles show much larger variation than iRT counterpart, as shown in Fig. 7 (c). RT design style has more coupling capacitance among lines,

which makes noisier environments. The increase of average delay time in RT is mainly due to the area increase and correspdoing load increase.

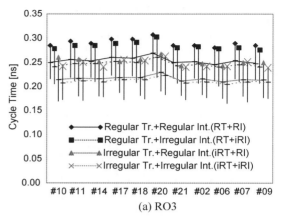

(a) RO3

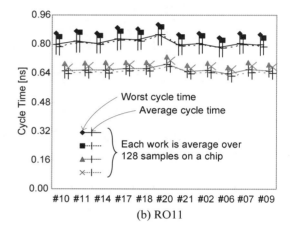

(b) RO11

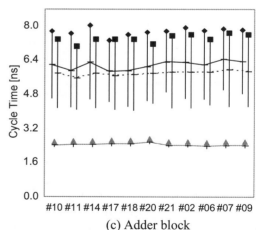

(c) Adder block

Fig. 7 Average and 3s variation error bar of measured cycle time. Numbers on x-axis indicates the chip number.

Normalized variation (σ/μ) increases as V_{DD} decreases, as seen in Fig. 8. But the conclusion that regular fabric does not help improve the worst-case performance is unchanged as is shown in Fig. 9 which depicts variation at 0.7V V_{DD}.

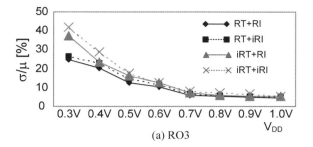

(a) RO3

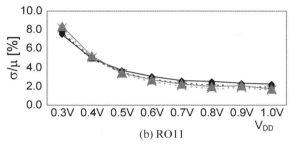

(b) RO11

Fig. 8 Normalized variation (σ/μ) of ROs at various V_{DD}

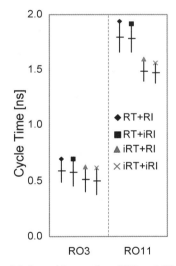

Fig. 9 Delay and 3σ error bar of ROs at 0.7V V_{DD}

IV. CONCLUSIONS

Three kinds of circuits are implemented with four layout styles with different regularities and the oscillating frequencies are measured to investigate the effect of regular structures on the performance. Regular transistor fabric significantly degrades the performance due to its larger parasitic capacitance but doesn't reduce the variations, since the variations mostly come from the random dopant effects. Regular interconnection fabric shows negligible performance reduction with no variation reduction. Thus, the regular fabric does not help improve the worst-case performance.

ACKNOWLEDGEMENT

This work is partially supported by STARC. The VLSI chips were fabricated through the chip fabrication program of VLSI Design and Education Center (VDEC), the University of Tokyo, with the collaboration by STARC, Fujitsu Limited, Matsushita Electric Industrial Company Limited., NEC Electronics Corporation, Renesas Technology Corporation, and Toshiba Corporation.

REFERENCES

[1] Marcel J.M. Pelgrom, et al., "Matching Properties of MOS Transistors," IEEE J. Solid-State Circuits, pp. 1433-1440, Oct. 1989

[2] Sani Nassif, "Delay Variability: Sources, Impacts and Trends," ISSCC Dig. Tech. Papers, pp. 368-369, Feb. 2000

[3] Saibal Mukhopadhyay, et al., "Statistical Characterization and On-Chip Measurement Methods for Local Random Variability of a Process Using Sense-Amplifier-Based Test Structure," IEEE Dig. Tech. Papers, pp. 400-401, Feb. 2007

[4] L. Pileggi, et al., "Exploring Regular Fabrics to Optimize the Performance-Cost Trade-Off," DAC, pp. 782-787, 2003

[5] V. Kheterpal, et al., "Design Methodology for IC Manufacturability Based on Regular Logic-Bricks," DAC, pp. 353-358, 2005

[6] T. Jhaveri, et al., "Maximization of Layout Printability/Manufacturability by Extreme Layout Regularity," SPIE Invited paper, Feb. 2006

[7] Borivoje Nikolic, et al., "Measurements and Analysis of Process Variability in 90nm CMOS," IEEE ICSICT, pp. 505-508, Oct. 2006

[8] Bowman, K. A., et al., "Impact of die-to-die and within-die parameter fluctuations on the maximum clock frequency distribution for gigascale integration," IEEE J. Solid-State Circuits, pp. 183-190, Feb. 2002

[9] LabVIEW by National Instruments: http://www.ni.com/labview/

Area/Yield Trade-offs in Scaled CMOS SRAM Cell

Vasudha Gupta* and Mohab Anis*†

*Department of Electrical and Computer Engineering, University of Waterloo, Waterloo, ON, Canada N2L3G1
†Spry Design Automation, Waterloo, ON, Canada N2J4P9
Email:{vgupta, manis}@vlsi.uwaterloo.ca

Abstract—A statistical design method, for the SRAM bit-cell, is proposed to ensure a high yield, while meeting the specifications of stability, writability, read speed, leakage and area. Optimal bit-cell designs in the 65nm, 45nm and 32nm technologies are derived. It is demonstrated that memory partitioning and longer transistors enable smaller transistor widths, and a close to 50% scaling of the bit-cell area with technology.

Index Terms—SRAM (Static random access memory), optimization.

I. INTRODUCTION

Increasing variability with technology scaling causes the design metrics of fabricated SRAMs to differ significantly from their respective targets, which degrades the memory yield [1]. Researchers have tried to incorporate upfront, the statistical variations in the design metrics, into the SRAM bit-cell design [2]. However, [2] considers only the within-die V_{th} variations due to random dopant fluctuations (RDF) and neglects the inter-die variations in the transistor dimensions. [2] uses transient metrics like the access and write times, which vary with the array size. Moreover, the resultant design need not be optimal because the joint failure probabilities are neglected. The use of analytical models in [2], for transistor characteristics and design metrics, is impractical for industry use. The contributions of this work are:

1) A statistical method for the SRAM bit-cell design is proposed. To the best of our knowledge, this is the first method that incorporates the impact of both types of variations on the design metrics; the inter-die variations in the transistor sizes and the within-die V_{th} variations due to RDF. No analytical modeling for either the transistor characteristics or the design metrics is involved. Modeling is used to estimate variability and yield. The current industrial SRAM bit-cell design relies on iterations of manual transistor size selection, verified by Monte Carlo (MC) simulations, and may take 3 to 4 weeks. Compared to this, the proposed method derives the optimal design in a day or two.

2) Optimal bit-cells in the 65nm, 45nm and 32nm are derived to study the impact of technology scaling on area and yield. The industry expectation of scaling the bit-cell area by 50%, is explored.

3) Memory partitioning and longer transistors are proposed to improve the bit-cell area scaling. Counter-intuitively, progressively longer than nominal transistor lengths (e.g., nominal length in the 45nm technology is 45nm) improve the bit-cell stability, allow narrower widths; therefore, a falling cell ratio provides close to 50% area scaling.

II. PRELIMINARIES

A. Design Constraints

The schematic and layout views of a 6T SRAM bit-cell are depicted in Fig.1. VL is at logic "0" and VR is at logic "1". In this paper, the static noise margin (SNM), write switching voltage (Vtrip), read speed, leakage and area are considered as the five metrics for the bit-cell design. These topics are well-understood in literature [1]. The first four are measured by DC simulation. The read speed or access time depends on the time t_{diff}, required to develop a differential voltage between the bit-lines, as one of them discharges during the *read* operation [1]. $t_{diff} = C_{BL} \times \Delta V / I_{read} \Rightarrow I_{read}/C_{BL} = \Delta V / t_{diff}$. Here, C_{BL} is the bit-line capacitance, ΔV is the differential voltage required for

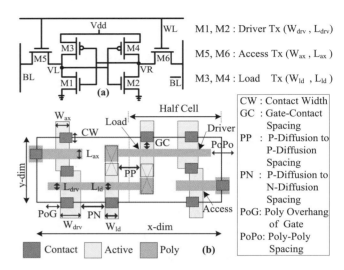

M1, M2 : Driver Tx (W_{drv}, L_{drv})

M5, M6 : Access Tx (W_{ax}, L_{ax})

M3, M4 : Load Tx (W_{ld}, L_{ld})

CW : Contact Width
GC : Gate-Contact Spacing
PP : P-Diffusion to P-Diffusion Spacing
PN : P-Diffusion to N-Diffusion Spacing
PoG: Poly Overhang of Gate
PoPo: Poly-Poly Spacing

Fig. 1. (a) 6T SRAM bit-cell and (b) Sample SRAM bit-cell layout [3].

correct read sensing, and I_{read} is the read current through M5 and M1, as WL is turned ON. The rate of differential build-up ($\Delta V/t_{diff}$, e.g. 10mV/100ps) is impacted by the change in C_{BL} (the interconnect and the junction capacitance). Consequently, in this paper, the normalized read current (I_{read}/C_{BL}) is the performance metric for the bit-cell. Leakage is the main cause of power dissipation in the SRAM due to the lower switching activity per bit-cell. The layout topology and the tight layout design rules for the SRAM bit-cell from [3] are used, as illustrated in (Fig.1 (b)). The x and y dimensions for the bit-cell area are calculated as a function of the layout design rules as follows:

$$Area = x_{dim} \times y_{dim}, x_{dim} = 2 \times max(x1, x2), y_{dim} = max(y1, y2),$$
$$x1 = (1/2)(PP) + W_{ld} + PN + W_{drv} + PoG + (1/2)(PoPo),$$
$$x2 = (1/2)(PP) + W_{ld} + PN + W_{ax} + PoG + (1/2)(CW),$$
$$y1 = 2[(1/2)(CW) + 2(GC) + L_{ld}] + CW,$$
$$y2 = 2[(1/2)(CW) + 2(GC)] + L_{drv} + L_{ax} + CW. \quad (1)$$

B. Preparatory Work

The design metrics are impacted by the operating parameters (voltage, temperature), the design parameters (transistor width, length), and the statistical parameters (process e.g., the threshold voltage).

1) Operating Parameters: -Accounted for, by evaluating the metrics at their respective worst-case operating conditions. E.g., the possible worst-case for leakage is 10% higher than nominal voltage, and a high temperature of 85°C [7]. The nominal voltages for 65nm, 45nm and 32nm are taken as 1.1V, 1V and 0.9V, respectively[7].

2) Design parameters (Inter-Die) {W_{drv} ,W_{ax} ,W_{ld} ,L_{drv} ,L_{ax} ,L_{ld}}: Variations in the transistor widths and lengths are considered as the main source of inter-die variations in this work. The inter-die V_{th} variations are accounted for implicitly, because these are predominantly caused by the variations in the transistor length [4]. Based on the *ITRS*

[7], the 3σ variation in the transistor dimensions is taken as 3nm, 3nm and 2nm for the 65nm, 45nm and 32nm, respectively.

3) Statistical parameters (Intra-Die): Because of the proximity of the bit-cell transistors, a highly regular layout and a fairly controlled array fabrication process, the within-die or intra-die (statistical) variations in the channel length and width are negligible [2]. Therefore, in this paper, intrinsic V_{th} variations due to RDF are considered to be the major source of intra-die variations in the design metrics. Since dopant fluctuation is random, the V_{th} of six transistors are considered as six independent and un-correlated Gaussian random variables [2]. By using a Pelgrom coefficient of $3mV\mu m$ [13], σ_{Vth0} (usually available in the vendor process kits) for 65nm, 45nm and 32nm is taken to be 35mV, 50mV and 70mV, respectively. Then, the σ_{Vth} (due to RDF) for a transistor is related to its size as follows [2]:

$$\sigma_{Vth} = \sigma_{Vth0} \sqrt{\frac{W_{min} L_{min}}{W L}}. \qquad (2)$$

Per unit interconnect and diffusion bit-line capacitances are assumed to be constant, for all technologies. Predictive Technology Models are used for simulation.

III. STATISTICAL DESIGN OF THE SRAM BIT-CELL

A. Intra-Die Variation

Because of the intrinsic V_{th} variations, the design metrics- SNM, Vtrip and read current exhibit gaussian distributions [1]. To statistically model the impact of the intrinsic V_{th} variations due to RDF, on the design metrics, the statistical average and variance of the gaussian distributions of the design metrics is estimated by using the Taylor series expansion as:

$$SNM_{avg} = SNM_0 + \frac{1}{2}\left\{ (\frac{\partial^2 SNM}{\partial Vth_1^2} + \frac{\partial^2 SNM}{\partial Vth_2^2})\sigma_{drv}^2 \right.$$

$$+ (\frac{\partial^2 SNM}{\partial Vth_3^2} + \frac{\partial^2 SNM}{\partial Vth_4^2})\sigma_{ld}^2 + (\frac{\partial^2 SNM}{\partial Vth_5^2} + \frac{\partial^2 SNM}{\partial Vth_6^2})\sigma_{ax}^2 \qquad (3)$$

$$\sigma_{SNM}^2 = \sum_{i=1}^{6} \sigma_i^2 \left(\frac{\partial SNM}{\partial Vth_i}\right)^2 = \left\{ (\frac{\partial SNM}{\partial Vth_1})^2 + (\frac{\partial SNM}{\partial Vth_2})^2 \right\} \sigma_{drv}^2$$

$$+ \left\{ (\frac{\partial SNM}{\partial Vth_3})^2 + (\frac{\partial SNM}{\partial Vth_4})^2 \right\} \sigma_{ld}^2 + \left\{ (\frac{\partial SNM}{\partial Vth_5})^2 + (\frac{\partial SNM}{\partial Vth_6})^2 \right\} \sigma_{ax}^2 \qquad (4)$$

SNM_0 and the partial derivatives are computed at the mean V_{th} values, by simulation. The results of modeling are verified by Monte-Carlo (MC) simulations. E.g., Fig.3(a) shows that the average leakage and standard deviation, from the 45nm bit-cell leakage MC results, are 77.2nA and 8.9nA, respectively. The estimated values are 77.7nA and 8.57nA, respectively. Similarly, the SNM average and standard deviation from MC simulations are 131.8mV and 22.1mV, respectively. The corresponding estimated values from modeling are 132.1mV and 21.6mV, respectively. For this work, this level of modeling accuracy is sufficient. The coefficient of σ_{drv}^2 on the RHS. of (4) contains the slopes of the SNM vs. V_{th1} and V_{th2}. These are numerically interchanged if the opposite data value (1 instead of 0) is stored at VL in the bit-cell, but the overall coefficient of σ_{drv}^2 remains the same. Thus, σ_{SNM} is the same, irrespective of the data value stored in the bit-cell.

The number of identical bit-cells and the expected electrical yield to the specifications determine the number of sigmas -N_σ, over which the bit-cell must operate correctly [1]. This concept is used to formulate the constraints of the optimization problem as follows:

$$\frac{SNM_{avg} - SNM_{residual}}{\sigma_{SNM}} \geq N_\sigma \qquad (5)$$

$$\frac{Iread_{residual}}{C_{BL}} = \frac{(Iread_{avg} - N_\sigma \times \sigma_{Iread})}{C_{BL}} \geq S_{differential} \qquad (6)$$

The constraint form in (5) is used for the SNM, Vtrip and leakage. Equation (6) is used for the read speed constraint. Eq.(5) constraints the

SNM yield instead of the SNM value. Both, SNM_{avg} and σ_{SNM}, are impacted by the choice of the nominal design parameters as observed from (2), (3) and (4). Therefore, the extent of the intra-die variations, and hence, the yield, can be controlled by the judicious choice of the nominal design. $S_{differential}$ is the desired slope of the read differential build-up in mV/ps, for the statistically weakest cell.

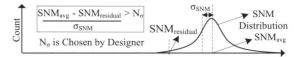

Fig. 2. Pictorial representation of the SNM design constraint.

The residuals, such as the $SNM_{residual}$ in (5), impart flexibility to design different versions of the bit-cell. Residuals for $Iread$ (lower limit) and leakage (upper limit) enable the design of a bit-cell with a high or moderate performance, and a low or ultra-low leakage. The SNM and Vtrip residuals build margin for reliability. The constraint is depicted in Fig.2. $S_{differential}$, N_{sigma} and the residuals are the inputs in (5) and (6).

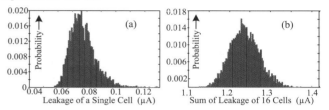

Fig. 3. Leakage (μA) distribution histogram for (a) single memory cell and (b) sum of the leakage of 16 cells.

The bit-cell leakage acquires a lognormal distribution with V_{th} variations (sub-threshold leakage, being the primary component of the total leakage). Therefore, (5) (applicable for the gaussian distribution) cannot be used directly. The central limit theorem [2] is used to model the sum of the leakage of 16 bit-cells as a gaussian distribution. Fig.3 signifies that the sum of the leakage of 16 bit cells (the V_{th} of every transistor in each of the 16 bit-cells is a random variable) displays a gaussian distribution. Because of the associated overhead of the peripherals in the memories, the deployment of memories as storage elements is justified for only a certain minimum number of bits (more than 16). Therefore, the use of 16 cells for leakage modeling does not restrict the minimum memory size. The mean and sigma values of the sum of the leakage of 16 cells is calculated as follows[12]: $Leakage\_mean_{16} = 16 \times Leakage\_mean_{1cell}, \sigma_{16}^2 = 16 \times \sigma_{1cell}^2$.

B. Yield Maximization

The previous section considers the intra-die variations in the design metrics. The inter-die variations in the transistor dimensions should also be considered for overall yield optimization. The design parameters- $\{W_{drv}, W_{ax}, W_{ld}, L_{drv}, L_{ax}, L_{ld}\}$ define a 6-D parameter space. The design constraints define a feasible region in this parameter space, within which a nominal design should be chosen. The problem is depicted graphically in 2-D (for illustration) in Fig.4, for an arbitrary feasible region, defined by arbitrary constraints. A tolerance box can be specified around a chosen nominal design, such that the dimensions of the tolerance box equal the spread of the design parameters e.g., $\pm 3\sigma$ value of the normally distributed widths and lengths. The smaller dots in the tolerance box represent the design variants around the nominal design. Therefore, the area overlap between the tolerance box and the feasible region represents the yield. The inner box in Fig.4, is the maximum orthogonal overlap between the feasible region and the tolerance box, and can be used very well to estimate the yield directly

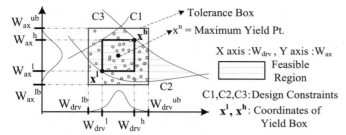

Fig. 4. Yield maximization method in 2-dimensions (for illustration).

[10]. Qualitatively, in 6-D, x^l and x^h (coordinates of the yield box) should be found, such that the six-dimensional volume (yield) of the yield box is maximized. Because design parameters have a symmetrical distribution, the final optimized design solution $x^n = (x^l + x^h)/2$. For complete derivations, the reader is referred to [10]. Using the double-bounded probability distribution function (DB-PDF), proposed by Kumaraswamy [5], the yield is computed as:

$$Yield(x^l, x^h) = \prod_{i=1}^{6} \left(F(\frac{x_i^h - x_i^l + t}{2t}) - F(\frac{x_i^l - x_i^h + t}{2t}) \right). \quad (7)$$

where x_i is the ith design parameter. t is the maximum spread of the design parameters. To check if the yield box lies in the feasible region, as a first order condition, it is sufficient to check the constraint violation at the extreme corners of the yield box, $\{x^l, x^h\}$. E.g., in 2-D, there are $2^2 = 4$ corners of the yield box, as displayed in Fig.5. However, SNM improves with increasing W_{drv}, and degrades with increasing W_{ax}. Therefore, the SNM should be checked at only $\{W_{drv}^l, W_{ax}^h\}$ (in 2-D) as shown in Fig. 5. By using this concept of constraint minimization in 6-D, the total number of constraint evaluations for every choice of the nominal design is reduced to six. This strategy suits the constraints in (5) and (6). Since the within-die variation is the same for all dies [8], the constraint in (5) is evaluated only at the die, which constitutes the global worst-case corner (worst SNM_{avg}) such as point d_2 in Fig.5. This implies that for the inter-die variants around d_0 (d_1, d_2 and so on), σ_{SNM} remains the same.

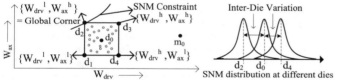

Fig. 5. Constraint Minimization

C. Final Optimization Problem

Maximize Yield $(x^l, x^h) \Rightarrow x^n = \frac{x^l + x^h}{2}$, use (7).

subject to the constraints: (1) $x^l < x^h$, (2) $x^h - x^l \leq t$, (3) $Area \leq Area_{max}$ and (4) design constraints for SNM, Vtrip, read current and leakage, as in (5) and (6) evaluated using (2), (3) and (4) at the worst-case inter-die design variant. SNM, Vtrip and read current have a lower bound; leakage of 16 cells has an upper bound.

IV. RESULTS AND DISCUSSION

A sequential quadratic programming based optimization engine [6] dynamically provides the transistor widths and lengths to the HSPICE templates, which are simulated to numerically compute the design constraints of the optimization problem. The following inputs are used. $N_\sigma = 4.763$, mathematically, corresponds to a single cell failure in an array of 1024×1024 cells [1], which covers a wide range of embedded memory sizes. The performance constraint is $Iread_{residual}/C_{BL} \geq$

$15mV/100ps$ for a bit line spanning 1024 rows. The maximum leakage of 16 bit-cells is set to 640nA, which implies an average maximum leakage of 40nA per bit-cell, as achieved in [9]. All constraints are evaluated at the respective worst-case voltage-temperature corners (as explained in Section II-B).

A. Statistical bit-cell design

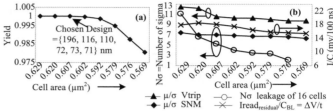

Fig. 6. Optimization results for 65nm (a) Area vs yield trade-off (b) Resultant N_σ for SNM, Vtrip, leakage, and $I_{residual}/C$

With the proposed method and the afore-mentioned speed and leakage constraints, optimal designs in the 65nm are obtained with varying $Area_{max}$ constraint (Fig. 6(a)). The displayed yield is obtained by MC simulations with 20000 points. A relaxed area constraint allows larger transistors. This reduces σ_{Vth}, and the intra-die variations, thereby giving a good yield. The chosen nominal design in Fig. 6(a), is the design of minimum area, for which all the design constraints are satisfied ($N_\sigma \geq 4.763$). Fig. 6(b) indicates that, for the chosen nominal design, N_σ of the leakage constraint is 5.17, but falls below 4.763, if $Area_{max}$ is further reduced.

B. The impact of technology scaling

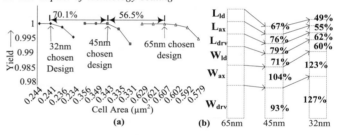

Fig. 7. (a) Optimization results for 65nm, 45nm, 32nm (b) Transistor sizes in optimal 45nm and 32nm designs, relative to 65nm sizes.

The bit-cell leakage is expected to increase with technology scaling. However, it is attempted to obtain 45nm and 32nm optimal designs, with the same maximum leakage as that for the 65nm, to impose stricter constraints. Therefore, the required performance is also kept the same. The results in Fig. 7(a), show that the area of the 45nm chosen design is 56.5% of that in the 65nm. The 32nm bit-cell area is 70.1% of that in the 45nm. This does not meet the 50% area scaling expectation. The reasons for unsatisfactory scaling can be detected from Fig.7 (b), which shows the transistor sizes in the nominal designs, relative to 65nm. The figure reveals that W_{drv} and W_{ax} have very poor scaling. Further analysis indicates that a wider W_{ax} is needed for higher read current. This necessitates a wider W_{drv} to maintain the cell ratio β ($= (W_{drv}/L_{drv})/(W_{ax}/L_{ax})$), to satisfy the SNM constraint.

C. Achieving 50% area scaling - partitioning and longer transistors

To achieve better area scaling, longer L_{drv} and L_{ax} are proposed, e.g. the maximum length for the 32nm design, which was previously set to 45nm, is increased to 52nm. This is based on the observations in Fig.8(a). During the read cycle, VL in Fig.1(a), rises to an intermediate

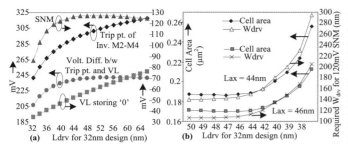

Fig. 8. SNM and Area analysis with varying L_{drv}

voltage (weak "0") due to the voltage division between M1 and M5. The voltage difference between the trip point of M2-M4 inverter and VL voltage, is an indicator of the SNM [1]. Fig.8(a) shows that very short L_{drv} (which strengthens M1, M2) reduces the M2-M4 trip point much more than the VL node voltage, thus degrading SNM (even though β improves). Therefore, a very short L_{drv} requires a larger W_{drv} to achieve the same SNM, which increases the bit-cell area significantly (Fig.8(b)). However, a very long L_{drv} does not give much area benefit. Therefore, an optimal L_{drv}, longer than nominal, is needed to reduce the W_{drv} required to meet the SNM constraint.

Secondly, memory partitioning is proposed. For the read current constraint $Iread_{residual}/(1024 \times C_{BL,single-bit-cell}) = \Delta V/t_{diff}$, the maximum number of rows is halved to 512 for the 45nm. Therefore, the $Iread_{residual}$ can be halved, but the slope of the weakest cell remains fixed at 15mV/100ps. This reduces the required access transistor strength. In turn, this enables a narrower driver. The number of rows for the 32nm design is limited to 256.

With these two modifications, optimal designs in the 45nm and 32nm are obtained. The results are displayed in Fig.9. Fig.9(a) shows that compared to Fig.7(b), all transistor widths scale with respect to 65nm. As expected, L_{drv} and L_{ax} do not scale as much. Fig.9(c) plots the transistor lengths in the optimal designs, relative to the respective nominal length. E.g., the relative L_{drv} increases from 1.11 in the 65nm design to 1.29 in the 45nm design, and to 1.5 in the 32nm design. The cell ratios are **1.722, 1.489 and 1.188** in the 65nm, 45nm and 32nm designs, respectively. Fig.9(b) signifies that a much better bit-cell area scaling for the 45nm and 32nm designs (51.7% and 53.7%, respectively) is achieved now. This defies conventional belief that a progressively higher cell ratio (as high as 4) is needed [11] with technology scaling to ensure an acceptable SNM yield. The results indicate that relatively longer transistors at scaled technology nodes, enable smaller widths, and a dropping cell ratio can provide an overall better area scaling for high-yield designs. The use of longer transistors improves the leakage N_σ. The Vtrip N_σ degrades, but meets the minimum requirement.

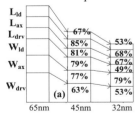
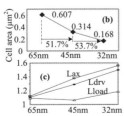

Fig. 9. Results with partitioning and longer lengths (a) transistor widths and lengths in the 45nm and 32nm optimal designs, relative to 65nm (b) cell area (c) transistor lengths/nominal lengths.

Fig. 10 compares the area of the 45nm optimal designs in Fig. 7 (non-partitioned) and Fig. 9 (partitioned). The column periphery

is duplicated in the partitioned memory. However, this overhead is compensated for, by the better bit-cell area scaling in the partitioned design, which provides a net gain of $42.3\mu m^2$ per block. 5 such blocks compensate for the $215\mu m^2$ increase in the WL decoder area. The periphery dimensions are industry estimates, based on layouts. Moreover, the column periphery can be shorter in the partitioned memory, because the write drivers can be smaller for the shorter bit lines. A similar comparison for the 32nm design also shows that the area benefit of the partitioned design compensates for the duplicated peripheral overhead.

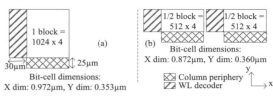

Fig. 10. Area comparison of (a) non-partitioned, and (b) partitioned memory banks. The column periphery Y-dim and WL decoder X-dim are assumed to be $25\mu m$ and $30\mu m$, respectively -industry estimates.

V. CONCLUSION

It is essential to use statistical design methods in scaled technology nodes, because increasing variations of the bit-cell metrics renders manual size selection more cumbersome and iterative. The proposed statistical method to design the SRAM bit-cell, accounts for the manufacturing variability in the transistor dimensions as well as the intrinsic V_{th} variations due to RDF. The developed method is flexible, requires only a small mathematical infrastructure and uses readily available models and tools in the industry. As a result, the extent of approximation in the proposed method is small. Optimal bit-cell designs for the 65nm, 45nm and 32nm technologies are derived. It is demonstrated that progressively longer than nominal transistor lengths and partitioning provide close to 50% area scaling. Longer transistors reduce variability, improve SNM and leakage and enable better width scaling. Partitioning improves performance, provides better area scaling and reduces the overall leakage (since unused banks can be disabled).

REFERENCES

[1] R. Heald, P. Wang, "Variability in Sub-100nm SRAM Designs," *IEEE/ACM ICCAD*, 2004, pp. 347-351.
[2] S. Mukhopadhyay et al., "Modeling of Failure Probability and Statistical Design of SRAM Array for Yield Enhancement in Nanoscaled CMOS," *TCAD*, 2005, pp. 1859-1879.
[3] F. Boeuf et al.,"0.248um2 and 0.334um2 Conventional Bulk 6T-SRAM bit-cells for 45nm node Low Cost - general Purpose Applications", *Sym. On VLSI Tech. Digest of Tech. Papers*, 2005, pp. 130-131.
[4] A. Srivastava, et al.,"Statistical Optimization of Leakage Power considering process variations using Dual-Vth and sizing", *DAC*, Jun. 04, pp. 773-778.
[5] P. Kumaraswamy, "A generalized probability density function for double-bounded random processes," *Journal of Hydrology(46)*, 1980, pp. 79-88.
[6] T. F. Coleman, Optimization Toolbox- Matlab, The Math works Inc. , 2005.
[7] Intl. Technology Roadmap for Semiconductors, *http://www.itrs.net/*, 2007.
[8] B. H. Calhoun and A. Chandrakasan, "Analysing Static Noise Margin for Sub-threshold SRAM in 65nm CMOS,"*ESSCIRC*, 2005.
[9] A. Goel et al., "Gate Leakage and its Reduction in Deep-Submicron SRAM,"*Intl. Conf. VLSI Design*, 2005, pp. 606-611.
[10] J. Jaffari and M. Anis, "Variability-Aware Bulk MOS Device design,"*ISLPED*, 2006, pp. 119-122.
[11] B. Cheng, et al, "Impact of Random Dopant Fluctuation on Bulk CMOS 6-T SRAM Scaling,"*IEEE Solid-State Dev. Res. Conf.*, 2006, pp. 258-261.
[12] A. Papoulis,*Probability, Random Variables and Stochastic Process*, New York, McGraw Hill, Third Edition.
[13] Y. Hirano, M. Tsujiuchi et al, "A Robust SOI SRAM Architecture by using Advanced ABC technology for 32nm node and beyond LSTP devices,"*Symp. on VLSI Tech. Digest of Technical Papers*, 2007, pp. 78-79.

A Monolithic Step-Down SC Power Converter with Frequency-Programmable Subthreshold z-Domain DPWM Control for Ultra-Low Power Microsystems

Ling Su, Dongsheng Ma
Department of Electrical and Computer Engineering
The University of Arizona, Tucson, AZ 85704, USA
{lings, ma}@ece.arizona.edu

A. Paul Brokaw
Analog Devices Inc.
Tucson, AZ 85718, USA
Paul.Brokaw@analog.com

Abstract— **This paper presents a fully integrated switched-capacitor (SC) power converter for ultra-low power microsystems. The design features an efficient step-down charge pump and a frequency-programmable digital feedback controller. The controller is designed in the subthreshold region to reduce power dissipation significantly. It employs a programmable switching frequency digital pulse-width modulation (DPWM) to maintain high efficiency under various loading scenarios, without causing random noise spectrum as in pulse-frequency modulation (PFM). The monolithic implementation effectively suppresses switching noises and glitches introduced by parasitic components from traditional bonding, packaging and PCB wiring. The test prototype was designed and fabricated with a 0.35-μm digital CMOS N-well process. It supplies a variable power output from 0.8 to 1.5V and from 400 μW to 7.5 mW precisely, with a variable switching frequency ranging from 200 KHz to 1 MHz. The converter achieves 66.7% efficiency with a controller power of only 147.5 μW.**

I. INTRODUCTION

Advances in biomedical and wireless sensing technologies bring the proliferation of self-powered energy-efficient devices [1, 2], where system miniaturization and power efficiency are paramount. To effectively implement these applications, the employment of on-chip power conversion and management system becomes essential. In particular, step-down conversion is very favorable in these applications to enable ultra-low power operations such as dynamic voltage scaling (**DVS**) [3]. As a solution, a switching buck converter is reported recently [4]. It employs a subthreshold-region controller to help maintain relatively high efficiency at light load. However, the presence of bulky off-chip inductors causes serious EMI noise and increases PCB profile. Although linear regulator can be very compact, its dropout voltage has to be very low to maintain high efficiency. Under these circumstances, a switched-capacitor (**SC**) power converter appears as a very attractive solution.

However, with new design specifications for these emerging applications, new design challenges arise: firstly, while majority of SC converters achieve step-up conversion, most reported step-down SC converters suffer the similar efficiency problem as linear regulators. Secondly, SC power converter usually includes many off-chip capacitors and thus on-chip pads and IC pins. This significantly increases system volume and causes large noise. For instance, each 5-mm gold IC bonding wire has 0.257-Ω ESR, 5.869-nH ESL and 0.242-pF ESC, which causes up to 500-mV glitch noises. Here **ESR**, **ESL** and **ESC** represent parasitic equivalent series resistance, inductance and capacitance, respectively. Thirdly, in order to facilitate a tight regulation and enable powerful power management schemes such as DVS, the converter should employ a closed-loop feedback control and its output voltage should be variable. Lastly, a lot of self-powered microsystems are designed at 10-mW level or below [1, 2, 4]. Within such a low power range, maintaining high efficiency becomes very challenging. Power consumption of the controller has to be significantly reduced.

In this paper, we propose a new SC power converter to overcome the above challenges. It features an efficient step-down power stage and a very low power frequency-programmable DPWM controller operating in the subthreshold region. The details are addressed as follows.

II. SYSTEM ARCHITECTURE & DESIGN STRATEGY

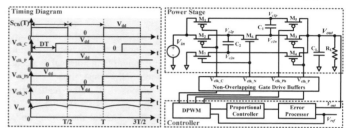

Fig. 1 Block and timing diagrams of the proposed converter.

Fig. 1 illustrates the timing and system block diagrams of the proposed design. It primarily comprises a step-down charge pump (**CP**) power stage and a feedback controller, which includes an error processor, a proportional controller and a digital pulse-width modulator (**DPWM**). The majority of the controller operates in the subthreshold region for low power operation. In addition, the switching frequency of the converter is programmable by adaptively controlling the biasing current of the oscillators in the controller. A direct benefit of this technique is the scalable power consumption in the controller, which helps maintain high efficiency at light load.

A. Power Stage Architecture: Step-Down Charge Pump

Different from the commonly used Dickson CPs and cross-coupled voltage doublers, this design employs a step-down CP power stage that efficiently achieves a 2-to-3 voltage conversion, as shown in Fig. 1. With reference to the timing diagram, the circuit operates in two complementary phases: the charge phase Φ_{charge} and the discharge phase $\Phi_{discharge}$, with respect to the operation states of the pumping capacitors C_1 and C_2. When Φ_{charge} is active ("1"), driven by the gate control signals V_{clk_C} and V_{clk_P} of the non-overlapping gate drive buffers, the PMOS power switches M_1, M_2, M_3 and M_4 are turned on. This creates two charging paths to pre-charge the pumping capacitors C_1 and C_2 and deliver power to the output V_{out}. When $\Phi_{Discharge}$ is active ("1"), the PMOS switches M_1, M_2, M_3 and M_4 are switched off, but the NMOS switches M_6 and M_7 and the PMOS switch M_5 are turned on by V_{clk_N} and V_{clk_Pb}. Accordingly, a discharging path is formed. Clearly, during $\Phi_{discharge}$, no current path exists between the output load and the input supply V_{in}. The power required by the load is supplied by discharging the pumping capacitors C_1 and C_2. The charge in C_1 and C_2, accumulated during the charging phase Φ_{charge}, is thus transferred to the output load. Note that, if $C_1 = C_2 = C_p$, the voltage across each of the capacitors will be equal to $V_{out}/2$ at the end of the discharging phase $\Phi_{discharge}$. Meanwhile, at the end of the charging phase Φ_{charge}, the voltage across each capacitor will be equal to $V_{in} - V_{out}$. Hence, as the

58

charge pump reaches the steady state, the total net charge difference on the pumping capacitors C_1 and C_2 should be equal to the charge consumed by the loading resistor R_L, leading to

$$2C_p\left(V_{in} - V_{out} - V_{out}/2\right) = V_{out}/R_L\,T \cdot \tag{1}$$

Here, T is the switching cycle of the CP, $C_1 = C_2 = C_p$. From Eqn. 1, we obtain

$$V_{out} = 2V_{in}/\left(3 + 2T/\left(R_L C_p\right)\right) \cdot \tag{2}$$

Hence, if $T/\left(R_L C_p\right) << 3/2$, then

$$V_{out} \approx 2V_{in}/3 \cdot \tag{3}$$

We thus achieve a 2-to-3 step-down voltage conversion.

B. Closed-Loop System z-Domain Feedback Control

For power converter designs, identifying the closed-loop gain behavior is critical to the controller design and loop compensation. Here we first derive the transfer function of the power stage, and then propose the control and compensation scheme accordingly.

In power electronics, there exists an age-old dilemma between the s-domain and z-domain loop gain analysis [5-7]. In a traditional power converter design, the power stage exhibits a nonlinear large-signal behavior due to the switching actions, and is thus more suitable to be modeled in the z-domain. However, because the controller is usually designed with linear analog circuits, it is commonly modeled in the s-domain. To model the entire closed-loop gain, domain transformation is unavoidable. State space averaging or other averaging modeling techniques [5-8] were thus proposed to approximately model the power stage in the s-domain. However, the averaging process could lose the high-frequency pole/zero information in the closed-loop gain transfer function. In this work, we model the entire system in the z-domain, by taking advantage of the digital nature of the proposed controller.

According to the charge conservation theory, the power stage transfer function can be derived as

$$V_{out}/V_{in} = az^{-1}/(1 - bz^{-1}) = a/(z - b), \tag{4}$$

where $a = 2C_p\Big/\left(C_L + C_p + \dfrac{T}{2R_L}\right)$, $b = \left(C_L - 2C_p - \dfrac{T}{2R_L}\right)\Big/\left(C_L + C_p + \dfrac{T}{2R_L}\right)$.

Eqn. (4) shows that the proposed power stage only has one single pole with $b < 1$. If no low-frequency pole is introduced by the controller design, the closed-loop converter will be stable and no extra compensation network is needed. This leaves a large design margin for regulation accuracy enhancement and low power design. Notice that, when the frequency is equal to zero and z=1 in Eqn. (4), the transfer function can be rewritten as

$$V_{out}/V_{in} = a/(1 - b) = 2/3, \tag{5}$$

which is consistent with the result obtained in Eqn. (3).

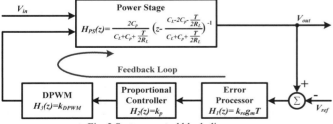

Fig. 2 System control block diagram.

Fig. 2 shows the system control block diagram. The proposed controller is to accomplish three major tasks: error processing, resolution enhancement (proportional control) and DPWM. As previously depicted in Fig. 1, in order to detect the regulation error between V_{out} and V_{ref}, both signals are fed into the controller as input signals. The error processor uses the two

voltage signals to initialize the low-power subthreshold region operation, thereby converting them into an error signal in a digital manner. This technique will be introduced in Section III. The computed error is modeled as

$$D_e(z) = k_{ro}g_m T V_e(z) \cdot \tag{6}$$

Here, k_{ro} represents the current-to-frequency gain of the ring oscillator, g_m represents the transconductance of the voltage-to-current conversion, and $V_e(z)$ is the error voltage, which is defined as $V_{out}(z) - V_{ref}(z)$. The transfer function for the error processor can then be modeled as

$$H_1(z) = k_{ro}g_m T \cdot \tag{7}$$

To enhance the processing resolution and improve the regulation accuracy, we include a proportional control stage. This process mainly "amplifies" the error signals from n to $n+k$ bits, and can be modeled as

$$H_2(z) = k_p \cdot \tag{8}$$

Another major part of the feedback control is the DPWM. The DPWM control imposes the computed error on a reference clock signal to generate the instant duty ratio, which determines the turn-on time of each power switch in the CP. In the z domain, DPWM is modeled as

$$H_3(z) = k_{DP} \cdot \tag{9}$$

As illustrated in Fig. 2, by combining Eqn. (9) with the power stage transfer function of Eqn. 4, we obtain the closed-loop gain of the converter as

$$T(z) = H_1(z)H_2(z)H_3(z)H_{PS}(z) = k_{DP}k_p k_{ro}g_m T\,a/(z - b). \tag{10}$$

Since this system has only one pole which meets $b < 1$, the converter is inherently stable.

III. CIRCUIT IMPLEMENTATION

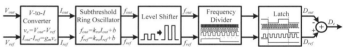

Fig. 3 Block diagram of the error processor.

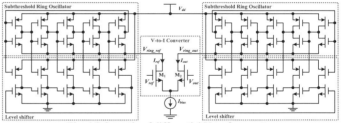

Fig. 4 Schematic of differential V-to-f converter

To implement the proposed system in silicon, we address the major circuit design issues in this section. Since the power stage design was discussed in Section II-A, here we focus on the design issues of the controller, including the error processor, the proportional controller, and the DPWM modulator. Fig. 3 shows the block diagram of the proposed error processor. The detailed circuit schematic of the differential voltage-to-frequency (V-to-f) converter, including the voltage-to-current (V-to-I) converter, subthreshold ring oscillators and level shifters, is shown in Fig. 4. At the input of the error processor, a differential V-to-I converter is employed to amplify the output voltage V_{out} and the reference voltage V_{ref}, and then convert them into the corresponding current signals I_{ref} and I_{out}. From Eqn. (7), in order to achieve a higher closed-loop gain and thus a finer regulation resolution, a large transconductance is preferred in the V-to-I converter. The differential circuit topology has the advantages of canceling even-order harmonics as well as temperature and process variations. In addition, wide common-mode input range and supply-independent current biasing are adopted to enhance circuit robustness to supply (V_{in})

and output (V_{out}) variations. As a result, the voltage error between V_{out} and V_{ref} is converted to the current difference,

$$\Delta I = I_{out} - I_{ref} = g_m (V_{vout} - V_{ref}) = g_m \cdot v_e. \quad (11)$$

I_{ref} and I_{out} are used to bias the two ring oscillators. By adjusting these currents, the oscillation frequencies of the oscillators vary accordingly. Note that the biasing current is very low, in order to ensure that the oscillators operate in the subthreshold region. Hence, the voltage swing of the subthreshold ring oscillator is below a MOSFET's threshold voltage, leading to significant switching power reduction. Our experimental results show that operating at 200 kHz causes the power consumption to drop significantly from 2.11 mW in traditional ring oscillator clock generator to just 54 μW in our design.

In subthreshold region [9], the oscillation frequency of each oscillator shows a linear dependence on the biasing current:

$$f_{osc} = k_{ro} \cdot I_{bias} + b. \quad (12)$$

The linear relationship between the oscillation frequency and the biasing current also makes the error signal linearly proportional to the oscillation frequency

$$\Delta f = f_{out} - f_{ref} = k_{ro}(I_{out} - I_{ref}) = k_{ro}\Delta I = k_{ro}g_m v_e. \quad (13)$$

This greatly simplifies the system modeling and circuit design.

Following the oscillators, level shifters are employed to ensure valid logic functions when interfacing traditional digital circuits. To further process the error signals, the frequency signals f_{out} and f_{ref} are converted into n-bit binary digital signals D_{out} and D_{ref} respectively, after passing through high-speed digital counters. The digital error is computed as

$$\begin{aligned}
(D_n D_{n-1}...D_1 D_0)_e \\
= (D_{n-1}D_{n-2}...D_1D_0)_{out} - (D_{n-1}D_{n-2}...D_1D_0)_{ref} \\
= (D_{n-1}D_{n-2}...D_1D_0)_{out} + \underbrace{10...0}_{n\ bits} - (D_{n-1}D_{n-2}...D_1D_0)_{ref} \quad (14) \\
= (D_{n-1}D_{n-2}...D_1D_0)_{out} + \overline{(D_{n-1}D_{n-2}...D_1D_0)}_{ref} + \underbrace{0...01}_{n\ bits}.
\end{aligned}$$

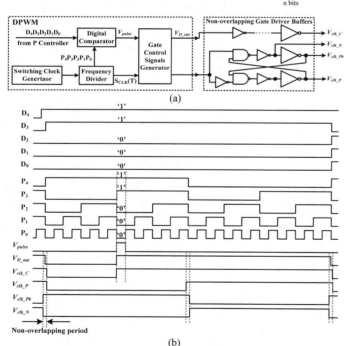

(a)

(b)

Fig. 5 The proposed DPWM controller and non-overlapping gate driver buffers: (a) circuit block diagram, and (b) control timing diagram.

This design also employs a proportional controller to further enhance the signal resolution from $n+1$ to $n+k+1$ bits. Since the entire system is modeled as a single pole system, no extra compensation circuit is needed in the proportional controller. The biasing current I_{bias} ensures that both oscillators operate in the subthreshold region. When the load significantly increases

(decreases), I_{bias} can be increased (decreased) accordingly. This adjusts the ring oscillator frequency, which determines the switching frequency of the converter, thereby achieving low switching power loss at light load. In this design, the entire power range is divided into eight regions, with the switching frequency also being adjustable at the corresponding levels.

For finer regulation within each power range, the digital pulse-width modulator takes charge. The detailed DPWM control scheme and timing diagram are illustrated in Fig. 5. A reference clock signal, generated by a switching clock generator, is converted into binary signals $P_4P_3P_2P_1P_0$. The amplified error signals at the outputs of the proportional controller then are compared with the reference data $P_4P_3P_2P_1P_0$ to compute the duty ratio of the converter, as demonstrated in Fig. 5b. For instance, when $(D_4D_3D_2D_1D_0)_e$ is "11000", a pulse signal is triggered when $P_4P_3P_2P_1P_0$ becomes "11000". This pulse signal then activates the duty ratio generator to determine DT. Five bits have been chosen to ensure accurate signal processing resolution, while maintaining low power and design complexity. Higher resolution can be easily achieved by increasing the data bit number and employing higher clock frequency, if power budget allows.

IV. EXPERIMENTAL VERIFICATION

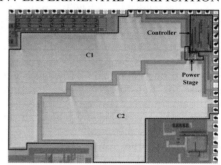

Fig. 6 Chip micrograph.

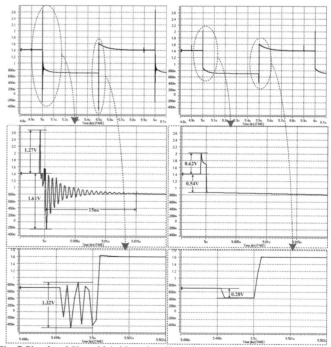

Fig. 7 Simulated V_{c1n} with/without bonding wire parasitics, and close-up view of V_{c1n} at instant of 5μs and 5.5μs, with/without bonding wire parasitics

The design was fabricated with a 0.35-μm digital N-well CMOS process. Fig. 6 shows the chip micrograph. The entire chip area is 7.8 mm², where the controller occupies only 0.26-

mm² area with 147.5-μW power dissipation. The chip layout is dominated by two 3.36-nF pumping capacitor C_1 and C_2, occupying 6.48-mm² silicon area in total. However, the on-chip capacitor implementation saves 4 on-chip pads and 4 IC pins, and largely reduces the system volume. Meanwhile, it also minimizes the parasitic components caused by bonding, packaging and PCB wiring, especially the ESR, ESL and ESC. These parasitic components are major contributors to large switching noises in power converter designs. For instance, even if just the bonding parasitic effect is considered, each gold bonding wire contributes 0.257-Ω ESR, 5.869-nH ESL and 0.242-pF ESC for 5-mm length [9]. The noise performance was simulated in this case and compared to our on-chip implementation, shown in Fig. 7. In this figure, we observe a typical voltage node V_{c1n} (see Fig. 1) at the on-chip power stage for both cases. Based on the results in Fig. 7, with the bonding wire, the switching glitches vary from 1.27 to 1.61 V. For the on-chip implementation, these glitches are suppressed to a range of 0.28 to 0.62 V. In addition, the ESC and ESL of the bonding wires cause oscillation ringing, which can be hardly observed in the on-chip design.

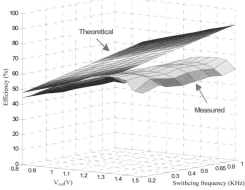

Fig. 8 Theoretical and measured power efficiencies.

With the 2.5-V input supply voltage V_{in}, the output voltage of the converter, V_{out}, is well-regulated at any level between 0.8 and 1.5 V, with the load current ranging from 500 μA to 5 mA. The switching frequency is programmable from 200 kHz to 1 MHz, depending on the instant load condition. Fig. 8 plots the efficiency versus V_{out} and the switching frequency. As a compromise to the closed-loop regulation, when the duty ratio becomes lower than 1/2 or/and V_{out} is lower than $2/3 V_{in}$, the efficiency will drop below 100%, even if we assume the controller consumes no power. We consider this efficiency as the "theoretical" maximum efficiency of the converter. With respect to the "theoretical" results, we plot our measured efficiency in Fig. 8. The measured efficiency is very close to the theoretical results due to subthreshold controller design and frequency-programmable operation. It stays above 50% in a voltage range of 0.9 to 1.5 V, with a maximum of 66.7% at 1.4 V, with 1-MHz switching frequency. To the best of our knowledge, this is the highest efficiency reported for step-down SC power converter in such a low power range.

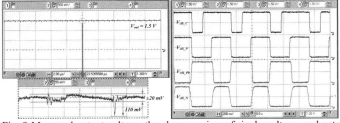

Fig. 9 Measured output voltage, the close-up view of ripple voltage, and gate control signals of the power transistors.

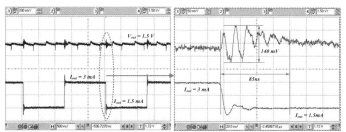

Fig. 10 Measured load transient performance and the close-up view at load dynamic transient.

Fig. 9 shows the measured voltage waveforms at key circuit nodes at steady state. The output voltage at 1.5 V is measured in Fig. 9. It clearly shows that the peak-to-peak ripple voltage at V_{out} is controlled to ±20 mV with 110-mV glitch, which is much improved from the off-chip implementations. The four non-overlapping gate-drive control signals are measured. As indicated in the figure, the control signals, V_{clk_P}, V_{clk_N} and V_{clk_Pb}, keep operating with a 50% duty ratio, while the control signal V_{clk_C} is modulated by the DPWM controller to achieve variable voltage regulation. The waveforms are consistent with the proposed control scheme addressed in Section III (Fig. 5). Fig. 10 shows the measured load dynamic performance of the converter. When the load current Iout quickly switches between 1.5 and 3 mA, the digital controller promptly responds to the changes with a negligible 85-ns delay and only 140-mV voltage variation at V_{out}.

V. CONCLUSIONS

In this paper, we propose a new monolithic step-down switched-capacitor power converter design. With the 147.5-μW subthreshold operated controller and a frequency-programmable DPWM regulation scheme, power consumption and signal processing speed are adaptively optimized. The fully on-chip implementation significantly reduces system volume and switching noises. The number of I/O pins and on-chip bonding pads as well as parasitic components is significantly reduced. The design provides a high performance solution for new generation, monolithic power supply designs for new-generation self-powered devices.

REFERENCES

[1] J. M. Rabaey, et. al., "PicoRadios for wireless sensor networks: the next challenge in ultra-low power design," *IEEE ISSCC*, pp. 200-201, Feb. 2002.

[2] N. Lajnef, S. Chakrabartty, N. Elvin, A. Elvin, "Piezo-powered floating gate injector for self-powered fatigue monitoring in biomechanical implants", *IEEE ISCAS*, pp. 89-92, May 2007.

[3] T. Burd, T. Pering, A. Stratakos, R. Brodersen, "A dynamic voltage scaled microprocessor system," *IEEE ISSCC*, pp. 294-295, Feb. 2000.

[4] Y. K. Ramadass and A. P. Chandrakasan, "Minimum energy tracking loop with embedded DC-DC converter delivering voltages down to 250mV in 65nm CMOS," *IEEE ISSCC*, pp. 64-65, Feb. 2007.

[5] R. D. Middlebrook and S. Cuk, "A general unified approach to modeling switching-converter power stage," *IEEE PESC*, pp. 18-34, 1976.

[6] W- H. Ki, "Signal flow graph in loop gain analysis of dc-dc PWM CCM switching converters," *IEEE TCAS-I*, vol.45, pp. 644-654, Jun. 1998.

[7] R. W. Erickson and D. Maksimovic, *Fundamentals of Power Electronics*, Norwell, MA: Kluwer, 2001.

[8] J. Sun, D. M. Mitchell, M. F. Greuel, P. T. Krein, R. M. Bass, "Averaged modeling of PWM converters operating in discontinuous conduction mode," *IEEE TPE*, pp. 482-492. Jul. 2001.

[9] P. R. Gray, P. J. Hurst, S. H. Lewis, R. G. Meyer, *Analysis and design of analog integrated circuits*, NY: John Wiley & Sons, 2001, pp. 65-73.

[10] D. E. Knuth, *The art of computer programming, Vol. 2: seminumerical algorithms*, Addison-Wesley, 1997.

[11] "MOSIS packaging and assembly packaging options: bond wire electrical parameters," http://www.mosis.com/Technical/Packaging.

A Fully-Integrated 130nm CMOS DC-DC Step-Down Converter, Regulated by a Constant On/Off-Time Control System

Mike Wens and Michiel Steyaert
ESAT-MICAS, K.U. Leuven
Kasteelpark Arenberg 10
B-3001 Leuven, Belgium
Email: mike.wens@esat.kuleuven.be

Abstract—**A fully-integrated DC-DC step-down converter in a 130 nm 1.2 V CMOS technology is realized, with an integrated metal-track inductor and integrated MOS and MIM capacitors. The converter is designed to generate an output voltage of 1.2 V out of a 2.6 V power supply. No external components are required. The maximum power conversion efficiency is 52 %, for a voltage conversion ratio of 0.46. This is a 12 % improvement compared to a linear regulator. Higher values are likely to be reached using a converter with external components, which is not the case here. Stacked transistors are used to cope with the high voltage. A novel control system based on a constant on/off-time keeps the output voltage constant at load conditions from 0 mW to 180 mW. The converter operates in discontinuous, asynchronous switching mode. The switching frequency ranges from 30 Hz to 300 MHz.**

I. INTRODUCTION

As technology scales down due to Moore's law, it becomes more cost-efficient to integrate all the building blocks of a system on a single die. These SoC's require multiple supply voltages. For instance the digital signal processing part typically needs a lower supply voltage than the power amplifier, which needs to be able to deliver sufficient output power into the communication medium. Therefore a dedicated power management system is required to accommodate each building block of the SoC with a proper supply voltage and power [1]. Moreover the increasing miniaturization leads to portable, wireless and battery-operated applications. The battery voltage however is usually too high for most parts of the circuitry in deep-submicron technologies. It therefore needs to be decreased. Using a linear regulator for this task will lead to excessive power loss. A switching step-down regulator can minimize this power loss, extending the battery lifetime.

In order to achieve a fully-integrated SoC the voltage converter(s) should be integrated on the same die, leading to distributed power management on-chip. Previous publications report fully-integrated step-down converters [2] [3], only requiring some commonly used technology options to integrate the passives. Other publications require extra (expensive) processing steps such as thick film and stacked-chip's [4] [5]. Clearly the most stringent problem on fully-integrated DC-

DC converters is the integration of the passives. The poor Q-factors of integrated capacitors and inductors make it difficult to achieve power conversion efficiencies which are higher than those achievable with linear voltage regulators. This is the reason why DC-DC converters using external components typically achieve higher efficiencies [6].

Equation 1 gives the power conversion efficiency η_{lin} of a linear voltage regulator, where P_{in} is the input power, P_{out} is the output power, I_{in} is the input current, U_{in} is the input voltage, U_{out} is the output voltage and U_{drop} is the voltage-drop over the linear regulator. In this equation the power consumption of the control system is assumed to be much lower than the output power P_{out} of the converter and is therefore not taken into account.

$$\eta_{lin} = \frac{P_{out}}{P_{in}} = \frac{I_{in}U_{out}}{I_{in}\left(U_{out} + U_{drop}\right)} = \frac{U_{out}}{U_{in}} = k_{lin} \quad (1)$$

As can be observed in equation 1 the power conversion efficiency η_{lin} of linear voltage regulators is only dependant of the voltage conversion ratio k_{lin}, and not of the output power P_{out}. From this point of view it is clear that the power conversion efficiencies for step-down voltage regulators, both linear and switched, should not be compared with each other at different voltage conversion ratios k. This is a common misunderstanding and it should be clear that the power conversion efficiencies of voltage regulators should only be compared at the same voltage conversion ratios k.

Obviously the most important reason to use a switched voltage converter instead of a linear voltage converter is the ability of a switched converter to achieve higher power conversion efficiencies. Therefore the power conversion efficiency of a switched step-down voltage regulator η_{sw} is to be compared with the power conversion efficiency of a linear voltage regulator η_{lin} at the same voltage conversion ratio k.

In order to benchmark a switched step-down regulator, in terms of power conversion efficiency, equation 2 can be used, where k_{sw} is the voltage conversion ratio of a switched voltage regulator. This expression gives the Efficiency Enhancement Factor (EEF) for switched step-down voltage regulators ver-

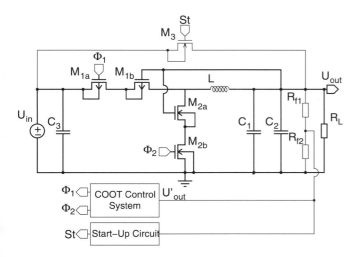

Fig. 1. The proposed architecture of the buck converter with feedback loop, control system and start-up circuit.

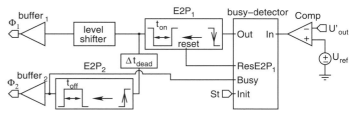

Fig. 2. The architecture of the COOT-control system.

sus linear voltage regulators. A negative EEF value indicates that the switched converter has a lower power conversion efficiency than its linear converter equivalent (unwanted) and vice versa (wanted).

$$EEF = 1 - \frac{\eta_{lin}}{\eta_{sw}}|_{k_{lin}=k_{sw}} \qquad (2)$$

The presented buck converter achieves an efficiency of 52 %, with a voltage conversion ratio k of 46 %. The efficiency improvement compared to a linear voltage regulator, according to the EEF, is 12 %. The input voltage range is 2 V to 2.6 V and the output voltage range is 1.1 V to 1.5 V. A novel constant On/Off-time (COOT) control system keeps the output voltage constant and stable at the desired level under varying load conditions, ranging from 0 mW to the maximum output power of 180 mW.

The architecture of the converter and the COOT control system is described section II. In section III the measurement results are discussed and a comparison is made between this work and other work. Finally conclusions are drawn in section IV.

II. ARCHITECTURE

A. Buck converter

Figure 1 shows the proposed architecture of the buck converter with the feedback loop, the COOT-control system and the start-up circuit.

The switch transistors are implemented in a waffle-shaped structure. Two transistors M_{1a}, M_{1b} and M_{2a}, M_{2b} are stacked to implement respectively the high-side and the low-side switch. The gates of M_{1b} and M_{2a} are biased with the output voltage U_{out} in order to divide the input voltage U_{in} over M_{1a}, M_{1b} and M_{2a},M_{2b}. This approach enables U_{in} to be higher than the nominal technology voltage. The high-side switch transistors M_{1a} and M_{1b} have a width of 1800 μm and the low-side switch transistors M_{2a} and M_{2b} have a width of 1100 μm, all at minimal length.

The output inductor L is implemented with a metal-track, hollow-spiral inductor, using the top thick copper layer of 2 μm thick and the aluminum layer of 1.2 μm thick. It consists of three windings, each having a width of 100 μm, resulting in a total inductance of 9.8 nH. The series resistance at a frequency of 1 GHz is 1.6 Ω. The dimensions of the inductor are 1 mm by 1.5 mm.

Output capacitor C_1 is implemented with a MOScap, using the gate capacitance of 1430 parallel nMOS transistors. Each of the individual nMOS transistors has a width of 100 μm and a length of 10 μm. This yields a capacitance of 14 nF, for an area of 1.43 mm^2. Output capacitor C_2 and input capacitor C_3 are both realized using MIMcaps, each with a capacitance of 1.07 nF. The MIMcaps are placed on top of the MOScap, reducing the required area.

As the control system uses the output voltage U_{out} as supply voltage, a start-up circuit is required. The start-up circuit switches transistor M_3 on until the output voltage U_{out} reaches a value of 0.9 V. Hereafter M_3 is switched off again and the COOT-control system takes over.

B. COOT Control system

Figure 2 shows the architecture of the constant on/off-time (COOT) control system, which keeps the output voltage U_{out} constant at the desired level under varying loads P_{out} and varying supply voltages U_{in}. The output voltage U_{out} is lowered to U'_{out} with the resistive divider formed by R_{f1} and R_{f2}. The comparator then compares U'_{out} with a reference voltage U_{ref}, which determines the desired output voltage U_{out}. The output of the comparator is used as an input for the busy-detector.

The busy-detector is initialized by the start-up circuit, by signal St. If U'_{out} is higher than U_{ref} no action is taken and the switches of the converter remain closed. The current through the load is then generated by the output capacitors C_1 and C_2. If U'_{out} is lower than U_{ref} the busy-detector detects wether the input of buffer$_2$ is low, meaning that the converter is in idle mode. If this is true the busy-detector outputs a falling edge to E2P$_1$ (edge-to-pulse-generator).

E2P$_1$ triggers on a falling edge and generates a low-pulse with a fixed duration t_{on} of 2 ns. Through the level shifter and buffer$_1$ the high-side switch is then turned on during a time t_{on}, charging the inductor L and the output capacitors C_1 and C_2.

The output of E2P$_1$ is also fed into a time-delay Δt_{dead} of 0.15 ns, providing a dead-time between the opening of the

TABLE I
SUMMARY OF THE MEASUREMENTS RESULTS.

Input voltage range	2 V-2.6 V
Output voltage range	1.1 V-1.5 V
Output power range	0 mW-180 mW
Switching frequency range	30 Hz-300 MHz
Power efficiency @ U_{in} =2.6 V and U_{out} =1.2 V	52 %
Efficiency Enhancement Factor	12 %
Maximum output ripple @ P_{out} =0 mW	110 mV
Minimum output ripple @ P_{out} =180 mW	60 mV
Load regulation $\delta u_{out}/\delta i_{out}$	$-0.51\ \Omega$
Line regulation $\delta u_{out}/\delta u_{in}$	-0.083

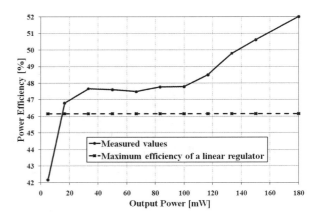

Fig. 3. The measured efficiency of the converter at varying loads compared with the theoretical maximum efficiency of a linear voltage regulator, having the same voltage conversion ratio k. The input voltage and the output voltage are kept constant at 2.6 V and 1.2 V respectively.

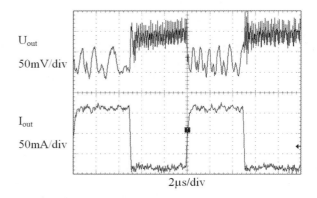

Fig. 4. The measured output voltage (upper curve) at a varying load current (lower curve).

high-side switch and the closing of the low-side switch. Time-delay Δt_{dead} drives E2P$_2$, which triggers on a rising edge and generates a high-pulse with a fixed duration t_{off} of 0.75 ns. The low-side switch is then turned on during a time t_{off} through buffer$_2$, discharging the inductor L into the output capacitors C_1 and C_2 and the load.

The busy-detector avoids a new switching cycle to be started until the previous switching cycle is finished. It also resets E2P$_1$ after one switching cycle, enabling a higher switching frequency and thus a higher output power.

In essence the COOT-control system makes sure that the converter always transfers a fixed amount of energy to the output during one switching cycle, due to the fact that both the on-time t_{on} and the off-time t_{off} are fixed. However the rate at which these fixed amounts of energy are transferred from the input voltage source to the output of the converter is dependant on the desired output power. Clearly when more power needs to be transferred to the output, more energy per unit of time needs to be transferred to the output. Since the transferred energy per cycle is fixed, the switching frequency will be increased. When no output power is needed, ideally the converter will stop switching. In reality it will still switch at a very low frequency, because the control system itself is powered by the output of the converter. The maximum switching frequency is designed to be 300 MHz, which determines the maximum output power of the converter.

When using asynchronous buck converters in discontinuous mode, normally current sensing through the low-side switch is required. However because t_{on} is set to be a constant value, t_{off} can be chosen fixed as well. This is due to the fact that t_{off} only depends on the value of the inductor L and the output capacitors C_1 and C_2, which in turn are fixed. Therefore no complicated and sensitive current sensing circuitry is required to determine when the low-side switch needs to be opened.

III. MEASUREMENTS AND COMPARISON

A. Measurements

This converter was implemented in a 130 nm 1.2 V CMOS technology. It measures 1.5 mm x 2.25 mm. Figure 5 shows a die photograph.

The solid line in figure 3 shows the measured power conversion efficiency of the entire converter at varying loads P_{out}. The input voltage U_{in} and the output voltage U_{out} are kept constant at 2.6 V and 1.2 V respectively. The dashed line

in figure 3 denotes the theoretical power conversion efficiency of a linear voltage regulator with the same voltage conversion ratio $k = 0.46 = 1.2/2.6$. The maximum power conversion efficiency is 52 %. This yields an Efficiency Enhancement Factor (EEF) of +12 % over a linear voltage regulator with the same voltage conversion ratio. It can be observed that the power conversion efficiency of the converter increases with an increasing output power. Clearly this behavior is desired due to the fact that the power losses will become proportionally more important at an increased output power demand.

The worst case output voltage ripple of the converter is 110 mV at zero load. This is less than 10 % of the output voltage and therefore acceptable for most applications. Because of the fact that the switching frequency increases as the output load increases, the output voltage ripple decreases as the output load increases. The minimum output voltage ripple occurs at the maximum output power, and is 60 mV.

The converter is capable of delivering any output power between 0 mW and 180 mW. Moreover it is intrinsically stable at every load condition in this power range. This is a huge advantage over Pulse Width Modulation control systems, which become intrinsically unstable at a low output power.

Figure 4 shows the measurement of the load regulation.

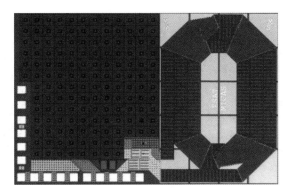

Fig. 5.   Micro photograph of the chip.

The lower curve represents the modulated current through the load, ranging from 4 mA to 150 mA. This is equivalent to an output power ranging from 5 mW to 180 mW. The upper curve represents the output voltage. Apart from the ripple due to the switching of the converter itself, an extra voltage drop of 75 mV appears when the output power is shifted to its maximum. This yields a load regulation of $-0.51 \ \Omega$. The line regulation is measured using an input voltage varying between 2 V and 2.6 V, it is measured to be -0.083.

Finally the input voltage range is 2 V to 2.6 V and the output voltage range is 1.1 V to 1.5 V.

Table I shows a summary of the most important measurements results.

B. Comparison with other work

Table II shows a comparison between the presented work and other publications in the field of integrated DC-DC step-down converters, known to the authors.

As can be observed no other fully-integrated buck converter introduces an efficiency improvement over a linear voltage regulator, having the same voltage conversion ratio k. This can also be seen through the EEF, which is negative for all other fully-integrated buck converters. Moreover the converters using special technology options, such as thick-film inductors or stacked-chip passives, fail to outperform a linear voltage regulator in terms of power conversion efficiency. The only solutions which present a positive EEF are this work and [6] which uses off-chip inductors. Furthermore the table shows that the presented work has the highest EEF of $+12 \%$, meaning that, at its specific voltage conversion factor, this work proves to deliver the highest power conversion efficiency benefit over a linear voltage regulator.

In absolute figures [6] and [2] provide a higher maximum output power, of 270 mW and 360 mW respectively, than the presented work. However the area requirement should also be taken into account, when making this comparison. It is indeed obvious that a larger area will lead to a higher maximum output power. Therefore it is more useful to compare the power per unit of area. From these figures it is clear that the converter which has a twice as high maximum output power of 360 mW also requires eight times the amount of area the presented

TABLE II
COMPARISON WITH OTHER WORK.

ref	[4]	[6]	[2]	[3]	[5]	this work
year	2005	2005	2006	2007	2007	2008
process (μm)	1.5 CMOS	0.09 CMOS	0.18 BiCMOS	0.08 CMOS	0.35 CMOS	0.13 CMOS
U_{in} (V)	5	1.2	2.8	1	3.3	2.6
U_{out} (V)	2.5	0.9	1.8	0.52	2.3	1.2
$P_{out,max}$ (mW)	75	270	360	53	161	180
$k=\eta_{lin}$ (%)	50	75	64	52	70	46
η_{sw} (%)	49	83(*)	58	48	62	52
EEF (%)	-2	+9.6(*)	-10	-8.3	-13	+12
f_{sw}	10MHz	233MHz	45MHz	3GHz	200MHz	30Hz-300MHz
L (nH)	80	4x6.8 off-chip(*)	2x11	0.32	22	9.8
C (nF)	3	2.5	6	0.35	1	15.07
area (mm^2)	16	1.267(*)	27	0.81	4	3.375
Power per area (mW/mm^2)	4.7	213(*)	13	65	40	53
level of integration	thick film L	* air core off-chip SMT L	full	full	stacked chip C and L	full

converter uses, leading to a four times lower power per unit of area ratio compared to the presented converter. Needless to say that [6] achieves a much higher power per unit of area, due to the fact that the area of the four off-chip inductors is not taken into account.

IV. CONCLUSIONS

A fully-integrated DC-DC step-down converter with a COOT control system, to keep the output voltage constant at varying loads and supply voltages, is realized. A maximum output power of 180 mW, generated with a power conversion efficiency of 52 %, is achieved without needing any external components. To the authors knowledge this is the first fully-integrated converter which has a power conversion efficiency benefit over a linear voltage regulator. This is translated in a Efficiency Enhancement Factor (EEF) of $+12 \%$.

The novel COOT control system keeps the output voltage constant and stable over the entire load range from 0 mW to 180 mW. Furthermore it enables the converter to work with input voltages from 2 V to 2.6 V and to generate output voltages between 1.1 V and 1.5 V.

REFERENCES

[1] C. Shi, B. C. Walker, E. Zeisel, B. Hu and G. H. McAllister. "A Highly Integrated Power Management IC for Advanced Mobile Applications". *IEEE Journal of Solid-State Circuits*, vol.42, no.8, pp. 1723-1731, August 2007

[2] S. Abedinpour, B. Bakkaloglu, and S. Kiaei. "A Multistage Interleaved Synchronous Buck Converter With Integrated Output Filter in 0.18 μm SiGe Process", *IEEE ISSCC Dig. Tech. Papers*, pp. 356-357, 2006

[3] M. Alimadadi, S. Sheikhaei, G. Lemieux, S. Mirabbasi and P. Palmer. "A 3 GHZ switching DC-DC converter using clock-tree charge-recycling in 90 nm CMOS with integrated output filter", *IEEE ISSCC Dig. Tech. Papers*, 2007, pp. 532-533

[4] S. Musunuri and P. L. Chapman. "Design of Low Power Monolithic DC-DC Buck Converter With Integrated Inductor", *Power Electronics Specialists*, 36th conference, pp. 1773-1779, September 2005

[5] K. Inizuka, K. Inagki, H. Kawaguchi, M. Takamiya and T. Sakurai. "Stacked-Chip Implementation of On-Chip Buck Converter for Distributed Power Supply System in SiPs", *IEEE Journal of Solid-State Circuits*, vol.42, no.11, pp. 2404-2410, November 2007

[6] P. Hazucha, et al. "A 233-MHz, 80 %-87 % efficient four-phase DC-DC converter utilizing aircore inductors on package", *IEEE Journal of Solid-State Circuits*, vol.40, no.4, pp. 838-845, April 2005

An On-Chip Dual Supply Charge Pump System for 45nm PD SOI eDRAM

J.B. Kuang[1], A. Mathews[1], J. Barth[2], F. Gebara[1], T. Nguyen[1], J. Schaub[1],
K. Nowka[1], G. Carpenter[1], D. Plass[3], E. Nelson[2], I. Vo[1], W. Reohr[4], T. Kirihata[5]
IBM Research Division and Systems-Technology Group   [1]Austin, TX
[2]Essex Junction, VT   [3]Poughkeepsie, NY   [4]Yorktown Heights, NY   [5]Hopewell Junction, NY
Email: kuang@us.ibm.com

Abstract - We present an on-chip word line (WL) dual supply system for server class embedded DRAM (eDRAM) applications. The design consists of switched capacitor charge pumps, voltage regulators, reference and clock circuits. Charge pump engines feature efficient charge transfer and energy conversion, boosting unregulated rails to 1.8x supply. At vdd=1V, regulated high (1.5 to 1.7V) and low (-0.3 to -0.6V) levels ensure WL overdrive and cell turn-off, respectively, with rippling $<\pm35$mV and maintenance power <780uW/2Mb-DRAM. The system supports >2GHz AC array access and can endure excessive DC load.

Keywords: eDRAM, SOI, switched capacitor circuits

I. INTRODUCTION

On-chip regulated level generation reduces the need of external supplies, and, therefore, system cost and power delivery complexity in large chips with multiple power islands. Supply generation for embedded DRAM (eDRAM) in server class applications entails special challenges due to the stringent power, frequency, cell retention, variability, and distribution requirements [1, 2]. Switched capacitor charge pumps have been traditionally used [3] in DRAM applications. In this paper, we report the design and hardware results of an integrated positive and negative voltage delivery system in a 45nm partially depleted (PD) SOI technology for high-performance processors, where two time constants need to be considered simultaneously: (i) fast FET native response time and, thus, faster computation time, and (ii) slow charge transfer time on pumped rails. The boosted word line (WL) high level (vpp) delivers overdrive to the DRAM cell access transistors, while the negative level (vwl) ensures strong cell turn-off and, thus, retention time yield. This energy-efficient adaptive on-chip voltage solution enhances eDRAM operation and scalability.

II. DESIGN FEATURES

The charge pump system, depicted in Fig. 1, consists of positive and negative pump engines, clock phase offset circuit, tunable non-overlapping clock block, voltage regulators, band-gap voltage reference, voltage delivery grids, and distributed high-density deep trench (DT) pumping and decoupling capacitors for pump engines and boosted rails, respectively. The positive and negative pump engines, shown in Figs 2 and 3, respectively, are designed with an internal slew-optimized voltage doubling topology,

This work is supported in part by the Defense Advanced Research Projects Agency under the Agreement No. HR0011-07-9-0002.

cross-coupled to transfer charges efficiently during both clock phases. A scheme to directly drive the DT pump capacitors is chosen, in contrast to prior work [4-6], to achieve well controlled internal slews and timing certainty, thus avoid contention at extreme process corners. The choice of a one-stage design reduces the technology qualification burden of high voltage device reliability.

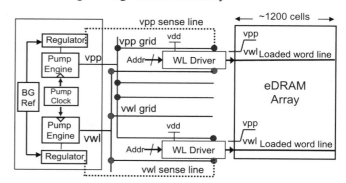

Fig. 1 Block diagram for the dual supply charge pump system in a 2Mb high-speed eDARM

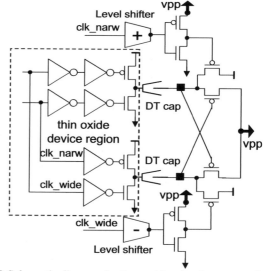

Fig. 2 Schematic diagram for the positive (vpp) pump engine. Thin oxide devices, enclosed in the dashed rectangle, are used in the regular vdd domain to the left of the deep trench capacitors (DT caps), whereas non-body contacted thick oxide devices are used in high bias region. The choice of floating body FETs conserves chip area. Positive and negative polarity level shifters, used for opposite clock phases, are labeled accordingly.

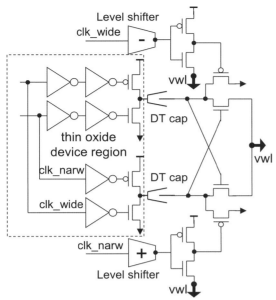

Fig. 3 Schematic diagram for the negative (vwl) pump engine. Thin and thick oxide devices, level shifters, and DT caps are noted as in Fig. 2. In this case of negative level generation, connections of the plate nodes of the DT caps to the higher potential prevent forward biased junction leakage to substrate.

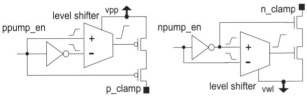

Fig. 4 voltage clamps for the positive and negative pumps. The clamping circuits are connected to the pump engine internal nodes at the right sides of the DT capacitors as shown in Figs 2 and 3.

High density DT capacitors (Fig. 5) enable the design of high capacity area-compact switched capacitor charge pumps to meet the overall DRAM array efficiency requirements.

On this test chip, the compact granular positive (1x) and negative (2x) pump engine areas for 2Mb eDRAM WL loads [7] are 0.0026 and 2x0.0026 mm², respectively. Thick oxide devices are used for high voltage regions to ensure reliability. Level shifters are used to interface different voltage domains. Voltage clamps shown in Fig. 4, which shut off internal current paths, permit direct external access for measurements or word line bias override during burn-in and debug modes.

The front-end clock phase offset block, shown in Fig. 6, divides the input pump clock, and produces a 90° phase separation to minimize aggregate peak switching currents at any given moment. This block also serves as local clock distribution buffer to individual pump engines. In a large dense embedded memory system, a four-way split that realizes 45° phase offset can be made to further cut down system peak power demand. The choice of adjustable lower frequency divided clock in the range of 50 to 150MHz,

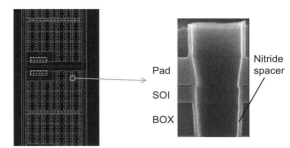

Fig. 5 A high-density deep trench (DT) capacitor cell array building block (left) and magnified view of a single DT cell cross section (right)

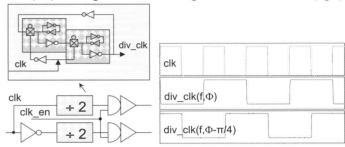

Fig. 6 Simplified schematic and phase diagram for clock divider block

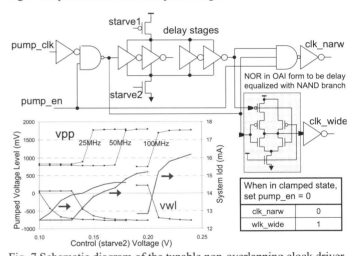

Fig. 7 Schematic diagram of the tunable non-overlapping clock driver and measured pump outputs over frequency and control voltage with starve1 tied to ground. Shown in the lower insert is the control voltage starve2 modulation to arrive at contention free settings in hardware.

instead of directly driving from the high frequency system clock, provides sufficient charge transfer to maintain DC and AC load needs of the WL circuit while optimizing energy conversion efficiency and reduce power consumption.

Fig. 7 shows the non-overlapping clock block, with adjustable edge separation knobs (starve1, starve2), that feeds the pump engines. The wide and narrow outputs are sized with equal delay from the input clock feed. When disabled, wide output is set to 1 and narrow output is set to 0 to shut off both phases of the pump engine.

Pumped levels are regulated by comparing divided sense point voltage to a reference level generated from the band-gap block, and turning each individual pump on and off by

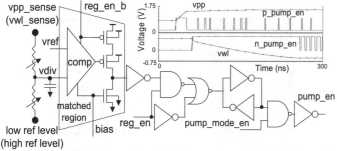

Fig. 8 Voltage regulator with exemplary start-up waveforms shown in the insert. The upper waveform insert shows the simulation results of vpp level regulation. As the current demands reduce after reaching steady state levels, individual regulator turns each pump engine on/off accordingly.

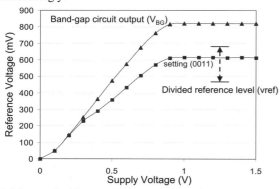

Fig. 9 Measured reference voltage vs. supply voltage. The lower curve shows an example setting of the divided reference level, which feeds the comparator block. (Upper curve) V_{BG} slope is -4.1mV/V.

enabling or disabling the clock feeds (Figs. 8 and 9). To prevent a high current condition due to delays in comparator decision registration, a latch structure, regulating switching thresholds, is incorporated prior to the pump clock enable feed. Exhaustive simulations, as well as post-fabrication hardware characterization, were performed to ensure start-up of both types of pumps in the presence of mutual interactions due to different pump enable times, regulation start times, and pump strength configurations. Fig. 8 insert shows an example of early vpp and late vwl engagement with both pumps under voltage regulation.

To control ripples, each pump output receives an additional 200pF DT capacitor load, in addition to distributed DT capacitor cells and circuit loads on vpp/vwl grids. Multiple feedback sense points are taken from calculated locations on vpp/vwl grids to optimize the regulation duty cycle and minimize RC drops. 15KΩ resistors, shunt to vdd and gnd, are connected to individual

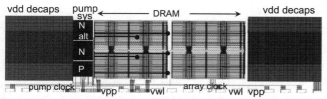

Fig. 10 Pump system test chip with sense points highlighted. Each pump engine receives one sense line from a pre-calculated location.

positive and negative pump outputs, respectively, to block low-frequency noise and ringing.

III. RESULTS AND DISCUSSIONS

The test chip, shown in Fig. 10, was fabricated in 45nm PD SOI logic technology with multiple threshold voltages, two oxide thicknesses 1.12/2.35nm, and eDRAM options. Aside from the pump clock input, a separate array clock input is provided to characterize multiple word line activation.

Measured voltage capacity curves, under the presence of pump-to-pump interactions at a divided pump clock frequency of 100MHz in the unregulated mode, are shown in Fig. 11. The region between inner curves represents suggested operation bias windows. Near voltage capacity operation is to be avoided as current supply diminishes and voltage rippling worsens. For instance, at vdd=1V, vpp peaks at 1.8V with a preferred regulated bias range from 1.5 to 1.7V; vwl reaches -0.77V where the regulated bias can be flexibly set between -0.3 to -0.6V to meet the required leakage specification.

Fig. 12 shows the measured frequency response of output voltages, where a broad range of functional frequencies is observed. This feature enables flexible adjustment of pump clock frequency in accordance with varying charge transfer

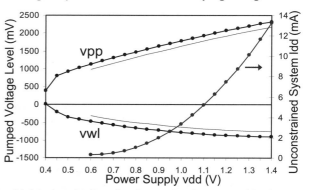

Fig. 11 Measured unregulated capacity for vpp and vwl pumps. Inner curves are the suggested voltage regulation range to ensure sufficient current supply capability under heavy load conditions.

rate, depending on the circuit load demand. As Idd increases with frequency, it is desirable to choose lower clock rate whenever possible. In this design, 50 - 150MHz internal pump clock frequency renders best energy efficiency. The insert of Fig. 7 shows the effect of clock edge separation measured at three pump clock frequencies, which reveal the importance of eliminating contention to reduce switching power and maximizing charging duty cycle while steering operations in the high energy conversion efficiency (>80%) region.

Fig. 13 shows load resilience characteristics, measured under extreme leakage assumptions or load demands. External shunt current loads are applied from the tester. Because of the complexity of word line circuits, three types of shunt loads are applied to track the output voltage levels, mimicking excessive device leakages due to skewed fabrication process conditions. The DC current supply capability of the vpp pump can also be used to burn the embedded fuses (eFUSE) [8] to program redundant array selection when multiple instances of the vpp pumps are simultaneously enabled.

The experiment pad cage includes an external array clock input, properly terminated on chip, to allow the feed of a high frequency clock. The dual supply charge pump system sustains AC loads of high-speed array access at 2GHz and reliably up to the instrument stimulation limit of 3.5GHz. This result demonstrates the suitability of embedded high-density switched capacitor charge pump methodology for high-performance processor designs.

Fig. 14 shows the measured output level tuning examples at low (0.8V) and high (1.3V) supplies. The flexibility to adjust band-gap circuit output and regulator resistor divider ratio (as in Fig. 9 lower curve) also enhances the circuit resilience at process corners and voltage scalability of eDRAM. Voltage ripples on vpp and vwl grids are observed to be <±35mV. Directly measured DC maintenance current to sustain boosted levels during ac inactivity for the 2Mb array is <780uA at vdd=1V, which includes contributions from regulators and reference blocks, as the result of pump efficiency and low device and DT capacitor leakage.

During the power down modes, energy efficiency is achieved by (1) selecting a lower pump clock frequency to retain the boosted voltage levels, or (2) enabling voltage trimmer settings with reduced vpp and vwl range, resulting in more 100x reduction in clock activation rate and, therefore, pump engine power consumption.

IV. CONCLUSION

We have designed and fabricated an integrated on-chip word line dual supply system for server class eDRAM applications on 45nm PD SOI. The design utilizes area compact deep trench capacitors for cross coupled switched capacitor charge pump engines, with voltage regulators and reference generators. Hardware results demonstrate highly tunable low-ripple output voltage ranges to meet access time and cell retention time requirements. At the nominal vdd of 1V, vpp regulates between 1.5 and 1.7V, vwl regulates between -0.3 to -0.5V. The design requires very low maintenance power, namely <780uW/2Mb-DRAM during array inactivity, while supporting >2GHz high speed stimulation during array access.

REFERENCES

[1] J. Barth, et al., "A 500MHz random cycle, 1.5ns-latency, SOI embedded DRAM macro featuring a three-transistor sense amplifier," ISSCC Dig. Tech. Papers, pp. 486-487, 2007.

[2] G. Wang, et al., "A 0.127µm² high performance 65nm SOI based embedded DRAM for on-processor applications, in IEDM Tech. Dig., 2006.

[3] Y. Nakagome, et al., "An experimental 1.5-V 64-Mb DRAM," IEEE J. Solid-States Circuits, vol. 26, no. 4, pp. 465-472, 1991.

[4] T. Cho and P. Gray, "A 10-bit 20 MS/s 35 mW pipeline A/D converter," Proc. CICC, pp. 499-502, 1994.

[5] P. Favrat, et al., "A high-efficiency CMOS voltage doubler," IEEE J. Solid-State Circuits, vol. 33, no. 3, pp. 410-416, 1998.

[6] H. Lee and P. Mok, "Switching noise and shoot-through current reduction techniques for switched-capacitor voltage doubler," IEEE J. Solid-State Circuits, vol. 40, no. 5, pp. 1136-1146, 2005.

[7] P. Klim, et al, "A one MB cache system prototype with 2GHz embedded DRAMs in 45nm SOI CMOS," Symp. VLSI Circuits, 2007.

[8] G. Uhlmann, et al., "A commercial field programmable dense eFUSE array memory with 99.999% sense yield for 45nm SOI CMOS, ISSCC Dig. Tech. Papers, 2008.

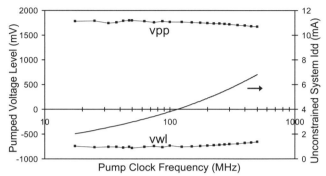

Fig. 12 Measured frequency response of the pump system unregulated capacity, including the effect of pump-to-pump interactions

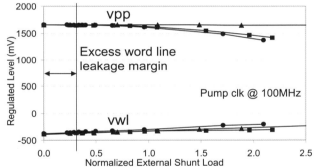

Fig. 13 Regulated output level vs. external shunt load current resilience. Shunt currents of vpp-to-gnd, vwl-to-gnd, and vpp-to-vwl were applied by the wafer tester to mimic various combinations of excessive WL circuit leakages. No level degradation is observed within the specified leakage load margin.

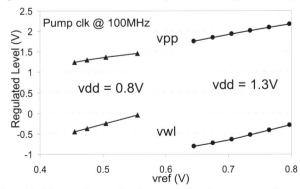

Fig. 14 Measured regulated output levels versus reference voltage (tied inputs for positive and negative regulators in this plot) for 0.8V low-power mode and 1.3V performance mode

A Time-Domain SAR Smart Temperature Sensor with -0.25~+0.35°C Inaccuracy for On-Chip Monitoring

Poki Chen, Kai-Ming Wang, Yu-Han Peng, Yu-Shin Wang
Dept. of Elect. Eng. and Grad. Inst. of Electro-Optical Eng.
National Taiwan University of Science and Technology
Taipei, Taiwan
poki@mail.ntust.edu.tw

Chun-Chi Chen
Dept. of Electronic Engineering
National Kaohsiung First University of Science and Tech.
Kaohsiung, Taiwan

Abstract—The first time-domain successive approximation register (SAR) smart temperature sensor is proposed in this paper. Without using any bipolar transistor, a temperature sensor composed of temperature-dependent delay line is utilized to generate a delay time proportional to the measured temperature. A binary-weighted time reference delay line is adopted for set-point programming. The effective delay of the reference delay line is adjusted to approximate that of the temperature-dependent delay line for digital output coding through the help of SAR control logic. With 10 output bits, the proposed smart sensor owns a chip area of 0.6 mm^2 in the TSMC 0.35-μm standard digital CMOS process. The consumption current is 11.12μA and an inaccuracy of -0.25~0.35°C over 0~90°C test temperature range is achieved for 23 test chips without any dynamic element matching, curvature correction, dynamic offset cancellation or BJT device.

I. INTRODUCTION

With the tremendous need of thermal sensing, the temperature sensors with digital I/O for easy interfacing gain much interest of many analog or mixed-mode IC designers. Usually, a temperature sensor with digital output is mounted close to the microprocessor or other significant heat source to continuously convert the operation temperature into digital output for thermal monitoring. The required resolution should be 0.5°C/LSB at least. At any time, the control chip can query the sensor for the current temperature though the digital interface to prevent the overheat disaster. The common problem is that the thermal probe is installed outside of the microprocessor or chipset. If the probe is not firmly attached or out of order, the monitored chip will be burned out easily. The best solution is to directly integrate the smart sensor into the VLSI chip to reduce the risk caused by device failure.

In the late twentieth century, the analog-to-digital converters (ADCs) were gradually integrated into thermal sensors by IC designers to compose the so-called smart temperature sensors [1]. Conventionally, the test temperature was converted by a temperature sensor into a voltage or current signal first, and then the corresponding ADC was utilized for the subsequent digital output coding. An ADC

with more than 10 output bits was usually required to obtain the necessary resolution at the expense of large chip area and high power consumption. In order to be fully compatible with the standard digital CMOS fabrication processes, the temperature sensor generally adopted the parasitic substrate or lateral bipolar transistor for temperature sensing [2, 3]. As the best choice for the integrated reference, a silicon bandgap circuit was normally utilized in the temperature sensor. However, it is not possible to keep the temperature of the reference constant in integrated smart sensors to achieve an accuracy comparable with that of the non-integrated version.

In reality, most researches of smart temperature sensors were focused on the accuracy enhancement at the expense of more elaborate calibration technique and larger die size. A micropower CMOS smart temperature sensor was presented to own an error of ±7°C without calibration [4]. The chip area was 1.5mm^2 in a 0.7μm CMOS process. By poly fuse trimming, the sensor error could be reduced to ±1°C with an external reference [5]. The die area was 3.3mm^2 in a 0.6μm CMOS process. The inaccuracy of the state-of-art smart temperature sensor was merely ±0.1°C (3σ) for –55~+125°C temperature range. However the chip size was as large as 4.5mm^2 in a 0.7μm CMOS process [6]. It makes the voltage-domain smart temperature sensors less attractive to VLSI on-chip temperature sensing. Moreover, the effective resolution becomes smaller as the supply voltage scaled down with the fabrication processes. The design of critical analog circuits, such as ADC and op amp, turns out to be even harder than before. Recently, a time-domain smart temperature sensor was invented to address the above issues [7]. The test temperature was converted into a pulse with a width proportional to the test temperature first. Then, the generated pulse was fed into a time-to-digital converter (TDC) rather than an ADC for digital output coding. The chip size was substantially reduced to 0.175mm^2 in a 0.35μm CMOS digital process with a measurement error of -0.7~+0.9°C. Later, a time-domain fully digital version was realized with only 140 FPGA logic elements to ease on-chip integration and IP reuse [8]. Neither full-custom design nor handcrafted device was required. However, the measured error was worsen to -1.5~0.8°C. Since

This research is funded by National Science Council under contract no. NSC 96-2221-E-011-151..

70

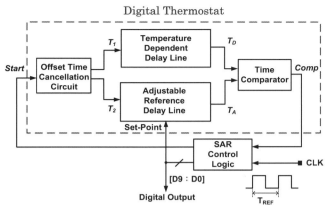

Figure 1. Architecture of the proposed smart temperature sensor.

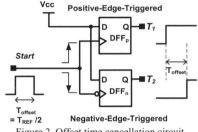

Figure 2. Offset time cancellation circuit.

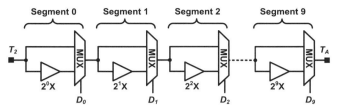

Figure 3. Adopted 10-bit ARDL with binary-weighted structure.

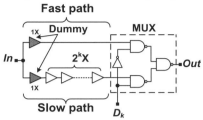

Figure 4. Schematic of the ARDL k-th segment.

no error reduction technique similar to the voltage-domain second-order curvature correction [9] could be adopted, the errors of time-domain thermal sensors were usually larger than those of the voltage-domain counterparts.

For error reduction, a novel time-domain SAR smart temperature sensor is proposed in this paper with the block diagram shown in Figure 1 which is evolved from the former time-domain digital thermostat [10]. Two delay lines with similar curvatures of the temperature-to-time transfer curves are utilized to lower the nonlinearity impact on the sensor's accuracy and the SAR control logic is adopted to fasten the digital output coding according to the temperature under test. The design consideration and detail circuit of the proposed sensor will be described in section II. The experiment results will be illustrated and discussed in section III. Finally, a conclusion will be given in section IV.

II. MAIN BUILDING BLOCKS

The proposed circuit consists of a offset time cancellation circuit to reduce the offset faced at the lower test temperature bound, a temperature-dependent delay line (TDDL) for temperature sensing to generate a delay T_D proportional to the measured temperature, a thermally compensated adjustable reference delay line (ARDL) to generate a delay T_A according to the programmed set-point, a time comparator for detecting the time difference between T_A and T_D, and a 10-bit SAR control logic to provide successive digital set-point programming. With a nominal temperature range of 0~90°C to fully support commercial IC on-chip sensing, an effective resolution finer than 0.1°C is promised. All sub-circuits will be illustrated in detail as follows.

A. Offset Time Cancellation Circuit

The output delay T_D of the temperature-dependent delay line at the lower temperature operation bound is usually much larger than zero. It is proven to cause large measurement offset, long conversion time and great power consumption [7]. One possible solution is to insert enough number of reference delay cells at the beginning of the reference delay line to compensate for this offset time [10]. As an expense, more chip area and dissipation power must be consumed. In order to solve the above problem, a simple but practical offset time cancellation circuit composed of only two D-type flip-flops (DFFs) is proposed as shown in Figure 2. At the beginning of each comparison, the pulse *Start* is fed into the clock inputs of both DFFs. The width of the pulse is designed to be equivalent to the offset time T_{offset} at the lower temperature operation bound. The flip-flop DFF$_p$ is triggered by the positive edge of *Start*, to generate the step signal T_1 which is sent to the TDDL input. Similarly, the negative edge of *Start* triggers the flip-flop DFF$_n$ to yield the step signal T_2 for ARDL input. The delay difference between T_1 and T_2 will be identical to T_{offset} for offset compensation. The large chip area occupied by the offset-compensation delay cells can be saved, and the ARDL length can be shortened correspondingly.

B. Adjustable Reference Delay Line

As depicted in Figure 3, the ARDL with a binary-weighted structure suitable for SAR operation is adopted [11]. The delay line consists of multiple delay segments whose delays are scaled with binary weights. The temperature compensation circuit adopted in the former time-domain sensor [7] is utilized likewise to reduce the thermal sensitivity of the ARDL delay cell to make its delay act as a unit reference time. However, the conventional thermal compensation circuit consumes continuous power. Some switches are added to shut down its quiescent currents between measurements to reduce self-heating effect. The 2-to-1 multiplexer in each segment is controlled by the corresponding input bit to include or bypass all unit delay cells of the segment in the signal transmission path of T_A whose overall delay is proportional to the ARDL input value.

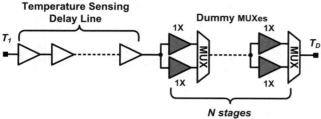

Figure 5. Temperature dependent delay

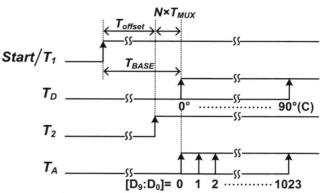

Figure 6. Timing diagram of the proposed sensor.

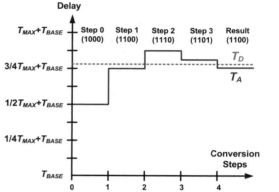

Figure 7 Exemplified operation of the 4-bit time-domain SAR sensor.

Figure 4 shows the entire schematic of the ARDL k^{th} segment. To balance the input loadings of both fast and slow paths in each segment for reducing the error caused by signal distortion at the input, one dummy delay cell is inserted in the beginning of each path at the expense of slightly increased circuit area and conversion time. The overall ARDL propagation delay T_A can be lumped as

$$T_A = T_{offset} + N \times T_{MUX} + \sum_{k=0}^{N-1} d_k 2^k T_X , \qquad (1)$$

where T_{MUX} is the multiplexer propagation delay taking the dummy delay cell in each path into account and T_X is the unit ARDL cell delay respectively. Due to that a multiplexer is placed in each ARDL segment, some extra delay $N \times T_{MUX}$ is included in the transmission path. However, the extra delay imposed on T_A can be easily compensated for by adding the same number of 2-to-1 multiplexers in the transmission path of T_D as illustrated in Figure 5.

To cut the delay line size and the conversion time in half, the delay cell of the ARDL can be theoretically implemented as a temperature-compensated NOT gate instead of a delay buffer [10]. However, the rise time and fall time of the temperature-compensated NOT gate are not equivalent due to the pull up and pull down currents cannot be kept exactly the same after fabrication. This mismatch between even and odd stages will cause additional errors. Therefore, a thermally compensated buffer (or 2 equivalent NOT gates) is used instead as the unit delay cell in ARDL.

C. Temperature-Dependent Delay Line

The TDDL consists of a temperature sensing delay line and N dummy multiplexers to compensate for the delay offset caused by the multiplexers resident in ARDL, as shown in Figure 5. Since there are only N 2-to-1 dummy multiplexers needed to be inserted in TDDL, the chip area consumed by the dummy devices is substantially decreased from that of one 2^N-to-1 dummy multiplexer used in the previous thermostat [10]. The temperature sensing delay line is simply composed of even number of NOT gates which are not thermally compensated. The higher the operation temperature is, the longer the propagation delay of NOT gate becomes [7]. Thus, the delay line composed of NOT gates can act as a time-domain PTAT (proportional to absolute temperature) circuit which owns much simpler structure than the conventional voltage-domain ones. The timing relationship between both delay lines is explicitly depicted in the timing diagram of Figure 6. The adjustable range of T_A is designed to fully cover the variation of T_D for 0~90°C temperature range.

D. Time Comparator and SAR Control Logic

The time comparator only needs to determine whether T_A leads or lags T_D. A simple DFF is good enough to be the time comparator by sampling T_D with the rise edge of T_A. The comparator output *Comp* is fed into the SAR control logic to determine whether the current SAR bit will be preserved ($T_A < T_D$) or cleared ($T_A > T_D$). As an example, the operation of the proposed time-domain sensor with 4 input bits is shown in Figure 7. The thermally sensitive delay T_D of the TDDL is fixed for a given temperature. On the contrary, the reference delay T_A with much less temperature sensitivity is varied by adjusting the effective length of ARDL according to the set-point value. The SAR algorithm is utilized to speed up the adjustment of T_A to approximate T_D. For simplicity, the delay faced by T_D, T_A at the lower temperature bound is denoted as T_{BASE} which equals $T_{offset} + N \times T_{MUX}$ and the maximum adjustable range of T_A is represented as T_{MAX} which equals $2^N \times T_X$. For a given test temperature, T_D is fixed and T_A is adjusted successively to approximate T_D. The final difference between T_A and T_D will be less than the unit reference delay T_X.

The time comparison error is mainly caused by the dead zone, or sampling window, of DFF. Fortunately, the signals can be easily stretched or amplified along the time axis since there is no hard limit similar to the supply voltage or full-scale voltage of the voltage-domain sensors imposed on the time-domain ones. The unit reference delay T_X is designed to be much larger than the DFF dead zone to make the corresponding time error less than 1 LSB. Thus, the impact of dead zone can be reduced straightforwardly by increasing the

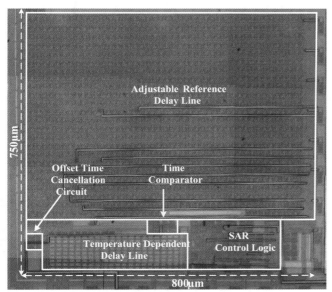

Figure 8. Microphotograph of the SAR sensor.

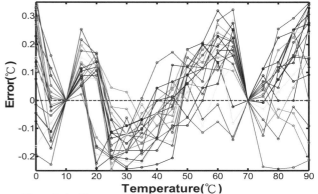

Figure 9. Architecture of the proposed smart temperature sensor.

number of SAR bits. With 10 SAR bits and a practical temperature range of -2~92°C to cover the possible process variations, the maximum error contributed by the dead zone is less than 0.1°C.

III. EXPERIMENTAL RESULTS

The proposed SAR smart temperature sensor was fabricated in a TSMC standard 0.35-μm 2P4M CMOS digital process. The chip area is 0.75mm×0.8mm as shown in Figure 8. The test input signal was issued by the FPGA control board and the digital output codes were collected by a logic analyzer.

To figure out the performance of the proposed circuit, the measurement of the SAR sensor was done in 5°C steps over 0°C~90°C temperature range in a programmable temperature and humidity chamber MHU-408LRBDA. With the excellent linearity achieved by making TDDL and ARDL have similar temperature-to-time curvatures, the measurement errors are -0.25~+0.35°C only for total 23 test chips after two point calibration as depicted in Figure 9. Compared with the former time-domain version [8], a four-fold improvement in accuracy is achieved. To reveal the effect of the process variation on the proposed circuit, all the effective resolutions of the test chips are calculated to be within 0.0908~0.0927°C/LSB. The chip-to-chip resolution mismatch is merely ±0.9% which is fairly low for most applications. The power consumption is 36.7μW at 2 samples/s.

IV. CONCULSION

A time-domain SAR smart temperature sensor was proposed in this paper. To reduce the chip size tremendously for portable or low cost applications, a simple offset cancellation circuit was explored to replace a large number of thermal-compensated delay cells for alleviating the large measurement offset faced at the lower temperature bound. The chip area of the 10-bit sensor is 0.6 mm^2. The measurement error is within -0.25~+0.35°C over 0°C~90°C which covers the full temperature operation range of commercial ICs. For total 23 test chips, the chip-to-chip resolution mismatch is merely ±0.9% which demonstrates the good immunity of the proposed sensor to process variations.

ACKNOWLEDGMENT

The authors would like to express their deep appreciation to National Chip Implementation Center (CIC) for the help of chip fabrication.

REFERENCES

[1] P. Krummenacher and H. Oguey, "Smart temperature sensor in CMOS technology", *Sensors and Actuators A: Physical*, vol. 22, issue 1-3, pp.636 - 638, June 1990.

[2] R. A. Bianchi, F. Vinci Dos Santos, J. M. Karam, B. Courtois, F. Pressecq, and S. Sifflet, "CMOS compatible temperature sensor based on the lateral bipolar transistor for very wide temperature range application," *Sensors, Actuators: A. Physical*, vol. 71, issue 1-2, pp. 3–9, Nov. 1998.

[3] G. Wang, and G. C. M. Meijer, "The Temperature Characteristics of Bipolar Transistors Fabricated in CMOS Technology," *Sensors and Actuators A: Physical*, vol. 87, issue 1-2, pp. 81-89, Dec. 2000

[4] A. Bakker and J. H. Huijsing, "Micropower CMOS temperature sensor with digital output," *IEEE J. Solid-State Circuits*, vol. 31, pp.933-937, July 1996.

[5] M. Tuthill, "A Switched-Current, Switched- Capacitor Temperature Sensor in 0.6-um CMOS," *IEEE J. Solid-State Circuits*, vol. 33, pp. 1117-1122, July 1998.

[6] M. A. P. Pertijs, A. Niederkorn, M. Xu, B. McKillop, A. Bakker, and J. H. Huijsing, "A CMOS Smart Temperature Sensor with a 3σ Inaccuracy of ±0.1°C from −55°C to 125°C," *IEEE J. Solid-State Circuits*, vol. 40, pp. 2805-2815, Dec. 2005.

[7] P. Chen, C.-C. Chen, W.-F. Lu and C.-C. Tsai, "A Time-to-Digital-Converter-Based CMOS Smart Temperature Sensor," *IEEE J. Solid-State Circuits*, vol. 40, no. 8, pp. 1642-1648, Aug. 2005.

[8] P. Chen, M.-C. Shie, Z.-Y. Zheng, Z.-F. Zheng and C.-Y. Chu, "A Fully Digital Time Domain Smart Temperature Sensor Realized with 140 FPGA Logic Elements", *IEEE Transactions on Circuits and Systems I*, vol. 54, pp. 2661-2668, Dec 2007.

[9] M. A. P. Pertijs, A. Bakker, and J. H. Huijsing, "A high-accuracy temperature sensor with second-order curvature correction and digital bus interface," *in Proc. ISCAS*, pp. 368–371, May 2001.

[10] P. Chen, C.-C. Chen, T.-K. Chen, and S.-W. Chen, "A Time-Domain Mixed-Mode Temperature Sensor with Digital Set-Point Programming," *in Proc. IEEE CICC*, pp. 821-824, Sept. 2006.

[11] A. Syed, E. Ahmed, D. Maksimovic, and E. Alarcon, "Digital Pulse Width Modulator Architectures," *in Proc. 35th Annual IEEE Power Electronics Specialirls Conference*, pp. 4689-4695, June 2004.

[12] T. A. Demassa, and Z. Ciccone, " Digital Integrated Circuits," *John Wiley & Sons, Inc.*, 1996.

A Temperature-to-Digital Converter Based on an Optimized Electrothermal Filter

S.M.Kashmiri, S.Xia, and K.A.A.Makinwa
Electronic Instrumentation Laboratory / DIMES
Delft University of Technology
Delft, The Netherlands
E-mail: S.M.Kashmiri@TUDelft.NL

Abstract— **The design of a CMOS temperature-to-digital converter (TDC) is presented. It operates by measuring the phase shift of an electrothermal filter (ETF), which is a function of the temperature-dependent thermal diffusivity of bulk silicon. Compared to previous work, this TDC employs an improved ETF, whose layout has been optimized to minimize the phase spread caused by lithographic inaccuracy. Furthermore, the TDC's front-end consists of a gain-boosted transconductor, whose wide bandwidth minimizes electrical phase spread. The resulting current is then digitized by a phase-domain $\Sigma\Delta$ modulator. The phase-subtracting node of the modulator is realized by a chopper demodulator, whose switching action, however, will give rise to a residual offset current. This is minimized by locating the demodulator at the virtual grounds of the transconductor's gain boosting amplifiers. Any residual offset is then eliminated by chopping the entire front-end. Measurements on 16 samples show that the TDC has an untrimmed inaccuracy of less than −0.4°C (3s) over the military range (-55°C to 125°C).**

I. Introduction

In earlier work [1, 2], it has been shown that absolute temperature can be accurately determined by measuring the phase shift of an integrated electrothermal filter (ETF). Using this approach, a temperature-to-digital converter (TDC) with an untrimmed inaccuracy of ±0.5°C has been realized [3]. This compares very favorably with the inaccuracy of untrimmed, band-gap temperature sensors, which is in the order of ±3°C.

An integrated ETF consists of a heater and a (relative) temperature sensor realized in close proximity on the same silicon substrate. AC power dissipation in the heater causes local temperature variations, which the sensor then converts back into electrical AC signals. Since the rate at which heat diffuses through the substrate is finite, the sensor's output will be phase shifted with respect to the heater's power dissipation. This phase shift is a function of the filter's geometry and of the *temperature-dependent* thermal diffusivity of the silicon substrate [4]. Since the thermal diffusivity of the substrate is insensitive to process spread [2, 5], the spread in an ETF's phase shift will be mainly determined by lithographic

inaccuracy, which can be minimized by optimizing its layout [6] and by making its critical dimensions sufficiently large.

In an ETF-based TDC, another important source of error is the *electrical* phase spread introduced by its front-end. In principle, this can be minimized by maximizing the front-end's nominal bandwidth. However, this must be done in a power efficient fashion, in order not to incur significant self-heating errors.

In this work, a new TDC front-end is described. It consists of a wide-band gain-boosted transconductor, which converts the ETF's output voltage into a current. The phase-shift of the resulting current is then digitized by a phase-domain $\Sigma\Delta$ modulator [3]. Compared to the multi-stage preamplifier used in previous work, this front end provides significantly higher bandwidth (115MHz vs. 25MHz) at roughly the same current consumption. To exploit the expected improvement in TDC accuracy, the new front-end has been combined with an improved ETF, whose layout has been optimized to minimize phase spread due to lithographic inaccuracy [6].

In the next section, the optimized ETF is described. Section III provides an overview of the implemented TDC. The circuit design is described in section IV, while the measurement results are presented in section V. The paper ends with conclusions.

II. Optimized Electro Thermal Filter

The layout of the optimized ETF is shown in Fig. 1. Like a previous ETF [3], it consists of an n+ diffusion heater, which is surrounded by a thermopile made of p+ diffusion/Aluminum thermocouples. However, its layout has been optimized to maximize the SNR at the thermopile's output, to maintain the same phase-shift at 100 kHz, and to minimize the sensitivity of this phase-shift to lithographic errors [6].

For the same power dissipation, reduced heater area will result in higher temperatures, and so, a folded heater was used. In addition, the thermopile's "hot" junctions were located on a roughly circular, constant phase-shift contour. This maximizes the thermopile's output amplitude, since this is proportional to the sum of the phase-shifted temperature variations at these junctions. Finally, the length of each arm, and hence its thermal noise contribution, was chosen to maximize the SNR at the thermopile's output. Compared to the ETF of [3], these considerations allowed the number of thermocouples, and hence the ETF's signal output, to be increased from 20 to 24.

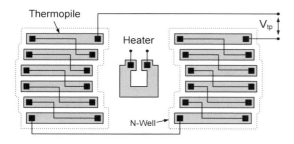

Figure 1.   Layout of the optimized ETF

Simulations show that at a driving frequency of 100 kHz and for the same lithographic inaccuracy, the optimized ETF exhibits 20% less phase spread than the ETF of [3]. In addition, its output SNR is 50% higher.

III.   SYSTEM DESIGN

A block diagram of the implemented TDC is shown in Fig. 2. Here, the optimized ETF is driven at a constant frequency f_{drive} by a square-wave derived from a crystal oscillator. Its output is then a small (sub-millivolt) AC signal, which is phase-shifted with respect to the square-wave. This signal is then converted into a current by the wide-band transconductor g_m, and then digitized by a phase-domain $\Sigma\Delta$ modulator.

The phase-domain $\Sigma\Delta$ modulator consists of a chopper demodulator, an integrator (C_{int}), a quantizer and a single-bit phase DAC. Depending on the output of the quantizer, the chopper demodulator will be driven by one of the two digitally phase-shifted versions of f_{drive}, $f_{drive}(\varphi_0)$ and $f_{drive}(\varphi_1)$, output by the phase DAC. The chopper demodulator acts as the modulator's summing node, and outputs a current whose DC

component is proportional to the difference in phase between the transconductor's output current and the output of the phase DAC. This DC component is then integrated by the capacitor C_{int}, which acts as the modulator's loop filter. The capacitor also filters out the harmonics of f_{drive} that are present at the output of the chopper demodulator. The voltage across the capacitor is then boosted by a differential-to-single-ended amplifier, which drives a digital latch in an off-chip FPGA. The latch thus serves as the modulator's quantizer.

Due to the charge injection mismatch of the demodulator's CMOS switches, and to the fact that a net DC current is required to establish a switching waveform across the parasitic capacitances at its input, there will be a significant DC offset current at the output of the demodulator. As in [3], this source of error can be eliminated by chopping the entire front-end (including the ETF) at a frequency f_{ch} (20Hz), which is much lower than f_{drive} (85 kHz).

Since the modulator is of 1st order, the bitstream was decimated by a 1st-order sinc filter, with a length of N/f_{ch}, where N is an integer, so that its notches perfectly eliminate the ripple caused by the low-frequency chopping. The decimation filter also sets the system bandwidth, and thus filters out most of the thermopile's wide-band noise.

The ETF's phase-shift is a near-linear function of temperature [3], and so achieving a resolution of 0.1°C (in line with the expected accuracy) over the military temperature range means that the phase-domain $\Sigma\Delta$ modulator must have a resolution of at least 12-bits. Since the modulator's over-sampling ratio can be made quite large, its resolution will be mainly limited by the leakage of its passive integrator, which, in turn, is determined by the finite output impedance of the transconductor. To achieve sufficient resolution, the transconductor's output impedance was increased by the use of gain boosting. As will be discussed in the following section, the CMOS switches of the demodulator can then be advantageously located at the virtual grounds established by the gain-boosting amplifiers. This significantly reduces the magnitude of the DC offset current at the output of the demodulator.

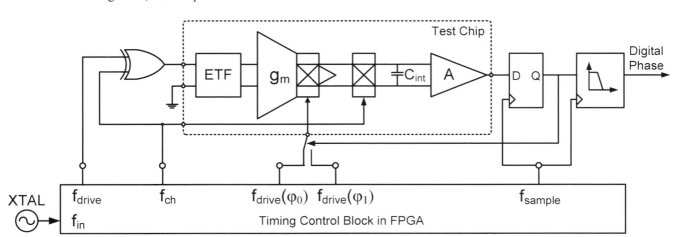

Figure 2.   System overview

IV. CIRCUIT DESIGN

As discussed above, the input transconductor should be designed to have wide bandwidth and high output impedance. To achieve this, the transconductor was implemented as a gain-boosted folded-cascode amplifier, with a PMOS input pair, and an embedded chopper demodulator (Fig 3). In order to compare the performance of the old ETF with that of the optimized ETF, two PMOS input pairs were connected in parallel. By multiplexing their tail currents, one of the two ETFs can be selected. The transconductance of each input pair is 300µS, which ensures that its noise contribution is negligible compared to the noise associated with the thermopile's resistance (20kΩ).

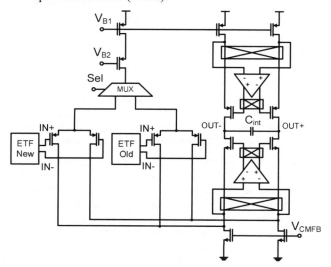

Figure 3.   The wide band transconductor

Simulations show that over temperature and process, the amplifier has a unity-gain BW greater than 115MHz and a corresponding phase-shift spread of less than 0.05 degrees at f_{drive} = 85kHz. Although this corresponds to a temperature-sensing inaccuracy of only 0.2°C, it should be noted that the phase spread *within a batch* should be significantly smaller. Furthermore, the amplifier's simulated DC gain is greater than 140dB, which corresponds to an output impedance of more than 33GΩ. With C_{int} = 70pF, a 2Hz signal bandwidth, and a 2.67 kHz sampling frequency, this means that the dead bands associated with integrator leakage are no wider than 0.02°C.

The demodulated DC current applied to C_{int} will be in the order of a few tens of nano-Amperes. This means that any DC error currents must be reduced to the pico-Ampere level. The chopper demodulator is itself a major contributor of such error currents. This is because any DC voltage across its output (e.g. due to the offset of the cascode transistors) will, because of its switching action, periodically charge and discharge the parasitic capacitance C_{par} (e.g. associated with the current sources and the PMOS input stage) at its input nodes. The resulting currents are then rectified by the chopper itself and cause a net DC offset current I_{off} at its output [8]. For an output voltage V_{off} and a chopping frequency f_{ch}:

$$I_{off} = 4f_{ch}C_{par}V_{off} \qquad (1)$$

To minimize I_{off}, the parasitic capacitances at the high impedance input nodes of the chopper demodulator should be *shielded* from the DC voltage across its outputs. As shown in Fig. 4, a suitable location for the chopper is between the source terminals of the cascode transistors and the input terminals of the booster amplifiers. This way, the booster amplifiers will establish a virtual ground at the high impedance, high capacitance, folding nodes of the main amplifier. The output of the boosters must then also be chopped in order to maintain the correct feedback polarity. This technique has two advantages. Firstly, fixing the chopper's input nodes at virtual ground reduces the magnitude of I_{off} by three orders of magnitude (from simulations), compared to the situation when the choppers are located outside the gain-boosting loop. Secondly, chopping the booster's output means that the contribution of its offset (and $1/f$ noise) to the amplifier's output current is also chopped. As discussed previously, any remaining residual offset current is then cancelled by chopping the entire front end [9].

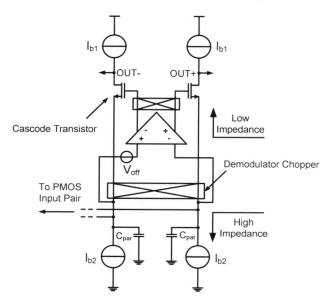

Figure 4.   Chopping at virtual ground nodes of the booster

Since the signal across C_{int} is too small to drive an off-chip latch, it is buffered by a differential to single-ended amplifier with a gain of 40dB. The output of this amplifier is a rail-to-rail signal, which drives an off-chip FPGA latch (Fig. 2). As described in [2], heater drive inversion (HDI) is used to minimize the effect of capacitive cross talk in the ETF.

V. MEASUREMENT RESULTS

The optimized ETF, the old ETF used in [3], and the TDC's analog front-end were realized in a standard 0.7µm CMOS technology. The chip has an area of 2.3mm^2 (fig. 5). The selected ETF and the temperature-to-digital converter each consume 2.5mW from a 5V supply. The timing signals were generated in an FPGA and derived from a 16MHz crystal oscillator. The ETF was driven at a frequency of 85 KHz, and the difference between the two reference phases φ_0 and φ_1, was chosen to be 90 degrees, which is large enough to cover the expected variation in the ETF's phase shift over the military temperature range. The sampling rate of the phase-domain $\Sigma\Delta$ modulator was 2.67 KHz, and the low frequency chopper was driven at 20Hz. A 14-bit counter was used as a 1st-order sinc filter, which limits the system bandwidth to 0.16Hz.

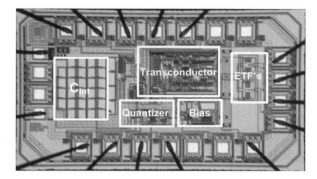

Figure 5.   Chip photo

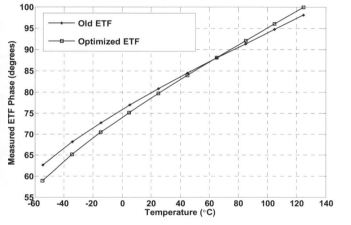

Figure 6.   Measured phase response of optimized and old ETF's

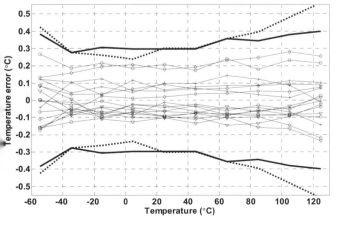

Figure 7.   Measured temperature error of 16 chips (new ETF). Bold line: 3σ spread for the new ETF, Dotted line: 3σ spread for the old ETF

As described in section IV, due to the implementation of an input multiplexer, both the old and the new ETF could be characterized. The measured phase shift of both filters (16 devices) is shown in Fig. 6 as a function of temperature. As a result of their different geometries, the two filters have significantly different phase characteristics. As shown in Fig. 7, the optimized ETF achieves an untrimmed inaccuracy of ±0.4°C (3σ) over the military range (-55°C to 125°C), while the old ETF only achieves an inaccuracy of ±0.54°C (3σ). These results are in line with the predicted 20% improvement in the phase spread sensitivity of the optimized ETF to lithographic inaccuracy.

VI.   CONCLUSIONS

A CMOS temperature-to-digital converter (TDC) based on thermal diffusivity sensing has been implemented. It consists of a phase-domain $\Sigma\Delta$ modulator, which measures the temperature-dependent phase shift of an electrothermal filter (ETF). By optimizing the layout of the filter, its sensitivity to lithographic errors was decreased by 20% and its SNR was increased by 50%. To minimize the phase error introduced by the interface electronics, a wide-band, gain-boosted, single-stage transconductor was used instead of the multi-stage pre-amplifiers used in previous work. In addition, the residual offset current introduced by the chopper demodulator of the phase-domain $\Sigma\Delta$ modulator was minimized by locating it at virtual ground nodes. Using these techniques, an untrimmed temperature-sensing inaccuracy of ±0.4°C (3σ) over the military range (-55°C to 125°C) was achieved (16 samples).

REFERENCES

[1]   K.A.A. Makinwa and J.F. Witte, "A temperature sensor based on a thermal oscillator, " Proc. of IEEE Sensors 2005, pp. 1149–1151, October 2005.

[2]   K.A.A. Makinwa and M.F. Snoeij, "A CMOS temperature-to-frequency converter with an inaccuracy of ±0.5°C (3σ) from -40 to 105°C," IEEE J. Solid-State Circuits, vol. 41, no. 12, pp. 2992–2997, December 2006.

[3]   C.P.L. van Vroonhoven and K.A.A. Makinwa, "A CMOS Temperature-to-Digital Converter with an inaccuracy of ±0.5°C (3σ) from -55 to 125°C," IEEE ISSCC Dig. Tech. Papers, pp. 576–577, February 2008.

[4]   V. Szekely, "Thermal monitoring of microelectronic structures," Microelectronics Journal, vol.25, no. 3, pp.157–170, 1994

[5]   C. Zhang and K.A.A. Makinwa, "The effect of substrate doping on the behaviour of a CMOS electrothermal frequency-locked-loop," Digest of Transducers, pp. 2283–2286, June 2007.

[6]   S. Xia and K.A.A. Makinwa, "Design of an Optimized Electrothermal Filter for a Temperature-to-Frequency Converter," Proc. IEEE Sensors, pp. 1255–1258, October 2007.

[7]   C. Zhang and K.A.A. Makinwa, "Interface Electronics for a CMOS Electrothermal Frequency-Locked-Loop," Proc. ESSCIRC, pp. 292–295, September 2007.

[8]   J.F. Witte, K.A.A. Makinwa and J.H. Huijsing, "A CMOS Chopper Offset-Stabilized Opamp," IEEE J. Solid-State Circuits, vol. 42, no. 7, pp. 1529–1535, July 2007.

[9]   A. Bakker and J. H. Huijsing, "Micropower CMOS temperature sensor with digital output," IEEE J. Solid-State Circuits, vol. 31, no. 7, pp. 933–937, July 1996.

A Fully Integrated Interface Circuit for 1.5°C Accuracy Temperature Control and 130-dB Dynamic-Range Read-Out of MOX Gas Sensors

A. Lombardi, M. Grassi, L. Bruno, P. Malcovati
Department of Electrical Engineering,
UNIVERSITY OF PAVIA,
Via Ferrata, 27100 PAVIA, Italy
[andrea.lombardi, marco.grassi, luca.bruno,
piero.malcovati]@unipv.it

A. Baschirotto
Department of Physics,
UNIVERSITY OF MILANO-BICOCCA
P.za Scienza, 20126 Milano, Italy
andrea.baschirotto@unimib.it

Abstract — **This paper presents a complete gas-sensing chip. It consists of a high-efficiency temperature control loop with a switching power stage and digital set-point and of a wide-dynamic-range interface circuit able to operate without calibration. Measurements results show that the controlled temperature of the sensor over a range of 250 °C exhibits an accuracy better than 1.5 °C with a maximum peak-to-peak ripple of 1.0 °C. The read-out circuit achieves, without calibration, a precision in sensor resistance measurement of 2.65% over a range of 5.3 decades (Dynamic Range, DR=138 dB). The overall system is flexible and can be interfaced to sensors with different fabrication parameters.**

The prototype chip, designed in a 0.35-μm CMOS technology, includes on the same 10-mm^2 die the precision read-out circuit and the switching power stage. In spite of the interferences produced by the power stage, the read-out circuit maintains always a DR performance above 130 dB.

I. INTRODUCTION

In order to keep under control the ambient pollution and to limit the human exposure to dangerous gases, portable gas-sensing systems are becoming very popular [1]. Nowadays miniaturized micromachined resistive gas-sensors can reach operating temperatures around 300-400 °C in few tens of milliseconds, consuming a small amount of power [2]. For these reasons, manufacturers are cutting down expensive ad-hoc instruments and large PCB solutions, while research institutions are working in order to develop devices based on the microsystem or micromodule approach [3] [4]. In order to develop a portable device, the system, composed by an array of gas-sensors, a temperature control circuit, an electronic read-out block and a data processor, has to be self-consistent and has to work without the need of any laboratory instruments. Nowadays the most suitable sensors for this target are devices with chemoresistive features. This kind of sensors are based on metal-oxide thin films (MOX), usually realized with the sol-gel technique and deposited by spin coating on silicon micromachined substrates, embedding an integrated platinum-titanium heater and thermometer. The interaction between the gas molecules and the MOX surface causes an adsorption of gases on the MOX surface itself,

leading to an electrical resistance variation of the sensing element. Considering the state of the art of the manufacturing [2], the sensor resistance value may vary across several decades, being the combination of three variable components: the nominal baseline (i. e. the resistance value in the absence of gas), the deviation from this nominal baseline, due to ageing and working temperature, and the resistance variation due to the bare gas concentration [5]. Since each contribution to the resistance variation is of the order of one-to-two decades and the sensor resistance measurement accuracy required to extract gas concentration information in the order of parts per million is about 1% over the resistance variation range due to the composite sensor response, a dynamic range up to 130 dB may be demanded. This is required if sensors with different specifications need to be read-out [3]. When, as often happens, the purpose of the interface circuit is to query one sensor, the required accuracy is only demanded in the sensor resistance range between the baseline and the value at maximum gas concentration at a given temperature. Significant improvement in gas sensing can be obtained using dynamic pattern recognition techniques, that are able to extract information also from the dynamic sensor response. Moreover, by using specific patterns to modulate the temperature of the sensor a higher selectivity with respect to different analytes can be obtained. In order to achieve the required accuracy in the chemical measurement, also the temperature of the sensor has to be accurately controlled, at least within ±5 °C, thus requiring a dedicated closed loop temperature control circuit. Typically, chemoresistive sensors are used over a temperature range from 200 °C to 450 °C.

II. GAS SENSING SYSTEM DESIGN OVERVIEW

The gas sensing system, as shown in Figure 1, consists of two parts: a temperature control circuit and a chemical read-out circuit. The first part is a closed loop circuit driven by a 9 bit digital set-point that allows the desired temperature pattern to be easily obtained with sufficient accuracy, exploiting two platinum-titanium embedded resistors (heater and thermometer). The first resistor, called R_H, has one terminal

Prototype fabrication has been funded by PRIN 2005092937 IT Project

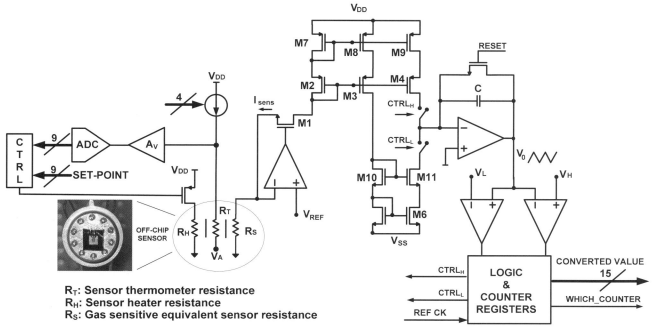

Figure 1. Block diagram of the gas sensing system.

R_T: Sensor thermometer resistance
R_H: Sensor heater resistance
R_S: Gas sensitive equivalent sensor resistance

connected to ground and the other connected to the chip power stage output. The second embedded resistor, R_T, is a thermometer, whose value, processed by suitable continuous time conditioning network, is sampled by a custom ADC, whose 9 bit output, compared with the temperature set-point, controls the gate of the p-MOS power switch. The actual gas-sensing element R_S is instead biased at a constant voltage by means of a voltage reference buffer with decoupled output current. The sensor current is then integrated with alternate sign, determined by the crossings of two fixed thresholds, thus leading to an oscillation, whose period is proportional to R_S. This oscillation drives a 15-bit counter while a reference clock drives another identical counter. The final count reached by the faster counter in the time needed by the slower one to reach count 256, that is the minimum value for a 8-bit precision, represents the A/D converted value. The additional flag signal *WHICH_COUNTER* indicates the faster counter in the last measure, leading to a final 16-bit output bus. This solution permits to operate the frequency conversion over a wider range with respect to traditional solutions for a given external reference frequency [5]. The maximum overall power consumption of the read-out circuit is 10 mW.

III. TEMPERATURE CONTROL CIRCUIT DETAILS

Table I shows the relationship between the power dissipated by R_H and the temperature that the gas-sensor would reach in an open-loop configuration delivering continuous DC power. The temperature control system has been optimized for a gas-sensor with a R_H whose value at room temperature is about 30 Ω and α, the thermal coefficient, is $2.2 \cdot 10^{-3}$ °C^{-1}.

TABLE I. STEADY STATE SENSOR TEMPERATURE GIVEN DC POWER

DC POWER	23 mW	40 mW	60 mW	70 mW
TEMPERATURE	200 °C	300 °C	400 °C	450 °C

Therefore, the value of R_H at 450 °C is less than 60 Ω and the power stage is capable of delivering much more power than the minimum required for this particular gas sensor and can also work with sensors characterized by a higher value of R_H at room temperature or with a higher thermal coefficient. The p-MOS switch that connects R_H to V_{DD} requires a large W/L ratio, in order to achieve a low ON-resistance and hence limit the power loss. A p-MOS switch with W=10 mm and L=0.5 µm achieves, for the used technology, an ON-resistance of about 1.5 Ω Thus, the power dissipated by the switch, e.g. at 300 °C, is 3% of the one dissipated by R_H.

R_T is biased by a digitally programmable current generator, in order to allow the adjustment of the feedback loop gain. The 4 bit selectable output currents are multiple of 160 µA with a maximum value of 2.40 mA. Varying the output current of the digitally programmable current generator I_{DC}, it is possible to use sensors with different resistance values at room temperature or to adjust the temperature operating range. Best performance is achieved setting the bias current to $I_{DC} \approx 800$ µA with the above mentioned sensors. In order to limit the thermometer bias current a fixed-gain amplifier (A_V=7) adjusts the thermometer signal amplitude to the single-ended A/D converter input swing of 1.1 V. The ADC, shown in Figure 2, is a 9-bit, 312.5-kHz data output rate, first order, single-bit sigma-delta modulator. A single-ended to fully-differential conversion is realized by using opposite sampling timing in the two paths of the switched-capacitor integrator input circuit, based on a fully differential folded-cascode op-amp. The integrator is followed by a latched sampled comparator, which controls the analog multiplexer for the feedback reference voltage selection. The A/D converter works with a clock frequency of 5 MHz and includes a dedicated decimation filtering logic. When the *RESET* is released, only *COUNT.0* starts to count the number of ones in the sigma-delta modulator output bitstream.

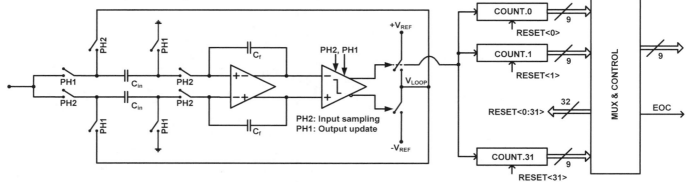

Figure 2. Block diagram of the A/D. converter

The counter COUNT1 is enabled 16 clock cycles later, *COUNT.2* after 32 clock cycles and so on. Finally, a multiplexer selects the output of last updated counter, providing the global output word every 16 clock cycles (3.2 µs). The digital section is actually a 512 order FIR filter with a decimation factor of 16. This solution is less area and power consuming with respect to a direct straight-forward implementation. The actual temperature reached by the gas-sensor is, therefore, measured in digital domain often enough to avoid that it moves too far from the set-point between two updates of the heater control signal. We remind that the average thermal time constant of the employed sensors is about 35 ms.

The power consumption of the control circuit, including A/D converter and conditioning network, is about 13 mW, which is much less than the power necessary to control the temperature of the gas-sensor in DC open loop configuration for high temperature set-point.

IV. CHIP DETAILS AND MEASUREMENTS RESULTS

The photograph of the test-chip is shown in Figure. 3. The area is 10 mm^2, including 94 pads. The block referred as "Voltage References" consists of several buffered resistive dividers, used for generating the voltage references that are required to bias the different blocks.

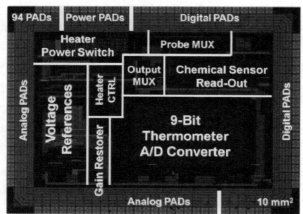

Figure 3. Microphotograph of the presented chip.

The block "Gain Restorer" is actually the digitally programmable I_{DC} current generator, while "Heater Control"

is the block that compares the output of the A/D converter and the set-point, generating the control signal for the "Heater Power Switch". By driving the "Output Mux" bus selector it is possible to read the 9-bit output of the thermometer and other control signals in test mode or the 16 output bits of the gas-sensor read-out circuit called "Chemical Sensor Read-Out" in operating mode. In this prototype, exploiting the "Probe Mux" analog selector, it is also possible to measure the voltage level of some critical internal nodes for characterization purpose. A detail of the layout is reported in Figure 4, showing the power switch implementation, which consists of five modules, each with 50 fingers with W/L=40 µm/0.5 µm. The V-shape of drain and source metal lines ensures the best current density distribution. The switch driver, consisting of a tapered chain of four inverters is necessary because the input capacitance of the power switch is about 15 pF. The measurement results in Figure 5 show the absolute error obtained for the temperature control circuit, which is lower than 1.5 °C over more than 200 °C range.

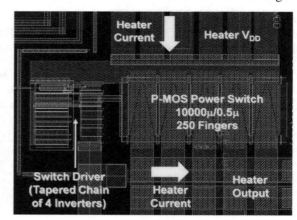

Figure 4. Layout of the P-MOS power switch and its driver.

The steady-state peak-to-peak temperature ripple around the mean temperature is always lower than 1.0 °C, as shown in Figure 6. The chemical sensor read-out circuit accuracy, instead, shown in Figure 7, is better than 2.65% over the range 10 kΩ÷2 GΩ, resulting in a dynamic range (DR) equal to 138 dB. Delivering the maximum power to R_H, in order to reach the highest operating temperature, slightly lowers the accuracy and the DR decreases to 130 dB, due to unavoidable cross-talk of the switching power block over the precision read-out circuit. This effect, of course, is more significant for the highest gas sensor resistance values, as again Figure 7 underlines. Operating the read-out circuit measurements on a reduced resistance range of 3 decades, an accuracy better than 0.8% is achieved.

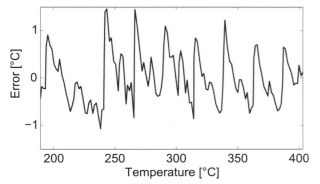

Figure 5.　Temperature control circuit linearity accuracy.

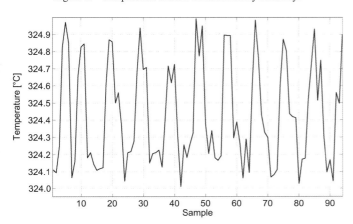

Figure 6.　Temperature control circuit steady-state ripple.

TABLE II.　Power efficiency of the temperature control circuit

TEMPERATURE	200 °C	300 °C	400 °C	450 °C
EFFICIENCY	67%	77%	82%	84%

The power efficiency of the temperature control circuit, driving a typical sensor at different temperatures, is reported in Table II. The system has been validated by several chemical measurements. An example is reported in Figure 8 and shows the digital output of the system, with the sensor at 350 °C exposed to different CO concentrations. The linearity error of the overall system, including chemical sensor response, is always lower than 4%.

V.　Conclusion

A complete integrated gas-sensing system with digital I/O, composed by temperature control and wide range read-out circuits, has been designed and characterized. The proposed system is able to control the temperature of different sensors up to 450°C with an accuracy of 1.5 °C, achieving a DR of 130 dB on 5.3 decades gas-dependent resistance value range and thus having a performance comparable or better than most of state-of-art systems, still partially based on discrete components and expensive laboratory instruments [6]. Furthermore, the developed chip is extremely flexible in terms of allowed sensor specifications and does not require calibration.

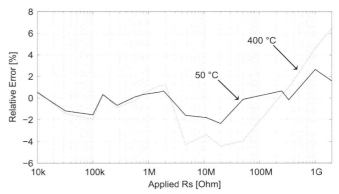

Figure 7.　Read-out circuit accuracy for different sensor temperatures.

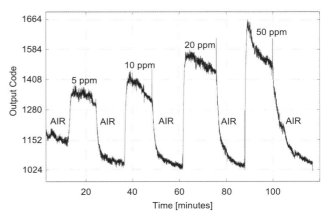

Figure 8.　Read-out digital output to very low concentrations of CO.

Acknowledgment

This work is funded by the Italian Government PRIN Project 2005092937.

References

[1] C. Liang Dai and M. Chen Liu, "Nanoparticle SnO$_2$ gas sensor with circuit and micro heater on chip fabricated using CMOS-MEMS technique", IEEE Nano-Micro Engineered and Molecular Systems Conference, pp. 959-963, 2007.

[2] S. Capone and P. Siciliano, "Gas-sensors from nanostructered metal oxides", Encyclopedia of nanoscience and nanotechnology, vol. 3, pp 769–804, 2004.

[3] "Interface and control circuits for high-selectivity gas sensors operated with temperature pattern", PRIN 2005092937, funded by Italian Government.

[4] "General Olfaction and Sensing on a European Level, GOSPEL", Network of Excellence funded by European Community, http://www.gospel-network.org.

[5] M. Grassi, P. Malcovati and A. Baschirotto, "A 141-dB dynamic range CMOS gas-sensor interface circuit without calibration with 16-bit digital output word", IEEE Journal of Solid-State Circuits, vol. 42, pp. 1543–1554, 2007.

[6] M. Malfatti, M. Peronzoni, N. Viarani, A. Simoni, L. Lorenzelli, A. Baschirotto, "A complete front-end system read-out and temperature control for resistive gas sensor array", IEEE European Conf. on Circuit Theory and Design, vol.3, pp. 31-34, 2005.

A 0.17-1.4GHz Low-Jitter All Digital DLL with TDC-based DCC using Pulse Width Detection Scheme

Dongsuk Shin[1,2], Won-Joo Yun[1,2], Hyun-Woo Lee[1], Young-Jung Choi[1], Suki Kim[2], Chulwoo Kim[2]

[1]Graphics Memory Design Team
Hynix Semiconductor, Icheon, Korea
E-mail: dongsuk1.shin@hynix.com
[2]Department of Electronics and Computer Engineering
Korea University, Seoul, Korea

Abstract☐ **A wide-range low-jitter digital DLL using 0.18um single-poly four-metal CMOS technology is proposed that uses an open-loop time-to-digital converter (TDC)-based DCC circuit with 10 cycles of maximum locking time by virtue of pulse width detection scheme. In addition, the DLL uses a semi dual delay line to remove the boundary switching problem and to optimize its area and power consumption. Thus, the proposed DLL operates over a frequency range from 170MHz to 1.4GHz. The peak-to-peak jitter is 13.8ps at 1.4GHz and the power consumption is reduced to 27mW.**

I. INTRODUCTION

The digital delay-locked loop (DLL) has been widely used in high-speed interface. Recently, as high-frequency operation over a wide range is necessitated, small jitter, low power and duty-cycle correction (DCC) capability have become critical in the DLL design. In general, digital DLLs suffer from jitter mainly caused by switching noise of the delay line [1, 2]. The conventional digital DLL has a dual loop, and each loop is composed of dual delay line which solves a boundary switching problem for small jitter and a dual loop for correcting duty ratio [3]. However, the dual delay line of the dual loop is not area and power efficient due to the increase of control logic and doubling of delay line.

A conventional dual-loop digital DLL has a phase mixer for DCC operation. Generally, a phase mixer designed for high frequency has a bad performance at low frequency. To improve the interpolation capability, several attempts have been achieved, for example, an enhanced phase mixer is used [4]. However, most conventional phase-mixing DCC circuits suffer from a trade-off between resolution and frequency range.

In this paper, we present a digital DLL with a time-to-digital-converter (TDC)–based DCC circuit using pulse width detection scheme for small jitter, low power and high resolution. And we propose a semi-dual delay line for low power consumption and small area.

II. ARCHITECTURE OF PROPOSED DIGITAL DLL

Figure 1 shows a block diagram of the proposed all digital DLL which consists of a semi-dual delay line and a TDC-based DCC. The proposed semi-dual delay line is composed of coarse single and dual delay lines, which solves the boundary switching problem as well as reducing area and

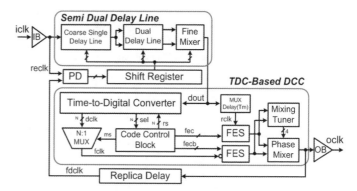

Fig. 1. Total Block Diagram of the Proposed All Digital DLL.

power consumption of conventional dual delay line by about 40% (M>>N). The TDC-based DCC starts to operate after DLL is locked. The DCC comprises a TDC, a falling-edge shifter (FES), a code control block, a phase mixer and a mixing tuner. The TDC detects high and low pulse widths of the input clock (*dout*) and generates digital codes (*sel*) and a clock delayed by the amount of low pulse width (*fclk*). For duty cycle correction, *dout* and *fclk* are mixed by the phase mixer.

The conventional DCC may not correct output duty properly if the input duty is not close enough to 50% because there is a limitation for precise phase mixing between two signals with a large delay difference. The mixing tuner and the falling-edge shifter are implemented to improve the mixing resolution. The code control block outputs control signals for mixing operation and power reduction of the TDC. As a result, the proposed DCC achieved power reduction, high resolution and wide range. Furthermore, it has a fast locking time of 10 cycles due to an open-loop scheme.

A. Semi-Dual Delay Line

A conventional delay line of DLL consists of a dual delay line and a fine mixer to solve the boundary switching problem when the DLL updates the locking information [3]. However, the additional coarse delay line and control logic for the dual delay line results in increase of area and power consumption as shown in Fig. 2. To remove the boundary switching problem and to optimize area and power consumption of the DLL, the semi-dual delay line is proposed, which is divided into three parts; coarse single delay line, dual delay line and fine mixer. The N-stage dual delay line is initialized at the middle of the stage, N/2-stage, then the (M-N)-stage coarse delay line and the fine mixer operate to lock the DLL. Once the DLL is locked, the dual delay line and the fine mixer track

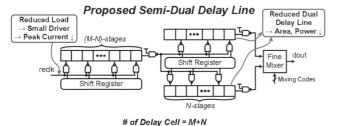

Fig. 2. Conventional and Proposed Delay Lines.

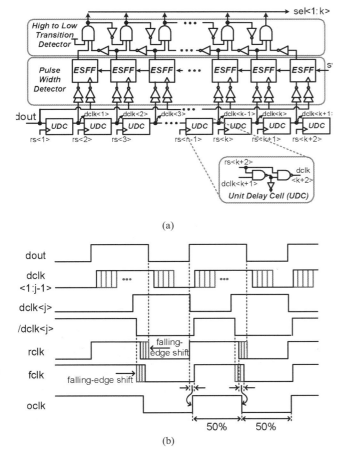

(a)

(b)

Fig. 3. Block Diagram of TDC(a) and Timing Diagram of DCC(b).

the phase difference between the reference clock and the feedback clock caused by supply voltage and temperature variations.

B. TDC-Based DCC

Figure 3 shows a block diagram of the proposed TDC and a timing diagram of the DCC using the TDC. The TDC consists of a high-to-low transition detector, a pulse width detector and a delay line. To prevent a harmonic lock of the TDC, the high-to-low transition detector detects the first position where the outputs of the pulse width detector change from high to low. The unit delay cell of the delay line has two NAND gates to cut off unused delay cells after the DCC is locked, resulting in reduction of overall DCC power consumption. The pulse width detector compares the input clock of the DCC, *dout*, with outputs of the delay line (*dclk<1:n>*) and then generates the digital codes (*sel<1:k>*) having pulse width information of both high and low pulses. In the code control block, the signals *sel<1:k>* are used to generate control codes (*fec, fecb, rs and ms*) as shown in Fig. 4. The pulse generator outputs the signals *hc* and *lc* to store the signals *sel<1:k>* during their high pulse. The signals *hc* and *lc* are synchronized with the signal *SW*. The control signals *fec* and *fecb* shift falling edges of mixing clocks (*fclk_sh, rclk_sh*) as shown in Fig. 5, the reset signals of unit delay cells (*rs<1:k>*) switch each unit delay cell and a select signal (*ms*) selects a clock delayed by the amount of low pulse width (*fclk*) as shown in Fig. 3.

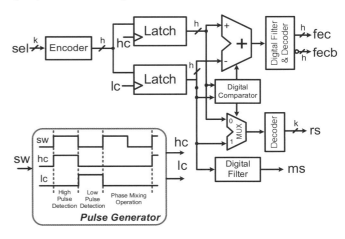

Fig. 4. Block Diagram of Code Control Block.

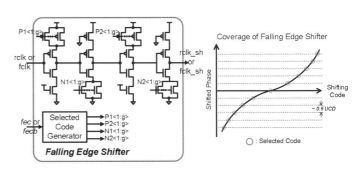

Fig. 5. Proposed Falling Edge Shifter.

The conventional DCC using a phase mixer suffers from poor mixing capability when the duty distortion gets worse. In the proposed DCC, falling edges of *fclk* and *rclk* are shifted by a half of the detected code difference between high and low pulse widths, which reduces the phase difference between falling edges of *fclk* and *rclk*, which in turn increases the accuracy of phase mixing even with large error from 50% duty ratio. Then, *rclk* and *fclk* are mixed by an advanced phase mixer whose phase resolution is improved. The open-loop TDC-based DCC achieves a locking time of 10 cycles, where high and low pulse width detection is four cycles each. The other two cycles are for phase mixing operation.

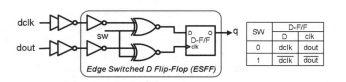

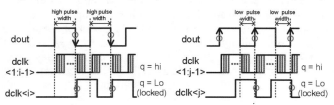

Fig. 6. Proposed Edge Switched D-F/F for Pulse Width Detection.

C. Edge Switched D-Flip/Flop

To detect each pulse width without an additional delay line or a TDC, the DCC needs a pulse width detector using a both-edge-triggered D-flip/flop. Figure 6 shows a block diagram of the proposed edge-switched D-flip/flop (ESFF) and a concept of the pulse width detection. The ESFF uses two XOR gates following a negative edge-triggered D-flip/flop to switch the triggering edge of sampling clock by signal *SW* every other cycle of input signal which gives a timing margin for correct pulse with detection. Therefore, the period of the signal SW is four times higher than that of DCC input. While the signal SW

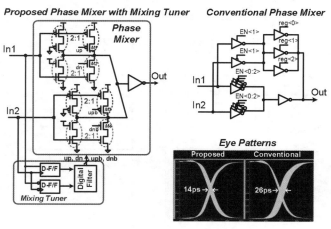

Fig. 7. Proposed Advanced Phase Mixer with Mixing Tuner.

is low, the pulse width detector operates as a negative edge-triggered D-flip/flop and detects high pulse width of the input clock. On the other hand, while the signal SW is high, the pulse width detector operates as a positive edge-triggered D-flip/flop and detects low pulse width. As a result, the proposed scheme detecting high and low pulse widths can achieve wider frequency range than one-cycle detection scheme of [5] provided the same delay line is used.

D. Advanced Phase Mixer

Most digital phase mixers suffer a trade-off between the mixing capability and the operating frequency range. In [4], a two-stage mixer is used to improve the DCC capability. However, it decreases the DCC capability as the phase difference between rising edges of two input clocks increases. Thus, the DCC circuit can not correct a duty distortion of the input clock at low frequencies. In this paper, the proposed phase mixer adopts the weighted inverters which are controlled by the mixing tuner in Fig. 7. Each PMOS and NMOS leg of the phase mixer is sized with a 0.6 ratio like in [6] by controlling each switch (M1~M4) independently according to the output signals of the mixing tuner (*up, dn, upb, dnb*). Two D-F/Fs of the mixing tuner sense a phase precedence of rising and falling edges of two input clocks,

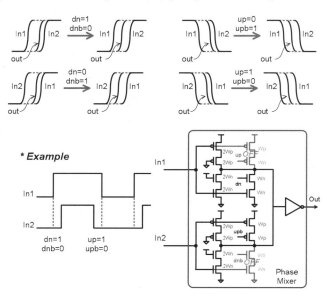

Fig. 8. Operation of the Proposed Advanced Phase Mixer.

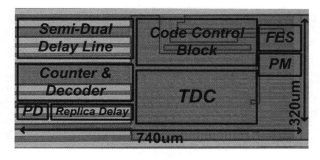

Fig. 9. Chip Microphotograph.

respectively. The signals *dn* and *dnb* represent the phase relation of the rising edges of input clocks. Similarly, the signals *up* and *upb* represent that of the falling edges. For example, if the rising edge of In1 leads that of In2 and the falling edge of In1 lags that of In2, the rising edges of In1 is weighted to 0.6 with *dn*=1 and *dnb*=0 and the falling edge of In2 is weighted to 0.6 with *up*=1 and *upb*=0 as shown in Fig. 8. As a result, the DCC capability of the proposed phase mixer has 12ps less jitter than that of the conventional one as shown in Fig. 7.

III. EXPERIMENTAL RESULTS

The proposed digital DLL is designed in a 0.18um single-poly four-metal CMOS technology with a 1.8V power supply voltage. The chip microphotograph of the proposed DLL is shown in Fig. 9. The active chip area is 0.740 x 0.320 mm2. The proposed DCC consumes ~60% of total area and the proposed semi-dual delay line has reduced total area of conventional register controlled DLL by about 40%. The duty ratio measurement result is shown in Fig. 10. The measured waveform at 1GHz shows 51.1% output duty ratio corrected from 60% input duty ratio. Figure 10 show peak to peak jitter of 13.8ps at 1.4GHz. The proposed DLL operates over a wide frequency range, from 170MHz to 1.4GHz, and consumes 27mW at 1GHz at a supply voltage of 1.8V. Table 1 shows the performance comparison of the proposed DLL with recent digital DLLs.

IV. CONCLUSION

In this paper, we present a semi-dual delay line composed of coarse single and dual delay line with fine mixer, which solves the boundary switching problem as well as reducing area and power consumption. The proposed TDC-based DCC circuit achieved power reduction, high resolution and wide frequency range along with a fast locking time of 10 cycles due to an open-loop scheme. To detect high and low pulse width in one TDC, the proposed edge-switched D-flip/flop was implemented. Also the advanced phase mixer with mixing tuner improved the DCC capability and the resolution. As a result, this DLL with DCC circuit can operate over a wide frequency range from 170MHz to 1.4GHz.

Table 1 Performance Comparison.

	SOVC03 [1]	JSSC06 [7]	ISSCC07 [5]	This Work
Process	0.13um-CMOS	0.35um-CMOS	0.18um-CMOS	0.18um-CMOS
Type	Closed-loop	Closed-loop (w/o replica)	Open-loop	Closed-loop
Operating Frequency	66MHz ~ 500MHz (f_{max}/f_{min}= 7.57)	140MHz ~ 260MHz (f_{max}/f_{min}= 1.86)	440MHz ~ 1.5GHz (f_{max}/f_{min}= 3.41)	170MHz ~ 1.4GHz (f_{max}/f_{min}= 8.24)
Jitter (peak-to-peak)	< 25ps	24ps@250MHz	7ps@1.5GHz	13.8ps @1.4GHz
Power	24mW @400MHz, 1.8V (60uW/MHz)	9.9mW @250MHz, 3.3V (39.6uW/MHz)	43mW @1.5GHz, 1.8V (28.7uW/MHz)	27mW @1GHz, 1.8V (27uW/MHz)

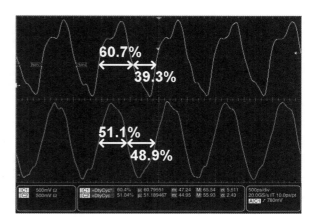

Fig. 10. Measured Waveform at 1GHz.

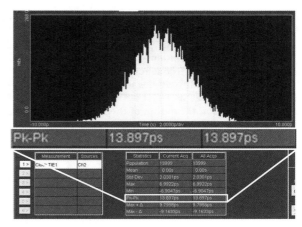

Fig. 11. Jitter Histogram of Proposed DLL at 1.4GHz.

REFERENCES

[1] Y. J. Jeon, et al., "A 66-333MHz 12-mW register-controlled DLL with a single delay line and adaptive-duty-cycle clock dividers for production DDR SDRAMs," *IEEE J. Solid-State Circuits*, vol. 39, no. 11, pp. 2087-2092, Nov. 2004.

[2] A. Hatakeyama et al., "A 256-Mb SDRAM using a register-controlled digital DLL," *IEEE J. Solid-State Circuits*, vol. 32, pp. 1728–1734, Nov. 1997.

[3] J. T. Kwak *et al.*, "A low cost high performance register-controlled digital DLL for 1Gbps x32 DDR SDRAM," in *IEEE Symp. VLSI Circuits*, pp. 283-284, 2003.

[4] D. U. Lee et al., "A 2.5Gb/s/pin 256Mb GDDR3 SDRAM with Series Pipelined CAS Latency Control and Dual-Loop Digital DLL," in ISSCC Dig. Of Tech. Papers, pp. 160-161, 2006.

[5] D. Shin et al., "A 7ps-Jitter 0.053mm² Fast-Lock ADDLL with Wide-Range and High-Resolution All-Digital DCC," in ISSCC Dig. Of Tech. Papers, pp. 184-185, 2007.

[6] B. W. Garlepp et al., "A portable digital DLL for high-speed CMOS interface circuits," IEEE J. Solid-State Circuits, vol 34, no 5, pp. 632-643, May 1999.

[7] Y-J. Wang et al., "All-digital delay-locked loop/pulsewidth-control loop with adjustable duty cycles." IEEE J. Solid-State Circuits, vol 41, no 6, pp. 1262-1274, Jun. 2006.

A 2-GHz 7-mW Digital DLL-Based Frequency Multiplier in 90-nm CMOS

Behzad Mesgarzadeh and Atila Alvandpour
Department of Electrical Engineering
Linköping University
Linköping - Sweden
{behzad, atila}@isy.liu.se

Abstract☐ **This paper presents a low-power low-jitter digital DLL-based frequency multiplier in 90-nm CMOS. In order to reduce the jitter and power consumption due to dithering in the lock condition, digital DLL operates in the open-loop mode after locking. To keep track of any potential phase error introduced by the environmental variations, a compensation mechanism is employed. The proposed frequency multiplier operates at 2-GHz utilizing a 1-V supply. It occupies 0.037 mm² of active area and dissipates 7-mW power at 2-GHz. The measured peak-to-peak and rms clock jitter at the output of the frequency multiplier are 9.5 ps and 1.6 ps, respectively.**

I. INTRODUCTION

Phase-locked loops (PLLs) are typically utilized in implementation of the conventional clock generators [1], [2]. However, they suffer from several drawbacks. First of all, PLLs are higher-order systems with stability issues. The loop bandwidth of a PLL can change due to PVT variation, resulting in stability problems. Furthermore, since the output of the VCO is fed back into the loop, jitter accumulates over the oscillation cycles causing a peak phase error considerably lager than the original phase variation [3]. These issues affect the overall performance of a PLL and make the design process of a PLL-based clock generator complex, time-consuming and challenging. Alternatively, delay-locked loop (DLL)-based clock generators with first-order loops have been proposed with more robust stability performance [4]-[11]. Unlike the PLL-based schemes, which employ the VCO for frequency multiplication, in DLL-based clock generators an additional frequency multiplier circuit is required to combine the phases produced by the delay line in order to multiply the frequency by a given factor. Different circuit techniques have been reported for DLL-based frequency multiplication [4]-[8].

Generally in a DLL-based clock generator, dithering around the average lock point increases the uncertainty at the output, resulting in performance degradation. In a digital DLL after lock, the best-case error caused by dithering is +/- 1 LSB. This error increases the total output clock jitter. Furthermore,

some extra power is dissipated since the delay control mechanism (e.g., phase detector, digital counter, etc.) operates consistently to keep the DLL in the lock condition. To solve this problem, a digital DLL-based clock generator locked in open-loop mode has been proposed in [9]. In this structure a lock detection mechanism disables the feedback loop after lock to eliminate the jitter and extra power consumption caused by dithering. However, once the loop is opened, the environmental variations (e.g., temperature, supply noise, etc.) might introduce phase error during the run time. In order to overcome this drawback, a phase-error compensation technique is proposed in this paper to take advantage of the open-loop mode during the lock condition and to eliminate the performance loss due to the introduced phase error. This paper describes a digital DLL-based frequency multiplier, which employs an open-loop system with phase-error compensation and utilizes a robust frequency multiplication technique.

The organization of this paper is as follows. In section II, the structure of the proposed digital DLL-based frequency multiplier is presented. Section III is dedicated to the experimental results followed by conclusions in section IV.

II. PROPOSED FREQUENCY MULTIPLIER

Fig. 1 shows the structure of the proposed DLL-based frequency multiplier. A phase detector compares the reference phase with the output of the delay line. Based on leading or lagging, the phase detector generates *up/down* signal for a 5-bit counter. The output of the counter controls the load of the delay elements in the delay line. The loop sampling frequency is 1/4 of the reference frequency to ensure the settlement of the loop before the next comparison. The counter continues to alter the total delay in the delay line until the delay is aligned with the reference clock period. Once the DLL is locked, dithering at the output of the counter generates a closed-to-open loop request for the loop control unit (LCU). LCU that consists of a set of controlling switches opens the feedback loop. This eliminates the jitter due to dithering during the lock condition, and shuts down the extra power needed for keeping the loop closed. At this point, the counter is disabled and its output is transferred to a register in order to keep a fixed load for the delay elements after opening the loop. While DLL is operating in the open-loop mode, a phase-error compensation (PEC) block is responsible to keep track of the potential phase errors. The open-loop operation is kept until the output and the reference phases are locked. However, if any phase error is detected, PEC block sends a closed-loop request to LCU and it closes the loop to keep track of the unwanted variations. After relock, based on variation at the output of the counter, LCU opens the loop once again. As shown in Fig. 1, the frequency multiplier block is responsible for frequency multiplication utilizing the multiphase clock output produced by the delay line. In the following subsections, a brief description of this block and other building blocks in the proposed structure is presented.

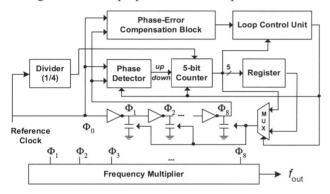

Figure 1. The block level structure of the proposed frequency multiplier.

A. Phase Detector

A transmission gate master-slave flip-flop is utilized as phase detector as shown in Fig. 2. Rising edges of the reference and output clocks are compared and the output of the flip-flop generates the control signal of the counter. In order to increase the precision of the phase detector, a delayed clock is utilized to control the keeper in the first latch as shown in Fig. 2. By using this technique the keeper will be open slightly before decision time of the first latch and it helps to increase the timing precision of the phase detector.

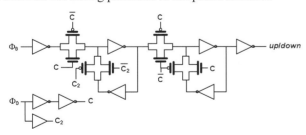

Figure 2. Phase detector.

B. Delay Elements

The structure of the delay elements is shown in Fig. 3. A delay element consists of an inverter stage with switch-controlled capacitive load. The load of each inverter stage is formed by five binary-weighted capacitors. The output of the counter adjusts the total delay of the inverter stages by controlling the switches connected to the binary-weighted capacitors.

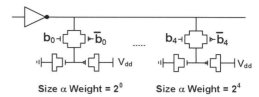

Figure 3. Delay element.

Fig. 4 shows the delay variation in the digitally controlled delay line versus the input code. The delay values are shifted by the minimum delay value toward the origin only to focus on the slope of the variation. The main concern in design of a delay line is the linear behavior of the total delay versus the input that controls the delay. As shown in Fig. 4 the utilized delay line exhibits an acceptable linear characteristic.

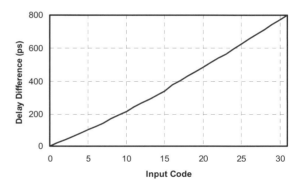

Figure 4. Delay variation in the delay line versus input digital code.

C. Phase-Error Compensation Block

As shown in Fig. 5, PEC block consists of an XOR gate followed by a low-pass filter and a comparator. It operates as an additional phase detector, which detects the difference between the input and output phases. The phase difference is detected by XOR gate. The output of XOR gate is filtered using a low-pass filter. The filter averages the generated phase difference. A comparator compares the output of the filter with a predefined reference (V_r) as shown in Fig.5. A binary signal is generated by comparator for LCU.

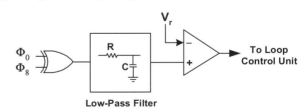

Figure 5. Phase-error compensation block.

While DLL is locked the phase difference between the reference and the output clock is small and the average at the output of the low-pass filter is close to zero. If because of any environmental variations a mismatch is introduced between the phases, the average starts to increase. When it increases to more than V_r, the output of the comparator toggles and LCU forces the DLL to enter to the closed-loop mode in order to compensate the phase error. When DLL relocks and compensates the unwanted phase errors, the average voltage deceases and the open-loop mode is reactivated. The timing diagram of PEC block is shown in Fig.6.

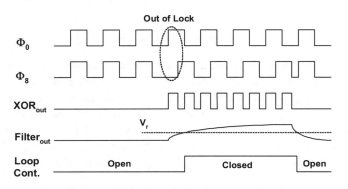

Figure 6.   Timing diagram of phase-error compensation block.

D.   Frequency Multiplier

A simplified block diagram of the frequency multiplier is shown in Fig. 7. A 2^n-input multiplexer selects the different phases generated by the delay line. The *select* signal of the multiplexer is generated by an n-bit counter. The output of the multiplexer provides the clock signal for the counter. To gain better understanding about the functionality of the frequency multiplier, consider the timing diagram shown in Fig. 8 for $n=2$ case. When the output of the counter is "0", the multiplexer selects Φ_0. It means Φ_0 becomes the clock signal for the counter. When the rising edge of Φ_0 is received by the counter, the output of the counter becomes "1" and the multiplexer selects Φ_1 as the clock signal for the counter. The output of the counter remains unchanged until the rising edge of Φ_1 is received. This process is repeated 2^n times in one period of the reference clock. Consequently the frequency at the output of the multiplexer is 2^n times of the reference frequency.

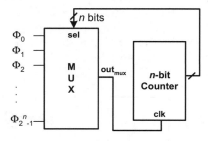

Figure 7.   Frequency multiplier.

Since the propagation delay of the counter is different in generating different outputs, the signal at the output of the

multiplexer suffers from variable duty cycle. Two solutions can be employed to solve this problem. One solution is to use an extra duty cycle correction if a multiplication factor of 2^n is required. The second solution is to trade off between the multiplication factor and utilizing an extra circuit. As shown in Fig. 8, the LSB output of the counter has a 50% duty cycle. However by utilizing this output the multiplication factor reduces by half (i.e. 2^{n-1} instead of 2^n). Depending on the given specifications and the required multiplication factor either of these two solutions can be applicable.

To find the relationship of the multiplication factor and the number of delay elements, we can consider that the number of generated phases is the same as the number of the delay elements in the delay line. Thus for an m-stage delay line

$$f_{LSB} = \frac{m}{2} \times f_{ref} \qquad (1)$$

where f_{LSB} is the frequency of the LSB output of the counter and f_{ref} is the frequency of the reference clock. The main constrain which determines the operating frequency of the proposed structure, is the total delay through the critical path in the feedback loop. If the worst-case delay of the counter from clock input to output is t_c and the worst-case delay of the multiplexer from select input to output is t_m, then for correct functionality, the period of the reference clock should satisfy

$$\frac{T_{ref}}{m} > t_c + t_m \qquad (2)$$

where T_{ref} and m are the period of the reference clock and the number of delay elements in the delay line. In (2) a lower limit for the period of the reference clock is determined, however other factors (e.g., clock jitter, interconnect delays, etc.) should be considered to determine more accurate boundary for the operating frequency.

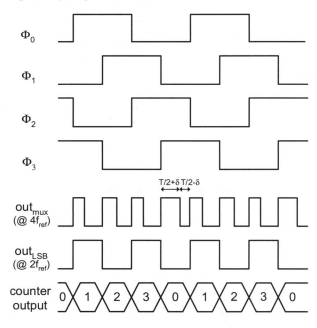

Figure 8.   Timing digram of frquency multiplier for $m=4$.

III. MEASUREMENT RESULTS

The proposed digital DLL-based frequency multiplier has been implemented in 90-nm CMOS process. Utilizing a 1-V supply, the frequency multiplier operates at 2 GHz. In the implemented test chip, a multiplication factor of 4 is employed. While operating in the open-loop mode at 2-GHz output frequency, the digital DLL and the frequency multiplier dissipate 6.75-mW and 0.25-mW power, respectively. The measured total power saving in the open-loop mode in comparison with the conventional closed-loop operation (i.e., without utilizing the loop-control circuits) is about 14%. The extra power required for loop-control circuits has been considered in the power-saving measurements. The measured frequency multiplier output at 2 GHz is depicted in Fig. 9. At this frequency, the measured peak-to-peak and rms clock jitter at the output of the frequency multiplier are 9.5 ps and 1.6 ps, respectively. The test-chip photograph is shown in Fig. 10. The proposed structure occupies 0.037 mm^2 of active area.

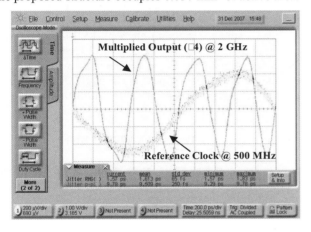

Figure 9. Measured output clock at 2 GHz (200 ps/div horizontal scale).

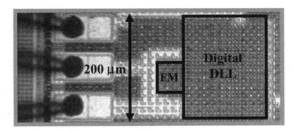

Figure 10. Chip photo.

A comparison between this work and the previously reported DLL-based frequency multipliers is shown in TABLE I. In this table the main characteristics such as operating frequency, jitter, power consumption, etc. are compared.

IV. CONCLUSIONS

A digital DLL-based frequency multiplication technique has been presented. In order to reduce the power consumption and jitter caused by DLL dithering, DLL operates in the open-

loop mode in the lock condition. An additional phase-error compensation circuit has been employed to keep track of the potential unwanted phase errors introduced by environmental variations. Proposed structure has been implemented in 90-nm CMOS and operates at 2 GHz consuming 7-mW power from a 1-V supply. Measured power saving achieved by utilizing the open-loop mode is about 14% at 2-GHz output frequency.

TABLE I. PERFORMANCE COMPARISON WITH PREVIOUS WORKS

	JSSC'02 [4]	JSSC'02 [5]	ISSCC'05 [6]	VLSI Symp.'07 [7]	This Work
Type	Analog	Analog	Analog	Digital	Digital
Process	0.18 μm	0.35 μm	0.35 μm	0.13 μm	90 nm
Frequency	2 GHz	1.1 GHz	1.8 GHz	1.6 GHz	2 GHz
Supply	1.8 V	3.3 V	3.3 V	1.2 V	1 V
Jitter (rms)	1.6 ps (@2 GHz)	2 ps (@1.1 GHz)	1.8 ps (@1.8 GHz)	1.4 ps (@1.6 GHz)	1.6 ps (@2 GHz)
Jitter (p-p)	13.1 ps (@2 GHz)	14.6 ps (@1.1 GHz)	12.2 ps (@1.8 GHz)	11.7 ps (@1.6 GHz)	9.5 ps (@2 GHz)
Area	0.05 mm^2	0.07 mm^2	0.07 mm^2	0.037 mm^2	0.037 mm^2
Power	12 mW (@2 GHz)	42.9 mW (@1.1 GHz)	86.6 mW (@1.6 GHz)	6 mW (@1.6 GHz)	7 mW (@2 GHz)

REFERENCES

[1] T. Fischer *et al.*, "A 90-nm variable frequency clock system for a power-managed Itanium architecture processor," in *IEEE J. Solid-State Circuits*, vol. 41, pp. 218–228, Jan. 2006.

[2] S. Desai, P. Trivedi, and V. V. Kanael, "A dual-supply 0.2-to-4 GHz PLL clock multiplier in a 65nm dual-oxide CMOS process," *in ISSCC Dig. Tech. Papers*, pp. 308–309, 2007.

[3] B. Kim, T. Weigandt, and P. Gray, "PLL/DLL system noise analysis for low jitter clock synthesizer design," in Proc. *Int. Symp. Circuits and Systems*, pp. 31–38, 1994.

[4] R. Farjad-Rad *et al.*, "A low-power multiplying DLL for low-jitter multigigahertz clock generation in highly integrated digital chips," in *IEEE J. Solid-State Circuits*, vol. 37, pp. 1804–1812, Dec. 2002.

[5] C. Kim, I-C. Hwang, and S-M. Kang, "A low-power small-area ±7.28-ps-jitter 1-GHz DLL-based clock generator," in *IEEE J. Solid-State Circuits*, vol. 37, pp. 1414–1420, Nov. 2002.

[6] J-H. Kim *et al.*, "A CMOS DLL-based 120MHz to 1.8GHz clock generator for dynamic frequency scaling," *in ISSCC Dig. Tech. Papers*, pp. 516–517, 2005.

[7] B. M. Helal, M. Z. Straayer, G. -Y. Wei, and M. H. Perrott, "A low-jitter 1.6 GHz multiplying DLL utilizing a scrambling time-to-digital converter and digital correction," in *VLSI Circuits Symp.*, pp. 166–167, 2007.

[8] Q. Du, J. Zhuang, and T. Kwasniewski, "A low-phase noise, anti-harmonic programmable DLL frequency multiplier with period error compensation for spur reduction," *IEEE Trans. Circuits Syst. II, Exp. Briefs*, vol. 53, no. 11, pp. 1205–1209, Nov. 2006.

[9] A. Alvandpour *et al.*, "A 3.5GHz 32mW multiphase clock generator for high-performance microprocessors," in *ISSCC Dig. Tech. Papers*, pp. 112–113, 2003.

[10] C-C. Chung and C-Y. Lee, "A new DLL-based approach for all-digital multiphase clock generation," in *J. Solid-State Circuits*, vol. 39, pp. 469-475, Mar. 2004.

[11] Y-S. Kim, S. J. Park, Y-S. Kim, D-B. Jang, S-W. Jeong, H-J. Park, and J-Y. Sim "A 40-to-800MHz locking multiphase DLL," in *ISSCC, Dig. Tech. Papers*, pp. 306-307, 2007.

A 15 MHz □600 MHz, 20 mW, 0.38 mm², Fast Coarse Locking Digital DLL in 0.13μm CMOS

Sebastian Hoyos[*], Cheongyuen W. Tsang, Johan Vanderhaegen[‡], Yun Chiu[¶], Yasutoshi Aibara[†], Haideh Khorramabadi, Borivoje Nikolić

Department of Electrical and Computer Sciences, University of California at Berkeley
[*] now with Department of Electrical and Computer Engineering, Texas A&M University
[¶] now with Department of Electrical and Computer Engineering, University of Illinois at Urbana Champaign
[‡] now with Robert Bosch Corporation   [†] Renesas Technology Corporation

Abstract - **A digital delay-locked-loop (DLL) suitable for generation of multiphase clocks in applications such as time-interleaved and pipelined ADCs locks in a very wide (40X) frequency range. The DLL provides 12 uniformly delayed phases that are free of false harmonic locking. The digital control loop has two stages: a fast-locking coarse acquisition is achieved in four cycles using binary search; a fine linear loop achieves low jitter (8.9 ps rms @ 600 MHz) and tracks PVT variations. The DLL consumes 20 mW and occupies a 470 □m X 800 □m area in 0.13μm CMOS.**

I. INTRODUCTION

Time-interleaved and pipeline ADC's require generation of multiple clock phases in a very wide operating frequency range with challenging jitter requirements in the upper frequency range. DLLs are often used in these applications, but they face design tradeoffs between the requirements for low jitter, fast locking, wide frequency-range and low power. Low voltage headroom, associated with supply voltages in scaled technologies presents a challenge for analog control loops in a DLL to achieve a very wide locking range. This limitation is solved by using digital control loops that ideally can use longer wordlengths to extend the dynamic locking range [1-11]. Jitter in digital DLL's is determined by the size of the DAC LSB that controls the delay line. However, the interaction of the wide dynamic range control with the delay line dramatically impacts other performance metrics such as the locking time, jitter, power consumption and silicon area.

In this DLL, a novel architecture allows the design to achieve 40X locking range together with fast locking, and low jitter at high frequencies in steady state. This locking range enables a wide set of operating modes as well as the testability of the ADC system that uses it. A 10-bit digital control is used to control the jitter, and the locking range. It is used to adjust the delay of the current-starved inverter based delay line, where the 4 most significant bits (MSB's)

coarsely select the frequency range (15MHz – 600MHz) using a fast binary search, and a binary-weighted DAC replicated at each delay cell. The 6 least significant bits (LSB's) linearly control the delay elements for a low jitter in steady state. The unit-element LSB DAC is shared among all delay cells. This split-control architecture enables the delay adjustment of delay elements with low supply voltage in the desired operating range. This design also allows for low power consumption and a moderate silicon area for a DLL with 12 clock phases.

II. ARCHITECTURE

Figure 1 shows the basic block diagram of the proposed DLL. The binary search brings the total delay D of the delay line within the locking range, $3T/4 < D < 5T/4$. If $3T/4 < D$ the UNDER signal is activated by the false-locking detection logic, Table 1.

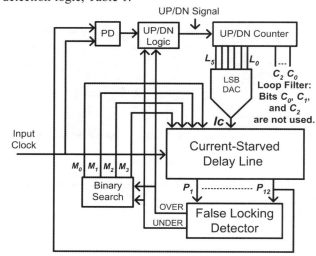

Fig. 1: Block diagram of the DLL.

Similarly, if $D > 5T/4$, the OVER signal is activated. The UNDER and OVER signals are correctly detected for duty cycles of the input clock from 25% to 75% making this DLL immune to duty-cycle variations.

The binary search machine gets triggered by either an external reset signal or by a sudden change in either the UNDER or OVER signals. This feature makes this DLL to track frequency changes in its entire range of operation which makes it suitable for broadband applications. When the binary search completes, the 6-bit LSB linear loop, whose counter is initialized at mid-range, makes the final fine adjustments to bring the total delay D within one LSB of the desired input clock period T. Only the top 6 bits of the 9-bit counter are used to drive the unit element DAC; the 3 LSBs provide low-pass filtering by slowing down the loop. Discarding the 3 LSBs also lowers jitter in steady state because it averages random up and down signals due to noise. The linear search stays on during the operation to provide compensation for voltage, temperature variations and aging.

The delay line is a chain of 24 current-starved inverters (Fig. 2). Each inverter receives the 4 MSBs from the binary search state machine and adds them to the mirrored current from the unit element DAC driven by the 6 LSB's.
Since a delay cell is the cascade of two of these inverters, the rising and falling times at the delay cell's output will be equal, preserving the duty cycle even if there are mismatches between the p-type and n-type devices of the current starvation sources.
The false locking detector is fully digital [7]. It determines the UNDER and OVER signals based on the delay line phases P1 to P12. Table 1 shows the logic levels of the delay line phases at the rising edge of the input clock.

TABLE 1: FALSE LOCKING DETECTION USING P1-P12 DELAY LINE PHASES

Delay	0.6T	0.76T	0.8T	T	1.22T	1.29T	1.33T	1.67T
P1	0	0	0	0	0	0	0	0
P3	0	0	0	0	0	0	0	0
P5	0	0	0	0	0	1	1	1
P7	0	0	0	0	1	1	1	0
P9	0	0	0	1	0	0	0	0
P10	0	0	1	1	0	0	0	1
P11	0	1	1	1	0	0	0	1
P12	1	1	1	0	0	0	0	1
UNDER		IN LOCKING RANGE					OVER	

The UNDER signal is high if all the phases from P1 to P10 are low. The OVER signal is high if a '...10...' pattern is found in any two consecutive phases from P1 to P8. As it can be inferred from Table 1, the UNDER and OVER signals are safely detected for duty cycles of the input clock from 25% to 75%. In the event that either the UNDER or OVER signals remain active after the binary search finishes, the UP/DN logic disables the phase detector (PD) output, to

avoid false locking. Instead, it uses the UNDER or OVER signals to bring the linear loop into a locking range.

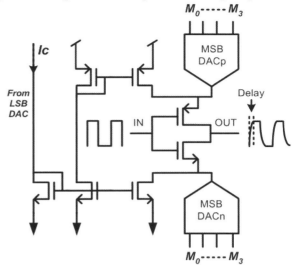

Fig. 2: Current-starved inverter.

The jitter of this DLL topology is inversely proportional to the squared value of the frequency of operation. This result can be derived as follows: for a frequency of operation F_1 that requires a nominal current I_1, where $F_1 = kI_1$, k being a constant that depends on the capacitance of the current starved delay cell and the number of cells that formed the delay line. Assuming linear low-to-high and high-to-low propagation delays, the proportionality constant is given by (1):

$$k \approx \frac{M * Vdd}{C} \text{ [V/F]}, \qquad (1)$$

where Vdd is the power supply, M is the number of current-starved inverters and C in the total capacitance that loads each inverter. The delay of the delay line is given by

$$T_1 = \frac{1}{kI_1}, \qquad (2)$$

and the peak-to-peak jitter will be,

$$\Delta t_1 = \frac{1}{k(I_1 - \Delta I)} - \frac{1}{k(I_1 + \Delta I)}, \qquad (3)$$

where ΔI is the current LSB value. Similarly for a frequency that is larger by a factor N, i.e., $F_2 = NF_1 = kI_2 = kNI_1$, the associated jitter is,

$$\Delta t_2 = \frac{1}{k(I_2 - \Delta I)} - \frac{1}{k(I_2 + \Delta I)}.$$ Thus, the jitter drop-off when the frequency rises from F_1 to F_2 is given by,

$$\frac{\Delta t_2}{\Delta t_1} = \frac{(I_1 - \Delta I)(I_1 + \Delta I)}{(I_2 - \Delta I)(I_2 + \Delta I)} \approx \left(\frac{I_1}{I_2}\right)^2 = \frac{1}{N^2}. \qquad (4)$$

In the prototype chip, the MSB and LSB currents are programmable, which gives flexibility for testing purposes. This also allows adjusting the LSB current to minimize the jitter at lower frequencies.

Replicating the MSB DAC across all the current starved inverters minimized DC current consumption, as only the dynamic current is drawn from these DACs. On the other hand, the LSB DAC current was mirrored to all current cells, since it is much smaller. The DC current in the LSB's corresponds to only the lower 6 LSBs of the total 10 bits in the dual digital control loop; furthermore, current scaling by a factor of 20 lowers the mirrored DC current. This current is scaled up to its nominal value locally at each delay cell where only the dynamic power is consumed.

III. IMPLEMENTATION AND TESTING

The DLL has been implemented in a general-purpose, 0.13μm 6M1P CMOS technology. The DLL occupies 470μm × 800μm area. Measured jitter performance is summarized in Table 2 and jitter measurement plot at 600 MHz and 380 MHz are shown in Fig. 3 and Fig. 4, respectively. Five chips were tested with almost the same measurement results. The DLL clock is driven off-chip using LVDS pads, which worsens the jitter by up to 7 ps rms. The actual on-chip DLL jitter variance is expected to be up to $(7\ ps)^2$ better that the squared of the rms values in Table 2. This expected on-chip jitter is also reported in Table 2. The linear control loop can be left running to absorb PVT variations in the locked state. The steady-state jitter produced by the LSB toggling is reduced with increased clock frequency as indicated in Eqn. (4). For frequencies larger than 300 MHz, the jitter produced by the LSB toggling is lower than the intrinsic jitter induced by the electronic noise. At low frequencies, however, the effect of the LSB toggling is higher, as the output will toggle between two phases as shown in Fig. 5. In the worst case, if the edge of the delayed clock gets very close to the input clock, the intrinsic jitter will make the linear loop to toggle between 3 LSBs producing a 3 edge clock eye diagram. As a result, the peak-to-peak jitter can be as big as 2 LSBs. This case is illustrated in the measured eye diagram of Fig. 6.

TABLE 2: RMS JITTER ACROSS THE OPERATING RANGE.

Freq. (MHz)	600	500	400	300	200	150	50	15
Measured rms off-chip jitter [ps]	8.9	8.9	9	9.5	10.2	20.5	100	116[1]
Expected on-chip jitter [ps]	4.1	4.5	5	5.7	7.4	19.2	100	116

[1] An LSB current that is lower than in the other measurements was used here to improve the jitter.

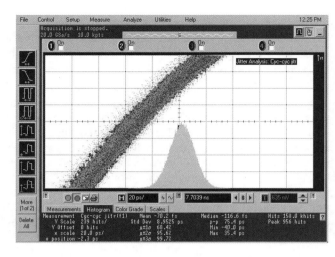

Fig. 3: Jitter measurement at 600 MHz.

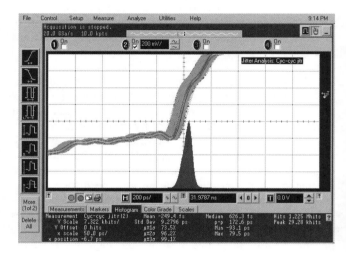

Fig. 4: Jitter measurement at 380 MHz.

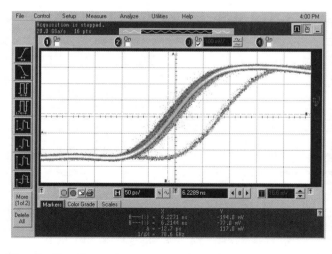

Fig. 5: Toggling of the LSB current for low frequency operation. The locking frequency is 15 MHz.

TABLE 3: COMPARISON BETWEEN THIS WORK AND RECENTLY REPORTED DLL S

	Tokun.[1]	Song[2]	Kim[3]	Kim[5]	Wang [6]	Bhor.[8]	Wang [9]	Yang[10]	Chang[11]	**This work**
Freq. (MHz)	20-300 (15X)	30-200 (6X)	40-800 (20X)	120MHz-1.8 GHz (15X)	400-600(1.5X)	200-1.2G (6X)	150-550 (3.7X)	40-500 (13.75X)	2-700 (350X)	15-600 (40X)
VDD	2 – 4 V	2.5 V	1.2 V	3.3 V	2.4-3.3 V	1.2 V	1 V	1.8 V	1.4-2.5 V	1.2 V
Power	9 mW	30 mW	43 mW	86.6 mW	9.9 mW	6.1mW	0.37 mW	12.6 mW	23 mW	20 mW
Type	Analog	Digital	Digital	Digital	Digital	Digital	Digital	Digital	Digital	Digital
Area	0.03 mm²	0.66 mm²	0.22 mm²	0.07 mm²	0.7 mm²	0.24 mm²	0.0119 mm²	0.2 mm²	0.88 mm²	0.38 mm²
Jitter (rms)	6.9ps@ 200 MHz	7.1 ps 200 MHz	1.6 ps @ 700 MHz	1.8 ps @ 700 MHz	24.4 ps peak-to-peak	4.6 ps	5.5 peak-to-peak	1.5 ps	17.6 ps peak-to-peak	8.9ps @ 600 MHz
Locking time	1.8 µs	-	-	1 cycles	10 cycles	-	4 cycles	134-14 cycles	32 cycles	4 cycles coarse lock
CMOS	0.30 µm	0.25 µm	0.13 um	0.35 µm	0.35 µm	0.13 µm	65 nm	0.18 µm	0.18 µm	0.13 µm

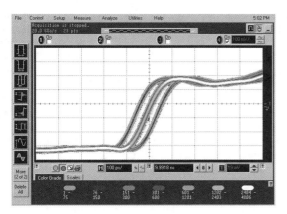

Fig. 6: Measured data showing the case of 3 LSBs flipping in the LSB DAC for low frequency operation. The locking frequency is 15 MHz.

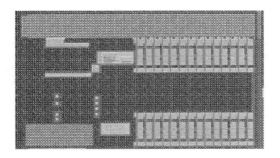

Fig. 7: Chip micrograph. DLL size is 470 m X 800 m.

IV. CONCLUSIONS

This paper presents an all digital implementation of a DLL with a 40X frequency locking range. A dual loop design, consisting in a coarse fast binary search combined with a linear search is proposed. This design achieves a large locking range with fast coarse locking while keeping the jitter and power consumption low. The chip occupies a 470µm X 800µm area and draws 20 mW @ 600 MHz in 0.13µm general-purpose CMOS. The 12 uniform phases of this DLL makes it suitable for providing the phases in applications such as time-interleaved and pipelined ADCs and broadband communications.

ACKNOWLEDGEMENTS

The authors acknowledge the contributions of the students, faculty and sponsors of the Berkeley Wireless Research Center. The National Science Foundation Infrastructure Grant No. 0403427, provided the infrastructure, and the research has been sponsored in part by the Center for Circuit & System Solutions (C2S2) Focus Center, one of five research centers funded under the Focus Center Research Program, a Semiconductor Research Corporation program, and ARO (Award #FD-W911NF-04-1-0418-NIKO-09/06). STMicroelectronics donated the chip fabrication. Charles Chen designed the PCB.

REFERENCES

[1] Y. Tokunaga, et. al., A 0.03mm/sup 2/ 9mW Wide-Range Duty-Cycle Correcting False-Lock-Free DLL with Fully Balanced Charge-Pump for DDR Interface," IEEE ISSCC 2006, Feb. 6-9, 2006 Page(s):1286 – 1295.

[2] E. Song, et. al., "A Reset-Free Anti-Harmonic Delay-Locked Loop Using a Cycle Period Detector," IEEE JSSC, vol. 39, no. 11, pp. 2055-2061, Nov. 2004

[3] Y-S. Kim, et. al., "A 40-to-800MHz Locking Multi-Phase DLL" IEEE ISSCC 2007, Feb. 11-15, 2007 Page(s):306 – 307.

[4] J-S. Wang, et. al., "An Ultra-Low-Power Fast Lock-in Small-Jitter All-Digital DLL," IEEE ISSCC 2005, Feb. 6-10, 2005 Page(s):422 – 423.

[5] J-H. Kim, et. al., "A CMOS DLL-Based 120MHz to 1.8 GHz Clock Generator for Dynamic Frequency Scaling," IEEE ISSCC 2005, Feb. 6-10, 2005 Page(s):516 – 517.

[6] Y-J. Wang, et. al., "All-Digital Delay-Locked Loop/Pulsewidth-Control Loop With Adjustable Duty Cycles," IEEE JSSC, vol. 41, no. 6, pp. 1262-1274, Jun. 2006.

[7] Y. Aibara, et. al., "A Novel False Lock Detection Technique for a Wide Frequency Range Delay-Locked Loop," IEICE 2006 E89-A(2):385-390

[8] P. Bhoraskar, Y. Chiu, "A 6.1-mW dual-loop digital DLL with 4.6-ps RMS jitter using window-based phase detector," ASSCC '07, 12-14 Nov. 2007 Page(s):79 – 82

[9] J-S Wang, C-Y Cheng, Y-C Liu, Y-M Wang, "A 0.67µW/MHz, 5ps jitter, 4 locking cycles, 65nm ADDLL, ASSCC '07, 12-14 Nov. 2007 Page(s):300 – 303

[10] R.-J. Yang, S.-I Liu, A 40–550 MHz Harmonic-Free All-Digital Delay-Locked Loop Using a Variable SAR Algorithm," ," IEEE JSSC 2007, vol. 42, no. 2, Page(s): 361-373

[11] H-H Chang, S-I Liu, A wide-range and fast-locking all-digital cycle-controlled delay-locked loop," IEEE JSSC 2005 vol. 40, no. 3, Page(s): 661-670

A 0.042-mm² Fully Integrated Analog PLL with Stacked Capacitor-Inductor in 45nm CMOS

Shih-An Yu and Peter Kinget,
Dept. of Electrical Engineering
Columbia University
New York, NY 10027, USA.

Abstract□ **We present a fully integrated Phase Locked Loop in an advanced 45nm CMOS technology. The loop filter is integrated on chip under the voltage-controlled oscillator inductor, resulting in significant area savings. The whole PLL measures only 280um by 150um. The PLL has a dual-band output for 2-2.5GHz and 4-5GHz. The circuit operates from a 0.85V supply and consumes 15.3mW for a -120dBc/Hz phase noise at a 1MHz offset from a 2.0 to 2.5GHz carrier.**

I. INTRODUCTION

Phase locked loops (PLLs) are essential building blocks for almost all integrated circuits; they are used for clock generation on digital ICs, for clock recovery in I/O circuits and for carrier frequency synthesis in wireless transceivers.

As CMOS technologies continue to scale to smaller feature sizes, the integration of analog and RF integrated circuits becomes progressively challenging. Reliability as well as power density reduction requirements have resulted in significantly lower supply voltages down to 1-V or sub-1-V supplies, e.g., 45nm CMOS technologies. Supply scaling poses significant challenges for the design of high performance analog and RF circuits. Additionally, the area of digital integrated circuits scales down quadratically with feature size reduction, whereas the size of passive components does not scale significantly. Every introduction of a new technology generation raises questions about the feasibility and/or the performance of analog and RF circuits

In this paper we investigate the design of a fully integrated

PLL for frequency synthesis in wireless applications in an advanced 45nm CMOS technology. All-digital PLLs have been introduced (see e.g., [1][2]) since they offer better compatibility to scaling, however, for wireless applications they still rely on LC-based oscillators to meet stringent phase noise and spur specifications [1]. We demonstrate that a very compact analog PLL design, comparable in size to a digital PLL and compatible with WLAN requirements, can be realized by the use of special design and layout techniques that allow the stacked integration of the PLL filter and the planar inductor of the on-chip voltage-controlled (VCO) oscillator. The VCO design further accommodates the low voltage requirements of deeply scaled CMOS.

II. PLL DESIGN

The block diagram of the PLL synthesizer is shown in Figure 1. The VCO oscillates between 8 and 10GHz and is locked to a 40MHz external reference. Scaling to smaller feature sizes allows the operation of the VCO and divider circuits at higher frequencies. This not only allows the easy generation of LO signals for multiple bands, it further allows the use of smaller on-chip planar inductors for the VCO to save area (see next section).

The VCO signal is buffered and drives a fixed divide-by-2 in the loop which has an output frequency between 4 and 5GHz. The programmable divider divides the signal further down to the reference frequency and feeds it back to the tri-state phase/frequency detector (PFD). The input of an

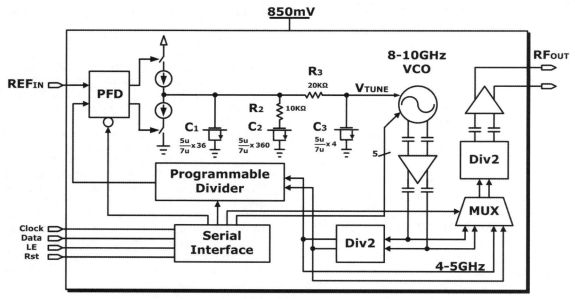

Figure 1   Block diagram of the phase locked loop test chip.

additional divide-by-2 can be connected to the VCO buffer output or the fixed divide-by-2 in the loop and generates quadrature local oscillator output signals between 4 and 5.2GHz or between 2 and 2.6GHz.

The programmable divider is a truly modular design consisting of a cascade of six divide-by-2/3 dividers [3]. The fixed divide-by-2 and the first four divide-by-2/3 dividers in the programmable divider are implemented with custom pseudo-differential CMOS logic cells using poly load resistors for higher speed and lower power performance. The last two divide-by-2/3 stages in the programmable divider, as well as the PFD, are implemented with standard CMOS logic gates. The PFD is a regular tri-state design with a lock detector. The charge pump is implemented with source switched PMOS and NMOS current sources.

The size and performance of the digital blocks such as the dividers and the PFD scale well with feature size and occupy only a small fraction of the overall area. The current design is an integer-N topology but the addition of a sigma-delta converter to convert the PLL into a fractional-N synthesizer will only incur a negligible area and power increase. These additional circuits similarly benefit significantly from transistor size scaling. We have focused our attention towards the scalability of the analog and RF blocks of the PLL. The significant area of the passive on-chip loop filter components and of the VCO inductor, as well as, the reduced supply voltage operation, have been identified as the major challenges.

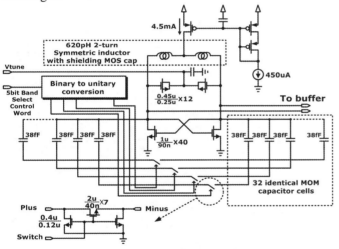

Figure 2   Schematic of the top-biased VCO.

III. VCO DESIGN

Deeply scaled transistors are more sensitive to reliability issues and can only operate under progressively smaller supply voltages. In a 45nm technology, the devices are designed for a nominal supply voltage below 0.9V for a GP technology and 1.1V for an LP technology [4]. Device reliability and performance degradation often depends exponentially on the applied gate voltage and over-voltage stress needs to be avoided to prevent degradation of the device characteristics or noise performance [5].

The VCO phase noise performance typically improves for larger voltage swings across the LC resonator (see e.g., [6]) and in many VCO topologies the gate voltage of the active

devices is allowed to go beyond the supply voltage. In this work in 45nm LP CMOS, we have used a top-biased VCO topology with an NMOS cross-coupled switching pair, shown in Figure 2. The VCO is operated from a 0.85-V supply and through proper sizing of the NMOS switching pair and the biasing current, the common-mode level of the LC tank was designed to be around 0.6V, such that the transistors of the cross-coupled switching pair are not over-stressed even when the tank operates with voltage limited swings (~1.1V_{PP}). The VCO uses differential switchable metal-oxide-metal (MOM) capacitors to provide discrete sub-band switching across the entire frequency range, and the continuous tuning is implemented with an NMOS inversion-mode varactor.

Technology scaling and faster transistor operation allows moving the VCO frequency towards a higher frequency. This enables the use of smaller inductors and thus a reduction of the circuit area. The quality factor of the inductive part of the impedance of an on-chip planar inductor is typically comparable, or even better for higher frequency designs. However, the quality factor of the capacitive part of the impedance, due to the capacitance between the planar inductor and the substrate, degrades when moving to higher frequencies. Therefore the use of a patterned ground shield [7] is desirable. In the next section we will demonstrate that the loop filter capacitors can be stacked under the inductor, thereby saving area, while at the same time improving the LC tank quality factor.

IV. DESIGN AND LAYOUT OF THE STACKED LOOP FILTER-RESONATOR STRUCTURE

As shown in the PLL block diagram of Figure 1 the on-chip loop filter requires several grounded capacitors that can be implemented with NMOS capacitors. Capacitor C2 in series with resistor R2 is by far the largest component. MOM capacitors are not area-efficient for such large value capacitance. In the 2nd order loop filter configuration, C2 does not need to have a high quality factor since it is in series with resistor R2. We can thus use MOS capacitors which offer a much higher capacitance density but with a limited quality factor. We found that the reference spur performance of the PLL was limited by charge pump mismatches or charge pump to VCO power supply cross talk, and was not affected by the gate leakage of the loop filter MOS capacitors.

To save area it is desirable to lay out MOS capacitor C2 under the on-chip inductor for the VCO. The layout and electrical equivalent model of the stacked MOS capacitor-inductor are shown in Figure 3. The NMOS inversion capacitor is sliced into L-shaped stripes so that magnetically induced eddy currents can be avoided [7][8]. The top plate of the capacitor is formed by the poly gates of the NMOS transistors that are laid out as a patterned ground shield for the inductor. The bottom plate of the capacitor is the inversion layer that is connected to the drain and source terminals, which are shorted to ground. The source and drains of neighboring stripes are laid out separately and only connected at the center of the capacitor so that no eddy currents can flow in the bottom plate.

Figure 3 also shows an equivalent lumped model for the stacked MOS capacitor-inductor structure. Traditionally a patterned ground shield is grounded; however, in this work, a

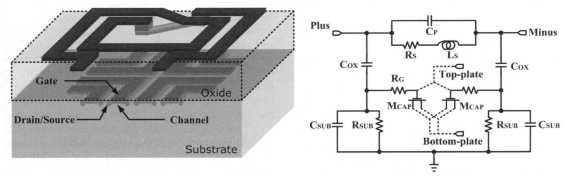

Figure 3 [Left] (Simplified) Layout of the stacked NMOS-loop-filter capacitor and VCO inductor and [Right] electrical equivalent model

DC bias is applied to the gates of the NMOS capacitors by the PLL to maintain the NMOS capacitor inverted. With different tuning voltages, the capacitance changes over a range of ±50% due to varying inversion levels. Even though the patterned ground shield is not shorted to ground anymore, it still improves the quality factor of the capacitive part of the inductor, especially when the inductor is driven differentially. Under differential drive, the differential capacitive currents through Cox will return through the poly gate and avoid the high losses in the substrate due to R_{SUB}. Our VCO uses a differential topology, and thus benefits from the presence of the NMOS capacitor poly gate shield. Figure 4 shows the results of an electro-magnetic simulation comparing the quality factor of an inductor without components underneath ('no shield'), and with a stacked MOS capacitor with a grounded gate ('grounded shield') or with a floating gate ('floating shield') when measured in a balanced or unbalanced configuration. We note indeed an improvement of the balanced quality factor with a MOS cap underneath compared to a bare inductor. All metal and poly wiring was included in the simulation. The source and drain N+ regions were not included but can be neglected since their resistivity is much large than the metal runners on top [8]. A simulation with the poly gates replaced by metal showed a negligible change in the losses and the effect of the losses in the MOS channel is thus assumed to be negligible.

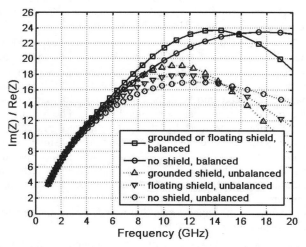

Figure 4 Electromagnetic simulation of the on-chip inductor with stacked MOS capacitors underneath.

V. EXPERIMENTAL RESULTS

A test chip was fabricated in an advanced LP 45nm CMOS technology from ST Microelectronics. The chip layout plot is shown in Figure 5. Thanks to the stacked loop filter-inductor layout the fully integrated PLL only occupies a very small area of 280μmx150μm or 0.042mm^2. The dividers, PFD, and charge pump occupy a very small area, and it is clear that the addition of additional digital functionality can be done without significant area increase.

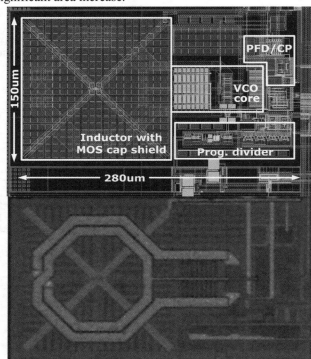

Figure 5 Composit layout plot and die photo of the fully integrated PLL in 45nm CMOS

The chips were packaged in a 64-pin QFN package and mounted on a PCB for testing. Due to package and board parasitics, a good output match for the output buffer could only be attained for the 2.0 to 2.5GHz band and measurements will only be reported for that band.

The chip operates with a nominal 0.85V supply and the VCO consumes 5mA, the synthesizer 13mA and the I/Q gneration divide-by-2 and the output buffer 3mA. Figure 6 shows the measured phase noise at various offset frequencies when the carrier is swept across the synthesizable range. A phase noise better than -120dBc/Hz at a 1MHz offset frequency is maintained across a range from 2.0GHz to 2.6GHz. The corresponding figure of merit for the VCO[*] at the center of the band is 182dBc/Hz. The 40MHz reference spurs were at -52dBc. Figure 7 shows the measured phase noise spectrum of the PLL for various output frequencies across the output frequency range. The PLL has a bandwidth of about 100kHz. The integrated phase error from 1kHz to 10MHz is 2.2deg$_{RMS}$. Some noise peaking is observed at the PLL filter cut-off frequency. This peaking is most likely due to deviations in the loop filter component values. The PLL had also a few small gaps in the output frequency range coverage due to variations in the MOS varactor and MOM capacitor values in the VCO. This chip was designed with a preliminary version of the device models and the design kit and so that deviations between the designed performance and obtained results is to be expected. These issues can easily be addressed in a redesign.

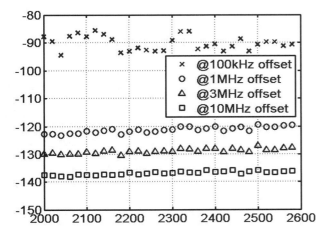

Figure 6   Measured phase noise at various offset frequencies across the synthesizable frequency range

The power consumption and noise performance of this PLL compares favorably to the state of the art in deeply scaled CMOS processes; it offers about 10dB better phase noise performance with a less than three times power consumption increase compared to [3]. The low voltage, high speed 10GHz VCO achieves an FOM of 182dBc/Hz at 0.85V compared to 177dBc/Hz for a 1.1-V 10-GHz DCO in [9] and 176dB/Hz for a 0.5-V 2.4-GHz VCO in [3]. The presented 45-nm analog PLL is very small (280um by 150um); interesting to note is that the size of the presented PLL is comparable to the 200um by 150um size of a fully digital 65-nm PLL of [2] or the 220um by 112um size of the 65-nm DCO in [9].

VI. CONCLUSIONS

We presented an ultra-compact fully integrated PLL designed in an advanced 45nm LP CMOS technology. A stacked loop filter-inductor structure allowed for a significant area reduction while offering a better resonator quality thanks to the shielding of the substrate electric losses. The VCO

---

[*] The FOM was calculated based on the divide-by-4 output and thus includes the effect of the noise of the dividers.

operates at two or four times the output frequency to enable scaling of the VCO inductor size and enable quadrature output generation with dividers. The VCO topology is further optimized to avoid gate oxide stress in the active VCO devices. The PLL operates from a low 0.85V supply and offers low noise and lower power operation.

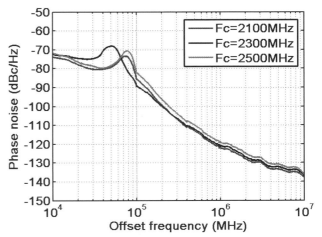

Figure 7   Measured phase noise spectrum for various PLL output frequencies.

ACKNOWLEDGMENT

ST Microelectronics donated the chip fabrication. The authors thank Ernesto Perea and his colleagues from ST and A. Balankutty from Columbia University for their help and technical support. S.A. Yu was supported through a research grant from Alcatel-Lucent. EM simulations were performed with the EMX simulator from Integrand Software.

REFERENCES

[1]   R. Staszewski et al., "All-digital PLL and GSM/EDGE transmitter in 90nm CMOS," *Digest of Technical Papers IEEE International Solid-State Circuits Conference (ISSCC)*, pp.316-317, Feb. 2005

[2]   A. V. Rylyakov et al., "A Wide Power-Supply Range (0.5V-to-1.3V) Wide Tuning Range (500 MHz-to-8 GHz) All-Static CMOS AD PLL in 65nm SOI," *Digest of Technical Papers International Solid-State Circuits Conference*, pp. 172-173, Feb. 2007.

[3]   S.A. Yu and P. Kinget, "A 0.65V 2.5GHz Fractional-N Frequency Synthesizer in 90nm CMOS" in *Digest of Technical Papers IEEE International Solid-State Circuits Conference (ISSCC)*, pp. 304-305, February 2007.

[4]   E. Josse et al, "A Cost-Effective Low Power Platform for the 45-nm Technology Node," *International Electron Devices Meeting (IEDM)* pp.1-4, 11-13, Dec. 2006

[5]   J.S. Suehle, "Ultrathin Gate Oxide Reliability: Physical Models, Statistics, and Characterization," *IEEE Transactions on Electron Devices*, vol. 49, no.6, pp. 985-971 , June 2002

[6]   P. Kinget, B. Soltanian, S. Xu, S. Yu and F. Zhang, "Advanced Design Techniques for Integrated Voltage Controlled LC Oscillators,", *IEEE Custom Integrated Circuits Conference*, pp. 805-811, September 2007.

[7]   C.P. Yue, and S.S Wong, "On-chip spiral inductors with patterned ground shields for Si-based RF ICs," IEEE Journal of Solid-State Circuits, vol. 33, no. 5, pp. 743-752, May 1998

[8]   F. Zhang and P. Kinget, "Design of Components and Circuits Underneath Integrated Inductors," *IEEE Journal of Solid-State Circuits*, Oct. 2006, pp. 2265-2271.

[9]   Nicola Da Dalt et al., "A 10b 10GHz Digitally Controlled LC Oscillator in 65nm CMOS," *Digest of Technical Papers International Solid-State Circuits Conference*, pp. 669-678Feb. 2006

A 1.7-GHz 1.5-mW Digitally-Controlled FBAR Oscillator with 0.03-ppb Resolution

H. Ito[1,3], H. Lakdawala[3], A. Ravi[3], S. Pellerano[3], R. Ruby[2], K. Soumyanath[3], K. Masu[1]

[1]Tokyo Institute of Technology, Yokohama 226-8503 Japan
[2]Avago Technologies, San Jose, CA 95131
[3]Intel Corporation, Hillsboro OR 97124 USA

Abstract — In this paper, a 1.5mW, 1.7GHz BAW oscillator with a multi-bit sigma-delta DAC based fine frequency tuning to achieve a frequency resolution of about 50mHz or 0.03ppb over a tuning range of 6.4MHz is presented. The oscillator achieves a phase noise of -97dBc/Hz at an offset of 10kHz.

I. INTRODUCTION

Crystal Oscillators have been the primary frequency reference sources used in communication circuits. However, their sizes and frequencies of operation are not easily scaled. Push towards miniaturization demands smaller form factor. The FBAR (Free standing Bulk Acoustic Resonator) technology is a proven technology used for RF front end filter applications. Their application for a frequency reference has been proposed in the literature [1], however, one of the challenges faced in the design of a frequency reference is the inaccuracy due to manufacturing variations and temperature changes. Some communication standards (like GSM and WiMAX) allow calibration of the frequency source using beacon information from the transmitter. This information can be combined with factory calibration to overcome these inaccuracies. The frequency resolution required for such a servo loop is in the 100ppb range. Analog techniques for trimming require small varactors and high accuracy voltage references.

In this paper, a digitally controlled FBAR based oscillator with a tuning resolution of 0.03ppb over 6.4MHz is presented. The resolution is achieved by a DAC composed of 3 sub-ranged capacitor banks, with fine resolution being obtained by 7-level sigma-delta capacitive DAC. The paper also addresses challenges due to spurious resonance in the oscillator output due to wire bonding from the chip to the FBAR. The wirebond resonance effects are eliminated by a resonance suppression circuit, implemented with a tuned circuit at the source of the gain stage.

II. THE PROPOSED OSCILLATOR

Figure 1 shows a block diagram of the proposed oscillator which consists of a core oscillator, a FBAR, a DAC including the 2nd-order sigma-delta modulator, a phase controller, a programmable divider and a buffer. The clock of the sigma-delta modulator is supplied from oscillator output through a divider and the phase controller which adjusts switching timing of fine capacitors for minimizing phase noise.

A. Oscillator Core

A differential topology is applied as shown in Fig. 2. The number of transistors operating in saturation region is limited to the cross-couple pair M1 and M2 for reducing flicker noises. FBAR resonators can be modeled using the modified Butterworth Van Dyke model (mBVD) [2]. Oscillation frequency f_{osc} is determined by

$$f_{osc} = \frac{1}{2\pi\sqrt{LC}}\left(1 + \frac{C}{2(C_m + C_L)}\right). \qquad (1)$$

$C_L = C_c\text{<}55{:}0\text{>} + C_{md}\text{<}71{:}0\text{>} + C_f\text{<}5{:}0\text{>}$ is total capacitance of capacitor banks, and oscillation frequency can be controlled by changing the number of capacitors; coarse $C_c\text{<}55{:}0\text{>}$, moderate $C_{md}\text{<}71{:}0\text{>}$ and fine $C_f\text{<}5{:}0\text{>}$. Coarse capacitors calibrate oscillation-frequency variations caused by process and temperature variations and are activated during start-up time. Moderate capacitors compensate temperature fluctuation. Fine capacitors improve the resolution of a frequency control and are explained in the next section. Features of the proposed oscillator are (1) 0.03ppb of fine frequency-tuning by the sigma-delta modulator with 19-control-bits, (2) the resonance suppression using a negative impedance circuit and (3) a stacked cross-coupled topology for increasing signal amplitude.

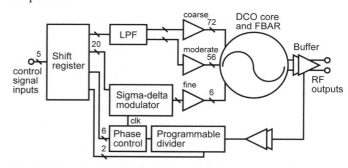

Figure 1. Block diagram of the oscillator with the subranged capacitive DAC including a sigma-delta modulator, a phase controller and a programmable divider.

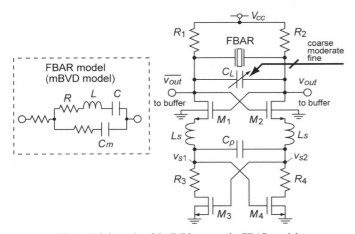

Figure 2. Schematic of the DCO core and a FBAR model.

B. Frequency Tuning by a Sigma-Delta Capacitive DAC

The second order sigma-delta has a 19bit input and drives 6 ouput-capacitors of the fine bank. The operation frequency of the modulator is a quarter the oscillator frequency. The sigma-delta is an error feedback structure that breaks cascades of adders with register insertion to operate at the high clock frequencies that is 1/4 the oscillator frequency at very low power. The quantization noise from the sigma-delta is filtered by the bandpass response of the FBAR, and allows the capacitive DAC to have a high resolution. Each bit of the sigma-delta $x_k<n>$ (= 0 or 1) at a cycle k turns on or off the nth capacitor with value C_{unit}. The effective capacitance of the fine bank over K cycles of the sigma-delta loop clock is

$$C_{eff} = \frac{\sum_{k=0}^{k=K-1} \sum_{n=0}^{n=N-1} x_k < n >}{K} C_{unit}. \qquad (2)$$

n is the fine capacitor index, ranging from 0 to $N-1$ (N=6) as shown in Fig. 3. The resolution of C_{eff} is the function of the cycles, K over which the measurement. This simplified analysis assumes that the out of band noise of the sigma-delta is removed by the FBAR filtering and that the switched capacitors are ideal. This scheme allows very fine capacitance change, without applying small capacitors that have poor process-variation robustness. The fine tuning method using the sigma-delta modulator has been proposed for LC-based and crystal-based digitally controlled oscillators (DCOs) [3,4], and this paper applies the technique to FBAR DCOs.

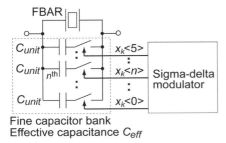

Figure 3. Simplified schematic of the fine capacitor bank connected to the FBAR

C. Spurious-Resonance Suppressor

A CMOS chip and the FBAR are connected to each other through a interconnect path that includes bonding wires and transmission lines as shown in Fig. 4 (a). Figure 4 (b) is a simplified model of the FBAR as seen by the oscillator. The simulation results in Fig. 5 illustrates the effect of the varying the length of the bonding wires, that changes its inductance (L_{wire}). Differential input impedance of the FBAR with wires and pads shows resonance around 1.7GHz (desired FBAR resonance). Resonances at over 7GHz are spurious and are induced by bonding wires. Spurious-resonance frequencies decrease as L_{wire} increases. The DCO core oscillates at spurious frequency if L_{wire} is large such as 3nH, which is realistic when the CMOS chip and the FBAR are loaded on a board.

Our approach is to neutralize the effect of the parasitic inductor by exploiting the negative impedance circuit. The concept of the cancellation scheme is shown in Fig. 6. Coarse, moderate and fine capacitors have been excluded for simplicity. The DCO core shown in Fig. 2 can be approximately modeled as Fig. 6 (a). The FBAR has high DC impedance, and R_s and C_p in Fig. 6 prevent the oscillator from latching and relaxation oscillation at low frequencies [6]. Impedance of inductors $j\omega L_s$ can be neglected at low frequencies and do not interrupt the effect of R_s and C_p. Impedance of the capacitor $1/j\omega C_p$ decreases as signal frequency increases, and a middle of the capacitor C_p becomes an AC ground. Then, an equivalent circuit model of a bottom portion at high frequencies can be represented by negative resistors $-1/g_m$ and negative inductors $-L_s$. Negative inductors can cancel out inductance of bonding wires L_{wire} and suppress spurious resonances.

A low pass filter (LPF) connected in parallel with the FBAR may be able to suppress spurious resonances, however the LPF will degrade Q of the oscillator tank and increases phase noise. An advantage of the proposed technique is that the spurious suppressor minimally degrades phase noise: Parasitic series-resistors in inductors slightly degenerate gain of cross-coupled transistors M1 and M2 and have to be made up by increasing the g_m of the cross-coupled pair.

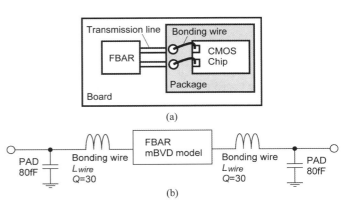

(a)

(b)

Figure 4 (a) Typical application of FBAR with CMOS chip on a PC board (b) Simplified model of the FBAR element along with the interconnect effects seen by the oscillators.

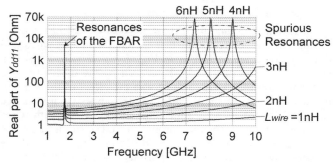

Figure 5. Input impedance of the circuit shown in Fig. 4 (b).

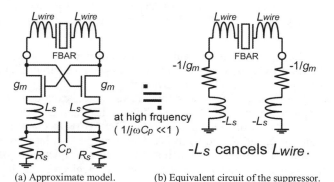

(a) Approximate model.　　(b) Equivalent circuit of the suppressor.

Figure 6. Proposed spurious-resonance suppressor circuit.

D. Stacked Cross-Coupled Topology

Resistors R_s and a capacitor C_p connected to source-nodes of transistors in Fig. 6 (a) are necessary for suppressing latch and relaxation oscillation at low frequencies. However, R_s reduces amplitude of oscillation signals, which is a disadvantage for phase noise characteristics. Thus, the stacked cross-couple topology as shown in Fig. 2 is used. Transistors M1 and M2 consist the negative resistance. M3 and M4 operate in linear region and increase amplitude of oscillation signals v_{out}. For example, when voltages v_{s1} and v_{s2} in Fig. 2 go up and down respectively, source-drain resistance of M3 and M4 becomes high and low, respectively. Then, voltage swings of v_{s1} and v_{s2} are emphasized, which boosts amplitude of oscillation signals v_{out}. From simulations, oscillation amplitude increase of 44mV and phase noise improvement of 0.9dB/Hz at 10kHz-offset improve without power penalties is seen.

III. MEASUREMENTS AND DISCUSSIONS

The test chip is fabricated by using 90nm Si CMOS process. Figure 7 is a micrograph of the CMOS chip. The chip is loaded on the board and is connected to the FBAR through bonding wires. An area of the DCO core is 280μm x 530μm including a differential inductor for the spurious suppression.

The measured output spectrum is shown in Fig. 8. Output power from buffer is about 2dBm. Spurious noise are observed and come from the shift register and equipments, outside the band of interest. Figure 9 is the measured close-in phase noise characteristic. A phase noise at 10kHz offset is -97dBc/Hz, with an integrated jitter (1kHz to 10MHz) is 300fs, with the instrument noise floor limiting the noise level over 1MHz. Figure 10 shows measured frequency tuning characteristics with changing of capacitances. The proposed

oscillator can change frequency from 1702.7MHz to 1709.1MHz. The tuning range is 6.4MHz.

Single-sideband modulation is used for measuring resolutions of fine bits controlled by the sigma-delta capacitive DAC. A measurement scheme is shown in Fig. 11. Several combinations of control bits for the sigma-delta modulator are measured. A measured resolution per a fine bit is 0.03ppb.

Performance of the oscillator is summarized in Table I. Power consumption of the DCO core is 1.5mW, and the sigma-delta modulator consumes 2.3mW. A commonly used figure of merit (FoM) is determined by

$$FoM = L\{\Delta f\} - 20\log\left(\frac{f_o}{\Delta f}\right) + 10\log\left(\frac{P_{DC}}{1mW}\right), \quad (3)$$

where $L\{\Delta f\}$ stands for phase noise at a given offset Δf, and f_o is the center frequency of the oscillator. P_{DC} is power consumption. A brief comparison among the present work and previously reported FBAR-based oscillators is shown in Table II. Phase noise of our oscillator at 10kHz offset is small as compared to other frequency-tunable oscillators. The present work achieves FoM of -200dBc/Hz which is comparable with other FBAR oscillators. The main contribution of the present work is very fine tuning resolution of 0.03ppb with a tuning range of 6.4MHz, while maintaining low phase noise characteristics.

Figure 7. Micrograph of the CMOS chip along with the FBAR

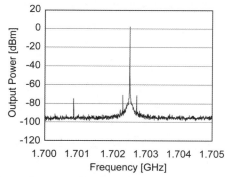

Figure 8. Measured spectrum. Numbers of coarse and moderate capacitors are 72 and 56, respectively. The control bit of the sigma-delta modulator is set to 10000 in hexadecimal.

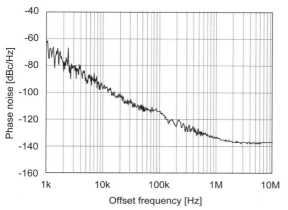

Figure 9. Measured phase noise. Numbers of coarse and moderate capacitors are 72 and 56, respectively. The control bit of the sigma-delta modulator is set to 10000 in hexadecimal.

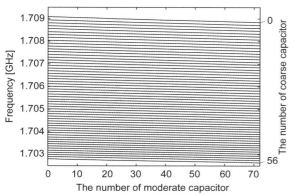

Figure 10. Output frequency as a function of the coarse and moderate tuning codes illustrating the linearity and overlap between banks.

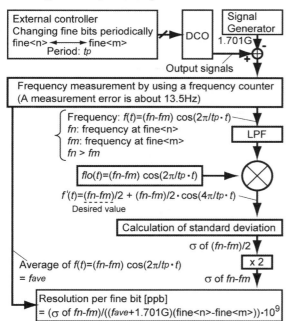

Figure 11. Algorithm for fine capacitor bank resolution measurement. When fine<n> and fine<m> are set to 10000 and 08000 in hexadecimal, (fine<n>-fine<m>) becomes 2^{14}.

TABLE I.   PERFORMANCE SUMMARY

Process technology	90 nm Si CMOS
Center frequency	1705.9MHz
Supply voltage	0.9V for the DCO core 1.1V for digital circuits
Power consumption	1.5mW for the DCO core 2.3mW for the sigma-delta modulator
Tuning range	6.4MHz
Phase noise	-97dBc/Hz at 10kHz offset
FoM	-200dBc/Hz at 10kHz offset
Tuning resolution	0.03ppb

TABLE II.   COMPARISON WITH THE PRESENT AND PREVIOUS WORKS

Ref.	Power [mW]	Center frequency [GHz]	Phase noise @10kHz offset [dBc/Hz]	FoM [dBc/Hz]	Tuning range [MHz]
This work	1.5 *	1.7	-97	-200	6.4
[1]	0.3	1.9	-100	-211	0
[6]	6.0	2.2	-85 **	-184	220
[7]	0.6	2.1	-95 **	-204	1.5
[8]	0.089	1.9	-98	-214	0
[9]	4.6	5.5	-93	-201	0
[10]	24.3	2.1	-94 **	-187	37

* Only the DCO core. ** These values are read off from graphs.

IV.   CONCLUSION

The paper proposes a fully digitally-controlled FBAR-based oscillator using a sigma-delta DAC for fine frequency tuning of 0.03ppb with spurious resonance suppression. The oscillator consumes 1.5mW and oscillates at 1.7GHz with a tuning range of 6.4MHz. The phase noise of -97dBc/Hz and FoM of -200dBc/Hz at an offset frequency of 10kHz.

ACKNOWLEDGMENT

The authors gratefully acknowledge Ralph Bishop, Hossein Alavi, Tomoki Saito and members of CCL at Intel Corporation and Mark Unkrich at Avago.

REFERENCES

[1]   B. P. Otis and J. M. Rabaey, IEEE J. Solid-State Circuits, vol. 38, no. 6, pp. 1271–1274, Jun. 2003.
[2]   J. D. Larson III, et al., in Proc. IEEE Ultrasonics Symposium, pp. 863-868, 2000.
[3]   R. B. Staszeski, et al., IEEE Trans. on CAS II, vol. 50, no. 11, pp. 815-828, Nov. 2003.
[4]   J. Lin, IEEE J. Solid-State Circuits, vol. 40, no. 12, pp. 2726-2734, Dec. 2005.
[5]   D. Ruffieux, in Proc. ESSCIRC, pp. 85-88, Sep. 2002.
[6]   P. Vincent, et al., in Digest Paper of IEEE ISSCC, pp. 478-479, 2008.
[7]   S. Rai and B. Otis, in Digest Paper of IEEE ISSCC, pp. 576-577, 2007.
[8]   Y. H. Chee, et al., in Proc. of IEEE RFIC Symp. Dig. Papers, pp. 123–126, 2005.
[9]   M. Aissi, et al., in Digest Paper of IEEE ISSCC, pp. 1228-1235, 2006.
[10] K. B. Östman, et al., IEEE J. Solid-State Circuits, vol. 41, no. 10, pp. 2248-2256, Oct. 2006.

24-GHz 1-V Pseudo-Stacked Mixer with Gain-Boosting Technique

Nobuhiro Shiramizu, Toru Masuda, Takahiro Nakamura, and Katsuyoshi Washio

Central Research Laboratory, Hitachi, Ltd.
1-280 Higashi-Koigakubo, Kokubunji, Tokyo, Japan
nobuhiro.shiramizu.fq@hitachi.com

Abstract—**Design techniques for a low-power mixer operating in the quasi-millimeter-wave frequency region were developed. A pseudo-stacked configuration and a pre-biasing technique, to reduce supply voltage and dynamic current consumption, respectively, were introduced. Furthermore, a gain-boosting technique, which actively utilizes a parasitic resonant caused by a transformer and parasitic capacitor, improves the power efficiency of the mixer. The proposed mixer fabricated by 0.18-μm SiGe BiCMOS technology achieves a conversion gain of 4.8 dB and NF of 10.4 dB at 1-V power supply. These performance results indicate that these design techniques are suitable for implementing low-power receivers for the quasi-millimeter-wave frequency region.**

I. INTRODUCTION

To extend the capability of high-speed wireless communication, the quasi-millimeter-wave region is a candidate band because it still has frequencies over a wide bandwidth usable for wireless communication systems. For instance, the Federal Communications Commission (FCC) has allocated bandwidth of 250 MHz around the 24-GHz frequency for unlicensed industrial, scientific, and medical (ISM) applications. Moreover, the local multipoint distribution systems (LMDS) band is similarly allocated in a frequency range of 24 to 30 GHz. On the other hand, the microwave frequency region under 10 GHz is already used by many applications, so the capacity of bandwidth in that region is not enough for high-speed wireless communication systems. The quasi-millimeter-wave region around 24 GHz is therefore expected to be further used for many applications, and several building blocks and receivers have been demonstrated at this frequency [1-3]. However, the circuits in the previous works consume much more power than circuits operating at less than 10 GHz. Regarding wide-spread commercial use, low-power-consumption operation an indispensable factor, even if a circuit is operated in the quasi-millimeter-wave region. A technique for designing high-frequency circuits featuring lower power-consumption operation has therefore been strongly required.

Figure 1 shows a simplified block diagram of a 24-GHz transceiver. The down-conversion mixer in the transceiver requires the characteristics of high conversion gain (CG), low noise figure (NF), and low distortion. To satisfy these requirements, the Gilbert-cell configuration is usually used for the down-conversion mixer because of its high performance in terms of low distortion and high gain [3-8]. However, since the Gilbert mixer consists of stacked transistors, the supply voltage of the mixer must be more than 2 V. A passive-type mixer can be operated at low supply voltage, but its conver-

sion gain is too small. To achieve both low power, low supply voltage around 1 V, and high gain, novel design techniques that break through the current limitation with conventional configurations should be investigated.

In this study, we developed design techniques for a mixer that can be operated at low supply voltage and thus lower power consumption. The performance of the fabricated mixer was experimentally investigated and the validity of the mixer-design concept was confirmed by the results.

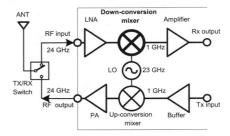

Fig. 1. Block diagram of 24-GHz RF-IC for wireless commnications

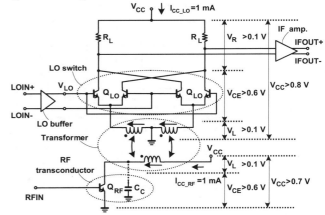

Fig. 2. Proposed pseudo-stacked mixer circuit

II. PSEUDO-STACKED MIXER

To achieve both high conversion gain and low power consumption, the mixer applies a combination of three techniques: supply-voltage reduction, gain boosting, and current-consumption reduction.

A. Pseudo-stacked mixer configuration

To reduce supply voltage (V_{CC}) for a mixer circuit topology, it is necessary to separate the DC stacking connection of transistors [9]. Figure 2 shows the proposed pseudo-stacked mixer circuit. An on-chip transformer is inserted between the RF-transconductor-stage and the LO-switching stage. By

102

introducing the transformer in this manner, the RF-transconductor stage and LO-switch stage are divided from the viewpoint of DC biasing. On the other hand, the RF-current signal amplified by the RF transconductor can be transmitted to transistor Q_{LO} by the electromagnetic-coupling effect of the transformer. The LO switch stage can then convert the frequency from the RF current signal to the IF current signal. Since the supply voltage can be the V_{CE} of one of the transistors in the proposed mixer, the supply voltage can be set to only 0.8 V. This supply-voltage reduction technique for operating at less than 1.0 V is attributed to the introduction of the transformer and pseudo-stacked topology.

The on-chip transformer is an important element in the pseudo-stacked mixer. Not to mention that the good characteristics of the coupling factor k and the quality factor Q should be obtained, the inductance and parasitic capacitor should be designed accurately in order to apply the gain-boosting technique described below. However, it is difficult to simulate the frequency response, especially in the quasi-millimeter-wave frequency region. To obtain an accurate model of the transformer, an electromagnetic simulator (Agilent Momentum) was used. The top view of the transformer and the simulation results of inductance and Q are shown in Fig. 3. The self-inductance and mutual-inductance fit the required values, and k of 0.5 and Q of 7 at 24 GHz are the enough to obtain CG of the proposed mixer. The frequency response of the on-chip transformer can be predicted by the simulation, and it is applicable to the proposed mixer circuit.

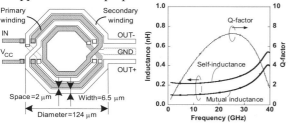

Fig. 3. Transformer layout and simulated characteristics of inductance and Q-factor of the pseudo-stacked mixer

B. Gain-boosting technique

To obtain both high gain and low-power consumption operation, we introduced the gain-boosting technique, which actively utilizes parasitic resonance caused by the transformer and parasitic capacitor. Usually, resonant frequency is calculated from the inductance of the transformer and capacitance of the resonant circuit [9]. However, in the case of the quasi-millimeter-wave frequency region, the transformer parasitic resistors significantly change the resonant frequency of the mixer, so the equivalent circuit model (including parasitic resistance) should be analyzed. Figure 4 shows the simplified transfer function of the pseudo-stacked mixer circuit. The equivalent circuit of the RF transconductor (Q_{RF}) is composed of an input capacitor (C_p), a transconductor, and collector parasitic capacitor (C_C). The transformer is represented by a T-shaped inductor network including parasitic resistors (R_S) to give an actual finite quality factor. The effective equivalent circuit of the differential LO switch block (shown in Fig. 2) is just an ideal switch with switching frequency f_{LO}. The IF voltage signal at the IFOUT node is generated by load resistor R_L. The input signal is v_{RF}, and the

output signal is v_{IF}. The output signal v_{IF} is expressed by the approximate equation below.

$$v_{IF} \approx \frac{g_m R_L}{\pi} \frac{2\pi f_{RF} k L_S}{Z_{RE}(f_{RF}) + j Z_{IM}(f_{RF})} V_{RF} \sin(2\pi(f_{RF} - f_{LO})t), \quad (1)$$

where,

$$Z_{RE}(f_{RF}) = (2\pi f_{RF})^2 L_S C_C (R_L + 2R_S) - (R_L + R_S), \quad (2)$$

$$Z_{IM}(f_{RF}) = 2\pi f_{RF} \left((2\pi f_{RF})^2 (k^2 - 1) L_S^2 C_C + R_S C_C (R_L + R_S) + L_S \right). \quad (3)$$

As Equations (1) and (2) indicate, in the case that $Z_{RE}(f_{RF})$ becomes zero, the transfer function of the proposed pseudo-stack mixer has resonant frequency f_{res}. If f_{res} can be set to be the RF input frequency, CG (i.e., v_{IF}/v_{RF}) becomes the maximum value.

$$f_{res} \approx \frac{1}{2\pi\sqrt{L_S C_C \left(1 + \frac{R_S}{R_L + R_S}\right)}} \quad (4)$$

$$CG_{max} \approx \frac{g_m R_L}{\pi} \frac{k}{\dfrac{k^2 - 1}{1 + \dfrac{R_S}{R_L + R_S}} + \dfrac{R_S C_C}{L_S}(R_L + R_S) + 1} \quad (5)$$

The maximum value CG_{max} of the CG function is also determined by coupling factor k and R_S (which depends on quality factor Q of the transformer). Here, Q is calculated from $2\pi f_{RF} L_S / R_S$. According to our on-chip transformer study, coupling factor k of 0.5, quality factor Q of 7, and R_S at 24 GHz of 4 can be used. As a result, CG_{max} is the same as the conventional one. Since the RF-transconductor can operate in single mode by transformer for single-to-differential conversion, if total CG is set equivalent to that of a conventional Gilbert-cell mixer, DC current consumption for biasing is reduced by 50%. For applying the gain-boosting technique to the proposed mixer, the transformer layout pattern and circuit parameters are determined by simulation. These parameters are then used to set the resonant frequency to the RF input frequency accurately. To confirm the effectiveness of gain-boosting technique, the transformer-layout pattern was applied to the fabricated proposed mixer in test element group (TEG).

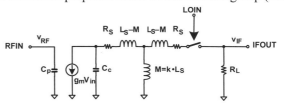

Fig. 4. Equivalent circuit of proposed mixer for small signal

C. LO pre-biasing technique

To reduce dynamic current consumption, pre-biasing is applied to the LO switch stage. Figure 5 shows simulated CG and LO-switch current dissipation I_{CC_LO} against LO input power at LO bias voltage V_{LO} of 0.75, 0.8, 0.85, or 0.9 V. The CG characteristics show LO input power with a peak gain, and the peak-gain value depends on both LO input power and V_{LO}. While the bias current of Gilbert-cell type mixers is usually controlled by a current-source circuit, the current dissipation of the LO-switch stage in the proposed mixer is not limited by the other transistors. Consequently, V_{LO} can be set to obtain high gain, low current dissipation, and low input power. There is thus an optimized V_{LO} and LO input power to obtain a given

CG and current dissipation. If the required CG is set to 6.2 dB, the lowest I_{CC_LO} of 0.9 mA can be obtained at 0.85 V of V_{LO} and LO input power of -6.5 dBm. The current consumption can be reduced by 55% (i.e., to 2 mA) from that of a conventional mixer at the same CG. Moreover, this technique contributes to reduce LO driving power so that total power consumption of a receiver (including the LO generation circuit) can be decreased. In short, the combination of the transformer-coupling technique and pre-biasing technique can reduce current consumption of quasi-millimeter-wave mixers.

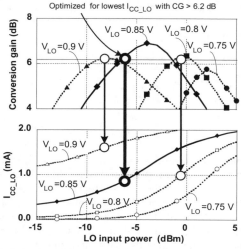

Fig. 5. Optimization of the Q_{LO} pre-biasing voltage for reducing LO-swtich current dissipation and LO input power by simulation

The proposed pseudo-stacked mixer circuit includes an IF amplifier, which is connected between the LO-switch stage and the output terminal. The IF amplifier consists of a transimpedance-type differential amplifier and emitter followers. To reduce the voltage swing at the output node of the LO-switch stage, the IF current signal at the LO-switch stage is transmitted in current mode to the output IFOUT by the amplifier. The supply voltage of the LO-switch stage can then be reduced because the V_{CE} headroom of the Q_{LO} for the voltage swing can be extended by this circuit. To drive a 50-Ω load, the IF amplifier consumes power of 2.4 mW. However, in the case of connection to an internal IF circuit in the RF-IC, the power can be reduced to less than 1 mW.

III. MEASUREMENT RESULTS

To confirm low-power-consumption operation of the proposed mixer, we fabricated a test element group (TEG) by using 0.18-μm SiGe BiCMOS technology with a cut-off frequency of 140 GHz. Figure 6 shows a chip micrograph of the proposed mixer. The mixer chip occupies an area of 1.05×0.75 mm, and the core circuit area is only 0.35×0.2 mm. We characterized the fabricated circuits by using on-wafer RF probes.

Figure 7 shows the measured and simulated CG responses and NF characteristic of the proposed mixer. The RF and LO power were set to be -50.5 dBm and -6.5 dBm, respectively. While there is almost 1-dB discrepancy between the measured and simulated data in the frequency range up to 24 GHz, the measured frequency response is similar to the simulated one. The peak frequencies of measured and simulated CG are almost the same at 23 GHz. At the operation frequency of 24

GHz, measured CG is 4.8 dB and simulated CG is 6.2 dB. These results indicate that the transformer design technique utilizing gain boosting for the quasi-millimeter-wave region is successful. Frequencies with minimum DSB-NF value were set to be in the frequency range between 23 and 24 GHz. The measured DSB NF characteristics have a minimum value in the frequency range between from 21 to 24 GHz. The measured NF of 10.2 dB and the simulated NF of 9.3 dB were obtained at 24 GHz. Due to the approximately-1-dB decrease in CG, the difference between measured and simulated NF characteristics is reasonable. Supply voltage, V_{CC}, is 1.0 V, and current consumption is 2 mA for the pseudo-stacked core circuit, 2 mA for the LO buffer, and 2.4 mA for the IF amplifier. Low power consumption of 6.4 mW is confirmed at 24 GHz. These results are attributed to the pseudo-stacked configuration with a transformer, the gain-boost peaking technique utilizing a parasitic resonant circuit, and the pre-biasing technique for LO switching transistors.

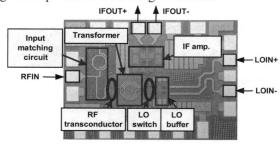

Fig. 6. Chip photodiagram of pseudo-stacked mixer

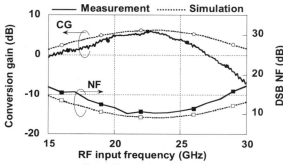

Fig. 7. CG and DSB NF versus frequency of pseudo-stacked mixer

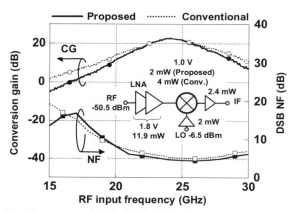

Fig. 8. Comparison of CG and DSB NF for the pseudo-stacked mixer with LNA and the conventional mixer with LNA

For a more practical evaluation of the proposed circuit, we also characterized it as a receiver configuration, which was combined with a low-noise amplifier circuit. A receiver with a Gilbert-cell (conventional) mixer was also fabricated for comparison. Figure 8 shows conversion gain and noise characteristics. The RF and LO power were set to -50.5 dBm and -6.5 dBm, respectively, for the receiver evaluation. At 24 GHz, CG of 22.7 dB for the proposed mixer and CG of 22.4 dB for the conventional mixer were obtained. The DSB noise figures (NF) for the proposed and conventional mixers are also very close. Instead of the almost the same small-signal characteristics at 24 GHz, power consumption is different. The low-noise amplifier consumes 12 mW at 1.8 V, and the gain and NF are 15 dB and 4.5 dB at 24 GHz. The proposed mixer can be operated at V_{CC} of 1.0 V, but the conventional Gilbert-cell mixer needs 2.0 V, at least. Consequently, the receivers with the proposed mixer and with the conventional mixer consume, respectively, 18.3 mW and 20.3 mW.

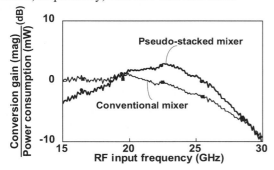

Fig. 9. Comparison of measurement data for the pseudo-stacked and Gilbert mixers

To compare the efficiency of the proposed pseudo-stacked and conventional Gilbert mixers, the ratio of CG versus power consumption was calculated (see Figure 9). At 24 GHz, the ratio for the proposed mixer is about 3 dB higher than that of the conventional mixer. This result confirms that power consumption can be reduced while maintaining CG by the proposed technique.

Measurements of the large-signal RF-IF down-conversion characteristics revealed P1dB and IIP3 of -32 dBm and -16.6 dBm, respectively. By analysis of the proposed circuit, it becomes clear that the large signal distortion is caused by the large voltage swing of the IF amplifier. Accordingly, we still have a room to improve the large-signal-distortion characteristic by optimizing the bias-condition of the IF amplifier.

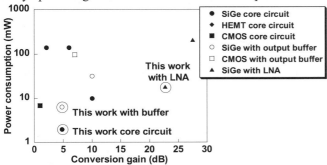

Fig. 10. Comparison of power consumption versus conversion gain for published down-conversion mixers

Figure 10 compares down-conversion mixer performances recently reported [3-10]. The previous works operated in the frequency range from 20 to 30 GHz are plotted. To our knowledge, the lowest power-consumption in previous works is achieved by a CMOS-based mixer with power consumption of 6.9 mW with CG of 1 dB in the 22-29-GHz band [6]. However, our proposed mixer-core circuit obtains CG of 4.8 dB with only 2-mW power consumption at 24 GHz. While including LNA for practical receiver conversion gain of more than 20 dB, the receiver configuration with the pseudo-stacked mixer consumes only 18.3 mW.

IV. SUMMARY

To achieve both high conversion gain and low power consumption, design techniques for quasi-millimeter-wave mixer are proposed. We introduced a pseudo-stacked mixer configuration, a gain-boosting technique, and an LO pre-biasing technique. The mixer applying the proposed design techniques was fabricated with 0.18-μm SiGe BiCMOS technology, and the measured conversion gain was 4.8 dB and the noise figure was 10.2 dB with low power consumption, i.e., 2 mW. Excellent efficiency of the conversion gain versus power dissipation can be achieved by the proposed circuit. The described techniques can be applied to 24-GHz wireless communication systems in the quasi-millimeter-wave region and to 60-GHz wireless communication systems in the millimeter-wave region.

ACKNOWLEDGMENT

This work was supported by "The research and development project for expansion of radio spectrum resources" of the Ministry of Internal Affairs and Communications, Japan.

REFERENCES

[1] H. Hashemi, et al., "A 24-GHz SiGe Phased-Array Receiver—LO Phase-Shifting Approach," IEEE Transactions on Microwave Theory and Techniques, Vol. 53, No. 2, pp. 614-626, Feb. 2005

[2] E. Sonmez, et al., "A single-chip 24 GHz receiver front-end using a commercially available SiGe HBT foundry process," 2002 IEEE Radio Frequency Integrated Circuits Symposium Digest of Papers, pp.159-162, Jun 2002

[3] S. Hackl, et al., "Benefits of SiGe over Silicon Bipolar Technology for Broadband Mixers with Bandwidth above 10GHz," 2001 IEEE MTT-S International Microwave Symposium, pp.1693-1696, May 2001

[4] N. Rodríguez, et al., "Comparing active Gilbert mixers integrated in standard SiGe process (Part I)," RF Design Magazine, January 2005, pp.51-58

[5] Y. Li, et al., "23GHz Front-end Circuits in SiGe BiCMOS Technology," 2003 IEEE Radio Frequency Integrated Circuits Symposium Digest of Papers, pp.99-102, Jun. 2003

[6] A. Verma, et al., "A K-Band Down-Conversion Mixer With 1.4-GHz Bandwidth in 0.13-μm CMOS Technology," IEEE Microwave and Wireless Components Letters, Vol. 15, No. 8, pp. 493-495, Aug. 2005

[7] K.B. Schad, et al., "Low-power active mixer for Ku-Band application using SiGe HBT MMIC," 2000 IEEE Radio Frequency Integrated Circuits Symposium Digest of Papers, pp.263-266, Jun. 2000

[8] C.S.Lin, et al., "A 9-50-GHz Gilbert-Cell Down-Conversion Mixer in 0.13-mm CMOS Technology," IEEE Microwave and Wireless Components Letters, Vol. 16, No. 5, pp. 293-295, May 2006

[9] C. Hermann, et al, "A 0.6-V 1.6-mW Transformer-Based 2.5-GHz Downconversion Mixer With +5.4-dB Gain and 2.8-dBm IIP3 ιν 0.13–μm CMOS", IEEE Transactions on Microwave Theory and Techniques, Vol. 53, No. 2, pp.488-495, Feb 2005

[10] K.L. Deng, et al., "A 3-33 GHz PHEMT MMIC Distributed Drain Mixer," 2002 IEEE Radio Frequency Integrated Circuits Symposium Digest of Papers, pp. 151-154, Jun. 2002

A 65-nm CMOS 8-GHz Injection Locked Oscillator for HDR UWB Applications

Romaric Toupé[1], Yann Deval[1], Franck Badets[2] & Jean-Baptiste Bégueret[1]

[1]IMS Laboratory
University of Bordeaux
Talence, France
benoit.toupe@ims-bordeaux.fr
[2]STMicroelectronics
Crolles, France

Abstract□ In this paper, an 8GHz 16th sub-harmonic Injection-Locked Oscillator based on LC-oscillators and pulse generators is presented. It has been fully implemented in a VLSI 65nm CMOS technology from STMicroelectronics and is dedicated to a double-loop frequency synthesizer. Under a nominal power supply of 1.2V, the ILO core dissipates 20mA (without buffers) for a measured phase noise of -107dBc/Hz at 100kHz offset from the 8GHz carrier. It also provides a synchronization bandwidth of 350MHz, thanks to a double synchronization network.

I. INTRODUCTION

Frequency synthesis is one of the most significant and critical RF function in telecommunication systems.

Nowadays, the main solution used to realize this function is the phase-locked loops (PLL) synthesizers. PLLs require circuits such as phase frequency detectors, charges pumps, loops filters and frequency dividers. To improve the RF performances of a local oscillator, an Injection Locked Oscillator (ILO) can be used in addition of a low frequency PLL. Thus, this ILO behaves as a frequency multiplier by using the pure low frequency signal generated by the PLL.

This system is called double-loop frequency synthesizer, as illustrated in Figure 1.

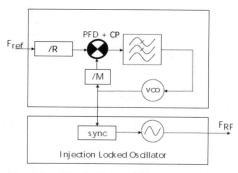

Figure 1.   The double-loop frequency synthesizer

The advantage of an ILO is its ability to detect an external signal and to synchronize its oscillation on it. It provides signals which frequency can be a sub-harmonic or a harmonic of this external signal. In our case, a 500MHz external signal is used to synchronize an 8GHz free running frequency oscillator [1]. The challenge is to realize the synchronization of an oscillator by its 16th sub-harmonic while reducing current consumption and silicon area.

This ILO has been realized in the framework of the SWANS European project, dedicated to the design of building blocks for sensors network.

The remainder of this article is as follows:

In Section II, the design of the ILO is discussed. Section III presents the implementation of the ILO in a VLSI 65nm CMOS from STMicroelectronics. Measurements results are reported in Section IV. Finally, conclusions are drawn in Section V.

II. CIRCUIT DESIGN

A. The ILO topology

As depicted in Figure 2, the 16th sub harmonic injection locked oscillator is based on a 2-differential negative resistance oscillators structure which free running frequencies are respectively 2GHz and 8GHz. The 2GHz oscillator receives the synchronization current pulses from an external 500MHz input signal (4th sub-harmonic of the 2GHz oscillator). When harmonics are included in the synchronization range of the oscillator, this latter is able to synchronize its frequency on that harmonic. The 2GHz differential output signals are modified by a pulse generator network in order to create the 2GHz synchronization currents. These pulses will drive the 8GHz oscillator, which frequency is the 4th harmonic of 2GHz. Thus, the overall injection locked oscillator provides 8GHz signals thanks to a 500MHz input signal synchronizing it on its 16th sub harmonic. Two output buffers (not represented on the figure 2) have been added in order to improve the slew-rate of the signals and to drive resistive and capacitive loads of RF pads.

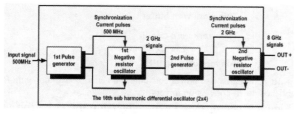

Figure 2.   The 16th sub-harmonic ILO architecture

B. Inductors Modeling

To control the two free running frequencies (2GHz and 8GHz), we have modeled and designed two integrated differential inductors with *Indentro* software. Classical negative resistance oscillators architecture need two serial integrated inductors to meet symmetry requirements. In the ILO topology, the two serial inductors are replaced by a differential symmetrical inductor for each oscillator of the system, in order to save silicon area.

The inductors values must be chosen very carefully in order to optimize the ILO synchronization bandwidth, which is the most important parameter for an injection locked oscillator.

We used 6nH inductor for the 2GHz oscillator and 1nH inductor for the 8GHz oscillator. The reason of these choices will be explained later. By including all properties of materials (dielectric and metallization layers) of 65nm CMOS technology in *Indentro*, we created a technological file that allows us to model and simulate inductors in terms of quality factor, values at working frequency and self resonating frequency, as shown in Figure 3 below.

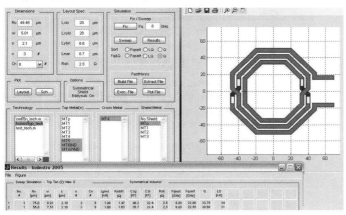

Figure 3. *Indentro* software for inductors modeling

The 65nm CMOS technology offers seven metallization layers excluding polysilicium and alucap layers. Coils of the inductors have been realized with the four upper metals (M5 up to M7 + Alucap) in order to reduce serial resistor.

C. Oscillators topology

The selected oscillator topology is a differential negative resistance oscillator as presented in Figure 4. This topology was chosen thanks to the large synchronization range that can be obtained and that is required for the ILO [2]. This oscillator is composed of a PMOS cross-coupled pair that provides voltage headroom to the architecture. It also reduces scattering effects, mismatching (thanks to differential configuration) and ultimately improves the synchronization.

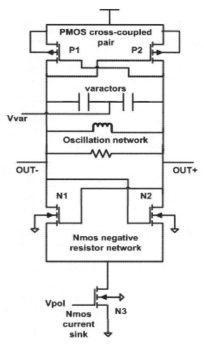

Figure 4. Oscillators topology

The oscillation network, with varactors, inductors (previously modeled) and parallel resistor, provides the free running frequencies of the 2GHz and 8GHz oscillators, according to the following theoretical formula (1):

$$f = \frac{1}{2\pi . \sqrt{L.C_{equ}}} \tag{1}$$

where L is the inductor value and C_{equ} is the overall capacitance value including transistors parasitic capacitors.

The process dispersions during wafer fabrication can affect the values of modeled inductors and as a result, the free running frequencies can be shifted. To prevent this phenomenon, we used for each oscillator two MOS varactors to guarantee oscillation frequencies.

Transistors N1 and N2 realize the negative resistor of the architecture. Transistor N3, used as a current sink, controls the current consumption of the differential oscillator through its gate voltage V_{pol}. The current consumption of each oscillator is about 2.5mA and the output differential amplitude voltage is 1.2V peak-to-peak.

D. Synchronization networks

In order to improve the synchronization efficiency, it is important to choose very carefully the capacitances values (lower values). Equation 2 shows that the synchronization range Δf is inversely proportional to this capacitance value. I_{sync} is the synchronization current while V_s is the output peak-to-peak amplitude. [3]

$$\Delta_f = \frac{I_{sync}}{2\pi . V_s . C_{equ}} \quad \text{with} \quad I_{sync} = \frac{I_o . \sqrt{2}}{n.\pi} \qquad (2)$$

The capacitor value must be as low as possible to improve the synchronization range. On the other hand, the inductor value must not be very high in order to minimize silicon area.

Therefore, there is a trade-off between the inductor and the capacitor values which both fix the free running frequency of the oscillator (1). Thus:

- for the 2GHz oscillator, we have chosen an inductor of 6nH and then, an overall capacitor of around 1pF (including all parasitic capacitors of transistors and varactors).

- for the 8GHz oscillator, we have chosen an inductor of 1nH leading to an overall capacitor of 395fF.

The two pulse generators that provide the synchronization current are built according to the "Design Oriented Delay" (DOD) principle. DOD is based on CMOS logic gates, inverters and NAND gates. These gates are used to realize the delays between the signals.

Figure 5 presents the architecture of the two pulse generators. To achieve an optimum synchronization range, it is necessary to carefully control the current pulses width. The current pulses width must be equal to half the period corresponding to the running frequency of the oscillator to be synchronized [4]. The 2GHz and 8GHz oscillators must be synchronized by opposite current pulses width of 250ps and 62.5ps respectively.

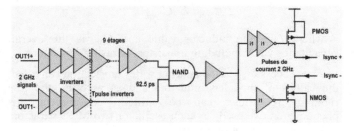

Figure 5.   Synchronization network architecture

A magnitude of 5mA (I_o) for current pulses can achieve a synchronization range of around 300MHz with free running differential oscillations amplitude of 1.2V (taking n equal to 16; see equation 2).

E. Output buffers

Two output buffers are required to drive the 50Ω resistors and the capacitors loads due respectively to the measurement system and the RF pads. These buffers are differential CML gates and dissipate 12mA under a voltage supply of 1.2V.

III.   IMPLEMENTATION

The ILO was fabricated by STMicroelectronics in a VLSI 65nm CMOS technology.

This advanced technology offers low power transistors and seven metallization layers excluding polysilicon.

We used 50Ω microstrip lines for single input and differential outputs interconnections.

Figure 6 depicts the microphotograph of the 0.6mm² (including pads) ILO die area.

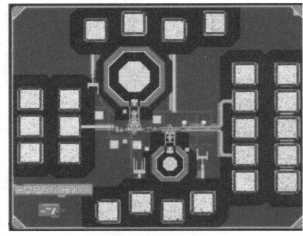

Figure 6.   ILO die photograph

IV.   MEASUREMENTS RESULTS

The 16th sub-harmonic injection locked oscillator was characterized by a Karlsuss Microtec probing tester. The test bench is also composed of an 8563E HP spectrum analyzer and an 83712B HP generator (for the 500MHz input signal).

The spectrum of the system output is presented Figure 7.

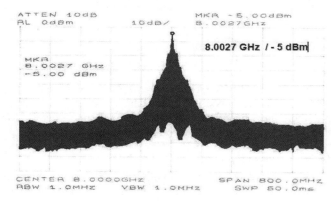

Figure 7.   Single output free running spectrum of ILO

The oscillator offers a power of -5dBm at 8GHz. There is no synchronization signal applied on the input of the system. The two oscillators work well and oscillate at frequencies close to their theoretical frequencies as expected. The dispersion of the modeled inductors value and parasitic capacitances create a little frequency shift. Thanks to the varactors of each oscillator, the outputs free running frequencies at 2GHz and 8GHz are achieved.

Applying the synchronization signal of 500MHz with 0dBm on the input of the system, the 8GHz fundamental ray is pure as shown on Figure 8 and all the oscillators are well synchronized.

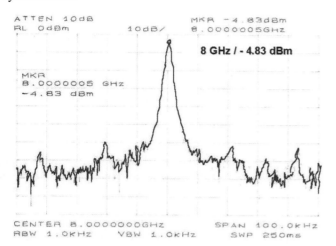

Figure 8. Single output synchronized spectrum of ILO

The ILO provides a measured synchronization range of 350MHz. This result is better than the synchronization range achieved in simulation (300MHz).

Figure 9 shows the plot of the synchronized phase noise versus the reference phase noise as a function of the frequency offset from the carrier.

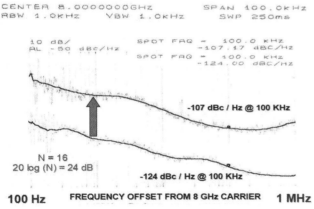

Figure 9. Synchronized phase noise of the ILO

In theory, the phase noise of an injection locked oscillator is linked to the reference signal phase noise with a factor of N, the rank of the sub-harmonic. In the case of this ILO design, N is equal to 16; hence, the synchronized phase noise plot of the ILO must follow the reference phase noise with a vertical shift of 2 dB, what is noticed in the figure 9.

The ILO exhibits a phase noise of -107dBm @ 100kHz offset from the 8GHz carrier, what is a quite good result for such an architecture.

V. CONCLUSIONS

An 8GHz 16th sub-harmonic Injection-Locked Oscillator was presented in this paper. Under a nominal voltage supply of 1.2V, the ILO dissipates 22.8mW for a synchronization range of 350MHz and a phase noise of -107dBc/Hz at 100kHz offset from the carrier. It provides a power level of -5dBm at 8GHz for a silicon area of roughly 0.6mm². This ILO meets the main requirements for SWANS European project and has been integrated in an whole transmitter.

VI. AKNOWLEDGMENT

The authors would like to thank Mathieu Koto, Birama Goumballa and Olivier Mazouffre of IMS Lab for design and layout support. We also wish to acknowledge STMicroelectronics Crolles for wafer fabrication.

REFERENCES

[1] V. Uzunoglu, M.H. White, "The Synchronous Oscillator: A Synchronization and Tracking Network", *IEEE Journal of Solid-State Circuits,* vol. SC-20, n°6, December 1985, pp.1214-1226.

[2] Y. Deval, J-B. Bégueret, A. Spataro, P. Fouillat, D. Belot and F. Badets, "HiperLAN 5.4 GHz Low-Power CMOS Synchronous Oscillator", *IEEE Trans. On Microwave Theory and Techniques*, vol.49, n°9, September 2001, pp. 508-513.

[3] F. Badets, Y. Deval, J-B. Bégueret, A. Spataro and P. Fouillat, "A 2.7 V 2.64 GHz Fully Integrated Synchronous Oscillator for WLAN Applications", *Proc. of the 25th European Solid-State Circuits Conf. (ESSCIRC 99)*, Duisburg, Germany, September 1999, pp. 508-511.

[4] P. Hellmuth, J-B. Bégueret, H. Lapuyade, O. Mazouffre, Y. Deval, "A 5.2GHz Tunable Synchronous Oscillator for IEEE 802.11a Applications", Proc. of the 2003 SBMO/IEEE MTT-S International Microwave and Optoelectronics Conference (IMOC2003), Foz do Iguaçú, Brazil, September 2003, vol. 1, pp. 153-156.

A 600-GHz CMOS Focal-Plane Array for Terahertz Imaging Applications

Ullrich R. Pfeiffer and Erik Öjefors

High-Frequency and Communication Technology
University of Wuppertal, Rainer-Gruenter-Str. 21, D-42119 Wuppertal, Germany
Email: ullrich@ieee.org and erik.ojefors@ieee.org

Abstract— A 600-GHz single-chip focal-plane array (FPA) has been fully integrated in a 0.25-μm CMOS process technology. The 3×5 array achieves a room temperature responsivity of 50 kV/W and a noise equivalent power (NEP) of 400 pW/$\sqrt{\text{Hz}}$. Each pixel comprises of an on-chip antenna, an NMOS incoherent power detection circuit based on resistive self-mixing, and a 43-dB amplifier with a 1.6-MHz bandwidth. The pixel size is 150×150 μm^2 and the overall array size is 680×980 μm^2 including bondpads. The circuit topology makes it possible to fully integrate terahertz focal-plane arrays for 600-GHz video-rate imaging applications in a low-cost CMOS process technologies for the first time.

I. INTRODUCTION

There is a vast amount of interest in millimeter-wave (mmWave) and terahertz applications today. Potential applications span across various scientific disciplines [1] and include radio astronomy, atmospheric sensing, medical diagnostics, biological research [2], label-free analysis of DNA molecules, wireless communication, radar [3], security screening, chemical and explosive detection. However, sensors and detectors that operate in the sub-millimeter wave band (300 GHz to 3 THz) have been a limiting factor for many applications in the past. Although great achievements have been made in terahertz science and technologies, detectors are often comprised of discrete components which are bulky and exhibit a low level of integration at high cost. Most terahertz images today are build up one pixel at a time, through raster scanning with single-point detectors or phased arrays. Therefore, a fully integrated CMOS focal-plane array is one of the key building blocks that will enable low-cost video-rate terahertz cameras in the future. It presents a crucial step towards the commercialization of terahertz imaging technologies.

Detection methods in this frequency range are commonly divided into two main categories: coherent detection and incoherent (direct) detection methods. Direct detectors have been around for many years and are based on the physical principle of energy/power absorption (calorimeters/bolometers [4], [5]), pneumatic detectors (Golay cell [6]), and square-law detectors (Schottky Barrier Diodes (SBDs) or transistor npn/FET non-linearities). Most of them are, however, incompatible with conventional microelectronics and require additional processing steps to be incorporated into today's semiconductor process technologies. Emerging detection principles include semiconductor nano-devices such as quantum dot arrays and plasma wave detectors [7]. Coherent detectors consist of heterodyne receivers often made of monolithic microwave integrated circuits (MMICs) [8]. The high cost of MMICs, however, limit the pixel count in a heterodyne receiver and the use of LNAs is typically limited to below 200 GHz in practical applications [3].

It is expected that future low-cost portable terahertz cameras will require sophisticated signal processing capabilities, paired with low power consumption and high sensitivity at room temperature. This fuels the growing interest in silicon integrated terahertz detectors. Promising low-cost alternatives include all electronic approaches, such as silicon SBD circuits with cut-off frequencies beyond 1 THz [9], SiGe hetero-junction bipolar transistors (HBTs) with cut-off frequencies as high as $f_{max}/f_T = 350/300$ GHz [10], and CMOS circuits reported at frequencies higher than 400 GHz [11].

In this paper the self-mixing of resistive mixers is used for incoherent (direct) power detection at 600 GHz, which is well above the used CMOS technologies cut-off frequency of $f_T = 35$ GHz. The detection principle has first been published in 1987 in discreet 10-500 MHz power detectors based on JFETs [12], and has been used later, for 0.1-3 GHz GaAs MESFET detectors in [13]. It is applied here to 600-GHz silicon integrated focal-plane arrays for the first time. The circuit architecture and the detection principle are described in Sec. II. Measured and simulation results are presented in Sec. III followed by the conclusions in Sec. IV.

II. CIRCUIT ARCHITECTURE AND DETECTION PRINCIPLE

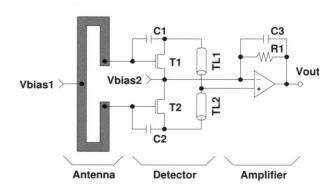

Fig. 1. Simplified single-pixel circuit schematic (R1=500 kΩ, C3=0.1 pF, C1 and C2=13 fF).

Self-mixing is usually unwanted and is caused by the parasitic FET gate-to-drain capacitance C_{gd}. It leads to dc-offset problems in resistive mixers as described in [14]. A resistive mixer converts a radio frequency (RF) signal applied at the drain of a FET to a lower frequency IF signal that is extracted through a low-pass filter. This is done while the local oscillator (LO) signal is used to modulate the conductance of a FET channel at the gate.

Unlike this, an incoherent (direct) power detection method is used in this paper as shown in Fig. 1. The 600-GHz RF input signal is received by an on-chip folded dipole antenna. It is then coupled from the gate to the drain of a differential FET structure (T1 and T2) via coupling capacitors (C1 and C2). Shunt transmission lines (TL1 and TL2) are used to tune out the reactance at the drains for maximum voltage swing and maximum self-mixing response. The detector is followed by an on-chip 43-dB amplifier with 1.6-MHz bandwidth. The amplifier is biased at ac-grounds through the common source contact of T1 and T2 to omit additional quarter-wave RF bias chokes. Similarly, the gate bias is applied at ac-grounds of the dipole antenna. The pixel circit draws 1.1 mA from a 5-V supply.

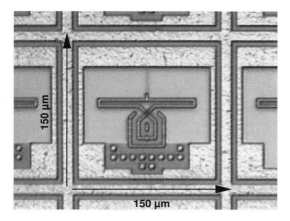

Fig. 2. Chip micrograph of one pixel showing the folded dipole antenna. The size of a pixel is 150×150 μm^2.

A chip micrograph of a single pixel including an on-chip dipole antenna is shown in Fig. 2. The chip was fabricated in IHP's 0.25-μm SG25 logic CMOS technology with an NMOS cut-off frequency of $f_T = 35$ GHz [15]. A five-layer aluminum back-end was used to implement antennas and low loss interconnects.

A. Expected Responsivity and Noise Considerations

The responsivity and NEP of a self-mixing FET detector can be analytically derived. For simplicity it is given here only for a single device in strong inversion ($V_{gs} > V_{th}$) and for a time-harmonic excitation. If an excitation voltage $v_{ds}(t)$ is applied over the drain source junction with zero V_{ds} bias (triode region), the drain current can be calculated as

$$i_{ds}(t) = v_{ds}(t)g_{ds}(t) = v_{ds}(t)\frac{W}{L}\mu Q_{ch}(t), \quad (1)$$

where $Q_{ch}(t) = C_{ox}(v_{gs}(t) - V_{th})$ is the time varying channel charge density and where W, L, and μ have their

usual meaning. Since the drain and the gate are connected through the capacitors, e.g. through C1 and C2, we obtain $v_{gs}(t) = V_g + v_{ds}(t)$ and for the drain current follows

$$i_{ds}(t) = \frac{W}{L}\mu C_{ox}(v_{ds}(t)^2 + v_{ds}(t)(V_g - V_{th})). \quad (2)$$

The dc-component of the drain current can be calculated for a time harmonic excitation of the form $v_{ds}(t) = V_{RF}\sin(\omega t)$ as

$$I_{ds} = \frac{W}{L}\mu C_{ox}(V_{RF}^2/2)). \quad (3)$$

This leads to the detected dc output voltage

$$V_{ds} = \frac{I_{ds}}{G_{ds}} = \frac{V_{RF}^2}{2(V_g - V_{th})} \quad (4)$$

and the expected responsivity is

$$R_v = \frac{V_{ds}}{P_{in}} = \frac{\frac{V_{RF}^2}{2(V_g - V_{th})}}{V_{RF}^2/R_{in}} = \frac{R_{in}}{2(V_g - V_{th})}. \quad (5)$$

For example, this yields a responsivity of 250 V/W with a detector input impedance of $R_{in} = 50$ Ω and $V_g - V_{th} = 0.1$ V. With a 43-dB voltage gain the responsivity increases to 35 kV/W. Note that the responsivity is only limited by the modulation speed of the channel charge density, and hence, the detection principle works well in the terahertz frequency range even in 0.25-μm CMOS process technologies. To the first order, it is not transit-time limited and only limited by the FET parasitic RC time constant.

The noise equivalent power (NEP), which is defined as the minimum power for unity signal-to-noise-ratio with a detector time constant of 1 s, is only limited by the thermal noise of the channel conductance G_{ds}. Since the channel of the NMOS detector is not dc-current biased, the noise spectral power density at the drain output terminal is $N_0 = 4k_BT/G_{ds}$ and the NEP follows as

$$\text{NEP} = \frac{\sqrt{N_0}}{R_v} = \sqrt{\frac{16k_BT}{R_{in}^2\frac{W}{L}\mu C_{ox}}(V_g - V_{th})}. \quad (6)$$

The self-mixing is predicted by the available BSIM device models and can be simulated from strong inversion to the sub-threshold region. See Sec. III for a model-to-hardware comparison.

B. On-chip Antenna Design

Previously published silicon-integrated terahertz dipoles have used high-resistivity substrates [16]. In this work, a 90-μm long dipole antenna was implemented directly in a standard low-resistivity (50-Ωcm) process technology and losses were minimized by placing the main radiator in the top-metal conductor of the back-end process. A folded dipole increases the antenna impedance at resonance by a factor of four [17] and provides a higher RF voltage for the FET power detector. It also provides a symmetry point (ac-ground) through which the FET gate bias can be applied. The antenna was designed and simulated using the 3D EM solver package HFSS, where a 200 μm thick 50-Ωcm conductor-backed silicon substrate was assumed. At 606 GHz the impedance is $100 - j75\ \Omega$ with an approximate bandwidth of 50 GHz. The simulated directivity is 7 dBi yielding a 5-dBi gain including losses.

C. Focal-Plane Array Configuration

The pixels were arranged in a 3×5 array with $150\times150\ \mu$m pitch (0.0225 mm^2 area per pixel). See Fig. 3 for a chip micrograph. With the resolution limit being $\lambda_0/2$, the aperture is oversampled unless a dielectric lens is used. The outputs of neighbour pixels can be combined by the readout electronics to improve the sensitivity if required.

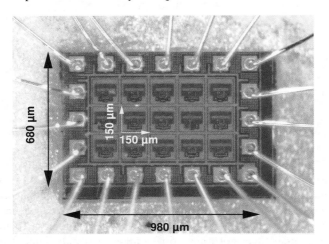

Fig. 3.   Chip micrograph of the 3×5 focal-plane array. Its size is $680\times980\ \mu$m^2 including bondpads.

Each antenna element has an effective area A_{eff}, which can be calculated as

$$A_{\text{eff}} = D\frac{\lambda_0^2}{4\pi}, \tag{7}$$

where D is the directivity of the radiator. This leads to a single-pixel antenna area of 0.1 mm^2 for a simulated 7-dBi directivity in the broadside direction. Note that the physical area of a pixel is smaller than the antenna area, and hence, the effective antenna areas overlap. Because of this, the available power per pixel is calculated as the physical area times the irradiance produced by the source.

III. Measured Results

Fig. 4 shows the measurement setup for responsivity and noise characterization. A 16.83-GHz source was AM modulated with a 16-kHz square-wave and multiplied by 36 to generate a pulsed 606-GHz signal with a peak power of 1.124 mW. The purpose of the AM modulation is to facilitate detection in the prescence of a dc-offset and a $1/f$ noise floor. A 22-dBi (estimated) horn antenna was used to illuminate the FPA with an intensity of 18.3 μW/mm^2 at a distance of 3 cm. The intensity was calculated from the measured radiation pattern, where the surface integral was normalized to the total power available from the source. The intensity in the center of the beam was verified using Friis transmission equation for the 22-dBi horn antenna at a 3 cm distance. This leads to an available power per physical pixel area of 0.4 μW. A lock-in

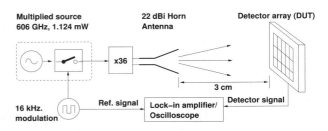

Fig. 4.   Measurement setup.

amplifier (LIA), tuned to the modulation frequency of 16 kHz, was used to measure the pixel output voltage and noise level. The pixel output waveform captured with an oscilloscope is

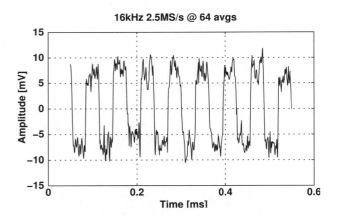

Fig. 5.   Captured pixel output waveform at 2.5 MSamples/s with an average of 64 traces. The 16-kHz square-wave modulated 606-GHz signal had a power density of 18.3 μW/mm^2 (0.4 μW/pixel).

shown in Fig. 5. It is sampled with 2.5 MS/s over 16 sweeps while it was illuminated with a 16-kHz square-wave modulated 606-GHz signal. In typical video applications a band-pass filter is used around the modulation frequency to improve the signal-to-noise-ratio accordingly. The responsivity, defined as the ratio between the detected voltage and the power available per pixel, is shown in Fig. 6 as a function of the FET dc bias voltage V_{gs}. The measured peak responsivity is 50 kV/W at a 350-mV V_{gs} bias. Note that this is below the 500-mV FET threshold voltage. The simulated peak responsivity is 90 kV/W and its shape and peak position correlates well with the measurements. The minor signal reduction can partly be explained by EM-modeling inaccuracies of the antenna, and the fact, that the device and parasitic models are used outside their specified frequency range.

Measured and simulated NEPs are shown in Fig. 7 versus V_{gs}. The measured minimum NEP (400 pW/$\sqrt{\text{Hz}}$) is slightly higher than the simulated NEP (150 pW/$\sqrt{\text{Hz}}$) due to a lower measured responsivity. Simulations show that the minimum NEP without amplifier drops to about 60 pW/$\sqrt{\text{Hz}}$ (not shown). Note that the V_{gs} bias differs for minimum NEP and maximum R_v. This is caused by a higher channel conductivity which improves the resistive noise voltage but degrades the responsivity R_v.

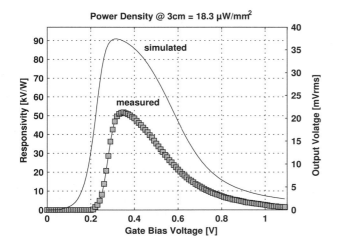

Fig. 6. Measured and simulated pixel responsivity (R_v) at 606 GHz versus the FET V_{gs} bias voltage. The power density was 18.3 μW/mm^2 (0.4 μW/pixel).

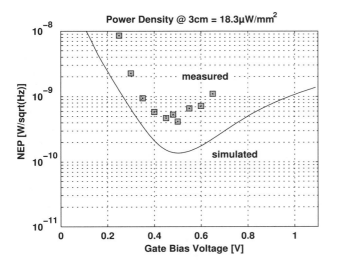

Fig. 7. Measured and simulated pixel NEP at 606 GHz versus the FET V_{gs} bias voltage. The power density was 18.3 μW/mm^2 (0.4 μW/pixel).

IV. CONCLUSION

A 3×5 600-GHz single-chip focal-plane array (FPA) has been presented. The FPA has been fully integrated in a 0.25-μm CMOS process technology. The array achieves a room temperature responsivity of 50 kV/W and a noise equivalent power (NEP) of 400 pW/$\sqrt{\text{Hz}}$ at 16 kHz. This performance is comparable with that of commercially available Golay cells (200-400 pW/$\sqrt{\text{Hz}}$, 45-10 kV/W @ 10-70 Hz [6]). The simulated minimum NEP of the detector without on-chip amplifier is about 60 pW/$\sqrt{\text{Hz}}$. The FPA is not thermal-time-constant limited and allows for a large modulation bandwidth of 1.6 MHz. As such, it will enable video-rate imaging applications at 600 GHz in a low-cost CMOS process technologies and leads to the construction of terahertz cameras which makes terahertz imaging practical for a wide range of high-profile applications.

ACKNOWLEDGEMENTS

The author would like to thank the IHP GmbH, Frankfurt-(Oder), Germany, for chip fabrication and the European Heads of Research Councils (EuroHORCs) and the European Science Foundation for partial funding of this work through an European Young Investigator Award. Many thanks also go to Peter Haring Bolívar, University of Siegen, Germany, and Hartmut Roskos, University of Frankfurt, Germany, for usefull discussions. Special thanks go to Francesco Voltolina and Gunnar Spickermann, University of Siegen, Germany, for measurement and wire-bonding support.

REFERENCES

[1] P. de Maagt, P. H. Bolivar, and C. Mann, "Terahertz science, engineering and systems – from space to earth applications," *Encyclopedia of RF and Microwave Engineering, Ed. by K. Chang, John Wiley & Sons, Inc.,* ISBN 0-471-27053-9, pp. 5175–5194, 2005.

[2] A. Markelz, "Terahertz dielectric sensitivity to biomolecular structure and function," *IEEE J. of Selected Topics in Quantum Electronics,* vol. 14, no. 1, pp. 180–190, Jan.-feb. 2008.

[3] H. Essen, A. Wahlen, R. Sommer, W. Johannes, R. Brauns, M. Schlechtweg, and A. Tessmann, "High-bandwidth 220 GHz experimental radar," *Electronics Letters,* vol. 43, no. 20, pp. 1114–1116, September 27 2007.

[4] S. Eminoglu, M. Tanrikulu, and T. Akin, "A low-cost 128 × 128 uncooled infrared detector array in CMOS process," *Journal of Microelectromechanical Systems,* vol. 17, no. 1, pp. 20–30, Feb. 2008.

[5] P. Helisto, A. Luukanen, L. Gronberg, J. Penttila, H. Seppa, H. Sipola, C. Dietlein, and E. Grossman, "Antenna-coupled microbolometers for passive THz direct detection imaging arrays," *European Microw. Conf.,* pp. 35–38, 10-13 Sept. 2006.

[6] QMC Instruments Ltd, "OAD-7 Golay detector operating manual," 4th Jan 2005.

[7] M. Dyakonov and M. Shur, "Plasma wave electronics: novel terahertz devices using two dimensional electron fluid," *IEEE Trans. Electron Devices,* vol. 43, no. 10, pp. 1640–1645, Oct 1996.

[8] W. Deal, L. Yujiri, M. Siddiqui, and R. Lai, "Advanced MMIC for passive millimeter and submillimeter wave imaging," *IEEE Int. Solid-State Circuits Conf.,* pp. 572–622, 11-15 Feb. 2007.

[9] U. Pfeiffer, C. Mishra, R. Rassel, S. Pinkett, and S. Reynolds, "Schottky barrier diode circuits in silicon for future mmWave and THz applications," *IEEE Trans. Microw. Theory and Tech.,* vol. 56, no. 2, pp. 364–371, Feb. 2008.

[10] M. Khater et. al., "SiGe HBT technology with $f_{max}/f_t = 350/300$ GHz and gate delay below 3.3 ps," *IEEE Int. Electron Devices Meeting,* pp. 247–250, Dec. 2004.

[11] E. Seok, C. Cao, D. Shim, D. J. Arenas, D. B. Tanner, C.-M. Hung, and K. K. O, "A 410 GHz CMOS push-push oscillator with an on-chip patch antenna," in *IEEE Int. Solid-State Circuits Conf.,* 2008, pp. 472–473.

[12] R. A. Barett, "Broadband RF detector using FET," US Patent 4 647 848, 1987.

[13] H.-G. Krekels, B. Schiek, and E. Menzel, "Power detector with GaAs field effect transistors," in *European Microw. Conf.,* 1992, pp. 174–179.

[14] S. A. Maas, "A GaAs MESFET mixer with very low intermodulation," *IEEE Trans. Microw. Theory and Tech.,* vol. 35, no. 4, pp. 425–429, 1987.

[15] B. Heinemann, R. Barth, D. Knoll, H. R"ucker, B. Tillack, and W. Winkler, "High performance BiCMOS technologies without epitaxially-buried subcollectors and deep trenches," *Semicond. Sci. Technol.,* vol. 22, pp. 153–157, 2007.

[16] C. Dietlein, J. Chisum, M. Ramirez, A. Luukanen, E. Grossman, and Z. Popovic, "Integrated microbolometer antenna characterization from 95-650 GHz," *IEEE MTT-S Int. Microw. Symp. Dig.,* pp. 1165–1168, 3-8 June 2007.

[17] R. Lampe, "Design formulas for an asymmetric coplanar strip folded dipole," *IEEE Trans. Antennas Propag.,* vol. 33, no. 9, pp. 1028–1031, 1985.

Single-Photon Synchronous Detection

Cristiano Niclass, Claudio Favi, Theo Kluter, Frédéric Monnier, and Edoardo Charbon
Ecole Polytechnique Fédérale de Lausanne
CH-1015 Lausanne
SWITZERLAND

Abstract[1]—**A novel imaging technique is proposed for fully digital detection of phase and intensity of light. A fully integrated camera implementing the new technique was fabricated in a 0.35μm CMOS technology. When coupled to a modulated light source, the camera can be used to accurately and rapidly reconstruct a 3D scene by evaluating the time-of-flight of the light reflected by a target. In passive mode, it allows building differential phase maps of reflection patterns for image enhancement purposes. Tests show the suitability of the technique and confirm phase accuracy predictions.**

I. INTRODUCTION

Evaluation of intensity and phase of an impinging ray of multi- or monochromatic light has shown its usefulness in a number of applications. One of the first applications of phase-based imaging has been historically optical rangefinding, where the time-of-flight (TOF) of a reflected ray of light is computed from the phase difference between an outgoing and an incoming optical signal. Traditionally, the evaluation of the phase of a light source is performed using techniques similar to homodyne and heterodyne receivers in radio frequency systems. In these devices the incoming radio signal is replaced with the impinging optical signal and the local oscillator with an electrical or optical signal synchronized with the outgoing modulated light source. The two signals are mixed and low-pass filtered, generally *in situ*, to obtain an intermediate frequency or baseband signal proportional to the phase difference between outgoing and incoming light.

Both CCD and CMOS implementations of this technique exist and have been commercially available for some time now [1],[2],[3],[4]. In these devices pixel-level mixing is performed during a light modulation cycle by selectively redirecting photocharges that are partially in and out of phase onto different locations for accumulation. In this approach, carrier selection and accumulation is limited by the relatively slow diffusion process below the photogate, thus limiting the time resolution of the measurement in each modulation cycle. In addition, due to the small number of charges in play in each cycle, generally millions of cycles are necessary to achieve reasonable phase accuracy. Consequently, the accumulation process may last tens of milliseconds to tens of seconds before TOF can be determined.

Several techniques have been proposed to increase the time resolution up to a few nanoseconds in CCDs [5] and in

CMOS [6]. However, all these methods still suffer from the fact that the phase signal is analog and thus it needs amplification and A/D conversion on a pixel-by-pixel basis. As a result, several sources of noise and non-idealities are present and may be severe. Moreover, in this approach background illumination can in principle be eliminated by virtue of the fact that it appears as a common-mode signal across the differential signal of each detector. However, when saturation is reached, the differential signal begins to compress, causing background effects to resurface and contrast to be slashed.

In this paper we propose a fully digital, multi-pixel phase detection method based on single-photon avalanche diodes (SPADs). We call this method single-photon synchronous detection (SPSD). In this method, a photon detected by a SPAD triggers a digital pulse that is accumulated in a digital counter. The charge redirection of conventional methods is replaced with a simple demultiplexer. Different locations for accumulation are replaced with as many independent counters. The phase can thus be computed by a simple manipulation of the counter outputs at the end of the accumulation period.

There are several advantages of SPSD if compared to conventional modulation based phase detection methods. First, the time resolution of a partial phase measurement during a modulation cycle is far superior, since it is dominated by the time resolution of a SPAD, typically a few tens of picosecond [7]. Thus, in principle a much smaller number of cycles are sufficient to achieve the same overall phase accuracy. Second, due to the digital nature of the phase measurement, no errors are introduced during the accumulation period, except for unavoidable Poisson noise. Moreover, the lack of amplification and A/D conversions removes quantization errors and the usual non-idealities associated with these components. Third, saturation is inherently prevented by detecting overflow in the counter and thus stopping accumulation on a pixel basis. This method, unlike global saturation control techniques (such as e.g. [3]), is both simple and accurate, and can be performed entirely digitally. Finally, the device is amenable to implementing multiple access techniques to enable coexisting rangefinding systems in close proximity based, for example, on FDMA or CDMA [9].

A camera implementing the proposed SPSD technique was fabricated in a 0.35μm CMOS technology. The camera comprises an array of 60x48 85x85μm² fully scalable pixels. Unlike recent implementations of SPAD arrays operating based on the TCSPC technique [8], the SPSD camera takes

[1] This work was supported by a grant in the framework of the Innovation Network initiative from EPFL (Innogrant).

advantage of full pixel parallelism. Thus in principle, no photons impinging upon the detector area are lost, if separated by at least the dead time of a SPAD. The camera was tested on a TOF rangefinder setup yielding an resolution of approximately 3.3cm with a frame rate of 22fps. The light source was achieved by sinusoidal modulation of an array of LEDs operating at 30MHz with a mean optical power of 800mW.

II. SINGLE-PHOTON SYNCHRONOUS DETECTION

The SPSD technique, introduced in [9] and described in detail in [10], involves the demodulation of the phase shift an optical signal experiences when travelling from source to target and back to the sensor. Figure 1 shows the basic setup involved in a solid-state 3D imager based on SPSD. It consists of a periodically modulated light source, typically a sine wave, used to illuminate the objects in front of the 3D image sensor, imaging optics, a band-pass filter used to block background light, and a single-photon image sensor comprising pixel-wise demodulation circuitry.

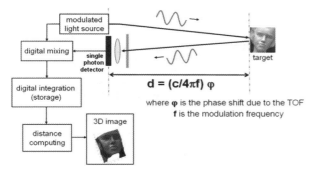

Figure 1. Solid-state 3D imaging setup based on the SPSD technique.

Thanks to the digital nature of single-photon detectors, phase demodulation may be achieved digitally. It involves a digital mixing operation with a reference signal, shared by the illumination source, and integration over a high number of cycles. Conveniently, these operations are implemented in a SPSD sensor by means of a demultiplexer (or a switch), driven synchronously with the reference signal, that connects the single-photon detector to two or more counters. When a photon is detected, depending on its arrival time with respect to the reference signal period, it increments a given counter. As a high number photons are detected, the contents of the counters follow a distribution that reproduces the optical signal waveform, over one reference period. Based on these values, it is possible to determine the phase, amplitude and offset of the optical signal.

In order to unambiguously demodulate the signal phase, at least, three counters are theoretically necessary. Practically, it is possible however to use only two counters and generate four samples. Figure 2 shows an example of illumination and demodulation waveforms, as adopted in this work. The sensor operates in an interlaced detection scheme based on two acquisition phases. In the first acquisition phase, the pixel-level demultiplexer switches between two counters so as to generate two samples, C_0 and C_{180}, corresponding to 0° and 180° of phase with respect S_{MOD}. Once these two samples are acquired and readout, the sensor operates in the second acquisition phase, in which S_{MOD} is delayed by a quarter of period with respect to the reference signal. As a result, the same in-pixel counters are used to acquire samples C_{90} and C_{270}, corresponding to 90°

and 270° of phase. Note that, although only two counters are used, the demodulation circuit does not miss any photon detection, unless the counter maximum value is reached.

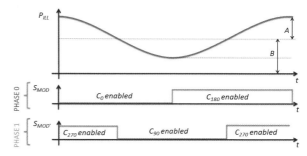

Figure 2. Incident optical signal and demodulation waveforms.

Once the four samples are acquired, the amplitude A, offset B, and phase φ are determined as

$$A = \frac{\sqrt{(C_{270} - C_{90})^2 + (C_0 - C_{180})^2}}{2}, \qquad (1)$$

$$B = \frac{C_0 + C_{90} + C_{180} + C_{270}}{4}, \qquad (2)$$

$$\varphi = \arctan\left(\frac{C_{270} - C_{90}}{C_0 - C_{180}}\right). \qquad (3)$$

Although φ is the most important result for a TOF rangefinder, A and B also carry interesting pixel information. A may be conveniently used to determine whether a pixel signal, in a given acquisition frame, has a sufficiently strong amplitude so as to be considered as a reliable measurement. Indeed, pixel signals with negligible amplitude could be simply disregarded. B may also be used to compute intensity images.

Theoretically, in Equations (1)-(3), all the four samples $\{C_i\}$ are assumed to be acquired simultaneously. When the objects in the scene are not static, the acquisition of four samples based on two counters may suffer from augmented motion artifacts. In order to solve this problem, the acquisition of C_0/C_{180} and of C_{90}/C_{270} should be interlaced at frequency sufficiently high that moving objects appear static and thus affects all $\{C_i\}$ simultaneously. Note that conventional motion artifacts may persist depending on the actual frame rate achieved by the image sensor.

III. IMAGE SENSOR ARCHITECTURE

The image sensor proposed in this work takes advantage of a fully digital realization, from photon detection to depth imaging. A simplified block diagram of the image sensor is shown in Figure 3. It consists of an array of 60x48 single-photon pixels, each one comprising its own SPSD demodulation circuit based on two 8-bit counters. The sensor also includes a bias generation circuit, a JTAG controller for testing/characterization purposes, and a readout circuit. The readout circuit is based on a controller that allows the image sensor to operate autonomously, only requiring a clock signal. The pixel matrix area is divided in 8 blocks, each one consisting of 8x48 pixels and being handled by an independent readout block. The first and last readout blocks handle six active and two blocked columns each. A decoder, driven by the readout controller, selects a row. In that row, a pipelined sequence of readout and reset is achieved in the 8 blocks in parallel, thanks to the 8 digital output buses of 16 bits implemented. In each row, the readout sequence is operated as follows. The first pixels in all the 8 blocks are read out, then, when the second pixels in all the blocks are read out, the first ones are simultaneously reset to zero. When the readout circuit finishes reading out the eighth pixels in all the blocks, it spends one additional cycle to reset them, before switching to the next row. As a result, 9 cycles of clock are necessary to read out and reset a full row. Since the sensor comprises 48 rows, the full frame rolling readout requires exactly 432 cycles. Note that in each readout cycle a digital signal, IDX[8:0], indicates the address of the pixels in the blocks that are currently being read out, and that each 16-bit bus outputs the contents of the two in-pixel counters simultaneously.

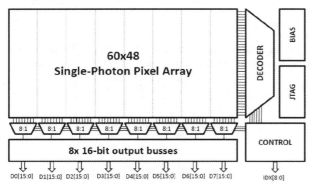

Figure 3.   Block diagram of the image sensor. The sensor consists of a 60x48 pixel array, a JTAG controller, and a fast parallel readout circuitry.

The readout circuit was designed to run at a clock frequency of up to 40MHz. At that frequency, a frame acquisition and readout takes 10.8µs. This time is short enough to be used in the interlaced acquisition of C_0/C_{180} and C_{90}/C_{270}, thus preventing motion artifacts as described previously. Moreover, since a pixel may be read out and reset in only 10.8µs, its 8-bit counters hardly ever reach their maximum values, assuming a dead time of 40ns.

IV.   SINGLE-PHOTON PIXEL

A.   Front-end Circuit

Single-photon detection with high timing resolution is achieved by means of a SPAD detector, whose performance characterization was reported in [11]. This device was carefully designed for the 0.35µm CMOS technology used in this work. Its front-end circuit involves 8 MOS transistors that perform passive quenching and active recharge. Figure 4 shows the schematics of the complete pixel circuit. Active quenching is achieved by adequately choosing two different thresholds for the inverter and nor gates [10]. At the inverter output, a digital inverted pulse reflects the detection of a photon. Its leading edge, i.e. high-to-low transition, accurately indicates the arrival time of the photon.

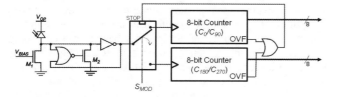

Figure 4.   Pixel circuit comprising front-end and digital demodulation. Passive quenching and active recharge ensures higher dynamic range with little impact on pixel size. Fully digital implementation enables noise-free demodulation and readout.

B.   Demodulation Circuit

As shown in Figure 4, the demodulation circuit consists of a 2:1 demultiplexer driven by a global signal S_{MOD}, synchronized with the light source, and two 8-bit counters. Each counter has a parallel tri-state output bus and a signal, OVF, indicating that the next increment would result in an overflow state. The OVF signals of both counters are combined, via an OR gate, to block the demultiplexer in a state in which neither counters could be incremented. Once one counter reaches its maximum value, the pixel is blocked until the next readout and reset operation.

V.   EXPERIMENTAL RESULTS

The fabricated image sensor, shown in Figure 5, has a surface of 6.5x5.5 mm^2.

Figure 5.   Photomicrograph of the SPSD image sensor. The circuit, fabricated in 0.35µm CMOS technology, has a surface of 6.5x5.5mm^2. The pixel pitch is 85µm.

As can be seen in the picture, the pixel matrix area occupies most of the integrated circuit area. Global distribution of S_{MOD} is implemented symmetrically, from a pad in the center of the top part of the padring. The image sensor was then mounted on a custom prototype of a camera, based on a FPGA for data interface and USB controller to provide a link with any PC, shown in Figure 6. An additional board comprising 48 NIR LEDs emitting at 850nm wavelength was mounted on the front face of the prototype. The LEDs provided a 30MHz sine wave illumination with an average optical power of 800mW and with a field-of-view of 50°.

Figure 6.   3D camera prototype based on SPSD.

The single-photon sensor was first characterized in terms of its main source of noise, i.e. dark count rate. Figure 7 shows the distribution of DCR over all the pixels in the array. As can been seen, most of pixels exhibit a DCR of a few hundred Hertz, thus leading to a typical temporal noise contribution of a few tens of Hertz. The median value was 245Hz while the average DCR showed to be higher, at 1261Hz, due to a small number of defected pixels, similarly to [8]. In our scheme these pixels may be ignored with no interference to surrounding pixels.

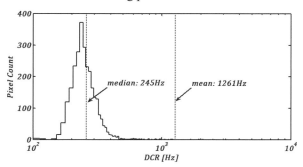

Figure 7. Distribution of DCR over 60x48 pixels under nominal V_E of 3.3V and at room temperature.

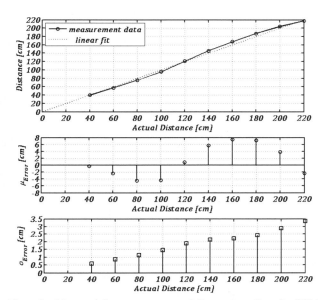

Figure 8. Measured distance versus actual distance, non-linearity (INL) and repeatability errors (1σ). Measurements based on an integration time of 45ms, i.e. 22fps.

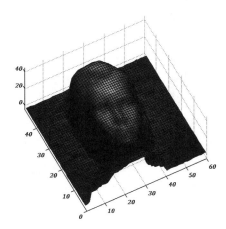

Figure 9. Experimental 3D image of a human-sized mannequin acquired with an integration time of 500ms.

The prototype was also evaluated with respect to its ranging capability. A flat panel was used as a target and displaced over a range of about 2.2m, starting at a distance of 40cm, so as to determine measurement linearity. Figure 8 shows the experimental results compared to the actual target distance. In the picture, integral non-linearity (INL) and 1σ

repeatability errors were also plotted as a function of distance. Relatively high INL was obtained due to third harmonic distortion in the illumination waveform, which resulted in aliasing effects through the SPSD demodulation based on four samples per period [10].

A 3D image of a human-sized mannequin was captured with the setup, using an integration time of 500ms. The model was placed at a distance of 1m from the prototype. A summary of performance parameters and operating conditions is given in Table I.

TABLE I.   SUMMRY OF PERFORMANCE PARAMETERS

Name	Value	[Unit]
Image resolution	60x48	-
Median DCR	245	Hz
Pixel dead-time	40	ns
Imaging lens f-number	1.4	-
Illumination central wavelength	850	nm
Narrowband optical filter width	40	nm
Illumination frequency	30	MHz
Illumination field-of-view	50	°
Illumination average power	800	mW
Resolvable distance range	5	m
Integration time	45	ms
Maximum distance INL up to 2.2m	7.4	cm
Maximum 1σ distance resolution at 2.2m	3.3	cm
Maximum ASIC feasible framerate[a,b]	46296	fps

a. assuming a complete SPSD demodulation per frame
b. currently not achieved due to prototype limitations

REFERENCES

[1] R. Miyagawa and T. Kanade, "CCD-Based Range-Finding Sensor", *IEEE Trans. on Electron Devices*, Vol. 44, N. 10, pp. 1648-1652, Oct. 1997.

[2] R. Lange, "3D Time-of-Flight Distance Measurement with Custom Solid-State Image Sensors in CMOS/CCD-Technology", Ph.D. Dissertation, ETH-Zürich, Switzerland, 2000.

[3] S. Kawahto, I. A. Halin, T. Ushinaga, T. Sawada, M. Homma, Y. Maeda, "A CMOS Time-of-flight Range Image Sensor with Gates-on-field-oxide Structure", *IEEE Sensors Journal*, 2007.

[4] B. Buxbaum, R. Schwarte, T. Ringbeck, M. Grothof, and X. Luan, "MSM-PMD as Correlation Receiver in a New 3D-Imaging System", in U. Schreiber, C. Wener, G. W. Kamerman, and U. N. Singh, Eds., Proc. *SPIE*, Vol. 4546, pp. 145-153, Jan. 2002.

[5] R. Büttgen, "Extending Time-of-Flight Optical 3D-Imaging to Extreme Operating Conditions", Ph.D. Dissertation, Univ. of Neuchatel, Switzerland, 2007.

[6] C. Bamji and E. Charbon, "Methods for CMOS-Compatible Three Dimensional Image Sensing using Quantum Efficiency Modulation", U.S. Patent 6,515,740, Feb. 2003.

[7] C. Niclass and E. Charbon, "A CMOS Single Photon Detector Array with 64x64 Resolution and Millimetric Depth Accuracy for 3D Imaging", *Intl. Solid-State Circuit Conference (ISSCC)*, pp. 364-365, Feb. 2005.

[8] C. Niclass, C. Favi, T. Kluter, M. Gersbach, E. Charbon, "A 128x128 Single-Photon Imager with on-Chip Column-Level 97ps 10bit Time-to-Digital Converter Array", *Intl. Solid-State Circuit Conference (ISSCC)*, pp. 44-45, Feb. 2008.

[9] C. Niclass, "Method and arrangement for measuring the distance to an object", U.S. Patent Application 182,949, 2007.

[10] C. Niclass, "Single-Photon Image Sensors in CMOS: Picosecond Resolution for 3D Imaging", Ph.D. Dissertation No. 4161, EPFL, Switzerland, 2008.

[11] C. Niclass, M. Sergio, E. Charbon, "A single-photon avalanche diode array fabricated in 0.35μm CMOS and based on an event-driven readout for TCSPC experiments", APCT Conference, SPIE Optics East, Oct. 2006.

Highly Sensitive UV-Enhanced Linear CMOS Photosensor

Daniel Durini, Erol Özkan, Werner Brockherde, Bedrich J. Hosticka
Fraunhofer Institute of Microelectronic Circuits and Systems (IMS)
Finkenstraße 61, D-47057 Duisburg, Germany
daniel.durini@ims.fraunhofer.de

Abstract☐ **This contribution describes a highly sensitive UV-enhanced linear CMOS photosensor which exhibits very low noise. The sensor features on-chip readout and control electronics, global synchronous shutter, programmable spectral responsivity, clock-independent variable integration time, two different acquisition modes, selectable region-of-interest readout, and a binning capability. The device has been designed and fabricated in the 0.5μm standard CMOS process available at the Fraunhofer IMS.**

I. INTRODUCTION

Many industrial applications require linear photosensors which exhibit high sensitivity and low noise. Recent advances in CMOS imaging enable design and fabrication of such sensors in standard CMOS technology at low cost, while enabling a complete cointegration of accompanying sensor electronics on the same chip. For several spectroscopy and other similar applications where CMOS photosensors are to be used, one of the main requirements is a sufficient optical sensitivity also in the UV part of the spectra (λ=250nm-400nm). The main goal in this kind of applications is not to create a digital image but to be able to detect an impinging radiation and measure its exact irradiance value in the optical spectrum ranging from UV to NIR. Although not pursuing a UV-blue light selective photodiode (PD) [1], but a photodiode with UV-enhanced quantum efficiency and acceptable values of quantum efficiency (η) for the entire spectra, several n^+ (NMOS *source/drain* implantation) PD and n-well PD based strip photodetectors were investigated in detail and compared. Based on the obtained results, a UV-enhanced linear CMOS photosensor has been designed and fabricated.

II. UV-ENHANCED STRIPE PHOTODETECTORS

The main problem in this application is the radiation absorption depth in the range between the 5.4nm (for λ=250nm) and 105nm (λ=400nm) depth [2]. The idea is to use photodiode stripes to be able to collect the carriers photogenerated within and below each PD stripe, but also at the silicon surface between the stripes, specially if the space-charge region (SCR) of neighboring PD stripes overlap so that no loss in the collected charge appears due to recombination. The four test structures fabricated for this purpose in the 0.5μm standard CMOS process available at the Fraunhofer IMS, were: 1) 10 interconnected 1mm long and 5μm wide n-well PD stripes, with a 5μm edge-to-edge distance; 2) and 3) the same photodetector stripes (5μm wide and with a 5μm edge-to-edge distance) fabricated using n^+ PD structures with and without field-oxide (FOX) isolation between the stripes, respectively; and 4) 8×10 n^+ PD based photodetector stripes connected in series, 1mm long, 0.6μm wide, with a distance of 0.6μm between the neighboring stripes. To avoid heavy absorption in the UV and blue/green part of the spectra, the original silicon nitride based passivation layer used in this process was replaced by a phosphosilicate glass (PSG) one which is practically transparent for radiation at these wavelengths. The layouts generated using *Cadence®* software tools, together with the electric field simulation results obtained after the first (n-well PD) and the last (0.6μm wide n^+ PD) test structures were simulated using the (*ISE-Synopsys*) TCAD software, and are shown in Fig. 1.

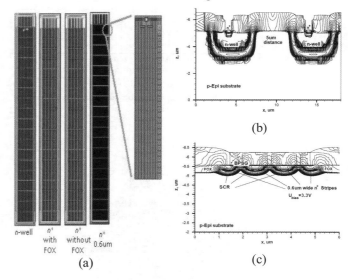

Figure 1. (a) Layout of the four test structure sets fabricated in the 0.5μm CMOS process for UV-enhanced quantum efficiency investigation; (b) 2-D electric field simulation of the n-well based stripe photodetector under V_{DD}=3.3V reverse biasing; (c) 2-D electric field simulation of the 0.6μm bright n^+ PD based reverse biased stripe photodetector [3].

The electric field simulation results shown in Fig. 1(b) suggest that the 5μm distance between the neighboring n-well PD based stripes is insufficient for their SCR to overlap, if reverse biased at V_{DD}=3.3V. On the other hand, from Fig. 1(c) it can be concluded that the 0.6μm wide n^+ PD based stripes do generate slightly overlapping SCRs when reverse biased at 3.3V. All four test structure sets fabricated were then electrically characterized. Considering the C-V and I-V curves [3] obtained at room temperature, the values listed in Table 1 were determined after a proper statistical analysis was performed of the measured data.

Photodetector Type	Capacitance V_{bias}=1V	Capacitance V_{bias}=3.3V	Dark Current V_{bias}=1V	Dark Current V_{bias}=3.3V
n-well Stripes	14.7pF	11.2pF	1.22pA	2.44pA
n^+ Stripes with FOX	28.6pF	21.5pF	0.53pA	1.2pA
n^+ Stripes without FOX	32.8pF	24.9pF	0.53pA	1.34pA
n^+ Stripes 0.6μm Edge-to-Edge Distance	54.5pF	40.1pF	0.57pA	1.35pA

Table 1. Electrical properties of the 4 photodetector test structures investigated.

The optical sensitivity and quantum efficiency measurements were also performed on all 4 test structures, using a Xe/Hg 1000W lamp based illuminator followed by a monochromator, results of which can be seen in Fig. 2 [3]. From Fig. 2 can be concluded that although the 0.6μm wide n^+ PD based stripe photodetector generates slightly overlapping SCRs between the neighboring stripes, its optical sensitivity and quantum efficiency performances in the UV part of the spectrum are poorer than those of the 5μm wide n^+ PD based stripes, although much better than those obtained from a (300x300)μm² n^+ single area PD. Also, the n^+ PD based stripes without the field-oxide isolation yielded a better performance than those with the field oxide structures between the stripes, as the "bird's beak" oxides penetrate the n^+ diffusion and diminish its effective depth as well as the SCR width generated beneath it, as it can be observed in Fig. 1(c) for the two n^+ stripes on the extremes.

From these results it can be concluded that the amount of photogenerated carriers lost due to recombination processes is much lower within the n-well or the n^+ diffusions than it is on the surface of the p-type epitaxial layer (or p-well) existent between the PD stripes. That also explains why 5μm wide n^+ PD based stripes had better quantum efficiency performance than the 0.6μm wide ones.

For the case of the n-well PD based linear photodetector, there was no difference in the quantum efficiency measured between the stripe photodetector and the (300x300)μm² single-area one, and it yielded the best optical sensitivity performance of all four test structure sets, with 55% quantum efficiency under λ=330nm of impinging radiation (and 10% for λ=910nm) as well as the lowest capacitance (Table 1).

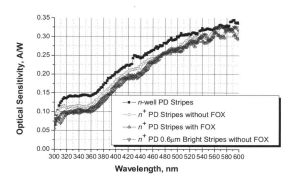

(a)

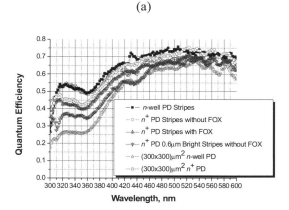

(b)

Figure 2. (a) Wavelength dependent optical sensitivity for the 4 test structure sets; and (b) wavelength dependent quantum efficiency curves for the four UV-enhanced stripe PD test structure sets compared to the quantum efficiency curves obtained from (300x300)μm² n-well PD and n^+ PDs.

The higher amount of dark current (2.44pA) is here compensated by its superior optical sensitivity performance. So, this stripe photodetector was selected for the application of interest. A simplified cross-section diagram of this detector can be found in Fig. 3. For this particular application, 3584 individual 5μm wide and 1mm long stripe photodiodes have been employed.

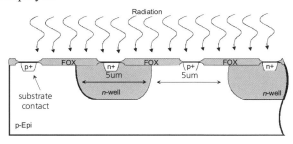

Figure 3. Cross-section of the chosen n-well PD based stripe photodetector structure fabricated in the 0.5μm standard CMOS process.

III. READOUT PRINCIPLE

The readout principle of the linear sensor is based on temporal integration of the photocurrent generated by each individual photodiode stripe. Here, each operational amplifier based individual integrator is followed by an amplifier performing both, a *correlated double sampling* (CDS) operation and an additional amplification.

A simplified circuit of the integrator used in this application is depicted in Fig. 4(a). Here, the important feature is the use of a capacitive feedback *T-network* which generates a very small effective feedback capacitance. This is essential for achieving a high output voltage at low photocurrents. The network works as a capacitive divider which attenuates the voltage across the integration capacitance, thus making this capacitance effectively smaller. The effective integration capacitance of the integrator shown in Fig. 4(a) can be theoretically expressed as shown in Eq. (1) without considering parasitic capacitances.

$$C_{int,1,2,3} = \frac{C_{int,1} \cdot C_{int,2}}{C_{int,1} + C_{int,2} + C_{int,3}} \quad (1)$$

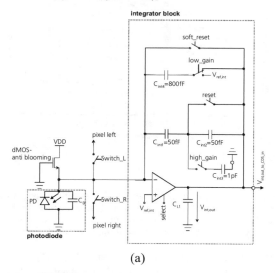

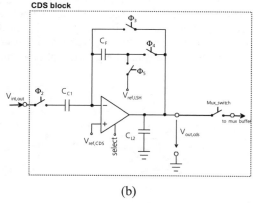

(b)

Figure 4. Schematics of the: (a) integrator block; (b) CDS block.

Table 2 shows that for the photodetector used we obtain three different gain settings due to different feedback capacitance combinations. For the high gain setting, the measured effective integration capacitance results somewhat larger than the calculated one, mainly due to parasitic capacitances not considered in the theoretical calculation.

Operation mode	Low-gain switch	High-gain switch	Reset-switch
$C_{int\,1,4}$=850fF	ON	OFF	ON
C_{int1}= 50fF	OFF	OFF	ON
$C_{int\,1,2,3}$ =4fF	OFF	ON	OFF

Table 2. Switch states for different integration capacitance values.

IV. CIRCUIT DESIGN

Figs. 4(a) and 4(b) depict the photocurrent integrator and the CDS amplifier, respectively. As described above, the integrator features three capacitors in the feedback loop to provide three different gain factors. These enable three different operational modes with different total responsivities of the photosensor. The responsivity values are determined by the three feedback capacitors present in the integrator block of the readout circuit, observed in Fig. 4(a), namely $C_{int1,2,3}$=4fF, C_{int1}=50fF, and $C_{int1,4}$=850fF, where $C_{int1,4}= C_{int1}+C_{int4}$. These values correspond to high, medium, and low gain settings, respectively. In Table 2 the switch states for each feedback capacitor are shown. Using the two binning switches, the *Switch_L* and the *Switch_R* shown in Fig. 4(a), two photodiode areas instead of a single one can be used, so that the total responsivity turns higher by a factor of two if compared to the case when only one photodiode is used. For blooming compensation, i.e. to avoid the effect of a single pixel photogenerated charge exceeding its saturation level and penetrating the adjacent pixels, an extra anti-blooming transistor has also been implemented in each pixel.

During a soft reset cycle, all capacitors are discharged to the voltage equivalent to the integrator offset voltage. After that, only one of the three feedback capacitors is connected, while the other capacitors remain in the reset condition. At the end of the simultaneous integration of the photocurrent being performed for all stripe photodiodes, using the selected feedback capacitor the charge accumulated at the selected capacitor is directly read out as voltage $V_{int,out}$ and stored at the load capacitor C_{L1} (Fig. 4(a)).

Offset and low-frequency noise caused by each pixel structure can be reduced by the CDS operation. Here, each pixel output is read out twice: once right after the reset operation, and a second time at the end of the integration cycle. The sample quantified after the reset is then subtracted from the one obtained after integration. The CDS amplifier holds the readout voltage sample obtained from each pixel throughout the soft reset phase to enable the time multiplexing operation of the output signals of the entire sensor (Fig. 4(b)).

V. LINEAR CMOS PHOTOSENSOR ARRAY

The integrator and the CDS blocks enable two different acquisition modes, namely the RAI (readout after integration) on one hand, and the MNRDI (multiple non-destructive readout during integration) on the other. In RAI mode, the pixel signals are simultaneously stored at the corresponding feedback capacitors of the integrator, and read out after the integration sequence. In MNRDI mode, the non-destructive multiple readout of the pixel data is performed during the integration process.

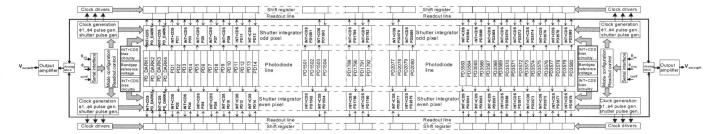

Figure 5. Block diagram of the linear photosensor array.

The multiple global synchronous shutter signal in this application can either be applied externally, or generated by the internal sensor electronics. The sensor also features programmable responsivity using three gain settings, as described above. The low, medium, and high gain settings yield a responsivity of 92, 1452, and 5500 V/W/m², respectively, for 625nm wavelength and integration time of 10ms.

The integration time can be varied independently of the clock frequency. An additional on-chip dark signal channel and temperature compensation are also implemented. The 120fA of dark current are delivered per each pixel without dark current compensation. With activated dark current suppression, the effective dark current is reduced to below 1fA per stripe PD. The sensor uses a single 3.3V power supply voltage, an external clock (up to 12 MHz) signal, and a configuration pin for readout mode setting.

Parameter	Value
Resolution (active pixels)	1 x 3580
Pixel size (µm x µm)	10 x 1000
Spectral range (nm)	250 - 1000
On-chip shutter	Synchronous
Reset	Synchronous
Max. clock rate (MHz)	12
Dynamic range (dB)	54
Fill factor (%)	98
Dark current per pixel (fA)	120
FPN (%)	2.4
Responsivity (V/W/m²)	1452
Noise eq. power (µW/m²)	2.75
Noise eq. exposure (pJ/cm²)	2.75
Image lag (%)	<1
Saturation irradiance (mW/m²)	1.45
Output swing (V)	2.1
Power consumption (mW)	580
Supply voltage (V)	3.3

Table 3. Measured parameters of the linear photosensor array (conditions: T_A=25°C, wavelength λ=625nm, T_{int}=10ms, medium gain setting).

The complete photosensor including the n-well photodiode stripe array, the readout control, the analog biasing, and the signal conditioning has been implemented on a (45.6×7)mm² chip, operational block diagram of which can be found in Fig. 5. Table 3 shows the measured optical and electrical parameters obtained at room temperature, the medium gain setting (C_{int1}=50fF), and 625nm wavelength of impinging

radiation when working with 10ms integration time. The UV optical sensitivity between the 250nm and 300nm wavelengths were verified in the application. The photograph of the photosensor is shown in Fig. 6. Fig. 6(a) shows the photodetector alone, while in Fig. 6(b), the entire photosensor placed in a ceramic package can be seen.

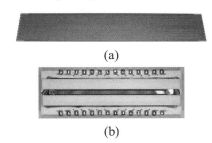

(a)

(b)

Figure 6. Photographs of (a) the fabricated linear photosensor array; (b) the same photosensor in a ceramic package.

VI. CONCLUSIONS

The linear CMOS photosensor featuring high responsivity, low dark current, and low noise has been presented. The complete readout control, the analog biasing, and signal conditioning are implemented on the chip fabricated in 0.5µm standard CMOS technology. Four different photodetector stripe test structures were simulated, fabricated, and characterized, which proved the n-well PD stripe photodetector to yield the best optical sensitivity performance in the UV-blue part of the spectra, also presenting the lowest capacitance, although a slightly increased dark current. The strong UV radiation absorbent silicon nitride based passivation layer has been replaced here by a UV transparent phosphosilicate glass (PSG) based one.

ACKNOWLEDGEMENT

The authors thank Armin Kemna and the wafer-fab team for their contributions to this undertaking.

REFERENCES

[1] A. Pauchard, P. A. Besse, R. S. Popovic, "A Silicon Blue/UV Selective Stripe-Shaped Photodiode", *Sensors and Actuators A, Physical*, vol. 76, 1999, pp. 172-177

[2] S. M. Sze, *Semiconductor devices. Physics and technology*, 2nd Edition, John Wiley & Sons, USA, 2002

[3] D. Durini, *Solid-State Imaging in Standard CMOS Processes*, Ph.D. thesis, University of Duisburg-Essen, 2008

A 3-TFT Hybrid Active-Passive Pixel with Correlated Double Sampling CMOS Readout Circuit for Real-Time Medical X-ray Imaging

N. Safavian, K.S. Karim
Electrical and Computer Engineering Department,
University of Waterloo
Waterloo, Ontario, N2L3G1, Canada
Email: nsafavia@engmail.uwaterloo.ca
kkarim@uwaterloo.ca

A. Nathan[1] and J. A. Rowlands[2]
1- London Center for Nanotechnology,
University College London
London, WC1HOAH, UK
2-Sunnybrook Health Science Centre,
University of Toronto
Toronto, Ontario, M4N3M5, Canada

Abstract- **This paper presents a new hybrid current-programmed, current-output active pixel sensor (APS) suitable for real time x-ray imaging (fluoroscopy) and an off-panel CMOS readout circuit. The pixel circuit is designed using hydrogenated amorphous silicon (a-Si:H) thin film transistor (TFT) technology. Measurements show that the proposed pixel circuit can successfully compensate for characteristic variations (e.g. mobility and threshold voltage shift) in a-Si:H TFTs under prolonged gate voltage stress. The readout circuit exploits correlated double sampling (CDS) technique to reduce the offset current, low frequency noise and fixed-pattern noise (FPN) on the array operation. Measurements show less than 5% change in the output current of the APS for 3V shift in the threshold voltage.**

I. INTRODUCTION

Active matrix flat panel technology based on a-Si:H TFTs has been extensively applied to digital x-ray diagnostic medical imaging. The technology has several desirable attributes such as uniformity, low temperature fabrication and economical advantage. The active matrix used for addressing and readout consists of many pixels each responsible for efficient transfer of collected charge to the external readout electronics. The collected charge is proportional to the x-ray radiation and can be obtained by both direct and indirect conversion methods [1]. So far, the most widely used and simplest circuit topology for each pixel is the passive pixel sensor (PPS) [2]. Although the PPS topology offers a very compact circuit, it is a destructive scheme which does not permit multiple readouts to reduce noise and is incapable of *in situ* signal amplification. As a result, the pixel dynamic range is relatively poor. To cope with this problem a 3-TFT active pixel sensor (APS) has been previously presented [3]. Although this pixel circuit provides on-pixel amplification, it does not completely compensate for the threshold voltage shift in the a-Si:H TFTs caused by their inherent instability [4].

In this paper, new hybrid 3-TFT current programmed APS pixel circuit suitable for real-time x-ray imaging along with the corresponding CMOS current-mode readout circuit suitable for performing CDS are presented. The pixel circuit extends the application of a-Si:H TFT from conventional switching element to on-pixel amplifier for enhanced signal-to-noise ratio and higher imager dynamic range. The capability of operation

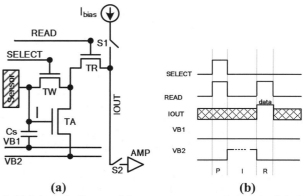

Fig. 1: (a) Schematic diagram of the current programmed pixel circuit in the active mode and (b) the corresponding programming waveforms.

in both passive and active modes as well as being able to compensate for inherent instabilities of the TFTs makes the architecture a good candidate for x-ray imaging modalities with a wide range of incoming x-ray intensities. By exploiting CDS technique in the current mode transresistance amplifier, input referred offset currents in the order of few nanoamps and settling times bellow 15μsec were achieved. Measurements show less than 5% change in the output current of the APS for 3V shift in the threshold voltage.

II. PROPOSED PIXEL OPERATION

The pixel circuit presented in Fig. 1(a) contains three TFTs (TA, TR and TW) coupled to the x-ray sensor. Using the pixel circuit in the active mode, TA is the amplifying TFT while TR and TW act as switches. Following the timing diagram displayed in Fig. 1(b), the pixel circuit operation can be described as follows. During the programming cycle (P), S1 is connected and the SELECT and READ control line signals turn on the switching TFTs TR and TW. Consequently the pixel is selected and in the steady state, the whole of constant bias current I_{bias} passes through TR and TA. In this cycle, when the steady state is reached, the current flowing through TW approaches zero and the diode-connected TFT, TA, will be biased in saturation region

$$I_{bias} = \frac{K_{TA}}{2}\left(VI - V_{B2} - VT_{TA}\right)^2 \qquad (1)$$

Here, K_{TA}, VI and VT_{TA} are the gain parameter, gate voltage and the threshold voltage of TA, respectively. After programming, both TR and TW are turned off. The storage capacitor C_S holds the previously established voltage value on the integration node (I). During the integration cycle, the photo-carriers caused by incident x-ray photons change the voltage at node I by ΔV_I

$$\Delta V_I = \frac{qN_h}{C_S}, \qquad (2)$$

where N_h is the total number of holes accumulated on C_S. In the readout cycle, S2 connects the output of the pixel (IOUT) to the off panel CMOS amplifier (AMP). The output current change of the common-source structure incorporating TA and TR as a result of charge integration across Cs is approximately equal to

$$\Delta I_{out} = g_{m-TA} \times \Delta V_I, \; g_{m-TA} = 2\sqrt{K_{TA}I_{bias}} \qquad (3)$$

Here, g_{m-TA} is the transconductance of TA. For exposure ranges in fluoroscopy, the corresponding small signal voltage, ΔV_I, is much smaller than $2(V_I-VT_{TA})$ and therefore usage of small signal model is justified.

Fig. 2(a) demonstrates the configuration of the pixel circuit in passive mode. By disabling TA, the circuit resembles that of a PPS structure to be used in high intensity modalities such as digital radiography [1]. In this mode, voltage levels that turn off TA are applied through VB1 and VB2 (Fig. 2(b)). If the readout operation is carried out through a low input impedance amplifier, the readout charge of the storage capacitor developed during integration and the reset of this capacitor are achieved simultaneously.

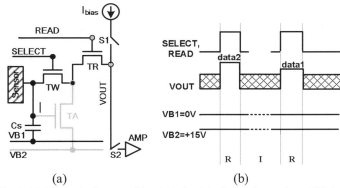

(a)   (b)

Fig. 2: (a) Schematic diagram of the pixel circuit in the passive mode and (b) the corresponding programming waveforms.

III. CMOS READOUT CIRCUIT

Fabricated transistors suffer from threshold-, mobility-, and geometry-induced mismatch effects as well as the low frequency 1/f noise resulting in dc offset and limiting the minimum detectable signal level [5]. To alleviate these problems, devices with large active areas are chosen for input stages because threshold voltage and mobility mismatches and 1/f noise are inversely proportional to the size of the device. However, to achieve input-referred offset currents in the range of few nano amps without sacrificing a large die area, dynamic offset-cancellation circuit techniques such as correlated double sampling CDS are usually employed. The CDS principle can be used to reduce the offset and low-frequency noise of the on-pixel amplifiers and off-panel readout circuits [6].

A simplified schematic of the proposed low offset approach is shown in Fig. 3. The method is based on a feedback loop. A second generation current conveyor topology (CCII) constitutes the forward amplifier of the feedback loop while the feedback network is comprised of a transconductance amplifier (i.e., g_m), two offset cancelling capacitors (i.e., C_{h1} and C_{h2}) and the clock signal φ. The input voltages V_{ref1} and V_{ref2} are used as virtual ac grounds. V_{ref1} determines the voltage across the low input resistance terminal of the transresistance amplifier and V_{ref2} is used as the reference for the amplifier's output voltage, V_{out}.

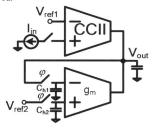

Fig. 3: Block diagram of the Transresistance Amplifier with offset compensation.

A. Offset Cancellation

Assuming that the capacitors C_{h1} and C_{h2} are initially discharged, the total input referred offset current of the amplifier originates mainly from the input offset current of the CCII and the input offset voltage of the g_m amplifier

$$I_{off-TOT} = I_{os} + g_m V_{os} \qquad (4)$$

Here, I_{os} is the input offset current of the CCII, V_{os} is the input offset voltage of the transconductance amplifier and g_m represents the gain of the transconductance amplifier. During the offset cancellation phase [Fig. 4(a)], the low resistance terminal of the CCII is disconnected from the signal path and the transconductance amplifier connected in unity-gain configuration. The voltage stored in the capacitor C_{h1} becomes

$$V(C_{h1}) = \frac{I_{os} \times R_{out} + (V_{ref2} + V_{os}) \times g_m R_{out}}{1 + g_m R_{out}} \approx \frac{I_{os}}{g_m} + (V_{ref2} + V_{os}) \qquad (5)$$

where R_{out} accounts for the total resistance at the amplifier's output node and $g_m R_{out}$ is the loop gain which is designed to be much larger than one. In the amplification phase, the input current data is connected to the CCII and the two switches connected to the storage capacitors are turned off, breaking the unity gain feedback loop. The previously stored voltage values remain across the storage capacitors except a small change, V_{inj}, due to charge injection and clock feed through errors of S1 and S2.

$$V(out) = \left[I_{in} + I_{os} + V_{ref2} + (V_{os} + V_{inj} - V(Ch1)) \times g_m \right] R_{out}$$

$$= \begin{bmatrix} I_{in} + I_{os} + V_{ref2} + (V_{os} + V_{inj}) \times g_m \\ -(\frac{I_{os}}{g_m} + (V_{ref2} + V_{os})) \times g_m \end{bmatrix} R_{out} \qquad (6)$$

$$\approx \left[I_{in} + V_{inj} \times g_m \right] R_{out}$$

In the above formulae it is postulated that the CCII, conveys the current to its output terminal with unity gain. Therefore, this method effectively reduces the offset currents and voltages at the inputs of the basic amplifier and the feedback network. Therefore, the input referred offset after the cancellation phase is limited by V_{inj} and can be alleviated by increasing the size of storage capacitors, C_{h1} and C_{h2}, at the differential input of the g_m amplifier. This method not only reduces offset of the off-panel amplifier, but also suppresses the low frequency noise of both the on-pixel amplifier and the

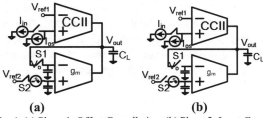

(a)   **(b)**

Fig. 4: (a) Phase 1: Offset Cancellation, (b) Phase 2: Input Current Amplification.

off-panel CMOS readout circuit.

B. Circuit Realization

To realize the current amplifier scheme utilizing CDS, the circuit in Fig. 5(a) is proposed. The class AB current conveyor (CCII) exhibits a current following action between the input node (X) and the output node (V_{OUT}) and a voltage following action between Y and X. It is comprised of transistors M1-M16, current sources I_{b1} and I_{b2} and two opamps (opamp(N) and opamp(P)) with nMOS and pMOS input differential pairs, respectively. The current source I_{in} represents the current data coming out of the pixel circuit in different modes of operation. The amplifiers opamp(N) and opamp(P) are standard two-stage, Miller-compensated opamps. The input terminals of opamp(N) are virtually short-circuited. Therefore it equates the drain voltages of M15 and M16 causing significant reduction in channel-length modulation related errors. Its other role is to provide bias for the cascading pMOS, M9. The same argument

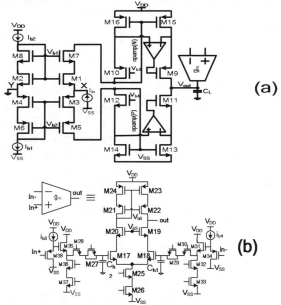

Fig. 5: (a) Proposed CCII transresistance amplifier and its offset cancellation transconductance stage, (b) Implementation of the transconductance (*gm*) stage.

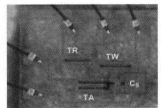

Fig. 6: Micrograph of a fabricated APS pixel circuit with a-Si:H TFTs

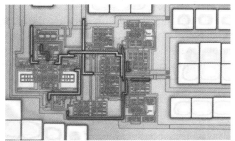

Fig.7: Die photomicrograph of the CMOS current amplifier

applies to opamp(P) and the devices M13, M14 and M11. The cascading devices M9 and M11 are added to the upper and lower branches to boost their respective output impedances resulting in overall increase in the output impedance of the current conveyor. The transconductance stage (g_m) used in the offset cancellation process is realized by the single-ended differential cascode topology to achieve high output impedance as shown in Fig. 5(b).

IV. EXPERIMENTAL RESULTS

Prototypes of the pixel circuit were fabricated with an in-house tri-layer inverted-staggered amorphous silicon TFT process. Plasma enhanced chemical vapor deposition (PECVD) is used for deposition of a-SiN (300 nm thick), a-Si:H, and passivation layers at a temperature of 300 °C. Fig. 6 shows a photomicrograph of a fabricated pixel circuit. The circuits were then diced and packaged. The transresistance amplifier was fabricated in a 0.35 μm CMOS technology. Fig 7 shows a die photomicrograph of the transresistance amplifier. The TFT pixel circuit, the transresistance amplifier and auxiliary circuitry were assembled on a printed circuit board. Discrete capacitors were used to emulate the effect of parasitic capacitance of the lines on the transient response of the pixel circuit. Fig. 8 demonstrates successful compensation for threshold voltage shift of TA for a programming current of 8.5 μA. The (W/L) of TA, TR and TW are 400μm/23 μm, 200μm/23μm and 200μm/23μm, respectively. The size of the storage capacitor is 2pF. For 3V V_T shift in TA, the relative change in the output current is less than 5%. To emulate the x-ray sensor a voltage source with amplitude varying from 14.5V to 15.5V is connected to the integration node (I) through capacitive coupling. The voltage gain is shown in the inset of Fig. 8, confirming that the pixel circuit maintains a relatively constant gain across a wide dynamic range of input signals.

In the current amplifier, the offset error originates primarily from mismatch of the transistors used to create current mirrors and the input stage. Fig. 9 shows the effectiveness of the offset cancellation scheme. Assuming that the bias current of 50μA flows in the input stage, the circuit is subjected to ±10% of this

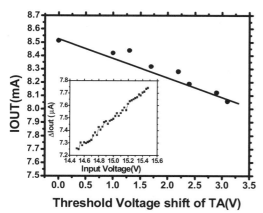

Fig. 8: Measured output current as a function of TA threshold voltage shift; the dynamic range is shown in the insert.

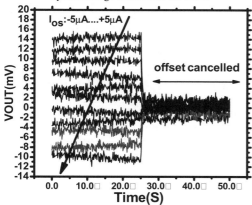

Fig. 9: Offset-cancellation functionality for the input offset current ranging from -5µA to +5µA.

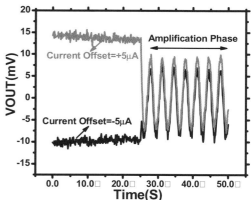

Fig. 10: Successful offset cancellation followed by amplification of the signal I_{in}=10nAsin(2π×300KHz×t).

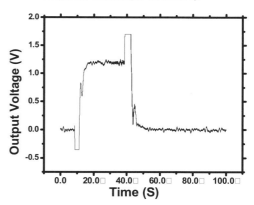

Fig. 11: Measured Transient output response of the transresistance amplifier to a 1µA input current pulse.

value as the input referred current offset. The first 25µs shows the output of the circuit during the offset cancellation phase and the second one demonstrates the timing response of the offset free circuit to the input signal. It is seen that the offset varying from -11mV to 15mV in the first phase is reduced to within 2mV or equivalently an input referred offset current of 2.4nA for the transresistance gain of 0.84MΩ. Fig. 10 is the transient output voltage response of the transresistance amplifier to the desired input current signal with the amplitude and frequency of 10nA and 300KHz, respectively superimposed on offset currents of ±5µA, showing the effective offset cancellation and amplification at the first and second phases of operation. Fig. 11 shows the measured output voltage transient response to a current pulse input with the amplitude of 1 µA during amplification phase. As can be seen, the output voltage of the transresistance amplifier settles to its final value in less than 12µsec.

V. CONCLUSION

A hybrid 3-TFT pixel circuit suitable for large area medical x-ray imaging along with a transresistance amplifier for the off-panel readout in the active mode has been proposed, designed and implemented. The presented pixel circuit can operate in active and passive readout modes, covering a wide range of incident x-ray intensities and therefore is an excellent candidate for incorporation in flat panels used in both

fluoroscopy and radiology imaging modalities. The feedback based offset cancellation scheme employed in the transresistance amplifier decreases the input referred offset and noise to the levels acceptable for precise detection of the signals generated by on-pixel TFT amplifiers. We show that current biasing is able to provide less than 5% change in the operating current of the APS for 3 V shift in the threshold voltage. The signal readout can be achieved in less than 12µs with 2.4nA input referred offset current making the scheme amenable towards low dose real time medical imaging.

REFERENCES

1. Eds. J. Beutel, H. L. Kundel, "Handbook of Medical Imaging, Physics and Psychophysics", SPIE 2000.
2. N. Safavian, J. Lai, J. A. Rowlands and A. Nathan., "Threshold voltage shift compensated active pixel sensor array for digital x-ray imaging in a-Si technology", IEE Electronics Letters, 2005, 41, Issue 7, pp. 411 – 412.
3. K. S. Karim, A. Nathan, J. A. Rowlands, "Amorphous Silicon Active Pixel Sensor Readout Circuit for Digital Imaging", IEEE Transactions on Electron Devices, 2003, 50, No. 1, pp. 200- 208.
4. P. Servati, S. Striakhilev, and A. Nathan, "Above-threshold parameter extraction and modeling for amorphous silicon thin film transistors," IEEE Trans. Electron Devices, 2003, 50, pp. 2227-2235.
5. H. P. Forghani-Zadeh, G. A. Rincon Mora, "A Programmable 210µV Offset Rail-to-Rail Gm–C Filter" , IEEE Transactions on Circuits and Systems-I, Vol. 54, No. 8, August 2007.
6. C. Enz and G. Temes, "Circuit technique for reducing the effects of circuit imperfections," *Proc. IEEE*, vol. 84, no. 11, pp. 1586–1614, Nov. 1996.

On-chip Jitter and Oscilloscope Circuits Using an Asynchronous Sample Clock

J. D. Schaub, F. H. Gebara, T. Y. Nguyen, I. Vo, J. Peña, D. J. Acharyya

IBM Austin Research Lab
11501 Burnet Road
Austin, TX
schaubj@us.ibm.com

Abstract□ We demonstrate digital circuits for measuring the jitter histograms of gigahertz clock and data signals. The circuits do not require calibration, and an asynchronous sampling technique alleviates the need for an on-chip sample clock generator with delay control. We combine measurements across swept reference voltages to create statistical clock signal and eye diagram waveforms at 6GHz and 5Gbit/s, respectively. The proposed technique produced RMS jitter measurements of 2.0ps on clock signals and 6.2ps on random data signals.

Keywords: jitter, oscilloscope, sub-sampling, and CMOS

I. INTRODUCTION

The amount of off-chip data transfer from high performance processors has grown beyond a terabit per second [1]. Jitter characterization of clock and data signals is critical for debug and model-to-hardware correlation, but measurement of each signal using external test equipment is impractical due to the sheer number of links and the difficulty in driving the signal to the instrument without distortion. An on-chip measurement solution would resolve these issues, but the circuits must provide good resolution with minimal area in order to be distributed around the die.

Jitter characterization of clock signals often involves comparing the input against a reference signal or a delayed version of itself (self-trigger). Ishida described a self-trigger technique for measuring period jitter using a phase frequency detector, charge pump, and digital delay line [2]. The 0.18μm circuits required a two-step calibration for measurement at a fixed frequency of 2.0GHz. Jenkins demonstrated 0.13μm circuits in which the input passed through both a fixed and variable delay to the data and clock inputs of a single latch [3]. After calibration of the analog delay line, the method achieved a resolution of 0.4ps. While both techniques provide good resolution, the calibration step is impractical for distributed use, and neither method can measure jitter on random data signals.

To characterize the jitter of data signals, on-chip oscilloscope circuits can be used. These are often implemented using sample and hold (SAH) circuits, an analog-to-digital converter (ADC), and a sample clock generation circuit. The design of the sample clock generator is particularly troublesome, since oscilloscope measurements often require both a wide timebase range and a fine timing resolution. A tradeoff between these two parameters is often encountered, and creative techniques such as phase interpolating delay lines [4] or dual delay locked loops [5] are used. These circuits are expensive in terms of area, design complexity and calibration. In [6], we reported the use of an asynchronous clock scheme with a SAH and external ADC for measurement of high-speed data patterns and eye diagrams. The SAH circuit required calibration, and an external oscilloscope was used as an ADC.

In this paper, we propose jitter characterization using a sub-Nyquist, asynchronous sample clock combined with digital comparators. The technique works for both clock and random data signals, and the asynchronous clock choice alleviated the need for a sample clock generator. The comparators provide simplified data conversion. The data are post-processed to produce statistical jitter histograms, and both clock and random data waveforms are synthesized from consecutive measurements at different reference voltages. Measurements indicate timing resolutions of 2.0ps for clock signals and 6.3ps for pseudo-random data signals.

II. PROPOSED SAMPLING TECHNIQUE AND CIRCUIT BLOCKS

A. Sampling technique

Traditional clock and data jitter measurement techniques involve creating a sample clock from either the system clock or a synchronous trigger signal. Alternatively, an asynchronous sample clock can be used to sweep the sample time across a clock edge or a unit time interval without having to generate the sample clock on-chip. The effective time at which each sample was taken can be re-constructed if the relationship between the system clock and the sample clock is known or can be derived from the sample data.

This work was supported under government contract NBCH3039004.

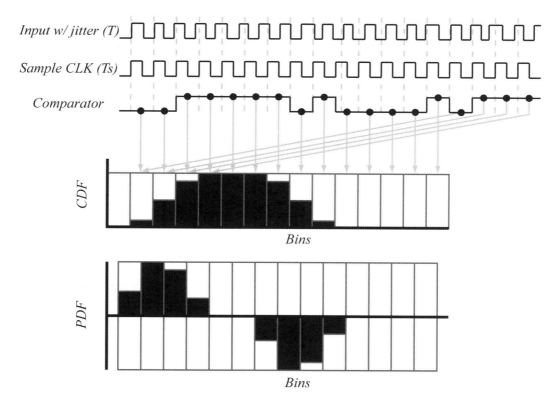

Figure 1. Illustration of effective timebase and sample binning for calculation of jitter histogram on clock signals.

This asynchronous technique, applied to jitter measurement of a clock signal, is illustrated in Fig. 1. At the rising edge of each sample clock, the input signal is compared against the reference voltage. Each subsequent sample effectively sweeps across the period of the input clock. The samples from the comparator are binned in 1ps steps after calculating the effective timebase,

$$tbase = \left[(1:N) \cdot T_S\right] \bmod T \qquad (1)$$

where N is the number of samples, Ts is the sample clock period, and T is the input signal period. The ratio of ones to the total number of samples in each bin yields an estimate of the cumulative density function (CDF) [3]. The probability density function (PDF) is found by differentiating the CDF. The jitter histogram of the rising and falling edges can be distinguished individually using this technique, as shown in the figure.

If the clock jitter technique were applied to random data signals, the resulting CDF would approach 50% across the unit interval since there is an equal probability of sampling a logical 1 or 0. Therefore, additional hardware that detects a rising or falling edge of the input signal is required. The output of this edge detector block is asserted only when an edge is captured within sampling window. The samples are binned in 1ps steps, and the PDF is constructed directly without differentiation. Note that this measurement technique could also be used to measure clock signals. However, the resolution would be lower than the clock jitter technique described above due to the fixed sample window in the edge

detector. In addition, the edge detector doesn't distinguish between rising and falling edges, so only a composite histogram of the 2 edges would be measured.

B. Top level sampling blocks

The measurement apparatus is shown in Fig. 2. The input clock or data signal was terminated with programmable 50Ω resistors. The sample clock was similarly terminated and passed to the clock input of a single comparator for clock jitter measurements or to the clock input of an edge detection circuit for data jitter measurements.

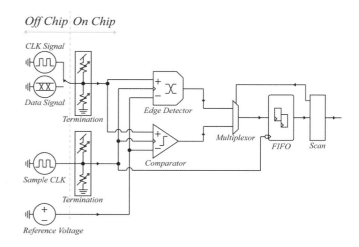

Figure 2. Block diagram of jitter measurement apparatus.

127

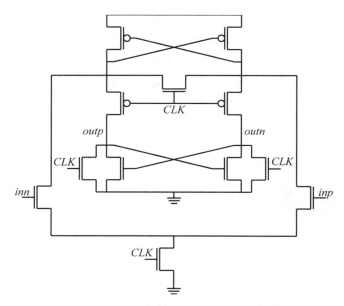

Figure 3. Comparator used directly in clock jitter measurements and within edge detector for data jitter measurements.

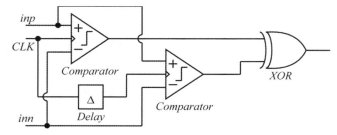

Figure 4. Edge detector used for data jitter measurements.

The asynchronous sampling technique requires that each consecutive comparison be captured without interruption. For low sample clock frequencies (<100MHz), the digital samples can be transferred off-chip and captured using a real time oscilloscope or a digital I/O board. We decided to capture the digital samples in an on-chip 4096 bit first in, first out (FIFO) memory, so that we could explore the impact of sample clock frequency on the measurement resolution. The memory contents were transferred off chip after each measurement via the digital scan interface.

C. Comparator

The clock jitter measurement requires comparing the input signal to a reference voltage across the sample window. If only the jitter near the midpoint of the signal is of interest, then a simple latch can be used for the comparison, as used in [3]. We were interested in characterizing the complete clock waveform at various voltages, so we used the comparator shown in Fig. 3. This circuit is a modified version of the comparator in [7] with improved kickback and lower power consumption. When the clock (CLK) is asserted, the comparator is in the reset phase and a low gain preamplifier is formed. The input voltage difference (inn & inp) is amplified via the top pfet pair and generates a voltage across the reset nfet. When CLK is low, the input differential stage is disconnected from the full cross-coupled pair and the input voltage difference is regenerated to a full rail decision. An external reference voltage provides a comparison point to the input signal.

D. Edge detector

The edge detector circuit is shown in Fig. 4. The input data signal was sampled using two of the comparators shown in Fig. 3. The comparators were clocked at a programmable delay offset, and the outputs were passed to an exclusive-OR gate. An edge is thus detected when each comparator produces different logical results.

III. RESULTS AND DISCUSSION

The circuit was implemented in a 65nm bulk technology [8] using a 1x25 pin digital macro layout, as shown in Fig. 5. During acquisition at a 1.2V supply, the samplers, memory subsystem, and termination circuits dissipated 1.4mA, 11mA, and 18mA, respectively. A 15pin wedge probe provided the RF inputs, supply voltage, and reference voltage to the comparators. A 5 pin needle probe provided the scan interface. A 12.5Gb/s pattern generator with 2 independently clocked channels produced the input signal and the asynchronous sample clock.

We experimented with different sample clock frequencies throughout our measurements, utilizing the ability of the on-chip memory to capture fast signals on-chip. We found that the measured jitter would generally increase as the sample clock frequency rose, possibly due to noise induced onto the power supply by the 4096 bit FIFO. As a result, the measurement results shown in Figs. 6 and 7 were recorded using sample clock frequencies near 125MHz.

A demonstration of the clock jitter technique is shown in Fig. 6. The input was a '1010' pattern at 12Gbit/s, equivalent to a clock frequency of 6GHz. The plot shows a series of jitter histogram measurements taken at different reference voltages. Since each independent measurement began independent of a common timing reference due to the asynchronous clock, the histograms taken at each reference voltage were aligned using a simple scoring algorithm that matched each histogram with

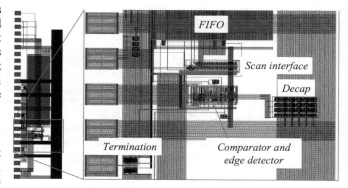

Figure 5. Layout (left) with zoomed view (right) of sampling circuits.

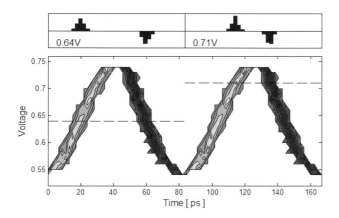

Figure 6. Statistical jitter measurement on a '1010' clock pattern at 12Gbit/s, equivalent to a clock frequency of 6GHz. The waveform was synthesized from a series of measurements recorded at different voltages. Individual histograms measured at 0.64V and 0.71V are shown at the top, corresponding to the dashed lines in the waveform.

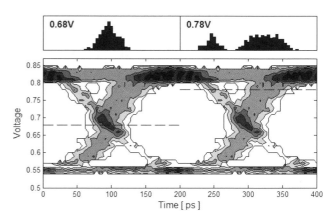

Figure 7. Statistical eye diagram of a 2^7-1 PRBS data pattern at 5Gbit/s. The waveform was synthesized from a series of measurements recorded at different voltages. Individual histograms measured at 0.68V & 0.78V are shown at the top, corresponding to the dashed lines in the eye.

its neighboring measurements. The RMS jitter near mid-rail (0.64V) was 2.1ps and 2.0ps for the rising and falling edges, respectively.

The edge detector, used to measure jitter of data signals, cannot distinguish between rising and falling edges of the input signal. Nevertheless, it is possible to infer the shape of a complete eye diagram by synthesizing a series of measurements taken at different reference voltages, as shown in Fig. 7. The input was a 5Gbit/s, 2^7-1 pseudo-random bit stream (PRBS) pattern. Aligning the histograms using an automated algorithm proved more difficult for the data jitter measurements compared with clock jitter measurements, so the histograms were aligned manually. At the crossing point of the eye diagram (0.68V), the measured RMS jitter was 6.2ps.

IV. CONCLUSION

We have demonstrated compact circuits for measuring jitter histograms and oscilloscope waveforms without the need for calibration. Comparators and a swept voltage reference are used for analog to digital conversion, and an asynchronous sample clock bypasses the need for an on-chip sample clock generator. The circuits produced RMS jitter measurements as low as of 2.0ps on clock signals and 6.2ps on data signals.

ACKNOWLEDGEMENTS

The authors would like to thank Volker Strumpen, Kevin Nowka and Gary Carpenter for helpful technical discussions throughout the course of this work.

REFERENCES

[1] H.Q. Le, W.J. Starke, J. S. Fields, F. P. O'Connel, D. Q. Nguyen, B. J. Ronchetti et al, "IBM POWER6 microarchitecture," *IBM Journal of Research and Development*, vol. 51, pp.639-662, 2007.

[2] M. Ishida, K. Ichiyama, T. J. Yamaguchi, M. Soma, M. Suda, T. Okayasu et al., "A Programmable On-Chip Picosecond Jitter Measurement Circuit without a Reference-Clock Input," *IEEE International Solid-State Circuits Conference*, pp. 512-513, Feb. 2005.

[3] K. A. Jenkins, A. P. Jose, D. F. Heidel, "An on-chip jitter measurement circuit with sub-picosecond resolution," *Proceedings of the 31st European Solid-State Circuits Conference*, pp. 157-160, Sept. 2005.

[4] M. Takamiya, M. Mizuno, K. Nakamura, "An On-chip 100GHz Sampling Rate 8-channel Sampling Oscilloscope with Embedded Sampling Clock Generator," *IEEE International Solid-State Circuits Conference*, pp. 457-458, Feb. 2002.

[5] Y. Zheng, K. L. Shepard, "On-Chip Oscilloscopes for Noninvasive Time-Domain Measurement of Waveforms in Digital Integrated Circuits," *IEEE Transactions on Very Large Scale Integration (VLSI) Systems*, vol. 11, pp. 336-344, June 2003.

[6] J. D. Schaub, F. H. Gebara, A. Jose, A. Saha, I. Vo, Y. H. Kwark, "13GHz On-chip Oscilloscope with Sub-picosecond Resolution Using Asynchronous Clock," *IEEE International SOI Conference*, pp. 123-124, 2006.

[7] G. M. Yin, F. Op't Eynde, and W. Sansen, "A High-speed CMOS Comparator with 8-b Resolution," *IEEE Journal of Solid State Circuits*. vol. 21, pp. 208-211, Feb. 1992.

[8] Z. Luo, A. Steegen, M. Eller, R. Mann, C. Baiocco, C. Nguyen, et al., "High performance and low power transistors integrated in 65nm bulk CMOS technology," *IEEE International Electron Devices Meeting*, pp. 661-664, 2004.

CMOS Unclonable System for Secure Authentication Based on Device Variability

D. Puntin, S. Stanzione and G. Iannaccone

Università di Pisa

Dipartimento di Ingegneria dell'Informazione: Elettronica, Informatica, Telecomunicazioni

Via Caruso 16, 56122, Pisa, Italy

daniele.puntin@gmail.com, {stefano.stanzione, g.iannaccone}@iet.unipi.it.

Abstract— **An unclonable system for product authentication in anti-counterfeiting has been implemented in standard 90 nm CMOS technology. The circuit exploits the intrinsic variability of the electrical characteristics of minimum size MOSFETs, in order to generate a physical one-way function that univocally identifies each particular IC. Effects of temperature, voltage supply and process variations have been internally compensated to obtain a robust and reliable behavior. Experimental measurements show that the circuit exhibits 30 μW power consumption, a bit error rate in response to a challenge smaller than 0.4% at 125□C or with a 10% voltage supply variation. Accelerated aging tests provide an estimate of a lifetime much in excess of the ten-year requirement. The very low power consumption makes the circuit also feasible for integration in RFID transponders.**

I. INTRODUCTION

Counterfeiting severely affects different industrial sectors, including the pharmaceutical, the aircraft, the automotive, and the luxury goods Industry. Recent solutions for secure authentication based on a secret key embedded in an RFID transponder are emerging [1].

One promising authentication method is the use of Physical One-Way Functions (POWF) [2] or Physical Unclonable Functions (PUF), that are functions based on the physical properties of real objects, too complex to be determined through brute force attacks, and impossible to clone because unknown even to the manufacturer. A significant number of proposed PUFs is based on optical properties [2,3]. They are obtained from the interference pattern of a transparent material containing randomly distributed scattering particles illuminated with a laser beam from a specified angle. Their unclonability derives from the uniqueness and unpredictability of speckle patterns resulting from multiple scattering of laser light in a disordered optical medium and from the impossibility of extracting the response function from a finite number of readings.

Silicon PUFs have been proposed, in which the random variability of the delays of logic gates [4-7] or of transistor threshold voltages [8] are used to generate a string univocally identifying a given circuit.

In the present work we propose a circuit – the "silicon nanokey" for generating a PUF to be used in a challenge-response authentication scheme. The circuit exploits the variability of the electrical parameters of minimum size MOS transistors, in particular of the threshold voltage, in order to generate a unique unclonable and reliable digital response to any digital challenge provided as input to the system. The nanokey is also robust to invasive attacks because a direct physical access would alter its properties.

Since the response of the nanokey to any challenge is unknown even to the manufacturer, we envisage a scheme in which an authenticating entity tests each nanokey before use, and collects and stores a large number of valid challenge-response pairs. In use, when one wants to authenticate the nanokey, it has to ask the authenticating entity a challenge, and then has to send the response back to the authenticating entity which matches the response to the stored one. Maximum security is obtained if each challenge-response pair is used only once.

II. CIRCUIT DESCRIPTION

Each bit of the response is obtained as a function of the analog output of a number of inverters biased around the point of maximum gain and realized with nMOSFETs of minimum length and width, in order to maximize threshold voltage variability and therefore output voltage dispersion. The block diagram of the nanokey is shown in Fig. 1. The core of the structure is the two-dimensional array of inverters. The digital challenge is a sequence of N inverter addresses. Each of the N-M+1 response bits is obtained from a group of M consecutive addresses, through a bit extractor circuit. In the simplest example realized we have M=2 and the bit extractor is an autozero comparator of the outputs of pairs of inverters. If the nanokey array and N are large enough the space of possible challenges can be easily made too large for a brute force attack.

The structure of a row of the array is shown in Fig. 2. Note that a single pMOSFET is used for each row, in order to reduce the total area occupation on the silicon die. This solution is especially useful if the number N of inverters in the array is large. In fact, in this way, it is possible obtain N^2

inverters by using only N pMOSFETs. Furthermore, pMOSFETs are large enough to exhibit negligible mismatch in comparison to the minimum sized nMOSFETs, so that they do not introduce a systematic shift of the output voltages on the same row.

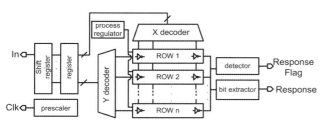

Figure 1.   Block diagram of the nanokey chip.

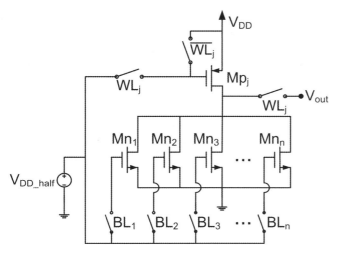

Figure 2.   Circuit of a row of the nanokey array. Bit lines BL_i are the outputs of the X decoder, Wordlines WL_j are the outputs of the Y decoder shown in Fig. 1.

It is important to bias the nanokey inverters in the maximum gain region, in order to maximize the inverter output dispersion, and to make the output response robust and reproducible in the presence of temperature, supply voltage, and process variations. To this aim, the input voltage of the inverters, V_{DD_half}, is provided by a process regulator circuit, shown in Fig. 3: The two pairs of nMOS and pMOS are perfectly matched and amplify the differential voltage (V_X-$V_{DD}/2$). These MOSFETs have a large size, in order to be mismatch insensitive.

The circuit labeled with A in Fig. 3 consists of 6 inverters identical to those forming the nanokey array connected in parallel and is equivalent to a single inverter of the array biased in the gain region but less sensitive to mismatch. Note that a larger number of inverters in parallel in the circuit A could reduce its sensitiveness to mismatch. On the other hand, since inverters biased in the maximum gain region require a considerable bias current, the circuit A absorbs a significant

portion of the power budget, and therefore the number of inverters in A has to be minimized.

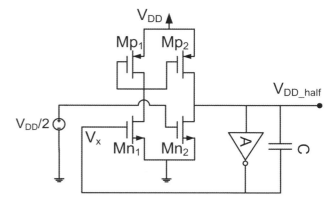

Figure 3.   Circuit of the process regulator.

The operation of the process regulator circuit is the following: if for any reason a change is induced in the value of V_X, the negative feedback of the circuit will compensate it, changing the input voltage V_{DD_half} of the matrix inverters. So, the voltage V_{DD_half} is regulated in order to keep A in the gain region even if undesired variations occur. Since A works in the maximum gain region, the gain loop of the circuit is high and V_X is very close to $V_{DD}/2$. The capacitor C of 250 fF allows Miller compensation to achieve loop stability. Given that A exhibits the same process dependence of the nanokey inverters, their average outputs will be compensated with respect to process, temperature, and voltage supply variations.

Let us describe now the authentication algorithm in the case M=2: every response bit is obtained by the sign of the difference between consecutive array outputs. So, the response bits can be easily extracted using an autozeroing comparator, as shown in Fig. 4. During the phase Φ_n the switches are closed and the inverters work on their trip point. Afterwards, during the phase Φ, the output array commutation occurs and, being the comparator inverters biased in the maximum gain region, the slightest variation of the array output unbalances the comparator inverters. The sensitivity to the array output variations is further increased by the use of large capacitances C (1pF), if compared with the input capacitances of the inverters. In this way the digital bits are correct only during the phase Φ. In order to complete the AD conversion, a Flip Flop D-latch has been used.

An additional measure to make the response robust and reliable is to discard those bits more likely to change as a result of noise, operation condition variations, or aging. To this aim a response flag is attached to each response bit upon the first reading, when the challenge-response pair is collected and stored: if the response flag is 1 the bit is unreliable (not valid), and is not considered in the validation of the response. In the case of M=2, the response flag is set to one for those bits obtained when the difference of inverter outputs is smaller than a "decision margin" V_{DM}.

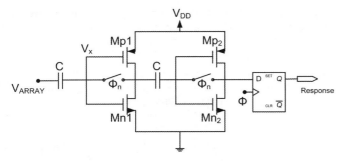

Figure 4.   Bit extractor.

The detector circuit, shown in Fig. 5, produces the response flag (*RF*) bits, that are function of two voltages, V_{DM} and V_{ARRAY}, as results from the following relation:

$$RF = \begin{cases} 0 \ , |\Delta V_{ARRAY}| > V_{DM} \\ 1 \ , |\Delta V_{ARRAY}| < V_{DM} \end{cases} \qquad (1)$$

The up and down chains simply evaluate if $\Delta V_{ARRAY} > V_{DM}$ and $\Delta V_{ARRAY} > -V_{DM}$ respectively. This means that a simple *XOR* operation between the two outputs of the chains evaluates if the absolute value of ΔV_{ARRAY} is lower than the decision margin V_{DM}.

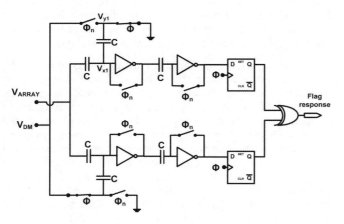

Figure 5.   Detector.

It is important to observe that V_{DM} is a result of a tradeoff: decreasing V_{DM} results in an increased bit error rate, increasing V_{DM} results in an increased number of bits to be rejected from the response. The False Rejection Rate (FRR) and the False Acceptance Rate (FAR) are a function of N, M, V_{DM}, the number of wrong bits accepted n_e in the response, and of system properties (noise, disturbs, and aging). Their evaluation is beyond the scope of the present paper. For the moment let us stress the fact that N, M, V_{DM} and n_e are obtained as a tradeoff between specifications on FRR and

FAR, and that an increase of N and M has a much stronger effect suppressing FAR than increasing FRR.

III.   EXPERIMENTAL RESULTS

The described nanokey has been implemented in a standard 90 nm CMOS process with an array size of 256 inverters and M=2, with the primary purpose of testing the robustness and reliability of the concept. At room temperature and with supply voltage of 600 mV the circuit absorbs 30 µW. The correlation between responses to the same input test challenge of 1500 addresses is essentially unitary if the same chip is considered and smaller than 1% if different chips are considered.

An important parameter of a nanokey is the Bit Error Rate (BER), that is the error probability of a valid response bit, that is a response bit not rejected in the first reference measurement.   By performing measurements for various values of the decision margin V_{DM}, the behavior of the BER as a function of V_{DM} has been obtained.   As shown in Fig. 6, the BER is a decreasing function of V_{DM}, and the fraction of non-valid bits in the response increases with V_{DM}, as shown in Fig. 7.   A good tradeoff is represented by a decision margin of 35 mV, for which the Bit Rejection Rate is lower than 20% and the BER for V_{DD}= 600 mV at room temperature is lower than 0.07%.

Measurements have been performed also varying the operating conditions.   Tests have been performed with operation at 125°C or with a 10% voltage supply variation. Although CMOS inverter outputs are strongly dependent on temperature and voltage supply, the process regulator makes the circuit robust to such of variations.   For a V_{DM} of 35 mV, in the worst case, the BER is lower than 0.4%.   This is comparable with the best result presented in literature, related to a different identification circuit [5].

Finally, accelerated aging tests have been performed. Circuits with no power supply have been put in an oven and periodically extracted, cycled to room temperature and tested. No observable degradation in their BER has been observed after 142 hours at 250°C, as shown in Fig. 6.

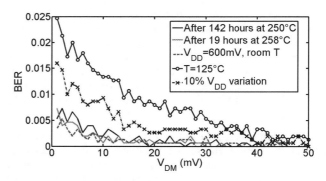

Figure 6.   BER as a function of the decision margin V_{DM}.

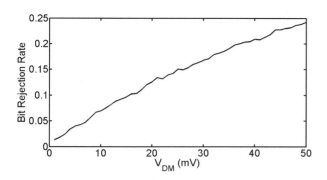

Figure 7. Bit Rejection Rate as a function of the decision margin V_{DM}.

In order to extract some additional information on their aging, we have evaluated the standard deviation of the difference between the comparator output voltages and those of the first reference measurements. Such value slowly increases with aging and is 7.8 mV after 142 hours at 250°C. Let us stress that this is a symptom of aging even if the circuit still works perfectly. At 258°C the same condition is reached after 19 hours. In Fig. 8 is shown the dispersion of the output voltage difference values with respect to those of the reference measurements as a function of the time during the accelerated aging tests. Higher temperatures could not be tested because of the large thermal time constants of the oven.

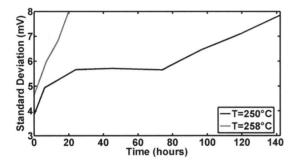

Figure 8. Standard deviation of the difference between comparator voltage outputs and those of the first reference measurement for the same challenge.

Such a strong temperature dependence is very promising from the point of view of the lifetime at room temperature: assuming an Arrenius-type aging process, it provides a lifetime well in excess of 10 years even at 120°C.

IV. CONCLUSION

A circuit for secure authentication, exploiting the intrinsic variability of the electrical characteristics of nanometric size MOS transistors, has been proposed and demonstrated. An internal compensation ensures a very good robustness to process, temperature and voltage supply variations. Measurements on the proposed IC have shown a 30 mW power supply and BER lower than 0.4% with operation at 125°C or with a 10% voltage supply variation. Finally, performing accelerated aging tests, a lifetime much in excess of the common ten-year requirement has been estimated. This work has been partially supported by Fondazione Cassa di Risparmio di Pisa and by Cassa di Risparmio di Pisa, Lucca e Livorno.

REFERENCES

[1] P. Tuyls, L. Batina, "RFID-Tags for Anti-counterfeiting", Topics in Cryptology – CT RSA 2006, Springer Berlin, pp. 115-131, 2006.

[2] Pappu, B. Recht, J. Taylor, N. Gerschen-Feld, "Physical one-way functions", Science, vol. 297, pp. 2026-2030, 2002.

[3] B. Škorić, P. Tuyls, and W. Ophey, "Robust key extraction from physical uncloneable functions", Proc. ACNS 2005, pp. 407-422, 2005.

[4] J. W. Lee, D. Lim, B. Gassend, G. E. Suh, M. van Dijk, and S. Devadas, "A technique to build a secret key in integrated circuits for identification and authentication applications", Proc. IEEE 2004 Symposium On VLSI Circuits, pp. 176-179.

[5] G. E. Suh and S. Devadas, "Physical unclonable functions for device authentication and secret key generation", Proc. DAC 2007, pp. 9-14, June 4-8, 2007.

[6] B. Gassend, D. Clarke, M. van Dijk, and S. Devadas, "Silicon physical random functions", in Proc. Computer Communication Security Conf., Nov. 2002, pp. 148-160.

[7] D. Lim, J. W. Lee, B. Gassend, G. E. Suh, M. van Dijk, and S. Devadas, "Extracting secret keys from integrated circuits", IEEE Trans. VLSI Systems, Vol. 13, no. 10, pp. 1200-1205, October 2005.

[8] K. Lofstrom, W. R. Daasch, D. Taylor, "IC identification circuit using device mismatch", IEEE International Solid-State Circuits Conference, Digest Tech. Papers, pp. 372-373, 2000.

Circuit Techniques for Suppression and Measurement of On-chip Inductive Supply Noise

Sanjay Pant

AMD Inc.

David Blaauw

University of Michigan

ABSTRACT

Increasing power consumption and clock frequency have significantly exacerbated the Ldi/dt drop, which has emerged as the dominant fraction of the overall power supply drop in high performance designs. We present the design and validation of a high-voltage, charge-pump based active decoupling circuit for the suppression of on-chip inductive power-supply noise. We also propose a low-power, high-resolution, digital on-chip oscilloscope technique, based on repetitive sampling, for measurement of high-frequency supply noise. The proposed circuits were implemented and fabricated in a 0.13μm CMOS process. Measurement results on the prototype demonstrate 48% and 53% reduction in power supply noise for rapidly switching current-loads and during resonance, respectively. On-chip supply noise is measured using the proposed on-chip oscilloscope and the noise waveforms are compared with those obtained from a traditional supply noise monitor and direct on-chip probing using probe pads.

1. INTRODUCTION

Aggressive technology scaling has exacerbated inductive (Ldi/dt) supply noise, impacting the robustness of power delivery networks. Ldi/dt is further aggravated by commonly used power reduction techniques such as power/clock-gating of macro blocks and frequency stepping in dynamic voltage scaled designs. Traditionally, decoupling capacitance or passive decap connected between V_{DD} and V_{SS} metal lines has been effectively used to suppress supply noise transients. However, the area and the leakage overhead places a limitation on the maximum amount of passive decap that can be added on the die.

Methods for IR-drop mitigation, such as increasing the on-chip power grid metallization are less effective in reducing Ldi/dt drop which is primarily caused by package inductance. This has given rise to an urgent need for the suppression of inductive noise in power distribution networks in the presence of large load-current transients. Active supply voltage regulation techniques employ circuits to enhance the amount of charge transfer to-and-from the power supply network during excessive supply-voltage fluctuations. The objective of these approaches is to reduce the supply drop for the same amount of explicit decoupling capacitance or to minimize the total decoupling-capacitance area for the same worst-case supply drop.

Several circuits have been proposed which enhance the charge transfer to or from decaps to suppress supply noise transients. In [1], a Miller-coupling based capacitance enhancement technique was proposed to reduce crosstalk between digital and analog regions on a die. A switched-capacitor circuit with two decap-banks switched between series and parallel configurations was proposed in [2]. In [3], a band-pass filter is used to detect supply noise resonance and an artificial shunt load is periodically switched on and off to dampen the resonance. A supply regulation technique using only nominal voltage supplies was presented in [4]. In [5], a shunt high voltage supply is connected to the regular power grid when power-gated logic blocks wake up from the sleep state. Several adaptive frequency-management techniques [6] have also been proposed to compensate for supply transients. These techniques employ supply-drop monitors at various locations on the die and the frequency of operation is altered to compensate for fluctuations in the power supply. In [7], the use of controlled incremental frequency changes to alleviate inductive noise in dynamically voltage scaled microprocessors was explored. In addition to these, several micro-architectural control techniques [8] such as selective issue, pipeline throttling and selective wake-up of clock-gated modules have also been proposed.

In this paper, we present a high-voltage, charge-pump based digital circuit technique for the suppression of inductive supply noise. The proposed circuit detects and suppresses excessive supply voltage fluctuations due to both sudden surges in load or due to excitation of supply resonance. The proposed circuit delivers a significantly larger amount of charge while ensuring that the charge transfer into the V_{DD} network is identical to that out of the V_{SS} network. This eliminates the possibility of any bounce in on-chip V_{DD} and V_{SS} relative to off-chip voltage references which can possibly interfere with the IO operation.

We also propose a power-efficient all-digital on-chip oscilloscope for accurate measurement of high-frequency supply noise. The proposed oscilloscope uses subsampling [9] to repetitively sample the supply noise waveform, capturing its time-shifted snapshots, each snapshot consisting of 38 sample points with 50ps resolution. The snapshots are then combined off-chip to reconstruct the complete supply noise waveform. The proposed circuit achieves a bandwidth of 20GS/s and is much more power efficient than analog supply drop monitors.

The proposed circuits for supply noise suppression and measurement were integrated in a prototype fabricated in a 0.13μm, triple-well CMOS technology. Measurement results on the prototype demonstrate 48% and 53% reduction in power supply noise during rapidly switching loads and during resonance, respectively. The on-chip supply noise waveforms, measured using the proposed on-chip oscilloscope are compared with those obtained from a traditional supply noise monitor and direct on-chip probing using probe pads. The measurements show good correlation in both the IR and the Ldi/dt drops.

The remainder of this paper is organized as follows. Sections 2 and 3 present the description of the supply noise suppression and measurement circuits, respectively. Section 4 presents the details of the prototype implementation and measurement results, and conclusions are drawn in Section 5.

2. SUPPLY NOISE SUPPRESSION

Figure 1(a) shows a simplified model of an unregulated power delivery network. The impedance of the power and ground distribution networks is modeled as a series combination of lumped elements, L_{VDD}-R_{VDD} and L_{VSS}-R_{VSS}, respectively. The total amount of non-switching as well as explicitly added on-die decap is represented by the lumped capacitance C_P. A time-varying current

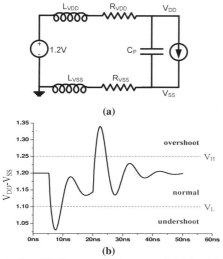

(a)

(b)

Figure 1. A simplified power delivery model (a) and a typical supply noise waveform with supply voltage thresholds (b).

source models the switching current of all the logic blocks in the chip. Figure 1(b) shows the unregulated supply voltage waveform with undershoot and overshoot supply voltage thresholds, V_L and V_H, respectively. V_L and V_H can be determined based on the performance constraints on the design. Three regions of operation: *normal* ($V_L < V_{DD} < V_H$), *undershoot* ($V_{DD} < V_L$) and *overshoot* ($V_{DD} > V_H$), are defined based on the amplitude of supply noise.

Figure 2 shows the schematic of the proposed supply noise suppression circuit technique. The proposed circuit employs decap banks, C_A, which store a higher than nominal supply voltage, V_{DDH}, across their terminals. C_A is connected between V_{DDH} and V_{SS} when the supply voltage is above the undershoot threshold, V_L ($S_N=1$, $S_{UN}=0$, $S_{OV}=0$). When a supply drop below V_L is sensed ($S_N=0$, $S_{UN}=1$, $S_{OV}=0$), T_0 turns off and T_1 turns on, discharging C_A from V_{DDH} to V_{DD}. The amount of charge transferred to the regular grid is $C_A(V_{DDH}-V_{DD})$. An artificial load T_2 is turned on to prevent excessive overshoots ($S_N=0$, $S_{UN}=0$, $S_{OV}=1$), sensed when the supply voltage bounces above the overshoot threshold, V_H.

For implementing the proposed supply-voltage regulation technique, a small portion of the total pads available for V_{DD} are allocated to V_{DDH} such that the total number of used pads is constant. Also, the total available decap-area is split between the passive decap C'_P and the decap bank C_A, while also accounting for the area overhead of the active circuits. The active decap bank, C_A, and transistors T_0 and T_1 are implemented using thick-oxide transistors to alleviate reliability concerns.

For a voltage regulation tolerance of $k \cdot V_{dd}$, the proposed circuit results in a decap amplification factor of $0.5+(V_{DDH}-V_{DD})/k \cdot V_{DD}$ as

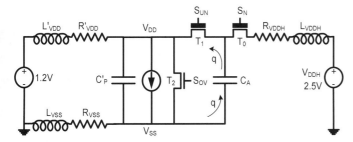

Figure 2. Proposed supply voltage regulation technique.

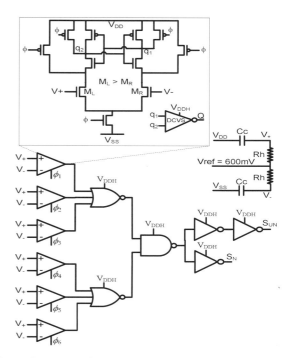

Figure 3. Level shifter and noise undershoot detector circuit.

compared to the use of only passive decap. During supply voltage undershoots, C_A is disconnected from V_{DDH} and forms a loop across V_{DD} and V_{SS}, enabling an equal amount of charge transferred into the power grid and out from the ground grid. This symmetric charge transfer ensures that the regular supplies V_{DD} and V_{SS} do not exhibit any bounce or spikes when switches T_{0-1} are turned on or off. Most of the prior published circuits [1,4,5] are inherently asymmetric and pump more charge into V_{DD} compared to the charge extracted out of V_{SS}, which may cause latch-up or errors in data transfer between different voltage domains.

The control signals S_N, S_{UN} and S_{OV} in Figure 2 are generated by integrated undershoot and overshoot detectors. The detectors are similar in design to the circuits presented in [4]. A level shifter (Figure 3) first couples V_{DD} and V_{SS} noise to a common reference voltage of 600mV. The translated waveforms V_+ and V_- are sampled by a bank of digital comparators clocked at 6 phases (ϕ_1-ϕ_6) of a 3.33GHz clock. The gain transistors M_L and M_R of the comparators are skewed to create thresholds V_H and V_L. The transistors in the comparators are implemented with larger than minimum length to minimize manufacturing variations. The comparator outputs use a DCVS stage for level conversion of outputs from V_{DD} to V_{DDH}. The outputs of the comparators are ORed together and buffered to generate S_N and S_{UN}. The overshoot signal S_{OV} is generated in a similar manner by another bank consisting of 6 clocked comparators. The latency of S_N, S_{UN} and S_{OV} generation was 380ps in simulations.

The next section describes the design of the proposed digital on-chip oscilloscope for supply noise measurement.

3. SUPPLY NOISE MEASUREMENT

Several circuits have been published to measure the on-chip supply noise. Circuits proposed in [10,11] constitute a sample-hold circuit to sample the supply voltage and a V-I converter circuit. The V-I converter circuit consists of a high-conductance transistor to convert the supply voltage samples into current, which is then amplified using a current mirror and transmitted off-chip using a transmission line. Current-based sensing is particularly attractive due to its robustness to coupling noise. However, the use of an analog V-I converter with high gain, followed by current amplifiers makes this technique power inefficient. A-D converters have also been proposed to convert the analog samples of supply noise into a digital code [12] which is then transmitted off-chip. This approach has high area overhead, making it less effective for fine-grained supply noise measurement. An analog circuit that reports whether power supply or ground voltage at the location of comparators within a microprocessor core crosses a pre-defined threshold voltage in every clock cycle was presented in [13].

The analog circuits have large power overhead and their non-linearity may adversely affect the accuracy of the detector in the presence of large fluctuations in supply voltage. To address these concerns, we propose a power-efficient and accurate all-digital on-chip oscilloscope. The proposed oscilloscope samples the supply noise waveform with a high frequency clock and generates its time-shifted snapshots, which are then combined off-chip to reconstruct the original waveform. Since the supply noise fluctuations are non-periodic in nature, the device-under-test (DUT) executes the same test-case repeatedly.

In the proposed on-chip oscilloscope (Figure 4), the measurement process is invoked by asserting a reference voltage, Vref, and the *trigger* signal. In this work, the reference Vref is supplied from off-chip. Since the supply voltage observed by the on-chip devices is V_{DD}-V_{SS}, we are interested in measuring V_{DD}-V_{SS} and not the absolute V_{DD}. Therefore, the reference voltage, Vref is translated to on-chip V_{SS} using an RC network. Cc is realized using a MIM-cap in order to minimize leakage. The on-chip oscilloscope consists of a coarse delay generator and a fine delay line. The coarse delay generator consists of a counter which asserts the *sample* signal whenever a user-specified (scanned-in) 12-bit count is attained after *trigger* has been asserted high. The fine delay line then generates time-shifted versions of the *sample* signal (s_1-s_{38}), with 50ps resolution. A set of clocked comparators sample the supply noise with the time-shifted versions of *sample* signal, resulting in an effective sampling rate of 20Gbps. The number of comparators is determined by the frequency of *clk* and the chip test time.

A calibration control signal, Δ_{calib}, connects the fine delay line in feedback to form a ring oscillator. During calibration, the divided ring oscillator frequency is measured off-chip and the delay of individual delay element is determined. The output of the clocked comparators is scanned-out as a thermometer code, indicating

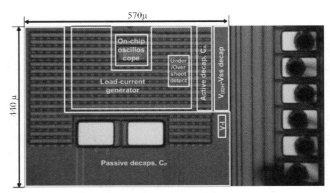

Figure 4. Die Micrograph.

whether each sample of V_{DD}-V_{SS} is greater or less than Vref. The test-case is repeatedly executed on the DUT, with different Vref and coarse delay values and the complete supply noise waveform is constructed off-chip.

The next section presents the implementation details of the prototype and measured results.

4. PROTOTYPE IMPLEMENTATION DETAILS AND MEASUREMENT RESULTS

The proposed supply voltage regulation and measurement techniques were implemented in a test-chip (Figure 5), fabricated in a 0.13μm, 1.2V CMOS process and packaged in a 108-pin PGA package. The test chip consists of unregulated and regulated test-cases, implemented for an iso-area and iso-pad comparison. The unregulated test-case used 3 V_{DD}, 3 V_{SS} pads and 670pF of C_P, while the regulated test-case had 1 V_{DDH}, 2 V_{DD}, 3 V_{SS} pads, 356pF of C'_P and 165pF of C_A. The total white space available for decaps in the regulated test-case was reduced to account for the area overhead of undershoot/overshoot detectors and the sampling clock (ϕ_1-ϕ_6) generator. A configurable load-current generator (10mA-120mA),

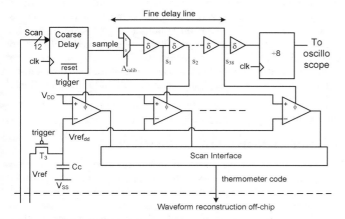

Figure 3. Digital on-chip oscilloscope for noise measurement.

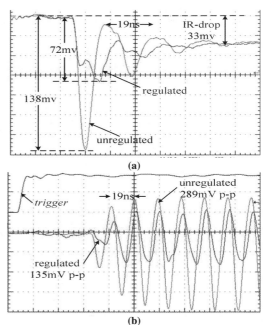

Figure 5. Measured unregulated and regulated supply noise waveforms for step load (a) and during resonance (b).

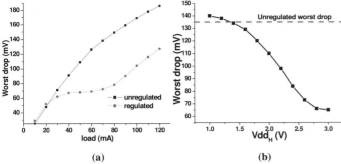

(a)   (b)

Figure 6. Measured worst drop as a function of load (a) and as a function of V_{DDH} (b).

with variable duty cycle and period (0.5ns-2μs) was implemented using an array of transistors connected between V_{DD} and V_{SS}. The proposed on-chip oscilloscope was used for the measurement of supply noise. An analog V-I converter based supply drop monitor [10] was implemented to validate the supply noise measurements. The measurements were also verified by direct on-chip probing of supply voltage at the top-level metal layers using probe pads.

Figure 6 shows a comparison of the measured on-die supply noise with and without supply regulation for a typical die. In Figure 6(a), the excitation load-current ramps up from 0 to 70mA, representative of the wake-up of a power/clock-gated module. Active regulation reduces the overall supply drop by 48% from 138mV to 72mV, and Ldi/dt drop by 63% from 105mV to 39mV, which represents a decap amplification factor of 9.9X. During resonance (Figure 6(b)), the peak-to-peak supply drop reduces from 289mV to 135mV, an improvement of 53%. The resonance frequency of the first droop was measured to be 52.7MHz. Figure 7(a) shows the measured worst supply drop as a function of peak load-current for one die. Figure 7(b) shows the measured regulated worst supply drop as a function of V_{DDH}. Figure 8 shows the measured supply noise waveforms for the ramp load with 70mA peak current demonstrating the reduction in worst supply drop with increasing V_{DDH}.

Figures 9(a) shows V_{DD}-V_{SS} waveforms measured using the V-I monitor and the on-chip oscilloscope, respectively, for ramp loads and during resonance. Both IR and Ldi/dt drops show good correspondence. A comparison with probe pads for resonance is shown in Figure 9(b). The difference in the amplitude of supply noise observed by the measurement circuits and the on-chip probes can be attributed to the probing of the top-layer grid by the probe pads which does not account for full IR drop in the power grid. The power consumption of the on-chip oscilloscope and the V-I monitor were measured to be 1mW and 29mW, respectively, showing that the on chip scope is significantly more power efficient.

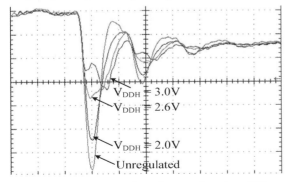

Figure 7. Measured supply noise as a function of V_{DDH}.

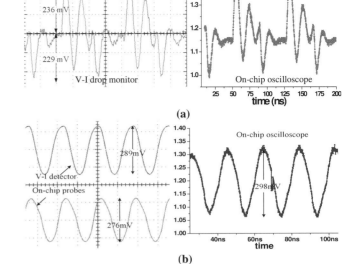

(a)

(b)

Figure 8. Measured supply noise waveforms using the V-I converter-based circuit and using the proposed on-chip oscilloscope, for ramp load (a) and during resonance (b).

5. CONCLUSIONS

In this paper, a high-voltage supply based supply noise suppression technique and a digital, subsampling based supply noise measurement technique were presented. Measurements on a 0.13m CMOS prototype demonstrate noise reduction by 48% and 53% for ramp loads and during resonance, respectively. Supply noise measurements from the proposed measurement circuit were validated against a traditional analog supply drop monitor and direct on-die probing and show good correlation.

ACKNOWLEDGMENTS

This work was supported by grants from NSF and Intel. The authors thank Visvesh Sathe and Carlos Tokunaga for helpful discussions.

REFERENCES

[1] T. Tsukada et al., *JSSC*, vol. 40, no. 1, pp. 67-69, Jan. 2005.

[2] M. Ang et al., *ISSCC Dig. Tech. Papers*, 2000, pp. 438-439.

[3] J. Xu et al., *ISSCC Dig. Tech. Papers*, 2007, pp. 286-287.

[4] S. Pant et al., *ISSCC Dig. Tech. Papers*, 2008, pp. 416-417.

[5] Y. Nakamura et al., *Symp. on VLSI Circuits*, 2007, pp. 124-125.

[6] J. Tschanz et al., *ISSCC Dig. Tech. Papers*, 2007, pp. 292-293.

[7] E. Hailu et al., *ISSCC Dig. Tech. Papers*, 2006, pp. 548-549.

[8] R. Joseph et al., *Proceedings of HPCA*, 2003, pp. 79-90.

[9] M. Takamiya et al., *ISSCC Dig. Tech. Papers*, 2002, pp. 182-183.

[10] M. Nagata et al., *JSSC*, vol. 40, no. 4, pp. 813-819, Apr. 2005.

[11] M. Fukazawa et al., *ISSCC Dig. Tech. Papers*, 2007, pp. 286-287.

[12] Y. Zheng et al., *Trans. on VLSI*, vol. 11, no. 3, pp. 336-344, June, 2003.

[13] A. Muhtaroglu et al., *JSSC*, vol. 39, no. 4, pp. 651-660, Apr. 2004.

A Fully Integrated Power Supply Unit for Fine Grain Power Management Application to Embedded Low Voltage SRAMs

E. Beigné[1], F. Clermidy[1], S. Miermont[1], A. Valentian[1], P. Vivet[1],

S. Barasinski[2], F. Blisson[2], N. Kohli[3], S. Kumar[3]

[1]*CEA-LETI, MINATEC, F-38054, Grenoble, France*
[2] *STMicroelectronics, F-38926, Crolles, France*
[3] *STMicroelectronics, Greater Noida, 201308 (U.P.), India*
{edith.beigne@cea.fr}

Abstract□ **In complex embedded applications, optimization and adaptation at run time of both dynamic and leakage power have become an issue at SoC coarse grain. We propose in this paper a fully integrated Power Supply Unit for fine grain DVFS and adaptive leakage control. The proposed PSU offers five power modes and can be easily integrated in any IP unit. The PSU has been implemented and validated in a STMicroelectronics 65nm technology. Dedicated Low-Voltage SRAMs have been designed to allow full DVFS. Using a Hopping technique, the dynamic power consumption can be reduced by a factor of 35%. Using an Ultra-Cut-Off technique, the static power consumption is strongly reduced in stand-by mode, 18 times better than classical MTCMOS.**

I.   INTRODUCTION

As leakage power and total power have become major issues in deep submicron technologies, advanced low-power strategies have to be explored from system level down to device level. For leakage control, power gating techniques have proved to be efficient but are not yet self-adaptive to PVT conditions [1][2]. We are aiming at providing leakage control taking into account process variability [3].

Regarding dynamic power, Dynamic Voltage and Frequency Scaling (DVFS) has been applied but mostly for CPUs, while requiring external DC-DC converters. We propose to provide DVFS which can be integrated at fine grain at low area cost within a SoC architecture. When addressing such DVFS technique, two design challenges must be resolved: the DVFS control must be fast and reliable to be transparent to the controlled IP, and the IP unit under DVFS control must be robust to low voltage operation and to voltage drop. Within IPs, standard-cell CMOS logic is usually robust to low-voltage operation with some known margins; the critical issue is to design embedded SRAMs allowing both normal and low-voltage operation. Low voltage SRAMs are mandatory to take benefit of dynamic power reduction through voltage scaling.

In this paper, we propose the design of an efficient and fully integrated Power Supply Unit which provides adaptive leakage control and fine grain DVFS, based on Hopping technique [4]. The proposed Power Supply Unit can be easily used in any SoC for controlling medium size IP units : each IP becomes an independent frequency and power domain. In terms of SoC architecture, a Globally Asynchronous Locally Synchronous paradigm associated to a NoC protocol is then a natural enabler to efficiently interconnect independent power controlled IPs [5].

In section II, we present in detail the proposed Power Supply Unit : its internal architecture, the local frequency and voltage control, the implementation of the Ultra-Cut-Off for adaptive leakage control, and finally the Hopping Unit for fine grain DVFS. In section III, we present the low voltage SRAM operation, which is necessary to cope with the proposed DVFS mechanism. Finally in section IV, we present the silicon results in terms of layout and power reduction.

II.   POWER SUPPLY UNIT

In this section is presented the Power Supply Unit (PSU), a CMOS fully integrated device which provides adaptive leakage control and fine grain DVFS. The proposed PSU can be integrated in any SoC to control power consumption at IP level. Each IP unit is then defined as an independent power domain (using its dedicated local voltage) and an independent frequency domain (using a dedicated local clock generator).

A.   PSU Architecture

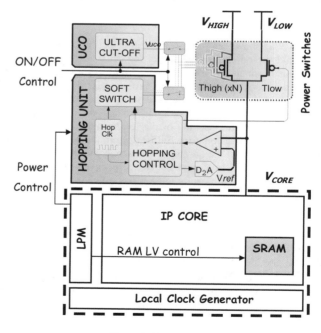

Figure 1 : Power Supply Unit

The IP unit handles a set of user-defined power modes (Figure 2). A Local Power Manager (LPM) integrated into the IP unit is in charge of controlling locally the IP unit's power modes. Moreover, the Local Power Manager handles low voltage SRAMs control to ensure safe transition between V_{HIGH} and V_{LOW} during memory accesses.

Reset	At reset, the unit is at VHIGH with no clock
High	The unit is supplied by VHIGH voltage
Low	The unit is supplied by VLOW voltage
Hopping	The unit is automatically switched between VHIGH and VLOW voltages, *for DVFS*
Idle	The unit is idle, with maintain of its current state at VLOW voltage, *for reduced leakage power*
Off	The unit is switched OFF, with no maintain of its current state, *for minimal leakage power*

Figure 2 : Power Supply Unit power modes

The Power Supply Unit (Figure 1) manages the internal V_{CORE} supply voltage according to the selected power modes, using two supplies V_{HIGH} and V_{LOW} provided off-chip. In the 65nm targeted technology, V_{HIGH} is 1.2V, V_{LOW} is 0.9V, but V_{LOW} could be any voltage between 0.6V and 1.2V.

The PSU is composed of three main devices: the Power Switches (Thigh and Tlow low-VT power transistors), the Ultra Cut-Off gate voltage generator (UCO), and the Hopping Unit. The UCO is used during 'Off' mode to reduce the unit leakage current. The Hopping Unit ensures automatic and smooth transitions between V_{HIGH} and V_{LOW} without stopping the unit clock and computations.

B. Local Frequency and Voltage Control

When designing such a Power Supply Unit, it is necessary to ensure the matching between the generated V_{CORE} voltage and the corresponding F_{CORE} frequency. The unit clock is generated by a programmable delay line [5], which is supplied by V_{CORE}. The obtained F_{CORE} frequency is thus related with any V_{CORE} variations. Due to synchronous design paradigm, F_{CORE} must be programmed according to the worst-case scenario and the critical path of the IP unit. In case of strong mismatch or variations between Delay Line timing and Unit timing, it is possible to reprogram the delay line accordingly: an automatic swap between V_{HIGH} and V_{LOW} delay configurations occurs at each Hopping transition. As a result, the Hopping transition is fast and reliable, with no hardware or software latency cost.

In a same manner, each Low-Voltage SRAM (see section III) must be configured in either V_{HIGH} or V_{LOW} mode for its internal efficiency. It is the duty of the Local Power Manager, not only to configure the delay line, but also to control the *ram_lv* signal. When a High↔Low Hopping transition occurs, the *ram_lv* signal is toggled accordingly to guarantee that all embedded SRAMs are in the proper state.

Finally, the PSU controlled IP unit behaves as an independent power and frequency domain. In order to have proper V_{HIGH} voltage levels at the IP unit interfaces (either in LOW state or in OFF state), it is necessary to insert Level Shifters on all external signals. These cells must also behave as isolation cells in order to offer a predetermined voltage level (0 or 1 according to protocol requirements) when the IP unit is powered off.

C. Ultra-Cut-Off for Leakage Control

Power switch transistors are used for their efficiency in cutting leakage currents when a given IP unit is not used. Among the existing power switch transistors, the SCCMOS-type (Super Cutoff CMOS [2]) was chosen since, being a low-VT transistor, it has the smallest size for a given on-current and is well suited to a low supply voltage environment (*Vlow* supply voltage). In order to exponentially decrease the leakage current of this low-VT power switch, its gate is reverse-biased by a control block called "Ultra Cut Off" [3] that automatically determines the point of minimum leakage (whose value depends on the temperature, the process parameters and the supply voltage).

Indeed, reverse-biasing the gate of the power switch decreases the subthreshold current but at the same time increases the gate-induced drain leakage and gate-tunneling currents. So a compromise has to be found in order to minimize the total leakage current. This "point of minimum leakage" is determined by comparing the former two current groups, thanks to two reference transistors representative of the power switch and a current comparator. This comparator (implemented using a current-to-voltage conversion and a voltage sense amplifier) generates Up and Down impulses to command a charge pump to respectively increase or lower its output voltage.

Of course, the automatic determination of the optimal bias voltage generates a power dissipation overhead. To avoid overhead, Ultra-Cut-Off power switches (UCPMOS) are not used when implementing a small width power switch. In that case, a classical MTCMOS-type Standard-VT transistor is used.

D. Hopping Unit for Fine Grain DVFS

Fine-grain Dynamic Voltage Scaling is the key element for a better power efficiency in heterogeneous SoC with wide applicative constraints. A technique called Vdd-Hopping [6] uses dithering between V_{HIGH} and V_{LOW} power supplies to precisely control the IP performance while minimizing power consumption. If hopping is fast enough, the number of cycles spent in 'High' and 'Low' mode is averaged on an applicative frame. The duty-ratio is controlled by a Pulse Width Modulator counter.

The proposed Hopping Unit [4] is used to seamlessly switch the supply sources. In steady state, the power is supplied through Thigh or Tlow transistors with minimal resistive losses. During transitions, the IP supply voltage V_{CORE} is controlled by a linear regulator connected to V_{HIGH}. The regulator uses the V_{REF} reference signal to adjust V_{CORE} by ramping up or down accordingly.

- to make a transition from V_{HIGH} to V_{LOW}, the Thigh transistor is used as a linear regulator and V_{CORE} is ramped down from V_{HIGH} to V_{LOW}. Then, Tlow transistor is switched on, and Thigh is switched off. The device is ready for the next transition.
- to make a transition from V_{LOW} to V_{HIGH}, Thigh is used as a linear regulator with a reference at V_{LOW}. The Tlow transistor is then switched off and V_{CORE} is ramped up to V_{HIGH}. When Thigh is fully on, the transition is over.

Thanks to smooth transitions, with no undershoot or overshoot, the IP does not need to be stopped. Hopping occurs without latency cost at application level. The transition duration can be adjusted from ~40ns to ~500ns. The Hopping Unit is fully integrated and is much smaller than any integrated capacitive or inductive DC/DC converter, and its power efficiency is similar or better. Hopping Unit efficiency has been evaluated to be close to 95%.

III. LOW-VOLTAGE SRAM OPERATION

For complete integration at SoC level, low voltage SRAMs are mandatory to take benefit of the proposed Power Supply Unit. The low voltage 6T SRAM used in the design uses both process and temperature tracking write-assist and read-assist circuits allowing a wide voltage range operation from 0.7V up to 1.3V.

A. Memory cell characteristics

The 6T SRAM cell is composed of two Pull-Down (PD), two Pull-Up (PU) that form the latch, and two Pass-Gate (PG) transistors. For deep submicron technology, the difficulty of making such a cell operate at low-voltage is due to the increase of the transistor parameters spread with technology scaling leading to stability and Write Margin (WM) related bit fails. Large L transistors are used to reduce the cell parameters spread; multi threshold transistors: low-VT for PU, high-VT for PD and PG are used to maximize the cell stability to the detriment of its WM for which a Memory Cell Supply (MCS) lowering write assist circuit is implemented.

B. Write operation

A closed-loop circuit is used in conjunction with a specific dummy write path. This feedback loop lowers the MCS as long as the Dummy Write Cells (DWC) have not flipped. Three phases can be distinguished. The dummy bit-lines are driven in order to write the DWCs and the dummy word-line is activated; the analog feedback loop starts lowering MCS. Then, the DWCs flip and the feedback loop starts powering the MCS up. Finally, a write completion detector triggers a faster MCS return to Vdd.

However, this write-assist scheme induces a write disturb for the unselected cells along the addressed columns resulting in potential data retention issues. Hence a trade-off is required between data retention capability and the ability to recover a strong write margin. As a consequence, the MCS voltage supplied to the addressed column during a write operation must be finely controlled over the Process, Voltage and Temperature ranges.

An Adaptive Weakest Write Margin Cell Configuration (AWWMCC) scheme has therefore been implemented to dynamically emulate the worst case bitcell for the write operation. In a deep submicron technology, like 65nm, the main factor determining the worst cell to write is the Vt spread as well as the lithography mismatch between all the devices. The worst memory cell to write is the one that has the weakest PG and the strongest latch. The AWWMCC consists in setting the proper ratio between the PG and the latch to write. In this implementation, 16 latches are tied together along the column and 16 pairs of independently

controllable PG are used. A 4-bit bus controls the number of PG to be selected during the write operation. It is hooked-up in a binary weighted fashion such that the number of selected PG can vary from 1 to 16. The configuration setting is a binary code that depends on the memory operating voltage. The chosen setting is 2 PG at low voltage (0.7V) and 16 PG at nominal voltage (1.2V). Moreover, this self adaptive write scheme allows keeping a single voltage supply to power the memory instance.

C. Read operation

The read operation margin and timing are mainly determined by the Bit Line Discharge Rate (BLDR) which varies according to the PVT corners and the Sense-Amplifier (SA) offset. The Adaptive BLDR (ABLDR) circuit consists in a selectable number of Dummy Read Cells (DRC) that discharge two dummy bit-lines (DBL) tied together per sub block. The DRC is composed of only the stacked transistor: the PG – dynamically controlled by a 4-bit bus - and the PD - controlled by the DWL. The trimming is therefore done by the very same devices as the memory cell ones. This circuit allows suppressing any other delay to trim the dummy path enabling the SA.

Finally, a special care has been taken to integrate both the AWWMCC and ABLDR circuits within the matrix in order to minimize the mismatch with the actual memory cell and reflect its topology. Beside the fact that the scheme implementation is highly integrated in the matrix; it is only 6 physical columns wide, and is shrinkable with the memory cell.

D. SRAM silicon results

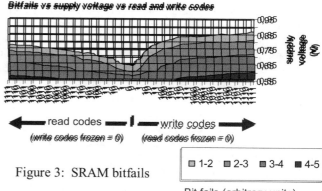

Figure 3: SRAM bitfails

SRAM silicon results are presented Figure 3. The rightmost side (1111) shows the number of failing bits with write assist not activated and slowest read time setting in read-assist. Decreasing the number of PG's (from right to center) corresponds to the activation of write-assist circuit (increased delay and column power supply drop). The left-most side (1111) shows the number of failing bits with fastest read time and most efficient write assist setup. Decreasing the number of DRC (from left to center) corresponds to an increase in read delay. By activating both write-assist and read-assist circuits, minimum functional voltage is achieved down to 0.7V @ 25MHz.

IV. SILICON RESULTS

The proposed Power Supply Unit has been implemented in the ALPIN prototype in a LP 65nm STMicroelectronics technology [7]. This chip contains 6 IP units all implementing their local PSU. We present in this section the layout architecture as well as power measurements on silicon.

A. Physical Implementation

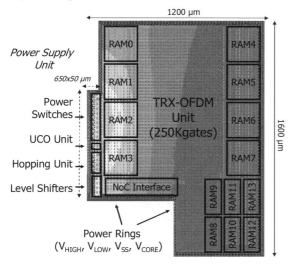

Figure 4: TRX-OFDM unit layout with its Power Supply Unit

Figure 4 shows the layout of one ALPIN unit, the TRX-OFDM unit with its attached PSU, and the corresponding IR drop distribution. The TRX-OFDM unit is a complex unit providing FFT computations for both RX and TX OFDM protocols, this unit integrates 14 Low-Power Low-Voltage SRAMs (290 Kbits total). The unit is supplied through 4 power rings: the external V_{HIGH}, V_{LOW}, V_{SS} and the generated V_{CORE}. The Power Supply Unit represents only 2.5% of the total OFDM unit area.

B. Leakage Power Reduction

Leakage measurements (Table 1) were performed on two IP units, namely TRX-OFDM and MEM units. The TRX-OFDM unit, with a bigger power dissipation (80mW) is driven by the UCPMOS-type LVT power switch, while the MEM unit with a lower power dissipation (30mW) is driven by a classical MTCMOS-type SVT power switch, as explained in Section II-C. In *high* mode, the voltage drop across the Power Switches is equal to 30mV in both cases. The difference between the *reset* and *off* modes illustrates the leakage gain provided by the Power Switches: leakage current of the UCPMOS transistor is 8 times lower than the MTCMOS one, while its I_{ON} current is 2.5 times higher.

Table 1: Measurement results of the power switches

	TRX-OFDM UCPMOS-LVT (5500µm)		MEM MTCMOS-SVT (2600µm)	
	VCORE	I(VCORE)	VCORE	I(VCORE)
high	1.166 V	30.5 mA	1.162 V	13.9 mA
reset	1.199 V	195 µA	1.198 V	284 µA
off	1.7 mV	276 nA	10.2 mV	2.4 µA

C. Dynamic Power Reduction

The Hopping Unit has been tested on 3 different IPs with the following parameters: V_{HIGH} = 1.2V, V_{LOW} = 0.9V, transition frequency = 150-300 kHz, ramp duration = ~80 ns. The IPs are fully functional during V_{CORE} dithering.

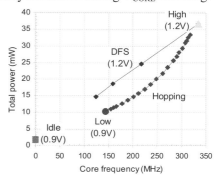

Figure 5: Dynamic power reduction with Hopping Unit

As illustrated in Figure 5, Vdd-Hopping technique offers a programmable Power/Performance ratio similar to a continuous DC/DC converter. Compared to frequency scaling (DFS only), Hopping technique (DVFS) reduces the dynamic power up to 35% for the same performance level.

V. CONCLUSION

We have presented in this paper a new Power Supply Unit, fully integrated in 65nm, offering adaptive leakage control and fine grain DVFS. The PSU and DVFS on advanced low voltage SRAMs were validated from 1.2V down to 0.9V. The proposed PSU offers five power modes and can be easily integrated in any IP unit at SoC level using two external voltages. Future work will focus on adapting these techniques to take into account intra-die variability.

ACKNOWLEDGMENT

This work was supported by the European Commission in the framework of FP6 with the IST-CLEAN project (Controlling Leakage Power in Nano CMOS SOC's) and with the Medea+ LOMOSA 2A708 project (Low-power expertise for Mobile and multimedia system applications).

REFERENCES

[1] M.H. Anis, S. Areibi, M. I. Elmsary. "Design and Optimization of Multi-Threshold CMOS (MTCMOS) Circuits". In IEEE transactions on Computer Aided Design, CAD'2003, vol. 22, issue 10, oct. 2003.

[2] H. Kawaguchi, K. Nose, T. Sakurai., "A Super Cut-Off CMOS (SCCMOS) Scheme for 0.5-V Supply Voltage with Picoampere Stand-by Current," IEEE JSSC, vol. 35, no. 10, pp. 1498-1501, Oct. 2000.

[3] A. Valentian et al. "Gate Bias Circuit for an SCCMOS Power Switch achieving maximum leakage reduction", ESSCIRC, Sept 07, Munich.

[4] S. Miermont, P. Vivet and M. Renaudin, "A Power Supply Selector for Energy- and Area-Efficient Local Dynamic Voltage Scaling", PATMOS'2007, 3-5 September, Göteborg, Sweden, 2007.

[5] E. Beigné et al. "Dynamic Voltage and Frequency Scaling Architecture for Units Integration within a GALS NoC", NOCS'2008, New-Castle, April 2008.

[6] H. Kawaguchi, G. Zhang, S. Lee, T.Sakurai, "An LSI for Vdd-Hopping and MPEG4 System Based on the Chip", IEEE ISCAS'01, May 2001.

[7] E. Beigné et al. "An Asynchronous Power Aware and Adaptive NoC based Circuit", Symposium on VLSI circuits, Honolulu, June 2008

A Single-Chip 8-Band CMOS Transceiver for W-CDMA(HSPA) / GSM(GPRS) / EDGE with Digital Interface

H. Yoshida, T. Toyoda, T. Yasuda, Y. Ogasawara, M. Ishii, T. Murasaki, G. Takemura, M. Iwanaga, T. Takida, Y. Araki, T. Hashimoto, K. Sami, T. Imayama, H. Shimizu, H. Kokatsu, Y. Tsuda, I. Tamura [††], H. Masuoka, M. Hosoya [†], R. Ito [†], H. Okuni [†], T. Kato [†], K. Sato, K. Nonin, K. Osawa, R. Fujimoto, S. Kawaguchi, H. Tsurumi, and N. Itoh

Semiconductor Company, Toshiba Corp., Yokohama, Japan
[†] Corporate R&D Center, Toshiba Corp., Kawasaki, Japan
[††] Toshiba Information Systems Corp., Kawasaki, Japan

Abstract— In this paper, a single-chip dual-mode 8-band 130nm CMOS transceiver including A/D/A converters and digital filters with 312 MHz LVDS interface is presented. For a transmitter chain, linear direct quadrature modulation architecture is introduced for both W-CDMA/HSDPA (High Speed Uplink Packet Access) and for GSM/EDGE. Analog baseband LPFs and quadrature modulators are commonly used both for GSM and for EDGE. For a direct conversion receiver chain, ABB (Analog Base-Band) blocks, i.e., LPFs and VGAs, delta-sigma A/D converters, and FIR filters are commonly used for W-CDMA/HSDPA (High Speed Downlink Packet Access) and GSM/EDGE to reduce chip area. Their characteristics can be reconfigured by register-based control sequence. The receiver chain also includes high-speed DC offset cancellers both in analog and in digital stage, and the self-contained AGC controller, whose parameters such as time constant are programmable to be free from DBB (Digital Base-Band) control. The transceiver also includes wide-range VCOs and fractional PLLs, an LVDS driver and receiver for high-speed digital interface of 312 MHz. Measured results reveal that the transceiver satisfies 3GPP specifications for W-CDMA/HSPA (High Speed Packet Access) and GSM/EDGE.

I. INTRODUCTION

Although W-CDMA has emerged as a potential mobile communication system standard and many mobile terminals support it, GSM is already in widespread use, and therefore, almost all mobile terminals still have to support GSM. Furthermore, reflecting the trend toward multiband mobile terminals in view of the rising demand for frequency resources, multiband transceivers, e.g., quad-band GSM transceivers or triple-band W-CDMA transceivers, have been reported[1-3]. However, no W-CDMA/GSM dual-mode multiband transceiver has been reported yet. In this paper, a fully integrated single-chip 8-band dual-mode CMOS transceiver, which is applicable in high-speed communication, i.e., HSPA (High Speed Packet Access) and EDGE, is presented.

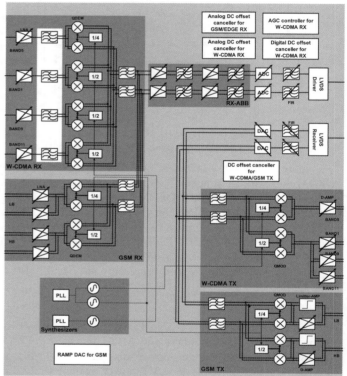

Figure 1.   Block diagram for entire transceiver

II. TRANSCEIVER ARCHITECTURE

An entire block diagram for the transceiver is shown in Figure 1. Direct conversion architecture is adopted both for the transmitter chain and for the receiver chain. The transceiver corresponds to eight bands; four bands for W-CDMA, namely, 800 MHz, 1.5 GHz, 1.7 GHz, and 2 GHz, and four bands for GSM/EDGE, namely, 850 MHz, 900MHz, 1.8 GHz, and 1.9 GHz and is equipped with mixed signal components, i.e., A/D and D/A converters and LVDS (Low

Voltage Differential Signaling) interface to communicate with a DBB (Digital Base-Band) LSI directly.

This transceiver introduces integrated A/D/A converters and digital signal processing circuitry in which a digitally assisted DC offset cancelling technique[4] with self-contained AGC (Automatic Gain Control) is implemented so that the transceiver is free from external AGC control, and thus, has flexible connectivity to various kinds of DBB LSIs.

A. Transmitter Chain

Direct quadrature modulation architecture is employed for transmitter chain both for W-CDMA and for GSM/EDGE. In order to reduce chip area, baseband LPFs and quadrature modulators can be commonly used in all bands of GSM/EDGE part due to introduction of direct modulation. A digitally assisted DC offset canceller is adopted to suppress carrier leakage. Complicated adaptive DC offset calibration is not required because DC offset in ABB (Analog Base-Band) is constant at any gain since the transmission power is controlled only with the RF amplifier. Dynamic range for transmission power control exceeds 90 dB with 10-bit digital control and 40 dB with 8-bit digital control for W-CDMA and EDGE, respectively.

B. Receiver Chain

The receiver also adopts direct conversion architecture. RF blocks, i.e., LNAs and QDEMs are arranged for each band; however, ABB blocks, i.e., LPFs and VGAs are commonly used for all bands both of W-CDMA and of GSM/EDGE. The ABB performances, namely, cut-off frequency, dynamic range, and input-referred noise can be changed by register-based control sequence via the LVDS interface in accordance with the reception mode of W-CDMA or GSM/EDGE. IQ imbalance of amplitude and phase is also digitally calibrated via the register setting to minimize EVM.

Different DC offset cancelling configurations are employed for W-CDMA and GSM/EDGE; for W-CDMA, closed-loop DC offset cancellers both in the analog and in the digital stage are cooperatively controlled by the digital DC offset detector that consists of an integrator and memory, so that continuous DC offset cancelling during reception is achieved to minimize residual DC offset and to prevent distraction in AGC. For GSM/EDGE employing TDMA (Time Division Multiple Access) system, a DC offset canceller is adopted only in the analog stage, which cancels DC offset in the predetermined time period before open-loop reception is operated during receiving time slot.

The self-contained AGC controller for W-CDMA is also included in the digital stage. Entire signal voltage for output of the A/D converter is measured to assign appropriate gain to LNA, VGAs and digital-AGC circuitry. The parameters for AGC such as time-constant and target voltage can be changed according to the specifications required by a DBB LSI.

A detailed block diagram for the DC offset cancellers and the AGC controller is illustrated in Figure 2.

C. Frequency synthesizers

Three wide-range VCOs for GSM, W-CDMA transmission and W-CDMA reception are introduced and they are controlled by two fractional PLLs; one is for GSM and W-CDMA transmission and the other is for W-CDMA reception.

D. Mixed signal and digital block

A 12-bit current-steering D/A converter applicable both for W-CDMA and for GSM/EDGE is introduced for the transmitter. This D/A converter works for W-CDMA with sampling clock of 15.36 MHz and for GSM/EDGE with sampling clock of 13.0 MHz. Also a 4-bit delta-sigma A/D converter with multi-decimated sampling clock is adopted for the receiver. This A/D converter works 15.36 MHz for W-CDMA and 541.667 kHz for GSM/EDGE.

The digital part includes programmable FIR filters for channel selection and phase equalization both for the transmitter chain and for the receiver chain. The tap coefficients of FIR filters are reconfigurable according to the frequency response in the analog stage. A high-speed LVDS driver and receiver of 312 MHz and peripheral A/D/A converters are also included in the transceiver.

Fig. 3 shows a chip photograph of the transceiver fabricated in 130nm CMOS, which occupies 6.5 mm x 6.5 mm chip area. Supply voltages for the transceiver are 2.8 V and 1.8 V.

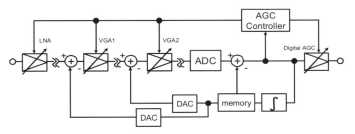

Figure 2. DC offset cancellers and AGC controller for W-CDMA

Figure 3. Die photograph for the transceiver

III. TRANSIMTTER PERFORMANCES

Measured overall EVM (Error Vector Magnitude) and ACLR (Adjacent Channel Leakage Ratio) for W-CDMA uplink signal of HPSK at 1950 MHz are shown in Figure 4.

EVM of 3.1 % and ACLR of less than –49 dBc at 4 dBm output with RX-band noise of less than –139 dBc/Hz were achieved. Fig. 5 also shows overall EVM for W-CDMA HSUPA (High Speed Uplink Packet Access) signal at 835 MHz to reveal that no degradation in EVM was found; i.e., less than 3 % was observed, whereas 2.4 % was achieved with normal uplink HPSK signal at 835 MHz.

Measured phase error and EVM in GSM/EDGE transmission are shown in Figure 6, which indicate that phase error of less than 1.2 degrees and EVM of less than 1.8 % were achieved for GMSK and 8-PSK, respectively.

The transmitter performance is summarized in Table 1.

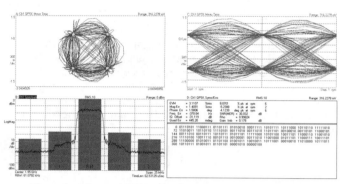

Figure 4.   Measured EVM and ACLR in W-CDMA transmission

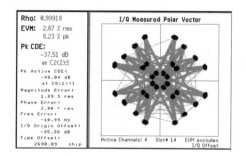

Figure 5.   Measured EVM for HSUPA in W-CDMA transmission

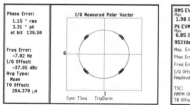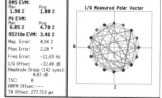

Figure 6.   Measured phase error and EVM in GSM transmission

IV.   RECEIVER PERFORMANCES

Measured EVM and eye diagram, which includes ADCs, decimation filters and FIR filters, for QPSK reception in W-CDMA are shown in Figure 7, which exhibits EVM of 3.3 % to ensure category 10 in HSDPA (High Speed Downlink Packet Access) reception. Measured BER (Bit Error Rate) performance for W-CDMA, i.e., RF input signal power of DPCH (Dedicated Physical Channel) versus BER, is shown in Figure 8. The sensitivity level defined in 3GPP is –117 dBm

for BER of 10^{-3}[5] and the evaluated result indicates that BER of DPCH for 10^{-3} was satisfied with the receiver input power of –125.0 dBm. Thus, assuming loss of 2.7 dB in front-end components such as an antenna switch and a duplexer, the sensitivity level for the receiver becomes –122.3 dBm, so that the 3GPP specification is satisfied by more than 5 dB margin. BER performance simulated from required CNR (Carrier to Noise Ratio) with measured gain and NF for the entire receiver chain is also shown in the same figure to indicate good agreement with the measured BER performance.

TABLE I.   TRANSMITTER PERFORMANCE

	W-CDMA	GSM/EDGE
Operation frequency (*1)	BAND 1 (1920—1980 MHz) BAND 5 (824—849 MHz) BAND 9 (1750—1785 MHz) BAND 11 (1427.9—1452.9 MHz)	GSM850 (824—849 MHz) GSM900 (880—915 MHz) DCS1800 (1710—1785 MHz) PCS1900 (1850—1910 MHz)
Dynamic range	> 95 dB	> 40 dB (8-PSK)
Output level	+14.6 dBm	+7.0 dBm (GMSK) +3.5 dBm (8-PSK)
RMS EVM / Phase error	2.4 % (BAND 5) 3.1 % (others)	1.15 deg. (GMSK) 1.8 % (8-PSK)
ACLR	–49.7 dBc @ +4 dBm	
Modulation spectrum	—	–36.2 dBc (200 kHz) –67.1dBc (400 kHz) –76.4 dBc (600 kHz)
Carrier leakage	< –50 dBc (w/ calibration)	–38 dBc
Power consumption	566.4 mW @ +4 dBm 478.5 mW @ –77 dBm (*2)	407.4 mW

(*1) Band name in 3GPP specifications
(*2) Including receiver chain

TABLE II.   RECEIVER PERFORMANCE

	W-CDMA	GSM/EDGE
Operation frequency (*1)	BAND 1 (2110—2170 MHz) BAND 5 (869—894 MHz) BAND 9 (1845—1880 MHz) BAND 11 (1475.9—1500.9 MHz)	GSM850 (869—894 MHz) GSM900 (925—960 MHz) DCS1800 (1805—1880 MHz) PCS1900 (1930—1990 MHz)
Dynamic range	69.6 dB (QDEM~)	100.9 dB
NF	1.84 dB (LNA) 7.9 dB (QDEM~)	5.4 dB
IIP3	–6.1dBm (LNA) +2.4 dBm (QDEM~)	—
IIP2	+ 56.3 dBm (QDEM)	—
RMS EVM	3.3 %	4.9 %
Sensitivity level	–122.3 dBm (*2)	–104.2 dBm (*3)
Blocker performance	—	–20.4 dBm (3 MHz) –18.4 dBm (20 MHz) (*3)
Power consumption	325.6 mW	317.0 mW

(*1) Band name in 3GPP specifications
(*2) Assuming front-end loss of 2.7 dB
(*3) Assuming front-end loss of 3.0 dB

Fig. 9 shows EVM and eye diagram for 8-PSK reception in GSM/EDGE mode, which indicates EVM of 4.9 % was achieved to make high-rate EDGE reception possible. Fig. 10 shows measured BER performance as a function of the receiver input power for GMSK reception in GSM/EDGE mode and simulated BER performance using required CNR with measured gain and NF for the entire receiver chain is also shown. Since the sensitivity level defined in 3GPP specifications is −102.0 dBm for BER of 2 % in TCH/FS class 2 channel[6], assuming loss of 3.0 dB in front-end components such as an antenna switch and an RF SAW filter, −104.2 dBm of sensitivity was achieved. Measured BER performance and simulation result indicate good agreement.

Measured receiver performance including other measured results is summarized in Table 2.

V. CONCLUSIONS

A fully-integrated 8-band W-CDMA(HSPA) / GSM(GPRS) / EDGE transceiver with high-speed digital interface implemented in 130nm CMOS has been developed. Compliant with 3GPP specifications, the transceiver's remarkable performance is suitable for accommodating high-rate communication in HSPA and EDGE, which performance is urgently required for 3G mobile terminals.

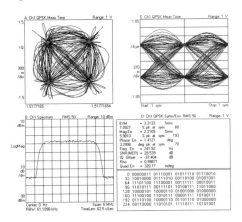

Figure 7. EVM and eye diagram for QPSK in W-CDMA reception

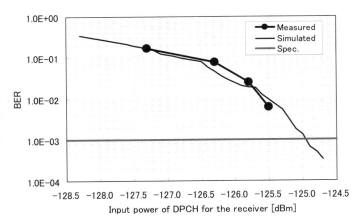

Figure 8. BER performances for DPCH in W-CDMA reception

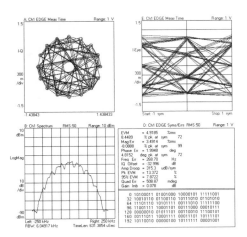

Figure 9. EVM and eye diagram for 8-PSK in GSM reception

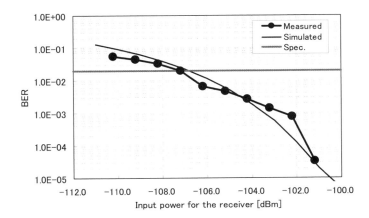

Figure 10. BER performance for GMSK in GSM reception

REFERENCES

[1] H. Darabi, A. Zolfaghari, H. Jensen, J. Leete, B. Mohammadi, J. Chiu, T. Li, Z. Zhou, P. Lettieri, Y. Chang, A. Hadji, P. Chang, M. Nariman, I. Bhatti, A. Medi, L. Serrano, A. Welz, K. Shoarinejad, S. Hasan, J. Castaneda, J. Kim, H. Tran, P. Kilcoyne, R. Chen, B. Lee, B. Zhao, B. Ibrahim, M. Rofougaran, and A. Rofougaran, "A Fully Integrated Quad-Band GPRS/EDGE Radio in 0.13μm CMOS," *IEEE ISSCC Digest of Technical Papers*, pp. 206—207, 2008.

[2] D. L. Kaczman, M. Shah, N. Godambe, M. Alam, H. Guimaraes, L. M. Han, M. Rachedine, D. L. Cashen, W. E. Getka, C. Dozier, W. P. Shepherd, and K. Couglar, "A Single-Chip Tri-Band (2100, 1900, 850/800 MHz) WCDMA/HSDPA Cellular Transceiver," *IEEE J. Solid State Circuits*, vol. 41, no. 5, pp. 1122—1132, 2006.

[3] B. Tenbroek, J. Strange, D. Nalbantis, C. Jones, P. Fowers, S. Brett, C. Beghein, and F. Beffa, "Single-Chip Tri-Band WCDMA/HSDPA Transceiver without External SAW Filters and with Integrated TX-Power Control," *IEEE ISSCC Digest of Technical Papers*, pp. 202—203, 2008.

[4] H. Okuni, R. Ito, H. Yoshida, and T. Itakura, "A Direct Conversion Receiver with Fast-Settling DC offset Canceller," *Proc. IEEE PIMRC 2007*, pp. 1—5, 2007.

[5] 3rd Generation Partnership Project; *3GPP TS 25.101 V8.2.0*, 2008.

[6] 3rd Generation Partnership Project; *3GPP TS 45.005 V8.0.0*, 2008.

A low power CMOS SAW-less Quad Band WCDMA/HSPA/1X/EGPRS Transmitter

Marco Cassia, Aristotele Hadjichristos, Hong Sun Kim, Jin-Su Ko, Jeongsik Yang, Sang-Oh Lee and Kamal Sahota

Qualcomm Inc.
5775 Morehouse Drive San Diego, CA 92121 USA

Abstract— **In this paper we present a multi-band CMOS transmitter for cellular applications. The transmitter covers a wide range of frequency bands and it is designed to minimize power consumption in order to increase hand-set talk-time. The output noise performance allows the removal of SAW for certain W-CDMA and CDMA bands; moreover it can be configured to be used for SAW-less GSM/EDGE operations while maintaining an excellent linearity.**

I. INTRODUCTION

The large commercial success of multiband and multi-mode 3rd generation cellular radios has been driving single chip integration, SAW filter reduction and low battery power consumption. State of the art solutions require quad-band EGSM combined with quad-band WCDMA/HSPA and C2K (CDMA) operation. Compact form factors make single chip SAW-less solutions highly desirable. Quad-Band SAW-less EGPRS transmitter examples have been presented in [1], [2] and [3] while Single-Band IMT SAW-less WCDMA transmitter solutions have been presented in [4] and [5]. Finally, Triple-Band WCDMA transmitter solutions that use TX SAW filters were presented in [6] and [7]. This paper describes the first SAW-less Quad-Band WCDMA/HSPA/CDMA/EGPRS low battery power single chip transmitter implemented in a low cost $0.18\mu m$ CMOS technology.

II. ARCHITECTURE

The main blocks of the transmitter architecture are presented in Fig. 1 and will be described in details in the next section. The transmitter is divided into two distinct signal paths, one for low frequency band (824 MHz to 915 MHz) and one for high frequency (1710 MHz to 1980 MHz). The two paths share the common baseband processing (Baseband Filter and Baseband Amplifier) and they are split at up-conversion; as shown in Fig. 1, separated mixers are used for GSM and WCDMA/CDMA in order to optimize current consumption and noise performance according to the various standard requirements.

For the same reason, two different VCOs have been designed to provide GSM LO signal or WCDMA/CDMA LO signal; the PLL is shared and it is based on a single bit $\Sigma\Delta$ architecture.

The transmitter operations can be summarized as follows: the external baseband I/Q differential current signals are applied to the baseband filter. Both common mode input voltage and input impedance are set by an input buffer: it is crucial to keep a low common-mode voltage as well as low impedance to allow low voltage operations. After filtering, the signal is mirrored to the up-converters, filtered, passed through a RF amplifier and transferred to a driver amplifier by means of a balun. The purpose of the RF filter is to attenuate any unwanted LO spurs to avoid in band signal aliasing due to intermodulation products.

To achieve the required WCDMA dynamic range (> 80 dB), the gain control is split into baseband gain stages and into 2 RF gain stages; the range as well as the slope of the gain control curve are

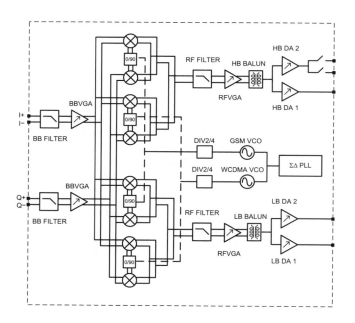

Fig. 1. Direct I/Q modulator transmitter block diagram

set by means of a programmable look-up table (LUT). Overall the transmitter provides two identical low band outputs operating from 824 MHz (US Cell) to 915MHz (EGSM) and three identical high band outputs, operating from 1710MHz (DCS) to 1980MHz (IMT). EDGE large signal polar modulation is implemented with collector voltage modulated PA.

III. MAIN BLOCKS

This section focus on the implementation details of the main transmitter blocks.

A. Baseband Filter and Baseband Amplifier

The purpose of the filter is to provide rejection for any external digital spurs, DAC sampling noise and also to attenuate noise in the receiver band of the various standards. The filter bandwidth is programmable from 1MHz to 5.6 MHz. A simplified schematic is shown in Fig. 2: g_{m1}, g_{m2} and C_2 form an active inductor providing an overall second order low pass bi-quadratic transfer function.

$$I_{upc}(s) = I_{in}G_{bbvga}\frac{1}{\left(\frac{s}{\omega_0}\right)^2 + \left(\frac{s}{\omega_0 Q}\right) + 1} \quad (1)$$

where I_{in} is the input current and G_{bbvga} is the gain of the baseband amplifier. The resonant frequency ω_0 and the quality factor Q can be expressed in term of circuit parameters as follows:

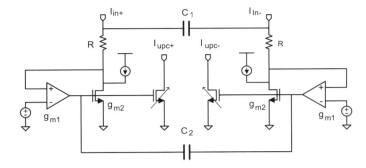

Fig. 2. Baseband filter/amplifier simplified schematic

$$\omega_0 = \sqrt{\frac{g_{m_1} g_{m_2}}{C_1 C_2}} \qquad (2)$$

$$Q = \frac{1}{R}\sqrt{\frac{C_2}{C_1 g_{m_1} g_{m_2}}} \qquad (3)$$

The filtering provided is typically sufficient to meet noise requirements and does not require the addition of an external board capacitor.

As shown in Fig. 2, the baseband amplifier is a simple scalable current mirror that can either attenuate or amplify the filtered current. The mirror ratio is linear in dB and can provide a control range over 40 dB. Given the extended range, matching of devices is critical to avoid LO leakage due to current mismatch.

B. RF-VGA

The up-converters (SSB mixing) are based on the standard Gilbert topology: the in-phase baseband signal is mixed with the in-phase RF LO signal and the quadrature baseband signal is mixed with the quadrature RF LO signal. The mixer outputs are summed and the resulting differential signal is passed through a variable attenuator (RFVGA).

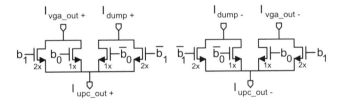

Fig. 3. RFVGA schematic

The VGA is a current attenuator implemented with binary weighted NFETs. In order to maintain good linearity of the output current with the control word, thermometer coding is implemented for the MSBs. A simplified schematic of two LSB cells is shown in Fig. 3: basically, the current from the upconverter is switched either to the balun or dumped to the supply. The layout of this block is critical to keep the isolation between the input and output signals greater than the required attenuation.

C. Driver amplifier

The last stage of the transmitter chain is the driver amplifier (DA). The DA core is presented in Fig. 4; the only difference between low band and high band is the RF choke. The RF signal at the RFVGA output is passed to the DA through a balun; the turns ratio is approximately 3:1 for low band and 1:1 for high band. The primary

side of the balun is connected to the VGA output and its center tap provides the bias for the mixer/VGA stack; the input impedance on the primary side is set by the reflected impedance of the DA input impedance.

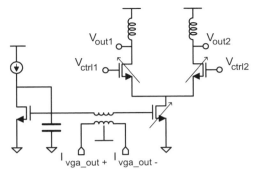

Fig. 4. Driver Amplifier schematic

The real part of this input impedance is approximately set by the bond wire inductance times the ω_T of the device. The secondary side of the transformer is connected to the driver amplifier g_m stages; gain control is achieved by switching the binary weighted cascode NFETs.

The output is combined in the output coil, that along with an external capacitor provides a 50 Ohm output match. Since the match is optimized for large signal, a VSWR circuit (programmable shunt resistors) has been added to the output to maintain constant VSWR across the entire power range. This is necessary since the output impedance changes significantly across the power range, due to on/off switching of the driver amplifier cells.

A total of four DAs have been implemented. To add a third high band output without increasing the die area, a low-insertion loss RF switch has been designed to multiplex a single DA output into two separate outputs.

D. $\Sigma\Delta$ synthesizer

A single bit 3rd order sigma delta fractional synthesizer provides GSM/EDGE and WCDMA/CDMA LO signals [1]. Two different VCOs are designed to meet GSM/EDGE performance and WCDMA/CDMA TX performance individually. The GSM/EDGE VCO can be also used for GSM/EDGE Rx mode. The synthesizer is programmable depending on different modes to optimize power consumption, settling time, and phase noise performance. On chip regulators are implemented to meet spur performance as well as to have good phase noise performance. The synthesizer requires only one external component for its loop filter, and the rest of components are integrated.

TABLE I

UMTS CDMA CHIP PERFORMANCE AT 5 dBm OUTPUT POWER

Band	Cell	900	AWS	PCS	IMT
WCDMA ACLR (dBc/3.84 MHz)	-50	-49	-47	-46.7	-46.5
1X ACPR (dBc/30 kHz)	-60.5	\	-62.5	-56	-56.9
HSPA ACLR (dBc/3.84 MHz)	-47.5	-47	-45.6	-45	-44.3

IV. CHIP LEVEL MEASUREMENTS

Table I presents a summary of UMTS/CDMA linearity performance at chip level across different frequency bands. The synthesizer draws 3.84 mA from a 2.7 V supply; the rest of the transmitter (including VCO and LO path) operates from a 2.1V supply. The total TX power consumption (including the synthesizer) vs chip output power level is presented in Fig. 5. Notice that -8 dBm and 5 dBm output power correspond to 0 dBm and 23 dBm (max output power) at the phone level. More than 80% of the TX power probability distribution function is below 0 dBm.

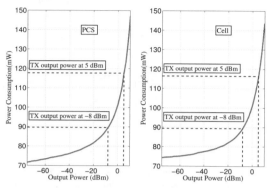

Fig. 5.   Total TX power consumption

The transmitter is able to output more power, while keeping ACLR well below -40 dBc/3.84MHz; a typical ACLR snapshot for 8 dBm (after de-embedding 0.7 dB of board trace and cable losses) IMT output power is presented in Fig. 6.

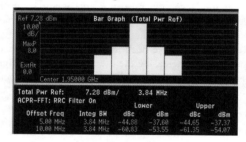

Fig. 6.   WCDMA ACLR snapshot

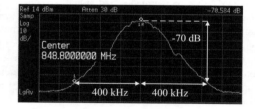

Fig. 7.   GSM 850 ORFS

As previously mentioned, the transmitter can be reconfigured to operate as quad-band GSM/EDGE. Good margin to GSM 0505 specifications is achieved, in particular ORFS 400kHz measurements (see Fig. 7) are within the lowest reported.

V. SYSTEM LEVEL MEASUREMENTS

Besides low WCDMA power consumption, output noise performance allows SAW filter removal across several frequency bands. Fig. 8 compares phone sensitivity measurements at max power for Cell, AWS and IMT with and without SAW filters. Notice that the TX output power is decreased by an amount equivalent to the filter insertion loss and this causes a degradation of the TX output SNR.

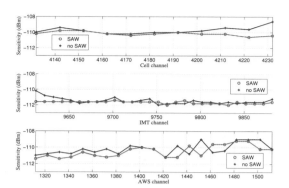

Fig. 8.   IMT, Cell and AWS receiver sensitivity performance with and without SAW filter across temperature

It can be observed sensitivity deltas for Cell higher channel (~ 1.5 dB desense) and IMT lower channel (~ 1 dB desense): Cell degradation is likely due to PA matching not optimized for SAW filter by-pass. For IMT the measured sensitivity in SAW-less mode is still below -110 dBm. A summary of UMTS measurements is presented in Table II.

TABLE II
UMTS SYSTEM PERFORMANCE AT 23 dBm OUTPUT POWER.

Band	Cell	900	AWS	PCS	IMT	System
WCDMA ACLR (dBc/3.84 MHz)	-43.4	-41.3	-40.9	-42.6	-43.1	-33
EVM (rms) %	4.1%	5.5%	5.6%	5.5%	5.6%	17.5%
HSPA ACLR ($\beta_c = 12, \beta_d = 15$) (dBc/3.84 MHz)	-40.2	-39.5	-40.1	-42.8	-43.5	-33
EVM (rms) %	5.25%	5.9%	5.3%	5.4%	4.7%	17.5%

A third achievement is the removal of TX SAW filter for GSM with good system margin: while for DCS and PCS the RX band noise needs to be below - 71 dBm, for GSM low band the requirement is 8 dB more stringent. While meeting the LB noise requirement with PLL modulation is nowadays typical [1], [2], [3], achieving the same goal in a direct I/Q transmitter topology is still a challenge: current in the up-converter path needs to be increased to improved the SNR, but at the same time the entire TX chain needs to maintain linearity.

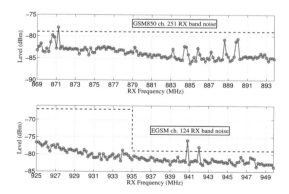

Fig. 9.   GSM850/ EGSM receive band noise

Typical GSM850/EGSM noise measurements at phone level are presented in Fig. 9: on average, there are 2/3 dB margin to the GSM specifications at the closest duplex frequency (channel 251 for

TABLE III

WCDMA COMPARISON TABLE

Design	Process	Power Consumption at min power	Power Consumption at 0 dBm	Power Consumption at nom. power	Bands	SAW	IMT ACLR at 5 MHz	Multi mode
[4]	CMOS 0.13μm	70 mW	175mW	230mW at +3.8dBm	IMT	NO	-46 dBc @ +3.8dBm	NO
[5]	0.35μm SiGe BiCMOS	not known	NA	113mW at -10dBm	IMT	NO	-49 dBc @ -10dBm	NO
[6]	CMOS 0.13μm	135.9 mW	not known	177.6mW at +9.5dBm	CELL PCS IMT	YES	-46 dBc @ +9.5dBm	NO
[7]	CMOS 0.13μm	74 mW est	not known	200mW (est) at +7dBm	CELL PCS IMT	YES	-43 dBc @ +7dBm	NO
This work	**CMOS 0.18μm**	**72 mW**	**100 mW**	**118mW at +5dBm**	**CELL 900 DCS PCS IMT**	**NO**	**-46 dBc @ +5dBm**	**YES**

GSM 850 and channel 124 for EGSM) and two fractional/reference spurs per channel (the GSM standard allows up to 5 exceptions per channel). Table IV summarizes the performance at phone level for the quad-band GSM/EDGE transmitter. A WCDMA performance comparison with previous published work is presented in table III.

TABLE IV

EDGE\GSM SYSTEM PERFORMANCE

Band	Parameter	Measured	GSM standard
GSM 850 MHz	Max Pout	32.1 dBm	33 dBm
	400 kHz mod	-69.11dBc	< -60 dBc
	Phase error rms	1.07°	< 5°
EDGE 850 MHz	Max Pout	27 dBm	27 dBm
	400 kHz mod	-63 dBc	< -54 dBc
	EVM rms	1.5%	< 9%
GSM 900 MHz	Max Pout	32 dBm	33 dBm
	400 kHz mod	-68.7 dBc	< -60 dBc
	Phase error rms	1.08°	< 5°
EDGE 900 MHz	Max Pout	27 dBm	27 dBm
	400 kHz mod	-63 dBc	< -54 dBc
	EVM rms	1.5%	< 9%
GSM 1800 MHz	Max Pout	29 dBm	30 dBm
	400 kHz mod	-67.17	< -60 dBc
	Phase error rms	1.12°	< 5°
EDGE 1800 MHz	Max Pout	26 dBm	27 dBm
	400 kHz mod	-64.1 dBc	< -54 dBc
	EVM rms	2.03%	< 9%
GSM 1900 MHz	Max Pout	29 dBm	30 dBm
	400 kHz mod	-66.7 dBc	< -60 dBc
	Phase error rms	1.3°	< 5°
EDGE 1900 MHz	Max Pout	26 dBm	27 dBm
	400 kHz mod	-63.1 dBc	< -54 dBc
	EVM rms	2.11%	< 9%

VI. CONCLUSIONS

The CMOS transmitter for multi-mode multi-band operations presented in this paper is part of a single chip Quad Band GSM/EDGE - Multiband WCDMA transceiver; it has been implemented in a standard CMOS 0.18μm process and operates from 2.1V and 2.7 supply voltages. Fig. 10 shows the micro-photograph of the chip. Even if the WCDMA power consumption is minimized, the circuit is capable of SAW less performance while exceeding WCDMA requirements. Moreover, to the authors knowledge, this is the first time a GSM SAW-less CMOS I/Q direct-upconverter has been reported.

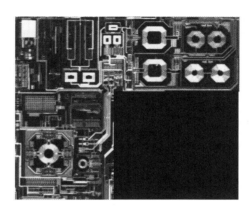

Fig. 10. Transmitter micro-photograph

ACKNOWLEDGMENTS

The authors would like to thank Pat Cantey and Rick Staszewski for supporting and providing the system level measurements. Thanks to Tim Nacita for leading the layout and to Sean Weng, Kevin Atkinson and Lee Lam for writing the phone drivers. Finally, we would like to thank Beomsup Kim and Cormac Conroy for their valuable inputs and support.

REFERENCES

[1] Erdogan, O.E.; Gupta, R.; Yee, D.G.; Rudell, J.C.; Jin-Su Ko; Brockenbrough, R.; Sang-Oh Lee; Lei, E.; Joo Leong Tham; Hongbing Wu; Conroy, C.; Kim, B.; "A single-chip quad-band GSM/GPRS transceiver in 0.18 μm standard CMOS", ISSCC. 2005 IEEE International 6-10 Feb. 2005 Page(s):318 - 601 Vol. 1
[2] Elliott, M.R.; Montalvo, T.; Jeffries, B.P.; Murden, F.; Strange, J.; Hill, A.; Nandipaku, S.; Harrebek, J.; "A polar modulator transmitter for GSM/EDGE" Solid-State Circuits, IEEE Journal of Volume 39, Issue 12, Dec. 2004 Page(s):2190 – 2199
[3] Hadjichristos, A.; Walukas, J.; Klemmer, N.; Suter, W.; Justice, S.; Uppathil, S.; Scott, G.; "A highly integrated quad band low EVM polar modulation transmitter for GSM/EDGE applications" CICC 2004. Proceedings of the IEEE 2004 3-6 Oct. 2004 Page(s):565 – 568
[4] Jones, C.; Tenbroek, B.; Fowers, P.; Beghein, C.; Strange, J.; Beffa, F.; Nalbantis, D.; "Direct-Conversion WCDMA Transmitter with 163dBc/Hz Noise at 190MHz Offset" ISSCC 2007. Digest of Technical Papers. IEEE International 11-15 Feb. 2007 Page(s):336 – 607
[5] Papadopoulos, D.F.G.; Qiuting Huang; "A Linear Uplink WCDMA Modulator with 156dBc/Hz Downlink SNR" ISSCC 2007. Digest of Technical Papers. IEEE International 11-15 Feb. 2007 Page(s):338 – 607
[6] Kaczman, D.L.; Shah, M.; Godambe, N.; Alam, M.; Guimaraes, H.; Han, L.M.; Rachedine, M.; Cashen, D.L.; Getka, W.E.; Dozier, C.; Shepherd, W.P.; Couglar, K.; "A single-chip tri-band (2100, 1900, 850/800 MHz) WCDMA/HSDPA cellular transceiver" Solid-State Circuits, IEEE Journal of Volume 41, Issue 5, May 2006 Page(s):1122 – 1132
[7] Koller, R.; Ruhlicke, T.; Pimingsdorfer, D.; Adler, B.; "A single-chip 0.13μm CMOS UMTS W-CDMA multi-band transceiver" Radio Frequency Integrated Circuits (RFIC) Symposium, 2006 IEEE 11-13 June 2006 Page(s):4 pp.

149

A 14-mW 2.4-GHz CMOS Transceiver for Short Range Wireless Sensor Applications

Reza Yousefi and Ralph Mason
Carleton University
Department of Electronics, Ottawa, Canada
Email:{gyousefi,rmason}@doe.carleton.ca

Abstract A low power and energy efficient transceiver architecture is introduced. It is implemented on a single chip intended for use in short range radios based on WPAN (IEEE802.15.4) at 2.4GHz. The transmitter is based on a constant envelope modulator built around a dual loop frequency synthesizer coupled through an injection locking mechanism. The core of the dual conversion receiver is realized by reconfiguring the transmitter building blocks. Techniques are presented for tuning the center frequency and bandwidth of the RF filter, as well as generating the required local oscillator frequencies. The transceiver is fabricated in a 0.18- m standard CMOS process. The receiver achieves 83-dBm sensitivity and 25dBm 1-dB compression point. The transmitter outputs 7-dBm QPSK signal, while carrier phase noise is better than 108-dBc/Hz at 5-MHz offset. Active mode power consumption is 11-mW and 14-mW in receive and transmit modes, respectively, on a 1.6-V supply.

I. INTRODUCTION

The constraints of a wireless microsensor network are different from those of conventional hand-held devices. They communicate small packet sizes, and the average data rate is low due to low event rate. Also, the traffic is mostly up-link from sensors to the base station with a very short transmission distance. Furthermore, the battery lifetime of the sensor network is crucial and must be maximized. Due to such unique characteristics of sensor networks, conventional design methodologies for wireless devices may result in an inefficient use of energy if they are applied to microsensor network [1].

The proposed architecture in this paper is tailored to the aforementioned characteristics to satisfy the expectations from such a link. Since the transmitter is activated more often than the receiver; and considering the facts that the packet size is small and transmit power required to communicate with a node at a short distance is low, special emphases are put on the transmitter capabilities to pass through the start-up time quickly and handle a high data rate while consuming very low power. The architecture takes advantage of the fact that in most microsensor networks, the transmitter and receiver are not in an active mode simultaneously and therefore explores opportunities to maximize the "re-use" of building blocks between two modes of operation. This results in at least 30%

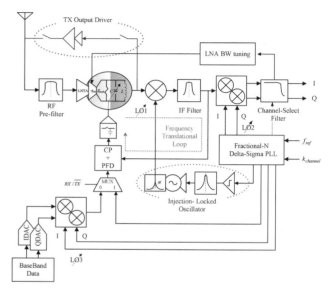

Figure 1. The proposed transceiver architecture

saving in the silicon real state and as a result, a reduction in the die cost, while completely avoiding the use of separate off-chip components to meet the requirements of the other mode. Therefore, the receiver is formed by reconfiguring the transmitter blocks, in particular the VCO and RF mixer, to act as the LNA and first downconvertor in a dual conversion scheme. Although not fundamentally required for proper functionality of the architecture, in a parallel effort, the paper challenges the idea of partial channel filtering at early stages of the receiver front-end and by incorporating it into the system, shows how it mitigates the dynamic range requirements of mixers and baseband channel select filters which results in a considerable power savings.

II. SYSTEM ARCHITECTURE

The proposed transceiver architecture is shown in Fig.1. The receiver (Rx) adopts a dual conversion architecture with a tunable LNA. It includes the preselect RF filter, LNA, RF mixer, quadrature IF mixers, baseband channel select filter and bandwidth tuning circuitry. The transmitter (Tx), on the other hand, is a constant envelope modulator which exploits the LNA (in an oscillatory state) and RF mixer as a part of the Frequency Translational Loop (FTL) used to translate the up-converted data from IF to a desired RF channel. The receiver and the transmitter share the Fractional-N Master PLL (MPLL) and the frequency multiplier (injection locked oscillator), which are providing the required local oscillator frequencies, LO1, LO2 and LO3, for IF and RF mixers.

In the transmit mode, the LNA, which has already been pushed into oscillation, acts as the VCO for the FTL. The QPSK data is first up-converted to the IF using LO3 and then fed into the Phase-Frequency Detector as the reference frequency of the FTL. Due to the high reference frequency, there are several hundred phase comparisons for one transmitted bit. Therefore the loop is able to copy the phase modulation of the reference path onto the output of the VCO, which is within the loop. In the FTL none of the local oscillator signals is at the carrier frequency, and thus the VCO will not suffer from frequency pulling.

In the receive mode, the narrow band LNA is first tuned to the desired channel. Once more the FTL is used to simply switching its PFD reference frequency from the Tx IQ mixer to LO2, from MPLL. Once the loop is settled, i.e. LNA is locked to the band of interest, the loop is opened and the tuning voltage is stored in the sampling capacitor of the loop filter. The bandwidth of the LNA can be adjusted to a set of discrete values. The narrow band LNA further attenuates the image frequency at 1800-MHz, which has already been attenuated by at least 40-dB at the off-chip ceramic pre-select filter. The LNA output is down-converted to a high IF. Due to the high frequency LO1, the RF mixer suffers from large 1/f noise at its output, but this does not corrupt the signal, which lies at the IF. The LO2 whose frequency is equal to the first IF, downconverts the signal in quadrature, to zero IF. Since, the first IF is well bellow RF, the flicker noise at the second mixer output is proportionally lower.

III. CIRCUIT IMPLEMENTATIONS

A. RxLNA or TxVCO

A common-gate topology with impedance transformation at its input is chosen for the LNA, shown in Fig.2, in order to decrease the power dissipation while achieving a relatively low Q matching network at its input [2]. Cascode transistors are added in order to further improve the input-output isolation. The isolation and wide-band matching network are crucial since the tuning of the LNA load affects the input matching characteristics. The cross-coupled transistors are for the tuning the LNA bandwidth [3-4]. They are designed such that for certain settings the LNA is pushed into an oscillatory state and act as the VCO. The bandwidth tuning is performed by the digitally controlled source degenerating NMOS transistors.

The LC tank inductors are realized by bond-wires connecting the pads to the PCB, in series with high-Q off-chip inductors. The capacitor is made of the parallel combination of a set of switched MIM capacitors and a pair of MOS varactors. The varactors are designed using PMOS transistors to protect them from substrate noise coupling. A tuning range of 150-MHz is achieved around the neighborhood of 2.44-GHz. The Kvco is kept relatively low in order to reduce the

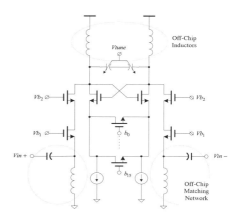

Figure 2. The schematic of the LNA

sensitivity of the tuning node in the receive mode when the FTL is opened. In the receive mode the achievable gain varies depending on the bandwidth setting. The LNA has a gain of 18-dB when it is tuned to a 20-MHz bandwidth. Such a high gain reduces the impact of the following stages on the sensitivity of the receiver.

The center frequency of the LNA is tuned first by switching to the VCO mode; then by turning off certain number of the degenerating transistors in the –gm-cell, it is switched into the amplification mode, and as a result, the Q of the tank is changed. During the tuning, when switching from VCO mode to the LNA mode with a limited but high Q , the center frequency of the LNA changes, however, the desired channel still falls in the extended bandwidth, which is what matters at the end of the tuning process. Also, the center frequency might change in the normal operation when the LNA is receiving small inputs due to voltage dependant parasitic capacitances. This sets a limit on the minimum tunable bandwidth, introducing a new trade-off between the maximum swing allowed in VCO mode and the linearity of the LNA. The smaller the VCO swing is, the lower the LNA linearity gets, albeit the narrower the tunable bandwidth is going to be. Therefore a co-design methodology has been developed to find the optimum setting.

B. Mixers

The RF mixer is designed based on the doubly-balanced Gilbert cell topology with a parallel LC tank as the load, which also acts as the IF filter. A 470-nH off-chip inductor with a relatively high Q of about 15 is used to achieve a 2-dB conversion gain with a very small biasing current of 58-μA. This choice allows the IF filter to be transparent for a 20-MHz of bandwidth at 305-MHz. The IF bandpass filter rejects the image frequency of RF+LO1 which is around 2.75-GHz. The IIP3 of the RF mixer is mainly determined by the overdrive voltage of its RF input transistors. A supply voltage of 1.6-V allows choosing a Vdsat of 0.4-V which results in about 15-dBm IIP3. The linearity of the RF mixer has a significant impact on the phase noise performance of the FTL.

A pair of IQ mixers forms the IF mixer in the receive chain. Each mixer adopts a Gilbert topology with diode connected NMOS as the load. This load also acts as the gm cell for the first Biquad filter in the baseband channel select filter which saves an intermediate transconductance stage. A similar structure is employed for the up-conversion mixers in the transmitter, where the described topology is combined with a differential-to-single ended converter to provide a CMOS level signal to the PFD in FTL. The input transistors are fed by a 100-mVpp binary data around 900-mV common-mode produced by single-bit DACs.

C. Frequency Synthesizer

The body of the frequency synthesis system can be decomposed and discussed in three major building blocks, the master PLL, the frequency multiplier, and the frequency translational loop. In order to be able to select any of the 16 channels located in between 2400MHz to 2480MHz, the master PLL needs to generate IF frequencies, LO2 (Rx mode) and LO3 (Tx mode), between 300-MHz to 310-MHz with a resolution of 625-KHz from a reference frequency of 10-MHz. A frequency multiplier generates the 7th harmonic of the IF, 2100-MHz to 2170-MHz, according to the LO2 (LO3), which is used as the LO1.

1) Master PLL.

A Fractional-N Delta-Sigma PLL is used as the master PLL (MPLL) to generate the local oscillator frequencies. The 4-stage ring oscillator is used to produce 8 phases of IF frequencies, capable of covering a tuning range of 280-MHz to 320-MHz. The delay cell used in the ring oscillator is shown in Fig.3. Experiments with various topologies showed that this structure provides a better PSRR and higher loop gain for a given current while it can operate at supply voltages as low as 1.3-V. The open loop phase noise of the MPLL is better than –130-dBc/Hz at 5-MHz offset. Each unit delay cell drains 450-μA from the supply.

Two stages of divide-by-2 are followed by a divide-by-7/8 to cover the required output range of 280-MHz to 320-MHz from a 10-MHz reference frequency. The latches used in the dividers are all based on True-Single-Phase-Clock (TSPC) topology which consumes very low power while it is fast enough for the frequency range of the MPLL. The divide-by-7/8 generates a non 50% output clock which is not an issue for the conventional tri-state PFD sensitive to rising edge only.

A single-bit third-order Delta-Sigma Modulator (DSM) based on [5], controls the mode bit of the Divide-by-7/8 according to the 6-bit control word, K-channel. This requires the use of a loop filter of second order or higher to compensate for the 40-dB/dec noise shaping caused by the DSM. The third order loop filter is made of off-chip components. A lock detector is implemented in order to turn on the FTL only after the MPLL is settled. The worst case settling time of 50-μs is observed for a 310-MHz output.

2) Frequency Multiplier

The frequency multiplier, shown in Fig.3, is designed based on the sub-harmonic injection locking of a system oscillating with free running frequency close to an odd harmonic of the original injected signal The efficiency of a pure sub-harmonic multiplier system strongly depends on the non-linearity of the slave oscillator and the offset between its free-running frequency and the closest harmonic of injected

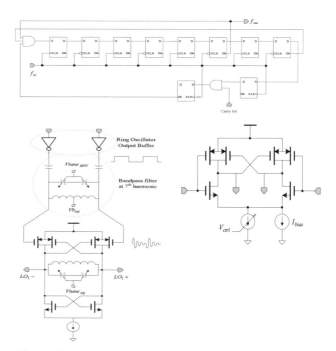

Figure 3. The schematic of a) divide-by-7/8, b) frequency multiplier, and c) ring oscillator delay cell

signal. It is observed that the oscillation amplitude is inversely proportional to its degree of non-linearity, with supply voltage as the upper limit. On the other hand, driving the mixer with a larger swing LO is desired since it results in a higher conversion gain and a less flicker noise power. Therefore, a lower linearity high swing oscillator is preferred to directly drive the mixer.

A complementary pair of phases of the ring oscillator is applied to CMOS inverters in order to enhance its harmonic contents. The pulse-shaped signal is then ac coupled to an oscillator through an on-chip bandpass filter with its pass band tuned around the 7th harmonic. The free-running frequency of the slave oscillator is also tuned accordingly, to be brought closer to this harmonic. This makes the phase noise degradation within a minimum 20*log(7) or 17-dB.

The CMOS drivers inject –40-dBm into the bandpass filter. The bandpass filter is made using a 9.4-nH symmetric on-chip inductor with a center tap used to provide biasing voltage for the PMOS injector. A set of binary weighted MIM capacitors in parallel with the inductor make the center frequency tunable. A similar LC tank is used as the resonator for the exploited complementary differential oscillator with a different decoder for the tuning. The average dc current drawn by the oscillator is 800-μA. The fundamental frequency spurs at the oscillator output are lower than –52-dBc.

3) Frequency Translational Loop.

The FTL is highlighted in Fig.1. The differential IF signal is converted to single-ended before being applied to the PFD. The integrator capacitor in the loop filter is connected to the charge pump through the sampling switch used during the receive mode. The minimum size NMOS switch is accompanied by dummy switches to minimize the sampling clock feed-through and charge re-distribution. The sampling capacitor is large enough to filter out the even-harmonics coupled to the common node of the varactors, but it is mediated by a buffer stage before being connected to the varactor in the LNA tank. This is necessary in order to prevent accumulation of the dc charge produced by the even-order non-linearity of the varactors, which eventually changes the voltage stored on the capacitor and as a result, the LNA gets out of tune.

The bandwidth of the FTL is determined by several factors. Ideally, since the FTL reference frequency is high, a wider loop bandwidth seems possible and therefore desirable in order to transfer a high bit rate up-converted data to the output of the modulator in transmit mode. A wider bandwidth reduces the settling time and as a result the energy consumption of the transceiver. Several other factors define a limit for such a choice; given the phase noise performance of the MPLL and the channel spacing, the loop bandwidth is set to 2-MHz. A settling time of about 7-µs is observed.

Due to the large loop bandwidth, the close-in phase noise of the FTL is dominated by that of reference frequency from MPLL and LO1 rather than VCO. The LO1 is correlated to the reference frequency via the frequency multiplier and there are reference spurs present on the spectrum of the injection locked oscillator at about –52-dBc.

D. Baseband Channel Select Filter

A pair of fourth order gm-C filters is designed for I and Q paths. The filters, shown in Fig.4, are based on the cascade of two Biquad filters. When it is tuned for 1-MHz bandwidth, it attenuates the edge of the adjacent channel at 4-MHz by about 48-dB. Combining this with the selectivity of the partial channel select filter built on the LNA the total adjacent channel attenuation is better than 60-dB.

Filter nonlinearity sets the upper bound on the dynamic range. The filter uses two-stage OTA (operational Transconductance Amplifier) to drive the capacitive load. Each OTA drains 64-µA and gives 82-dB dc gain with a unity gain frequency of 11-MHz and 60-degree phase margin. Large gate area is used for the input NMOS transistors to lower the flicker noise corner. The lower *ft* of the transistors is not an issue because the maximum input frequency of the filter is 10-MHz. The combined gain of the IF mixer and channel-select filter is 7-dB. The baseband filters consume an estimated total current of about 750-uA.

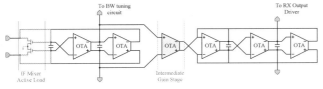

Figure 4. The schematic of the baseband channel select filter

TABLE I.   SUMMARY OF THE CHIP CHARACTERISTICS

Receiver Sensitivity	–83-dBm
Receiver 1-dB Compression Point	–25-dBm
LO1 Phase Noise	–113-dBc/Hz @5MHz offset
MPLL Phase Noise	–132-dBc/Hz @5MHz
Blocker Rejection (BW=2-MHz) @ 2.398-GHz	–60-dB
Transmitter Start-up Time	55-µs
Transmitter Output power	–7-dBm
Power Dissipation	Rx < 11-mW Tx < 14-mW
Technology	0.18-µm CMOS
Die Area	2.7mm by 2.5mm

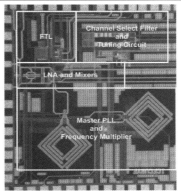

Figure 5. The die microphotograph

ACKNOWLEDGMENT

The authors would like to acknowledge the Micronet and Canadian Microelectronics Corporation (CMC) for their supports. Also, one of the authors, Reza Yousefi, thanks Mr. Yasser Soliman for his valuable comments in the course of preparing this paper.

REFERENCES

[1] A. Wang, S. Cho, C. Sodini, and A. Chandrakasan"Energy efficient modulation and MAC for asymmetric RF microsensor systems," in Proc. Int. Symp. Low Power Design (ISLPED), 2001, pp. 106–111.

[2] H. Darabi, Abidi A. A., "A 4.5-mW 900-MHz CMOS receiver for wireless paging," IEEE Journal of Solid State Circuits, vol. 35, pp. 1085--1096, August 2000.

[3] DeVries C., R. Mason, "A 0.18-µ CMOS, high Q-enhanced bandpass filter with direct digital tuning," Proceeding of IEEE Custom Integrated Circuits Conference CICC2002, pp. 279-282, Florida, USA, May 2002.

[4] W. B. Kuhn, D. Nobbe, D. Kelly, A. W. Orsborn, "Dynamic range performance of on-chip RF bandpass filters," IEEE Transactions on Circuits and Systems –II: Analog And Digital Signal Processing, vol. 50, pp. 685-694, October 2003.

[5] T. A. D. Riley, M. A. Copeland, T. A. Kwasniewski, "Delta-Sigma Modulation in Fractional-N Frequency Synthesis," IEEE Journal of Solid State Circuits, vol. 28, pp. 553-559, May 1993.

A Multi-Standard Mobile Digital Video Receiver in 0.18μm CMOS Process

Kenneth Barnett[1], Harish Muthali[1], Susanta Sengupta[1], Yunfei Feng[1], Bo Yang[1], Zhije Xiong[1], Tae wook Kim[4],
James Jaffee[2] and Cormac Conroy[3]

[1]Qualcomm Inc., Austin, Texas
[2]Qualcomm Inc., San Diego, California
[3]Qualcomm Inc., Campbell, California
[4]Dept. of Electrical Engineering, Yonsei University, Seoul, Korea

Abstract A multi standard direct conversion receiver for digital video broadcast application is presented. This receiver supports MediaFLO[TM], DVB-H and ISDB-T standards. Broadband multi-standard operation is achieved with a reconfigurable LNA, broadband mixer, programmable bandwidth baseband filter, wide tuning range LC VCO with a fully integrated fractional-N synthesizer. A high linearity signal path enables concurrent operation with GSM transmitter. Out of band transmitter (TX) blockers (DCS/IMT, Bluetooth) are attenuated by a novel integrated elliptic low pass filter. The receiver is implemented in 0.18μm CMOS process. In MediaFLO[TM] mode this design achieves a cascaded noise figure (NF) of 2.7dB and IIP3 of -8.2dBm in the highest gain mode. In DVB-H mode this design achieves a cascaded noise figure of 2.5dB and IIP3 of -3.3dBm in the highest gain mode. The peak power dissipation is 162mW and 190mW (@2.1V) in MediaFLO[TM] and DVB-H mode respectively.

I. INTRODUCTION

Digital video broadcasting for handheld devices in UHF band is governed by three main standards MediaFLO[TM] (698-746MHz), DVB-H (470-750MHz) and ISDB-T (470-770MHz). These standards are based on orthogonal frequency division multiplexing (OFDM) modulation, which has an efficient physical layer for providing common source data to multiple users. DVB-H standard [1] defines 5/6/7/8MHz channel bandwidths while MediaFLO[TM] & ISDB-T defines a 6MHz channel bandwidth only.

The ability to have the DVB-H receiver operate concurrently with a GSM or DCS/Bluetooth Transmitter is a desirable feature.

This paper presents a wideband direct conversion UHF tuner capable of concurrent operation with a GSM/DCS & Bluetooth transmitter.

II. MOBILE TV RECEIVER DESIGN CHALLENGES

Mobile TV receivers have to cover at least an octave of bandwidth 470-770MHz as a result direct conversion receivers are sensitive to any harmonic conversion with integer multiples of LO mixing down to baseband frequency thereby corrupting the wanted signal. Fig. 1 shows such a case where the Jammer at LO harmonics [DCS/Bluetooth transmitter] down converts to baseband after mixing with harmonics of the mixer LO. Fig. 1 also shows that a GSM transmitter signal can generate an IM2 component at the baseband

Harmonic conversion is addressed with an on chip elliptic LPF integrated in the LNA, which attenuates the transmitter signals and a high linearity signal path to minimize IM2 due to a GSM transmitter (TX). In order to maintain a good S/N the elliptic LPF needs to attenuate the TX signal by at least 60dB.

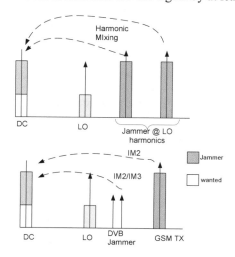

Figure 1. Harmonic mixing and IM3/IM2 cases for a wideband receiver

Following are some of the challenges posed by DVB-H standard:

A. Analog TV jammer (S1 Jammer):

The UHF spectrum has analog TV signals which will de-sense the wideband receiver and has a protection ratio of 35dB against the wanted signal.

B. Digital TV jammer (S2 Jammer);

A digital TV jammer signal 40dB stronger than the wanted signal can exist and can cause IM2 in the direct conversion receiver. This requires a high linearity RF front end.

C. Analog jammer and digital jammer (L1 jammer):

A digital TV jammer and analog TV jammer can intermodulate and result in IM3 at baseband. High IIP3 needs to be maintained in the highest gain mode.

III. WIDEBAND RECEIVER DESIGN

Fig. 2 shows a simplified block diagram of the receiver. A direct conversion architecture has been chosen due to its simplicity wherein the baseband stages could be shared for different RF front ends. As described in [2] there are two timing modes for this OFDM receiver: acquisition mode and slotted mode. The receiver enters acquisition mode upon power-up. The slotted mode is defined as the receiver powered-up and switches between "active" and "sleep" modes.

The DVB-H RF front end is fully differential in order to achieve high IIP2. The MediaFLO^{TM} LNA's are single ended and use the same pins as the DVB-H LNA. The receiver can be configured to operate in either DVB-H or MediaFLO^{TM} mode. The G_m stages convert the output of the LNA (voltage) to current which drives passive down-conversion mixers. The G_m stage limits the IIP3 performance of the receiver.

DC offset correction and IM2 calibration circuits can be used to further improve the IIP2 performance of the receiver.

The VCO achieves a tuning range of 1880-3080MHz, wide range is achieved with a single VCO. The PLL is a 3rd order $\sum\Delta$ fractional N synthesizer with an integrated loop filter similar to the design described in [3].

Some of the key building blocks of the receiver are described below:

A. LNA Design

Fig. 3 shows a simplified block diagram of the LNA. For DVB-H the differential LNA is active and for MediaFLO^{TM} one of the two single ended LNA's is active. The LNA's for these two standards share the same RF inputs. The single ended LNA's utilize the package bond wire inductance for source de-generation.

DVB-H LNA is a double cascoded structure with integrated elliptic filters. The notch of the elliptic filter is designed to be at 1.8GHz. The cascade of the two elliptic filters and bandpass filter results in at least 60dB of notch depth. Careful layout of the filter stages is done in order to minimize magnetic and substrate coupling.

Both the LNA's have digital gain control with a total of 6 gain steps resulting in at least 50dB gain control range. Gain control is done by baseband digital processor.

B. Mixer Design

The down-conversion mixer stage comprises of a G_m stage, passive mixer and a single pole trans-impedance amplifier (TIA). Passive mixer is preferred for its superior linearity and low flicker noise [4]. The mixer stage has been designed such that it could be reconfigured [5] to further minimize components resulting from harmonic mixing.

Since the passive mixer operates in current mode the G_m stage is the dominant contributor to the IIP3 of the entire receiver. Fig. 4 shows a simplified diagram of the mixer stage.

The G_m stage achieves IIP3 of greater than +20dBm. The cascode devices M3 and M4 sense the non-linearity in the drain current of M1 and M2 and feed-forward an IM3 cancellation current through transistors M_{aux1} and M_{aux2} (biased in weak inversion).

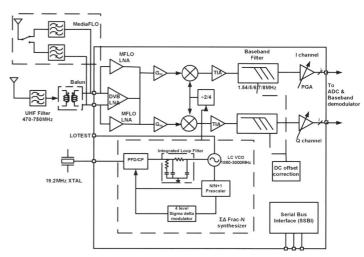

Figure 2. Block diagram of the wideband receiver

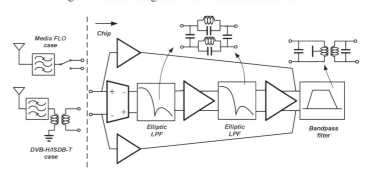

Figure 3. Simplified block diagram of the LNA

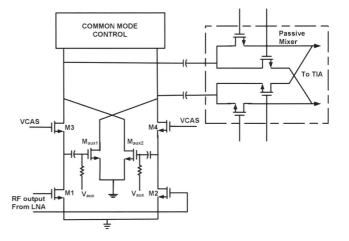

Figure 4. Circuit schematic of the Mixer stage

C. Baseband Filter Design

The Baseband filter is a 7th order Chebyschev opamp RC LPF. The filter bandwidth can be programmed to accommodate 5/6/7/8MHz channel bandwidths. The biquad is a Tow-Thomas implementation as shown in Fig. 5.

The biquad consists of two opamps, R and C elements to implement second-order low-pass transfer function with the desired Q and pole locations. In the TIA and bi-quad stages, parallel R and C banks are switched to change the filter bandwidth. The filter has a process calibration circuit, which automatically compensates resistor and capacitor variations.

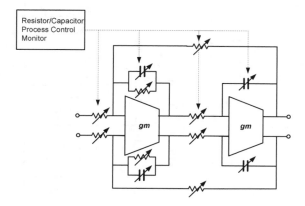

Figure 5. Tow Thomas BiQuad stage

D. Wideband VCO design

A simplified schematic diagram of the VCO is shown in Fig. 6. Complementary MOS transistors provide negative g_m to the lossy tank. This topology has been chosen as it has the lowest power consumption for a given oscillation amplitude. Wide tuning range (1880-3080MHz) is achieved with the use of MOS varactors and an 8-bit switched MIM (metal insulator metal) capacitor bank. The inductors at the tails of the VCO improve phase noise as a result of better waveform symmetry and suppression of $2f_o$ thermal noise from the PMOS current source [6].

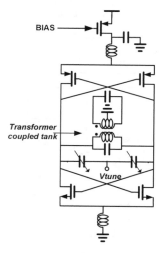

Figure 6. VCO schematic

IV. Measurement Results

A die photo of the receiver is shown in Fig. 7. The receiver is packaged along with the digital baseband demodulator and the ADC in a 9mm x 9mm SiP (System in Package). Measurement results for MediaFLO™ & DVB-H mode are summarized in Table I.

A. DVB-H results:

Fig. 8 shows the bandpass response of the LNA (observed at the baseband output), it can be seen that the attenuation is about 60dB. NF & Gain plot of the receiver in this mode is shown in Fig. 9. Sensitivity of the DVB-H tuner for QPSK ½ encoding (referred to LNA input) is shown in Fig. 11.

B. MediaFLO™ measurement results:

The NF of the receiver is 2.7dB in the highest gain state. Sensitivity plot of the tuner @ 719MHz (referred to LNA input) is shown in Fig. 12

TABLE I.   DVB-H & MediaFLO™ Measurement Summary

Specification	DVB-H Mode	MediaFLO™ Mode
NoiseFigure (dB)	2.8 to 2.2[a]	2.7
Gain Control Range (dB)	40	63
IIP3 (dBm)	-3.3 to +1[a]	-8.2
Uncalibrated IIP2: adjacent channel jammer (dBm)	+32	+24
Uncalibrated IIP2: GSM TX jammer (dBm)	+55	>+55
Sensitivity of the Tuner (dBm) [QPSK ½]	-96.6	-101.8

a. variation across DVB-H band

C. PLL/VCO measurement results:

The phase noise of the VCO (measured at LO test output) is -128dBc/Hz (before divide by 2 for UHF) @ 1MHz offset with VCO running @ 2088MHz. The phase noise plot of the synthesizer is shown in Fig. 10. The integrated phase noise (IPN) is -39dBc (integration from 1kHz to 3.8MHz). Plot of the phase noise is shown in Fig. 10.

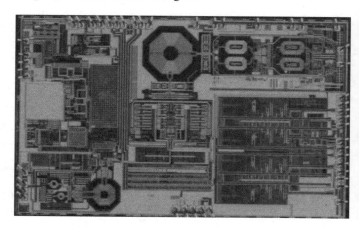

Figure 7. Die photo of the Receiver

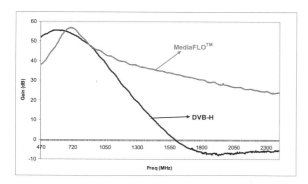

Figure 8. LNA tank response in DVB-H & MediaFLO^{TM} mode

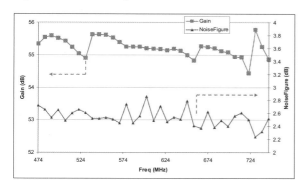

Figure 9. Gain and NF in DVB-H Mode

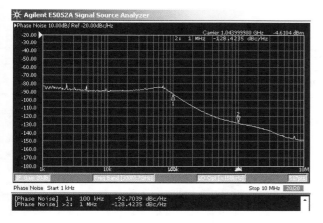

Figure 10. Synthesizer phase noise plot (Fvco=2088MHz)

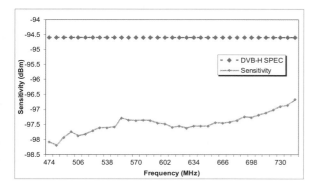

Figure 11. Sensitivity plot of the DVB-H tuner with QPSK ½ rate

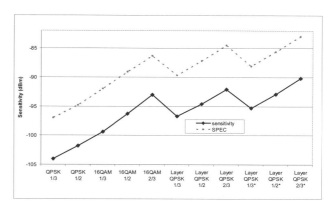

Figure 12. Sensitivity plot of the MediaFLO tuner for various modulations [@ 719MHz]

V. CONCLUSION

A low power, fully integrated, multi-standard mobile digital video receiver is implemented in 0.18μm CMOS process which integrates a novel elliptic LPF. Using this scheme receiver achieves greater than 60dB attenuation of the out of band TX jammers. Additional rejection of LO harmonic spurious is obtained with high linearity harmonic rejection mixers.

VI. ACKNOWLEDEGEMENTS

The authors would like to thank C. Bailey for layout support, M. Zeidan, A. Kolsrud, R. Chen, P. Bugyik, H. Nguyen for RF test and automation support & T. Marra, Z. Janosevic, H. Weissman, A. Wong for RF system support.

VII. REFERENCES

[1]   Mobile and Portable DVB-T Radio Access Interface Specification, MBRAI, version 1.0

[2]   V. Peluso, et. al "A Dual-Channel Direct-Conversion CMOS Receiver for Mobile Multimedia Broadcasting", ISSCC Dig. Tech. Papers, Feb. 2006.

[3]   Erdogan, O.E , et al "A single-chip quad-band GSM/GPRS transceiver in 0.18μm standard CMOS", ISSCC Dig. Tech. Papers, Feb. 2005.

[4]   Chehrazi, S.; Bagheri, R.; Abidi, A.A "Noise in passive FET mixers: a simple physical model", CICC October 2004, pp 375-378

[5]   Weldon, J.A.; et al "A 1.75 GHz highly-integrated narrow-band CMOS transmitter with harmonic-rejection mixers", ISSCC Dig. Tech. Papers, Feb. 2001

[6]   Hegazi, E., Sjoland, H., Abidi, A.A. "A filtering technique to lower LC oscillator phase noise", IEEE JSSC vol 36, Dec 2001, pp. 1921-1930

On-chip auto-calibrated RF Tracking Filter for Cable Silicon Tuner

Olivier Jamin, Vincent Rambeau, Frederic Mercier, Insaf Meliane
NXP Semiconductors, 2 esplanade Anton Philips, Campus Effiscience, 14906 Caen, France
olivier.jamin@nxp.com

Abstract□ **An integrated RF tracking filter based upon a programmable LC resonator and an auto-calibration is presented. Its 10dB unwanted power rejection improves the tuner performance above 54dB CNR and 57dB C/I under loaded spectrum conditions. This filter enables a low-cost high-performance silicon tuner for both analog and digital Set-Top-Boxes and Cable Modems.**

I. INTRODUCTION

State-of-the-art fully integrated cable silicon tuners don't need external filter components [1], but can only meet the requirements for receiving digitally modulated signals. As analog modulated TV signals will stay present on TV cable networks for many years, it is desirable to have a cable silicon tuner that can meet both the requirements for analog and digital reception. This silicon tuner should minimize the bill of material to enable low-cost multi-channel systems that are required for new services as high-speed Internet (channel bonding) and watch-and-record.

The main issue of dealing with analog TV is the necessary high Carrier-to-Noise-plus-Interferers ratio, which requires a very large dynamic range. This paper deals with the integration of a tunable RF filter that removes part of the loaded spectrum input power, what in turn improves the tuner dynamic range necessary for high performance analog TV reception.

II. SILICON TUNER ARCHIECTURE CONSIDERATIONS AND RF FILTER REQUIREMENTS

The passive LC RF tracking filter presented in this paper is part of a single down-conversion low-IF [2,3] silicon tuner designed in 0.25um BiCMOS technology (Fig.1).

Compared to a double conversion architecture (standard-IF, up-down), the direct conversion architecture allows integration of RF and IF selectivity. Low-IF architecture also avoids problems encountered in Zero-IF concept [3,4] like DC offsets, RF and LO self-mixing, and 1/f noise. The issue of the down-conversion at LO harmonics of unwanted signals contained in the input broadband spectrum is prevented using a combination of RF filters and double-quadrature mixer architecture [5].

Considering analog channels reception in the 50-550MHz frequency range, 49dB Carrier-to-Noise ratio (CNR) [6] is required to demodulate channel levels above 60dBuVrms (during sync). In addition, fully loaded spectrum conditions put severe demand for even and odd linearity performances since 2nd and 3rd order non-linearities generate Composite Second Order (CSO) and Composite Triple Beat (CTB) products that partly fall in the wanted channel. Analog TV reception requires these interferences to be lower than 57dBc in order not to be visible on the image.

As a consequence, the large dynamic range requires RF filtering in order to increase the ratio between wanted and unwanted power, and thus maintain a low RF tuner power consumption. The reduction of unwanted signal power allows for more gain (AGC2 on Fig.1) therefore improving overall tuner noise figure (NF), and relaxing linearity constraints on blocks following the RF filter.

In order to select any analog channel, the filter has to be tunable between 50MHz and 550MHz. Considering the Low-IF architecture (Fig.1), and to meet CNR / CSO / CTB constraints, the filter NF should not exceed 8dB, its power rejection must be greater than 8dB under flat input spectrum conditions, and its input IP2 and IP3 must be respectively larger than 155dBuV and 130dBuV. Finally, the tuner maximum lock time must be less than 500ms at start-up and 30ms at channel change.

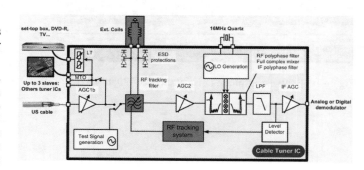

Figure 1. Silicon Tuner architecture

III. FILTER DESIGN

The above-mentioned requirements led to the choice for a passive LC filter topology (Fig.2-a) because of its intrinsically good noise and linearity characteristics. Resonance frequency tuning is achieved with an integrated programmable capacitor bank. In contrast with integrated varactors, integrated capacitor bank enables higher tuning range and better linearity performance. The best trade-off between quality factor and linearity was found by splitting the filter into two bands. As a consequence, two external coils are necessary to cover the full frequency range. The 20 MHz loaded bandwidth was chosen from several trade-offs: a narrow-bandwidth filter provides a high rejection, but at the cost of high NF, low IP2 and IP3, and numerous MOS switches due to the high number of filter sub-bands that are required to cover the full RF band. Furthermore, a too narrow bandwidth causes tilt inside the wanted channel.

The RF filter bandwidth BW is set by the LC tank loaded quality factor Q and its resonance frequency (f_R):

$$BW = f_R / Q(f_R) \qquad (1)$$

The quality factor Q of the LC tank is proportional to its equivalent parallel resistance R_P:

$$Q(f_R) = R_P \cdot \sqrt{C_{tank} / L_{tank}} \qquad (2)$$

Since a constant filter bandwidth requires a quality factor proportional to f_R, R_P also needs to be proportional to f_R. R_P resistance could be implemented by designing a variable source resistance Rs (Fig2.b). Unfortunately, this resistance causes too much noise, due to a lowering of the available signal power from the previous stage. Therefore, an impedance transformation is applied. In this design, the source resistance transformation is achieved using a variable capacitor Cmatch (Fig2.c), implemented as an integrated capacitor bank. This ensures ability to provide a good impedance matching over the full frequency range and provides additional filter roll-off toward lower frequencies, where in traditional cable plants, most of the power is located.

It is worth noting that a tunable constant-bandwidth filter means that both the quality factor and the voltage amplitude at the tank node are increasing with frequency. Consequently, at high frequencies not only the non-linearities of ESD protections at tank node (Fig.1) are not negligible anymore, but the VGA block (AGC2) is potentially overloaded. In this design, the voltage swing at the tank node is kept under control by allowing some increase of bandwidth toward higher frequencies. This is acceptable as some margin exists on filter rejection at high frequencies (thanks to the coupling capacitor Cmatch). The remaining frequency-dependent gain is compensated with a capacitive divider (Ctap, Cload) (Fig.2.d), which also avoids LC resonator detuning by reducing the capacitive load from the following amplifier to the LC tank.

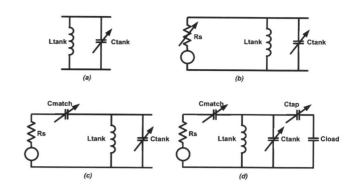

Figure 2. (a) LC tank, (b) LC tank with resistive coupling, (c) LC tank with capacitive coupling, (d) capacitive divider

IV. TRACKING SYSTEM

During normal operation, the resonance frequency of the RF filter must be tuned to the wanted channel frequency with a sufficient accuracy to maintain acceptably low loss (<4dB) and tilt (<2dB). Internal capacitors and external coils are subject to manufacturing tolerances (capacitor maximum deviation: +/-10%, coil maximum deviation: +/-5%). This spread is too high to tune the filter within the specifications without calibration.

In this design, there are 70 sub-bands (capacitor banks) to ensure overlapping of RF filters (Fig.3a). This overlap between filters guarantees that receiving any analog channel, a filter exists that has sufficiently low tilt and loss (Fig.3b). This corresponds to a 4MHz tuning resolution on the resonance frequency at 50MHz, and 12MHz at 550MHz. Furthermore, LC filters located within the same band (low band, high band Fig.3a) are built with the same coil and designed with matched capacitors. Consequently, all these LC filters exhibit the same dispersion on the resonance frequencies and bandwidths. The tracking filter calibration exploits this specificity.

The filter selection is successively operated in a coarse and fine step. For both steps, the input signal (either test or available) is down-converted using the normal tuner path. At IF, the low-pass filter properly selects the test signal using a narrow-band mode. Finally, a level detector provides its amplitude. This two-step approach has the advantage of minimizing the calibration time at channel change, when timing is critical. Using the available signal for the second calibration step at channel change also ensures no spurious is injected into the tuner signal path. This is crucial especially when slave tuners and loop-through outputs are provided, which might otherwise be disturbed by a residue of test signal. The two steps are detailed in the next sections.

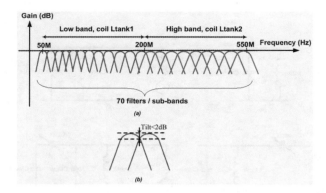

Figure 3. Tracking principle

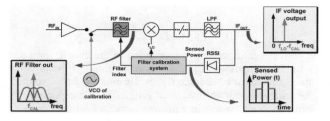

Figure 4. Scanning at start-up

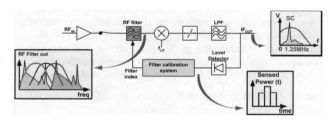

Figure 5. Tuning at channel change

A. Coarse step: Transfer Function scanning at start-up

At IC start-up, a continuous-wave signal generated on-chip is applied to the RF filter input (Fig.4). Among 18 potential candidates, the filter that maximizes the IF signal magnitude is identified. This process is repeated for six RF frequencies distributed across the whole RF frequency band (50-550MHz). The total scanning time is less than 100ms. Once the scanning of the RF filters is achieved, the deviation from nominal filters transfer functions has been sampled across the RF frequency band. Under the assumption that filters in the same frequency range experience the same spread, a rough estimate of deviation can be made for every RF filter.

Start-up scanning is fast and accurate enough to ease the fine tuning achieved in the second step.

B. Fine step: Filter Tuning at Channel Change

At each channel change, the second calibration is operated (Fig.5). The desired analog-modulated input channel is down-converted to IF. The internal LPF selects the sound carrier (SC). This sound carrier has the property to be narrow-band and frequency-modulated (NTSC). Its constant envelope facilitates level detection. Nevertheless, this design provides sufficient flexibility to also allow the use of the internal test signal for this second calibration step. This can be useful when the chip is used in systems where SC is amplitude modulated. Thanks to start-up transfer function scanning, a first estimate of the most suitable filter has already been determined. Therefore only five additional filters, with a center frequency in proximity of the first estimate filter, need to be measured in order to identify the one that maximizes IF signal magnitude. This process is achieved in less than 5ms.

V. MEASUREMENTS

The RF tracking filters transfer functions have been measured within the Silicon Tuner (Fig.6). Under flat input spectrum conditions, they provide more than 12dB rejection at low frequencies, and more than 9dB at high frequencies. This suits initial requirements.

Figure 7 shows the IF signal magnitude during scanning at start-up. It lasts 100ms, which is acceptably low compared to the maximum 500ms for the whole tuner.

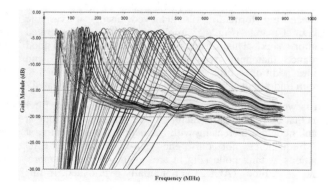

Figure 6. Measured transfer functions

160

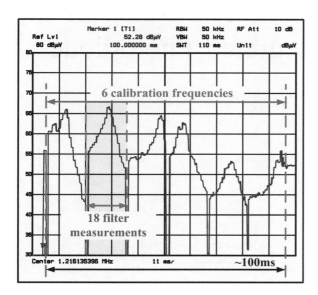

Figure 7. Transfer function scanning at start-up – Spectrum analyser in zero-span mode

As illustrated in Fig.8, noise and linearity performance of the whole tuner has been measured across RF frequency band and meets CNR / CSO / CTB initial targets with respectively more than 2dB, 5dB, 5dB margin.

Figure 9 shows a chip micrograph of the IC. The RF filter and digital control areas are respectively 0.2mm^2 and 0.3mm^2.

VI. CONCLUSION

An RF tracking filter has been demonstrated, which design is based on a capacitive-coupled passive LC resonator. Its fully integrated two-step auto-calibration allows a fast selection of the best filter setting at each channel change. This filter minimizes application costs and enables a silicon tuner having high performance analog cable reception.

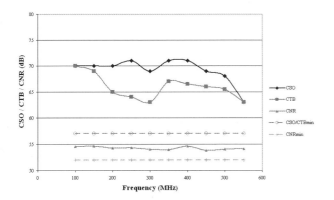

Figure 8. CNR, CSO, CTB – Fully loaded spectrum: 64dBuV (sync) analog channels, 59dBuV digital channels

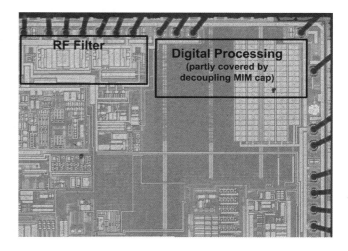

Figure 9. Chip micrograph

ACKNOWLEDGMENT

The authors want to thank Maxime Bernard for his design leading, Luca Lo Coco for his support and management, Jean-Marc Paris and Olivier Crand for some initial ideas, and Evelyne Le Guennec for her layout work.

REFERENCES

[1] J. van Sinderen, et al., "A 48MHz to 860MHz Digital Cable Tuner IC with Integrated RF and IF selectivity", ISSCC2003, paper 25.4, pp. 444-445, Feb. 2003.

[2] J.R Tourret, S. Amiot, M.Bernard et Al, "SiP Tuner With Integrated LC Tracking Filter for Both Cable and Terrestrial TV Reception", IEEE Journal of Solid State Circuits, Vol. 42, No. 12, p.2809, December 2007

[3] Jan Crols and Michiel S. J. Steyaert, "Low-IF Topologies for High-Performance Analog Front Ends of Fully Integrated Receivers", IEEE Transactions On Circuits And Systems—II: Analog and Digital Signal Processing, Vol. 45, No. 3, March 1998

[4] B. Razavi, "Design Considerations for Direct-Conversion Receivers", IEEE Transactions On Circuits And Systems—II: Analog and Digital Signal Processing, Vol. 44, No. 6, June 1997

[5] F. Behbahani, Y. Kishigami, J. Leete, A.A. Abidi, "CMOS Mixers and Polyphase Filters for Large Image Rejection," IEEE Journal of Solid-State Circuits, Vol. 36, No. 6, p. 873, June 2001

[6] Cisco White Paper, "Digital Transmission: Carrier-to-Noise Ratio, Signal-to-Noise Ratio, and Modulation Error Ratio", November 2006, http://www.cisco.com/en/US/prod/collateral/video/ps8806/ps5684/ps2209/prod_white_paper0900aecd805738f5.pdf

Power Efficient 4.5Gbit/s Optical Receiver in 130nm CMOS with Integrated Photodiode

Filip Tavernier and Michiel Steyaert
K.U. Leuven ESAT-MICAS
Kasteelpark Arenberg 10
3001 Heverlee, Belgium
Email: filip.tavernier@esat.kuleuven.be

Abstract—An optical receiver with integrated photodiode in 130nm CMOS is presented. The extremely unfavourable optical and electrical performance of a differential photodiode in this technology, namely a very low responsivity of only 5mA/W, an optical bandwidth of 500MHz and a large photodiode capacitance of 1pF, have been solved so that bitrates of 4.5Gbit/s and higher can be received for BER values as low as 10^{-12}. The power consumption for this is only 74.16mW due to a biasing in weak inversion.

I. INTRODUCTION

Optical fiber communication is nowadays largely deployed for shared long-haul communication links (ex. transatlantic telephone lines). For such applications the major specification is speed, so a fiber is preferred over an electrical wire as its bandwidth-length product is much higher. The conversion from the electrical to the optical domain and back is however very expensive. The components that take care of these conversions, a laser diode at the transmitter and a photodiode at the receiver, are fabricated in very specialized technologies to make sure they have very good optical characteristics. For a high responsivity and a large optical bandwidth, the photodiode is thus integrated in GaAs [1], InP [2] or other expensive technologies. The high cost of such a solution is however not important for these applications as it is carried by a large number of users.

Recent trends in multimedia require ever increasing amounts of data to be processed and stored. As computing power over time follows Moore's law and the price per Gigabyte of storage drops very fast, processing and storing these huge amounts of data is becoming less of a problem. The performance bottleneck nowadays is in the transfer of the data between the different processing and storage units. The speed of the communication channel must increase accordingly which is becoming a huge problem. Traditionally, such communication links use copper wires as medium. However, as the bandwidth demands keep increasing, copper is just not able to fulfill this need. A transition to optical fiber will thus become necessary. In order to make the use of optical fiber communication for such short-haul communication links economically viable, the optical components must decrease in cost. The receiver, described in this paper, can be seen in this view as the ultimate reduction in cost, namely the integration of the complete receiver, from the photodiode to the post amplifier, on a single

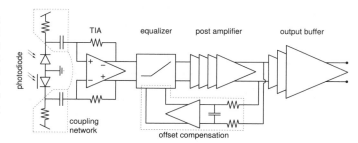

Fig. 1. Architecture of the presented integrated optical receiver.

chip, fabricated in 130nm CMOS without any post-processing steps.

Previous publications show realisations in 180nm CMOS enabling speeds ranging from 1.2Gbit/s [3] to 2Gbit/s [4], 3Gbit/s [5] and 3.125Gbit/s [6]. The receiver presented in this paper is integrated in 130nm CMOS and is able to handle bitrates up to 4.5Gbit/s for a very low Bit Error Ratio (BER). The inherent responsivity of a differential photodiode in this 130nm technology is 4 [4], 6 [3] to 14 [6] times lower than for a differential photodiode in 180nm CMOS. However, the measured sensitivity for a BER lower than 10^{-12} is only 4.6dBm [3] to 0.6dBm [6] lower due to an extremely low-noise design. In [4] the sensitivity is -8dBm but for a much larger BER of 10^{-9} which makes a comparison of the sensitivity invalid. Moreover this has been achieved with a very low power consumption of 74.16mW which is much lower than in [3] and [6]. The lower power consumption in [5] can be explained by the single-ended implementation of the circuit, whereas the presented receiver is fully differential, and the absence of a post amplifier.

The architecture of the presented optical receiver is described in section II. In section III the key design issues are discussed. The measurement results are shown in section IV and in section V a conclusion is drawn.

II. RECEIVER ARCHITECTURE

The architecture of the presented receiver can be seen in fig. 1. When light impinges, the differential photodiode generates two small photocurrents with a relatively large common-mode component and only a small differential component. As described more thoroughly in [7], the common-mode compo-

162

nent originates from slowly diffusing substrate carriers. For a fast photodiode response, this component needs to be suppressed. The differential component on the other hand contains the wanted high-frequent data and needs to be amplified. This is accomplished in the differential transimpedance amplifier (TIA). To extend the optical bandwidth of the photodiode even more, an analog equalizer has been included in the receiver [5], [8]. The post amplifier, which is a limiting amplifier, amplifies the signal in order to obtain a signal with a swing of several 100mV which is high enough for a clock- and data-recovery circuit to work with. In order not to amplify the offset voltage of the circuit, an offset compensation loop has been included. Finally, the output buffer is able to drive the 50Ω of the measurement equipment.

III. DESIGN

A. Photodiode

For the photodiode, technology downsizing has a negative impact on the responsivity. In 180nm CMOS, the responsivity of a differential photodiode has been shown to be 70mA/W [6]. The measured DC-responsivity for a photodiode in the technology this design has been integrated in is only 5mA/W for the same photodiode layout as in [6]. Moreover, the optical bandwidth is not higher than about 500MHz [6], so the responsivity is even much lower in the GHz-range where this design is aimed for. As the optically generated currents are thus very small, noise is a major issue during the design of the receiver, especially for the TIA which is the first block after the photodiode.

The diameter of the photodiode is 60μm for which the parasitic junction capacitance to ground equals 1pF at each side.

As can be seen in fig. 1, the photodiode is connected to the TIA through a coupling network. Its function is dual. Firstly, it biases the photodiode with the highest voltage available, namely the supply voltage (1.2V). Doing so, the photodiode capacitance is minimized. Secondly, it removes the offset between both outputs of the differential photodiode.

B. Transimpedance amplifier

The topology of the implemented differential TIA can be seen in fig. 2(a). The feedback resistors, which determine the gain from input current to output voltage, have been implemented as PMOS transistors in their linear region. Polysilicon resistors suffer from large parasitic capacitances to the substrate and thus limit the bandwidth. Using PMOS transistors, these parasitic capacitances can be made very small so high speed operation is assured.

A first order estimate for the bandwidth of the TIA (BW_{TIA}) is given by:

$$BW_{TIA} = \frac{A}{2 \cdot \pi \cdot R_f \cdot C_d} \quad (1)$$

in which A, R_f and C_d represent the voltage gain of the voltage amplifier, the value of the feedback resistor and the value of the photodiode capacitance respectively. The photodiode has a large capacitance of 1pF at each of its ouputs and R_f should be large to amplify the very small currents from the photodiode.

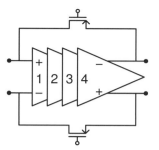
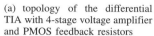

(a) topology of the differential TIA with 4-stage voltage amplifier and PMOS feedback resistors

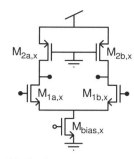

(b) implementation of a voltage amplifier stage (x=1,2,3,4)

Fig. 2.   The differential TIA.

To obtain a high BW_{TIA}, the voltage amplifier of the TIA should thus have a high gain (1). However, as the poles of the voltage amplifier represent non-dominant poles in the feedback loop of the TIA, the bandwidth of the voltage amplifier should also be very high to have enough phase margin in the loop. Combining a high gain with a high bandwidth for the voltage amplifier has been obtained by cascading differential stages as can be seen in fig. 2(a). The transistor implementation of such a stage can be seen in fig. 2(b). Each differential stage has linear PMOS transistors as load to make the bandwidth as high as possible. However, the gain is quite low for such a topology. As the gain of a cascade of stages increases much faster than the bandwidth decreases, the GBW of the cascade is much higher than that of one stage as described more thoroughly further on. Four stages are thus cascaded so that the gain is high enough to enable high speed operation (1) and the bandwith is high enough to guarantee enough phase margin in the feedback loop. Cascading differential stages is also beneficial for the common-mode rejection of the TIA which is directly related to the common-mode rejection of the voltage amplifier and needs to be high to suppress the large and slow common-mode component of the photodiode signal. During the design of the TIA, there are two parameters that mainly determine the added noise of the receiver, namely the value of the feedback resistor R_f and the equivalent transconductance of the voltage amplifier g_m. The latter is approximately equal to $g_{m,M_{1a,1}} = g_{m,M_{1b,1}}$ if the gain of the first stage is sufficiently high. As well R_f as g_m need to be made as large as possible to obtain a good low-noise performance. Making R_f large requires a large voltage gain A to obtain a high bandwidth (1) as was already discussed above. However, for a large transconductance, a large biasing current is required if the input transistors are biased in saturation. To increase the current efficiency g_m/I, the first amplifying stage is designed in weak inversion. For a large transconductance of 110mS, the current can thus be reduced to only 6.8mA.

The designed TIA has a gain from input current to output voltage of 4.5kΩ and a bandwidth of 2.9GHz. The integrated noise voltage at the output is 3.32mV which corresponds to an integrated noise current at the input of 0.738μA.

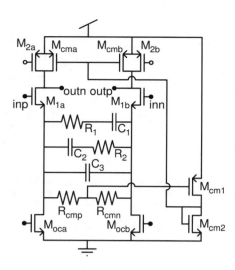

Fig. 3. The pseudo-differential equalizer.

C. Equalizer

The equalizer is needed to extend the photodiode optical bandwidth which is not higher than 500MHz [6]. In contrast to [5] where a single-ended implementation is discussed, the equalizer discussed here is of the pseudo-differential type as can be seen in fig. 3. As in [5] and [8], the equalization is realized through frequency dependent source degeneration of M_{1a} and M_{1b}. This source degeneration is implemented by R_1-C_1, R_2-C_2 and C_3. These filter branches are placed differentially to boost only the differential signal and not the common-mode signal. The common-mode signal is even suppressed by a high-frequent common-mode feedback path built up by components M_{cmx} and R_{cmx}. A high performance differential equalization is thus achieved while a high bandwidth common-mode rejection is maintained. Transistors M_{oca} and M_{ocb} are, besides for the biasing of the equalizer, also used to close the offset compensation feedback loop. Therefore, their gates are driven with the fed back offset voltage at the output of the post amplifier, as can be seen in fig. 1, and regulate the DC-voltages of both outputs of the equalizer.

The implemented equalizer has a DC-gain of 0dB and is able to extend the photodiode bandwidth from 500MHz to about 3GHz. Due to the need for frequency dependent source degeneration of M_{1a} and M_{1b}, a differential topology is not possible. However, common-mode signals are rejected with more than 8.5dB due to the common-mode rejection circuit.

D. Post amplifier with offset compensation

The post amplifier amplifies the output signal of the equalizer so as to supply a rail-to-rail signal to the next block which will in most cases be a clock- and data-recovery circuit. To achieve a high gain as well as a high bandwidth, a cascade of four resistively loaded differential pairs has been used. As they all have a first order response and in the assumption that the capacitive load of the last stage is the same as for the other stages, the transfer function of the cascade of four stages is

given by:

$$A = A_{1st}^4$$
$$= \frac{A_{0,1st}^4}{\left(1 + \dfrac{s}{2 \cdot \pi \cdot f_{-3dB,1st}}\right)^4} \qquad (2)$$

A_{1st}, $A_{0,1st}$ and $f_{-3dB,1st}$ represent the transfer function, DC-gain and -3dB-bandwidth of one stage respectively. Four poles coincide at $f_{-3dB,1st}$. The -3dB-bandwidth of the post amplifier will thus be lower than this value. It is given by:

$$f_{-3dB} = \sqrt{\sqrt[4]{2} - 1} \cdot f_{-3dB,1st}$$
$$\approx 0.435 \cdot f_{-3dB,1st}. \qquad (3)$$

Whereas the -3dB-bandwidth thus only drops with about a factor of 2, the gain increases with the power of 4. The gain-bandwidth product of the cascade of four stages is thus much higher than that of one stage if $A_{0,1st}$ is considerably higher than 1 which is always the case for an amplifier.

To prevent the offset voltage from being amplified, an offset compensation circuit is included. As can be seen in fig. 1, the DC-voltage of both outputs of the post amplifier is measured through an R-C low-pass filter and the difference is amplified. The loop is closed in the equalizer as discussed before. Implementing the capacitor of the low-pass filter differentially instead of using two single-ended capacitors to ground, has two important advantages. Firstly, for a certain lower cut-off frequency, only a fourth of the total capacitance value and thus only a fourth of the area is needed. Secondly, unwanted common-mode components in the signal are fed back without low-pass filtering and are thus rejected over the entire frequency band.

The designed post amplifier has a gain of 32dB and a bandwidth of 4.8GHz. The lower cut-off frequency due to the offset compensation is 5MHz which is low enough for the bitrates this design is aimed for.

IV. MEASUREMENT RESULTS

The complete receiver, from photodiode to output buffer, has been integrated in a standard 130nm CMOS technology. The chip photograph can be seen in fig. 4. The total power consumption at a supply voltage of 1.2V is only 74.16mW including biasing currents.

The transient behaviour of the chip is verified with a Parallel Bit Error Ratio Tester (ParBERT). A commercially available laserdriver and laserdiode with a center wavelength of 850nm are used to generate the light pulses. The laserdriver is therefore modulated by the ParBERT with a 2^7-1 PRBS data pattern. The modulated light is guided through a fiber and at the end focused on the integrated photodiode. The output of the chip is then analyzed by the ParBERT. The measured BER versus modulated optical input power for various bitrates is presented in fig. 5. As can be seen in this figure, for a bitrate of 4.5Gbit/s and an optical input power of -3.4dBm, the BER is only 10^{-12}. The circuit is even functional up to 5Gbit/s.

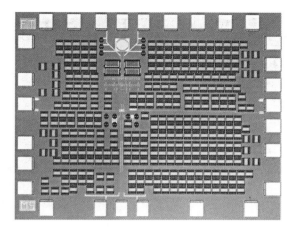

Fig. 4. Chip photograph of the integrated optical receiver. The die size is $1.5 \times 1.18 \text{mm}^2$.

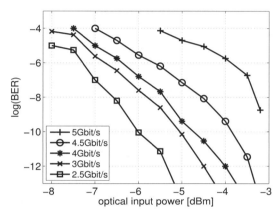

Fig. 5. Measured BER versus optical input power for various bitrates.

Fig. 6 shows the measured eye diagrams for a 3Gbit/s and a 4.5Gbit/s signal with an optical input power of -3.2dBm.

V. CONCLUSION

In this paper, an optical receiver with integrated photodiode in 130nm CMOS is presented. The photodiode has both a low responsivity and a low optical bandwidth. The bandwidth problem has been solved by making use of a differential photodiode topology and by including an optimized analog equalizer in the receiver chain. The low responsivity of 5mA/W imposes very stringent requirements on the added noise of the receiver. Conciliating a low noise performance with a low current consumption has been achieved by biasing the first stage of the TIA in weak inversion. After the equalizer, a post amplifier with offset compensation amplifies the signals to a rail-to-rail level.

In table I, a comparison is made between the presented receiver and the current state-of-the-art in CMOS. All mentioned implementations are done in 180nm CMOS whereas the presented receiver is realized in 130nm CMOS. This explains the lower sensitivity figure as the photodiode responsivity is 4 [4], 6 [3] to 14 [6] times lower than in 180nm CMOS. Measurements show that signals up to 4.5Gbit/s can be received

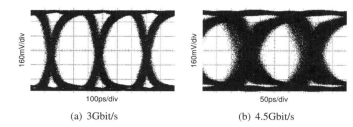

| (a) 3Gbit/s | (b) 4.5Gbit/s |

Fig. 6. Eye diagrams for -3.2dBm optical input power.

TABLE I
COMPARISON WITH THE STATE-OF-THE-ART.

	speed	sensitivity	BER	power
[3] / 180nm [1]	1.2Gbit/s	-8dBm	10^{-12}	450mW
[4] / 180nm [2]	2Gbit/s	-8dBm	10^{-9}	50mW
[5] / 180nm [3]	3Gbit/s	-19dBm	10^{-11}	34mW
[6] / 180nm [4]	3.125Gbit/s	-4.2dBm	10^{-12}	145mW
this work / 130nm	4.5Gbit/s	-3.4dBm	10^{-12}	74.16mW

[1] power includes output buffer

[2] 3.3V supply voltage needed; epi process

[3] no post amplifier; single-ended

[4] extra 3.3V supply voltage needed

at very low BER values. Moreover, this is achieved at a very low power consumption of only 74.16mW.

To the authors' knowledge, this is the fastest optical receiver, fully integrated in standard CMOS, reported up till now.

REFERENCES

[1] J. Choi, B.J. Sheu, and O.T.-C. Chen, "A monolithic GaAs receiver for optical interconnect systems", *IEEE Journal of Solid-State Circuits*, vol. 29, no. 3, pp. 328-331, Mar. 1994.

[2] M. Yung, et al., "Highly integrated InP HBT optical receivers", *IEEE Journal of Solid-State Circuits*, vol. 34, no. 2, pp. 219-227, Feb. 1999.

[3] C. Hermans, F. Tavernier, and M. Steyaert, "A Gigabit Optical Receiver with Monolithically Integrated Photodiode in 0.18μm CMOS", *Proceedings of the IEEE European Solid-State Circuits Conference*, pp. 476-479, Montreux, Switzerland, Sep. 2006.

[4] M. Jutzi, M. Grözing, E. Gaugler, W. Mazioschek, and M. Berroth, "2-Gb/s CMOS Optical Integrated Receiver With a Spatially Modulated Photodetector", *IEEE Photonics Technology Letters*, vol. 17, no. 6, pp. 1268-1270, Jun. 2005

[5] S. Radovanovic, A. J. Annema, and B. Nauta, "A 3-Gb/s optical detector in standard CMOS for 850-nm optical communication", *IEEE Journal of Solid-State Circuits*, vol. 40, no. 8, pp. 1706-1717, Aug. 2005.

[6] Wei-Zen Chen, et al., "A 3.125 Gbps CMOS fully integrated optical receiver with adaptive analog equalizer", in *Proceedings of the IEEE Asian Solid-State Circuits Conference*, pp. 396-399, Nov. 2007.

[7] C. Rooman, D. Coppée, and M. Kuijk, "Asynchronous 250-Mb/s Optical Receivers with Integrated Detector in Standard CMOS Technology for Optocoupler Applications", *IEEE Journal of Solid-State Circuits*, vol. 35, no. 7, pp. 953-958, July 2000.

[8] F. Tavernier, C. Hermans, and M. Steyaert, "Optimised equaliser for differential CMOS photodiodes", *IEE Electronics Letters*, vol. 42, no. 17, pp. 1002-1003, Aug. 2006.

5.75 to 44Gb/s Quarter Rate CDR with Data Rate Selection in 90nm Bulk CMOS

George von Bueren, Lucio Rodoni, Heinz Jaeckel
Electronics Laboratory
ETH Zürich
CH-8092 Zürich, Switzerland

Alex Huber
Institute of Microelectronics
University of Applied Sciences Northwestern Switzerland
CH-5210 Windisch, Switzerland

Roland Brun, Daniel Holzer
Bern University of Applied Sciences
CH-3400 Burgdorf, Switzerland

Martin Schmatz
IBM Zurich Research Laboratory
CH-8803 Rüschlikon, Switzerland

Abstract□ **This paper presents a quarter rate clock/data recovery (CDR) circuit for plesiochronous serial I/O-links. This 2x-oversampled phase-tracking CDR, implemented in 90nm bulk CMOS technology, covers the whole range of data rates from 5.75 to 44Gb/s thanks to a data rate selection logic. A bit error rate < 10^{-12} was verified up to 38Gb/s using a 2^{7-1} PRBS pattern. The CDR is able to track a maximum frequency deviation of −615ppm between incoming data and reference clock.**

Keywords: clock data recovery, quarter rate, CMOS.

I. INTRODUCTION

The aggregate data communication bandwidth of key components in telecommunication equipment and computer servers has shown a continuous increase in the past. This progress has been reached by increasing the serial data rate and by integrating more links on a single chip. In order to achieve multi-channel integration into a CMOS logic process, these transceivers should be low power and area efficient. One of the most crucial and speed-limiting circuit blocks in these link macrocells is the clock and data recovery (CDR) circuit in the receiver. The first 40Gb/s CMOS CDR has been presented in 2003 [1]. This 40Gb/s CDR has been realized in 0.18μm CMOS, employs a quarter-rate architecture with a multiphase VCO and passive loop filter, achieves a the bit-error rate (BER) of 10^{-6} and consumes a current of 144mA from a 2V supply. In case of plesiochronous systems, where every participant gets nearly the same frequency, the CDR tracking loop with the area-consuming passive loop filter can be replaced with a digital phase tracking loop [2]. A half-rate 25Gb/s CDR implemented in 90nm CMOS achieving a BER < 10^{-12} incorporates a digital first order loop filter, consumes 98mA from a 1.1V supply and its area consumption is 0.064mm² only, and is therefore suited for high-density integration [3]. It has been shown with a quarter rate CDR [4]

that area and power consumption can be further reduced thanks to two accomplishments. First, the application of a phase-programmable PLL [5] allows realizing a dual loop CDR [2] without phase rotators. Second, the use of static-CMOS design style in most analog circuits instead of current mode logic (CML). This 40Gb/s CDR is implemented in 65nm SOI CMOS and its area and power consumption are 0.03mm² and 72mW, respectively. The use of static-CMOS design style is only possible with regulated supply voltages [5], [6]. Compared to static-CMOS design style CML circuits have a better immunity to supply variations and generate less switching noise. The 40Gb/s CDR presented in this paper employs fully differential CML in all analog high-speed circuits. With a 90nm CMOS technology CML circuits are mandatory to processes a 40Gb/s data stream. Only the digital loop filter consists of CMOS gates. We propose a data rate selection logic that allows covering the whole range of data rates from 5.75 to 44Gb/s. This feature makes the circuit especially suitable in multi-standard applications enabling new link rates while supporting compatibility with legacy rates.

II. CDR TOPOLOGY

In high-density serial I/O links, the transmitter (TX) and receiver (RX) are clocked by two independent reference clocks having the same nominal frequency. These reference clocks are multiplied from a quartz crystal oscillator with a frequency tolerance ranging from ±10 to ±100ppm. In these plesiochronous systems the CDR has to track a slowly drifting phase difference between the incoming data and the RX clock caused by the small frequency offset between the TX and RX clocks. Hence, a phase-tracking loop in the CDR is sufficient.

The architecture of our phase tracking loop is shown in Fig. 1. It is a 2x-oversampled quarter rate CDR with the advantage that only the first latch of the sampling flip-flop must be able to track the data at full speed. Eight parallel

This work was supported by the Swiss Federal Office for Professional Education and Technology, contract/grant number KTI 7995.1

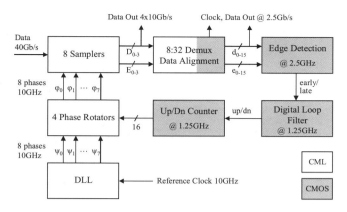

Fig. 1 Architecture of the phase tracking loop.

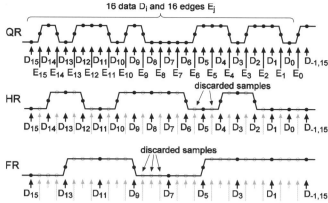

Fig. 3. Principle of the rate selection quarter-rate (QR), half-rate (HR), and full-rate (FR) mode, • sample points, ∘ discarded samples

samplers acquire the four data bits ($D_{0..3}$) and four edges ($E_{0..3}$) needed to evaluate the sampling position [7]. Eight parallel 1:4 demultiplexers reduce the data rate form 10 to 2.5 Gb/s and align the sampled bits, which are separated by one eighth of the period of the reference clock signal, to one single clock phase, generating 16 data ($d_{0..15}$) and 16 edge ($e_{0..3}$) bits. The transition from differential signaling to full swing CMOS signal levels is performed in the demultiplexers. The phase tracking loop is implemented by a digital delay locked loop. The digital control logic consists of an edge detection logic, a digital loop filter and an up/down counter, which controls the output phases (φ_i) of the four phase rotators. The reference clock phases (Ψ_i) are generated in an analog delay locked loop (DLL). The four 10Gb/s data bits $D_{0..3}$ are buffered and fed to output pins for testing and measurement purposes.

III. CIRCUIT DESIGN

A. Sampler

The first stage of the master-slave flip-flop is a shunt inductive peaked CML latch. The bandwidth enhancement is necessary since this latch has to track the 40Gb/s input data. With a 0.7nH on-chip inductor a maximal bandwidth enhancement by a factor of 1.8 [8] has been achieved. The area of one multi-layer spiral inductor amounts to $20 \times 20\mu m^2$. In the second latch of the master-slave flip-flop no inductive peaking is required because this latch operates with a 10Gb/s data stream only.

B. Digital Control Loop with Rate Selection

Fig. 2 illustrates the block diagram of the digital control loop. All circuit blocks are synthesized circuits and are placed and routed with a digital design tool.

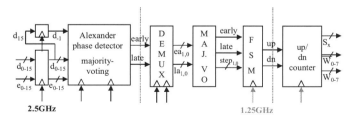

Fig. 2. Block diagram of the digital loop filter.

The edge detector solves the Alexander equations [7] and outputs a single early or late signal after majority voting. In order to relax the speed requirement for the digital loop filter, the early and late output signals of the edge detector are demultiplexed by a factor of 2. The loop filter is realized as finite state machine and accumulates the incoming early and late bits. A phase step (up or down) is induced when the overhang of early or late signals is greater than three. This edge detection logic can work in three operation modes as depicted in Fig. 3. Quarter rate (QR) operation is used for an input data rate from 23 to 44Gb/s. The early/late generation logic generates for each of the 16 data/edge bit pairs an early/late signal by solving the Alexander equations [7]. When the data rate is lower and the bit length larger, between 11.5 and 23Gb/s, the CDR operates in half rate (HR) mode. The edge samples used in the quarter rate mode are omitted and only the data samples are evaluated. In this mode, the even data samples take the role of the edge bits and the odd data samples are still data bits. From the eight data/edge pairs the early/late information is generated. For a still lower input data rate from 5.75 to 11.5Gb/s, the full rate (FR) mode is appropriate. Here, every other sample of the odd data samples are alternately used as data and edge bit, respectively. In this case, the early/late logic generates 4 early/late signals. Hence, our receiver can cover the full range of data rates from 5.75 to 44Gb/s, even though the multi phase delay lock loop (DLL), which generates the reference clock phase Ψ_i, is band limited. The DLL operates from 5.75 to 11.5 GHz and limits the lower data rate of the CDR.

C. DLL, Phase Rotator and Clock Buffer

In order to update the sample position, we use four parallel phase rotators, which are controlled by a thermometer coded up/down counter. Using a full thermometer code, glitches or discontinuities, in the phase rotator characteristics can be avoided. The four differential reference clock phases (Ψ_i), which are generated by the DLL, are fed to the four phase rotators. One phase rotator, shown in Fig. 4(a), consists of a phase selection stage followed by a phase interpolation stage [2]. The first stage selects two clock phases from two adjacent phase octants. Using eight clock phases provides a better phase linearity compared to using six phases or I/Q

167

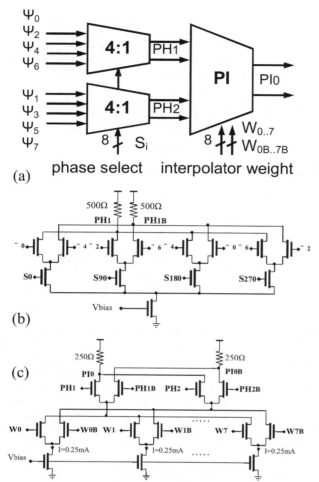

(a)

(b)

(c)

Fig. 4. (a) Phase rotator, (b) phase selector, (c) phase interpolator

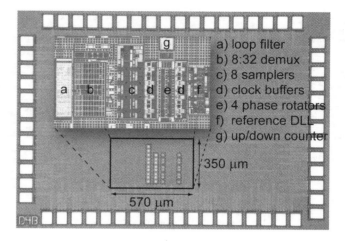

Fig. 5. Chip photo and layout of the CDR

interpolation schemes. The phase interpolator that blends the two selected phases is controlled by the 8-bit thermometer coded value $W_{7..0}$. The schematic of the used 4:1 multiplexer and interpolator are depicted in Fig. 4(b) and Fig. 4(c), respectively. Retiming flip-flops between the up/down counter and the phase rotator guarantee that all control signals S_i, $W_{7..0}$, $W_{7B..0B}$ change at the same time. The common mode outputs of the selector and the interpolator are regulated by a replica bias as all CML circuits of this CDR. An important practical requirement is that amplitude and common mode voltage of sampling clock are valid always, even after start-up, to assure the presence of the CDR system clock. This implies that the control signals S_i, $W_{7..0}$, $W_{7B..0B}$ are initialized correctly. As can be seen Fig. 4(b) and Fig. 4(c), the regulated output common mode voltages of the proposed selector and interpolator circuits are always valid because their output common mode voltages are independent of the digital control signals.

A total number of 64 phase steps for one 100ps reference clock period or 16 steps for one data unit interval (UI) of 25ps are provided, resulting in a nominal timing resolution of 1.56ps. As a consequence, the maximal possible frequency offset between TX and RX clocks that can be tracked correctly amounts to $10^6/(64 \cdot 8 \cdot 3)$ppm = 615ppm. The reference clock

signals (Ψ_i) as well as the sample clock signals (φ_i) are driven by clock buffers using inductive and capacitive peaking to have enough driving capability and to remove any DC-offset in the differential clock signal. The inductive shunt peaking is used to expand the bandwidth of the buffer. With capacitive peaking, the gain at lower frequencies (<5 GHz) is decreased. In addition, the output DC levels are regulated actively to reduce DC-offset and duty cycle distortion of the clock signal.

IV. MEASUREMENT RESULTS

Our CDR circuit is fabricated in a 90nm bulk CMOS technology and consumes 230mA from a 1V power supply voltage (analog 215mA, digital supply 15mA). All inputs and outputs are ESD protected except the differential 40Gb/s data inputs. The layout of the core circuit that occupies $570 \times 350 \mu m^2$ (=0.2mm^2) and the die micrograph of the CDR circuit are shown in Fig. 5. The CDR is able to lock to a PRBS data stream at up to 44Gb/s when the input signal is applied to the chip using on-wafer probes. The 40Gb/s input eye diagram with a 10GHz sinusoidal clock signal is illustrated in Fig. 6(a). The recovered data at 10Gb/s is shown in Fig. 6(b). The operating ranges for full-, half- and quarter-rate modes are 5.75 to 11.5Gb/s, 11.5 to 23Gb/s and 23 to 44Gb/s, respectively. In all operating ranges, the maximum frequency offset that can be tracked is ±615ppm for a BER of <10^{-12} up to 38Gb/s. The limit was set by the measurement setup because the input pattern was not error free above 38Gb/s. The value of ±615ppm is sufficient to countervail inequalities of

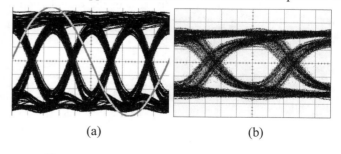

(a)   (b)

Fig. 6. (a) 40Gb/s input data, 10GHz sinusoidal clock signal.
(time scale: 10ps/div, amplitude scale: 50mV/div)
(b) Recovered 10Gb/s data
(time scale: 20ps/div, amplitude scale: 50mV/div)

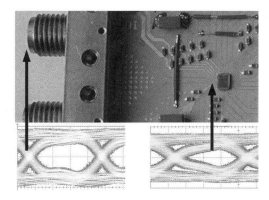

Fig. 7. Eye diagram of a 24Gb/s data stream at the input of the package (left eye diagram) and at the pad of the circuit (right eye diagram)

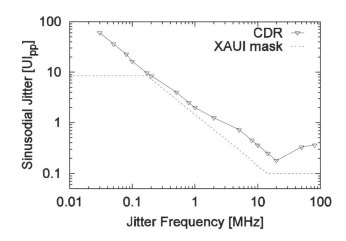

Fig. 8. Jitter tolerance of the packed CDR at 24Gb/s achieving a BER<10^{-12}.

the clock frequencies of two chips clocked from different crystal oscillators. Besides the frequency offset, which can be tracked, the jitter tolerance is the second key parameter for CDRs employed in chip-to-chip communication. The jitter tolerance measurements have been performed in a packaged module (Fig. 7). Fig. 7 also shows the eye diagram of the 24Gb/s input data before (left eye diagram) and after (right eye diagram) a trace of 1.6cm length on the substrate. The jitter tolerance plot at 24Gb/s of the packaged CDR and the extended jitter tolerance mask for XAUI [9] are illustrated in Fig. 8. For all jitter frequencies and all jitter amplitudes, the XAUI mask can be fulfilled by our circuit.

TABLE I. shows a comparison with previously published 40Gb/s CMOS CDRs with analog [1], [10] or digital loop filters [4], [11]. Fully analog CDRs are area consuming and dissipate less power but have a larger BER (>10^{-12}) compared to [4], [11]. Among the three CDRs with a digital loop filter our CDR covers the largest range of data rates. Furthermore, it consumes less power and has a smaller chip area than the 3x-oversampling CDR [10]. Only the circuit in [4] reaches superior performance with respect to power and area, but uses a more advanced transistor technology that allows to implement the speed-critical circuit blocks in CMOS logic instead of the more power- and area-consuming CML logic.

TABLE I.   40GB/S CMOS CDRS

	[1]	[4]	[10]	[11]	**This**
Data-rate [Gb/s]	40	27-40	40	40-44	5.75-44
T_{bit}/T_{clock}	1/4	1/4	1/2	1/4	1/4
Demux data	1:4	1:8	1:2	1:16	1:16
Loop filter	passive	digital	passive	digital	digital
Supply [V]	2	1	1.2	1.4	1
Power [mW]	144	72	48	900	230
Area [mm²]	0.64ᵃ	0.03	0.42	1.44	0.2
Gb/s/mW	0.28	0.56	0.83	0.048	0.174
Tb/s/mm²	0.06	1.33	0.09	0.03	0.2
BER	10^{-6}	<10^{-12}	10^{-9}	<10^{-12}	<10^{-12}
CMOS	0.18μm	65nmᵇ	90nm	90nm	90nm

a. Estimated   b. Silicon on insulator technology (SOI)

V.   CONCLUSION

A clock-data-recovery circuit implemented in 90 nm bulk CMOS for 40Gb/s chip-to-chip communication is presented. Thanks to the novel rate selection feature in the fully digital

loop filter a very large data rate range from 5.75 to 44Gb/s can be covered. From 5.75 to 38Gb/s a BER <10^{-12} is achieved even for a frequency offset of ±615ppm and data jitter amplitudes above the XAUI mask.

ACKNOWLEDGMENT

The authors thank T. Toifl, C. Menolfi, T. Morf, C. Kromer, M. Kossel, J. Weiss for fruitful discussions, M. Lanz and M. Witzig for bonding and the IBM foundry team for manufacturing the CMOS chips.

REFERENCES

[1] J. Lee and B. Razavi, "A 40-Gb/s Clock and Data Recovery Circuit in 0.18-μm CMOS Technology," IEEE Journal of Solid-State Circuits, vol. 38, pp. 2181–2190, Dec. 2003.

[2] S. Sidiropoulos, M. Horowitz, "A Semi-Digital Dual Delay-Locked Loop," IEEE JSSC, vol. 32, no. 11, pp. 1683-1692, Nov. 1997.

[3] C. Kromer, G. Sialm, C. Menolfi, M. Schmatz, F. Ellinger, H. Jäckel, "A 25-Gb/s CDR in 90-nm CMOS for High-Density Interconnects", IEEE J. Solid-State Circuits, vol. 41, no.12, pp. 2921-2929, Dec. 2006.

[4] T. Toifl, C. Menolfi, P. Buchmann, C. Hagleitner, M. Kossel, T. Morf, J. Weiss, and M. Schmatz, "A 72mW 0.03mm² Inductorless 40 Gb/s CDR in 65 nm SOI CMOS," ISSCC Dig. Technical Papers, pp. 226–227, 11–15 Feb. 2007.

[5] T. Toifl, C. Menolfi, P. Buchmann, et al., "0.94ps-rms-Jitter 0.016mm² 2.5GHz Multi-Phase Generator PLL with 360° Digitally Programmable Phase Shift for 10Gb/s Serial Links," IEEE J. Solid-State Circuits, vol. 40, no. 12, pp. 2700–2712, Dec., 2005.

[6] E. Alon, J. Kim, S. Pamarti, K. Chang, and M. Horowitz, "Replica compensated linear regulators for supply-regulated phase-locked loops," IEEE J. of Solid-State Circuits, vol. 41, pp. 413-424, Feb. 2006.

[7] J. D. H. Alexander, "Clock Recovery from Random Binary Data," Electronics Letters, vol. 11, pp. 541–542, 1975.

[8] S. S. Mohan, M. Hershenson, S. P. Boyd, and T. H. Lee, "Bandwidth Extension in CMOS with Optimized On-Chip Inductors", IEEE Journal of Solid-State Circuits, vol. 35, no. 3, pp. 346–355, March 2000.

[9] IEEE Std. 802.3ae-2002, Media Access Control (MAC) Parameters, Physical Layers, and Management Parameters for 10 Gbps Operation.

[10] C. F. Liao, and S. I. Liu, "40 Gb/s Transimpedance-AGC Amplifier and CDR Circuit for Broadband Data Receivers in 90 nm CMOS," IEEE JSSC, vol. 43. no. 3, pp. 642-655, March 2008.

[11] N. Nedovic, N. Tzartzanis, H. Tamura, H. Rotella, M. Wiklund, Y. Mizutani, Y. Okaniwa, T. Kuroda, J. Ogawa, and W. Walker, "40-to-44 Gb/s 3× Oversampling CMOS CDR, 1:16 DEMUX," in IEEE ISSCC Dig. Technical Papers, pp. 224–225, 11–15 Feb. 2007.

A Robust 1.5Gb/s + 3Gb/s Serial PHY with Feed-Forward Correction Clock and Data Recovery

W Redman-White[1,3], M Bugbee[1], S Dobbs[1], X Wu[1], R Balmford[1], J Nuttgens[1], U Kiani[1], R Clegg[1], G W den Besten[2]

1. NXP Semiconductors, Southampton UK
2. NXP Semiconductors Research, Eindhoven, NL
3. also with University of Southampton, UK

Abstract—**This paper describes a 1.5Gb/s and 3Gb/s serial PHY architecture aimed at robust operation and ease of porting to smaller technologies. A minimum of precision analogue functions are used, and all digital functions use rail-to-rail CMOS. A single fixed low-jitter PLL serves the transmit and receive paths in both modes, and a new oversampling CDR relaxes the requirements for the analogue front-end as well as for the signal quality. The design occupies <0.4mm^2 in 90nm CMOS and consumes 75mW.**

I. INTRODUCTION

Rivalling analogue-to-digital conversion channels, embedded high-speed serial data interfaces are now an essential component of modern system-on-chip (SoC) designs, reducing cost, power and pin-count. Interfaces are needed between processor ICs, with displays, disk drives, other memory functions, etc.. Typical data rates are in the Gb/s region, and are increasing over time. To the system designer, such interfaces are just another set of pins, but there is significant subtlety in realising a robust and efficient architecture. Traditionally, there are a number of precision analogue functions employed in such sub-systems, and porting these blocks between foundries has been challenging compared with the digital parts. Further, with demands for very high data rates, small devices must be used in the critical analogue blocks; hence mismatch effects can affect yield if there is no strategy to calibrate or correct.

This paper describes a low-power embedded Serial-ATA physical layer capable of 1.5Gb/s or 3Gb/s operation, where the architecture has been optimised to minimise the sensitivity to the analogue limitations of nanometre CMOS and allow porting to new and smaller technologies.

A. System Requirements

Many standards exist depending on the application and technology, (e.g. Ethernet, PCI-e, HDMI, SATA, MIPI, DisplayPort, etc,) but most have strong similarities, often using 50Ω terminated, balanced lines with defined low signal swing. In the case of SATA [1] this is nominally 0.5Vp-p differential. The data rate is normally well defined, but there can be some small degree of frequency modulation added to spread the spectrum of any electromagnetic radiation from the link. In this case, the receiver must be able to cope with 0.53% frequency deviation. The transmitted random and deterministic jitter are defined for a worst-case eye opening allowing straightforward symbol recovery. Short and long term jitter are often specified with regard to tracking PLL bandwidths. As is common, SATA uses an embedded clock with a run length of 5 requiring clock and data recovery (CDR) function to allow the symbols to be re-sampled accurately.

B. CDR Techniques

The CDR is one of the most critical aspects of the PHY architecture, determining how well the receiver can acquire and track the incoming data rate, and how well the symbol eye is sampled. The classical technique is to use a tracking PLL [eg, 2, 3]. The incoming signal is fed to a phase detector able to handle the random transitions in the data. The VCO in the loop has an output in quadrature with the input so that its edge is ideally aligned with the centre of the data eye for sampling the symbol values. Hence, a PLL is needed with a precise settling time to acquire and track the frequency of data bursts, while the relative phase of the sampler is set by dead reckoning so that phase errors must be well controlled. Since this PLL must track the incoming data frequency, it cannot be used for the transmit path. With a lot of precision analogue functionality, porting this architecture to another technology requires significant effort.

With the availability of denser, faster logic, the possibility of using a blind oversampling approach has become practical [4], where the symbol recovery is handled in the digital domain. A major advantages is that the PLL does not need to track the incoming data eliminating start-up and tracking issues, and thus can also be used to control the transmitter at the same time. It is a development of this approach that is used in this PHY.

II. RECEIVER ARCHITECTURE

Figure 1 shows the receiver input amplifier. Adaptive line terminations are set by comparing fabricated on-chip values with an external resistor. A differential grounded gate amplifier outputs a signal level sufficient for direct sampling by a fast rail-to-rail CMOS latch. Whilst this amplifier is very fast, it and the succeeding latch are designed with very small devices, so the input referred offset over process statistics is not negligible.

To achieve 5X oversampling at 3Gb/s the PLL runs at 1.5GHz with 10 output phases. Each phase samples the amplified signal into one of 10 parallel latches (Figure 2), whose outputs are then aligned first with two phases and then with a single phase. 4 consecutive blocks of 10 samples are then assembled for processing in the CDR. For 3Gb/s the samples are taken 40 bits wide at 375MHz; for 1.5Gb/s the sample stream is decimated by 2 and the output words are at 187.5MHz, this being almost the only mode switching required. Normal CMOS library logic can handle both modes, and so the PLL is not required to switch frequency or to track incoming signal variations, simplifying the design and giving more freedom to optimise jitter.

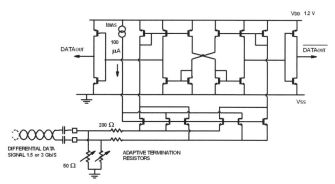

Figure 1 Receive Input Amplifier

The PLL sampling phases are only separated by 67ps, and the p-p jitter should thus be significantly less than this. At the core is a differential 5-stage ring oscillator based on current controlled inverters, thus helping with noise isolation. The time resolution between stages is a function of transistor matching parameters, requiring larger devices and hence significant current to maintain speed. The layout of the core and the sampling phase routing is carefully optimised to balance the parasitics and avoid any loss of symmetry.

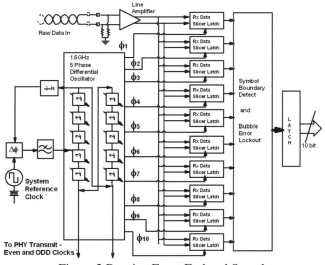

Figure 2 Receive Front-End and Sampler

A. Synhronisation and Symbol Extraction Strategies

The simplest method of extracting bit transitions and hence the data is to use an EXOR function on the incoming samples, and look for non-zero outputs. This works well if the sampling function is near ideal, but can be less reliable if there are imperfections. If the receiver is subject to noise, jitter or offset due to small, poorly matched transistors in the high bandwidth pre-amp (represented as a decision threshold variation) errors can arise making it extremely difficult to determine the symbol transition times.

B. Window Algorithm

Noise and jitter could, in the worst case, corrupt two consecutive samples, one either side of the ideal transition boundary. However, if the signal is not completely lost, the three centre samples (for 5X O/S) are generally reliable. We can thus use a simple window function to look for differences between symbols separated by two samples, implying finding sample strings having the same sign, followed by strings of the opposite sign. Note with that this strategy, clean data leads to results which show where the transitions could possibly be, but not exactly. However, if the raw sample data have noise or offsets, the window function gives results which are easily averaged to show the correct position. Combining both types of detectors with a voting system can achieve more robust data recovery for a wide range of input signal qualities.

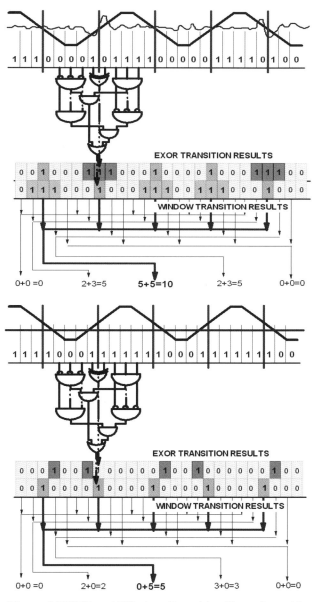

Figure 3 EXOR and Window Transition Detection with Noise and Offset

Since there may be clock slippage as well as jitter, offset and noise, the bit transition timing is estimated from a buffer long enough such that there are always at least 8 transitions in the data. (200 raw samples in this case). The window function is implemented using a simple AND-OR network (Figure 3). Results from all 200 window edge detections are weighted and combined with the 200 weighted EXOR results before then being summed in 5 groups (since there is 5X oversampling). The group with the largest vote sum is deemed to be the sample index modulo 5 which represents the best estimate of the clock edges. Bit values are then extracted from the central 40 samples of the 200 tested, using the preceding and succeeding data only as run-in and run-out for the algorithm. In this case, the central 3 samples from each group of 5 are used to determine the symbol value (Figure 4) by a majority vote.

To evaluate 200 samples and perform the weighting multiplication, five summations, and maximum value test could consume considerable power and area if done without some very careful design, so extensive use is made of arithmetic simplifications and data pipelining.

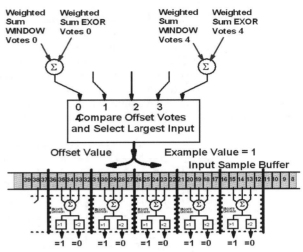

Figure 4 Symbol Extraction Scheme

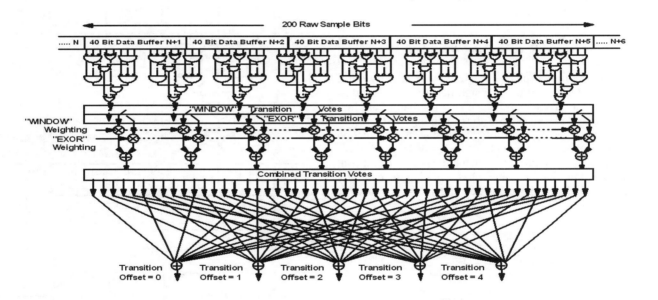

Figure 5 CDR Pipeline Conceptual Flow

Vote weighting is performed with left/right shift operations. Only 40 samples are actually processed at one time, and the intermediate operations and results are pipelined until all are summed at the end.

Clock slip is handled by extracting more bits than normally needed at each step. Normally, one bit frame (5 samples) is dumped each time. If the received signal is fast, the extra bit is periodically kept so that 9 bits are output. In the opposite case, 2 bits are dumped so that only 7 are output. A buffer with flag signals controls the transfer rate to the link.

III. TRANSMIT ARCHITECTURE

The top level follows broadly conventional structure. 8-bit wide parallel data are encoded into 10 bits and delivered from the link layer to the PHY Tx at a moderate clock speed. The low jitter PLL oscillator is used to control the parallel to serial conversion function and the transition timing in the line driver. EVEN and ODD data bits are parallel loaded into a shift register and then and clocked out serially at half the data rate. The serial data are then interleaved and re-timed with edges fed directly from the master oscillator (Figure 6).

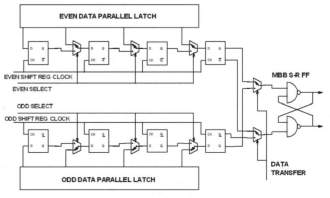

Figure 6 Transmit Architecture

The transmit buffer uses a simple current steering scheme. An externally referenced replica bias allows the output amplitude to be programmed and then track over process and temperature. Make-before-break and slew rate control are included in the driver to ensure precise and symmetrical eye crossing points. The output terminations are adaptively set with an external resistor and a replica circuit (Figure 7).

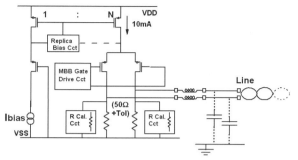

Figure 7 Transmit Buffer

IV. IMPLEMENTATION AND RESULTS

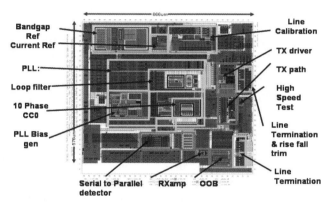

Figure 8 PHY Layout

The layout of the complete PHY is shown in figure 8. The total area is less than 0.4mm^2 in standard 90nm CMOS, including a significant decoupling capacitance. Note that the circuit is embedded in a large multimedia IC, and the measurements are taken in this environment, not as an isolated test chip. The design is fully functional at 3Gs/s (Gen 2), but the product has not been qualified at this rate at the time of writing. A special test mode allows direct measurement of the PLL behaviour at the pins. The one-σ jitter is less than 3ps, and the transmit eye pattern shows less than 170ps jitter at 250 Unit Intervals (UI).

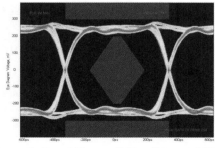

Figure 9 Gen 1 Transmit Eye Jitter at 250 UI

The receiver front end shows excellent sensitivity, being able to recover clean signals down to 100mV p-p and can handle 100mV p-p noise on a 200mV p-p signal. There are

no lock time issues, and the system easily follows more than the 0.53% frequency differences such that no special spread spectrum tracking is needed. Full compliance with SATA Gen 1 requirements has been verified.

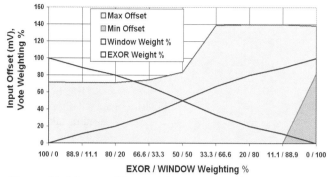

Figure 10 Measured Input Offset at Threshold of Failure.

The performance can be tuned by altering the weighting of the Window and EXOR detection paths Figure 10 shows the improvement in offset tolerance where a differential DC voltage is added to the line signal. When only the EXOR detector is operating, the link fails with around 70mV extra offset. As the proportion of the Window detector added is increases beyond about 67% (the system default), the offset tolerance increases by 2X to 140mV. As predicted by MATLAB simulations, if the only Window detector is used, the link cannot work with an ideal clean signal, but is still functional if a minimum offset is present.

TX Jitter MEASUREMENTS			Specification	
	DJ	**TJ**	**DJ**	**TJ**
5 UI	<35ps	<100ps (soldered)	117ps	237ps
250 UI	<35ps	<170ps	147ps	313ps
Rx PLL	Test Mode	σ (10 cycles, 1 UI) < 3ps		
Power	**Total**	**Analogue**	**Digital**	
	75mW	65mW	9mW	
Die Area	0.4 mm^2			
Tech.	90nm CMOS			

V. CONCLUSIONS

A robust SATA Gen 1/2 PHY has been developed with minimum use of precision analogue blocks for yield and process portability. A single fixed low-jitter PLL is used for both transmit and receive paths in both modes, saving power and eliminating locking problems. An enhanced oversampling CDR with a high sensitivity front end and dual transition detectors is shown to have excellent immunity to offsets and poor signal quality. Optimisation of conventional CMOS digital circuitry and extensive pipelining is used to achieve small die are and low power consumption.

REFERENCES

[1] Serial ATA 2.6 Specification, 15 Feb 2007

[2] H. Greshishchev and Schvan, JSSC, Sept. 2000

[3] R. Walker, et Al, *ISSCC Dig.*1997

[4] LEE *et al.*: CMOS JSSC, Apr 1995

A Low-jitter 1.5-GHz and 350-ppm Spread-spectrum Serial ATA PHY Using Reference Clock with 400-ppm Production-frequency Tolerance

Takashi Kawamoto and Masaru Kokubo

Hitachi Central Research Laboratory

1-280, Higashi-Koigakubo Kokubunji-shi, Tokyo 185-8601 Japan

E-mail: takashi.kawamoto.hv@hitachi.com

Abstract□ A serial ATA PHY was fabricated in a 0.15-μm CMOS process with a technique of calibrating a spread spectrum clock generator (SSCG). This technique involves calibrating the SSCG output signal frequency, which does not meet the serial-ATA specifications due to large variations in the reference oscillator, by utilizing the received signal during a power-on sequence. This is achieved by shifting the SSCG divide ratio, which is the input signal of the $\Sigma\Delta$ modulator. A feed-forward delay cell and voltage to the current converter with a high current limiter are applied to a VCO to achieve low jitter and prevent the SSCG from malfunctioning. This technique enables a serial ATA PHY to use reference oscillators with a production-frequency tolerance of less than 400 ppm, i.e., higher than the permissible TX frequency variations (i.e., 350 ppm). The calibrated SSCG achieved a total jitter of 3.9 ps.

I. INTRODUCTION

As the need for viewing motion pictures on portable devices becomes more intense, the interface between signal-processing units and other peripheral-storage devices must become faster. A "serial AT attachment" (SATA), which is one of the most promising high-speed storage interfaces, is widely used between hosts and external storage devices like HDDs and disk media, such as Blu-ray Discs, DVDs, and CDs, because SATA has a large bandwidth [1–6]. It thus provides significant improvements in storage and features for both desktops and mobile platforms. It is difficult in SATA communications using multi-GHz clock signals to reduce large EMI radiation noise and control low-jitter high-speed clock signals in various electronic systems. A spread-spectrum clock generator (SSCG) based on a sigma-delta PLL is the most attractive solution to these issues in SATA applications [2–6]. The SSCG must achieve an EMI reduction of more than 7 dB, 250-cycle jitter of less than 12 ps, and variations in 1.5-GHz output signal frequency of less than +/- 350 ppm in a non-SSC mode [1]. According to SSCG jitter, the permissible variations in reference-signal frequency may be less than +/- 100ppm. Inexpensive oscillators, such as those made from ceramics, have not been used as the reference signal in SATA PHYs because their production frequency tolerance is larger than +/- 100 ppm. Highly precise but expensive oscillators, such as those from crystal, have therefore been used. This has resulted in more expensive SATA PHYs. A novel architecture for SATA PHYs is proposed in this paper to achieve low-cost versions by using a reference oscillator with large variations. Section II describes the overall architecture for the proposed SATA PHY and a technique of calibrating the SSCG output-signal frequency by utilizing the received signal during a power-on sequence. Section III presents the VCO circuit we applied and Section IV presents the results of measurement. Section V concludes the paper.

II. ARCHITECTURE

Figure 1 is a block diagram of the proposed SATA PHY and SSCG. The SATA PHY consists of the clock and data recovery (CDR), the spread spectrum clock generator (SSCG), the serializer (SER), the deserializer (DES), and the counter (CNT) as an additional block to calibrate the SSCG output-signal frequency. The CDR recovers the clock signal (F_R) and data signal (DC) from the received signal (RX). The SSCG is based on a fractional-N PLL and it consists of the phase frequency detector (PFD), the charge-pump (CP), the loop filter (LF), the VCO, the multi-modulus prescaler (PRS), the programmable counter (PGC), the $\Sigma\Delta$ modulator (SDM), and the wave generator (WG) [3, 6]. The SSCG generates the clock signal (F_T) for the transmit signal (TX) from the reference signal (F_{REF}). If the FREF frequency has variations larger than +/- 100 ppm, the FT frequency may not be able to meet the SATA specifications. This causes SATA communications to fail. The proposed technique calibrates the FT frequency by utilizing F_R during a power-on sequence. Figure 2 illustrates the power-on sequence in the SATA specifications [1]. If the host recognizes the end of the device COMWAKE sequence, it starts the D10.2 sequence and sends the D10.2 signal to the device. If the device finishes the COMWAKE sequence, it starts the ALIGN sequence. Here, if the SSCG does not lock, the device sends the D10.2 signal to the host in the ALIGN sequence. Then, if the SSCG locks, the device sends the ALIGN signal. If the host can recognize the device's ALIGN signal, it changes from the D10.2 sequence to the ALIGN sequence. The host can only recognize the device's ALIGN signal that satisfies the SATA specifications. If the host cannot recognize the device's ALIGN signal within a set period of time, it cannot move onto the ALIGN sequence. The proposed technique makes the device's ALIGN signal meet the SATA specifications by utilizing the host D10.2 signal even if the SATA PHY uses the reference oscillator with large variations. Consequently, the proposed calibration must finish within 873.8 μs, which is from the starting point of the host D10.2 sequence to the permissible time the host can wait for the fine device's ALIGN signal. Figure 3 shows the calibration procedure and Fig. 4 is a block diagram of the proposed $\Sigma\Delta$ modulator to achieve proposed calibration technique. It consists of a 3rd-order $\Sigma\Delta$ modulator and an additional calculation block. The integer value of the divide ratio (I) is through the $\Sigma\Delta$ modulator and is added to the $\Sigma\Delta$ modulator output signal (Y). The decimal value of the divide ratio (F) and the modulation wave signal (W) is entered into the $\Sigma\Delta$ modulator as the input signal (X). S is the SSC mode-select signal. The proposed procedure for calibration is described as follows. First, the CNT counts the FR to detect the host SSC mode. If the count result (N_C) is less than a certain threshold value (N_T), the CNT determines the operation mode of the host is the SSC-ON mode and it then sets S to 1..

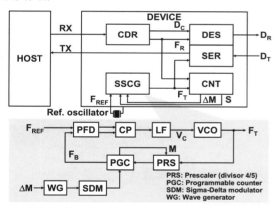

Figure 1.   Block diagram of SATA PHY and SSCG

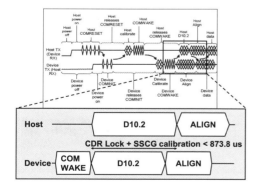

Figure 2.   SSCG calibration procedure in power-on sequence

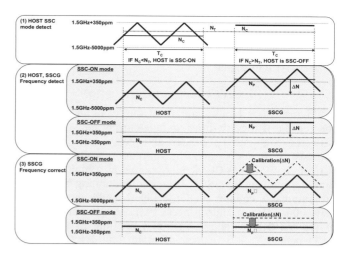

Figure 3.   SSCG calibration explanation figure

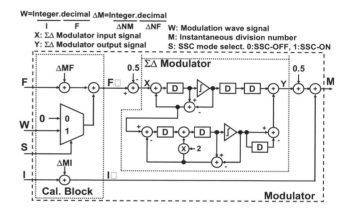

Figure 4.   Block diagram of $\Sigma\Delta$ modulator

Second, the CNT counts F_R and F_T to measure the difference between the F_R count results (N_C) and the F_T count results (N_P). In this case, F_R and F_T are defined as

$$F_R = N_C / T_C ,\qquad(1)$$

$$F_T = N_P / T_C = F_{REF} \times M ,\qquad(2)$$

where M is the SSCG divide ratio and T_C is the count time. T_C is set to 16 μs according to the calibration accuracy and calibration time. The proposed technique involves adding M to ΔM so that the F_T frequency equals the F_R frequency. ΔM is calculated as

$$F_{REF} \times (M + \Delta M) = N_C / T_C ,\qquad(3)$$

$$F_{REF} \times \Delta M = N_C / T_C - F_{REF} \times M = (N_C - N_P)/T_C ,\qquad(4)$$

$$\Delta M = \Delta N / (T_C \times F_{REF}),\qquad(5)$$

where ΔN is (N_C-N_P). Finally, the CNT calculates ΔM and it sets ΔM to the value in the wave generator (WG). The integer value (ΔMI) of ΔM is added to F and the decimal value (ΔMF) is added to I. Therefore, the SSCG divide ratio changes from M to M+ΔM and the calibrated frequency of the SSCG output signal then equals the F_T frequency, which satisfies the SATA specifications. This results in successful SATA communications because the host can recognize the device's ALIGN signal.

III. VCO CIRCUIT DESCRIPTION

Figure 5 is a block diagram of the VCO and shows the schematics of the low-jitter voltage-current converter (VIC) with the high-current limiter and delay cell. The VCO consists of the VIC and the current-controlled oscillator (CCO) [3, 6]. The VCO should operate as a high-frequency limiter to prevent the SSCG from malfunctioning because the programmable counter (PGC) in Fig. 1 could operate at less than 600 MHz in our process. The divide ratios of the prescaler (PRS) as shown in Fig. 1 are four or five. If the VCO generates a frequency of more than 2.4 GHz in the SSCG settling state, the PGC malfunctions. This causes the SSCG to fall into an unlock state. The VCO must generate an output frequency of less than 2.4 GHz. In our approach, by utilizing the VIC to achieve a high-current limiter, the VCO could operate as a high-frequency limiter. The VIC converts a VCO-controlled voltage (V_C) to a CCO-controlled current (I_P). When the M1 source current (I_C) is smaller that the reference current (I_R), I_P is IC because the M8 drain current (I_{CM}) defined as $I_C - I_R$ is zero. However, when I_C is larger than I_R, I_P equals I_R because I_{CM} is not zero. As a result, I_P defined as $I_C - I_{CM}$ becomes I_R. When I_P is I_R, the CCO generates an output frequency of 2.4 GHz

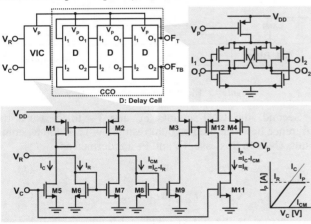

Figure 5. VCO block diagram

IV. MEASUREMENT RESULTS

The proposed SATA PHY was fabricated in a 0.15-μm-CMOS process. Figure 6 shows the spectrum of the CDR output signal and the SSCG output signal by using an oscillator with large variations as a reference. The CDR output signal frequency was measured as 37.5 MHz because it was divided by 40. Without the proposed calibration, the SSCG output-signal frequency does not satisfy the SATA specifications because of the large variations in the reference oscillator. With the proposed calibration, on the other hand, this is almost the same as the CDR output-signal frequency and can satisfy the SATA specifications. Figure 7 shows the SSCG output-signal spectrum without (a) and with (b) the

SSC. Our SSCG achieved an EMI reduction of 10.0 dB. Figure 8 is a screen shot of the measured power-on sequence for our SATA PHY obtained by using the 400-ppm frequency variation oscillator as the reference. The host could recognize the device's ALIGN signal and changed from the D10.2 sequence to the ALIGN sequence. The host and the device could then change to the SYNC sequence. This means that the host and device could send random commands in SATA applications. Figure 9 plots the results of measuring the Vc-frequency characteristics, which are linear from V_C=0.5 V to 1.2 V. The VCO gain, Kvco, is 2.2 GHz/V at 1.5 GHz and the Vc-frequency characteristics are almost flat from V_C=1.2 V to 1.5 V due to the high-frequency limiter. The maximum VCO output-signal frequency is 2.2 GHz (i.e., less than our target of 2.4 GHz). Figure 10 is a micrograph of our SATA PHY chip. Its dimensions are 2120 × 1000 μm. The results for SATA PHY measurement are summarized in Table 1. We achieved SATA random-command communication by using an oscillator with large variations of +/- 400 ppm, which exceeds the permissible variations of +/- 100 ppm. In the power-on sequence, the SSCG's calibration time (including CDR locking time) was shorter (i.e., 850 μs) than 873.8 μs.

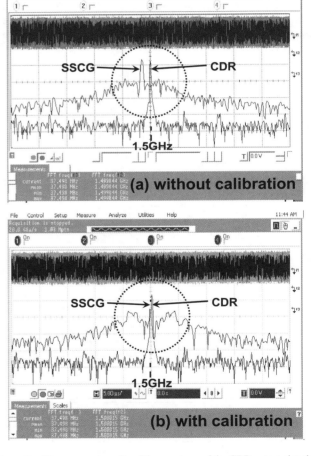

Figure 6. Measurement results of the spectrum of the CDR output signal and the SSCG output signal generated by our SATA PHY with 400-ppm frequency variation oscillator (a) w/o and (b) with calibration

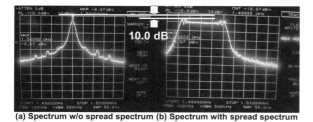

(a) Spectrum w/o spread spectrum (b) Spectrum with spread spectrum

Figure 7. SSCG output signal spectrum (a) w/o and (b) with SSC

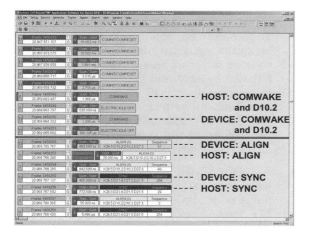

Figure 8. Measured power-on sequence of SATA PHY by using 400ppm variation oscillator as the reference oscillator

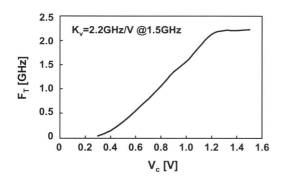

Figure 9. Measurement result of Vc-frequency characteristics

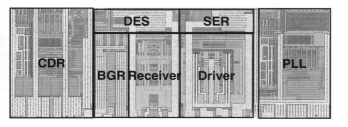

Figure 10. Chip micrograph

TABLE I. COMPARISON OF THE MEASURED OTHER-WORK SSCGS AND OUR SSCG

	This work	[2]	[3]	[4]	[5]	Spec. [1]	Unit
EMI reduction	10.0	(5.4)	(7)	10.0	9.8	> 7	dB
Random jitter of PLL	1.4	-	9.3	8.1	3.2	< 12	ps rms
Total jitter of PLL	3.9	-	-	8.4	16.8	< 133 (with driver)	ps p-p
Modulation bandwidth	+0/ -0.500	+0/ -0.37	+0/ -0.515	+0.035/ -0.500	+0.0/ -0.500	+0/ -0.500	%
Technology	0.15	0.15	0.13	0.15	0.18	-	µm
Power	29	-	-	54	77	-	mW

The SSCG achieved random jitter in a 250-cycle averaging a period of 1.4 ps and total jitter averaging a period of 3.9 ps. These values are about half those in previous work and sufficient to satisfy the SATA specifications. Moreover, the SSCG power consumption was 29 mW, which is half that reported in previous work [2-5].

V. CONCLUSION

A novel architecture for a SATA PHY obtained with a technique of calibrating an SSCG was proposed using an oscillator with large variations as the reference oscillator. The proposed technique is that the frequency of the SSCG output signal is calibrated by utilizing the host signal while a SATA power-on sequence. The proposed technique involved calibrating the SSCG output-signal frequency by utilizing the host signal during a SATA power-on sequence. The proposed SATA PHY was fabricated in a 0.15-µm CMOS process. It achieved SATA random-command communication, a total jitter of 3.9 ps, and an EMI reduction of 10.0 dB by using a reference oscillator that had 400-ppm frequency variations. This architecture should be an extremely attractive solution to reducing the cost of SATA applications.

VI. REFERENCE

[1] Serial ATA International Organization, "SATA: High Speed Serialized AT Attachment," Rev. 2.6, Oct. 2006.

[2] M. Aoyama, et al., "3Gbps, 5000ppm Spread Spectrum SerDes PHY with Frequency Tracking Phase Interpolator for Serial ATA," Dig. Symp. VLSI Circuits, pp. 107-110, June 2003.

[3] M. Kokubo, et al., "Spread-Spectrum Clock Generator for Serial ATA using Fractional PLL Controlled by Delta-sigma Modulator with Level Shifter," ISSCC Digest of Technical paper, vol. 48, pp. 162-163, Feb. 2005.

[4] H. R. Lee, O. Kim, G. Ahn, and D. K. Jeong, "A Low-Jitter 5000 ppm Spread-Spectrum Clock Generator for Multi-Channel STAT Transceiver in 0.18µm CMOS," IEEE ISSCC, Digest of Tech. Papers, pp. 162-163, Feb. 2005.

[5] J-S. Pan, et al., "Fully Integrated CMOS SoC for 56/18/16 CD/DVD-dual/RAM Applications with n-Chip 4-LVDS Channel WSG and 1.5 Gb/s SATA PHY," IEEE ISSCC, Digest of Tech. Paper, pp. 266-267, Feb. 2006.

[6] T. Kawamoto, et al., "Low-jitter and Large-EMI-reduction Spread-spectrum Clock Generator with Auto-calibration for Serial-ATA Application," IEEE CICC, pp. 345-348, Sept 2007.

An Adaptive 4-Tap Analog FIR Equalizer for 10-Gb/s Over Backplane Serial Link Receiver

Ori Eshet, Adee Ran, Amir Mezer, Yaniv Hadar, Dror Lazar and Miki Moyal

Intel

Haifa, Israel

Abstract — An adaptive 4-tap transverse-form differential analog finite impulse response (AFIR) filter in 65-nm CMOS is described in this paper. The filter is used for receiver-side equalization of severe inter-symbol interference (ISI) encountered in 10-Gb/s serial-link over legacy backplanes in 10GBASE-KR mode of the IEEE802.3ap standard [1] and over passive direct-attach SFP+ cables [2]. The AFIR is accompanied by an integrated in-die digital adaptation engine, employing the zero-forcing (ZF) equalization with the sign-sign block least mean square (LMS) adaptation algorithm. The AFIR uses an LC delay line structure which was optimized for low area and enhanced frequency behavior. The design has been fabricated as part of the receiver in a fully functional 10GBASE-KR compliant chip, achieving bit-error rate lower than 10^{-12} over several different backplane channels. It consumes 7.9 mW from a 1.2-V supply and occupies an area of 0.26 mm†.

I. INTRODUCTION

Inter-symbol interference (ISI) becomes a fundamental obstacle as data rates approach 10-Gb/s in serial-links over backplane. The frequency dependent loss in FR4 traces calls for challenging receiver architectures. In many of the legacy backplanes the signal at the receiver's input exhibit a completely closed eye. The pulse (single-bit) response of a typical backplane channels reveals considerably large pre-cursor energy, in addition to post-cursor signal spread and reflections from connectors and stubs, as shown in Fig. 1.

A system which is required to operate under these impairments with a bit-error rate (BER) lower than 10^{-12} has to manipulate the input signal to counteract these effects. Such systems usually employ some kind of equalization – either in the transmitter, the receiver or both. The equalization generates a high-pass response, which aims to match the inverse of the channel loss profile, resulting in an extended overall bandwidth and lower ISI [3]. A specific approach to the channel equalization problem is specified for 10GBASE-KR systems (subset of the IEEE 802.3ap standard [1]). This standard specifies a transmit-side equalization scheme using an adjustable 3-tap finite impulse response (FIR) filter, known as a feed-forward equalizer (FFE). The tap weights are tuned by the link-partner's receiver during link establishment, using a specified handshake protocol between receiver and transmitter. In addition to the transmit-side FFE, a common practice in high speed serial links is to provide additional equalization at the receiver side. Common approaches for equalization include combinations of passive high-pass networks and/or active high-frequency boosting stages [3].

However, these circuits have several drawbacks and limitations:

- To achieve the boosting factor required for backplane equalization at 10-Gb/s rate, several boosting stages are needed. These stages must be followed by additional gain stages to restore the low-frequency signal swing. Each stage contributes to the total noise, non-linearity and offset, which accumulates along the receive path. An architecture that uses fewer active stages is therefore favorable.

- A 10GBASE-KR system is targeted to operate with various different backplane channels [1] and therefore required to be highly adaptable. An FFE solution can provide the flexibility to adapt to different frequency responses and signal reflections by relatively simple means, in contrast to the tuning of peaking stages, which is usually done by complex analog circuitry [3].

- For backplane channel equalization, a non-linear equalizer, which can perform ISI cancellation without amplifying the high frequency noise, and which can mitigate spectral nulls due to reflections, is desired. A decision-feedback equalizer (DFE) is one type of such non-linear equalizer. An FFE set to cancel pre-cursor ISI, combined with a DFE, set to cancel post-cursor ISI, form a well-established channel equalization solution [4].

The use of LC delay-line analog finite impulse response (AFIR) filters at the receiver end of multi-gigabit links has shown promising results in recent publications [5]–[8]. In this work we present an automatically adaptive 4-tap LC delay-line AFIR filter optimized for low area and fully integrated into a 10-Gb/s transceiver. We describe how to optimize the LC delay line architecture for low area and how to improve the frequency behavior along the delay line. The rest of this

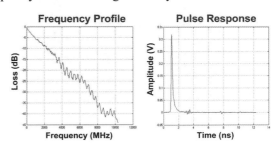

Figure 1. Example of a backplane channel frequency profile and pulse response.

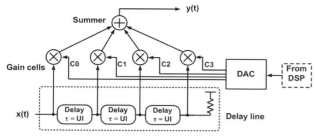

Figure 2.   Block diagram of the 4-tap AFIR filter.

paper is organized as follows. Section II describes the architecture of the AFIR and describes the main building blocks. In section III the adaptation method is discussed. Section IV presents results from both simulations and measurements of fabricated devices.

II.   AFIR IMPLEMENTATION

The blocks diagram of the 4-tap AFIR filter is depicted in Fig. 2. The main building blocks and design techniques will be described in the sub-sections which follow.

A.   Delay Line

At the heart of the AFIR filter lays the delay line. The delay line is designed to carry the analog continuous-time waveform across equally spaced delay intervals of one unit interval (1-UI)[1] separating the gain taps. The delay line should exhibit a controlled characteristic differential impedance of 100 Ω with a bandwidth larger than 9 GHz. Inductor-free active methods for implementing a delay line [8] were revoked due to lack in voltage headroom at 1.2-V supply. In addition, a cascade of active delay cells would introduce additional noise, non-linearity and offset to the signal.

LC-ladder artificial transmission lines are the common choice for implementing a passive delay line [5]–[7]. On chip monolithic inductors and capacitors are used to construct the passive delay element. The choice of inductance, L and capacitance C, in one LC section and the number of sections grouped into a segment, N_{LC}, defines the characteristic impedance, Z_0, the time delay of each segment, T_{delay} and the cutoff frequency (BW) of the delay line, f_{cutoff}, as given by

$$Z_0 = \sqrt{L/C}$$

$$T_{delay} = N_{LC}\sqrt{LC} \qquad (1)$$

$$f_{cutoff} = N_{LC}/(p \cdot T_{delay})$$

As the frequency in the delay line approaches f_{cutoff} the impedance becomes reactive, distorting the gain and phase of the signal. Tap spacing, T_{delay}, of 1-UI can be implemented by choosing $N_{LC} \geq 1$. As N_{LC} grows, smaller inductor and capacitor values are used in each stage. However, the total area becomes bigger since inductors have keep-away spacing constraints and limited placing flexibility among bumps.   From that perspective, we would like to use the lowest N_{LC} possible; nevertheless, the lower limit on N_{LC} is determined by the selected delay line topology and by the minimum required delay-line BW, as evident in (1).

In our design f_{cutoff} was specified to be greater than 9 GHz in order to achieve smooth frequency response up to 5 GHz. This calls for $N_{LC} \geq 3$ with each section having $T_{delay\_LC} = 1\text{-UI}/N_{LC}$, as shown in Fig. 3(b). On the other hand, had we selected the widespread symmetric traveling-wave topology shown in Fig. 3(a)– consisting of identical and symmetric input and output delay lines[5]–[7], we would have been restricted to using an even number of LC sections per segment – 4 in this case. The area penalty for a 4-tap FIR structure would sum up to a total of 16 differential inductors.

To reduce the total area the following measures were taken:

- Use the single delay-line topology [Fig. 3(b)] instead of the symmetric traveling-wave topology [Fig. 3(a)], to avoid the bump-pitch separation zone that would be forced between the input and ouput delay-lines, in the later.

- Use the lowest possible number of LC sections for every 1-UI segment that still meets the delay line BW requirement (3 in this case). Since the topology is a single delay-line, an odd number of LC section is allowable. Hence, we have a total of 12 LC sections vs. 16 if the symmetric traveling-wave topology was in use.

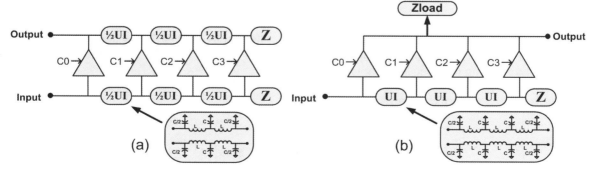

Figure 3.   AFIR topology comparison. (a) Symmetric traveling-wave topology. (b) Single delay-line topology.

---

[1]   1-UI roughly equals 97 ps at the system rate of 10.3125 GHz.

179

- Use stacked intertwined differential inductors that achieve a higher quality factor per area.

B. Anti-reflection Matching Resistors

A novel technique was developed to improve the frequency behavior across the delay line due to reflections. Anti-reflection matching resistors were added on each node across the delay line to repair the low-frequency impedance mismatch. The delay line has 50 Ω termination resistors at the end to match the 100 Ω differential characteristic impedance of the delay line at mid-high frequencies. In the low frequency region, the DC resistance of the inductor's metal lines dominates, and the inductor behaves as a ~4.5 Ω resistor, denoted in Fig. 4 as r. Owing to the 12 LC sections placed in series, considerable impedance mismatch exists at each node. These impedance discontinuities cause signal reflections and a non-smooth frequency response over the delay line in addition to failing to meet the return loss spec. This can be mended by adding anti-reflection resistors. Starting at the end of the delay line and going backwards, the equivalent resistance, R_{eq}, in each node is the parallel combination of the supplementary resistor, R, and the impedance looking ahead into the delay line, as shown in Fig. 4. R is selected such that R_{eq} becomes 50 Ω.

C. Gain Cells

The gain cells are realized by differential pairs whose tail currents are produced in a DAC. The gain cell schematic is shown in Fig. 5. To control the weight and polarity of the gain we use positive and negative g_m pairs driven by separate tail currents. The sum of all tail currents that drive the gain cells must remain constant to maintain a stable CM level at the output summation nodes. For this reason, the DAC, generating the tail currents, is of a current-steering type. In addition to the aforementioned positive and negative g_m pairs, the gain cells have yet another positive g_m, driven by a larger tail current. This current is steered to the one particular tap, assigned as the main tap, and remains zero for all other taps.

D. Summer

As mentioned before, the summer is realized by current summation load resistors. In order to reduce current consumption, the largest possible resistors that can still conform to the output bandwidth requirement are desirable. Inductive peaking was used at the summer to relax the bandwidth constraint, allowing the use of larger load resistors.

III. EQUALIZER ADAPTATION

The AFIR coefficients are adapted by an in-die digital block operated at 1/32 of the baud rate. The update is carried out using zero forcing (ZF) equalization with the

sign-sign block least mean square (LMS) adaptation algorithm [4], which is set to minimize ISI by constructing a filter response approximating the inverse frequency profile of the channel.

Since the AFIR operates in series to an adaptive transmitter-side equalizer at the remote partner front-end, their adaptation algorithms are relatively similar and can share hardware resources. In order to enable correct adaptation, the receiver-side AFIR adaptation begins only after the remote-partner transmitter FFE adaptation is completed.

IV. RESULTS

The AFIR was fabricated in a standard 65-nm CMOS technology. It is embedded in the receiver section of a 10-Gb/s transceiver chip. The dimensions of the circuit are 950 μm x 280 μm. The die photograph of the AFIR is depicted in Fig. 6. To implement a complete 10-Gb/s system, the AFIR is followed by a VGA block, thus its outputs are not accessible for direct high-speed measurements. To gain some insight into the performance and capabilities of the AFIR filter, simulation results and lab measurements are presented in the following figures. Fig. 7 shows the LC delay line response to an input transient step, obtained from a SPICE simulation. As can be seen, the delayed copies of the input step are spaced roughly 97 ps (±1 ps) apart. The smooth and settled behavior of the step response at the four tapped locations along the delay line indicates the significance of the anti-reflection matching resistors. The apparent attenuation of the signal, as it propagates across the delay line, is due to inductor losses (low quality factor of monolithic inductors), however, the adaptation engine should adjust the corresponding tap gains to compensate it, provided that the taps are designed with sufficient variable gain range.

Test-chip lab measurements offer additional insight into the equalization capabilities of the AFIR. As a test case, operation in 10-Gb/s over a 3 m Twinax cable in SFI mode [2] was examined. In order to demonstrate the AFIR performance, the first tap of the DFE was turned off. This setting should create a closed eye unless additional equalization is employed, and in this case, that can only be done by the linear equalizer implemented by the AFIR (in SFI mode the transmitter-side FFE is disabled). The system was allowed to converge, first with the adaptation turned off and then with the adaptation turned on. Fig. 8 shows the vertical eye openings at the point sampled by the recovered clock, which were measured using on-chip eye-monitoring circuitry. When allowed to adapt (Fig. 8, bottom), the AFIR was able to equalize the channel to provide operation with BER of less than 10^{-12}. The low residual ISI can be compared to

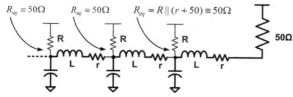

Figure 4.   Insertion of R, the anti-reflection matching resistors.

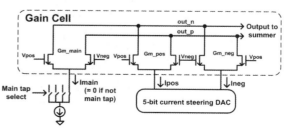

Figure 5.   Schematic view of the tap gain cell.

Figure 6. Die photograph of the test chip area housing the AFIR.

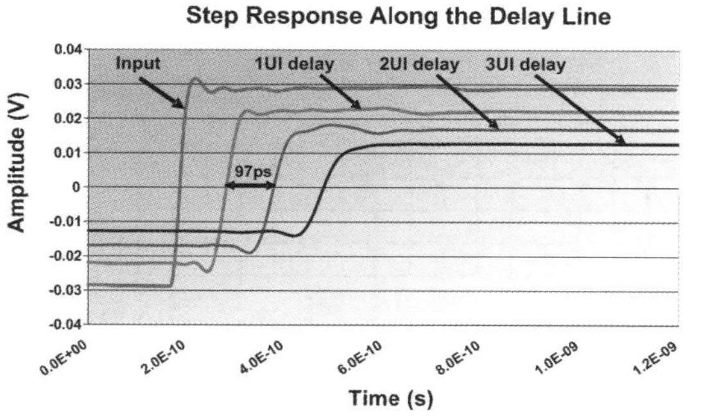

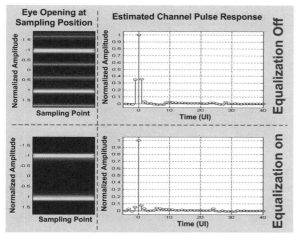

Figure 7. SPICE simulation of a propagation of an input transient step along the delay line.

Figure 8. Lab measurements of AFIR equalization over a 3 m Twinax cable in SFI mode - adaptation off (top) and on (bottom).

the sever ISI, displayed by the multiple horizontal levels at the centre of the eye, when adaptation is off (Fig. 8, top-left). In addition, the estimated channel pulse-responses at the input to the slicer, are presented for both cases (right side), revealing the proper equalization of the pre and post cursors.

V. CONCLUSION

We have presented an area efficient, automatically adjustable, transverse-form, 4-tap AFIR filter used for receiver-side equalization in a 10-Gb/s serial link transceiver chip. We discussed the rationale and advantages of a receiver architecture using an AFIR set as an FFE together with a DFE. We described the topology of the AFIR in comparison to recent reported works, and the techniques used to reduce the area and enhance the waveform's dynamic behavior across the

delay line. We presented the main building blocks of the AFIR and discussed the adaptation method. Finally, we demonstrated the delay line performance and equalization capabilities of the AFIR with simulation results and lab measurements, obtained from a 65-nm CMOS fabricated test chip.

REFERENCES

[1] IEEE Draft P802.3ap, Draft 3.0, Draft amendment to IEEE Std 802.3-2005, July, 2006.

[2] SFF-8431, Enhanced 8.5 and 10 Gigabit Small Form Factor Pluggable Module "SFP+" Revision 2.2, December 2007, ftp://ftp.seagate.com/sff/SFF-8431.PDF

[3] S. Gondi and B. Razavi, "Equalization and clock and data recovery techniques for 10-Gb/s CMOS serial-link receivers", IEEE J. Solid-State Circuits, vol. 42, pp. 1999-2011, Sep. 2007.

[4] S. U. H. Qureshi, "Adaptive equalization," Proc. IEEE, vol. 73, no. 9, pp. 1349-1387, Sep. 1985.

[5] C. Pelard, et al. "Realization of multigigabit channel equalization and crosstalk cancellation integrated circuits", IEEE J. Solid-State Circuits, vol. 39, pp. 1659-1670, Oct. 2004.

[6] S. Reynolds, P. Pepelijugoski, J. Schaub, J. Tierno and D. Beisser, "A 7-tap transverse analog-FIR filter in 0.13um CMOS for equalization of 10Gb/s fiber-optic data systems", ISSCC Dig. Tech. Papers, pp. 330-331, Feb., 2005

[7] J. Sewter and A. Chan, "A CMOS finite impulse response filter with a crossover traveling wave topology for equalization up to 30 Gb/s", IEEE J. Solid-State Circuits, vol. 41, pp. 909-917, April 2006.

[8] F. Bien, H. Kim, E. Gebara and J. Laskar, "Analog CMOS equalizer circuits for 10-Gb/s serial data transmission", presented at the DesignCon, Santa Clara, CA, 2007.

A 2.9Tb/s 8W 64-Core Circuit-switched Network-on-Chip in 45nm CMOS

Mark Anders, Himanshu Kaul, Martin Hansson, Ram Krishnamurthy, Shekhar Borkar

Circuit Research Lab, Intel Corporation

Hillsboro, OR, USA 97124

Email: mark.a.anders@intel.com

Abstract—An on-die multi-core circuit-switched network for tera-scale computing, achieving 2.9Tb/s throughput for random data transmissions on a 64 core 2D mesh and consuming 8W in 45nm CMOS at 1.0V, 50°C is described. Use of pipelined circuit-switched transmission, coupled with circuit path queue circuits and packet-switched request circuits enable power consumption of 125mW/router and efficiency of 363Gb/s/W, with scalable traffic-dependent throughput up to 6.2Tb/s.

I. INTRODUCTION

As integration densities continue to increase in a power limited environment, multi-core processors provide increased performance vs. power efficiency through parallel processing at reduced voltages and frequencies. Interconnect networks, for on-die communication between cores, are key to enabling scalable performance as the number of cores increases [1-4]. Circuit-switched networks offer a dedicated channel during data transmission without the need for intermediate buffering or arbitration. This can offer lower power consumption and higher throughput compared with packet-switched networks [5]. However, by avoiding buffering and arbitration, the dedicated channel resources must be reserved prior to data transmission, possibly preventing other more optimal data transmissions from occurring. Unlike pre-scheduled source-directed routing schemes [6-7], distributed routing schemes are not limited to predefined traffic patterns or applications, but determine packet routes and priorities for the reservation of resources based on incomplete real-time information. In order to overcome challenges of resource allocation and distributed control while maintaining energy savings of a circuit-switched network, the proposed circuit-switched network for on-die multi-core communication uses efficient circuits to enable i) pipelining of circuit-switching phases to improve throughput, ii) channel allocation using packet-switching without holding circuit-switched network resources, iii) queue slots to hold future channels for more optimal channel allocation, iv) 5.9Tb/s bisection bandwidth for a 2D mesh of 64 routers with 512b bidirectional interconnect in 45nm CMOS [8], and v) 2.9Tb/s maximum throughput for random data transmissions with energy efficiency of 363Gb/s/W.

The remainder of the paper is organized as follows: Section II provides an overview of the network and router organization; Section III illustrates the network operation; Sections IV and V provide more details on circuits that route request packets and circuit-switched data, respectively; finally, results are shown in Section VI.

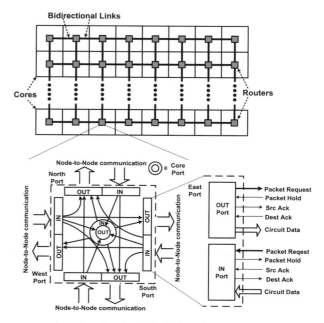

Figure 1. Circuit-switched 2D mesh organization.

II. NETWORK AND ROUTER ORGANIZATION

The circuit-switched 2D mesh network is composed of a packet-switched request address network alongside a circuit-switched acknowledge and data network (Fig. 1). During the setup period for a circuit-switched data transmission, request packets containing the destination address are routed using the packet-switched network. As the request packet passes each router and interconnect segment, the corresponding circuit-switched data channel for that segment is allocated for the future circuit-switched data transmission. When the request packet reaches its destination, a complete channel or circuit has been allocated. This channel has a latching or storage element only at the destination, with only multiplexers and repeaters along the way. Acknowledge signals indicate that the channel is ready for the data transfer, thus completing the setup period. When the channel is ready, the source router drives the data onto its output, where it propagates to the destination without interruption by state elements. When the destination has received the data, the channel is automatically deallocated.

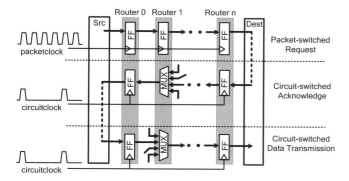

Figure 2. Circuit-switched pipeline and clocking.

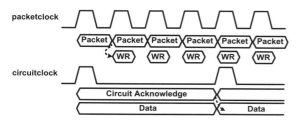

Figure 3. Network timing diagram.

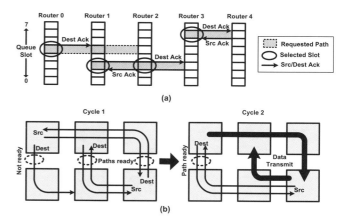

Figure 4. (a) Slot selection and (b) Path selection and data transmission.

To improve the data throughput, the three routing phases are pipelined, with different clocks to synchronize the request packet-switched and data circuit-switched portions of the network (Fig. 2). Since each request packet travels only between neighboring cores each cycle, it operates with a higher frequency clock (**packetclock**) than the circuit-switched portion (**circuitclock**), where data may travel across the whole network each cycle. During circuit-switched data transmissions, acknowledges for future transmissions are sent (Fig. 3). Also, request packets are simultaneously creating new channels by writing (WR) the routing direction for future data transmissions. This pipelining removes the request and acknowledge phases from the critical path, improving circuit-switched throughput by 3X.

III. NETWORK OPERATION

Each router within the network is divided into five separate ports: north, south, east, west, and core (Fig. 1). Each of these ports is further divided into IN and OUT ports, for receiving and transmitting data, respectively. All ports within a router are fully connected as a crossbar. In order to avoid deadlocks, the 2D mesh uses x-first, y-second routing, and unused paths are removed from within the router. Request packets of 10b are sent between neighboring routers with packet hold signals providing flow control. Bidirectional acknowledge signals, from source (**Src Ack**) and destination (**Dest Ack**), indicate that a circuit-switched path is ready for data transfer during the next **circuitclock** cycle. Finally circuit-switched data is routed from source to destination.

In order to improve resource utilization with distributed control, queue slots added to each router port store multiple request paths. This provides several potential paths for the circuit-switched network to choose from during the acknowledge phase, improving total throughput and resource utilization by 69%. As each request packet propagates from

one router to the next, its routing direction is stored in a queue slot. During a **circuitclock** cycle, each router port selects one of its queue slots, based on a rotating priority (Fig. 4a). The direction previously stored in that queue slot is used to route source and destination acknowledge signals. Arrival of both acknowledges at any router along the path indicates that the complete path is ready for data transmission in the next cycle (Fig. 4b). Paths that are not ready must wait for a future **circuitclock** cycle, while ready paths free their resources following data transmission.

IV. REQUEST PACKET ROUTING CIRCUITS

The request packet circuits route 10b packets containing destination address and queue slot (Fig. 5). The IN port compares the router and destination addresses to determine the routing direction and corresponding OUT port. Round-robin priority circuits select one of the valid packets at each OUT port and send **Hold** signals to the unselected IN ports. As each request packet is transmitted, the routing direction is written to the queue slot entry within a register file, creating request paths from router to router. The **Hold** signal is also asserted when the requested queue slot is full, preventing that request packet's IN port from continuing.

The **Hold** signal to the previous router is delayed by one cycle using a flip-flop, reducing the **packetclock** cycle time by one interconnect traversal. To accommodate the delayed **Hold** signal, an additional latch at the request packet IN port is closed whenever a **Hold** is asserted, while the previous router sends the next request packet. After the one cycle delay, the previous router will also stop transmitting. Pipelining of the flow control results in 30% **packetclock** cycle time reduction.

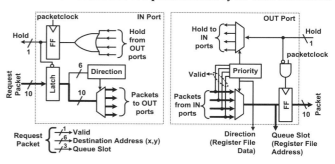

Figure 5. Request packet router circuits.

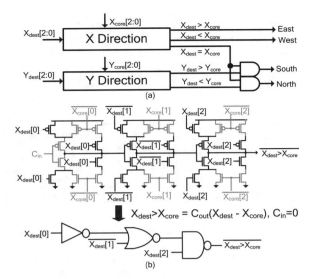

$$X_{dest} > X_{core} = C_{out}(X_{dest} - X_{core}), C_{in} = 0$$

(b)

Figure 6. Request packet (a) direction circuits and (b) 3b comparator.

Direction circuits for the IN port coming from a core are shown in Fig. 6a. Each IN port compares the $X_{dest}[2:0]$ and $Y_{dest}[2:0]$ fields of a request packet with the fixed $X_{core}[2:0]$ and $Y_{core}[2:0]$ address of the router to determine routing direction. A chain of ripple-carry gates implementing 3b compare is optimally sized to account for fixed core addresses, resulting in worst-case delay of an inverter followed by two gates (Fig. 6b).

Following the direction circuits, the priority circuits in each OUT port choose one from among the valid request packets (Fig. 7). Round-robin priority selection is implemented using six circuits that select earliest arriving valid signals by comparing all pairs of valid signals in parallel, yielding 50% delay reduction compared to a tree implementation [9]. These signals are sent on the same clock edge, and increasing the delay of certain bits avoids any simultaneous arriving signals. Since the circuits hold state when multiple **Valid** signals arrive, deasserting the selected **Valid** following transmit allows the next request packet to proceed.

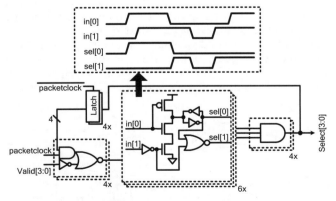

Figure 7. Request packet round-robin priority circuits.

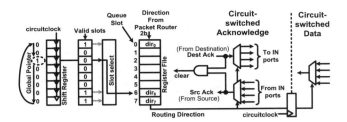

Figure 8. Circuit-switched acknowledge circuits.

V. CIRCUIT-SWITCHED ROUTING CIRCUITS

Each **circuitclock** cycle, bidirectional source and destination acknowledges are sent across the network. A global pointer provides the starting point for a valid queue slot selection. Rotating this pointer each cycle using a shift register improves fairness and prevents starvation. Use of a global pointer across all routers ensures that common paths are selected. The direction information stored in the selected queue slot sets the routing direction for the two acknowledges (Fig. 8).

The interface between the request packet circuits and circuit-switched routing is shown in Fig. 9. All register file storage is static latch-based with interrupted feedback for robust operation. At each **packetclock**, the 2b direction is written to latches addressed by the 3b queue slot. At the same time, a separate latch is set to indicate to the request packet network that the slot is now full. Each **circuitclock** cycle, the **full** bits are transferred to a second latch indicating **valid** queue slots. The selected queue slot is cleared if both source and destination acknowledges are asserted, indicating that data will be transferred the following cycle.

The slot select circuit searches for the next valid queue slot starting at the pointer position (Fig. 10). This operation is similar to an adder carry chain in which the pointer generates a one that propagates through the chain as long as the queue slots are empty. Using a logarithmic carry tree with intermediate carries that wrap around from MSB to LSB provides this functionality after three logic gates, a 63% delay reduction. A leading one from the carry merge tree indicates the position of the one-hot slot select.

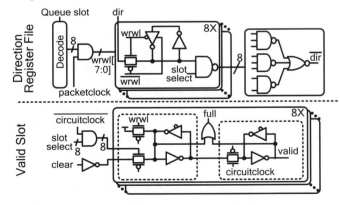

Figure 9. Direction and valid queue slot static register file circuits.

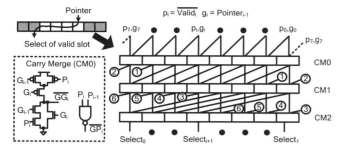

Figure 10. Slot select circuit.

During circuit-switched data transfer, data bits are routed through multiplexers and across interconnect and repeaters from the source to the destination. Selecting new paths each **circuitclock** cycle may change the routing direction at each router, causing glitches. Propagation of multiple glitches along a path significantly increases power consumption. Converting transitions to pulses through the multiplexer avoids these glitches by ensuring a common low value at all inputs when selecting new paths (Fig. 11). This pulse is then converted back to a transition before driving the next interconnect segment to reduce switching power on global interconnects. This reduces data switching power by up to 30%.

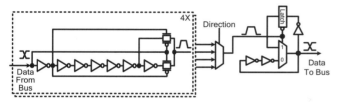

Figure 11. Circuit-switched data router circuit.

VI. RESULTS

The circuit-switched network-on-chip is simulated with 64 routers (Fig. 15) with 2mm distance between routers in 45nm CMOS at 1.0V, 50°C. Data transmission width is 512b with 350ps **packetclock** and 1.4ns **circuitclock** periods, yielding bisection bandwidth of 5.9Tb/s. The network achieves a maximum 2.9Tb/s throughput for random data transmissions at the optimal **packetclock** to **circuitclock** ratio of 4 (Fig. 12). Lowering this ratio by reducing the **packetclock** frequency reduces available paths during the acknowledge phase, while increasing the clock ratio by decreasing **circuitclock** frequency slows the circuit-switched transmit rate. For a 64 core network, four queue slots provide 69% throughput increase with diminishing returns for additional slots. Link utilization measures average circuit-switched interconnect use to indicate routing efficiency. Utilization of total interconnects averages 20% while utilization of interconnects with available paths averages 50%.

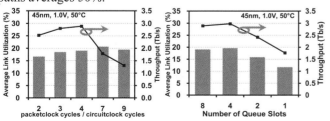

Figure 12. Throughput and link utilization vs. clock ratio and queue size.

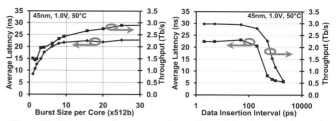

Figure 13. Network performance vs. burst size and data insertion interval.

Saturation of the network with bursts of 512b data transmissions from all 64 cores or varying of the rate at which data is transmitted both result in a maximum throughput of 2.9Tb/s, while latencies increase from 6ns to 23ns (Fig. 13). Limiting maximum number of router to router hops for data transmissions increases the throughput by 29% for four hops and to more than 6.2Tb/s for one hop (Fig. 14). Total network power peaks at 8W or 125mW/core at a maximum throughput rate of 2.9Tb/s. Power scales as throughput decreases, reaching less than 4W for 1.16Tb/s of throughput.

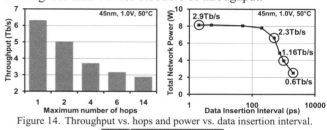

Figure 14. Throughput vs. hops and power vs. data insertion interval.

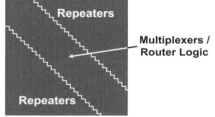

Figure 15. 45nm CMOS router layout.

VII. CONCLUSION

Pipelined circuit-switched transmission, coupled with circuit path queue circuits and packet-switched request circuits enable maximum power consumption of 125mW/router and efficiency of 363Gb/s/W for a multi-core circuit-switched network-on-chip. Throughput of 2.9Tb/s for random data transmissions across a 64 core 2D mesh is achieved while consuming only 8W in 45nm CMOS at 1.0V, 50°C.

REFERENCES

[1] L. Benini and G. Micheli, "Networks on Chips: A New SoC Paradigm," in Computer Magazine, vol. 35 issue 1, pp. 70-78, 2002.

[2] W. J. Dally and B. Towles, "Route Packets, Not Wires: On-chip Interconnection Networks," DAC 2001, pp. 684-689.

[3] Z. Yu et al., "An Asynchronous Array of Simple Processors for DSP Applications," ISSCC, pp. 428-429, 2006.

[4] S. Keckler, et al., "A Wire-Delay Scalable Microprocessor Architecture for High Performance Systems," ISSCC, pp. 168-169, 2003.

[5] P. Wolkotte et al., "An Energy-Efficient Reconfigurable Circuit-Switched Network-on-Chip," Proc. IPDPS, pp. 155a, 2005.

[6] C.-M. Wu and H.-C. Chi, "Design of a High-Performance Switch for Circuit-Switched On-Chip Networks," ASSCC, pp. 481-484, 2005.

[7] S. Vangal et al., "A 5.1GHz 0.34mm2 Router for Network-on-Chip Applications," Symposium on VLSI Circuits, pp. 42-43, 2007.

[8] K. Mistry et. al., "A 45nm Logic Technology with High-k+Metal Gate Transistors, Strained Silicon, 9 Cu Interconnect Layers, 193nm Dry Patterning, and 100% Pb-free Packaging," IEDM, pp. 247-250., 2007.

[9] K. Lee, S.-J. Lee, and H.-J. Yoo, "A High-Speed and Lightweight On-Chip Crossbar Switch Scheduler for On-Chip Interconnection Networks," Proc. ESSCIRC, pp. 453-456, 2003.

Standby Power Reduction Techniques
for Ultra-Low Power Processors

Yoonmyung Lee, Mingoo Seok, Scott Hanson, David Blaauw, Dennis Sylvester

Department of Electrical Engineering and Computer Science
University of Michigan, Ann Arbor, MI

Abstract ☐ **Standby power can dominate the power budgets of battery-operated ultra-low power processors, and reducing standby power is the key challenge for further power reduction. State-of-the-art ultra low voltage sensors consume hundreds of nW in wake mode and 100 pW or less in standby mode. Therefore, applying known circuit techniques for further standby power reduction is very challenging. In this paper, we extend known standby power reduction techniques for use in ultra-low power processors. In particular, we propose structures that enable the use of super cut-off voltages throughout the design with minimal power overhead. Different strategies for power gated logic blocks and memory cells are investigated.**

I. INTRODUCTION

The size of ultra-low power sensor systems is a critical concern, especially for medical applications requiring implantation. Cost, which is related to system volume, is also an important limitation in sensor systems. Since the size of the power source is restricted in such applications, ultra-low power consumption on the order of nanowatts (nW) and picowatts (pW) is required for these sensor processors.

One of the most promising approaches to achieving ultra-low power consumption is supply voltage scaling into the subthreshold regime [1] to minimize wake mode energy. However, many sensor systems spend much more time in standby mode than wake mode. Previous approaches have neglected the power consumed in this standby mode despite the fact that standby power can dominate the system budget [2]. Recent work [3] has shown that a better balance between wake mode power and standby mode power can be achieved by designing the system with standby power as a primary constraint. Careful technology selection for balancing active and standby power, stacking high-V_{th} transistors in memory cells for less subthreshold leakage, power gating for less standby power and other architectural/circuit techniques were shown to reduce standby power to tens of pW, giving ~1 year lifetime with a 1mm^3 system size including battery.

However, even with the sleep strategies presented in [3], standby power is still a dominant (>75%) source of total power consumption. Standby power consists of two components. The first component is the power consumed by circuits that are turned off (power gated) during standby mode. The second component is the power consumed by circuits that must retain state and remain turned on (e.g., memory). The ratio between these two types of standby power can vary depending on the complexity of logic and amount of memory required, though the second type dominated the standby power in [3]. Therefore, developing different techniques for reducing each type of standby power is the key challenge for extending the lifetime of ultra-low power applications to the multi-year range.

However, reducing the standby power for circuits that only consume tens of pW is very challenging for several reasons: 1) the power overhead for using any leakage reduction techniques must be a few pW in order to be beneficial, 2) since these systems are typically battery operated, only a single supply voltage is available, 3) any locally generated voltages for power reduction that are greater than power supply voltage (V_{DD}) or less than the ground voltage, should be

controlled without level converters or other switches that introduce new leakage paths.

In this paper, we develop standby power reduction techniques that can be applied to ultra low power processors. First, we explore the use of super cut-off MTCMOS for reducing standby power in power gated blocks. Our key contribution is the development of an ultra-efficient charge pump and cut-off circuit designed for low frequency operation (1~10Hz). Next, we investigate leakage paths in memory and propose a leakage reduction strategy that uses a super cut-off voltage to reduce bitline leakage. To support charge pump operation, a sub-pW clock generator with a unique current starving scheme is also introduced.

A test chip is fabricated in a 0.18μm CMOS technology to demonstrate the proposed leakage reduction techniques. This older process was strategically selected due to the availability of devices with high V_{th} and negligible gate leakage. The target V_{DD} of the chip is 0.5V, which is typical for ultra-low power processors. Measured results show that a 4.6Hz charge pump clock is generated with a 0.64pW power overhead and a standby power reduction of 2.3-19.3X is achieved for power gated logic blocks. For memory, standby power is reduced by 29%.

II. STANDBY POWER REDUCTION FOR LOGIC BLOCKS

Large logic blocks in ultra low power processors, such as the CPU, are often power gated to minimize standby power. For such circuits, using super cut-off is a straightforward and effective method for further reducing standby power [4]. In the super cut-off technique a negative voltage is applied to the power gating NMOS footer or a voltage greater than V_{DD} is applied to the PMOS header. However, the power cost of generating this super cut-off voltage has been shown to be large (50nW in [4]) relative to the sub-nW standby power budget targeted in this work. Consequently, the application of this technique becomes challenging in ultra low power processors. To apply the super cut-off strategy to a block with tens of pW standby power, the generation of the super cut-off voltage must have a power overhead on the order of several pW, or ~1000X lower than the results presented in [4].

As shown in Figure 1, the proposed system includes a charge pump that generates the super cut-off voltage and an output driver to

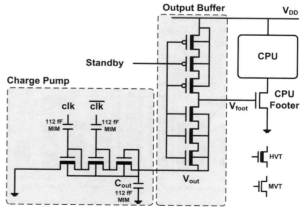

Figure 1. Proposed circuit for reducing standby power of power gated blocks

switch the gate voltage on the footer (V_{foot}) between the super cut-off voltage (V_{out}) in standby mode and V_{DD} in wake mode. The charge pump consists of three high-V_{th} NMOS transistors and three metal-insulator-metal (MIM) capacitors. Two clock signals with opposite phases (to be described further in Section IV) are applied to the pumping capacitors. To ensure maximum power efficiency, the clock must oscillate at the lowest possible frequency, so all leakage paths at V_{out} must be eliminated. Leakage is minimized along the pumping stack by using high-V_{th} devices and by reverse biasing the bodies of the pumping transistors using V_{out}.

To further improve power efficiency, a triple stacked inverter is used for connecting V_{out} to the footer. The PMOS stack minimizes subthreshold leakage during standby mode thereby lessening the pumping overhead and the required pumping frequency, while the NMOS stack plays a critical role when switching from standby mode to wake mode. The long NMOS stack cuts the connection between V_{out} and the gate of the footer to eliminate contention between the PMOS stack and the charge pump. It is also crucial to bias the bodies of the entire NMOS stack with V_{out} to ensure that the NMOS stack is not forward biased during wake mode. The negative voltage developed at V_{out} is preserved during wake mode, which is typically very short (on the order of milliseconds) [2], thus minimizing the time and power overhead of switching back to standby mode.

The carefully designed configuration described in this section allows the charge pump to be operated with low clock frequency (<10 Hz) and sub-pW power while guaranteeing sufficiently low (<-150mV) super cut-off voltage at the output at room temperature (25°C). Measurement results will be discussed in Section V.

III. STANDBY POWER REDUCTION IN MEMORY

Various SRAM structures, such as the modified-6T [5], 8T [6] and 10T [7] topologies, have been explored for low voltage applications. Despite obvious differences, each of these structures has similar components: a cross-coupled inverter pair, bit-lines, word-lines, access transistors and read buffers. Consequently, we can identify several sources of leakage that are common across all structures. To explore standby power reduction for memory, we study the low-leakage memory cell proposed in [3]. Given the general similarities between various SRAM structures, many of the conclusions in this work may be extended to other cells. As depicted in Figure 2, the memory cell under investigation uses cross-coupled inverters with stacked high-V_{th} transistors to minimize the subthreshold leakage. A separate read buffer with medium-V_{th} transistors is used to boost the read performance and improve cell stability at low voltage.

A. Leakage reduction for power gated blocks

Figure 2 shows the most important leakage paths within and between memory cells. Path 1 is the leakage path for circuits that are power gated (i.e., turned off) during standby mode. Only the read buffer is shown in Figure 2, but this category of circuits also includes memory peripherals such as row/column decoders, bit-line drivers and other control logic. Since these circuits are all turned off by a footer, our analysis shows that Path 1 contributes only ~2% of the total standby power. A separate power gating transistor is used to ensure that the current drawn from other power intensive modules, such as the CPU, does not induce read/write errors during wake mode. However, the super cut-off voltage that is generated by the charge pump introduced in Section II can be shared with virtually no power overhead.

B. Bit-line leakage reduction

Path 2 in Figure 2 shows the bit-line leakage path in the array structure of the memory. During standby mode, the bit-lines (BL and $\overline{BL}$ in Figure 2) float to some intermediate voltage, V_{BL}, between 0

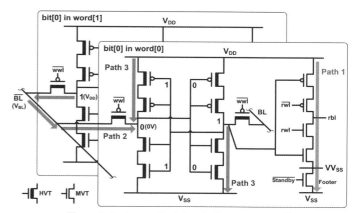

Figure 2. Leakage paths in low leakage memory cell

and V_{DD}. The value of V_{BL} depends on the number of bit cells storing 0's and 1's in the bit-line column. As a result, the transistors that connect the bit-lines and the memory cell (pass transistors) will have a drain-source voltage of V_{BL} or $V_{DD} - V_{BL}$ when the cell stores 0 or 1 in the adjacent node, respectively. This drain-source voltage induces subthreshold leakage on the bit-line, which contributes ~50% of total standby leakage.

In order to reduce the bit-line leakage, a super cut-off voltage (> V_{DD}) can be applied to the gate of the pass transistors during standby mode. This can be achieved by using a charge pump to boost the power supply for the wordline driver connected to the pass transistor control. The basic concept of this strategy is similar to the strategy used with power gated logic blocks, but it raises the following new challenges: 1) a new power supply for the pass transistor control logic must be kept near V_{DD} or higher at all times since low voltage at the gate of pass transistors will turn on the transistors, resulting in data loss, 2) the new power supply should be able to supply enough current to meet the demands of the pass transistor control logic during a memory write operation, and 3) all these criteria should be met with a power budget on the order of pW.

The proposed circuit that meets these criteria is presented in Figure 3. An ultra-low power charge pump similar to the one presented in the previous section is used for boosting the power supply. PMOS transistors are used to generate a positive super cut-off voltage V_{out} (>V_{DD}). The output of this charge pump is tied to the power rail of the wordline drivers. Charge is continuously pumped into the output capacitor (C_{out}) to develop V_{out}. The wordline drivers are structured to always provide full V_{out} in standby mode while also enabling wordline control during the wake mode. However, there can be no direct connection to the power supply at the output node during wake mode because a direct connection to V_{DD} would prevent V_{out} from rising higher than V_{DD} in standby mode. As a result, write operations that lead to a transition at the output of the wordline drivers will consume the charge stored in C_{out}, thereby lowering V_{out}. Therefore, consecutive write operations that occur between pumping cycles (due to the low pumping frequency) may bring V_{out} below V_{DD}. As the voltage reduces, the pass transistors of memory cells will be turned on, resulting in data loss.

To prevent this data loss, a "holder" transistor is introduced. The holder transistor indirectly connects V_{DD} with the output of the charge pump and is turned on during wake mode. When V_{out} drops below V_{DD}, the holder transistor is forward biased and can effectively "hold" V_{out} near V_{DD}. A wide low-V_{th} transistor would be preferable for the holder transistor, but in standby mode, the holder transistor acts as a direct leakage path from the output of the charge pump to V_{DD}, thereby reducing pump efficiency. Thus, a moderately sized (W:0.55μm L:0.35μm) high-V_{th} transistor is chosen to alleviate this

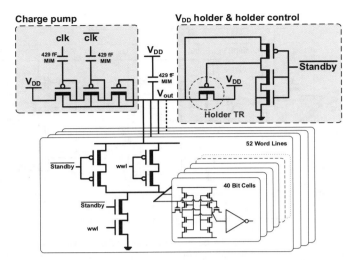

Figure 3. Proposed circuit for bit-line leakage reduction

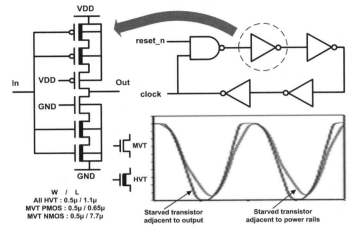

Figure 4. pW clock generator with current starved transistors and output waveform comparison between different starved transistor placement schemes

side effect. Worst case simulations show that this configuration maintains V_{out}>489mV at V_{DD}=0.5V.

C. Intra-cell leakage

Finally, Path 3 in Figure 2 shows the intra-cell subthreshold leakage path. In each cell, the primary leakage paths include a single NMOS stack and a single PMOS stack. For example, with a bit value of 1 stored in the front memory cell in Figure 2, the top left PMOS stack and bottom right NMOS stack will leak. Our analysis shows that this leakage amounts to ~48% of total standby power.

In order to suppress intra-cell subthreshold leakage, a reverse body bias can be applied to all transistors or high V_{th} transistors can be used. However, according to our analysis, the standby power of our target memory module was 60.5pW and the overhead of generating enough well bias current to compensate for junction leakage was greater than the projected leakage improvement. Therefore, our memory structure uses high-V_{th} transistors as in [3].

IV. ULTRA LOW POWER CLOCK GENERATION

The clock generator is one of the most important elements in our proposed ultra-low leakage system. Without proper design, the clock generator can easily exceed the pW budget allotted. Figure 4 illustrates the proposed clock generator with a unique current starved inverter. In this inverter, current starved transistors are placed next to the output node whereas conventional design places them next to the power and ground rails.

To achieve minimum power, the clock generator is designed for operation at very low frequencies (1~10Hz). Each inverter in the clock generator uses stacked high-V_{th} transistors adjacent to the power and ground rails and current-starved medium-V_{th} transistors in the off-state adjacent to the output node. In this configuration, the on-current of the inverter is determined by the subthreshold leakage of the starved medium-V_{th} transistors, which makes the current consumption very small. When the input is low, the NMOS stack is turned off and a small voltage is developed at the source of the starved NMOS due to stack effect. Thus, a reverse body bias is generated for the starved NMOS, making the off-current smaller and thereby improving the power efficiency over the case where the starved transistors are adjacent to the power and ground. The same effect can be observed in the PMOS stack. Our analysis shows that the 10%-90% rise/fall time can be reduced by 19.6% with our proposed design, making the clock generator more stable and robust.

V. MEASUREMENT RESULTS

A. Measurement of standby power for power gated blocks

A large CPU block with 23,472 transistors has been tested using 4 different medium-V_{th} footer sizes at room temperature (25°C). Figure 5 shows the generated super cut-off voltage and charge pump power consumption as functions of the charge pump clock frequency. The charge pump clock was supplied externally in this specific experiment to give maximum tunability. Strong super cut-off voltages (<-150mV) are generated with low pumping frequency (<10Hz) and sub-pW power consumption. The leakage reduction achieved using super cut-off MTCMOS is shown in Figure 6. With a footer width of 17.16μm, the CPU block consumes 15.4pW in standby mode without super cut-off MTCMOS. For low pumping frequencies (<10Hz), increasing the pumping frequency reduces total standby power since the super cut-off voltage reduces. However, as frequency exceeds 10Hz, the charge pump overhead becomes dominant and increases total power consumption. Total standby power reaches a minimum of 0.8pW at 10Hz, a 19.3X reduction over normal operation.

Figure 7 shows the standby power reduction for different footer sizes. Despite different footer sizes, the standby power converges to ~1pW for all cases at an optimal pumping frequency of 10Hz. Therefore, the power gain is largest (19.3X) with the widest footer and smallest (2.3X) with the narrowest, which suggests that this power reduction technique may also enable active power reduction by allowing more freedom when choosing the size of the power gating transistor.

The size of the power gating transistor is constrained by the standby mode power budget and wake mode current demand. In wake mode, a wider power gating transistor is preferred to minimize the voltage drop across the power gating transistor. However, since the standby power of a circuit block is determined by the size of the power gating transistor, narrow width is preferred for minimum standby power. Energy consumption in standby mode dominates wake mode energy consumption for ultra-low power processors, so a power gating transistor with very narrow width is typically used (a footer width of only 0.66μm was used in [3]). The voltage drop across such a narrow power gating transistor effectively reduces V_{DD} for the logic, making the circuit block slower, less robust and less energy efficient. In light of our measured results, a wider power gating transistor can be used with a minor standby power penalty and significant wake mode energy reduction (estimated at 23% by eliminating 116mV out of 500mV).

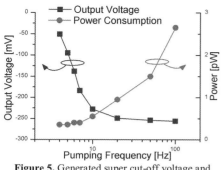

Figure 5. Generated super cut-off voltage and charge pump power for CPU leakage reduction

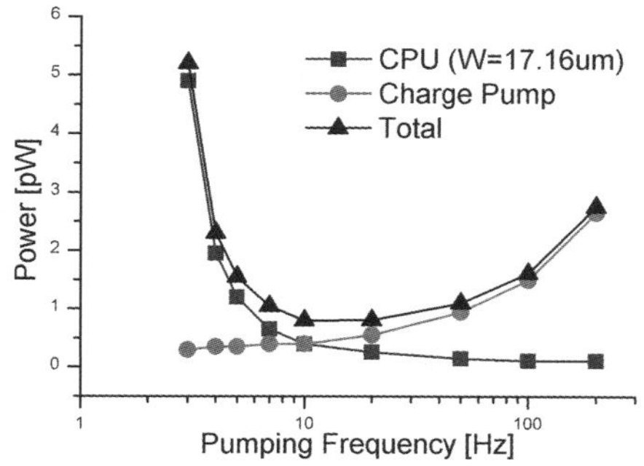

Figure 6. CPU and charge pump power in standby mode

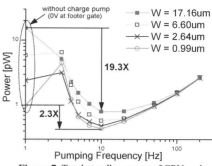

Figure 7. Total standby power of CPU and charge pump with various footer size

B. Measurement of standby power for memory

A memory with 2,720 bit cells has been tested at room temperature (25°C). Figure 8 shows the generated super cut-off voltage and charge pump power consumption as functions of charge pump clock frequency. The power overhead for the charge pump is significantly higher than for the previous section due to the larger number of leakage paths such as the pass-transistor controllers and the holder transistor. At the power optimal pumping frequency of 20 Hz, the charge pump overhead is below 5% of original memory standby power. Total standby power is shown in Figure 9. At a pumping frequency of 20 Hz, standby power is reduced by 29.1% compared to normal operation. Note that power actually increases at low frequencies since the output of the charge pump can fall below V_{DD} (0.5V) in this region and cause increased leakage across pass transistors.

C. Low power clock generator

Testing of the low power clock proposed in Section IV shows an average oscillating frequency of 4.6 Hz with a power consumption of only 0.64pW. Simple calculations suggest that, at the optimal frequency for the two previously described charge pumps (10Hz, 20Hz), clock power can be maintained below 3pW. Since the power characteristic in Figure 6 is flat near the minimum, applying the memory-optimal clock frequency of 20Hz to the CPU charge pump results in a negligible power penalty of only 1.3%. This result suggests that a single clock generator can be shared between the memory and CPU.

Measurements at temperatures ranging from 0-80°C reveal that the low power clock tracks the power optimal frequency well. Figure 10 shows the power optimal charge pump clock frequency for CPU and generated frequency, both normalized at 40°C. Over this temperature range, discrepancies between the optimal frequency and the generated frequency result in a maximum power penalty of only 14% compared to the optimal operation point.

VI. CONCLUSION

Super cut-off circuit techniques for reducing the standby power of ultra-low power processors have been presented along with a supporting low power clock generator. A standby power reduction of 2.3-19.3X is achieved for power gated logic blocks, while standby power is reduced by 29.1% for memory using the proposed techniques.

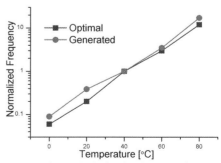

Figure 11. Die Micrograph and Dimensions

Dimensions	
CPU Pump	960 μm²
Memory Pump	1,365 μm²
Low power Clock Gen.	658 μm²

REFERENCES

[1] A. Wang, A. Chandrakasan, "A 180mV FFT processor using subthreshold circuit techniques," Int. Solid-State Circuits Conf., 2004, pp. 292-293

[2] M. Seok, et al., "Analysis and Optimization of Sleep modes in Subthreshold Circut Design," ACM/Design Automation Conference, 2007

[3] M. Seok, et al., "The Phoenix Processor: a 30pW platform for sensor applications," Symposium on VLSI Circuits, June 2008, in press

[4] H. Kawaguchi, et al., "A super cut-off CMOS (SCCMOS) scheme for 0.5-V supply voltage with picoampere stand-by current," JSSC, Oct. 2000, pp.1498-1501

[5] B. Zhai, et al., "A sub-200mV 6T SRAM in 130nm CMOS," Int. Solid-State Circuits Conf., 2007, pp. 332-333

[6] L. Chang, et al., "Stable SRAM cell design for 32 nm node and beyond", Symposium on VLSI Technology, Jun. 2005, pp. 128-129

[7] B. Calhoun, A. Chandrakasan, "A 256kb Sub-threshold SRAM in 65nm CMOS," Int. Solid-State Circuits Conf., 2006, pp. 2592-2601

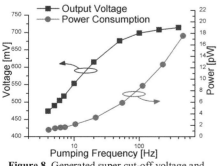

Figure 8. Generated super cut-off voltage and pump power for Memory leakage reduction

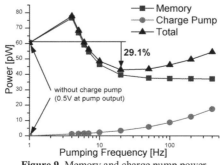

Figure 9. Memory and charge pump power in standby mode

Figure 10. Optimal and generated clock frequency normalized at 40°C

Low-Power 32-bit Dual-MAC 120 µW/MHz 1.0 V icyflex DSP/MCU Core

C. Arm, S. Gyger, J.-M. Masgonty, M. Morgan,

J.-L. Nagel, C. Piguet, F. Rampogna, P. Volet
CSEM
Neuchâtel, Switzerland

Abstract—**A low-power programmable combined digital signal processor (DSP) and micro-controller unit (MCU), named icyflex, was designed. It is implemented as a customizable, synthesizable and reconfigurable VHDL software intellectual property core. Performance values are given for a 0.18 micron technology integration.**

I. INTRODUCTION

Today's portable appliances – such as portable phones, MP3 players, PDAs, audio and image processing systems, hearing aids, wired and wireless communication devices – increasingly use programmable combined DSP/MCUs. The advantage of combined DSP/MCUs compared to standard DSPs are their ease of programming in high-level languages such as C or C++. They combine hardware support to efficiently handle and access various data types which is inherent to MCUs, with the efficiency of number crunching and digital signal processing algorithms which are typical for DSPs.

DSP processors are designed to efficiently execute DSP algorithms by reducing the amount of clock cycles for their execution. An analysis of this type of algorithms – for instance in digital filters, data correlation and Fast Fourier Transform computation – shows that optimizing the multiply-and-accumulate (MAC) operations is key to achieving good performance, i.e. to reduce the required clock cycles and power consumption. The goal of an efficient DSP is to execute an operation such as the MAC in a single clock cycle. This entails two architecture features: pipelining the data path of complex operations, and guaranteeing sufficient bandwidth to/from the data memory.

The presented combined DSP/MCU has a load/store (RISC) architecture; the data paths are fed by input registers. Load/store architectures seem better suited for "low-power" programming since input data fetched from the data memories may be reused in latter computations. It implements various indexed data memory accessing modes required to efficiently manipulate stack-stored local variables of many types. In addition, it implements DSP specialized indirect addressing modes. Data memories are addressed via pointers with pre- or post- decrements / increments as well as circular addressing (modulo) capability. All these addressing modes are especially efficient when managing data arrays to avoid extra clock cycles for calculating addresses. These operations are performed in a specialized address generation unit (AGU).

As with DSPs, loops are efficiently handled without overhead: LOOP or REPEAT instructions can repeat 1 to N instructions without having to explicitly initialize and update a loop counter; and they do not require an explicit branch instruction at the end of the loop.

Another important feature of both DSPs and embedded MCUs is their capability to efficiently handle external hardware generated interrupt requests. Both the latency and the overhead for context switching need to be as low as possible.

II. CUSTOMIZABLE AND RECONFIGURABLE ICYFLEX DSP/MCU CORE

The icyflex DSP/MCU is implemented as a synthesizable VHDL software intellectual property (soft IP) core which is both customizable and reconfigurable [1]. This processor core is designed to be used in systems-on-chip (SoC), either in a single or multi-processor environment.

The range and complexity of embedded applications that can be implemented in SoCs is quite broad. Digital signal processing-oriented applications can range from baseband data processing in wireless communication devices, image and audio compression or decompression algorithms in multimedia devices, to a whole set of other algorithms such as speech recognition. Control-oriented applications can range from the handling of simple man-machine interfaces, to complex graphical user interfaces (GUI), to the search and manipulation of large data sets contained in external storage devices (flash memory, hard-disk, network), through the use of a real-time multitasking kernel. As a consequence, it is rather difficult for any programmable microprocessor to cover all these applications in the most efficient way. The efficient implementation of DSP-oriented embedded applications depends on:

– operating constraints such as the required data precision, the required processing speed, and/or power consumption, of the data handled

– the various kinds of data to be handled by the algorithms (e.g.: 8-12 bit integer pixels, 16-24 bit fixed point audio samples, 32-bit floating-point data), their organization in memory (e.g.: 1-D vectors, 2-D arrays, complex data structures, etc.), and the amount of available memory.

The designer can customize the architecture of the icyflex DSP/MCU for each implementation in order to best fit the requirements of the embedded application being targeted. This is done by selecting the appropriate:

- data memory bandwidth (up to 32 or 64-bit wide memory transfers),

- address word size (program and data: up to 32 bits),

- data processing and address computation hardware.

The resulting silicon will only contain the required hardware which will save power consumption and reduce the size (and cost) of the chip.

Aside from being customizable at integration time, the icyflex processor is also reconfigurable at run-time. Both the address generation unit (AGU) and the data processing unit (DPU) can be reconfigured [3]. It is very interesting to re-configure addressing modes, as they are often the bottleneck for intensive computation algorithms. The few bits in a 32-bit instruction which are available to select among addressing modes only allow a few basic addressing modes. More powerful addressing modes are required to achieve better performance, i.e. to reduce the amount of clock cycles and power consumption. These additional addressing modes can be selected by the programmer on the fly for a given algorithm. They are selected through specific registers within the AGU (registers Cxn and Cyn in Fig. 2). Four run-time reconfigurable complex addressing modes are available per AGU index register.

The data processing unit is also re-configurable. The icyflex DSP/MCU has a relatively complex DPU data path allowing it to execute multiple operations in parallel. However, because of the limited number of bits in the 32-bit instruction, it is not possible to always fully exploit the data path capabilities in terms of computational power. In order to speed-up the execution of intensive computation and digital signal processing algorithms, configuration registers are available which allow a much finer control over the data path than most standard icyflex instructions will allow. By appropriately reconfiguring both the available AGU addressing modes and the DPU data path, it is possible to speed-up digital signal processing kernel execution by an order of magnitude over simple 32-bit MCUs.

III.   ARCHITECTURE OF THE ICYFLEX DSP/MCU CORE

The icyflex core is made of four units (Fig. 1): the program sequencing unit (PSU), the data move unit (DMU), the data processing unit (DPU) and the host and debug unit (HDU).

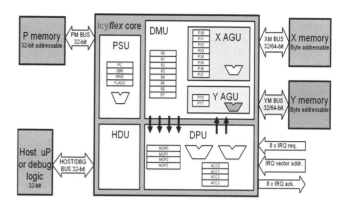

Figure 1.   icyflex DSP/MCU processor core

The PSU handles instruction fetches, hardware loops, instruction repeats, branches, subroutine calls and external interrupt requests (8 priority levels, vectorized). It dispatches operations to the DMU and to the DPU.

The DMU (Fig. 2) is responsible for the handling of the data moves among the core's registers, and between data memories (X, Y) and the core's registers. It contains a register file of eight 32-bit registers and two reconfigurable AGUs. The DMU is a pure load/store unit that implements independent and parallel accesses to the two data memory banks. During each clock cycle, up to four 32-bit data words can be transferred between the DMU and the memory.

The reconfigurability of the AGUs allows the icyflex core to best fit the needs of DSP algorithms in terms of data memory address computation. There are two classes of indirect memory addressing modes, of which the second is run-time re-configurable:

- Basic addressing modes: indirect, ±1, ±offset, pre/post/ and no index modifications

- Pre-defined addressing modes: a choice of four distinct pre-defined addressing modes can be selected among the 32 available (Fig. 2). The selection of pre-defined operations is performed in the Csn configuration register associated to each Psn index register (where s refers either to memory bus X or Y). For instance, a pre-defined operation for index register Psn could be:

$$Psn := (Psn + Psn + 1 + OFFA) \% Msn$$

The DPU (Fig. 3) implements both basic ALU operations needed by any MCU (such as: ADD, SUB, MUL, SHIFT, etc.), as well as digital signal processing and single instruction multiple data (SIMD) operations (such as: ADD2, MAC, MAC2, etc.). DPU operations read their operands from the DMU's general-purpose registers. The large data throughput available between these two units allows the parallelization of many algorithms (such as: convolutions, FFTs, etc.). Up to six 32-bit data words can be read from the DMU registers, and up to two 32-bit data words can be written back to the DMU during each clock cycle. The DPU contains two 32-bit multipliers, as well as two 32-bit ALUs, two 64-bit barrel shifters and two 64-bit accumulator ALUs. A set of four 64-bit accumulator registers and of four 128-bit re-configuration registers are also implemented. The data-path of this unit, just as those of the AGUs, is run-time re-configurable. It is possible to redefine up to four new instructions by configuring the behavior of each of the boxes in the DPU data path. This re-configurability allows to best match the class of algorithms and data to be processed, without pre-defining and coding these instructions in the instruction-set prior to hardware implementation time. As an example, the radix-2 FFT butterfly kernel can be entirely implemented in hardware through the use of three re-configurable operations.

The Host and Debug Unit (HDU) allows the control of the icyflex DSP/MCU core from either an external 32-bit host microprocessor or from a JTAG debug interface. During the software development phase, the software designer uses the HDU's debug logic to place breakpoints and execute algorithms in step-by-step mode.

The icyflex DSP/MCU instructions are 32-bit wide. Since instructions are fetched from the program memory at every clock cycle, this short instruction width is very beneficial for power consumption. However, the limited instruction width restricts the number of parallel operations that may be encoded. The icyflex supports the parallel execution of up to two independent operations in a single clock cycle. Additional parallelism (e.g. SIMD, specialized, or re-configurable operations) may be available within each of these two operations.

A tool suite was developed for icyflex. It is based on the GNU tools (gas, gcc, gdb) and the Eclipse development toolset, to which a C++ model of the icyflex was added for debugging applications when not using the on-chip debug (OCD) capability.

IV. Performance of the icyflex Core

A frequently used benchmark for microprocessors is the number of clock cycles to execute well-documented algorithms. Among these algorithms, the 16-tap FIR filter and the complex FFT are significant DSP algorithms which are often published for a variety of processors. Table I shows that the icyflex core performance is similar, for these algorithms, to the fastest dual-MAC architectures (BF53x [2], SP5 [3] or ZSP500).

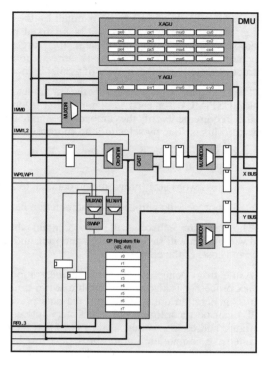

Figure 2. icyflex DMU data path

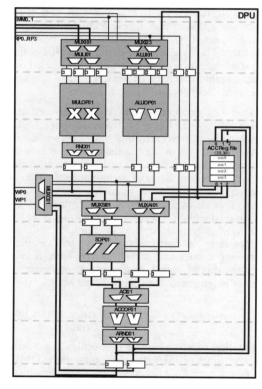

Figure 3. icyflex DPU data path

TABLE I. NB OF CLOCK CYCLES FOR DIFFERENT MCUS & DSPS

Company / DSP	Clock Cycles for:	
*) estimated	16-tap FIR 40 samples	Complex FFT 256 points
CSEM / icyflex	535	2'700
CSEM / MACGIC Audio-I	195	1'410
Philips / Coolflux	* 640	* 5'500
ADI / BF535	741	2'400
TI / TMS320C5509	384	4'800
ARM / ARM9		3'900
3DSP / SP5		2'420
LSI / ZSP 500		2'250

The first integration of the icyflex DSP/MCU, named icyfirst, works with 8-, 16-, 32- and 64-bit wide words, 32- and 64-bit wide transfers, and a dual multiply-and-accumulate (MAC) data path. Targeting a broad range of applications, it was integrated with:
- a Direct Memory Access (DMA) controller
- a vectorized interrupt and DMA request controller
- a JTAG controller,
- 4 timers (32 bits) and a watchdog,
- multiple bus interfaces: 2 SPI, 2 I2C and 2 inter-IC sound (I2S) controllers,
- a 32-bit general purpose input/output GPIO controller,
- a unified program and data memory made up of 128 kiBytes of low-power SRAM memory.

Figure 4. Test chip of the icyflex DSP/MCU core

The chip was integrated by Taiwan Semiconductor Manufacturing Company (TSMC) using their 180 nm technology (Fig. 4). The resulting 32-bit icyflex DSP/MCU counts about 110'000 equivalent gates on 1.6 mm^2. In 130

nm and 90 nm technologies, an icyflex DSP/MCU would have an area of respectively 0.43 mm^2 and 0.21 mm^2.

The samples were verified to run on a power supply as low as 1.0 V. By raising the power supply to 1.8 V, the icyflex can be clocked at up to 50 MHz. At 1.0 V, the icyflex has a typical power consumption normalized to the clock frequency of 120 µW/MHz, which can reach 215 µW/MHz for a power-hungry algorithm such as a Fast Fourier Transform (FFT). The targeted maximum clock frequency for the processor is 75 MHz in a 130 nm TSMC technology at 1.5V. These results were compared to those of other DSPs available on the market (Table II).

TABLE II.   COMPARISON OF ENERGY CONSUMPTION

Features *) estimated **) single precision	Freescale Starcore [4]	Philips CoolFlux [5]	CSEM MACGIC Audio-I	CSEM icyflex
Bits per instruction	128	32	32	32
Bits per data word	16	24	24	32
Number of MAC	4	2	4	2
Memory transfers per cycle	8	2	8	8
Thousands of gates	600	45	150	110
Cycles to run an FFT 256	**1'614	* 5'500	1'410	2'700
Avg. power @1V (µW/MHz)	*350	*75	170	120
Avg. power @1V for FFT (µW/MHz)	*600	*130	300	215
Avg. energy @1V for FFT (normalized)	* 2.3 x	* 1.7 x	1 x	1.4 x

V. CONCLUSION

The icyflex DSP/MCU designed at CSEM offers a customizable and reconfigurable soft-IP solution. It combines the benefits of the support for high level languages and a high performance (both memory throughput and computing power) for digital signal processing applications. Its best-in-class energy consumption per operation make it especially well suited for portable systems where extending battery life plays a key role.

REFERENCES

[1]   F. Rampogna et al. « MACGIC, A Low Power Re-configurable DSP », Chapter 21, in "Low Power Electronics Design", Edited by C. Piguet, CRC Press, 2005)

[2]   Analog Devices, www.analog.com/processors/blackfin

[3]   STMicroelectronics, www.st.com/mcu/inchtml-pages-st10.html

[4]   T. R. Halfhill, "StarCore DSPs Boost VoIP," Microprocessor Report, May 18, 2004

[5]   "CoolFlux DSP", Philips Digital Systems Labs, www.coolfluxdsp.com

A 5.2Gb/p/s GDDR5 SDRAM with CML Clock Distribution Network

KyungHoon Kim, SangSic Yoon, KiChang Kwean, DaeHan Kwon, SunSuk Yang, MunPhil Park, YongKi Kim, ByongTae Chung

Design Team, Memory R&D, Hynix Semiconductor Inc.
Ichon-Si, South Korea
Kyunghoon.kim@hyix.com

Abstract □ **A 1Gb Density, 5.2Gbps/s/pin data rate GDDR5 SDRAM was developed using 66nm DRAM process. It uses traditional Core architecture, 8-bit pre-fetch with 16-banks, but the clocking and interface topology are fully changed for operating more than 4Gbps without using differential signaling. Major barrier to achieving high data bandwidth is the clock jitter. To overcome this limitation, this project utilizes a CML clocking scheme.**

I. INTRODUCTION

Today's graphic memory applications are rapidly evolving with high speed and large bandwidth requirements. But the traditional memory interface topologies posed barriers. The main barriers can be summarized as: (1) single-ended signaling which has crosstalk and simultaneous switching noise (SSN) disadvantages, (2) increasing clock jitter due to long delay path and large power noise, and (3) data in/output pin skews from variations of inner and outer DRAM. The barrier number (1) can be solved by adapting differential signaling at the system. But differential signaling increases cost in the DRAM and also the system. It needs to double the number of data in/output PADs and channels when it runs at the same operation frequency as single-ended signaling. So the current DRAM should search other ways to increase the maximum operation speed without changing the single-ended scheme. To surmount the item number (3), per-bit de-skewing is needed, it is GPU's ability. But the item number (2) is fully DRAM's role. For better performance in clocking, current mode logic and CMOS clocking are implemented together. In this paper, we will announce systematic changes briefly and then will review the clocking scheme which proposed to reduce jitter.

II. ARCHITECTURE OVERVIEW

The GDDR5 SDRAM has various different interface schemes from the GDDR3/4 SDRAM. Fig. 1 shows the interface topology of the GDDR5 and the GPU. The write clock (WCK) is adapted, and data strobe signal (DQS) is removed. There are various transfer rates, for example, when we assume the HCK has 1X frequency, the CMD has 1X transfer rate, the ADD has 2X transfer rate, the WCK has 2X frequency, and the data has 4X transfer rate.

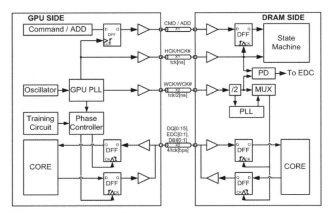

Figure 1. Simplified block diagram of the interface between DRAM and GPU

This is to maintain channel efficiency without sacrificing stable operation of the DRAM. There are more detailed views of major differences.

A. Forward Clocking

In the previous generations of graphic DRAMs used data strobe signal (DQS) for data in/output schemes. This strobe signal just toggles during data transfer, and it causes inter symbol interference (ISI). To remove the ISI and extra demerit of the DQS scheme, the forward clocking (WCK) is adapted in the GDDR5 SDRAM. The WCK always toggles during the entire operation for the removal of ISI, except in the self-refresh mode. In the previous case, a main clock is commonly used for controlling command, address and data. In this case, the total clock path is increased, and there is additional delay by the DLL. Clock jitter is almost proportional to the delay, so the previous clock scheme has large jitter values. In the GDDR5 SDRAM, a pair of WCK/WCK# is used to decrease the total range of coverage in the chip, and it can reduce the delay from the clock input pad to the data output pads.

B. Various Trainings

1) Address Training

In the GDDR5 SDRAM, the address transfer speed is almost the same as the data transfer rate of the previous graphic DRAMs. For this reason, the address can be erroneous if the training isn't used. During the address training mode, the GPU inserts the address into the DRAM with the phase of the address shifted, and monitors the DQ of the DRAM. The DRAM sends out the received address data through the DQ pins. The GPU can find the stable points of the address.

2) WCK2CK Training

There are two kinds of clocks, the HCK and the WCK. The HCK is used for handling the command and the address, and the WCK is used for handling the data. If two clocks are misaligned in their phases, then errors can occur in read/write operation. If the read/write command – it is treaded by the HCK – arrives at wrong time, unstable latency or error during the write/read operation can be shown. The training used a phase detector in the DRAM. The phase detector compares the WCK / HCK and sends the result to the GPU for aligning the phases.

3) Read Training

The read training is commonly used for the previous graphic memory but just aligns with byte or word. In the GDRD5 SDRAM, each DQ output pins is trained separately. It can remove pin skews due to inner DRAM's process, package process, and channel variations. The pin variation can be almost 100ps, and it is one of the speed limiting factor in the previous graphic DRAMs. The training data inputs from the address pins are transferred to the data output pins. The GPU can center its inner strobe clock based on the DRAM's outputs.

4) Write Training

As in the read training, the per-bit de-skewing is adapted for the write training. The write training sequence is after the read training, and the GPU shifts the input data's phase and monitors the DQ. And the DRAM passes the received data over to the output data pins. The GPU can decide the stable points of the phases of the write data.

C. Phase Locked Loop

A Phase Locked Loop (PLL) is used in the GDDR5 SDRAM. The PLL filters high frequency input jitter and re-aligns clock phase when its input duty is distorted. If the external WCK noise is greater than the PLL's output clock jitter, the PLL can improve internal clock quality. So the PLL is an optional scheme which depends on the quality of the input clock. The PLL can change its loop bandwidth by the MRS codes to avoid the peaking frequency of the input jitter and power noise in DRAM.

D. Error Detection Code

When using the PLL, data interface schemes do not follow source synchronous clocking. So, random jitter (RJ) is considered for calculating error rate. Error detection code is adapted for improving bit error rate (BER). If the data has errors, the GPU knows it by receiving the CRC data which is calculated by the DRAM, and then re-transfer the data. Cyclic Redundancy Check-8 algorithm is adapted in the GDDR5 SDRAM.

III. INTERNAL CLOCK NETWROK DISTRIBUTION

A new interface scheme helps the high speed operation of the GDDR5 SDRAM, but clock jitters are the most

TABLE I.   THE CML/CMOS POWER SENSITIVTY

	CMOS	CML
DC	0.759	0.054
10MHz	0.759	0.031
50MHz	0.759	0.071
100MHz	0.759	0.107
500MHz	0.713	0.513
1GHz	0.500	0.840
4Ghz	0.140	0.336
8GHz	0.121	0.244

jitter source is divided into input clock source jitter, power noise, and duty mismatch. The power noise is the major clock jitter source in the DRAM, and the power of the DRAM is not filtered well due to the limitation of reservoir capacitors. A LDO regulator can be a solution, but it decreases the operating voltage and it limits the speed of transistors in the DRAM. So in this project, current mode logic (CML) is used to implement a clock distribution network for increasing power supply rejection ratio (PSRR) [1]. And effort was to design the clock distribution network compactly to reduce the delay.

A. CMOS / CML Clocking Methods

The CMOS signaling is commonly used in the DRAM for transferring a clock. But the CMOS clocking is commonly known as lower PSRR. But realistically, the CMOS is just weak in the low and mid-band (till a hundred megahertz) frequency's noise, but it has high immunity to high frequency noise. The CML shows inversely. It has higher immunity to power noise in lower frequency, but noise immunity decreases during mid-band till a giga hertz frequency region. Jitter is induced only in transitional situations, and the CMOS has higher capacitance value than CML circuits. (It depends on MOS parameters.) The power noise is presented in 1) low frequency (<20MHz): external noise from the board RLC, 2) mid band frequency (around a hundred MHz): internal noise from package resonance, and 3) high frequency (>1GHz): internal noise from the SERDES logic [3]. So the realistic power noise frequency decides the performance of both clocking schemes. And also situations in real boards and electrical tests can be different, because electrical tests have more ideal power environments. Table 1 shows the power noise sensitivity factor (1) of CML and CMOS scheme. To obtain these simulation results, the single tone sinusoidal noise source is induced to the power (both VDD and VSS) of CMOS / CML chains.

Power Sensitivity =
{ (Max (Δ delay) – min (Δdelay)) / delay } / (Δ Supply Voltage / Supply Voltage)   (1)

Using single or differential signaling is different between CMOS and CML. The differential signaling offers higher common mode rejection ratio (CMRR), so the CML has better performance than the CMOS clocking. But because the SERDES and Tx uses the CMOS signaling, the CML signaling level needs to convert to the CMOS signaling level by a CML2CMOS converter. The CML2CMOS converter has poor CMRR properties and needs a current to improve the CMRR. But the CML2CMOS are used in

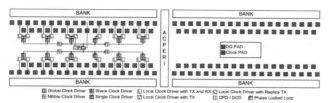

Figure 2. The block diagram of the total clock distribution network

many places of the clock distribution, so the current is limited to use. And the lower PSRR of CML2CMOS detracts merits of the CML clock distribution.

The total delay from the WCK/WCK# input to the data output pin is decided by the total number of stages and unit propagation delay. The CML clocking has lower delay, because the propagation delay of a unit stage is smaller than that of an inverter. Also the total number of stages in the CML is less than that of the CMOS. The CML can be enabled or disabled by the switch MOS between the current source and the input stage, so there is no burden to inserter enable/disable NAND (or NOR) gate in the CMOS clocking scheme.

For these reasons of CMOS and CML properties, this project implemented both clocking drivers to compare their performances. The CMOS clocking driver can offer higher noise immunity to high frequency noise, easy implementation and was confirmed by previous device. And from the CML clocking driver, higher immunity to lower frequency noise and lower delay can be obtained

B. Clock Distribution Network

Fig. 2 shows the CML clock distribution network in the GDDR5 SDRAM. The CMOS clock distribution network is almost same as the CML's. Each WCK/WCK# pair takes care of 20 DQs (16 DQ, 2 EDC, and 2 DBI). The WCK pad is located at the center of DQ, and the global driver distributes the clock across the upper and the lower side of the chip. Two SERDES blocks share the final driver, which is named "share clock driver." Fig. 3 shows the block diagrams of the global, nibble, and share clock driver.

The global clock driver generates a half rate 4 phase clock, performs duty cycle correction (DCC) and quadrate phase correction (QPC), and distributes the clock to the nibble clock driver. The 4 phase half rate clock can reduce power and achieve stable operation to release CML bandwidth limitation. And the other reason for using the half rate 4 phase clocking is that the divided WCK must be used for synchronizing with the HCK – the HCK is the half rate of WCK. The nibble clock driver takes 4 DQ blocks, and it just buffers the clock. The share clock driver converts the CML level to CMOS level and re-distributes the CMOS clock level to each SERDES block. The CML2CMOS consumes large power. To reduce the number of CML2CMOSs and to maintain the CML clock level to the final stage, CML2CMOSs are inserted at the share clock driver. The Tx local clock driver generates a full rate clock base on logic at figure 3.

IV. EXPERIMENTAL RESULT

Fig. 4 is the read training result. It shows the clock

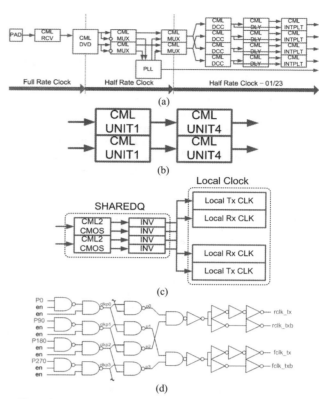

Figure 3. The block diagram of (a) global clock driver, (b) nibble clock driver, (c) share clock driver, and (d) local Tx clock

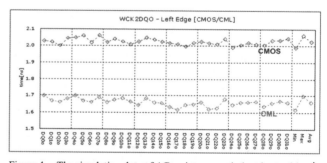

Figure 4. The simulation data of AC resistance variation due to driver's capacitance

TABLE II.   THE CML/CMOS CLOCK DELAY DUE TO POWER

	CML		CMOS	
	Delay[ns]	Delta[ps]	Delay[ns]	Delta[ps]
1.4V	1.84	80	2.29	150
1.5V	1.76	0	2.14	0
1.6V	1.72	-40	2.03	-90
1.7V	1.68	-80	1.94	-180
1.8V	1.66	-100	1.87	-250

delay path and the Tx delay path. But the Tx circuit is the same as the one in CMOS/CML clocking, so the delta means the delay difference between the CMOS and the CML. The CML has 300~400ps shorter than the CMOS clocking unit. And the table 2 shows the variation due to dc power. The CMOS is more sensitive to power variation as expected.

Fig 5 shows the output jitter from the CMOS and the CML clocking. It was measured from electrical test

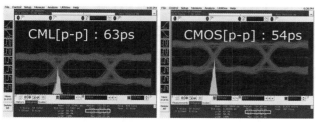

Figure 5.   The Data eye and jitter measurement from CML / CMOS

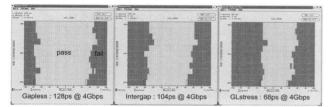

Figure 6.   The single DQ tDH/S of CMOS clocking with various pattern

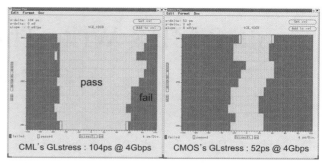

Figure 7.   The all DQ tDH/S of CML/CMOS with GLstress pattern

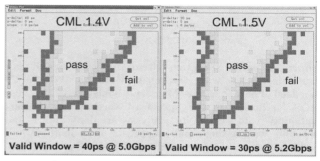

Figure 8.   The tAC-tCK shmoo of GDDR5 SDRAM

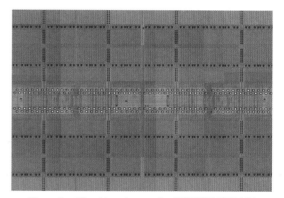

Figure 9.   The chip micrograph of GDDR5 SDRAM

equipment with an oscilloscope. The measured conditions were 1.5V, 3.2Gbps operation and used 128bit length PRBS data patterns. The CMOS jitter is 54ps and the CML jitter value is 63ps. These values contain input clock jitter (around 15ps), clock jitter, and Tx jitter. From the Tx simulation result, the jitter of Tx driver is around 50ps with the real channel and GPU IO models. Even though the system model is worse than electrical test equipment model, the clock jitter of less than 20ps would be expected. This testing pattern doesn't use many active commands, so major power noise is high frequency noise from the SERDES logic. The result shows the CML and the CMOS clocking are not different in their performances at low noise condition. And it can be correlated with the power sensitivity simulation results. But the higher noise conditions show different results. Fig. 6 is the data setup/hold of single DQ with various patterns in the CMOS clocking. The X-axis means the setup/hold time, and the Y-axis means the operating frequency. The input data patterns are the same and just the active commands are different in those patterns. The CMOS clocking depends on the data patterns, and shows weakness to pattern which has more low frequency noise made of active-precharge commands as in GLstress. But the CML has more immunity to low-mid band frequency noise than the CMOS as figure 7. The CMOS shows the same results with figure 6, but the CML decreases just 20ps.

The shmoo data in the figure 8 show the maximum operating frequency at 1.5 / 1.4V with the GLstress pattern. They are all DQ probing, and the data valid window is more than 30ps at 5.2Gbps in 1.5V condition. And the CML clocking scheme shows the same shmoo at 1.4V.

V.   CONCULSION

This work has implemented the GDDR5 SDRAM with 66nm 3 metal process. Fig 9. is the chip micrograph. This GDDR5 SDRAM with the various techniques such as forward clock, training with per-bit de-skewing, and optimized clocking, can achieve higher speed operation than the previous GDDR3/4 SDRAM. To maximize operating frequency, the project implements both the CML

and the CMOS clocking scheme and optimized the clock distribution network. Both clocking schemes are compared under various testing environments. In the lower noise condition, the CMOS shows about the same or a little better performance than the CML. But the CML clocking scheme is more robust in its operation. By using the CML clock distribution network, 5.2Gbaps at 1.5V condition and 5Gbps at 1.4V accomplished at even the worst condition

Reference

[1]   H. Hassan, et al., "MOS Current Mode Circuits: Analysis, Design, and Variability", IEEE Transactions of VLSI SYSTEMS, VOL. 13 pp.885-898, AUG 2005.

[2]   Ki-Won Lee, et al., "A 1.5-V 3.2 Gb/s/pin Graphic DDR4 SDRAM With Dual-Clock System, Four-Phase Input Strobing, and Low-Jitter Fully Analog DLL", IEEE J. Solide-State Circuits, VOL 42 pp 2369-2377.

[3]   Wong, K.L, et al □Enhancing microprocessor immunity to power supply noise with clock-data compensation" IEEE J. Solide-State Circuits, VOL. 41, pp. 749-758, Aprile 2006.

Program Circuit for a Phase Change Memory Array with 2 MB/s Write Throughput for Embedded Applications

G. De Sandre, L. Bettini, E. Calvetti, G. Giacomi,
M.Pasotti, M. Borghi, P. Zuliani, R. Annunziata
Front End Technology and Manufacturing
STMicroelectronics
Agrate Brianza (MI), ITALY
guido.de-sandre@st.com

I. Tortorelli, F. Pellizzer, R. Bez
Flash Memory Group R&D
ST M6 s.r.l.
Agrate Brianza (MI), ITALY

Abstract□ **A flexible program circuit for chalcogenide non-volatile memories was developed within a 4Mb ePCM (embedded Phase Change Memory) implemented in 90nm CMOS technology. The proposed architecture ensures adaptability with respect to process variations and is fully compatible with a single pulse approach or a multiple pulse algorithm for multi-level operation. In the former a write throughput of 2 MB/s is achieved.**

I. INTRODUCTION

The increasing need for high-performance, low-power and highly scalable storage devices required the investigation, in the last years, of alternative solutions to the currently widely diffused Flash technology. Phase Change technology is one of these. Compared to Flash memories, PCM offer shorter access time, higher write throughput, higher endurance and superior scalability [1][2]. A further advantage is that any single memory cell can be independently programmed without requiring the entire block to be erased and then overwritten. All of this, together with a great compatibility with a standard CMOS process, makes PCM technology one of the most likely candidates for next-generation non-volatile memories. PCM are based on a ternary alloy of Ge, Sb and Te, in our case $Ge_2Sb_2Te_5$ (GST), which shows a reversible transformation from a crystalline highly conductive state, called SET, to an amorphous highly resistive state, called RESET. The resistance window between the two states can be as large as two orders of magnitude, thus allowing to associate binary information to the phase in which the active material is brought. Moreover the active material can be led into any intermediate state between the two so to permit multi-level storage in each memory cell. The phase transition can be electrically induced by applying proper current pulses. In order to reset the phase-change cell it is common to apply a rectangular current pulse whose amplitude is high enough to

bring, by means of Joule Effect, the GST above its melting temperature T_m and whose falling edge is fast enough to cause a rapid cooling of the material itself. On the other hand there is not a unique method for setting a phase-change device. The technique implemented in our design was proposed in [2] and is schematically depicted in Fig. 1. It consists in applying a conventional RESET pulse to melt the GST but with a very slow stepped or linear quenching so that, thanks to the slow falling edge, the material has time enough to crystallize and to move into the low resistance state.

In this work we present a compact program circuit able to generate SET and RESET program pulses with a complete flexibility on the write parameters. Experimental results were collected from a 4Mb ePCM macro in order to prove the effectiveness of the proposed architecture.

II. DESIGN AND IMPLEMENTATION

A. Program Circuit Architecture

The program circuit was implemented within a 4Mb µTrench MOS-selected ePCM [3] fabricated in 90nm CMOS technology. The memory macro is characterized by a 32 bits data word, extended to 38 bits including ECC, and is organized in four 1Mb sectors where n-MOS transistors are employed as cell selectors. The cell size is 0.29 µm². In order to supply the required current levels during a write operation, a two-stage charge-pump block is included in the system. Program pulses are shaped and then applied by means of a p-MOS current generator to the selected memory cell through the write path shown in Fig. 2.

The architecture of the circuit providing SET and RESET current pulses is schematically depicted in Fig. 3. After enabling the write operation, a programmable constant current generator is used to charge the capacitance C through the resistance R_1, while keeping transistor M_1 on and

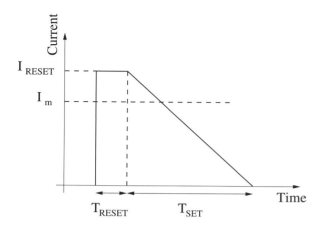

Figure 1. Set program pulse. The constant current level I_{RESET} is higher than the melting current I_m in order to melt the chalcogenide before the slow cooling.

transistor M_2 off. As steady state is reached, M_1 is turned off and the constant voltage across the capacitor is reproduced across the resistance R_2 by means of a unity gain feedback loop and then buffered across a third resistor R_3 thanks to a simple source follower. This gives rise to a constant current flowing in R_3. The open-loop replica of the source follower was implemented in order not to affect the stability of the feedback loop when a parallel approach is used, as will be discussed later. After a programmable delay, transistor M_2 is turned on, the capacitance is thus discharged by means of a constant current and its voltage, again buffered and applied across R_3, linearly decreases from its initial value. The current flowing into the third resistor thus assumes the shape shown in Fig. 1. This current pulse is mirrored with a proper gain factor and directed to the selected memory element.

The program circuit operates in two different ways, according to the information carried by the data word. The mirror output switch, implemented by transistor M_6 in Fig. 3, is controlled by timing signals together with the input data bit. When a SET pulse is to be applied (data bit is 1), the current pulse is simply mirrored, amplified and sent to the storage element. If a RESET is required (data bit is 0), the mirror can truncate the current pulse just before the beginning of the linear discharge. In the latter case, in order to guarantee the correct amorphization of the active material, it is necessary to provide an extremely fast quench of the current pulse. For this reason, a pull-down n-MOS is connected to the MMBL, as shown in Fig. 2, so to discharge the bit-line within few nanoseconds. The mirror gain factor is 4 in order to obtain a very high current level, up to 650 μA.

The constant current I_{RESET} of Fig. 1 depends only on the programmable current charging the capacitance, whereas the duration of the constant current region is a multiple of the clock period and can be digitally controlled. The slope of the falling edge depends only on the programmable discharge current. Moreover the duration of the T_{SET} can be reduced by truncating the tail of the falling edge, which is useless for the

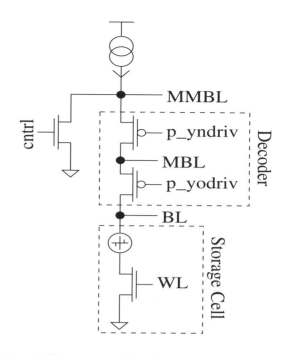

Figure 2. Write current path along the global and the local bit-line.

crystallization, by comparing the voltage across the capacitor with a threshold voltage and eventually generating a digital signal which abruptly terminates the current pulse.

Table I summarizes the ranges of variability of the three main parameters defining a program pulse. This great flexibility makes this architecture suitable both for a single pulse program approach and for the implementation of an optimized write algorithm for multi-level operation [4].

B. Single-Pulse Programming

In a single pulse write method one single current pulse is applied to each storage element in order to obtain the maximum possible write throughput. However, due to process parameters control, identical electrical pulses can result in different temperatures in different cells. Thanks to the flexibility offered by the proposed architecture, each process variation, as the amount of current needed to reset a phase change element or the time needed to cool the chalcogenide after melting during a SET operation, can be compensated by simply controlling the charge or the discharge current.

TABLE I.   PROGRAM CIRCUIT PROGRAMMABLE PARAMETERS

Parameter	Min.	Nom.	Max.
I_{RESET}	300 μA	450 μA	650 μA
T_{RESET}	T_{CLOCK}	100 ns	32 T_{CLOCK}
T_{SET}	350 ns	400 ns	2.5 μs

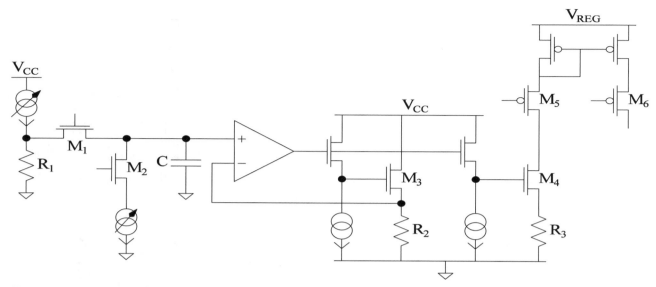

Figure 3. Schematic diagram of the program circuit. Note that the p-MOS current mirror providing current for the write operation is connected to a regulated version of the charge-pump voltage named V_{REG}.

One further important advantage is the possibility of implementing parallelism in order to write more than one cell simultaneously. The open loop follower $M_4 - R_3$ of Fig. 3 was replicated eight times in order to obtain eight identical currents all having the shape of Fig. 1. Moreover each replica was used to feed a current mirror having three outputs. Despite the theoretical possibility of achieving complete parallelism over the whole data word, it is worthwhile to say that the number of source followers connected in parallel is limited by the desired frequency response of the feedback loop, whereas the number of outputs of the current mirror is the result of a trade-off between the mirror response time and the sizes of the unwanted spikes in the output current pulses. The maximum number of cells programmable simultaneously was set to ten in the macro in order to limit the current absorption from the supplies. Considering a typical T_{RESET} of 100 ns, a minimum T_{SET} of 350 ns and an extra time of 175 ns to take into account analog settling times, we can guarantee a write throughput of (10 bit / 625 ns), that is, 2 MB/s.

C. Multi- Level Operation

A pulse and verify algorithm might prove to be necessary for the write operation, in order to obtain the greatest control in setting the PCM cell conductance level. As was shown in [4], the algorithmic approach opens the possibility of multi-level programming of a PCM array. The proposed program circuit easily adapts to a program and verify scheme. A modify signal is associated to each data bit according to the result of the verify step, indicating whether the cell needs further programming. Both data and modify bits are input into the logic that controls the current mirror output switch, represented as transistor M_6 in Fig. 3. The switch can selectively disable the current pulse when the cell has reached

the desired conductance value. Thus, a pulse and verify algorithm can be implemented by properly controlling the output switches of all mirrors so to simultaneously generate SET and RESET pulses, or no pulse, when it is not needed. After each verify step the circuit programmable parameters can be updated to reshape the program pulse according to technology requirements.

III. EXPERIMENTAL RESULTS

Within the validation activity of the 4Mb ePCM a specific analysis was carried on in order to evaluate the performance of the proposed circuit within a single pulse write scheme. The main control signals involved in the programming of a data word are shown in Fig. 4. The write operation starts when signal CSN is sampled low and its timing is defined by output signal WAITN. The internal signal PDPULSE shows the generation of the subsequent pulses needed to program the word. Thanks to the ten bit parallelism, we can guarantee a write throughput of 2 MB/s. This rate is reduced to 1.85 MB/s if a 200 ns latency per word, due to verify time, is considered. The correct characteristics of the current pulse were directly verified by probing the bit line voltage. The conversion of current into voltage across the storage element can be considered linear as the MOS selector works in linear region and the storage element resistance is approximately linear [1]. The shapes of the current pulses obtained for SET and RESET operations are shown respectively in Fig. 5 and Fig. 6. The dependence of the SET shape on parameter T_{SET} is also shown, as well as the actual slope of the falling edge in the RESET shape. A very fast falling edge of about 4 ns is achieved. The functionality of the program pulse is evaluated by reproducing well-known results related to the PCM cell behavior [5][6]. The measured cell current after a RESET pulse is sketched in

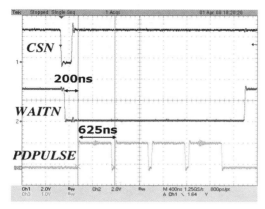

Figure 4. Measured control signals defining the programming of a data word.

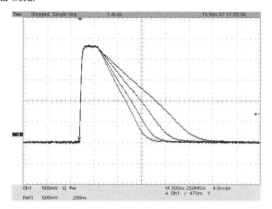

Figure 5. Measured BL voltage waveforms during a SET operation for four different values of the T_SET parameter.

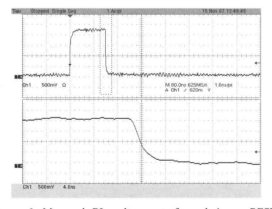

Figure 6. Measured BL voltage waveform during a RESET operation. At the bottom, the zoom on the falling edge shows a quench time of about 4 ns.

Fig. 7 as a function of parameter I_{RESET}. The results obtained are consistent with a typical programming (R-I) characteristic of a PCM cell. In Fig. 8 the measured cell current after a SET pulse is represented as a function of parameter T_{SET}, both for the ePCM macro and for the analytical cell. The result of a RESET pulse is shown too as a limiting case with very small quench time. Data collected from the macro show a good agreement with results obtained on analytical cells.

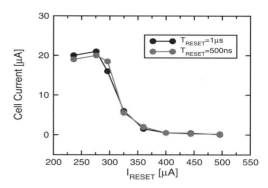

Figure 7. Cell current after RESET as a function of the I_{RESET} current, for different values of the RESET duration.

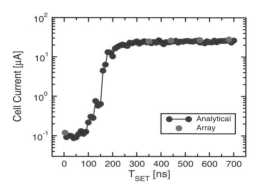

Figure 8. Cell current after SET as a function of the T_{SET} duration.

IV. CONCLUSION

A compact and flexible programming circuit for an ePCM macro in 90nm technology is proposed. The circuit generates current pulses of trapezoidal shape and allows complete control of the pulse parameters over a wide range. Experimental results show programming curves of the PCM cell as obtained by the circuit. Furthermore the circuit features simultaneous generation of SET and RESET pulses and hence enables full parallelism over the data word. The specific way in which the output current is controlled allows using the circuit either in a single pulse or in a pulse and verify write scheme. In the current implementation, a throughput of about 2 MB/s has been achieved using a single pulse write method.

REFERENCES

[1] M. Gill *et al.*, "Ovonic unified memory – A high-performance nonvolatile memory technology for stand-alone memory and embedded applications," *ISSCC, Dig. Tech. Papers,*vol. 1, Feb. 2002, pp. 458-459.

[2] E. Park and T. A. Lowrey, "Programming a phase-change memory with slow quench time," US Patent 6,487,113 B1, Nov. 2002.

[3] F. Ottogalli *et al.*, "Phase-change memory technology for embedded applications," *Proc. ESSDERC, 2004*, pp. 293-296.

[4] T. Nirschl *et al.*, "Write strategies for 2 and 4-bit multi-level phase-change memory," *IEDM Tech. Dig.*, pp. 461-464, 2007.

[5] F. Bedeschi *et al.*, "4-Mb MOSFET-Selected µTrench phase-change memory experimental chip," *IEEE J. Solid-State Circuits*, vol. 40, no. 7, pp.1557-1565, Jul. 2005.

[6] D. Mantegazza *et al.*, "Effects of the crystallization statistics on programming distributions in phase-change memory arrays," *Proc. ICMTD, 2007*, pp. 43-46.

A 3.6GHz, 16mW ΣΔ DAC for a 802.11n / 802.16e transmitter with 30dB digital power control in 90nm CMOS

P. Seddighrad[1,2], A. Ravi[1], M. Sajadieh[1], H.Lakdawala[1], K. Soumyanath[1]

[1]Communication Technology Lab
Intel Corp.
Hillsboro OR USA.

[2]Department of Electrical Engineering
University of Washington
Seattle WA USA.

Abstract□ **This paper presents a ΣΔ DAC based transmitter (TX) baseband for 802.11n / 802.16e with channel filtering and gain control performed in the digital domain. The effect of circuit imperfections on TX EVM is analyzed for a robust line-up with gain control and the design of the high speed ΣΔ modulator is described. The ΣΔ DAC fabricated in a 90nm CMOS process operates up to 3.6GHz while drawing 16mW from a 1.3V supply.**

I. INTRODUCTION

Integrated CMOS radios are required to be low cost and flexible to meet the variety of emerging wideband wireless LAN and WAN data standards such as 802.11n, 802.16e. In addition to the multiplicity of channel frequencies, these standards require the radio to support different channel bandwidths, modulation orders, power levels and operational modes. High dynamic range sigma-delta (ΣΔ) ADCs have been used [1], [2] to move the bulk of receiver baseband circuits into the digital domain. This paper presents a ΣΔ DAC based transmitter (TX) baseband that is compatible with this elimination of signal conditioning circuits from the analog chain. Variable bandwidth channel selection, gain control, IQ correction and LO feed through cancellation are performed in the digital domain. The ΣΔ DAC running at either half or the full local oscillator frequency has been optimized for good dynamic range in-band while relaxing the residual analog filtering requirements.

II. TRANSMITTER ARCHITECTURE

A conventional transmitter baseband incorporates a high resolution (8-10 bits), low over-sampling ratio (1x-2x OSR) DAC followed by a high order elliptic or chebyshev filter to suppress the sampling images. Additional stages of variable gain amplifiers are used to provide gain control at baseband before up-conversion. Fig. 1 shows the multi-mode TX incorporating the ΣΔ DAC presented in this paper. The TX baseband consists of a digital front end (DFE) and a ΣΔ DAC. The 10-bit quadrature baseband modulation signals generated at 40MHz by the IFFT/FFT unit are interpolated to the ΣΔ

sampling rate in the DFE (inset to Fig. 1). The sampling images of the baseband signals are suppressed by the cascade of filters in the DFE.

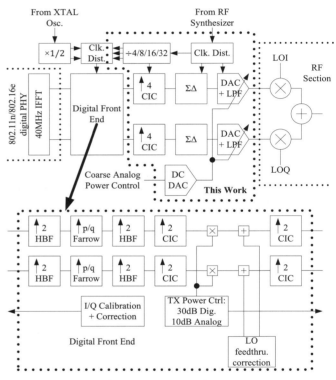

Figure 1: Block diagram of ΣΔ DAC TX. DFE details expanded in inset.

A 2x- interpolating 21-tap half-band filter (HBF) with multipliers is required to suppress the closest images at 40MHz. The fixed 40MHz and 80MHz clocks are derived from the crystal oscillator. Since the ΣΔ modulator operates at a frequency synchronous with the local oscillator, a fractional re-sampler converts the data from the fixed clock domain to a variable channel frequency dependent domain. The re-samplers are implemented using a Farrow filter architecture with a cubic polynomial interpolation for the fractional values

[3] to ensure that for all required channel frequencies the degradation from aliasing of sampling images and quantization noise is below -55dB.

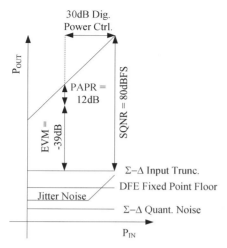

Figure 2: TX baseband EVM line-up. The TX in-band noise floor supports a digital power control range of 30dB.

The programmable polynomial coefficients are a function of the p/q ratio. Another stage of 2x-interpolating HBFs and one stage of a 2x-interpolating cascade-integrator-comb (CIC) with zero-order hold (ZOH) and a third order SINC filter increase the sampling frequency to the range 280MHz – 450MHz. Fine digital power control scaling (TX AGC) is performed at this stage to trade-off the higher available dynamic range against power dissipation and circuit realization. LO feed through correction is also introduced here as DC offsets in the I and Q paths. A 2x-CIC with ZOH + second order SINC and a 4x-CIC with only ZOH provide the final stages of interpolation and image suppression while minimizing power dissipation.

The I/Q DFE outputs are truncated to 10-bits and drive the digital sigma-delta modulators. A second order 3-bit $\Sigma\Delta$ modulator provides adequate in-band SQNR and out-of-band emissions to support all operational modes without significant DAC and filter complexity. Higher order modulators impose tougher filtering requirements on the TX chain and are more susceptible to EVM degradation due to non-linearity and mismatch.

The TX is required to have an EVM of at least -30dB at the PA output. With a 6dB margin for the PA and an equal partitioning of the remaining EVM budget between the up-conversion mixer impairments (phase noise, linearity) and the baseband, the DAC output modulation quality is required to be at least -39dB. Fig. 2 shows the TX baseband EVM line-up. The noise shaping supports an in-band integrated noise floor of less than -102dB in the worst case. The in-band noise is limited to -80dBFS in the worst case by the truncation at the sigma-delta input. The fixed point precision noise in the digital filtering chain is set to be 10dB below this absolute level. Starting with the -39dB for the worst case baseband EVM budget and accounting for an additional 12dB for PAPR, this TX can support nearly 30dB of fine digital power control. Coarse analog power control of 10dB is implemented through a single step of the DAC current. Additional coarse

RF power control is implemented in the PA to reduce power dissipation at large back-offs.

The modulator and DAC clock is derived from the main local oscillator (LO) RF frequency synthesizer used for up-conversion. The buffered LO signal used in up-conversion directly clocks the $\Sigma\Delta$ DAC for the 2.4GHz 802.11 band, the 2.3-2.7GHz and the 3.5GHz 802.16 band. To ensure that the $\Sigma\Delta$ DAC never has to run faster than 3.6GHz for all bands, the LO signal is divided by 2 for operation in the 5-6GHz 802.11 band. This choice of clock frequencies guarantees that mixing products in the RF transmit chain do not fold the out of band quantization noise into the signal band [4]. The low integrated phase noise from the RF synthesizer (-38dBc) minimizes the jitter induced noise floor in the DAC output spectrum. The 0.3ps jitter results in an baseband signal frequency dependent noise contribution of -83dBc and an absolute noise floor of -98dBFS [5]. The latter term adds to the DAC quantization, thermal and flicker noise and determines the jitter limitation on digital power control.

III. $\Sigma\Delta$ DAC

Fig. 3 shows the schematic of the 2nd order digital $\Sigma\Delta$ modulator. The error-feedback topology can directly handle inputs with both polarity and can easily be reconfigured for different quantization levels. This implementation breaks cascades of adders with registers to operate at high speed. The input 10-bit word in 2's-complement format is sign extended internally by 1 additional bit to provide over-range protection. The output is quantized to 3 bits to drive the DAC. The quantizer is implemented as simple wire routing and does not incur additional delays. The one additional bit guarantees unconditional stability for a normalized input range of [-1, 1]. The feedback coefficient of -1 is implemented by inverting all bits and setting the LSB carry-in to 1. The +2 is a single upward bit position shift. A 15-stage linear feedback shift register (LFSR) generates a pseudo-random sequence to dither the input and is used to break up any tonal limit cycles. The random statistics of OFDM inputs are often sufficient to self-dither the modulator. The dither input is can be selectively switched on or off and the dither amplitude is programmable from ±0.5LSB to ±2LSB.

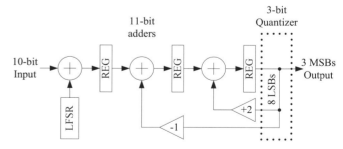

Figure 3: Schematic of 2nd order 3-bit $\Sigma\Delta$ modulator (error-feedback topology)

Each adder is further pipelined into three 4-bit slices for speed (Fig. 4). The three 4-bit adders are cascaded to create a 4-bit slice of the $\Sigma\Delta$ modulator. Additional pipelining registers are required at the overall input to the modulator to correctly time align the bits across the three 4-bit slices. The total latency of 5 clock cycles has a negligible impact on the baseband signal. A ripple carry implementation of a 4-bit adder is very modular and involves only local routing compared to the routing complexity of a carry look-ahead topology. A mirror adder implementation further eliminates redundant signal inversions in the critical carry propagation path [6]. The sum inversions are absorbed into the flip-flops implementing the registers. The 4-bit pipeline offers a better trade-off between speed and power compared to the 1-bit case [7]. The last interpolation stage, LFSR and $\Sigma\Delta$ share a global clock grid with four distributed drivers. A very simple H-tree pre-global grid on the top metals provides the input to the global drivers. The local clock drivers are distributed across the 4-bit slices and drive the slice registers. The local clock grid equalizes the skew at the flip-flops.

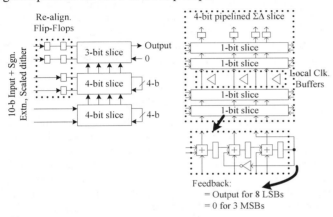

Figure 4: $\Sigma\Delta$ modulator implemented as 4-bit slice on the left. Details of each 4-bit slice (built from 1-bit slices) on the right

The 3-bit (7-level) output of the $\Sigma\Delta$ controls the 6-element thermometric differential current steered DAC array (Fig. 5). The 0.5mA long channel length current source unit elements are designed for better than a 1% 3-σ mismatch. The corresponding DAC thermal + flicker noise floor is -84dBFS and mismatch induced floor is -85dBFS worst case. The cascode transistor sizing is optimized for high output impedance at the clock frequency to minimize noise folding into the passband. It is combined into the switch array to shield the output from the routing parasitics of the larger current source array. A final retiming level sensitive latch close to the switches eliminates timing mismatch between the different elements. The make before break current steering bit controls and switches in saturation minimize clock feed through, charge injection and signal dependent modulation of the DAC current. The DAC current drives a 30MHz 1-pole filter. An additional RC passive pole at ~200MHz suppresses the high frequency quantization noise. The filters do not need tuning or trimming since the quantization noise is shifted away from the passband. Additional filtering with relaxed requirements is provided by the RF section of the transmit chain. This is in contrast to the RF-DAC proposed in [8], [9], where the mixer is absorbed into the current steering core of the DAC. Unfortunately, an RF DAC transforms a relatively simple baseband filter into a tougher RF filtering requirement. The high levels of out-of-band quantization noise can fold back into the passband due to non-linearities in the up-conversion mixer and the RF amplifiers. The low-Q on-chip passives and the conflict between filtering out-of-band noise

and the wide-span of channel frequencies limit the use of the RF-DAC technique.

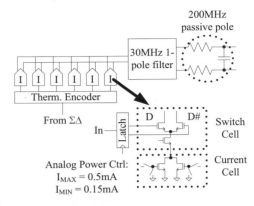

Figure 5: 6-Element DAC with coarse analog power control

IV. MEASURED RESULTS

The TX was fabricated in a 90nm CMOS process [10]. The $\Sigma\Delta$ DAC occupies an area of 0.3mm^2 including the analog filters (Fig. 6). Figs. 7 and 8 show the DAC response to a single tone power sweep and to two tone testing in both analog power control (APC) states. The DAC has a peak SNDR better than 70dB and was limited by the linearity of the probing buffer and noise in the test fixturing. Fig. 9 shows the EVM and WiMAX mask compliance at the maximum average output power for a 64-QAM OFDM signal. Fig. 10 plots the measured EVM as a function of average output power. The EVM was measured using a 100MS/s ADC and a vector signal analyzer (VSA) in software and the measurements were limited by the implementation loss of the ADC and VSA to about -40dB. The usable power control range is at least 32dB. Each $\Sigma\Delta$ DAC, including the high speed digital, draws 16mW (digital: 11mW, analog: 5mW) from a 1.3V supply at 3.6GHz.

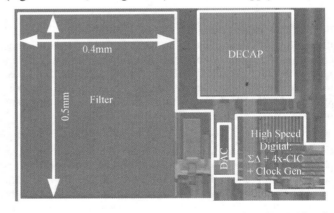

Figure 6: Die shot of $\Sigma\Delta$ DAC (including last interpolator, $\Sigma\Delta$, DAC and filters). Core circuits occupy 0.3mm^2.

V. CONCLUSIONS

A 90nm $\Sigma\Delta$ DAC based TX baseband for 802.11n/802.16e is presented. An error-feedback topology using 4-bit pipelined slices with mirror adders achieves 3.6GHz operation while dissipating only 16mW. The TX generates OFDM modulation with an EVM better than -39dB over a 32dB power control range while meeting the toughest 802.16e mask.

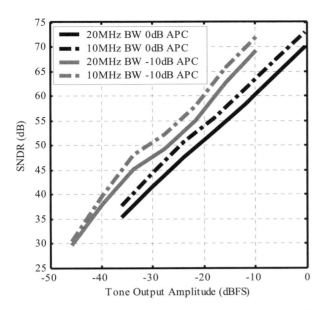

Figure 7: SNDR measured over 10MHz and 20MHz channels for both steps (0, -10dB) of analog power control (APC)

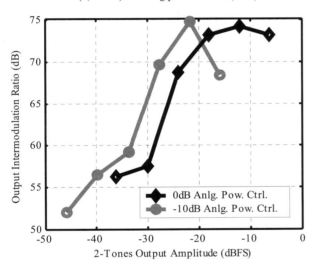

Figure 8: Ratio of signal tone to 3rd order intermodulation as a function of signal amplitude for both steps of analog power control

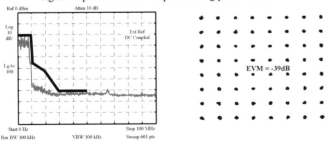

Figure 9: Output power spectrum and EVM for 64-QAM OFDM. The mask shown for 802.16 is 10dB tougher (far-out) than 802.11.

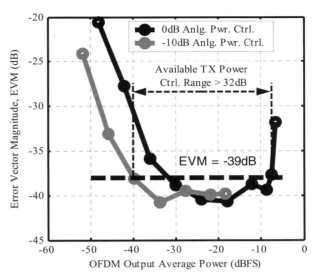

Figure 10: Measured EVM as a function of input average power. Target is -39dB. EVM degrades on high side due to PAPR compression and on the low side due to noise and distortion floor. Available average power control range is 32dB

ACKNOWLEDGMENT

The authors thank Yorgos Palaskas, Gordon Compton, Cuong Le, Ralph Bishop, Chris Hull, Wesley Kwong and Hossein Alavi for their contributions.

REFERENCES

[1]   T. Christen, T. Burger, and Q. Huang, "A 0.13μm CMOS EDGE/UMTS/WLAN Tri-Mode ΣΔ ADC with -92dB THD," ISSCC Dig. Tech. Papers, pp. 240-241, Feb. 2007.

[2]   P. Malla, H. Lakdawala, K. Kornegay, and K. Soumyanath, "A 28mW Spectrum-Sensing Reconfigurable 20MHz 72dB-SNR 70dB-SNDR DT ΣΔ ADC for 802.11n/WiMAX Receivers," ISSCC Dig. Tech. Papers, pp. 496-497, Feb. 2008.

[3]   f. j. harris, "Performance and design of Farrow filter used for arbitrary resampling," IEEE Int. Conf. DSP, vol. 2, pp. 595-599, Jul. 1997.

[4]   A. Jerng and C. G. Sodini, "A Wideband ΔΣ Digital-RF Modulator for High Data Rate Transmitters," IEEE J. Solid-State Circuits, vol. 42, no. 8, pp. 1710-1722, Aug. 2007.

[5]   H. Tao, L. Toth and J. M. Khoury, "Analysis of timing jitter in bandpass sigma-delta modulators," IEEE Trans. Circuits Syst. II, vol. 46, no. 8, pp. 991–1001, Aug. 1999.

[6]   J. M. Rabaey, A. Chandrakasan, and B. Nikolic, Digital Integrated Circuits, Prentice Hall, 1999.

[7]   A. Pozsgay et al., "A Fully Digital 65nm CMOS Transmitter for the 2.3-2.7GHz WiFi/WiMAX Bands using 5.4GHz ΣΔ RF DACs," ISSCC Dig. Tech. Papers, pp. 360-361, Feb. 2008.

[8]   S. Luschas , R. Schreier and H. Lee "Radio frequency digital-to-analog converter," IEEE J. Solid-State Circuits, vol. 39, no. 9, pp. 1462-1467, Sep. 2004.

[9]   P. Eloranta and P. Seppinen, "Direct-Digital RF Modulator IC in 0.13μm CMOS for Wideband Multi-Radio Applications," ISSCC Dig. Tech. Papers, pp. 532-533, Feb. 2005.

[10] K. Kuhn et al., "A 90 nm communication technology featuring SiGe HBT transistors, RF CMOS, precision R-L-C RF elements and 1μm² 6-T SRAM cell," IEDM Tech. Dig., pp. 73-76, Dec. 2002.

A 12-bit 3.125-MHz Bandwidth 0-3 MASH Delta-Sigma Modulator

Ahmed Gharbiya and David A. Johns

Department of Electrical and Computer Engineering, University of Toronto

10 King's College Rd., Toronto, Ontario, CANADA, M5S 3G4

a.gharbiya@utoronto.ca, johns@eecg.utoronto.ca

Abstract—A 12-bit 0-3 MASH delta-sigma modulator with a 3.125MHz bandwidth is implemented in 0.18μm CMOS technology. The modulator has an oversampling ratio of 8 (clock frequency of 50MHz) and achieves a peak SNDR of 73.9dB (77.2dB peak SNR) and consumes 24mW from a 1.8V supply. For comparison purposes, the modulator can be re-configured as a single-loop topology where a peak SNDR of 64.5dB (66.3dB peak SNR) is obtained with 22mW power consumption. The energy required per conversion step for the 0-3 MASH architecture (0.95 pJ/step) is less than half of that required by the feedback topology (2.57 pJ/step).

I. INTRODUCTION

Delta-sigma (ΔΣ) modulators are widely used for high-resolution and moderate-bandwidth *analog-to-digital* (ADC) converters. In particular, the multi-stage topology (MASH) [1] is attractive for high-order low *oversampling ratio* (OSR) ADC. The popularity of MASH for low OSR stems from the improvement in the achievable SQNR when compared to single-loop topologies. The SQNR advantage is due to the enhanced stability which allows for a larger input-signal level in MASH structures. In previous implementations, cascades of ΔΣ (ΔΣ MASH) and cascades of ΔΣ followed by a zero-order quantizer (ΔΣ-0 MASH, also known as the Leslie-Singh architecture [2]) have been reported.

In this work, the missing piece of MASH topologies, the 0-ΔΣ MASH structure [3], is demonstrated in a 0.18μm CMOS process. It is found that the 0-ΔΣ MASH is stable for a larger input-signal level than any traditional topology. The enhanced stability improves the achievable SQNR in the 0-ΔΣ MASH. A proof-of-concept 0-3 MASH ΔΣ prototype is fabricated to evaluate the concept and compare it to a 3rd order single-loop feedback ΔΣ topology. The improved resolution and superior power efficiency of the 0-ΔΣ MASH topology are shown.

II. 0-ΔΣ MASH MODULATOR

The 0-ΔΣ MASH is illustrated using a cascade of two stages (0-L) as an example and is shown in Fig. 1. The first stage generates a quantization noise signal q_1 which is fed to a ΔΣ

modulator in the second stage after an optional inter-stage gain G. Linear analysis of the 0-L MASH leads to the following result:

$$y = H_1\, x - H_2\, NTF_2\, q_2 + \left(H_1 - H_2\, G\, STF_2\right)q_1 \qquad (1)$$

where STF_2 and NTF_2 are the *signal transfer function* (STF) and the *noise transfer function* (NTF) of the second stage respectively and q_1 and q_2 are the quantization noise from the quantizers in the first and second stages respectively. The output from both stages is processed in the digital domain to obtain the final output y. By choosing H_1 to be $\left(G\, STF_2\right)$ and H_2 to be the NTF of the first stage (which is unity), the final output becomes:

$$y = G\, STF_2\, x - NTF_2\, q_2 \qquad (2)$$

To get an understanding of the mechanism that leads to the enhanced stability of the 0-L MASH topology, consider the output of the first stage q_1 as shown graphically in Fig. 2 for a sinusoidal input and 8 levels in Q_1 as an example. As long as the input does not overload the first-stage, the signal into the second-stage is the quantization noise of the first stage. Once the input exceeds the reference voltage of the quantizer in the first stage $V_{ref,Q1}$, the signal into the second-stage includes an input-signal component. However, the modulator is still stable and operational after overloading Q_1. Therefore, the maximum input-signal level into the 0-L MASH topology can be determined:

$$x_{\max} = k\, \frac{V_{\text{ref},Q2}}{G} + V_{\text{ref},Q1}\left(1 - \frac{1}{M_1}\right) \qquad (3)$$

where k is a constant ranging from 50 to 80% [4] and depends on the loop order and number of bits in the quantizer Q_2. The maximum input given in (3) holds as long as the inter-stage gain is bound by:

$$G \le k\, \frac{V_{\text{ref},Q2}}{V_{\text{ref},Q1}}\, M_1 \qquad (4)$$

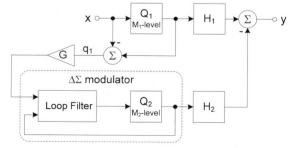

Fig. 1: The 0-L MASH ΔΣ modulator

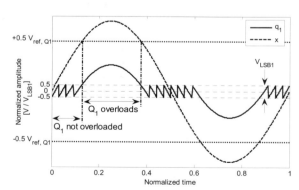

Fig. 2: 1st stage input and output in the 0-L MASH

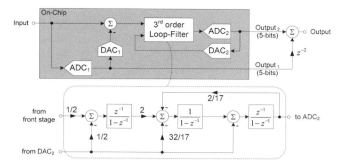

Fig. 3: System level of the experimental 0-3 MASH modulator

The enhanced stability of the 0-L MASH is clear when comparing (3) to the maximum input level into a traditional $\Delta\Sigma$ modulator:

$$x_{\max} = k\, V_{\mathrm{ref,Q}} \tag{5}$$

where $V_{\mathrm{ref,Q}}$ is the reference voltage of the quantizer. As an example: for unity inter-stage gain, the 0-L MASH can tolerate an input that is larger than a traditional topology by $V_{\mathrm{ref,Q1}}\left(1 - M_1^{-1}\right)$. Therefore, the 0-L MASH improves the achievable SQNR even for a small number of levels in the first-stage quantizer.

An addition advantage of the 0-L MASH is the low swing and low distortion characteristics of the $\Delta\Sigma$ modulator if the input is limited to $V_{\mathrm{ref,Q1}}$. This occurs because the input to the second stage is quantization noise only if Q_1 is not overloaded. Processing quantization noise reduces the swing at the internal nodes of the modulator which relaxes the headroom requirements, and allows for more efficient opamp architectures to be used. Distortion becomes also independent of the input signal, which relaxes linearity requirements. This advantage is similar to input-feedforward topologies where the loop filter processes quantization noise only [5].

III. DESIGN OF THE EXPERIMENTAL MODULATOR

The objective of the test chip is to build a re-configurable modulator that is capable of operating as either a 0-$\Delta\Sigma$ MASH or as a single-loop feedback $\Delta\Sigma$ modulator. The re-configurability feature facilitates evaluation of the proposed modulator and allows for a comparison with a

traditional architecture.

The design of the modulator follows a typical top-down methodology. Firstly, the system level, which provides the mathematical description of the modulator, is developed. The system model is then mapped into the equivalent switched-capacitor circuit. Finally, the building blocks are designed at the transistor level.

A. System Level Design

The system level of the MASH modulator is shown in Fig. 3. The second stage is a third-order feedback $\Delta\Sigma$ topology with optimized NTF zeros. It uses a 17-level internal quantizer ADC_2 with reference voltage levels of $\pm0.5\ V_{\mathrm{diff}}$ which is limited by opamp swing. In the first stage, ADC_1 also uses a 17-level quantizer but with reference voltage levels of $\pm1.0\ V_{\mathrm{diff}}$. The same number of levels is used in the two quantizers to allow design reuse for the ADC and *data weighted averaging* (DWA) [6] blocks. The digital filter and digital adder are implemented off-chip. The inter-stage gain is chosen to be unity to simplify the re-configurability of the modulator.

B. Structural Level Design

The system model in Fig. 3 is mapped into the equivalent switched-capacitor circuit as shown in Fig. 4 in the single ended form for simplicity (the actual implementation is fully-differential). Linearity of the two DACs feeding into the first integrator is critical to ensure the performance of the modulator. Therefore, DWA is used for both front-end DACs. However, linearity is less important for the DACs in the second and third integrators since nonlinearities are noise shaped when referred back to the input. Therefore, DWA was omitted from the second integrator because it uses a non-delaying topology which reduces the time available to perform DWA.

The first integrator uses the double sampled input technique [7]-[8] to mitigate the timing constraint introduced at the input of the 0-$\Delta\Sigma$ MASH topology. The constraint is due to the delay free path from the input through ADC_1, DWA_1, and DAC_1 to the integrator input as shown in Fig. 4. The front-end sampling capacitor is 1pF to achieve the desired resolution of 12 bits for the 0-3 MASH topology. The

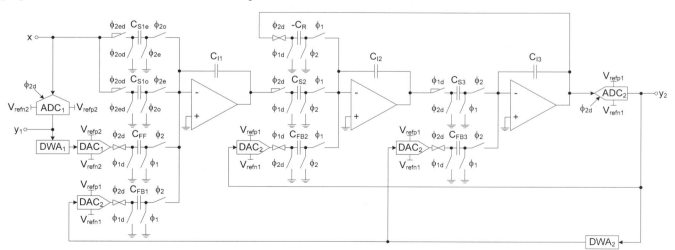

Fig. 4: $\Delta\Sigma$ modulator structural level

207

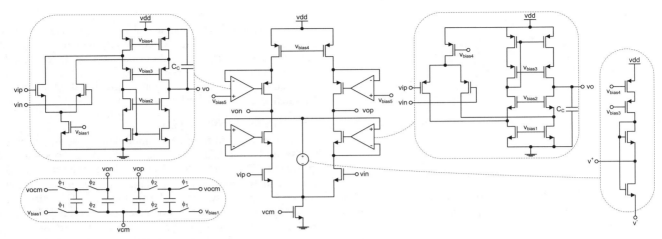

Fig. 5: Telescopic opamp

capacitors in the following stages of the modulator are scaled down.

The modulator in Fig. 4 can operate in single-loop feedback mode by simply turning off ADC_1, DWA_1, and DAC_1. Furthermore, C_{FF} is not switched in single-loop mode to eliminate its noise contribution to the modulator.

C. Circuit Level Design

The next step is to implement each of the building blocks at the transistor level. The telescopic opamp architecture is picked for implementation and is shown in Fig. 5. Telescopic opamps with NMOS inputs have the advantage of high-speed operation because of the all NMOS signal path. The output common-mode voltage is set using a typical switched-capacitor common-mode feedback circuit where the control voltage vcm is fed back to the tail transistor. The DC gain from the telescopic opamp is not sufficient and gain boosters are needed to achieve the desired gain. All the biasing voltages for the opamps and their gain boosters are generated using typical wide-swing cascode current mirrors except for the NMOS cascode gain boosters which are generated as shown in Fig. 5. This biasing scheme improves the common-mode rejection.

The quantizers ADC_1 and ADC_2 are implemented as 17-level flash. Each ADC has 16 parallel comparators and each comparator is a cascade of a preamplifier, regenerative latch, and RS latch. The total input capacitance of the flash is 0.24 pF which is about one-fourth the input sampling capacitor (1 pF). Therefore, the extra load at the input due to ADC_1 is insignificant.

The preamplifier shown in Fig. 6 compares the differential input and differential reference and amplifies the difference.

The difference is then processed by the dynamic regenerative latch shown in Fig. 6 [9]. The gain of the preamplifier is important to reduce the offset and kick-back from the regenerative latch. The latch is reset when the control signal *latch* is low. Therefore, a simple RS-latch is used to hold the output of the dynamic latch for the remainder of the period.

IV. MEASURED PERFORMANCE

The $\Delta\Sigma$ modulator is implemented in a 0.18µm 1P6M CMOS process with the MIM capacitor option. The chip active area is 1.8mm^2 as shown in Fig. 7. The die is packaged in a 44-pin CQFP package.

The measured performance of the $\Delta\Sigma$ modulator is summarized in Table 1. The improvement in the performance of the MASH modulator is reflected in its *figure of merit* (FOM) which is less than half of that achieved by the feedback topology.

The main advantage of the 0-$\Delta\Sigma$ MASH topology is allowing a larger input-signal which results in an improvement in the achievable SNR and SNDR as illustrated in Fig. 8.

The output spectrum for the two configurations at their maximum SNR is shown in Fig. 9. The input frequency is at 780kHz and with amplitude of -3dBFS for the feedback modulator and 8dBFS for the 0-$\Delta\Sigma$ MASH modulator.

The internal nodes of the 0-3 MASH modulator contain quantization noise only before overloading the first quantizer. Although this feature is difficult to measure for all three opamps in the modulator, it can be confirmed for the third opamp. This is because the third opamp output is quantized

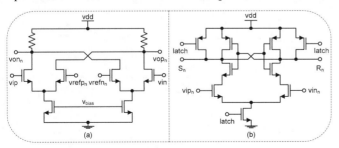

Fig. 6: (a) Preamplifier and (b) Regenerative latch

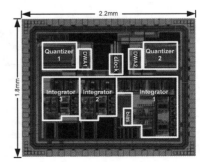

Fig. 7: Micrograph of prototype

and processed off-chip, therefore, its distribution can be analyzed. By confirming the output of the third opamp, we can deduce the validity of the quantization noise only feature for the other opamps.

The 17-level outputs of the third opamp are shown in Fig. 10. For a zero input-signal, the outputs from both configurations are normally distributed since the input is thermal noise. The 0-3 MASH topology maintains similar distribution up to 6 dBFS (maximum point before the ADC_1 overloads). However, at an input of -3 dBFS (maximum SNR point for the feedback modulator), the feedback modulator distribution shows more occurrences at the reference limit which indicates that the modulator is getting closer to overloading.

The 0-3 MASH performance can be compared to a recent $\Delta\Sigma$-0 MASH modulator implemented in 0.18μm 1P6M CMOS process with similar resolution [10]. The first stage is a second-order feedback topology with 4-bits internal quantizer and the second stage is a 9-bits pipeline ADC. The modulator is clocked at 80MHz with an OSR of 4 and achieves a peak SNDR of 73 dB while consuming 240mW, therefore, it has a FOM of 3.29 pJ/step.

V. CONCLUSION

A configurable $\Delta\Sigma$ modulator is implemented in 0.18μm CMOS technology to evaluate the 0-$\Delta\Sigma$ MASH concept and compare it to the single-loop feedback modulator. Both topologies are tested at 50MHz with an OSR of 8 and powered from a 1.8V supply. The 0-$\Delta\Sigma$ MASH modulator achieves 77.2dB peak SNR (73.9dB peak SNDR) which is 10.9dB (9.4dB) better than the feedback modulator at the expense of 9% increase in power consumption. The energy required per conversion step for the 0-$\Delta\Sigma$ MASH architecture is 37% of that required by the feedback architecture.

REFERENCES

[1] T. Hayashi *et al.*, "A multistage delta-sigma modulator without double integration loop," *ISSCC Dig. Tech. Papers*, pp. 182 – 183, Feb. 1986.

[2] T. C. Leslie and B. Singh, "An Improved sigma-delta modulator architecture," *IEEE International Symposium on Circuits and Systems.*, vol. 1, pp. 372 – 375, May 1990.

[3] A. Gharbiya and D. A. Johns, "Fully Digital Feedforward Delta-Sigma Modulator," *IEEE PhD Research in Microelectronics and Electronics*, July 25-28, 2005.

[4] S. R. Norsworthy, R. Schreier, and G. C. Temes, Delta-Sigma Data Converters. John Wiley & Sons, 1996.

[5] J. Silva, U. Moon, J. Steensgaard, and G. C. Temes, "Wideband low-distortion delta-sigma ADC topology," *Electron. Lett.*, vol. 37, pp. 737 – 738, 2001.

[6] R. T. Baird and T. S. Fiez, "Improved $\Delta\Sigma$ DAC linearity using data weighted averaging," *IEEE International Symposium on Circuits and Systems.*, vol. 1, pp. 13 – 16, May 1995.

[7] Y. Fujimoto *et al.*, "An 80/100MS/s 76.3/70.1dB SNDR $\Sigma\Delta$ ADC for digital TV Receivers," *ISSCC Dig. Tech. Papers*, pp. 76 – 639, Feb. 2006.

[8] A. Gharbiya and D. A. Johns, "On The Implementation of Input-Feedforward Delta-Sigma Modulators," *IEEE Trans. Circuits and Systems II*, vol. 53, pp. 453 – 457, Jun. 2006.

[9] T. Kobayashi *et al.*, "A current-controlled latch sense amplifier and a static power-saving input buffer for low-power architecture," *IEEE J. Solid-State Circuits*, vol. 28, pp. 523 – 527, Apr. 1993.

[10] A. Bosi *et al.*, "An 80MHz 4x oversampled cascaded $\Delta\Sigma$-pipelined ADC with 75dB DR and 87dB SFDR," *ISSCC Dig. Tech. Papers*, pp. 174 – 591, Feb. 2005.

Table 1: Summary of the measured performance

	0-3 MASH	**Feedback $\Delta\Sigma$**
Supply	1.8 V	
$f_{sampling}$	50 MHz	
OSR	8	
BW_{signal}	3.125 MHz	
Analog Power	19 mW	18 mW
Digital Power	5 mW	4 mW
Total Power	24 mW	22 mW
Peak SNR	77.2 dB	66.3 dB
Peak SNDR	73.9 dB	64.5 dB
FOM*	0.95 pJ/step	2.57 pJ/step

*FOM=Power/(2BW$_{signal}$ 2^((SNDR-1.76)/6.02))

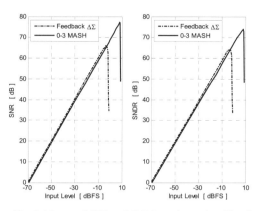

Fig. 8: Measured SNR and SNDR vs. input-signal level

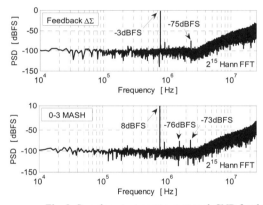

Fig. 9: Sample output spectrum at peak SNR for the feedback and the 0-3 MASH $\Delta\Sigma$ modulators

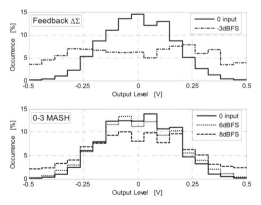

Fig. 10: Measured output level distribution

A 20.7 mW Continuous-time $\Delta\Sigma$ Modulator with 15 MHz Bandwidth and 70 dB Dynamic Range

Karthikeyan Reddy and Shanthi Pavan
Indian Institute of Technology, Madras
shanthi.pavan@iitm.ac.in

Abstract—We present a CT-$\Delta\Sigma$ modulator operating at a sampling rate of 300 Msps in a 0.18μm CMOS process. A low power four bit flash ADC and a complementary current-steering DAC are used to reduce power and noise. The opamps used in the active-RC loop filter are deliberately made slow to further reduce current consumption and the resulting loop delay is compensated. The modulator achieves a peak SNR of 67.2 dB in a 15 MHz bandwidth (OSR=10) while dissipating only 20.7 mW from a 1.8 V supply.

I. INTRODUCTION

Continuous-time $\Delta\Sigma$ modulators are attractive low-power alternatives to other ADC architectures due to their low power dissipation and implicit anti-aliasing. Several high performance modulators targeting 10-12 bit resolutions with signal bandwidths in the 10-15 MHz range have been reported recently [1] [2] [3]. In this paper, we present the design and experimental results of a multibit $\Delta\Sigma$ ADC with 15 MHz signal bandwidth and a sampling rate of 300 Msps. The modulator achieves 11 bit resolution while dissipating only 20.7 mW from a 1.8 V supply. This is made possible by choosing a large full scale voltage of 2.4 V and a complementary current-steering feedback DAC that result in reduced circuit noise requirements. A power efficient flash ADC capable of handling large signal swings is another key block employed in this design. The rest of the paper is organized as follows. Section II describes the architectural choices made in the converter. Circuit design details and measurement results from a testchip are given in Sections III and IV respectively. Section V gives the conclusions.

II. ARCHITECTURAL CHOICES

We justify the various architectural choices made in the design.

A. Choice of Noise Transfer Function :

At low oversampling ratios, increasing the NTF order does not significantly improve the inband SNR. Hence, a third order loop filter was chosen. By using a multibit quantizer, the modulator can be made stable even with Out of Band Gains (OBG) larger than 1.5. While larger OBGs result in lower inband quantization noise, they have a smaller Maximum Stable Amplitude (MSA), as well as increased sensitivity to component variations. An OBG of three was chosen as a compromise between the above conflicting considerations. A maximally flat NTF with complex zeroes is commonly used in $\Delta\Sigma$ modulator design. Simulations predict a peak SQNR

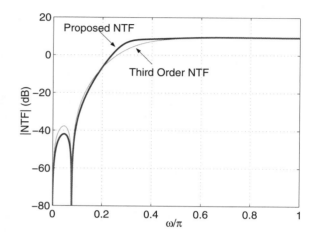

Fig. 1. Magnitude of the proposed NTF in comparison with that of a third order maximally flat NTF with an Out of Band Gain (OBG) of three. The inband SNR is improved by 5 dB.

of about 71 dB for such an NTF. To reduce the in-band quantization noise, we exploit excess loop delay as described below. In a high speed design such as this, significant excess loop delay can be expected (in our design, this delay is about 60% of the bit period). The usual strategy to mitigate the effect of excess loop delay is the following - a direct path is added around the quantizer and the loop filter coefficients are retuned so that the NTF magnitude is restored to the original value. Excess loop delay increases the order of the modulator - the resulting extra pole can be placed so that the transition band of the NTF is narrower, while keeping the OBG the same. This results in lesser inband noise - a result that can be understood from fundamental analytical limitations on NTFs as described in [4]. Fig. 1 shows the magnitude responses of the proposed NTF and a maximally flat NTF with OBG=3 (as obtained from [5]). The peak SQNR for our optimized NTF is about 77 dB.

B. Loopfilter Topology:

A "cascaded integrators with feedforward summation" (CIFF) architecture was chosen to implement the loop filter, as shown in a simplified single-ended schematic of the modulator of Fig. 2. Notice that a separate summing amplifier is used to develop the weighted summation of the three integrator outputs. DAC1 provides a direct path around the quantizer and is used to compensate for excess loop delay and finite bandwidth of the loopfilter opamps. Active-RC integrators were used to allow high swing and low noise operation. The integrating capacitors were realized as digitally programmable capacitor banks to mitigate the effect of systematic RC time-constant variations. The full-scale voltage of $2.4\,V_{pp,diff}$ relaxes thermal noise requirements of the first integrator, as well as offset requirements in the flash ADC. This enables the use of an inherently monotonic flash ADC *without comparator offset correction* in the quantizer.

C. Quantizer Design:

A multibit quantizer with an NRZ feedback DAC results in reduced sensitivity to clock jitter, as well as lower distortion due to the nonlinearities in the first opamp. We settled for a four-bit quantizer as a compromise between the benefits offered by multibit quantization and the exponential complexity of implementation. A current-steering DAC was chosen in the feedback path of the modulator. Apart from the the potential for high speed operation, such a DAC has the following additional benefits :

1) The gain from the equivalent input referred noise voltage of the first opamp to the modulator is reduced when compared to a resistive DAC.
2) The high loop gain around the first integrator reduces the "delay" through the first integrator.
3) For a given opamp design, in-band RMS noise due to opamp nonlinearity is reduced by a factor of 8 [6].

Dynamic element matching based on Data Weighted Averaging (DWA) was used to mitigate the effect to mismatch in the DAC unit elements.

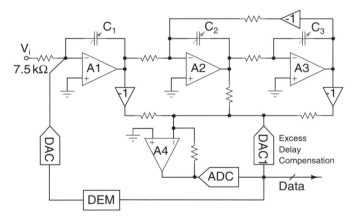

Fig. 2.   Architecture of the modulator.

III. CIRCUIT IMPLEMENTATION DETAILS

A. Operational Amplifiers

Active-RC integrators based on a single-stage OTA are commonly used (see for example [3]) in $\Delta\Sigma$ loopfilters. Using a two stage opamp can result in reduced inband noise due to opamp nonlinearity as explained below.

Consider two integrators built using a single stage OTA and a two stage Miller compensated opamp as shown in Fig. 3. The transconductors in both designs weakly nonlinear. For the

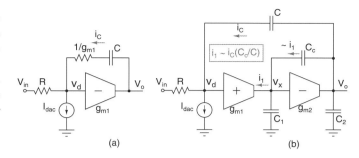

Fig. 3.   Comparison of one and two stage opamps when used in a $\Delta\Sigma$ modulator.

integrator of Fig. 3(a), the entire capacitor current has to be supplied by the transconductor g_{m1}. In a well designed Miller-opamp based integrator (Fig. 3(b)), it is seen that v_x and v_d are small in relation to v_o. The voltages across the integrating and compensating capacitors are nearly equal, resulting in

$$i_1 = i_C \frac{C_c}{C} \qquad (1)$$

Thus, the current demanded of the first stage transconductor is a factor $\frac{C_c}{C}$ smaller in a two stage design when compared to a single stage OTA. This means that the effect of transconductor nonlinearity is greatly reduced in a Miller opamp [6]. In our design, $\frac{C_c}{C} \approx 0.14$ in the first integrator.

The first and fourth amplifiers (A1 and A4 in Fig. 2) consume $1.6\,mA$ and $1.2\,mA$ respectively, while A2 and A3 draw $650\,\mu A$ each. A CAD routine and methodology were developed to determine the relative weighting factors and the current required in DAC1 to realize the desired NTF. The routine accounts for the frequency response of the operational amplifiers and the excess delay introduced by the ADC & DEM logic.

B. Flash ADC, DAC and DEM Logic

The block diagram of the 4-bit flash ADC used in this work is shown in Fig. 4. It consists of 15 differential comparators, a resistor ladder and a digital backend. The nominal LSB size is $150\,mV$, which relaxes the offset requirements of the comparators. The comparator array generates a thermometer code and the 4-bit ADC output code is generated by summing the number of 1's in the thermometer. This makes the quantizer characteristic inherently monotonic.

The circuit diagram of the comparator and the corresponding clock waveforms are shown in Figs. 6(a) and (b) respectively. The comparator operates as follows. When LC is high, the nodes X & Y are connected to ip & im through two coupling capacitors C_b, which have been charged to $V_{refp} - V_{cm}$ and $V_{refm} - V_{cm}$ respectively. Thus, the differential voltage between nodes X & Y at the end of the on-phase of LC is $(V_{ip} - V_{im}) - (V_{refp} - V_{refm})$. L goes high after LC goes low. In this phase, the back to back inverters formed by M1, M2, M3 & M4 are activated, thereby regenerating the difference between the voltages at nodes X & Y. The decision made by the latch is held on C^2MOS inverters, which are clocked by Ld.

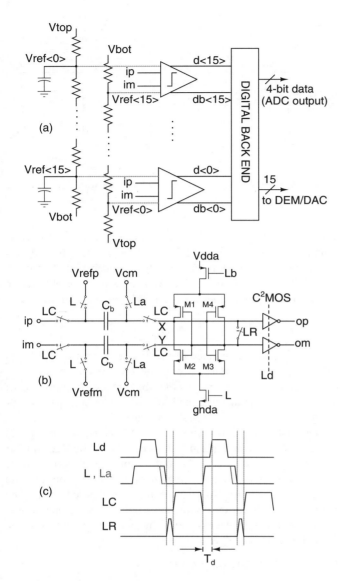

Fig. 4. (a) Flash ADC architecture (b) comparator circuit and (c) clock waveforms.

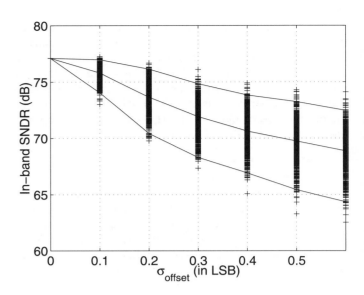

Fig. 5. Effect of comparator random offset on in-band SNDR - for each level of offset, 1000 trials were simulated. The lines show the modulators with the best 1% SNDR, mean SNDR and the worst 1% SNDR respectively.

the characteristic of the quantizer is monotonic.

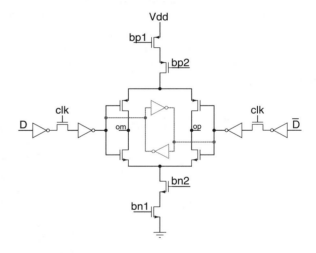

Fig. 6. DAC unit-cell with drive circuitry.

A small reset phase LR is necessary to prevent latch hysteresis [7]. The estimated 3σ random offset of the comparator is about 40 mV. The comparator does not consume any static power and is highly suited for $\Delta\Sigma$ work, where flash ADC nonidealities are largely shaped out of the signal band. The capacitive coupling used to subtract the differential references from the input enables the ADC to handle large input swings, which is not possible with other comparator architectures (like the ones used in [1] [2]).

The modulator was simulated for various levels of Gaussian distributed offsets in the comparators. 1000 trials for each level of offset were run. Fig. 5 shows the results. The lines represent the mean, the best and the worst 1% of the SNRs. It is thus seen that to achieve a 11 bit performance from the modulator, random offsets in the comparator with a standard deviation of up to 0.4 LSB can easily be tolerated, as long as

A complementary current steering DAC is used in the modulator feedback path. The unit-cell is shown in Fig. 6. Using both NMOS and PMOS current sources obviates the need for extra current to be injected into the virtual ground nodes of the first opamp to maintain a reasonable input common-mode voltage, thereby reducing thermal noise added by the DAC.

A 4-layer barrel shifter based implementation [1] was used to implement the Data Weighted Averaging algorithm.

IV. MEASUREMENT RESULTS

The chip was fabricated in a 0.18 μm CMOS technology through Europractice. The active area of the ADC is about 1 mm^2, and was mounted in a 44-pin JLCC package. Figure 7

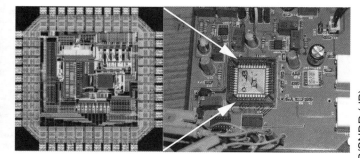

Fig. 7. Chip layout and test-board.

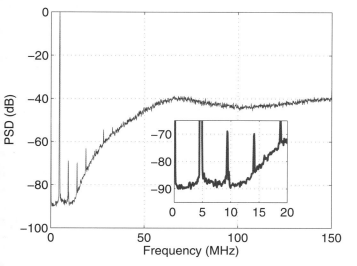

Fig. 8. PSD of the modulator for a 4.7 MHz input tone at the maximum stable amplitude.

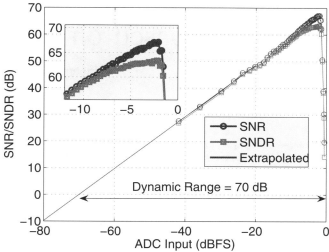

Fig. 9. Measured SNR, SNDR and dynamic range. The peak SNR is 67.2 dB.

lower energy per level resolved.

V. CONCLUSIONS

We presented a $\Delta\Sigma$ modulator achieving 70 dB dynamic range in a 15 MHz bandwidth. The factors that enable such performance at a power dissipation of 20.7 mW are the choice of a large full scale voltage, an active-RC loopfilter implemented using Miller compensated opamps, a complementary current steering feedback DAC and a low power flash ADC. The efficacy of the proposed design techniques are borne out through measurement results from test chips fabricated in a 0.18 μm CMOS process.

REFERENCES

[1] S. Paton, A. Di Giandomenico, L. Hernandez, A. Wiesbauer, T. Potscher, and M. Clara, "A 70-mW 300-MHz CMOS continuous-time $\Sigma\Delta$ ADC with 15-MHz bandwidth and 11 bits of resolution," *IEEE Journal of Solid-State Circuits*, vol. 39, no. 7, pp. 1056–1063, July 2004.
[2] J. Arias, P. Kiss, V. Prodanov, V. Boccuzzi, M. Banu, D. Bisbal, J. Pablo, L. Quintanilla, and J. Barbolla, "A 32-mW 320-MHz continuous-time complex delta-sigma ADC for multi-mode wireless-LAN receivers," *IEEE Journal of Solid-State Circuits*, vol. 41, no. 2, pp. 339–351, February 2006.
[3] L. Breems, R. Rutten, and G. Wetzker, "A cascaded continuous-time $\Sigma\Delta$ modulator with 67-dB dynamic range in 10-MHz bandwidth," *IEEE Journal of Solid-State Circuits*, vol. 39, no. 12, pp. 2152–2160, December 2004.
[4] J. Harrison and N. Weste, "Analytic limitations on sigma-delta modulator performance," *Proceedings of the IEEE International Symposium on Circuits and Systems*, vol. 3, 2000.
[5] R. Schreier, "The Delta-Sigma toolbox for MATLAB," *Matlab code and documentation*, vol. 2003, 1997.
[6] P. Sankar and S. Pavan, "Analysis of integrator nonlinearity in a class of continuous-time $\Delta\Sigma$ modulators," *IEEE Transactions on Circuits and Systems - Express Briefs*, vol. 54, no. 12, pp. 1125–1129, December 2007.
[7] S. Pavan, N. Krishnapura, R. Pandarinathan, and P. Sankar, "A 90 μW 15-bit delta-sigma ADC for digital audio," in *Proceedings of the European Solid-State Circuits Conference*, 2007, pp. 198–201.
[8] S. Kuichycki, R. Trofin, K. Vleugels, and B. Wooley, "A 1.2-V 77-dB 7.5-MHz continuous-time/discrete-time cascaded $\Delta\Sigma$ modulator," *IEEE Symposium on VLSI Circuits*, pp. 238–239, 2007.

shows the IC layout and a photograph of the test board used to characterize the converter.

Figure 8 shows the PSD of the modulator output for a 4.7 MHz input tone for an amplitude that results in the peak SNDR. A 4800-point Blackman-Harris window was used in the PSD computations. The measured SNR and SNDR of the modulator for a 4.7 MHz input tone are shown in Figure 9. The peak SNR and SNDR are 67.2 dB and 63.2 dB respectively. The measured dynamic range of the modulator is 70 dB. Table

TABLE I
COMPARISON WITH OTHER CT-$\Sigma\Delta$ MODULATORS

Reference/Feature	Bandwidth	SNDR/SNR/DR	Power (mW)	FOM pJ/lvl
[1],0.13μm	15 MHz	63.7/64.6/67.0	70	1.68
[2],0.25μm	10 MHz	53.9/55.5/58.0	15.2	1.56
[3],0.18μm	10 MHz	63.0/63.0/67.0	122.4	5.30
[8],0.18μm	7.5 MHz	67.0/71.0/77.0	89.0	2.05
This work(0.18μm)	15 MHz	64.2/67.2/70.0	20.7	0.37

I compares the performance of the ADC proposed in this work to other state-of-the-art converters designed in similar technologies. Thanks to the architectural and circuit techniques employed in this design, our work achieves a significantly

A 11 mW 68dB SFDR 100 MHz bandwidth ΔΣ-DAC based on a 5-bit 1GS/s core in 130nm

Pieter Palmers, Michiel Steyaert

Abstract—**This paper presents a delta-sigma current-steering digital-to-analog converter implemented in a standard 130nm CMOS technology. The 5-bit core DAC provides 13-bit static linearity without calibration, using only $0.44mm^2$. The delta-sigma converter achieves 68dB SFDR over a 100MHz signal bandwidth at 1GHz sampling frequency. A novel very low power thermometer decoder was used, resulting in a power consumption of 11mW. In terms of power efficiency this converter outperforms all comparable D/A converters published in open literature. The design demonstrates the viability of multi-bit delta-sigma D/A converters as an alternative for Nyquist-rate DACs in highly integrated broadband applications. It also shows that in deep sub-micron processes the use of a delta-sigma converter extends the usable bandwidth for D/A converters.**

Index Terms—**D/A Converters; current-steering; CMOS; delta-sigma; deep sub-micron**

I. INTRODUCTION

Along with the emerging demand for multi-standard large bandwidth digital communication systems comes a need to implement higher performance data converters. For cost and integration reasons these are preferably implemented on the same die as the digital baseband section. This enforces the use of a modern deep sub-micron CMOS technology to implement these data converters. At very high conversion speeds integration is also beneficial with respect to interfacing, since connecting multiple chips with multi-bit interfaces running gigabit/s per pin data rates is non-trivial and power hungry. Implementing data converters in modern day deep sub-micron technologies however imposes new design challenges as a result of their lower analog performance.

This paper presents a 5-bit delta-sigma modulated current-steering Digital-to-Analog Converter (DAC) achieving 68dB of SFDR for a 100MHz signal band. It was manufactured in a pure-digital 130nm technology and consumes only 11mW at its nominal 1GS/s update rate.

The motivation and problem at hand are explained in section II. Section III describes the basic architecture, topology and floor plan and the different building blocks of the DAC. The measurement results of the prototype are presented and commented in section IV. Finally, some conclusions are formulated.

II. IN-BAND HARMONIC DISTORTION

From a system point of view, D/A converters are blocks that should generate a predefined signal bandwidth at a specified precision and linearity. The major challenge in the design of D/A converters is not merely achieving a high update rate, but achieving high linearity over a large signal bandwidth. In-band

distortion can be considered more important than out-of-band distortion since the latter can be filtered (e.g. spectral images in Nyquist rate D/A converters).

One of the main sources of non-linearity in current steering D/A converters is recognized to be the code dependency of the converters output impedance [1][2]. Sufficient output impedance has to be maintained over the complete output signal bandwidth. As calculated in [2], the relation between second order distortion performance ($SFDR_{HD2}$), load impedance (R_L), number of bits (B) and the required output impedance (Z_{req}) of the unit current cells is given by:

$$Z_{req} = \frac{SFDR_{HD2} \cdot R_L \cdot 2^B}{4} \quad (1)$$

This equation shows that in order to evaluate the maximum usable bandwidth for a given linearity specification, the impedance of the switched current cell is a key parameter. Therefore it is useful to examine the maximal output impedance a current cell can provide over the desired frequency range, given a certain technology.

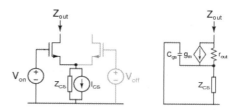

Fig. 1. Ideal switched current cell and it's simplified small signal equivalent

Fig. 1 shows an idealized switched current cell that consists of a current source having an output impedance equal to Z_{CS}, and a saturated CMOS transistor operating as switch. Neglecting the complementary switch as it is turned off, and all device capacitances except for the gate-source capacitance, the small signal equivalent circuit reduces to the circuit shown on the right. The output impedance of this configuration is easily calculated to be (assuming $Z_{CS} \gg |sC_{gs}|$ and $g_m r_{out} \gg 1$):

$$Z_{out} = r_{out}(1 + g_m \frac{Z_{CS}}{1 + sZ_{CS}C_{gs}}) \approx r_{out}(1 + g_m \frac{1}{sC_{gs}}) \quad (2)$$

Recognizing that $\frac{g_m}{2\pi C_{gs}}$ is the transition frequency (f_T) of the saturated switch transistor, equation (2) can be rewritten as:

$$Z_{out} \approx r_{out}(1 - j\frac{f_T}{f}) \quad (3)$$

Equation (3) can now be used to determine the maximum frequency f_{max} up to which the switched current cell achieves a certain required output impedance Z_{req}. Starting from

$$|Z_{req}| = \left| r_{out}(1 - j\frac{f_T}{f_{max}}) \right|$$

and assuming that $f_{max} \ll f_T$, we obtain:

$$f_{max} \cdot Z_{req} = f_T \cdot r_{out} \qquad (4)$$

This equation reveals a trade-off between circuit performance and technology. It reveals that for broadband high output impedance current cells the used transistors should not only have high-speed, but also exhibit high output impedance. The relations obtained in this section are summarized in Fig. 2. It shows that the output impedance drops with 20dB/dec to reach r_{out} when frequency passes f_T of the switch transistor, as indicated by equation (3). For a certain required impedance, the maximum operating frequency can be determined using equation (4).

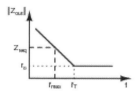

Fig. 2.   Output impedance for a switched ideal current source

The presented calculations consider only the gate-source capacitance of a switch transistor that cascodes very high impedance current source, hence present an optimistic view of the problem. Other significant capacitances are present at the switch source node (e.g. wiring capacitance, source-bulk capacitance), and current source output impedance is limited. Nevertheless it gives insight in the core problem of current cell design in deep sub-micron CMOS technologies: since equation (1) limits the impedance, the maximum signal bandwidth is fixed by the $f_T r_{out}$ product of the switches. Although these technologies provide every increasing transition frequencies, short channel effects cause r_{out} to drop, resulting in a stagnating, in some cases even decreasing, $f_T r_{out}$ product. In this design, the used 130nm CMOS technology limits f_{max} to approximately 80MHz for a 60dB $SFDR_{HD2}$ specification.

The presence of higher order distortion for higher signal frequencies is usually not a problem since it falls out of band and hence is filtered by the reconstruction filter. Any distortion present in the output spectrum however will interact with the sample frequency and will be folded back (mixed) into the band of interest. It is therefore beneficial to use higher degrees of oversampling such that the magnitude and the number of harmonics that are folded back is decreased.

III. ARCHITECTURE AND CIRCUIT DESIGN

Fig. 3 shows the floor plan of the experimental prototype. The clock and binary input data is brought on chip by a high-speed low-voltage differential signaling input stage. The binary input words are decoded by a 5-31 decoder that provides the input signals for the switch drivers, driving the switched current cells. Current matching is provided by the current

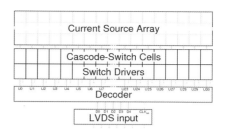

Fig. 3.   Prototype floor plan

source array (CSA). For clock and output routing, balanced trees have been used to ensure low delay mismatch.

Aside from the clock distribution, the thermometer decoder is the main contributor to the total power consumption of a unary DAC. The lack of regularity in the thermocode conversion operation, since every output is dependent on all of the inputs in a unique way, results in a separate logic function for each output. This requires a full custom design process and a high power consumption since all data lines have to be routed over the complete decoder. For this design, a 5-31 decoder was designed that achieves the required speed with a very low power overhead. The decoder is inspired by the mux-based topology proposed in [3].

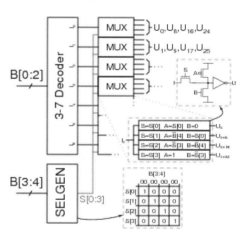

Fig. 4.   Multilevel 5-31 decoder architecture

Fig. 4 shows the 5-31 thermometer decoder architecture. In a first stage, the lower 3 bits are converted by a 3-to-7 decoder. Such a decoder can be built using logic functions that consist of either one-level NAND3 gates or two-level NAND2 gates. By restricting the decoder functions to these two logic functions the transition speed through the decoder can be fast and well equalized. The second stage consists of a set of equal mux blocks that select among three levels: logic 0, logic 1 or first stage output. This selection is based upon the S[0:4] select signals that are generated by the SELGEN block. The truth table for this block is included in the figure. This design results in high speed capability with low power consumption.

The specification for the static linearity of the DAC requires adequate current source matching. The first order Pelgrom relationship [4] between current matching and area is given by:

$$\left(\frac{\Delta I}{I}\right)^2 = \left(A_\beta^2 + \frac{4 \cdot A_{VT}^2}{(V_{gs} - V_T)^2}\right)\frac{1}{WL} \qquad (5)$$

Aside from the well-known fact that matching is largely determined by area, the equation also indicates the sensitivity of matching to the gate overdrive of the current source transistor. On the other hand section II shows that the switches should also have a high f_T, hence also high gate overdrive to maximize their speed. In deep sub-micron technologies with a low power supply it becomes increasingly difficult to meet both specifications simultaneously. Designing for high switching speed results in very large area requirements for the current source transistors.

In order to lower the area requirements, this design uses PMOS transistors as current sources and a 1.5V power supply for the current source array. Doing so allows for more current source transistor gate overdrive and hence lowers the effect of V_T mismatch, reducing the total area of the system. The main disadvantage of this, aside from extra power consumption, is that one has to ensure that no voltage difference exceeds the maximum operation voltage of the transistors (1.2V). The commonly used cascoded current cell however inherently provides a cascode that can be used to shield the high-voltage CSA from the switches. To overcome systematic mismatch errors, the spatial averaging technique proposed in [5] has been used.

IV. MEASUREMENT RESULTS

All measurements are performed on a single ended output signal with 5-mA load current. If not specified otherwise, measurements are performed at the nominal sample rate of 1GS/s. Since the circuit is still functional at 2GS/s, measurements for this sampling frequency have also been performed. The noise shaped input signal was generated externally using a 3rd order digital noise shaping loop. It was applied to the chip over a high-speed LVDS interface.

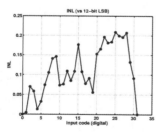

Fig. 5.   INL plot illustrating an uncalibrated static linearity of 0.21 LSB_{12-bit}.

Fig. 5 shows a typical measured INL plot, showing that the converter provides 0.21LSB referred to 12-bit accuracy, corresponding to better than 13bit static accuracy. This indicates the effectiveness of the used current source array scrambling and cell biasing.

Fig. 6 shows the output spectrum of the converter both when 6MHz signal and 99MHz signals are applied. The plots show the very limited harmonic downmixing due to the high oversampling ratio, notwithstanding the presence of a

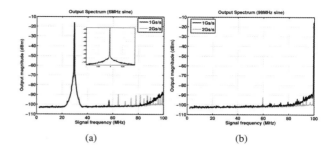

(a)   (b)

Fig. 6.   Output spectrum for a 6MHz (a) and 99MHz (b) output signal, converted at 1Gs/s and 2Gs/s. The inset shows a zoomed-in version of the converted signal to illustrate the fact that the signal smearing observed in the main plot is a measurement artifact. The lower quantization noise due to the higher oversampling when using a 2GS/s update rate can be observed. The extra spurious at 2GS/s are due to decoding errors starting to occur.

significant second order harmonic originating from the limited output impedance of the current cell. At 2GS/s decoding errors start to occur, generating extra spurious. An example output spectrum ranging up to the sample frequency is shown in Fig. 7. The third-order noise shaping and the out-of-band distortion can be observed.

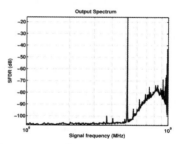

Fig. 7.   SFDR up to the sample frequency of 1GS/s. The signal applied is a 50MHz sine, since this is the highest frequency that causes the second order harmonic to fall in-band. The third order noise-shaping and out-of-band distortion can be observed.

A summary of the spectral performance within the band of interest is shown in Fig. 8, indicating better than 68dB SFDR for signals up to 100MHz.

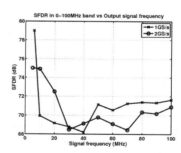

Fig. 8.   SFDR within the DC-100MHz band, for signals from 5 to 100MHz sampled at 1Gs/s and 2Gs/s.

For multi-carrier signal generation applications, the higher order harmonic distortion is not that important since it is effectively filtered by the reconstruction filter. A more significant distortion mechanism for such systems is intermodulation distortion, since these spurious appear in the desired signal band. Fig. 9 shows an overview of the third-order intermodulation performance of the converter. It shows better than 70dB intermodulation over a 50MHz band, and maintains at least 58dB over the 100MHz signal band. .

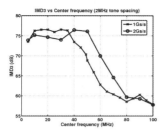

Fig. 9.   IMD3 versus center frequency for two tones spaced 2MHz apart, sampled at 1Gs/s and 2Gs/s.

A. Design summary and comparison

Fig. 10 shows a chip micrograph, marking the current cell array, swatches and decoder. Table I summarizes the design.

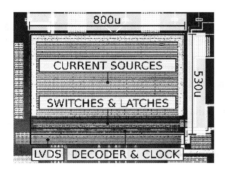

Fig. 10.   Chip photograph

TABLE I
DESIGN SUMMARY

Technology	130nm CMOS	
Area	$0.42mm^2$	
INL	$0.21 \, LSB_{12-bit}$	
Load current	5mA	
Analog supply	1.5V	
Update rate	1Gs/s	2Gs/s
Digital supply	0.9	1.2
Power	11.1mW	21.9mW
Bandwidth	100MHz	100MHz
SFDR@50MHz	70db	71dB
IMD3@50MHz	70dB	76dB
SFDR@100MHz	70db	71dB
IMD3@100MHz	58dB	58dB

To indicate the advantage of the delta-sigma oversampled architecture, Table II compares this design with the current state of the art deep sub-micron converters capable of converting a 100MHz band with at least 60dB of SFDR. The comparison clearly shows the power merits of the presented concept and design.

A side remark is that the bandwidth of low oversampling converters is severely limited by the presence of Nyquist images, resulting in a significant power penalty in the reconstruction filter.

TABLE II
COMPARISON WITH RECENTLY PUBLISHED CMOS DAC AT 100MHZ
SIGNAL BANDWIDTH

	This work	[6]	[7]	[8]	
Bandwidth	100	100	120	125	MHz
Resolution	5 (12)	12	12	10	bit
Load current	5	5	5 (15)	5	mA
Update rate	1000	200	350	250	MS/s
SFDR@100MHz	70	55	70	58	dB
Power	11.1	25	198 (216)	14	mW
FOM	36900	4100	620 (570)	7140	MHz/mW
Technology	0.13	0.13	0.18	0.18	μm

V. CONCLUSIONS

In this paper, a simple analysis was presented to assess the maximal distorion performance of current steering D/A converters in nanometer CMOS technologies. It relates the maximal achievable bandwidth for a certain linearity specification to technological parameters of the used process. This results in a clear trade-off indicating the significance of signal bandwidth rather than raw update rate. By leveraging the high speed of modern CMOS processes to achieve a large degree of oversampling, some of these limitations can be circumvented and the usable bandwidth of the converter can be increased.

A multi-bit delta-sigma modulated D/A converter is presented that achieves 12-bit performance over a signal bandwidth of 100MHz. It is based upon a 5-bit current steering DAC that is operated at 1GS/s. The use of a 5-times oversampling not only allows for the application of a 3rd order noise shaping function, it also reduces the downconversion of distortion products into the band of interest. The converter achieves 13-bit static linearity without calibration by employing current source array averaging and extended overdrive biasing of the current source transistors. A novel multilevel decoder circuit was developed to reduce power consumption to only 11mW. When comparing the converter to current state of the art designs, the proposed techniques achieve an improvement of power efficiency by approximately a factor 5.

REFERENCES

[1] R. V.D. Plassche, CMOS Integrated Analog-to-Digital and Digital-to-Analog Converters, Kluwer Academic Publishers, 2003.

[2] A. van den Bosch; et. al., "SFDR-bandwidth limitations for high speed high resolution current steering CMOS D/A converters," Proc. IEEE Int. Conf. El., Circuits and Systems, pp. 1193-1196, Sept. 1999

[3] Van Der Plas, G.A.M.; et. al., "A 14-bit intrinsic accuracy Q2 random walk CMOS DAC", IEEE Jnl. Solid-State Circuits, vol.34, no.12, pp.1708-1718, Dec 1999

[4] Pelgrom, M.J.M.; et. al., "Matching properties of MOS transistors", IEEE Jnl. Solid-State Circuits, vol.24, no.5, pp. 1433-1439, Oct 1989

[5] Deveugele, J.; et. al. , "A gradient-error and edge-effect tolerant switching scheme for a high-accuracy DAC," Circuits and Systems I: Regular Papers, IEEE Trans. on Circuits and Systems I, vol.51, no.1, pp. 191-195, Jan. 2004

[6] Clara, M.; et. al., "A 1.5V 200MS/s 13b 25mW DAC with Randomized Nested Background Calibration in 0.13u CMOS", IEEE Solid-State Circuits Conference, Dig. of Tech. Papers, 2007, pp.250-251

[7] Doris, K.; et. al., "A 12b 500MS/s DAC with >70dB SFDR up to 120MHz in 0.18um CMOS", IEEE Solid-State Circuits Conference, Dig. of Tech. Papers, 2005, pp.116-117

[8] Deveugele, J.; et. al., "A 10-bit 250-MS/s binary-weighted current-steering DAC", IEEE Jnl. Solid-State Circuits, vol.41, no.2, pp. 320-329, Feb. 2006

Third-Order ΣΔ Modulator with 61-dB SNR and 6-MHz Bandwidth Consuming 6 mW

Edoardo Bonizzoni, Aldo Peña Perez, Franco Maloberti

Department of Electronics
University of Pavia
Via Ferrata, 1 – 27100 Pavia – ITALY
[edoardo.bonizzoni, aldo.perez, franco.maloberti]@unipv.it

Miguel Garcia-Andrade

Departamento de Eléctrica y Computación
Universidad Autónoma de Ciudad Juarez
Ciudad Juarez, Chihuahua – MEXICO
miguel.garcia@uacj.mx

Abstract— **This low-power sigma-delta modulator targets the DVB-H requirements and achieves about 10 bit with 6-MHz signal band and a FoM of 0.59 pJ/conversion. The used scheme is a multi-bit third order modulator that, with suitable topological modification, enables using two op-amps and enjoying a swing reduction at the quantizer input. The area of the circuit, fabricated with a 0.18-μm analog CMOS technology, is 0.32 μm². The nominal supply voltage is 1.8 V and the clock frequency is 96 MHz (OSR = 8). Experimental measurements confirm the behavioral study made accounting for the op-amps limitations.**

I. INTRODUCTION

Sigma-delta modulators are more and more used for portable telecom applications. Well-known advantages are: minimum requests of analog accuracy, good figure of merit (FoM) and medium-high resolution with a relatively low oversampling ratio (OSR). According to this trend it is expected that the challenging band (4-8 MHz) and power consumption (less than 10 mW) requirements for digital video broadcast for handhelds (DVB-H), [1], can be satisfied with power optimized ΣΔ solutions.

This paper uses a third order ΣΔ architecture with a 5-bit quantizer, [2]. Therefore, if the expected resolution is 10 bit, an OSR as low as 8 can be used, as it grants an extra 42-dB SNR. The circuit does not use any DEM because the expected linearity of the resistor-based DACs is sufficient. The key characteristics of the circuit to reduce the power consumption is the use of only two op-amps, [3], and just 18 voltage comparators instead of 31 in the flash while ensuring an overall 5-bit accuracy.

The proposed third-order sigma-delta modulator has been integrated by using a 0.18-μm analog CMOS technology. Experimental results show 9.8 bit of accuracy at 96-MHz clock (6-MHz signal bandwidth). The resolution slightly increases at lower clock and equal SNR because of the reduced spur noise injected by the DAC, especially the one on the second stage. The total power consumption is as low as 6.18 mW with 1.8-V supply voltage, resulting in a remarkable FoM of 0.59 pJ/conversion.

II. LOW POWER STRATEGIES

In order to reduce the power consumption it is necessary to identify power hungry components and to limit their power request and, possibly, their number. Since the power of an op-amp increases in a quadratic way with its bandwidth, it is mandatory to keep at the minimum the clock frequency and, accordingly, the OSR. However, with low OSR, it is necessary to use high-order modulators, that means more op-amps, or to augment the resolution in the quantizer, that means more comparators. The trade-off depends on the power required by the single blocks. For this reason, we made preliminary transistor level simulations with the used technology. We obtained that an op-amp with 600-MHz bandwidth, 300-V/μs slew-rate, and 60 dB of gain consumes 2.3 mW, and a comparator with 5-mV sensitivity clocked at 100 MHz consumes about 60 μW. The numerical result provides the architecture recommendation: use the maximum number of bit in the quantizer and the lowest OSR.

A. Reduction of the number of op-amps.

Fig. 1 shows the chosen basic sigma-delta scheme, [2]. It is a third order modulator with a cascade of three integrators without delay. The coefficients that makes the noise transfer function (NTF) equal to $(1 - z^{-1})^3$ are shown in the diagram.

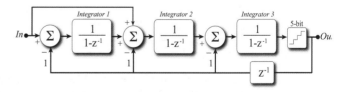

Fig. 1 – Third order sigma-delta modulator with 5-bit quantizer.

Since a large output swing of an op-amp demands for high slew-rate, it is worth using a feed-forward path, as shown in Fig. 1, that limits the swing of first op-amp to almost the quantization noise.

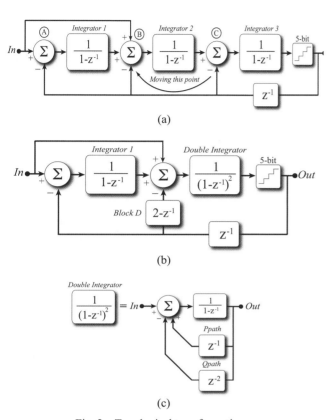

(a)

(b)

(c)

Fig. 2 – Topological transformations.

Starting from the basic architecture we performed a number of topological transformations to eliminate one op-amp. As shown in Fig. 2(a), the feedback at the input of the third op-amp is moved at the input of the second one multiplied by $(1 - z^{-1})$. Therefore, the transfer function of the second block becomes $1/(1 - z^{-1})^2$ and its feedback turns out to be equal to $-1 - 1 + z^{-1} = -(2 - z^{-1})$ (Fig. 2(b)). The double integrator of Fig. 2(b) can be realized with a scheme similar to the one proposed in [3] without the double-sampling. Namely, the sampled-data implementation of the diagram of Fig. 2(c) requires an extra analog delay to achieve the z^{-2} term (referred to as *Qpath*). This is done by a pair of capacitors operated at half the clock frequency.

B. Reduction of the number of comparators.

The power required by the quantizer is mainly due to the flash. Indeed, the power of the DAC is negligible because it is mainly given by the generator of the quantized voltages.

The technique used to reduce the number of comparators in the flash starts by observing that for many bit and a given OSR, there is a good correlation between two successive flash inputs. Therefore, it is more convenient to quantize $(V_O(n) - V_O(n - 1))$ than $V_O(n)$. This leads to the scheme of

Fig. 3, which, indeed, foresees the quantization of $(V_O(n) - V_{O,Q}(n - 1))$, where $V_{O,Q}(n - 1)$ is the result of the previous quantization. The z^{-1} term after the quantizer represents a full clock delay. However, in the real implementation it is divided in two half delays, one used in the flash and the other in the previous block in the modulator.

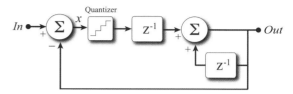

Fig. 3 – 5-bit quantizer with reduced input range.

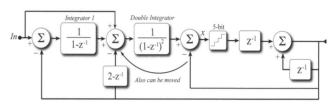

Fig. 4 – Modulator with reduced input range quantizer.

The use of the scheme of Fig. 3 into the modulator gives the diagram of Fig. 4. Since the subtraction at the input of the quantizer would require an additional active block, that branch is moved back multiplied by $(1 - z^{-1})^2$. The result is that the feedback signal at the input of the block referred to as *Double Integrator* becomes

$$-(2 - z^{-1}) - (1 - z^{-1})^2 = -3(1 - z^{-1}) - z^{-2} \qquad (1)$$

leading to the block diagram of Fig. 5.

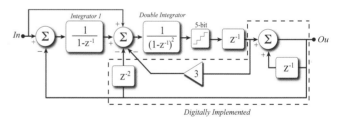

Fig. 5 – Proposed modulator architecture.

The reduction of the swing at the input of the flash determines two benefits: the slew-rate of the second op-amp is relaxed and the number of comparators decreases from 31 to 18 for 5-bit quantization.

The cost that must be paid is due to the coefficient 3 in the block diagram depicted in Fig. 5 that imposes a non favorable feedback factor. This requires a more demanding bandwidth and slew-rate in the op-amp. The problem can be possibly limited by using an attenuation factor in the *Double Integrator* block that is compensated for with a corresponding reduction in the flash quantization interval. The possible need of a higher gain in the comparators is likely demanding a smaller increase of power than the one needed by the op-amp. A study of the problem at the transistor level showed an expected but limited benefit so that, to ensure a more robust solution, we opted for the original approach.

III. CIRCUIT IMPLEMENTATION

The two op-amps used to implement blocks *Integrator 1* and *Double Integrator* have the same scheme but use different bias currents as requested by the slew-rate and bandwidth: they are fully-differential folded cascode amplifiers with switched capacitor common mode feedback. The input capacitor in the first integrator is 80 fF and the feedback capacitors in the *Double Integrator* is 40 fF. The op-amps key features are summarized in Table 1.

TABLE I.   OP-AMPS PERFORMANCE

Feature	First op-amp	Second op-amp
Supply voltage	1.8 V	1.8 V
Bandwidth	580 MHz	890 MHz
Slew-rate	300 V/µs	400 V/µs
Gain	51 dB	48 dB
Power consumption	1.9 mW	2.4 mW

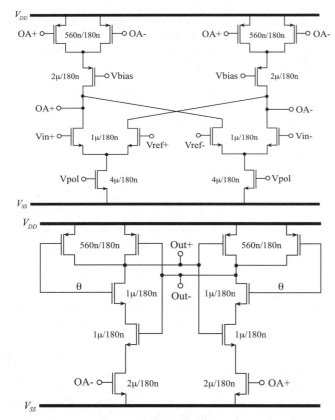

Fig. 6 – Schematic diagram of the used voltage comparator: preamplifier (top) and latch (bottom).

A 5-bit DAC made by an array of capacitors would require using 32 unity elements whose value should be too small to ensure the required matching performance. For this reason, the DACs have been realized by using a resistive divider with 32 equal resistances of 200 Ω. Moreover, in order to avoid interferences and reduce the digital processing, the input of the *Double Integrator* uses two DACs. The used solution implies some additional power consumption, that is, however, about the 15% of the total.

Fig. 6 shows the schematic diagram of the voltage comparators used in the sigma-delta modulator. It is a two-stage fully differential scheme. The first stage (top of the Fig. 6) is a preamplifier with a gain of 9.3 dB and continuous time common mode feedback. The second stage (bottom of Fig. 6) is the regenerative latch. Simulation results show a response time of about 2 ns after the signal clock (Φ) triggering. The bias current of the preamplifier is 25 µA.

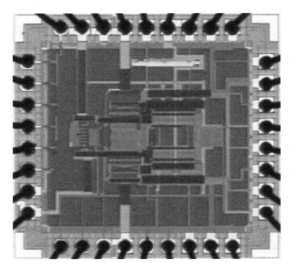

Fig. 7 – Chip microphotograph.

IV. MEASUREMENT RESULTS

The proposed third order sigma-delta modulator has been integrated by using a 0.18-µm, double poly, 5 metal levels CMOS technology. The die, whose microphotograph is shown in Fig. 7, has an active area equal to 0.32 µm². The reference voltages are external to the circuit; no internal buffer is used to enforce the strength of the references. To limit the effects of parasitic inductances due to the bonding, a 40-pins LLP package has been used. The nominal supply voltage is 1.8 V.

The proposed modulator has been measured for different sampling frequencies, f_s. At 96-MHz clock, the measured spectrum is given in Fig. 8. Considering an OSR = 8, the signal bandwidth is 6 MHz and the achieved SNDR is 60.7 dB, corresponding to 9.8 bit. The spectrum shows a second and a third harmonic whose amplitudes are -88 and -77 dB$_{FS}$, respectively. The second harmonic tone is likely due to a small mismatch in the input differential signal.

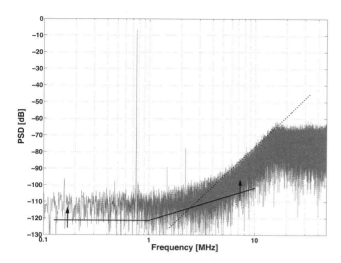

Fig. 8 – Measured output spectrum
(FFT with 65536 points; dashed line: -60 dB/dec slope).

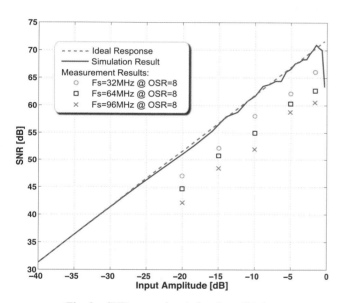

Fig. 9 – SNR versus input signal amplitude.

Fig. 9 compares the measured SNR versus input amplitude for different conditions. The dashed and the solid lines are the ideal and the behavioral simulation results, respectively. For the behavioral study, the used model foresees the real limit caused by the gain, bandwidth and slew-rate of the op-amps given in Table 1, [4]. The experimental data show that when the clock frequency is reduced to 64 MHz and 32 MHz (bandwidth equal to 4 MHz and 2 MHz, respectively), the SNR improves by approximately 3 and 6 dB. The reason of the SNR degradation is ascribed to the noise affecting the DAC signals. Since the circuit does not use internal buffers, the DAC voltage experiences a ringing that settles well within the clock period at f_s = 32 MHz, but has some residual for f_s = 64 MHz and 96 MHz. Computer simulations show that a white noise injected at the input of the first integrator

gives rise to a white spectrum while a white noise injected at the input of the second integrator causes a first order shaped component. This contribution, because of the 3 and the z^{-2} terms and because of the layout of the DACs, is dominant. Its effect is visible in the spectrum of Fig. 8 as it hits the corner of the signal band.

The total measured power with 96-MHz clock is 6.18 mW. Therefore, the achieved FoM is 0.59 pJ/conversion, value that is remarkable if we consider the wide band of the input signal. Table 2 summarizes the performance of the modulator.

TABLE II.   PERFORMANCE SUMMARY

Sampling frequency	96 MHz
Supply voltage	1.8 V
Full scale input signal	600 mV p.p.
Signal bandwidth	6 MHz
Peak SNDR	60.7 dB
Active area	0.32 μm²
Power consumption	6.18 mW
FoM	0.59 pJ/conversion

V.   CONCLUSIONS

In this paper a low-power third order sigma-delta modulator has been presented. The proposed circuit uses only two op-amps and a reduced number of voltage comparators in the quantizer (18 to achieve 5 bit of resolution). Measurement results show 60.7-dB peak SNDR considering 96-MHz clock and a signal bandwidth of 6 MHz. The total measured power consumption is equal to 6.18 mW. This leads to a FoM of 0.59 pJ/conversion.

ACKNOWLEDGMENTS

The authors would like to thank Ivano Galdi for his valuable contribution to this work, National Semiconductor Corporation for chip fabrication, FIRB, Italian National Program #RBAP06L4S5, and CONACyT Mexico project #J45732-Y for partial economical support.

REFERENCES

[1] M. Kornfeld and G. May, "DVB-H and IP Datacast – Broadcast to Handheld Devices", IEEE Trans. on Broadcasting, vol. 53, no. 1, pp. 161-170, March 2007.

[2] S.R. Norsworthy, R. Schreier, and G.C. Temes, "Delta-Sigma Data Converters", IEEE Press, 1996.

[3] J. Koh, Y. Choi, and G. Gomez, "A 66dB DR 1.2V 1.2mW Single-Amplifier Double-Sampling 2nd-order DS ADC for WCDMA in 90nm CMOS", IEEE International Solid-State Circuits Conference Dig. Tech. Pap., pp. 170-171, Feb. 2005.

[4] P. Malcovati, S. Brigati, F. Francesconi, F. Maloberti, P. Cusinato, and A. Baschirotto, "Behavioral Modeling of Switched-Capacitor Sigma-Delta Modulators", IEEE Trans. on Circuits and Systems – I: Fundamental Theory and Applications, vol. 50, no. 3, pp. 352-364, March 2003.

Parallel Double Error Correcting Code Design to Mitigate Multi-Bit Upsets in SRAMs

Riaz Naseer and Jeff Draper
Information Sciences Institute
University of Southern California
Marina del Rey, CA 90292
{naseer, draper}@isi.edu

Abstract□ **The range of SRAM multi-bit upsets (MBU) in sub-100nm technologies is characterized using irradiation tests on two prototype ICs, developed in 90nm commercial processes. Results reveal that MBU, as large as 13-bit, can occur in these technologies, limiting the efficacy of conventional SEC-DED error-correcting codes (ECC). A double-error correcting (DEC) ECC implementation technique suitable for SRAM applications is presented. Results show that this DEC scheme reduces errors by 98.5% compared to only 44% reduction by conventional SEC-DED ECC.**

I. Introduction

SRAM reliability faces serious challenges from radiation-induced soft errors in sub-100nm technologies [1]. SRAM cells are designed with minimum geometry devices to increase density and performance; however, a consequence is that the critical charge (Q_{crit}) that can upset such cells has become very small, potentially increasing the upset frequency. Therefore, it has become conventional to protect memories with the application of error correcting codes (ECC) such as single-error-correcting (SEC) Hamming code, single-error-correcting-double-error-detecting (SEC-DED) extended-Hamming, or SEC-DED Hsiao codes [2][3][4]. With increasing multi-bit upset (MBU) trends [5][6], conventional single-bit correcting ECC may not be sufficient to meet reliability goals. The problem is further exacerbated for space electronics where galactic cosmic rays carry heavy-ions with much higher linear energy transfer (LET) characteristics compared to terrestrial radiation sources.

This work presents heavy-ion induced upset results for two prototype SRAM ICs designed in two characteristic 90nm processes revealing the extent of MBU in these processes. These results show that the multi-bit upsets in these processes can be as large as 13-bits, implying that current ECC architectures which use column interleaving by 2 or 4 with conventional SEC/SEC-DED codes ([7][8]) are not sufficient to mitigate the expected soft errors. This deficiency motivates the exploration of more powerful ECC implementations, such as double error correcting (DEC) BCH (Bose-Chaudhuri-Hocquenghem) codes. Commonly employed iterative BCH decoding schemes such as Berlekamp-Massey, Euclidian and Minimum Weight Decoding algorithms require a multi-cycle decoding latency [9][10][11], which is not tolerable for embedded memories. Therefore, a new parallel implementation approach is presented for DEC BCH codes. This parallel approach is suitable for SRAM applications where data is accessed in words on every transaction. In addition, a design space for various ECC techniques has been explored by implementing SEC Hamming, SEC-DED Hsiao, DEC and DEC-TED BCH codes using IBM's 90nm standard cell ASIC technology. The implementation results demonstrate the practicality of the proposed decoding implementation approach and also offer insights for various trade-offs for selecting soft error mitigation techniques. Accelerated irradiation test results on prototype SRAM ICs demonstrate the relative reliability efficiency of SEC-DED and DEC ECC techniques.

II. Heavy-ion-induced Upsets

This section presents heavy-ion-induced soft error results for two SRAM ICs designed using commercial 90nm processes. One IC has been designed in a low-power process (henceforth labeled LP), while the other IC has been designed in a standard high-performance process (labeled SF), employing a foundry provided 6T SRAM cell designed for each process. To characterize the intrinsic radiation response of the processes, each IC contains a *baseline* SRAM module of 64-kbits without ECC protection and any hardening applied on peripheral logic. In addition, each IC also contains a *hardened* module that applies ECC on the memory array to mitigate upsets and triple-modular redundancy (TMR) on peripheral logic to guard against single-event transients. The size of the hardened array increases in proportion to the redundancy required by the applied ECC scheme in each IC. Both SRAMs have been extensively tested using a 10MeV cocktail beam at the Lawrence Berkeley National Laboratories (LBNL) 88-inch cyclotron. Fig. 1 shows the distribution of raw upsets for LP and SF SRAMs versus ion LET value, before any ECC correction is applied.

This work was supported by the Defense Advanced Research Projects Agency (DARPA) Microsystems Technology Office under award No.: N66001-04-1-8914. Any opinions, findings, and conclusions or recommendations expressed in this work are those of the authors and do not necessarily reflect the views of DARPA/MTO or the U.S. Government.

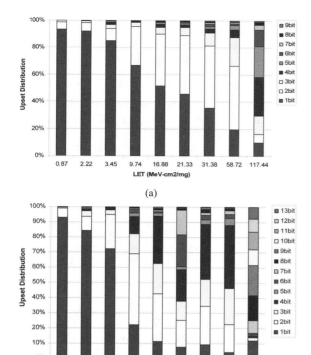

(a)

(b)

Figure 1.   Single- and Multi- Bit Upset Distributions versus Effective
LET (a) LP SRAM (b) SF SRAM

At onset, single-bit upsets (SBU) dominate the total soft error distribution; however MBU quickly become the main contributor as the LET increases. A wide difference in MBU distribution can be noted for the two ICs, in addition to observing that the largest MBU is 9 bits for LP versus 13 bits for SF. The difference in LP and SF upset distributions can be understood by investigating the 6T SRAM cell critical charge in each process. Our prior simulations show that the Q_{crit} of the LP cell is slightly higher than the SF (1.58fC vs. 1.23fC), due to variations in cell design and nominal operating voltages (1.2V and 1V, respectively). These MBU distributions suggest that much larger column interleaving factors must be implemented if only the conventional single error correcting ECC is employed. However, the aspect ratio of memory array and column multiplexer design may potentially restrict the interleaving factor to 8 or 16. Moreover, if the increasing MBU trend continues with technology scaling as expected, it will become necessary to utilize more powerful codes such as double error correcting ECC.

III.   PARALLEL IMPLEMENTATION APPROACH FOR BCH CODES

Having projected increasing MBU trends in SRAMs, it is important to begin exploring stronger ECC schemes. Though such schemes have been explored in communication applications, some re-design is necessary to make them suitable for memory protection. Particularly, a pure combinational logic approach has been adopted to implement double error correcting BCH codes in order to overcome the multi-cycle decoding latency of conventional BCH decoders.

This approach is constructed on a standard array based syndrome decoding procedure, where a set of syndromes is pre-computed corresponding to correctable error patterns. The error correction bits are then set according to a Boolean function mapping of syndrome patterns. This allows a Boolean function implementation using a standard cell ASIC design methodology.

For the following, recall from coding theory that a binary (n, k) linear block code is a k-dimensional subspace of a binary n-dimensional vector space. Thus, an n-bit codeword contains k-bits of data and r (= n − k) check bits. An r x n parity check matrix H, or alternatively k x n generator matrix G, is used to describe the code [9]. Due to the cyclic property of BCH codes, a systematic generator matrix of the form $G_{k,n}$ = [$I_{k,k}$ | $P_{k,r}$] can be generated by combining two sub-matrices. $I_{k,k}$ is an identity matrix of dimension k, and $P_{k,r}$ is a parity sub-matrix consisting of the coefficients of k parity polynomials of degree r. The k parity polynomials can be obtained from a polynomial division involving the generator polynomial g(x) of the BCH code as:

$$P_i = remainder\left(X^{n-k+i} / g(x)\right) \bmod 2 \qquad i = 0,1,...k-1 \qquad (1)$$

A.   DEC Encoder

The encoding process converts a data word (row vector $\underline{b}$) into a codeword (row vector $\underline{c}$) by multiplying it with the generator matrix G of the code using modulo-2 arithmetic, i.e., $\underline{c} = \underline{b} * G$. With systematic generator matrix G, data bits are passed as-is in the encoding process and only the check bits need to be computed. The computation of check bits is accomplished through XOR trees, e.g. an encoder is shown in Fig. 2 for DEC (26, 16). The inputs to each XOR tree are data bits chosen according to non-zero entries in respective columns of the parity sub-matrix which is part of the G matrix. The depth of the XOR tree has an upper bound of $\log_2(k)$ if implemented using 2-input XOR gates.

B.   DEC-TED Encoder

A DEC-TED encoder is similar to a DEC encoder except that an additional overall parity bit is added. Since this is an overall parity bit covering the data as well as check bits, it can only be computed after all other check bits have been computed. Therefore, this bit becomes the critical path in a DEC-TED encoder and can considerably increase the latency of the encoder.

C.   DEC Decoder

For decoding purposes, a parity check matrix H, of the

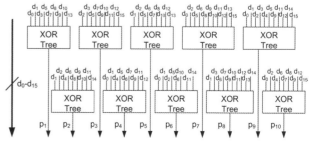

Figure 2.   Encoder Circuit for DEC (26, 16)

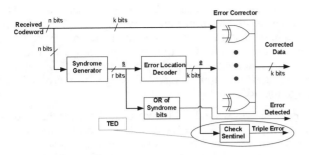

Figure 3. Block Diagram of BCH Decoder

form: $H_{r,n} = [P^t_{r,k} | I_{r,r}]$, is required where P^t is the transpose of the parity sub-matrix in systematic G. The input to the decoder is the read codeword vector $\underline{v}$ which may contain errors in data or check bit locations. A block diagram of the decoder is shown in Fig. 3 (ignore the TED portion for now) containing three main parts: 1) Syndrome Generator, 2) Error Location Decoder and 3) Error Corrector. The circuit for the syndrome generator is similar to the encoder circuit. Essentially, it re-computes the check bits and compares those with the received check bits. In algebraic form, this process translates to $\underline{s} = H * \underline{v}^t$; where $\underline{v}^t$ is the transpose of the read codeword vector $\underline{v}$ and $\underline{s}$ is the syndrome vector. A non-zero syndrome implies the presence of errors and is checked by ORing the syndrome bits to flag error detection. The erroneous bit positions are identified by feeding the syndrome into an error location decoder. The error location decoder circuit is implemented using combinational logic that maps the respective pair of syndromes and correctable error patterns. This mapping is pre-computed by multiplying all correctable error patterns with the parity check matrix H. For binary vectors, an erroneous bit is corrected merely by complementing it; therefore, the error corrector circuit is simply a stack of XOR gates.

D. DEC-TED Decoder

The decoder for a DEC-TED code is similar to the decoder for DEC with modifications necessary to handle triple-bit error detection, as shown in Fig. 3. In particular, an all-0 column and an all-1 row are added to the DEC H matrix to obtain the parity check matrix for DEC-TED. This increases the syndrome vector by 1-bit, doubling the number of syndromes. The error location decoder then maps the syndromes for 3-bit errors to a sentinel pattern. A simple sentinel value of the least three bits being set in the error pattern $\underline{e}$ can be ANDed to flag triple error detection.

IV. RESULTS AND DISCUSSION

For demonstrating the practicality of the parallel implementation approach, DEC and DEC-TED encoder and decoder circuits have been implemented for typical memory word sizes of 16, 32 and 64 bits. For analyzing trade-offs with conventionally used ECC schemes, SEC and SEC-DED codes have also been implemented. Since the Hsiao code is an optimal SEC-DED code [3], we have included only the Hsiao code for SEC-DED ECC for our comparisons. Synopsys Design Compiler (DC) has been used for synthesizing all encoder and decoder circuits targeted to an IBM 90nm standard cell library. Table I shows the latency and area results for encoder circuits while Table II shows the latency and area results for decoder circuits.

A major inference from the synthesis results is that the decoding latency for the DEC codes is reasonably small, and it is much better compared to multi-cycle shift register based decoders used in communication systems [9][10][11]. Therefore, this parallel implementation of DEC codes makes it feasible for memory applications.

As expected, the overall parity bit results in increasing the latency penalty of the DEC-TED encoder by 80% to 85% as compared to the DEC encoder. Therefore, DEC is preferred wherever possible as compared to DEC-TED. Looking at the decoder results, we see that the latency of SEC and Hsiao SEC-DED decoders is identical. On the other hand, the decoding latency for DEC and DEC-TED varies significantly, between 21% to 36% for 16 and 64 bit decoders respectively. The latency increases between DEC and DEC-TED because the corresponding syndrome and correctable & detectable error patterns are doubled by adding the overall parity bit. For DEC-TED, the computed overall parity cannot simply be compared with the received overall parity to infer triple bit error detection since the computed overall parity will be the same for single- and triple-bit errors, but single-bit errors are correctable while triple-bit errors are not. In contrast, in the Hsiao SEC-DED case, the number of syndromes and correctable error pattern pairs remains the same as for SEC. If

TABLE I ECC ENCODER LATENCY AND AREA RESULTS

Data Width	Ham. SEC		Hsiao SEC-DED		DEC		DEC-TED	
	Latency (ns)	Area (μm^2)	Latency (ns)	Area (μm^2)	Latency (ns)	Area (μm^2)	Latency (ns)	Area (μm^2)
16	0.4	296	0.4	291	0.5	496	0.9	786
32	0.5	598	0.5	605	0.6	1250	1.1	1424
64	0.65	1302	0.7	1168	0.7	2335	1.3	2546

TABLE II ECC DECODER LATENCY AND AREA RESULTS

Data Width	Ham. SEC		Hsiao SEC-DED		DEC		DEC-TED	
	Latency (ns)	Area (μm^2)	Latency (ns)	Area (μm^2)	Latency (ns)	Area (μm^2)	Latency (ns)	Area (μm^2)
16	0.9	576	0.9	935	1.4	4288	1.7	5432
32	1.1	1303	1.1	1376	1.8	11735	2.2	13757
64	1.3	2412	1.3	2681	2.2	37279	3	42976

TABLE III REDUNDANCY FOR ECC

	SEC	DEC
Data bits	Check bits	Check bits
16	5	10
32	6	12
64	7	14
128	8	16

TABLE IV ACCELERATED TEST RESULTS

	LP IC-SEC-DED	SF IC-DEC
Errors Observed before ECC	13,004	12,117
Errors Observed after ECC	7,305	195

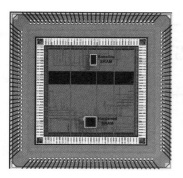

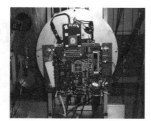

(b) SRAM IC mounted on test board for irradiation

Figure 4. (a) SF IC layout

we compare the latency penalty between Hsiao SEC-DED and DEC-TED, it is almost double both for encoder and decoder. However, in comparing SEC-DED to DEC, the percentage decoder latency penalty varies by 55% to 69% for different block sizes, implying again that DEC is strongly preferred over DEC-TED unless there is strong evidence that the target application requires triple-error detection.

Another important implication can be made from the almost identical latencies of the Hsiao SEC-DED and DEC encoders. Since the syndrome generator circuit is similar to the encoder circuit, error detection can be accomplished with quite similar latency for both SEC-DED and DEC codes. The ECC implementation architecture can benefit remarkably from this observation. In particular, as most memory accesses would be error-free, data can be passed for processing to the next stage without the full decoder delay. In erroneous cases, when a non-zero syndrome is detected, only then is the full decoder latency needed to correct the errors. For these cases only, the next processing stage can be stalled for a cycle or two depending on the speed of the processing stage, minimizing the overall performance penalty.

The spread of the area results for the encoder and decoder circuits is quite large for various ECC schemes, but the overall area for each is very small compared to typical ASIC sizes. Thus, these ECC encoders and decoders can be implemented without a significant area impact. Notice that the extra redundancy required within the memory array for a particular code is a function of the error detection and correction capability of that code and block size. Table III lists the redundancy requirements for SEC and DEC codes for typical memory word sizes, showing that DEC requires twice as many check bits as SEC ECC.

For evaluating the relative reliability efficiency of the ECC techniques, we implemented the Hsiao SEC-DED code on the LP prototype SRAM IC and the DEC code on the SF IC following our parallel decoding approach. Fig. 4 (a) shows the layout of the SF IC embedded in the chip micrograph, and Fig. 4(b) shows the SRAM chip mounted on the tester board for irradiation. As can be seen from the layout, the hardened array is larger compared to the baseline array due to extra redundancy required for the DEC BCH code. The accelerated heavy-ion irradiation testing, performed on the prototype SRAM ICs according to a JEDEC standard, showed that the SEC-DED code reduced the error count only by 44%. On the other hand, the implemented DEC code reduced the error count by more than 98%, as shown in Table IV. This increased error coverage of DEC ECC easily justifies its associated implementation cost for many applications.

V. CONCLUSION

Heavy-ion-induced soft error results for SRAM ICs designed in two characteristic 90nm processes have been presented. The upset distributions exhibit that MBU are the dominating contributor to overall soft error rate, and these MBU can range as large as 9-bits for LP and 13-bits for SF necessitating the usage of more powerful ECC schemes. Implementations of DEC and DEC-TED ECC using a parallel implementation approach in 90nm technology demonstrate that these codes can effectively be applied for SRAM applications. Synthesis results for different ECC circuits reveal various trade-offs and provide guidelines for choosing a particular solution depending on the application requirements. Test results on prototype SRAM ICs demonstrate that DEC reduces the error count by more than 98% compared to only 44% for SEC-DED ECC.

ACKNOWLEDGMENT

The authors would like to thank Michael Bajura and Younes Boulghassoul for design collaboration and collecting the test results. The authors also thank Jeff Sondeen for physical design of the ICs and Scott Stansberry for the tester board design.

REFERENCES

[1] R.C. Baumann, "Radiation-induced soft errors in advanced semiconductor technologies," IEEE Trans. Device Mater. Reliab., vol. 5, no. 3, pp. 305–316, Sep. 2005.

[2] R.W. Hamming, "Error Correcting and Error Detecting Codes", Bell Sys. Tech. Journal, Vol 29, pp. 147-160, April 1950

[3] M. Y. Hsiao, "A Class of Optimal Minimum Odd-weight-column SEC-DED Codes", IBM Journal of R & D Vol. 14, July 1970, pp. 395-401

[4] C.W. Slayman, "Cache and memory error detection, correction, and reduction techniques for terrestrial servers and workstations", Device & Materials Reliability, IEEE Trans. on Vol. 5, Sept. 2005 pp. 397 – 404

[5] D. Radaelli, H. Puchner, S. Wong, S. Daniel, "Investigation of multi-bit upsets in a 150 nm technology SRAM device", IEEE Trans. On Nucl. Sci. Vol. 52, Issue 6, pp. 2433- 2437, Dec 2005

[6] D. Giot, P. Roche, G. Gasiot, R. Harboe-Sorensen, "Multiple-Bit Upset Analysis in 90 nm SRAMs: Heavy Ions Testing and 3D Simulations", IEEE Trans. Nucl. Sci., Vol. 54, Aug. 2007 pp.904 – 911

[7] K. Osada, Y. Saitoh, E. Ibe, K. Ishibashi, "16.7fA/cell Tunnel-Leakage-Suppressed 16Mb SRAM for Handling Cosmic-Ray-Induced Multi-Errors", ISSCC Dig. Tech. Papers, pp. 302-303, Feb. 2003

[8] T. Suzuki et al, "0.3 to 1.5V Embedded SRAM with Device-Fluctuation-Tolerant Access-Control and Cosmic-Ray-Immune Hidden ECC Scheme", ISSCC Dig. Tech. Papers, pp. 484-612, Feb. 2005

[9] S. Lin, D. J. Costello, "Error Control Coding: Fundamental and Applications", Prentice-Hall, 1983

[10] Shyue-Win Wei, Che-Ho Wei, "High-speed hardware decoder for double-error-correcting binary BCH codes", Communications, Speech and Vision, IEE Proceedings Jun 1989 Vol. 136, Issue 3, pp. 227- 231

[11] W.M. El-Medany, C.G. Harrison, P.G. Farrel, and C.J. Hardy, "VHDL Implementation of a BCH Minimum Weight Decoder for Double Error", Radio Science Conf., Proc. of the 18th 2001 Vol. 2, pp. 361-368

A Multiword Based High Speed ECC Scheme for Low-voltage Embedded SRAMs

Shah Jahinuzzaman, Tahseen Shakir, Sumanjit Lubana, Jaspal Singh Shah, and Manoj Sachdev

Department of Electrical & Computer Engineering
University of Waterloo
Waterloo, ON, N2L 3G1, Canada
E-mail: {smjahinu, msachdev}@uwaterloo.ca

Abstract—This paper presents a multiword based error correction code (MECC) scheme to mitigate SEUs in low-voltage SRAMs. MECC combines four 32 bit data words to form a composite 128 bit ECC word and uses optimized transmission-gate XOR logic, thus significantly reducing check-bit overhead and error correction time, respectively. Use of composite word warrants a unique write operation where MECC updates check-bits by simultaneously writing one data word and reading the other three data words. Two composite words are interleaved in a row to tackle multi-bit SEU. In addition, the supply voltage of the SRAM is reduced to save leakage and active power. A 64kb SRAM with MECC implemented in 90nm CMOS technology consumes 154 µW leakage power and 375 µW active power at 0.6 V and 100 MHz, showing improved area and speed-power efficiency than conventional single-word ECC and existing multiword ECC schemes.

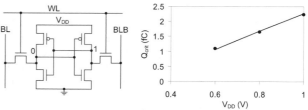

Figure 1.   6T SRAM cell and variation in critical charge with V_{DD}.

I. INTRODUCTION

Due to reduced signal charge and noise margin, nanoscale integrated circuits experience more particle-induced single event upset (SEU) than ever before [1],[2]. Primarily, high energy neutrons from cosmic radiation and alpha particles from packaging materials cause the upset. These particles directly or indirectly generate additional charge in silicon and corrupt the signal charge [3]. Since they usually do not damage the device, SEU is often referred to as soft error. However, the rate of system malfunction can be much higher due to SEU than all hard failure mechanisms combined. Accordingly, ensuring SEU tolerance of integrated circuits has become critical. This is particularly true for static random access memory (SRAM), which occupies 70% die area of system-on-chips (SoC) and microprocessors.

The SEU vulnerability of SRAMs is accentuated by process variations [4]. Process variations change the SRAM cell critical charge, Q_{crit}, which is the minimum charge required to cause a SEU. If Q_{crit} in the fabricated SRAM population decreases, the SEU rate exponentially increases [5]. The decrease in Q_{crit} is often intentional. Being the largest building block of SoC, SRAM dominates the total leakage power of the chip. As a result, different leakage reduction techniques, such as, supply voltage scaling, gated grounding,

etc., are employed to un-accessed SRAM blocks [6], [7]. These techniques decrease the voltage difference between SRAM logic states and thus reduce Q_{crit}, making SRAM more vulnerable to SEU (see Figure 1). This necessitates employing error protection technique in order to ensure SEU robustness of the SRAM and hence the SoC.

Typically, architecture level technique like error correcting code (ECC) is used to tackle SEUs in SRAMs. While circuit level techniques, such as cell hardening [8], can also be used, they incur significantly higher (30-100%) area overhead. In addition, two factors make ECC more attractive. First, the definition of what an error is, in fact, lies at the architecture level. An upset cell does not cause any problem if it is written before being read. Second, the error may result from physical weakness of the cell (e.g., high leakage). In that case, circuit hardening cannot help. Furthermore, ECC can improve the yield of the SRAM. However, the cost associated with ECC can be significant. For example, a Single Error Correction Double Error Detection (SECDED) code requires storing 7 check-bits for a 32bit data word, thus increasing memory array size by 22% [9]. This increase manifests in higher cost coupled with larger leakage and active power dissipation. In addition, ECC operates on read data path, causing read delay, which can be as large as four clock cycles [10].

In this paper, we present a high speed multiword based ECC (MECC) scheme for low-voltage embedded SRAMs. The scheme incurs minimal delay penalty while consuming smaller area and lower power than conventional single-word ECC scheme and recently reported multiword schemes [10], [11]. While MECC has some similarities with the "alternate ECC" architecture reported in [11], MECC has a number of

This work was financially supported by Gennum Corporation, Burlington, ON and NSERC, Canada.

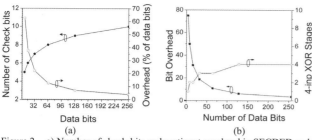

(a)   (b)

Figure 2. a) Number of check-bits and pertinent overhead in SECDED code and b) 4-input XOR stages in check-bit generator as a function of data bits.

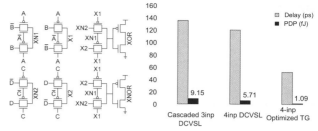

Figure 3. Optimized 4-input TG XOR gate and its power-delay comparison.

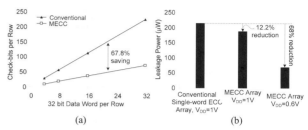

(a)   (b)

Figure 4. a) Check-bits for MECC and conventional ECC as a function of data words per row, and b) Array leakage power saving in MECC.

key differences. First, MECC uses 9 check-bits instead of 10 check-bits to perform error correction on a 128 bit *composite word* while providing the same error protection. The composite word consists of multiple 32 bit data words instead of 16 bit words. Second, MECC uses a transmission-gate XOR logic optimized for 4-inputs, thus significantly reducing read delay and power penalty. In addition, the scheme uses high threshold voltage (high-V_t) transistors in memory array and lower supply voltage in order to reduce leakage current. The paper is organized as follows. Section II provides the basics of an ECC scheme. Section III presents the proposed MECC scheme. Section IV demonstrates a 0.6V 64kb SRAM implemented with MECC. Section V presents measurement results. Finally, Section VI draws the conclusion.

II. ECC CIRCUIT FOR SRAMs

Typically, an ECC circuit consists of check-bit memory, check-bit generator, syndrome decoder, and error corrector. Check-bits store the information for any given data word so that in case of a bit error, the erroneous bit can be detected and corrected. The check-bits are generated by XOR operation of the bits of a data word. In a write operation to the SRAM, when data are written into the data memory, check-bits are also generated and written into the check-bit memory. In a read operation, both data-bits and check-bits are read out from corresponding memories. Check-bits are regenerated and XORed with the stored check-bits to generate syndrome bits. If there is no bit error, syndrome bits are all zero. Otherwise, syndrome bits represent erroneous data bit's location, which is decoded and corrected.

The number of check-bits required in ECC is a function of the data word size and the number of correctable errors. For SECDED code, the number of check-bits, k, is given by $2^{k-1} \geq n + k$, where n is the number of bits in the data word [9]. Figure 2a shows the number of check-bits and pertinent overhead for SECDED code as a function of data word size. Clearly, larger the word size, smaller the overhead.

III. HIGH SPEED MECC SCHEME

Since the overhead for check-bits decreases with increasing word size, it is preferable to use larger data words. However, ECC operation on larger data word increases logic complexity. In order to take the advantage of larger data word and reduce pertinent implementation complexities, we propose the MECC scheme. As seen in Figure 2a, overhead reduction beyond 128 bits of data is not appreciable. Accordingly, we choose word size of 128 bits for ECC operation. Since typical

data word size is less than 128bits, we combine multiple data words to get a composite 128 bit word. In particular, we consider 32 bit data word so that the composite word consists of four such words. In order to limit the complexity of ECC logic, we choose SECDED code, which is based on single error correctable Hamming code. In addition, we use 4-input XOR gates in the ECC logic to reduce the number of stages and hence the delay in the check-bit generator. Check-bit generator is a vital block on the critical path. Figure 2b shows the number of stages required to implement check-bit generator using 4-input XOR gate. As evident from the figure, only one additional stage is required if word size for ECC increases from 32 bits to 128 bits. Therefore, using 128 bit composite word does not incur significant delay penalty. Furthermore, in order to minimize the delay, we use a 4-input-optimized transmission gate (TG) XOR gate, which exhibits smaller delay and power-delay-product (PDP) compared to other 4-input XOR gates like DCVSL (see Figure 3).

Each 128bit composite word, which consists of four 32 bit data word, needs 9 check bits according to the SECDED code. On the other hand, in a conventional scheme, each of the 32 bit data words would require 7 check-bits, implying 28 check bits for four data words. Thus, the MECC scheme reduces the number of check-bits by 67.8% as shown in Figure 4a for varying number of 32 bit data word per row. This saving directly translates into significant amount of area and power savings. Less check-bits mean smaller array, i.e., shorter word lines (WLs) and lower number of transistors. Shorter WL reduces decoder active power while less transistors decrease the leakage power. In fact, MECC reduces array leakage by 12.2% as shown in Figure 4b. In order to decrease the leakage power further, we reduce the supply voltage (V_{DD}) of the SRAM array and the peripheral circuits. Lower V_{DD} significantly reduces leakage current by reducing i) the drain-induced barrier lowering (DIBL) effect on OFF transistors and ii) gate tunneling of ON transistors. The total array leakage saving by using MECC is thus 68% (see Figure 4b).

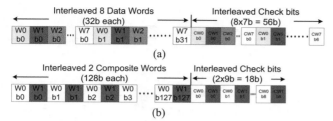

(a)

(b)

Figure 5. Bit arrangement in a row of a) conventional ECC and b) MECC.

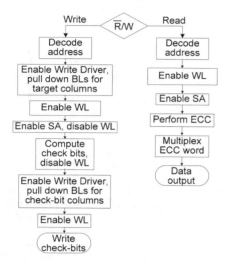

Figure 6. Flow chart of read and write operations in MECC scheme.

One limitation of MECC scheme is that it can correct only one error and detect two errors in the 128 bit composite word. However, cosmic radiation at the ground level can induce multiple bit errors [11]. In order to deal with this problem, we interleave two composite words in a row as shown in Figure 5. As a result, two adjacent bit errors will belong to two different composite words and will easily be corrected. In case of three bit errors in a row, two of the errors will belong to one composite word and the third error to the other composite word. MECC will then detect (double error) and correct (single error) these errors. In case of three bit errors in a column, each of the errors will belong to a different composite word and will be corrected. However, the probability of occurring three bit errors is extremely low (0.1%) compared to a single bit error.

The use of multiple words in ECC requires special read and write operations. In a read operation, one of the two composite words on the selected row is read, passed through the ECC logic, and multiplexed (4-to-1) to provide the requested 32 bit data as shown in the flow chart in Figure 6. In contrast, the write operation is a combination of both read and write functions. In a write cycle, the selected WL is raised twice - *first* to write into target data word and simultaneously read from other three data words in the same composite word, and *second* to write the updated check-bits that are computed based on the new composite word. To reduce power in this case, row decoder decodes the row once; however, WL is activated by a control signal (WLE), which is ANDed with the outputs of the row decoder.

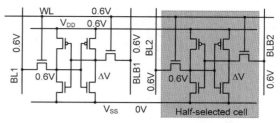

Figure 7. Two adjacent cells in a row: one belongs to selected or read composite word while the other belongs to half-slected composite word.

IV. A LOW-VOLTAGE 64 KB SRAM WITH MECC

We make a 256x256 bits data array by designing a high-V_t (~0.46V) memory cell that balances area and speed tradeoffs in a commercial 90nm process. The row decoder, write drivers, and sense amplifiers (differential input, latch type) are optimized based on power and performance tradeoffs. All control signals are generated from the clock signal using static delay elements. The ECC block is designed to work on 128 bit composite word using 9 check-bits: 8 bits to correct a single bit error (SBE) while the 9th bit to detect a double bit error (DBE). The syndrome decoder is, therefore, a 8-to-137 decoder, which decodes the erroneous bit location. Thus, the ECC block uses one less bit compared to [11] for the same error protection. In order to test the functionality of the ECC block, four set/reset switches are placed before SA latches. These switches enable changing read bit values (1↔0) for locations 1, 95, and 96 in the composite word and 1 in the check-bits. The operating voltage of the SRAM is kept 0.6V. Below 0.6V, the timing block (TB) fails to generate required timing signals. In fact, this constraint stems from the fact that TB is shared with another on-chip low-power SRAM array.

In a read operation, depending on the address input, one of the two composite words in the selected row is read and ECC is performed. If no error is found in ECC operation, the read word is multiplexed to provide 32 bit data word. If an error (two errors) is found, ECC corrects (detects) the error and signals SBE (DBE). Data on the other composite word in the same row, which we refer as *half-selected* composite word, remain stable as the gate-to-source voltage of access transistors cannot go below V_t. In other words, the 'logic 0' voltage, ΔV, of a half-selected cell (see Figure 7) is clamped at (0.6-V_t) V, thus retaining the data. In a write operation, WLE signal activates the WL of the decoded row twice. In the first WL activation, new data is written into the target 32 bit word. At the same time the sense amplifier is enabled to read the new data and the other three words in the composite word. Then ECC generates new check-bits, which replace stored check-bits in the second WL activation. Figure 8a shows the micrograph and the block diagram of the MECC chip.

V. MEASUREMENT RESULTS AND PERFORMANCE ANALYSIS

Due to multiword ECC operation, the MECC scheme reduces the number of check-bits by 67.8%, which means 58,368 less transistors than conventional single-word ECC for a 64 kb array. MECC with 0.6V V_{DD} exhibits 1.62nA cell leakage (simulated, typical process). Less cell leakage has been reported in [11], however, for 130nm technology with a

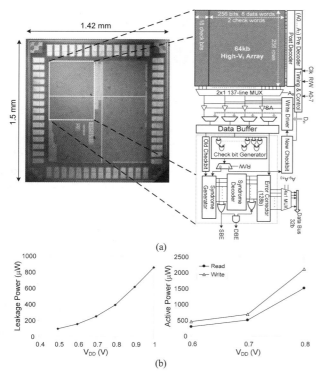

1.42 mm

1.5 mm

256 bits, 8 data words
2 check words

18 check bits

64kb
High-V, Array

256 (Rows)

(A0...A7) Pre Decoder Post Decoder Timing & Control

Clk R/W A0-7

2x1 137-line MUX

SA

Write Driver

New Checkbit

D_in

Data Buffer

Old Checkbit Check bit Generator

R/W

Ag-A10

Syndrome Generator

Syndrome Decoder

Error Corrector (128b)

4x1 MUX

Data Bus 32b

SBE   DBE

(a)

(b)

Figure 8. a) Micrograph and block diagram of the MECC chip and b) measured leakage and active power of the chip.

TABLE I.   MEASURED MECC CHIP PERFORMANCE AND COMPARISON

	This work	**Ref. [11]**	**Ref. [10]**
Technology	90 nm	130 nm	130 nm
Array size, word size	64 Kb, 32 b	16 Mb, 16 b	4 Mb
ECC-word, check-bit	128 b, 9 b	128 b, 10 b	64 b, 8 b
Check-bit overhead	7%	7.8%	12.5%
Data latency for SBE	10 ns	27 ns	2.86 ns
Average power	0.375 mW @ 0.6 V, 100 MHz	19 mW @ 1.5V & 3.3V, 14.3 MHz	2.6 W @ 1.3V,1.4GHz
Average energy	3.75 pJ	1330 pJ	1857 pJ
Avg. energy per bit	0.06 fJ	0.08 fJ	0.44 fJ

area and 68% array leakage savings than a conventional single word ECC are achieved. In addition, a 0.6V 64kb macro implemented in 90nm CMOS with the proposed ECC scheme exhibits better speed and energy performance than existing multiword ECC schemes. Thus, the proposed scheme manifests itself as a faster and cost-effective alternative to existing schemes for SEU mitigation in low-voltage SRAMs.

ACKNOWLEDGMENT

The authors are thankful to Dr. M. Sharifkhani for numerous stimulating discussions and to Pierce Chuang for help in PCB design and testing.

variety of control voltages (0.5V V_{GND}; 1V V_{BL}, 1.5V internal, 3.3V external). The measured chip leakage power and active (read and write) power are shown in Figure 8b. The leakage power saving is 82% for reducing V_{DD} from 1V to 0.6V. The read and write power saving is also significant. At 0.6V the read and write powers are 295 μW and 454 μW, respectively, meaning an average active power consumption of 375 μW. Since the chip operates at 100 MHz, the active energy consumption is 3.75 pJ. Table I shows a comparison of the MECC scheme with [10] and [11], which are multiword ECC schemes working on 64 bits and 128 bits, respectively. Since these schemes have different array sizes, we convert their energy consumptions into bit level. Accordingly, we find that MECC has 86% less energy consumption and 5.5% less check-bit overhead than [10]. Conversely, MECC has similar area overhead but better energy efficiency than [11]. However, [11] is much slower and requires a number of voltage references, requiring on-chip voltage converters and additional timing and control signals.

The data latency of MECC with an SBE inserted by one set/reset switch is 10 ns, which is 2.7 times smaller than the latency reported in [11] and larger than the latency reported in [10]. However, MECC is much energy efficient than [10].

VI. CONCLUSION

We have presented a multiword based ECC scheme that is capable of handling multiple bit SEUs in SRAMs. The scheme combines four 32 bit data words to perform ECC on a 128 bit composite word and reduces the supply voltage to minimize leakage and active power consumption. Thus, 67% check-bit

REFERENCES

[1] Y. S. Dhillon, A. U. Diril, A. Chatterjee, and A. D. Singh, "Analysis and optimization of nanometer CMOS circuits for soft-error tolerance," *IEEE Trans. Very Large Scale Integr. (VLSI) Syst.*, vol. 14, no. 5, pp. 514-524, May 2006.

[2] T. Granlund, B. Granbom, and N. Olsson, "Soft error rate increase for new generations of SRAMs," *IEEE Trans. Nucl. Sci.*, vol. 50, no. 6, pp. 2065–2068, Dec. 2003.

[3] P. E. Dodd and L. W. Massengill, "Basic mechanisms and modeling of single-event upset in digital microelectronics," *IEEE Trans. Nucl. Sci.*, vol. 50, no. 3, pp. 583–602, Jun. 2003.

[4] S. M. Jahinuzzaman, M. Sharifkhani, and M. Sachdev, "Investigation of process impact on soft error susceptibility of nanometric SRAMs using a compact critical charge model", in Proc. *Int. Symp. on Quality Electronic Design 2008*, San Jose, CA, pp. 207-212.

[5] P. Hazucha and C. Svensson, "Impact of CMOS technology scaling on the atmospheric neutron soft error rate," *IEEE Trans. Nucl. Sci.*, vol. 47, no. 6, pp. 2586-2594, Dec. 2000.

[6] K. Flautner, N. S. Kim, S. Martin, D. Blaauw, and T. Mudge, "Drowsy caches: Simple techniques for reducing leakage power," in *Proc. Int. Symp. Computer Architecture*, 2002, pp. 148–157.

[7] A. Agarwal, H. Li, and K. Roy, "DRG-cache: A data retention gated-ground cache for low power," in *Proc. Design Automation Conf.*, 2002, pp. 473–478.

[8] T. Calin, M. Nicolaidis, R. Velazco, "Upset hardened memory design for submicron CMOS technology," *IEEE Trans. Nucl. Sci.*, vol. 43, no. 6, pp. 2874–2878, Dec. 1996.

[9] C. L. Chen and M. Y. Hsiao, "Error-correcting codes for semiconductor memory applications: a state-of-the-art review," *IBM J. Res. Dev.*, vol. 28, no. 2, pp. 124-134, Mar. 1984.

[10] J. L. Shin, B. Petrick, M. Singh, and A. S. Leon, "Design and implementation of an embedded 512-KB Level-2 cache subsystem," *J. Solid-State Circuits*, vol. 40, no. 9, pp. 1815-1820, Sep. 2005.

[11] K. Osada, Y. Saitoh, E. Ibe, and K. Ishibashi, "16.7-fA/cell tunnel-leakage-suppressed 16-Mb SRAM for handling cosmic-ray-induced multierrors," *J. Solid-State Circuits*, vol. 38, no. 11, pp. 1952-1957, Nov. 2003.

Importance Sampling Monte Carlo simulations for accurate estimation of SRAM yield

T.S. Doorn[1], E.J.W. ter Maten[1], J.A. Croon[1], A. Di Bucchianico[2], O. Wittich[2]

[1]NXP Semiconductors, Eindhoven, The Netherlands
[2]Eindhoven University of Technology, Eindhoven, The Netherlands

Abstract—**Variability is an important aspect of SRAM cell design. Failure probabilities of $P_{fail} \leq 10^{-10}$ have to be estimated through statistical simulations. Accurate statistical techniques such as Importance Sampling Monte Carlo simulations are essential to accurately and efficiently estimate such low failure probabilities. This paper shows that a simple form of Importance Sampling is sufficient for simulating $P_{fail} \leq 10^{-10}$ for the SRAM parameters Static Noise Margin, Write Margin and Read Current. For the SNM, a new simple technique is proposed that allows extrapolating the SNM distribution based on a limited number of trials. For SRAM total leakage currents, it suffices to take the averages into account for designing SRAM cells and modules. A guideline is proposed to ensure bitline leakage currents do not compromise SRAM functionality.**

I. INTRODUCTION

Decades of scaling according to Moore's law have shrunk devices to such an extent that variability has become a serious issue at all levels of circuit design. The effects of variability are most noticeable in SRAM design, since SRAM cells use very small transistors. For this reason, statistics have long been part of SRAM cell design. Intra-die transistor Vt mismatch is still the main statistical parameter, although others are gaining importance. Downscaling of transistors leads to widened Vt-distributions (Figure 1 left). In addition, the amount of SRAM on large System-on-Chips (SoCs) continues to increase, causing the amount of variation that has to be taken into account to increase as well (Figure 1 right).

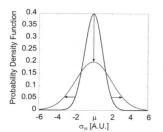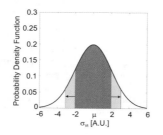

Figure 1: Increased variability leads to widening mismatch distributions (left). Increasing number of memory bits per SoC leads to a larger part of the mismatch distribution being taken into account in memory bitcell design (right).

On top of this, there is a clear trend towards voltage scalable systems [1]-[2], resulting in an increased demand for voltage scalable SRAM as well. At lower supply voltages, SRAMs are more susceptible to variability, leaving less design margin for the designer. Hence it is becoming increasingly hard to guarantee correct SRAM operation under all process, voltage and temperature conditions. This translates to very tough requirements on SRAM parameters like Static Noise Margin (SNM), Write Margin (WM) and read current (I_{read}).

SRAM yield should not be limited by design parameters. To guarantee no more than 0.1% yield loss for a 10Mb SRAM, a failure probability of $P_{fail} \leq 10^{-10}$ is taken into account in SRAM bitcell design for all relevant parameters. Provided the probability distribution is Gaussian, $P_{fail} \leq 10^{-10}$ corresponds to μ-6.4σ (with μ the mean and σ the standard deviation of the distribution). Using Monte-Carlo (MC) simulations, the 6.4σ limits of the SRAM parameter distributions are estimated. Accurate estimation of the relevant parameters at μ-6.4σ with plain Monte-Carlo takes billions of simulations and is too time consuming. Hence, a limited number of simulations is done (10^3-10^4), the μ and σ of the distribution are extracted and μ-6.4σ is determined by extrapolation. This technique is not always accurate, since the SNM distribution is not Gaussian at all [1] and the distribution I_{read} is not Gaussian in its tail.

This paper presents the use of the simplest form of Importance Sampling (IS) to drastically increase the accuracy of Monte-Carlo simulations. This technique was applied before in a complex adaptive fashion, requiring complex sampling algorithms and post-processing [3]. This paper presents a form of IS that requires less implementation effort. The applicability of the method is demonstrated by estimating the yield and probability distribution functions of SNM, WM and I_{read}. In the case of the SNM, a new method is presented for accurately estimating $P_{fail} = 10^{-10}$ by extrapolation. For SRAM total leakage currents, it suffices to take the averages into account for designing SRAM cells and modules. A guideline is proposed to ensure bitline leakage currents do not compromise SRAM functionality.

II. IMPORTANCE SAMPLING

Monte-Carlo analysis in circuit design normally assumes Gaussian distributed Vts of the transistors in the circuit. This results in many samples being drawn from around the average of the distribution. The extreme Vts are responsible for the extremes in the distributions of the output parameters (SNM, WM, I_{read}, etc.). Therefore it makes sense to have more samples drawn from the tails of the Vt distributions. Using a Gaussian distribution with a higher standard deviation for the Vt is the simplest way to achieve this.

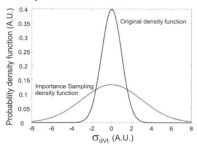

Figure 2: The principle of Importance Sampling. Using a density function with a higher standard deviation in Monte-Carlo analysis results in more samples being drawn from the extremes of the distribution.

From Figure 2 it is clear that using a wider Gaussian density function for Monte-Carlo sampling, indeed more samples are drawn from the extremes of the density. Using a wider Vt sampling distribution is a very practical choice, since no modifications to the circuit simulator are necessary. Using a wider density instead of the original distribution leads to distorted SNM, WM and I_{read} distributions. The correct density functions and distributions are obtained by a mathematical transformation based on the ratio of the original and IS distribution. The resulting distributions are now estimated over a much larger range compared to applying standard MC.

IS can be more formally described as follows. Suppose parameter x has a density $f(x)$. With IS, parameter x is sampled according to density $g(x)$. To compensate for sampling according to $g(x)$ instead of $f(x)$, the distribution function y, the sampled version of x, has to be multiplied by the ratio $f(x)/g(x)$. The sampled distribution function of parameter y is given by equations 1 and 2.

$$F^{MCIS}(y) = \frac{1}{N} \sum_{i=1}^{N} I_{\{x_i < y\}} \frac{f(x_i)}{g(x_i)} \qquad (1)$$

with

$$I_{\{x_i < y\}} = \begin{cases} 0 & x_i \geq y \\ 1 & x_i < y \end{cases} \qquad (2)$$

where N is the number of trials.

III.   APPLICATION OF IS TO SRAM BIT CELL ANALYSIS

This section shows that with the same number of trials, IS MC can estimate much lower failure probabilities than is possible with normal MC. It is also shown that extrapolated MC can lead to over- or under-estimation of the $P_{fail} \leq 10^{-10}$ for two of the most important SRAM parameters: SNM and I_{read}. Moreover, for the SNM, a new method allows estimating $P_{fail} \leq 10^{-10}$ using extrapolated MC with high accuracy.

A 65nm SRAM cell is simulated using PSP MOS transistor models. A supply voltage $V_{dd} = 0.9V$ is used, to bring the cell closer to its operating limits. At this Vdd, the accuracy with which all parameters are determined becomes more important. The IS simulations use Gaussian distributions with a $\sigma = 3\sigma_{Vt}$ for the Vts of all transistors in the SRAM cell.

A.   Static Noise Margin (SNM)

An SRAM cell has to be stable enough to be read without changing the data in the cell. The SNM is a measure for the read stability of the cell. The SNM is the amount of noise that can be imposed on the internal nodes of the SRAM cell before it changes its state. The SNM is determined by plotting the voltage transfer curve of one half of the SRAM cell together with the inverse of the voltage transfer curve of the other half of the cell. The sides of the largest squares that can be drawn inside the eyes are SNMh and SNMl (Figure 3). Both SNMh and SNMl have a Gaussian distribution. The minimum of SNMh and SNMl is traditionally defined as the SNM [4]. Since taking the minimum of SNMh and SNMl is a non-linear operation, the distribution of SNM is no longer Gaussian. Therefore using extrapolated MC to determine $P_{fail} \leq 10^{-10}$ does not yield accurate results.

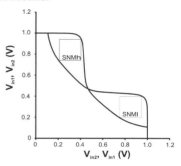

Figure 3: The butterfly curve of an SRAM cell, used to determine the SNM.

Figure 4 left, shows the cumulative distribution function (CDF) of the SNM, determined by a MC simulation using 50k trials, both for normal MC (solid) and IS MC (dotted). Normal MC can only simulate down to $P_{fail} \approx 10^{-5}$. Statistical noise becomes apparent below $P_{fail} \approx 10^{-4}$. Using the simple form of IS, $P_{fail} \leq 10^{-10}$ is easily simulated. The correspondence between normal MC and IS MC is very good down to $P_{fail} \approx 10^{-5}$. Figure 4 clearly shows that using extrapolated MC leads to overestimating the SNM at $P_{fail} = 10^{-10}$.

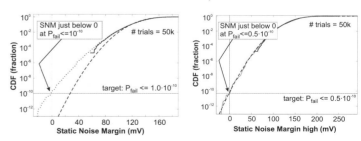

Figure 4: SNM (left) and SNM high (right) cumulative distribution function for extrapolated MC (dashed), normal MC (solid) and IS MC (dotted).

A new simple method is now presented to estimate the SNM by evaluating the distribution of only SNMh or SNMl. Figure 4 right shows the CDF of SNMh. The distribution of SNMh is a Gaussian distribution and extrapolation leads to a good estimate of SNMh at $P_{fail} \leq 10^{-10}$. The $P_{fail} \leq 10^{-10}$ limits for SNMh and SNM appear be to almost identical. At first sight, this is surprising, since the SNM and SNMh have different distributions. However, a small difference exists between SNM and SNMh/SNMl. The following describes how they are different.

The SNM is defined as the smaller value of *SNMh* and *SNMl*

$$SNM \equiv \min(SNMh, SNMl) \qquad (3)$$

Also, using a probability rule,

$$P(A \cup B) = P(A) + P(B) - P(A \cap B) \qquad (4)$$

We now apply equations (3) and (4) with $A=\{SNMh \leq a\}$ and $B=\{SNMl \leq a\}$. The probability that SNMh and SNMl are simultaneously very small is extremely low. Therefore $P(A \cap B) \approx 0$. Assuming that SNMh and SNMl are identically distributed, it follows for the values of interest for a that:

$$
\begin{aligned}
P(SNM \leq a) &\approx P(SNMh \leq a) + P(SNMl \leq a) \\
&= 2P(SNMh \leq a) \qquad (5) \\
&= 2P(SNMl \leq a)
\end{aligned}
$$

A failure probability for SNMh of $P(SNMh \leq a)=0.5 \cdot 10^{-10}$ is required to get the same failure probability $P(SNM \leq a)=10^{-10}$. In the example shown in this paper, the difference between a for $P(SNMh \leq a)=0.5 \cdot 10^{-10}$ and $P(SNM \leq a)=1.0 \cdot 10^{-10}$ is only 1.2mV, which is within the statistical accuracy of IS MC. The extrapolated version of $P(SNMh<a)=0.5 \cdot 10^{-10}$ deviates from $P(SNM \leq a)=1.0 \cdot 10^{-10}$ by only 0.3mV. Effectively, using $P(SNMh<a)=0.5 \cdot 10^{-10}$ means extrapolating to μ-6.5σ. This analysis shows it is possible to use extrapolated MC as an accurate estimate of the far tail of the SNM distribution.

B. Read Current

The read current is a measure for the speed of the memory cell and is therefore an important parameter. Figure 5 shows the extrapolated MC, regular MC and IS MC distribution for the read current of an SRAM cell. Again, there is a good match between regular MC and IS MC, down to $P_{fail} \leq 10^{-4}$.

These read current simulations were done on one side of the cell. Therefore, $P_{fail} \leq 0.5 \cdot 10^{-10}$ has to be targeted for the read current as well. The correspondence with the SNMh simulation is very good. The cells start flipping during a read action at almost exactly the same failure probability as where SNM=0mV.

These simulations show that extrapolated MC can result in serious underestimation of the read current. This can lead to over-design of the memory cell. To be able to accurately simulate the worst case read current as a result of mismatch,

IS MC is required for simulating the read current. Extrapolated MC is by no means accurate enough.

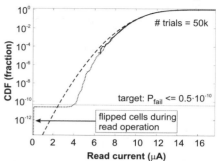

Figure 5: Read current Cumulative Distribution function of the extrapolated distribution (dashed), regular Monte-Carlo (solid) and IS Monte-Carlo (dotted).

C. Write Margin

An SRAM cell should not only be stable during read, it also has to be sufficiently instable to be written when desired. The write margin is a measure for the writeability of the SRAM cell. A cell is written by precharging one bitline to Vdd and discharging the other bitline to ground, with the wordlines at Vdd. The write margin can be defined as the highest acceptable voltage on this low bitline (Figure 6).

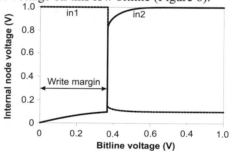

Figure 6: The internal node voltages of an SRAM cell versus the low bitline voltage. The write margin (WM) is defined as the highest bitline voltage at which de SRAM cell flips.

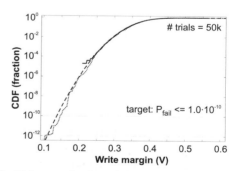

Figure 7: Write margin Cumulative Distribution function of the extrapolated distribution (dashed), regular Monte-Carlo (solid) and IS Monte-Carlo (dotted).

The distribution function of the write margin was also simulated using extrapolated MC, normal MC and IS MC (Figure 7). Again, a good match is obtained between normal MC and IS MC. The WM is underestimated by about 10 mV, which is not a significant deviation. Therefore the far tail of the WM distribution can be estimated using extrapolated MC.

D. Leakage currents

Leakage currents can be divided into two important components: total leakage current and bitline leakage current. Total leakage current is important for the standby power consumption of the memory. This can be estimated by multiplying the average of the total cell leakage by the number of cells in the memory instance. The large number of cells in an SRAM results in a small variation on this estimate, making this method sufficiently accurate.

Bitline leakage is the sum of the leakage currents of the non-selected cells in the column being accessed. Too much bitline leakage current can result in a non-functional memory. During reading, one of the two bitlines of the column is discharged to develop sufficient differential voltage for the sense amp to detect. In a worst case situation, all non-accessed cells connected to the column being read are discharging the opposite bitline with their leakage currents. If the sum of the leakage currents is in the order of the worst-case read current, there is a risk of developing insufficient differential voltage on the bitlines and a read failure.

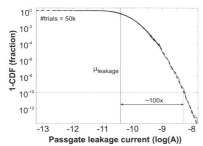

Figure 8: 1-CDF of the logarithm of the Passgate leakage current: extrapolated MC (dashed), regular MC (solid) and IS MC(dotted).

Short columns with fewer cells have lower bitline leakage currents than longer columns. Hence, if a memory with long columns can handle the worst case bitline leakage, a smaller instance of that memory with shorter columns can also handle the bitline leakage.

Figure 8 shows the logarithm of the passgate leakage current. Since the leakage current depends exponentially on the transistor Vt, the distribution of the logarithm is excellently Gaussian. The probability of a passgate leakage current that is 100x higher than the average is approximately $P(I_{leak,pg} \geq 100\ I_{leak,pg,\mu}) \approx 10^{-10}$ for this cell, meaning this is a very rare event. Hence it is safe to assume only one cell has worst-case leakage and all other cells have an average leakage current. Equation 6 is proposed as a guideline to ensure bitline leakage does not compromise SRAM functionality.

$$I_{read,wc} \geq x \cdot \left(I_{leak,pg,6.4\sigma} + (L-2)I_{leak,pg,\mu} \right) \qquad (6)$$

where $I_{read,wc}$ is the worst case read current, L is the maximum number of cells in a column and x is a margin factor at the discretion of the designer.

IV. Conclusion

Continuous scaling according to Moore's law and an increasing number of bits used in SRAM memories strongly increase the need for incorporating statistical information into the design of SRAM bit cells. To guarantee sufficient yield for a 10 Mb SRAM, failure probabilities of $P_{fail} \leq 10^{-10}$ are required, probabilities found in the far tails of the parameter distributions. Accurate statistical techniques are a must to be able to simulate such failure probabilities.

In this paper it is shown that accurate statistical DC SRAM cell simulations are possible using a relatively simple statistical technique like Importance Sampling (IS) Monte Carlo (MC) with widened Vt distributions. The technique has been successfully applied to accurately estimate the distributions of Static Noise Margin (SNM), Write Margin (WM) and read current I_{read}.

For the SNM, it is shown that extrapolation of normal MC simulations overestimates the yield. In addition to the benefit of IS MC simulations, it has been shown that extrapolation of the Gaussian distributions of the individual eyes yields results in accurate yield estimation. The results of the latter method are in agreement with IS MC simulations.

The read current distribution deviates strongly from a Gaussian distribution and its distribution can therefore not be extrapolated. The use of extrapolated distributions would result in a pessimistic I_{read} and could thus lead to over-design of the memory cell and/or memory architecture. Importance Sampling or a technique with similar statistical accuracy is required to make correct decisions in the design process.

The WM can be estimated with extrapolated Gaussian distributions. Although a small difference of the WM at $P_{fail} \leq 10^{-10}$ is observed between extrapolated MC and IS MC, this difference is not significant.

To determine the SRAM total leakage currents the average current per cell is multiple by the number of cell in the instance. A guideline is proposed to guarantee that bitline leakage currents do not compromise SRAM functionality.

V. Acknowledgements

Roelof Salters, Patrick van de Steeg, Jwalant Mishra, Dick Klaassen, Gerben Doornbos and Thomas Merelle (all NXP Semiconductors) are acknowledged for many fruitful discussions.

References

[1] B.H. Calhoun, A.P. Chandrakasan, "Static Noise Margin Variation for sub-threshold SRAM in 65-nm CMOS", IEEE Journal of solid-state circuits, vol. 41, no. 7, pp. 1673-1679, July 2006

[2] H. Onoda et al., "0.7V SRAM technology with stress-enhanced dopant segregated Schottky (DSS) source/drain transistors for 32 nm node", Symp. on VLSI Technology digest of technical papers, pp. 76-77, 2007

[3] R. Kanj, R. Joshi, S. Nassif, "Mixture importance sampling and its application to the analysis of SRAM designs in the presence of rare failure events," Design Automation Conference, pp. 69-72, July 2006.

[4] E. Seevinck, F.J. List, J. Lohstroh, "Static Noise Margin Analysis of MOS SRAM cells", IEEE Journal of solid state circuits, vol. 22, no. 5, pp. 748-754, October 1987.

A Robust Single Supply Voltage SRAM Read Assist Technique Using Selective Precharge

Mohamed H. Abu-Rahma[1,2], Mohab Anis[2] and Sei Seung Yoon[1]

[1] Qualcomm Incorporated, San Diego, CA 92121
[2] Electrical and Computer Engineering Department
University of Waterloo, Waterloo, ON N2L 3G1
Email: marahma@qualcomm.com

Abstract— **In this paper, we present a new read assist technique for SRAM to improve bitcell read stability. The new technique utilizes selective precharge where different parts of the bitlines are precharged to V_{DD} or GND. Using charge sharing, the required value of bitline voltage can be precisely set to increase bitcells' SNM, while using only one supply voltage. A 512kb memory was designed to demonstrate this technique in an industrial 45nm technology. Results show large improvement in SNM and high robustness against process variations. In addition, the proposed technique reduces the memory access time compared to the conventional approach. Moreover, the proposed technique demonstrates higher operating margin which makes it an attractive option to deal with SRAM read stability in nanometer technologies.**

I. INTRODUCTION

The large increase in random variations in advanced CMOS technology nodes is creating huge challenges for SRAM design. This is exacerbated by the high demand for low voltage and high density memories for SoC [1]. Dealing with SRAM cell stability is currently one of the biggest challenges in SRAM design [2], [3], [4].

Bitcell stability is defined depending on the SRAM operation mode. In read operation, the static noise margin (SNM) is used as the measure of SRAM robustness and is defined as the maximum internal noise voltage that the bitcell can tolerate [5]. It has been shown that SNM limits the bitcell stability and dictates the minimum supply voltage at which the memory can operate [6].

To mitigate the impact of variations on bitcell SNM, several single supply read assist techniques have been proposed [2], [7], [8]. Other read assist techniques, such as using dual supply voltages have also been proposed [9], [10], [11], [12]. However, they require adding level shifters which can cause speed penalty and have large area overhead. In addition, a dual supply approach requires adding a different power grid for memories, which adds to the complexity of power delivery, especially in SoCs.

In this paper, we present a new read assist technique which requires only one supply voltage. The proposed technique uses selective precharge and charge sharing to precisely control the bitline voltage before a bitcell is accessed. To show the effectiveness of the proposed technique, a 512kb memory was designed in 45nm technology. Selective precharge technique improves bitcell SNM and can reduce memory access time. The technique is robust against process and temperature variation and improves the read operation window.

II. BACKGROUND

In SRAM design, the bitlines' voltages are typically precharged to V_{DD} before accessing the bitcell. However, in [13], it was shown that reducing the bitline voltage V_{BL} before accessing a bitcell improves the bitcell's read stability. This is because the pass gate (access transistor) strength reduces as the bitline voltage decreases. This effectively increases the bitcell α ratio (defined as the ratio of

pull down to pass gate strength). Hence, SNM improves as ΔV_{BL} increases where ΔV_{BL} is defined here as $V_{DD} - V_{BL}$ just before the wordline (WL) is asserted. Note that as ΔV_{BL} increases, SNM reaches a maximum point, and further increase in ΔV_{BL} causes significant SNM reduction. This is mainly due to read disturbs. Therefore, accurate control of ΔV_{BL} level is important to prevent ΔV_{BL} from exceeding the maximum SNM point.

From a circuit point of view, the relation between ΔV_{BL} and SNM has been exploited in [2], [8] to increase bitcell stability. In [8], a pulsed bitline approach is used where a pulse is presented to control an NMOS pull-down. This pull-down device discharges the bitline, which increases ΔV_{BL}, and SNM. However, this technique is sensitive to PVT variations since ΔV_{BL} is a strong function of the pulse duration which will vary with PVT variations. Therefore, a complex timing scheme is required to control ΔV_{BL} at different PVT conditions. In [2], an NMOS device is used to precharge the bitlines, hence, having one V_{th} drop on the bitlines. Due to the strong sensitivity of V_{th} to PVT variations, the effectiveness of this technique reduces in different PVT corners. Moreover, low V_{th} devices are required to ensure that ΔV_{BL} does not cause read disturbs in the worst case conditions, which adds additional cost (especially for low cost SoCs).

III. SELECTIVE PRECHARGE TECHNIQUE

In our proposed technique, different parts of the bitlines are precharged to V_{DD} or (predischarged) GND. Using charge sharing, the final required value of bitline voltage can be precisely controlled. This technique relies on the capacitance ratio to control the bitline voltage. Therefore, this technique shows high immunity against process variations (both front-end and back-end) since the capacitance ratio shows very weak dependence on PVT corners.

Fig. 1 shows a simple schematic for the selective precharge technique with four bitline columns connected to the read and write circuitry (sense amplifier and write drivers). Bitlines, BL/BLB, refer to the upper part of the bitlines connected directly to the bitcells (before the column select). Sense/Write lines, SL/SLB, refer to the lower part of the bitline connected to the sense amplifier and write drivers (after the column select).

Selective precharge operation can be divided into three main steps. First, BL/BLB are precharged to V_{DD} as in conventional approaches, while SL/SLB is precharged (pre-discharged) to GND, as shown in Fig. 1(a). In the second step, the column select devices (MUX) on each bitline column are enabled. Hence, charge sharing occurs between the upper and lower bitlines. Note that $BL0 - BL3$ all experience charge sharing. The final bitlines voltage after charge sharing is determined by the capacitance ratio of upper and lower bitlines (BL and SL). Using charge sharing, the bitline voltage can

234

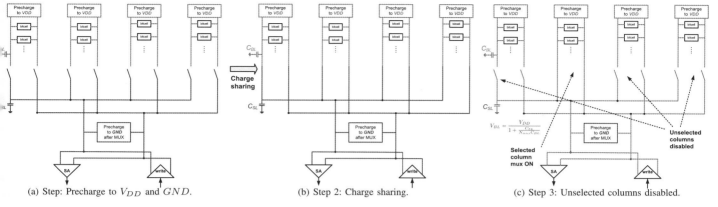

(a) Step: Precharge to V_{DD} and GND. (b) Step 2: Charge sharing. (c) Step 3: Unselected columns disabled.

Fig. 1. Selective Precharge operation

be reduced. Therefore, SNM improves as discussed in Section II. In the third step, the MUX devices for all unselected columns are disabled, while the selected column MUX stays on. In this case, the selected column allows access to the required bitcell, while half-selected[1] bitcells also see improvement in SNM since their bitline voltages have also been reduced.

Fig. 2 shows the implementation of selective precharge technique. A NOR gate is added for each bitline column to control the column select. Fig. 3 shows the precharge circuits for both V_{DD} and GND. Fig. 4 shows the timing diagram for selective precharge operation. ch_sh is activated using the rising edge of precharge disable (for PMOS pull-up). When ch_sh is high, the PMOS devices in the column select MUX are on. Hence, charge sharing between all bitlines sharing the same read/write circuitry and SL/SLB line is enabled. Therefore, BL/BLB voltage decrease while SL/SLB voltage increase. ch_sh is disabled using disabled using mux_state which is a dummy column select signal. Therefore, bitcells see reduced bitline voltage when the bitcell is accessed. At the end of operation, BL/BLB are precharged back to V_{DD} while SL/SLB are precharged to GND, as shown Fig. 4.

By selecting the location of precharge to V_{DD} or GND, the required value of ΔV_{BL} is set. For example, if a larger ΔV_{BL} is required, one or more of the bitlines can be precharged to GND instead of V_{DD}. Therefore, the proposed technique allows changing ΔV_{BL} by selecting which points to be precharged to V_{DD} or GND. Note that in this technique, no additional supply voltages are required to generate the desired bitline voltage, which reduces the design complexity. In addition, since the final ΔV_{BL} voltage depends solely on capacitance ratio, it is very robust against process variations.

IV. Access Time Improvement

In SRAM memories, the read operation determines the access time of the memory. The clock to WL enable contributes to memory's access time, hence, it is usually optimized for speed. However, the proposed technique introduces another signal, ch_sh, which should be enabled before the WL is asserted. To accommodate the ch_sh signal shown in Fig. 4, the WL enable path may be delayed. This delay will therefore increase the memory access time. Hence, a technique to reduce (or recover) access time is required.

[1]Half-selected bitcells: bitcells on the same row where WL is asserted, although they are not accessed for read or write operations.

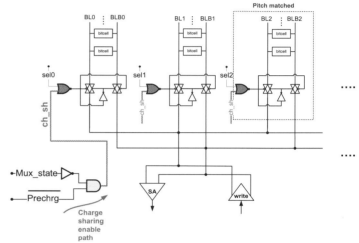

Fig. 2. Selective precharge schematic.

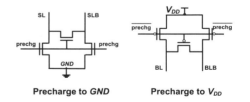

Precharge to GND Precharge to V_{DD}

Fig. 3. Precharge to V_{DD} and GND circuits, including equalize transistors.

In addition to the clock to WL delay, another part of the critical path is the WL pulse width T_{WL}. T_{WL} is the time required for the bitcell to discharge the bitlines and generate sufficient input differential for the sense amplifier to allow correct read operation. T_{WL} typically contributes to approximately 30% of the memory access time [12]. To reduce this delay component, we exploit the relation between ΔV_{BL} and the SA input offset.

There are many types of sense amplifiers used in SRAM design. However, current latch sense amplifier (CLSA) is one of the most widely used due to its high speed and isolation. Moreover, it has been shown in [14] that reducing bitline voltage (common mode)

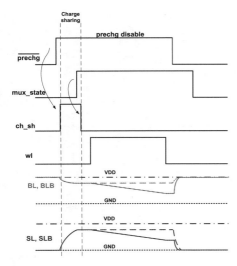

Fig. 4.   Selective precharge timing diagram.

improves the SA robustness. This characteristic of CLSA makes it very attractive in the proposed selective precharge technique. By reducing the bitline voltage (increasing ΔV_{BL}) the SA offset ($\sigma_{SA,offset}$) reduces, hence, allowing T_{WL} to be reduced for a give failure probability. The reduction in T_{WL} can therefore compensate for any increase in clock to WL delay, as will be shown in Section V.

V. RESULTS AND DISCUSSION

To test the proposed read assist technique, a 512kb memory was designed and implemented in an industrial 45nm technology. In this section, we show post-layout simulation results for this memory.

In Fig. 5, the read operation is shown for a bitcell on the first column (enabled using MUX0). In the beginning of the operation, $BL0$ and $BLB0$ are set to V_{DD} while SL and SLB are set to zero. Charge charing operation is activated using ch_sh, which activates all the MUX transistors. Therefore, $BL0/BLB0$ voltage decrease while SL/SLB increases as shown in Fig. 5, and they settle to a value determined by the capacitance ratio. Note that charge sharing happens quickly and that it is not sensitive to the ch_sh pulse width (wider pulse does not affect the settling voltage after charge sharing). After charge sharing is completed, the MUX devices (PMOS) for all unselected columns are disabled (MUX1), while the selected column stays selected (MUX0). Therefore, when WL is asserted, the accessed and half-selected bitcell see a reduced bitline voltage, which increase the bitcell's SNM. At the end of read operation, the bitlines are precharged to V_{DD} while the sense lines are precharged to GND.

The impact of bitline voltage on the CLSA speed and input offset is shown in Fig. 7. Monte Carlo transient simulations were used to measure the SA's offset. As ΔV_{BL} increases, the SA delay slightly decreases until it reaches a minimum point. Beyond that point, the SA delay increases. In the mean time, the SA input offset (σ_{offset}) decreases monotonically with the increase in ΔV_{BL}. The reduction in σ_{offset} improves the robustness of the SA and decreases the probability of read access failures. Therefore, the WL pulse width can be reduced accordingly based on the following:

$$\frac{T_{WL2}}{T_{WL1}} = \frac{\sigma_{SA,offset_2}}{\sigma_{SA,offset_1}} \tag{1}$$

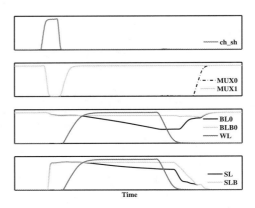

Fig. 5.   Results for selective precharge read operation. MUX0/1 are the gates voltages for the PMOS devices in the column select for column 0 and 1, respectively.

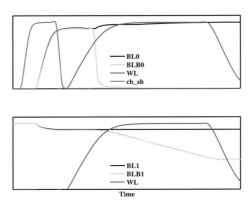

Fig. 6.   Results for selective precharge write operation. $BL0/BLB0$ are accessed for write operation while $BL1/BLB1$ are half selected bitlines.

where T_{WL} is the time allowed for bitcell to generate bitline differential before enabling the SA. This large reduction in σ_{offset} reduces access time of the memory. Typically, T_{WL} is about 30% of memory access time. As shown in Fig. 7, SA offset can be reduced by up to 25%. Therefore, access time improves by 7%. In reality, to accommodate the ch_sh pulse, the WL enable path may be slightly delayed. Hence, this improvement in speed is reduced. Nevertheless, since charge sharing requires very short time, the impact on access time improvement is negligible. Therefore, in the worst case scenario, the proposed technique will allow having the same access time as in conventional approach.

Charge sharing operation is also enabled when a bitcell is accessed for write operation, as shown in Fig. 6. In that case, half-selected bitcells experience reduced BL voltage to improve read stability (bitlines $BL1$ and $BLB1$). To improve the write-ability of the selected bitcell, a CMOS write driver is used for write operation. Therefore, BL voltage lost in charge sharing is recovered using the write driver as shown in (Fig. 6). Hence, the write margin for the selected bitcell is not deteriorated.

The improvement in SNM using the proposed technique is shown in Fig. 8. Monte Carlo simulations are used to measure the impact of local variation on the bitcell's SNM. To ensure high yield target for the embedded memories, 6σ of SNM local variation is included. As

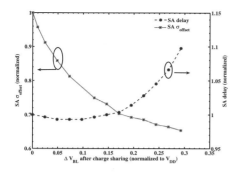

Fig. 7. Sense amplifier delay and input offset versus ΔV_{BL} after charge sharing.

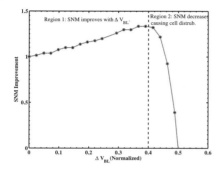

Fig. 8. SNM improvement using the proposed technique versus ΔV_{BL} after charge sharing.

ΔV_{BL} increases, SNM increases linearly until it reaches a maximum point. Any further increase in ΔV_{BL} causes SNM to decrease significantly, which deteriorates cell read stability.

To evaluate the robustness of the proposed scheme in precisely controlling ΔV_{BL}, different process and RC extraction options were simulated to measure how ΔV_{BL} is affected. Table I shows ΔV_{BL} for different process corners, interconnect capacitances and temperature. It is clear that ΔV_{BL} shows negligible change across different conditions, which shows the robustness of the proposed technique against PVT variations.

TABLE I
ΔV_{BL} FOR DIFFERENT CONDITIONS.

Process	Slow	Slow	Nominal	Fast
Temp.	-40	125	25	-40
Parasitic C	max	max	nominal	min
ΔV_{BL}[A]	9.8%	9.4%	11.1%	12%

[A] Normalized to V_{DD}.

Fig. 9 shows the process window curves (V_{th}), which is used to determine the operating limit of the memory with 6σ of local variation coverage. Using the selective precharge technique (solid-line) the operating window is expanded as compared to the conventional approach. This increase in operation window reduces the failure probability by more than 100X.

The proposed technique has small area overhead ($< 2\%$) and shows strong robustness against process variations. In addition, it requires only one supply voltage. Hence, does not require any additional level-shifters that cause significant area and speed penalty. Moreover, the timing generation is simple since it re-uses timing

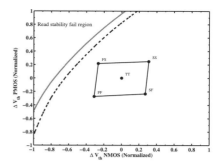

Fig. 9. V_{th} windows showing the improvement in read stability operating window for selective precharge (solid line) compared to the conventional approach (dotted line). Simulation accounts for 6σ of local variations.

signals available in SRAM design. The memory speed also improves using the proposed technique. The large improvement in bitcell SNM and operation window show the effectiveness of this technique. Measurement results for the 512kb macro will be provided in the future after testing the macro.

VI. CONCLUSION

The increase of local variations in nanometer technologies strongly affect SRAM cell stability. In this paper, we propose a novel read assist technique to improve SRAM static noise margin. The proposed technique, selective precharge, allows precharging different parts of the bitlines to V_{DD} and GND and uses charge sharing to precisely control the bitline voltage, which increases the bitcell stability. In addition to improving SNM, the proposed technique also improves memory access time. Moreover, it only requires one supply voltage. The proposed technique has been implemented in the design of 512kb memory in 45nm technology. Results show improvements in SNM and read operation window which confirms the effectiveness of this technique.

REFERENCES

[1] K. Itoh et al., "Low-voltage limitations of memory-rich nano-scale CMOS LSIs," ESSCIRC, pp. 68–75, 2007.
[2] A. Bhavnagarwala et al., "A sub-600mv, fluctuation tolerant 65nm cmos sram array with dynamic cell biasing," VLSI Circuits Symp., pp. 78–79, 2007.
[3] S. Mukhopadhyay et al., "Modeling and estimation of failure probability due to parameter variations in nano-scale srams for yield enhancement," Symp VLSI Circuits, pp. 64–67, 2004.
[4] E. Grossar et al., "Read stability and write-ability analysis of SRAM cells for nanometer technologies," JSSC, pp. 2577–2588, Nov. 2006.
[5] E. Seevinck et al., "Static-noise margin analysis of mos sram cells," JSSC, pp. 748–754, Oct 1987.
[6] J. Lin et al., "Prediction and control of nbti induced sram vccmin drift," IEDM, pp. 1–4, 2006.
[7] M. Yabuuchi et al., "A 45nm low-standby-power embedded sram with improved immunity against process and temperature variations," ISSCC, pp. 326–606, 2007.
[8] M. Khellah et al., "Wordline and bitline pulsing schemes for improving SRAM cell stability in low vcc 65nm CMOS designs," Symp. VLSI Circuits, pp. 9–10, 2006.
[9] ——, "A 256-kb dual-V_{CC} SRAM building block in 65-nm cmos process with actively clamped sleep transistor," JSSC, pp. 233–242, Jan. 2007.
[10] J. Pille et al., "Implementation of the cell broadband engine in a 65nm SOI technology featuring dual-supply SRAM arrays supporting 6GHz at 1.3V," ISSCC, pp. 322–606, 2007.
[11] K. Zhang et al., "A 3-GHz 70MB SRAM in 65nm CMOS technology with integrated column-based dynamic power supply," ISSCC, pp. 474–611 Vol. 1, 2005.
[12] M. Yamaoka et al., "Operating-margin-improved sram with column-at-a-time body-bias control technique," ESSCIRC, pp. 396–399, 2007.
[13] A. Bhavnagarwala et al., "Fluctuation limits & scaling opportunities for CMOS SRAM cells," IEDM, pp. 659–662, 5-7 Dec. 2005.
[14] B. Wicht et al., "Yield and speed optimization of a latch-type voltage sense amplifier," JSSC, pp. 1148–1158, July 2004.

A 90nm CMOS mm-wave VCO
using an LC Tank with Inductive Division

Lianming Li, Patrick Reynaert and Michiel Steyaert

KU Leuven ESAT-MICAS

Leuven, Belgium

{Lianming.Li, Patrick.Reynaert, Michiel.Steyaert}@esat.kuleuven.be

Abstract□ this paper presents a low supply voltage, fundamental-frequency 90nm CMOS mm-wave oscillator using an enhanced LC tank with inductive division to improve the oscillator performance. The oscillator achieves a tuning range from 53.2GHz to 58.4GHz while consuming 8.1mW from a 0.7V supply. The phase noise at 58.4GHz is -90.08dBc/Hz @ 1MHz offset. The oscillator can also be operated from a supply voltage as low as 0.43V with a phase noise of -90.10dBc/Hz @ 1MHz offset from a 61.7GHz carrier, while consuming only 1.2mW.

I. INTRODUCTION AND MOTIVATION

Driven by the ever-increasing data-rate requirements, wireless communication enters the millimeter-wave era. The unlicensed wideband spectrum around 60GHz, for example, allows a wide variety of emerging consumer product. Conventionally, millimeter-wave (mm-wave) circuits are constructed with III-V compound devices like GaAs or InP [1], [2], or SiGe [3], [4]. Thanks to the scaling, the f_T and f_{MAX} of CMOS process are improved quite a lot, thus making the design of mm-wave CMOS circuits possible [5], [12]. Considering the SoC trends, it is very attractive to implement mm-wave circuits using CMOS technology. However, with the scaling of CMOS technology, the intrinsic analog performance of the transistor like output impedance, leakage, low supply voltage, is degraded and process variation becomes worse, while the transistor speed is increased. The degradation of analog performance poses many challenges to circuit designers.

Recently, several mm-wave oscillators -a key component of a frequency synthesizer- have been presented using SiGe BiCMOS or CMOS technology [7]-[12]. However, achieving high tuning range and low phase noise are still major challenges, especially when the oscillator operates from a low supply voltage. Traditional oscillator design tries to achieve good phase noise performance by maximizing the amplitude of the tank signal. But at a low supply voltage, the oscillator will enter the voltage limited region and phase noise cannot be improved any more with conventional techniques.

This paper will first focus on the challenges for mm-wave oscillator design at a low supply voltage. Next, a novel LC tank structure with inductive division is presented that provides a solution to these challenges. Finally the measurement results are discussed and conclusions are given.

II. DESIGN OF LOW-VOLTAGE CMOS MM-WAVE VCOs

As mentioned before, a low supply voltage is a major design challenge for all oscillators. To cope with this challenge at GHz frequencies, an enhanced LC tank using bonding wires can be implemented [6]. But when moving to higher frequencies, many more challenges arise.

1. In a mm-wave oscillator, the capacitive parasitics from the transistors, varactors and inductors are very large compared to the tank capacitance. Therefore it is very difficult to realize a large tuning range at mm-wave frequencies. To increase the tuning range, an SOI technology could be used, which inherently has lower parasitics [9], [11].

2. The quality factor of an LC tank at GHz frequencies is usually limited by the inductor Q. The Q of the varactor is very large, so the design of the varactor can be optimized for maximum tuning range. But in the mm-wave region, it is the varactor which largely determines the quality factor of oscillator tank. Optimizing the varactor for high tuning range typically further reduces its quality factor.

3. Design kit device models are typically valid only up to ~20GHz. Using compact device models for high frequency application often incurs some accuracy issues.

4. Parasitic extraction is crucial at mm-wave frequencies, and is more complicated since accurate EM field solvers are needed.

The above issues underscore why it is difficult to design mm-wave oscillators in CMOS that simultaneously achieve good phase noise and large tuning range, while operating from a low supply voltage.

III. PROPOSED MM-WAVE VCO CIRCUIT

Figure 1 depicts the proposed mm-wave oscillator structure including the buffer. In the oscillator core, the enhanced LC tank consists of the magnetically coupled inductors L_{C1}, L_{C4}, L_{C2}, L_{C3}, and the accumulative nMOS varactor M_V. The cross-coupled pair transistors compensate the tank loss. Only nMOS transistors are used because of their speed benefit. For operation at a low supply voltage, the tail current source is eliminated which has the advantage of reducing the thermal and flicker noise. This also makes the signal amplitude larger, resulting into better phase noise performance. Different from [8], where inductors L_{c1} and L_{c3} function as lossy choke inductors, in this circuit L_{c1} and L_{c3} are an important part of the oscillation tank. It will be shown that with this enhanced LC tank, the oscillator tuning range and phase noise are heavily improved.

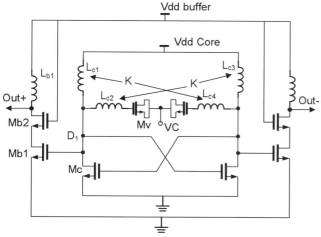

Figure 1.   Schematic of proposed mm-wave VCO including the cascode buffer

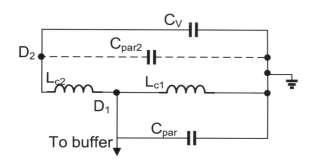

Figure 2.   Operating principle of the enhanced LC tank with inductive division

As it was mentioned before, the capacitive parasitics are a significant part of the oscillator tank capacitance. To achieve a large tuning range, a large varactor value needs to be used to meet the large ratio of the variable capacitance value to the fixed capacitance. This results in a very small tank inductance and very small characteristic tank impedance. As a result, a large DC power is needed to sustain the oscillation.

Figure 2 shows the operating principle of the proposed LC tank. This network by definition is a fourth-order network, having two potential oscillation frequencies. Special consideration has been taken to make sure the circuit can only oscillate at the fundamental frequency by reducing the loopgain at the higher potential oscillation frequency. Inductors L_{C2} and L_{C1} can be understood as an inductive voltage divider, which will upconvert the impedance of the parasitic capacitance C_{par}. The latter consists of the parasitic capacitance of the negative g_m transistors, the output buffer transistors and also the interconnections. The impedance

upconversion results in C_{par2}, whose relationship can be understood intuitively as below:

$$C_{par2} \approx C_{par}/n^2 \quad \text{and } n=(L_{C1}+L_{C2})/L_{C1} \qquad (1)$$

Thus, the inductive voltage divider reduces the capacitive parasitics across varactor capacitance C_V, directly resulting in a larger tuning range. The four inductors L_{C1}, L_{C2}, L_{C3} and L_{C4} are implemented using a two-turn inductor structure. The inherent transformer effect of the two-turn inductor increases the quality factor of the tank and also reduces the required Silicon area. As shown in the micrograph of the oscillator, this two turn inductor makes good capacitive decoupling to supply voltage, thus suppressing pickup noise. The inductor is realized using the top metal to reduce the loss from the substrate and also to minimize the parasitic capacitance. To optimize the inductor quality factor and also the capacitive parasitics, the inductors L_{C1}, L_{C2}, L_{C3} and L_{C4} have a different trace-width. The inductors are simulated using CST Microwave.

Apart from the improved tuning range, the inductive division also improves the phase noise. Normally, good phase noise is obtained by increasing the signal amplitude of the tank. The maximum signal amplitude at the transistor drain point $D1$ is limited by the supply voltage, which constraints the signal to noise ratio of the tank. As such, it is difficult to achieve good phase-noise performance at a low supply voltage. By using the inductive divider technique, the tank voltage is two times higher if $L_{C1}=L_{C2}$.

$$V_{D2}=n{\cdot}V_{D1} \quad \text{and} \quad n=(L_{C1}+L_{C2})/L_{C1} \qquad (2)$$

where V_{D1} is the voltage swing at the negative g_m transistor drain point, limited by the supply voltage, and V_{D2} is the tank voltage swing across inductor L_{C1} and L_{C2}. The higher tank voltage directly results in a better phase-noise performance. As will be demonstrated by the measurements, excellent phase-noise performance is achieved even at a low supply voltage.

Stand-alone oscillators always need a buffer in order to perform measurements. Usually, a two stage tapered buffer amplifier [10] or source follower is used to decrease the capacitive loading to the oscillator tank [11]. In this design, a cascode buffer amplifier is used to isolate the VCO core from the test equipment and to provide enough power to the load impedance. However, the gain stage will also present a capacitive load to the oscillator tank which would typically reduce the tuning range, as already indicated. However the inductive divider decreases the capacitive loading from the buffer amplifier. As such, a single buffer can be used without reducing the tuning range of the VCO. The buffer has a load of about 16fF.

As mentioned before, the varactor performance heavily affects the oscillator performance at mm-wave frequencies. Special efforts were taken to optimize the Q of varactor and also to increase the tuning ratio. Here, an accumulative nMOS varactor in n-well is used. A large tuning range is achieved despite the small varactor value about 25fF.

IV. MEASUREMENT RESULTS

The micrograph of the oscillator is shown in figure 3. The circuit is fabricated in 90nm CMOS. The VCO core area is about 96x80um². The two-turn coupled inductor arrangement allows the placement of the varactor on top of the oscillator core. As a result, the AC bypassing of the tuning voltage to the power supply is improved, which reduces the noise pickup of the tuning voltage.

The phase noise is measured with both an R&S FSU67 67GHz spectrum analyzer and the PN9000 phase noise measurement system using the delay-line method. Good agreement was achieved between both measurements.

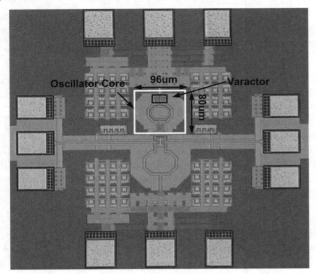

Figure 3.   micrograph of the oscillator

At 0.7V supply voltage, the oscillator consumes 8.1mW (excluding the buffer power consumption) and the measured tuning curve at 0.7V supply is given in figure 4, showing that the oscillator can be tuned from 53.2 to 58.4GHz. The circuit can work down to 0.43V supply with a tuning range from 58.8 to 61.7GHz while consuming only 1.2mW.

For a 0.7V supply, figure 5 shows the measured phase noise performance at 58.4GHz. The spurs around 621 kHz and 927 kHz are due to nearby MW transmitters. Figure 6 shows the measured phase noise performance across the frequency range. When the varactor control voltage is very low or very high, the C-V curve of the varactor is flat, resulting in good supply noise immunity. In the center of the frequency range, the varactor C-V curve is very symmetrical resulting in less AM-FM conversion. Figure 7 shows the measured output power performance when both core supply voltage and buffer supply voltage are 0.7V. When the buffer supply voltage is increased to 1V, a single ended output power about -9.67 dBm is measured across 50 Ω.

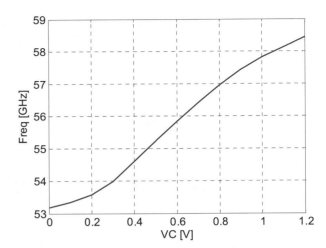

Figure 4.   Measured frequency tuning range versus tuning voltage (V_{DD}=0.7V)

Table I summarizes the measurement results of this oscillator and makes the comparison with other mm-wave oscillators with comparable frequency range. To make a comparison of the performance of the oscillators, two finger-of-merits FOM and FOM_T are used. At 0.7V supply, the oscillator achieves a FOM and FOM_T of -176.32 and -175.71 respectively. At 0.43V supply, the oscillator achieves a FOM and FOM_T of -185.1 and -178.76 respectively. To the authors' best knowledge, this advances the state-of-the art.

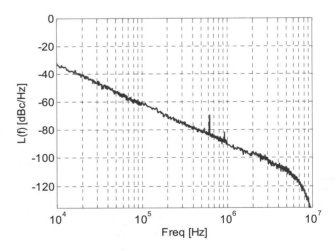

Figure 5.   Measured phase noise curve @ 58.4GHz (V_{DD}=0.7V)

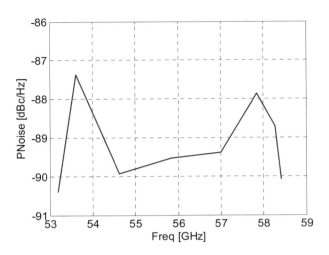

Figure 6.   Measured phase noise@1MHz versus frequency (V_{DD}=0.7V)

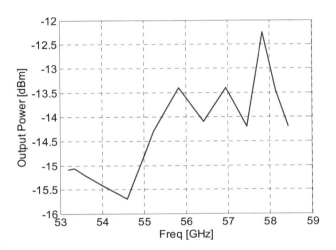

Figure 7.   Measured output power versus frequency (V_{DD}=0.7V)

TABLE I.   STATE-OF-ART OF OSCILLATORS ABOVE 50GHZ

VCO [Ref]	FO (GHz)	FTR (%)	PNoise (dBc/Hz)	P_DBS (mW)	V_dd (V)	FOM (dBc/Hz)	FOM_T (dBc/Hz)	Tech.
M. Tiebout [7]	51.2	1.39%	-85 @1M	1.0	1	-179.19	-162.03	0.12um CMOS
H.Wang [8]	49.5	2.21%	-99.67 @1M	13	1.3	-182.42	-169.31	0.25um CMOS
F. Ellinger [9]	56.5	14.70%	-92 @1M	21.0	1.5	-173.81	-177.16	90nm SOI
C. Cao [10]	56.5	10.27%	-108 @10M	9.8	1.5	-173.13	-173.36	0.13um CMOS
D.D. Kim [11]	70.2	9.55%	-106.14 @10M	5.4	1.2	-175.76	-175.36	65nm SOI
This work	58.4	9.32%	-90.08 @1M	8.1	0.7	-176.32	-175.71	90nm CMOS
	61.7	4.81%	-90.10 @1M	1.2	0.43	-185.1	-178.76	

a. FOM=PNoise-20log($f_0/\Delta f$)+10log(P_{DISS}/1mW)

b. FOM$_T$= PNoise-20log(($f_0/\Delta f$)*(FTR/10))+10log(P_{DISS}/1mW)

V.   CONCLUSION

An enhanced LC tank using inductive division was proposed to improve the phase noise performance and to increase the tuning range of a low voltage mm-wave VCO. Using a 90nm CMOS technology, the presented oscillator achieves a tuning range of 9.32% and a phase noise of -90.08dBc/Hz @ 1MHz offset from 58.4GHz carrier, while consuming 8.1mW from a 0.7V supply voltage. The circuit can work down to 0.43 V supply, achieving a phase noise of -90.10dBc/Hz @ 1MHz offset from the 61.7GHz carrier and consuming only 1.2mW. The implemented VCO achieves the best FOM using the lowest supply voltage among mm-wave oscillators working near 50GHz

ACKNOWLEDGMENT

The authors would like to thank Ilja Ocket (ESAT-TELEMIC), Prof. Dominique Schreurs (ESAT-TELEMIC) and Frederik Daenen (ESAT-MICAS/Imec) for their support during the measurements and Noella Gaethofs (ESAT-MICAS) for the packaging. R&S Belgium is acknowledged for their excellent support with the measurement setup. Lianming Li is supported by a Fellowship from the Chinese Scholarship Council.

REFERENCES

[1] S. Gunnarsson, C. Karnfelt, H. Zirath, R. Kozhuharov, D, Kuylenstierna, A. Alping, and C. Fager, "Highly integrated 60GHz transmitter and receiver MMICs in a GaAs pHEMT technology," IEEE Journal of Solid-State Circuits, Vol. 40, No.11 Nov. 2005. pp. 2174-2186

[2] Y. Baeyens, C. Dorschky, N. Weimann, Q. Lee, R. Kopf, G. Georgiou, J. –P, Mattia, R. Hamm, and Y.-K Chen, " Compact InP-based HBT VCOs with a wide tuning range at W- and D-band, IEEE Trans. Microwave Theory Tech., vol. 48, no.12 Dec. 2000, pp. 2403-2408.

[3] B. Floyd, S. Reynolds, U. Pfeiffer, Y. Beukema, J. Grzyb, and C. Haymes, "A silicon 60GHz reciever and transmitter chipset for broadband communications," ISSCC Digest of Technical Papers, pp. 184–185, Feb. 2006.

[4] W. Winkler, J. Borngraber, B. Heinemann, and F. Herzel, "A fully integrated BiCMOS PLL for 60 GHz wireless applications," ISSCC Digest of Technical Papers, pp. 406–407, Feb. 2005.

[5] C. H. Doan S, Emami, A. Nikenejad, and R. Brodersen, "Milimeter-Wave CMOS design," IEEE Journal of Solid-State Circuits, Vol. 40, No.1 Janu. 2005. pp. 144-155

[6] J. Craninckx, M. Steyaert, "A CMOS 1.8GHz Low-Phase-Noise Voltage-Controlled Oscillator with Prescaler," ISSCC Digest of Technical Papers, pp. 266–267, February 1995.

[7] M. Tiebout, H.Wohlmuth, and W. Simburger, "A 1V 51GHz Fully-Integrated VCO in 0.12 um CMOS," ISSCC Digest of Technical Papers, pp. 300–301, Feb. 2002.

[8] H. Wang, "A 50GHz VCO in 0.25 um CMOS," ISSCC Digest of Technical Papers, pp. 372–373, Feb. 2001.

[9] F. Ellinger, T. Morf, G. Buren, "60GHz VCO with Wideband Tuning Range Fabricated in VLSI SOI CMOS Technology," IEEE Int. Microwave Symp. Dig. Papers, pp. 1329-1332, June. 2004.

[10] C. Cao, K.K.O, "Millimeter-Wave Voltage Controlled Oscillator in 0.13um CMOS Technology," IEEE Journal of Solid-State Circuits, Vol. 41, June.2006. pp. 1297-1304.

[11] D. D. Kim, H.Wohlmuth, and W. Simburger, "A 70GHz Manufacturable Complementary LC-VCO with 6.14 GHz Tuning Range in 65nm SOI CMOS," ISSCC Digest of Technical Papers, pp. 540–541, Feb. 2007.

[12] A. Cathelin, B. Martineau, N. Seller, S. Douyere, J. Gorisse, S. Pruvost, et al "Design for Millimeter-wave Applications on silicon Technologies," ESSCIRC Digest of Technical Papers, pp. 464–471, Sept. 2007.

A Fully Integrated 60 GHz Transmitter Front-End with a PLL, an Image-rejection Filter and a PA in SiGe

Srdjan Glisic[1], Yaoming Sun[2], Frank Herzel[3],
Maxim Piz[5], Eckhard Grass[6] and Christoph Scheytt[7]
IHP
Frankfurt Oder, Germany
glisic@ihp-microelectronics.com

Wolfgang Winkler[4]
Silicon Radar GmbH
Frankfurt Oder, Germany

Abstract□ **This paper presents a fully integrated transmitter front-end for 60 GHz wireless communication, produced in 0.25 □m SiGe:C BiCMOS technology. The transmitter features a mixer, a phase-locked loop (PLL), a preamplifier, an image-rejection filter and a power amplifier (PA). The measured single-ended 1dB compression point at the output is 10.5 dBm and the saturated power is 14.9 dBm. Error free data transmission with a QPSK OFDM signal and data rate of 360 Mbit/s over 5 m was demonstrated.**

I. Introduction

A large license free band of 7 GHz, centred around 60 GHz was assigned as Industrial, Scientific and Medical (ISM) band, offering opportunity for wireless communication with data rate in the order of Gbit/s. Initially III/V technologies had the advantage of high speed for this frequency band, but advances in silicon germanium (SiGe) Bipolar/BiCMOS technologies, with hetero-junction bipolar transistor (HBT) cut-off frequencies reaching $f_T/f_{max} = 300/350$ GHz, made them competitive. Fully integrated 60 GHz chipsets in BiCMOS technologies for wireless communication with data rates in the order of 1 Gbit/s have already been reported [1], [2]. Work was also done in CMOS [3], but no functional transceiver has yet been reported.

In this paper, we present a fully integrated transmitter front-end, built for a system presented in [2]. Moreover, it can be used with any system operating at a frequency around 5 GHz – for dual-radio (5/60 GHz) applications as proposed in the IEEE 802.11 Very High Throughput (VHT) Study group [4]. So far only two integrated designs at 60 GHz with a similar performance have been reported [1], [2]. This is the first transmitter with integrated image-rejection filter.

II. Transmitter Architecture

The transmitter was designed in IHP 0.25 μm production qualified SiGe:C BiCMOS technology. HBT cut-off frequencies are $f_T/f_{max} = 200/200$ GHz [5]. The HBT breakdown voltages are $BV_{CEO} = 1.9$ V and $BV_{CBO} = 4.5$ V. Five metal (aluminium) layers are available.

Transmitter architecture is show in Fig. 1. The transmitter front-end consists of a mixer, phase-locked loop, a preamplifier, an image-rejection filter and a power amplifier.

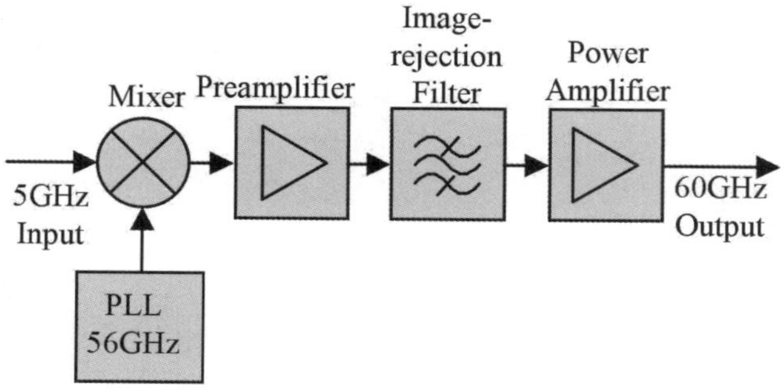

Figure 1. Transmitter architecture.

A. Mixer

A Gilbert cell is used as up-converter mixer core. The simplified schematic of the mixer is shown in Fig. 2. Transistors Q1 to Q6 together with two load resistors Rc form the Gilbert cell core. The up-converter is optimized for high linearity and output power. To achieve a high voltage swing at the output a large resistor value is required for the load resistor Rc. However, the voltage drop across the resistor rises with increasing load resistance. This will deteriorate the transistor performance. A 200 Ω load resistor is a good trade-off.

The IF signal is up-converted in the mixer with the 56 GHz oscillator signal from the integrated PLL. The result is a double-sideband spectrum with a signal at 61 GHz and an out-of-band image at 51 GHz. When the 5 GHz signal is up-converted to 60 GHz, there is a conversion loss. The maximum 60 GHz output 1dB compression point (1dBCP) is -15 dBm in simulation. This signal has to be filtered to remove the image at 51 GHz. Due to the high insertion loss of the image-rejection filter, the 61 GHz signal is additionally attenuated. Because of this, this signal has to be amplified in an amplifier, which follows the mixer.

This paper was funded by the German Federal Ministry for Education and Research (BMBF), under grant number 01 BU 371 (WIGWAM).

242

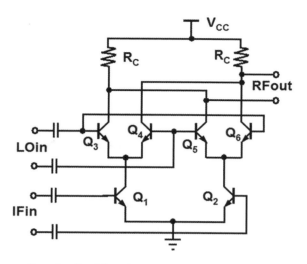

Figure 2.   Simplified schematic of the up-conversion mixer.

The mixer draws 10 mA from a 3.5 V supply. For optimal performance, the mixer requires a 4 dBm differential input signal at 56 GHz from the PLL.

B. PLL

A 56 GHz PLL is used for the LO signal generation. It is a critical component for the performance of the whole system because OFDM signals are sensitive to PLL signal phase noise. The spur level is not critical, but it should be below -45 dBc to keep the integrated phase error small.

The PLL features a VCO with differential output, a divider, a phase-frequency detector, a charge pump and a loop filter (Fig. 3). The divider consists of nine consecutive divide-by-two stages resulting in a division ratio of 512. A higher divider ratio would raise the reference phase noise to an unacceptable level.

The PLL is implemented using a fourth-order topology as shown in Fig. 3. Since the PLL is fully integrated, the Q-factor of the VCO coil cannot be high, so the phase noise level is relatively high, typically between -90 and -95 dBc/Hz at 1 MHz offset. The phase noise has to be suppressed by using a PLL. The PLL acts as a high-pass filter for the phase noise generation in the VCO, requiring a large PLL bandwidth [6]. Reference phase noise is inside the PLL bandwidth amplified by $20\log(512) = 54$ dB. A low-noise reference is required to counteract this large amplification. As discussed in [6], a high PLL bandwidth requires a large charge-pump current, boosting the spurious tones. In order to suppress the spurs, we use a fourth-order PLL topology and a new technique for the calculation of PLL parameters, which gives additional 10 dB spur suppression. Adding a low-pass filter (R3 and C3) creates an additional pole in the loop filter, which reduces the spur level.

The PLL has a 4.5 MHz measured bandwidth and a spur level below -55 dBc. The VCO phase noise at 1 MHz offset is -90 dBc/Hz. The PLL consumes 80 mA from 3 V supply and 60 mA form 2.6 V.

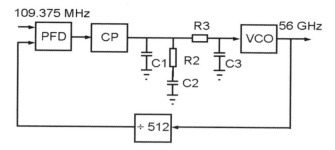

Figure 3.   Fourth-order PLL topology.

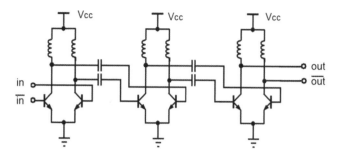

Figure 4.   Simplified schematic of the preamplifier.

C. Preamplifier

The preamplifier features a three-stage common-emitter differential topology. Fig. 4 shows the simplified schematic. Inductors for matching are realized as metal lines. A metal line inductor occupies the smallest chip area for a given inductance and has a medium Q-factor [7]. The loss of microstrip transmission lines is high due to the relatively thin silicon dioxide layer between the top conductor and ground metal.

In order to obtain a symmetrical design, a single-ended preamplifier was laid out first, and then it was copied upside down. The emitters of the differential pairs are connected directly to the chip ground. By doing so, the preamplifier is single-ended measurable. It has a measured gain of 18 dB at 61 GHz. The preamplifier consumes 60 mA from a 2.6 V supply.

D. Image-rejection Filter

The purpose of the filter is to attenuate the signal at 51 GHz. Simulations show that the insertion loss of integrated filters around 60 GHz is significant. The substrate is lossy and ohmic losses are significant because of small cross-section of integrated lines. This reduces Q-factor of resonant structures and limits selectivity. It is possible to design a very good filter (high selectivity and low insertion loss) for this frequency range, but only on a printed circuit board with high accuracy and low loss.

A very important aspect for integrated filters is size, because chip area is expensive. For compact design a hairpin bandpass filter type was chosen. The filter layout can be seen in the transmitter chip photo in Fig. 7. To achieve lower insertion loss, the filter was designed as broadband, but only the lower part of the passband - around 61 GHz - is used. This approach gives sufficient selectivity and better insertion loss.

Measured results (Fig. 5) show that the insertion loss is 11 dB at 61 GHz. The signal at 51 GHz is attenuated by 35 dB resulting in 24 dB image rejection. Electro-magnetic simulations of the filter were done with ADS Momentum program by Agilent. We have relatively good matching between simulation and measurements (Fig. 5). The filter dimensions are 0.6x0.4 mm^2, which is acceptable size.

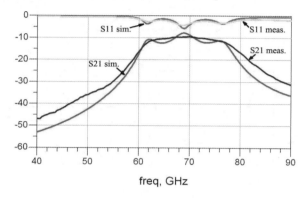

Figure 5.   Measured and simulated S-parameters of the filter.

E. Power Amplifier

The PA features a multi-stage differential cascode topology. Cascode offers high gain, of around 11 dB per stage for IHP technology, and possibility of good matching at both input and output. To achieve the required PA amplification of 25 dB, a three-stage cascode was chosen. The PA, as the rest of the system, is fully differential, for better common-mode noise rejection and robustness. Differential circuits are layed out in close proximity, giving good AC ground at the base of common-base transistors. This reduces the impact ionization, and collector voltage swing is than limited by BV_{CBO}, rather than BV_{CEO}.

The modulation scheme to be used in the system is OFDM, which is sensitive to nonlinear distortion. This means that the PA parameter of interest is the output 1dB compression point rather than saturated output power. To achieve a high 1dBCP – class-A was chosen for the PA.

The matching topology between stages is an L-C structure. It is simple and frequency selective, fulfilling PA selectivity requirement. The inductance was realized as a line in the top metal layer for lower loss. A common solution would be if this line were perpendicular to symmetry axes. But they have been bent to connect at the symmetry axes. This gives good ac ground and a more compact layout (see PA layout in Fig. 7). The stages have been separated by approximately 200 μm to reduce coupling and to alleviate heat conduction.

Simulation of all parasitics and cross-coupling effects in the layout is very important to prevent any oscillations. Passive structures were simulated with Agilent electro-magnetic simulator Momentum. Figure 6 shows a comparison of measured and simulated PA S-parameters. The PA consumes 162 mA from 3.7 V supply.

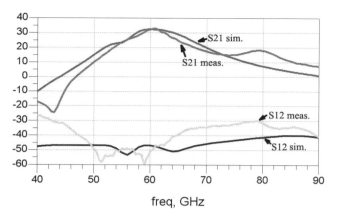

Figure 6.   Comparison of measured and simulated S21 and S12 parameters.

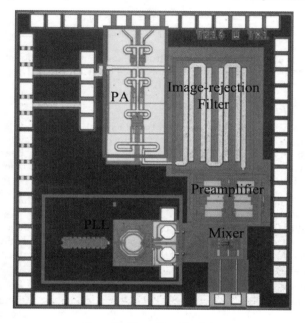

Figure 7.   Tranmitter chip photo.

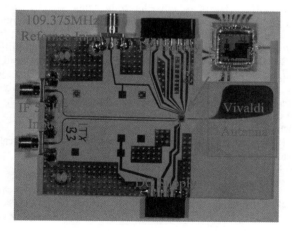

Figure 8.   Transmitter board photo with chip close-up

III. MEASUREMENT RESULTS

The complete transmitter front-end can only be measured on board. The PA was measured on-wafer. The measured single-ended 1dBCP of the PA at 61 GHz is 10.5 dBm and the saturated power is 14.9 dBm. The transmitter chip was mounted on a board and wire bonded (Fig. 8). Since the Vivaldi antenna is single ended, the PA cannot be used differentially, which would double the power and increase the 1dBCP because of symmetrical load. We should note here, that since the system uses an OFDM signal (sensitive to nonlinear distortion) the signal level at the output of the transmitter has to be 6-to-10 dB lower than the 1dBCP. The simulated conversion gain of the transmitter front-end is 40 dB, and the measured image-rejection is better than -40 dB.

The transmitter front-end was measured as a part of the 60 GHz OFDM system for wireless communication [2]. A block diagram of the system is show in Fig. 9. Figure 10 presents a lab photo of the setup. Measurements have shown that the maximum distance for error free data transmission is 5 meters. This is done with a QPSK signal, ¾ coding, and a data rate of 360 Mbit/s. Figure 11 shows measured constellation diagram. The transmitter front-end allowed transmission at a five times larger distance, which corresponds to 14 dB more in the link budget, compared to the system in [2]. The chip size is 1.8x1.4 mm^2 and total power consumption is 1.15 W.

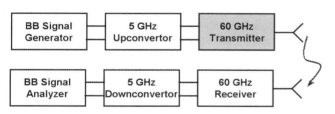

Figure 9. Transmitter and receiver constellation measurement setup.

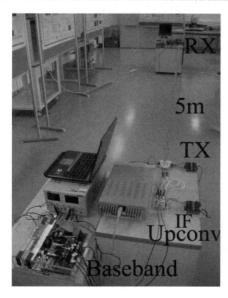

Figure 10. Measurement setup

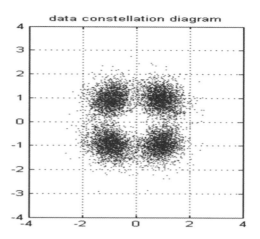

Figure 11. Constellation diagram for QPSK, ¾ coding, OFDM signal with 360 Mbit/s data rate over 5 m distance

IV. CONSLUSION

We presented a fully integrated transmitter front-end for a 60 GHz wireless communication system, fabricated in SiGe:C BiCMOS technology. The transmitter front-end features a mixer, a PLL, a preamplifier, an image-rejection filter and a power amplifier. This is the first 60 GHz transmitter with integrated image rejection filter. The chip was produced, mounted on a board and wire bonded. The board has an integrated Vivaldi antenna. The simulated conversion gain is 40 dB. The measured single-ended PA 1dBCP is 10.5 dBm and the transmitter image-rejection is below -40 dB. Error free data transmission at 360 Mbit/s over 5 m was demonstrated. The transmitter can be used with any system operating in the frequency band around 5 GHz, thereby forming a 5/60 GHz dual-radio as proposed in [4].

ACKNOWLEDGMENT

The authors thank Markus Ehrig for his help with the measurement.

REFERENCES

[1] B. Floyd, S. Reynolds, U. Pfeiffer, T. Beukema, J. Gryzb, C. Haymes, "A Silicon 60GHz Receiver and Transmitter Chipset for Broadband Communications," in *Proc. ISSCC,* 2006, pp. 649–658.

[2] Y. Sun, S. Glisic, F. Herzel, K. Schmalz, E. Grass, W. Winkler and R. Kraemer, "An Integrated 60 GHz Transceiver Front-End for OFDM in SiGe: BiCMOS," in *Proc .of the 16th. Wireless World Research Forum,,* 2006, pp. 121–127.

[3] B. Razavi, "A 60 GHz Direct-Conversion CMOS Receiver," *ISSCC Dig. Tech. Papers,* Feb. 2005, pp. 400-401.

[4] H. Singh, S. S. Lee, C. Chaplin and J. Park, "Potential benefits of dual-radio VHT systems," IEEE 802 11-08-0349-01-0vht. IEEE 802.11 VHT Study Group.

[5] B. Heinemann et al., "Novel Collector Design for High-Speed SiGe:C HBTs," IEDM Tech. Dig. 2002, pp. 775-778.

[6] S. Glisic and W. Winkler, "A Broadband Low Spur Fully Integrated BiCMOS PLL for 60 GHz Wireless Applications," *RWS 2006,* San Diego, USA, pp. 451-454.

[7] Y. Sun, J. Borngraeber, F. Herzel and W. Winkler, "A fully integrated 60 GHz LNA in SiGe:C BiCMOS technology," *BCTM,* Santa Barbara, Oct. 2005, pp. 14-17.

60GHz Quadrature Doppler Radar Transceiver in a 0.25µm SiGe BiCMOS Technology

Hugo Veenstra, Marc Notten

Philips Research
High Tech Campus 37
5656 AE Eindhoven, The Netherlands
hugo.veenstra@philips.com

Xiongchuan Huang, John R. Long

Electronics Research Laboratory/DIMES
Delft University of Technology
Mekelweg 4, 2628 CD Delft, The Netherlands

Abstract□ A 60GHz Doppler radar for short-range presence detection applications in the unlicensed 60GHz band is described. The 1.1x2.1 mm^2 SiGe:C BiCMOS IC includes a 60GHz VCO, a polyphase filter for quadrature signal generation, a low-noise amplifier with current reuse quadrature down-conversion mixer and a power amplifier. The VCO can be tuned from 59.5-61.5GHz. The receiver quadrature accuracy is better than 27dB across a ±10MHz IF bandwidth. With a single-ended input drive of the differential input, the receiver achieves a conversion gain of 55dB and a DSB noise figure of 22.9dB. Assuming 4dBi antenna gains, the radar IC supports up to 5m range.

I. INTRODUCTION

Doppler radar systems are widely used for speed detection. An un-modulated carrier is continuously transmitted and, after reflection by any object, received. The received frequency is identical to the transmitted frequency for static objects. With a direct conversion receiver, the reflection from static objects corresponds to dc at the IF output. For moving objects, the received frequency is shifted due to the Doppler effect:

$$f_d = \frac{2v}{\lambda} \qquad (1)$$

with λ the wavelength of the transmitted signal and v is the relative speed of the object. For example, a relative speed of 2.5m/s at 60GHz results in a 1kHz Doppler frequency shift. Thus, the relative speed of objects can be found from the IF output frequency in a direct conversion radar receiver. The sign of the Doppler frequency is positive for objects approaching the radar and negative for objects moving away and may be detected by quadrature down-conversion in the receiver. Note that a Doppler radar cannot be used for distance detection. If the distance to objects must be determined, modulation must be applied in the transmitter. However, presence detection is readily realized using Doppler radar. The attenuation of walls at 60GHz is attractive for frequency reuse across rooms. The received signal power P_r can be calculated from the radar equation:

$$P_r = \frac{P_T G_T G_R \sigma \lambda^2}{(4\pi)^3 d^4} \qquad (2)$$

with P_T the transmit power, G_T and G_R the antenna gains, σ the radar cross section (RCS) of the object, λ the wavelength and d the distance to the object. For example, the received signal power reflected from an object with $\sigma = 0.2m^2$ at $d = 5m$ and -5dBm transmit power is $P_r = -111$dBm. The double-sideband input noise power N_i across a bandwidth B follows from $N_i = 2kTB$, with k Boltzmann's constant and T the absolute temperature. Across a 10kHz detection bandwidth, the input noise power is therefore -131dBm. From the comparison of P_r and N_i, it follows that a 20dB receiver noise figure is sufficient for 0dB signal-to-noise ratio (SNR). Such requirements can be met with a low-cost SiGe BiCMOS technology.

The radar transceiver block diagram is shown in Fig. 1.

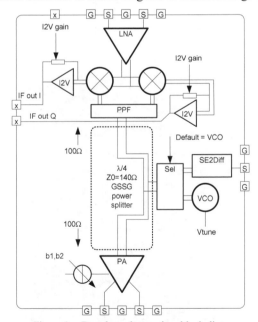

Figure 1. Doppler radar receiver block diagram.

The IC includes a 60GHz VCO, a polyphase filter (PPF) for quadrature signal generation, a quadrature down-conversion mixer with current reuse low-noise amplifier and a power amplifier. The IF path is dc-coupled to enable detection of slow-moving objects that generate low-IF signals. The VCO signal is shared between the receiver and transmitter.

In Section II, the VCO and polyphase filter are explained to more detail. Section III discusses the passive power splitter used at the VCO output. The LNA and down-conversion mixer are discussed in Section IV. Several inductors on the IC are realized as shorted transmission line stubs. The trade-offs between spiral inductor and shorted stub are discussed in Section V. Experimental results are presented in Section VI.

II. LC-VCO AND POLYPHASE FILTER

A. Varactorless VCO

Since the quality factor of the varactor at 60GHz is approximately 3 in the BiCMOS process, a varactorless VCO topology is used. The simplified circuit diagram of the VCO is shown in Fig. 2.

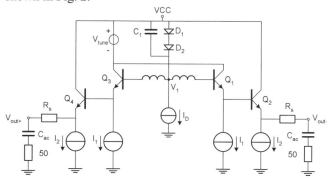

Figure 2. Varactorless LC-VCO topology.

Each emitter follower provides approximately 90° phase shift between its emitter and base currents. The double emitter follower translates the resistive output load into a negative resistance at the input of the first emitter follower, realizing undamping to start and sustain oscillation. The LC-tank capacitance is dominated by the collector-base capacitance of the first emitter followers Q_1, Q_3. The collector-base bias voltage of Q_1, Q_3 can thus be used for frequency tuning. The differential output power into on-chip 50Ω loads is approximately -6dBm. More details on the VCO can be found in [1].

B. Polyphase filter (PPF)

A two-stage 60GHz passive RC polyphase filter is used to generate quadrature signals from the VCO output signal. The circuit diagram of the first filter section is shown in Fig. 3. This PPF topology enables a wideband phase matching. The amplitudes of the I and Q outputs are designed to be equal at 60GHz. The second filter section is identical, although the RC time-constants of the two sections are slightly different to achieve optimum phase accuracy across a wide frequency range.

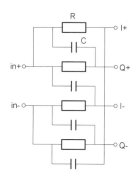

Figure 3. First polyphase filter section.

The filter employs thin-film resistors and MiM capacitors. With a filter resistor value of 50Ω, a practical value for the filter capacitor of 53fF is needed. The impact of the finite quality factors of the passives (e.g, Q(MIM) $\approx$ 17 at 60GHz) and the interconnect were analyzed during the design of the PPF. With transmission line models, the simulated quadrature phase accuracy remains within 2°.

Since the down-conversion mixer requires at least -6dBm from the VCO, the 10dB attenuation of the PPF is compensated for by an amplifier. More details on the PPF can be found in [2].

III. POWER SPLITTER

The VCO output signal drives the PA in the transmitter and the down-conversion mixer via the PPF in the receiver. To split the VCO output signal, a passive power splitter based on transmission lines is used, see Fig. 4.

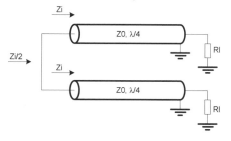

Figure 4. Passive power splitter.

The two transmission lines each have a length $\lambda/4$ at 60GHz and a characteristic impedance of $Z_0 = 70\Omega$. With two equal load impedances of $R_l = 50\Omega$, the input power is split in two halves. The impedance transformation from $R_l = 50\Omega$ to $Z_i = 100\Omega$ across each transmission line results in a 50Ω load impedance for the VCO.

Each transmission line has a physical length of 630μm. The relatively large size of the power splitter is exploited to create distance between the PA output and LNA input. Since this radar uses a zero-IF receiver, cross-talk from transmitter to receiver leads to dc-offset in the IF-path which may saturate the receiver and thus must be minimized.

IV. CURRENT REUSE LNA/MIXER

The receiver uses a common-emitter LNA followed by Gilbert cells for quadrature down-conversion. To reduce the power dissipation, the bias current of the LNA is reused in the Gilbert cell mixers. The circuit diagram of the LNA/mixer circuit is shown in Fig. 5. The quadrature LO inputs LO_I_{in} and LO_Q_{in} are driven by the outputs of the PPF. The LNA/mixer design requires a minimum supply voltage of 3.5V. However, in this design, the mixer operates from a 4.5V nominal supply. The extra headroom is used across the mixer load resistors. Since only a few kHz of IF bandwidth is required in this application, the value of the load resistors can be chosen relatively high to enable a high conversion gain.

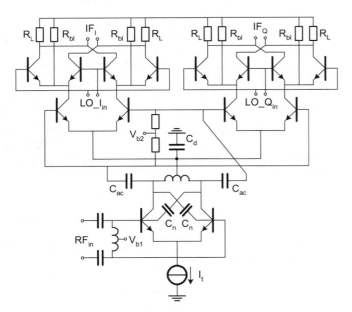

Figure 5.   Current reuse LNA / Quadrature mixer.

The LNA uses an LC input network for impedance matching. Neutrodyne capacitors C_n are applied to improve the reverse isolation from the VCO signal to the LNA input. The LNA output capacitance is tuned out at 60GHz using a parallel inductor. The center tap of this inductor is decoupled to ground via capacitor C_d. The LNA output signal is ac-coupled to the Gilbert cell RF inputs via capacitors C_{ac}. The 10mA LNA bias current I_t is split in two equal halves at the center tap of the LNA load inductor to bias the Gilbert cell mixers. Large area mixer load resistors R_L at the IF output are used for low 1/f-noise and low dc-offset. Current bleeding resistors R_{bl} are used to reduce the dc voltage across the mixer load resistors and enable a further increase in conversion gain.

The differential IF outputs are converted to single-ended signal using op-amps as shown in Fig. 1. The feedback resistors are programmable for gain control.

V. INDUCTOR VERSUS SHORTED STUB

Inductors are often realized as spiral inductor. For low inductance values, a transmission line shorted at one terminal behaves as a (frequency dependent) inductor.

The inductance L_{eq} realized by a shorted stub depends on the length l and characteristic impedance Z_0 of the transmission line, the effective relative permittivity $\varepsilon_{r,eff}$ and the frequency, via

$$L_{eq} = \frac{Z_0 \tan(\frac{2\pi f l}{c} \sqrt{\varepsilon_{r,eff}})}{2\pi f} \qquad (3)$$

Here, c is the speed of light in vacuum. The input impedance of the shorted stub behaves inductively if the length l of the line is less than $\lambda/4$ [3].

Compared to a spiral inductor, a shorted stub offers usually a lower quality factor and lower self-resonant frequency. Moreover, the inductance of the shorted-stub shows more variation across frequency, leading to narrower bandwidths in impedance matching circuits. Thus, it seems logical to prefer spiral inductors over shorted stubs. However, the spiral inductor has some drawbacks that are overcome by the shorted stub. Firstly, the spiral inductor cannot be shielded from the substrate by a solid ground plane. Shorted metal loops around the inductor lower the inductor quality factor and must be avoided. A shorted stub built from a coplanar transmission line on top of a ground shield enables simple distribution of power supply and ground across the IC. Secondly, the shorted stub provides excellent shielding from the substrate and from nearby components. Coupling between multiple inductors realized from shorted stubs is nearly absent, whereas coupling between spiral inductors is often a concern. Thus, shorted-stub inductors are much simpler to use in practical designs.

In this design, spiral inductors are only used when the quality factor is critical for circuit performance. This is the case in the VCO, at the PA output and the LNA input. In all other cases, shorted stubs are used.

VI. EXPERIMENTAL RESULTS

The IC has been realized in NXP Semiconductors' QUBiC4X 0.25µm SiGe:C BiCMOS process with f_T/f_{max} = 130/140 GHz [4]. The IC measures 1.1x2.1mm^2 and dissipates 0.5W from a nominal 4.5V supply voltage. The IC photomicrograph is shown in Fig. 6. The IC is intended for flip-chip mounting, so several ground bondpads are distributed across the IC to reduce thermal resistance and minimize the ground impedance.

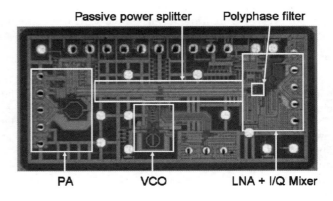

Figure 6.   IC photomicrograph.

Since there is no modulation in the transmitter, the VCO operating frequency can be monitored at the PA output. The measured VCO tuning range is between 59.5-61.5GHz.

A typical IF output spectrum is shown in Fig. 7. This result is obtained with an RF input frequency 17.5MHz above the on-chip VCO frequency of 61.113GHz, leading to a 17.5MHz IF output signal. The receiver input signal level was -74dBm, driven into one side of the differential receiver input. The inverted receiver input is terminated into a dummy 50Ω resistor. This is sub-optimum for noise and gain, but no 60GHz balun was available at the time of evaluation. The IF output was evaluated with a FET probe with unity gain.

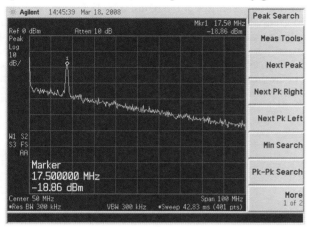

Figure 7.   Example IF output signal at -74dBm input signal.

The -18.86dBm output level corresponds to a receiver conversion gain of 55.14dB. From the -38dBm noise floor at the IF output across a 300kHz resolution bandwidth, a receiver noise figure of 22.9dB follows. With differential excitation, a 3dB increase in conversion gain and reduction in noise figure are expected.

The quadrature accuracy has been evaluated using a Rohde & Schwarz SMIQ vector signal analyzer. The quadrature IF output signals are up-converted inside the vector signal analyzer. The quadrature accuracy can be analyzed from the sideband suppression of the up-converted signal. Moreover, the SMIQ allows programmable correction of amplitude and phase inaccuracy, so that a detailed analysis of the quadrature mismatch can be performed. The results are shown in Fig. 8.

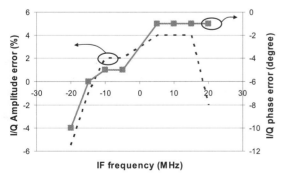

Figure 8.   Measured quadrature accuracy across the IF band.

The image rejection is better than 27dB for IF frequencies between -10MHz and 10MHz.

The power amplifier, designed for 0dBm differential output power, showed instability when operated at its nominal 4.5V supply voltage. At 3.3V supply, the amplifier was stable. Since the amplifier bias current is about half the intended bias current when operated at 3.3V supply, the output power strongly reduces. The measured output power was -13dBm at 60GHz. The measured chip performance is summarized in Table I.

TABLE I.   SUMMARY OF EVALUATION RESULTS.

Supply voltage	4.5V
Power dissipation	0.5W
VCO frequency	59.5-61.5GHz
IF bandwidth	+/-10MHz
I/Q accuracy	>27dB
Rx conversion gain (single-ended receiver in)	55dB
Rx DSB noise figure (single-ended receiver in)	22.9dB
PA output power (at 3.3V supply voltage)	-13dBm single-ended
Chip size	1.1x2.1mm^2

VII.   CONCLUSIONS

A 60GHz Doppler radar transceiver IC has been presented. Quadrature signals are derived from the single-phase 60GHz VCO using a two-stage passive polyphase filter. The bias current from the common-emitter LNA is reused to bias the Gilbert cell down-conversion mixers. Assuming 4dBi transmit and receive antenna gains, the IC supports up to 5m range.

ACKNOWLEDGMENT

The authors would like to thank Dave van Goor and John Mills for measurement support.

REFERENCES

[1]   H. Veenstra, M. Notten, "Varactorless, tunable LC-VCO for microwave frequencies in a 0.25µm SiGe BiCMOS Technology," in *Proc. IEEE BCTM*, 2007, pp. 54-57.

[2]   M. Notten, H. Veenstra, "60GHz quadrature signal generation with a single phase VCO and polyphase filter in a 0.25µm SiGe BiCMOS Technology, " in *Proc. IEEE BCTM*, 2008, unpublished.

[3]   D. M. Pozar, Microwave Engineering, 3rd ed., Wiley, 2005, pp. 60.

[4]   P. Deixler et al, "QUBiC4X: An f_T/f_{max}=130/140GHz SiGe:C-BiCMOS Manufacturing Technology with Elite Passives for Emerging Microwave Applications," in *Proc. IEEE BCTM*, 2004, pp. 233-236.

A 60GHz Digitally Controlled Phase Shifter in CMOS

Yikun Yu, Peter Baltus, Arthur van Roermund
Department of Electrical Engineering,
Eindhoven University of Technology
Eindhoven, the Netherlands

Dennis Jeurissen, Anton de Graauw, Edwin van der
Heijden, Ralf Pijper
NXP Semiconductors, Research
Eindhoven, the Netherlands

Abstract — **This paper presents a 60GHz digitally controlled phase shifter in the 65nm CMOS technology. Using a differential varactor-loaded transmission-line architecture, the phase shifter achieves a phase resolution of 22.5□, an average insertion loss of 8.5 to 10.3dB and a return loss of better than 10dB from 55 to 65GHz. The phase shifter occupies an area of only 0.2mm². To the knowledge of the authors, this is the first 60GHz digitally controlled phase shifter with a phase resolution of 22.5□ in silicon reported to date. It is well suited for a 60GHz phased array.**

I. INTRODUCTION

Recently there is much interest in the 60GHz frequency band for high-speed short-range wireless communication [1] – [7]. The large bandwidth available around 60GHz, with at least 3GHz worldwide overlap (59 to 62GHz), offers the possibility of data transmission at rates of several gigabits per second.

At 60GHz the path loss is high due to the small wavelength thus it is necessary to use a high gain antenna. Phased array [8] is a well-known technique to provide an increased antenna gain and directionality as well as electronic-controlled beam steerability by using multiple antennas. This is highly beneficial to the 60GHz wireless system.

Phase shifters are essential components in a phased array to adjust the phase of each antenna path and steer the beam. As shown in Figure 1, by placing the phase shifters after the LNAs, the received signals from the multiple antennas are amplified, phase shifted and combined before frequency down conversion. The RF beam forming architecture does not require any additional mixers, LO signals, analog-to-digital or digital-to-analog converters as compared to a standard single-antenna transceiver. Furthermore, because of the spatial filtering of interferers, the dynamic range and therefore the power dissipation of the mixers and subsequent stages can be reduced. Thus RF beam forming has the advantage of low cost and low power. The main challenge is to design a low-loss broadband and high-resolution phase shifter with a phase control range of 360° at 60GHz [6], [7] especially in a low cost CMOS technology.

This work presents the design of a 60GHz digitally controlled phase shifter in the 65nm CMOS technology. Using a differential varactor-loaded transmission-line architecture, the phase shifter has a phase resolution of 22.5°, an average insertion loss of 8.5 to 10.3dB and a return loss of better than 10dB from 55 to 65GHz. To the knowledge of the authors, this is the first 60GHz digitally controlled phase shifter with a phase resolution of 22.5° in silicon reported to date.

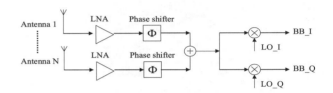

Figure 1. An RF beam forming receiver in which the received signals from multi antennas are amplified, phase shifted and combined before down conversion.

II. DESIGN OF PHASE SHIFTER

A phase shifter with a phase control range of 360° and a phase resolution of 22.5° is the typical requirement in phased array systems [8]. Phase shifters can be designed by tuning the lumped element equivalent of a transmission line.

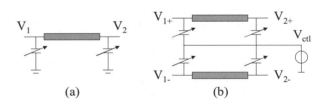

Figure 2. A schematic of (a) a conventional varactor-loaded transmission-line phase shifter; (b) a proposed differential phase shifter consisting of a differential transmission line loaded with a differential varactor at each side.

Figure 2(a) shows a conventional varactor-loaded transmission-line phase shifter [9], [17]. It consists of a transmission line loaded with a varactor at each side. The varactor capacitance can be varied by the DC control voltage and creates a perturbation in the insertion phase and characteristic impedance of the π section.

In this work, a differential varactor-loaded transmission-line phase shifter (Figure 2(b)) is used. The phase shifter consists of a differential transmission line loaded with and a differential MOS varactor at each side. The cross-sectional view of a differential MOS varactor is shown in Figure 3 [18]. The top and bottom plates of the varactor are formed by the poly gates and n-well. The differential gate terminals of the varactor are connected to the transmission line and the n-well of the varactor is connected to the DC control voltage.

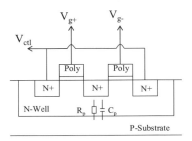

Figure 3. A cross-sectional view of a differential poly/n-well MOS varactor

One advantage of using a differential phase shifter is that the differential path could be swapped to provide a discrete phase step of 180°. Thus the differential phase shifter is only required to achieve a phase control range of another 180°.

Another advantage of using a differential phase shifter is that a differential varactor has better capacitance-control range and better quality factor as compared to a single-ended varactor. This is because that operating in a differential mode, the n-well node of a varactor is a virtual ground and not sensitive to any parasitics. In contrast, it is difficult to create a low-impedance broadband AC ground at the n-well node of a single-ended varactor especially at 60GHz. As a result, a differential phase shifter has better performance as compared to a conventional single-ended phase shifter.

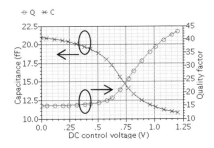

Figure 4. The capacitance and quality factor of a differential MOS varactor at 60GHz in simulation.

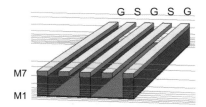

Figure 5. A differential coplanar transmission line with solid metal-1 ground underneath the metal-7 signal lines.

The transmission line in Figure 2 could be replaced by distributed low-pass structures consisting of spiral inductors and capacitors [9]. The advantage of using a transmission line instead of a spiral inductor is that a transmission line is easy to model, scalable and has better isolation between lines.

The phase control range of a phase shifter depends on the capacitance-control ratio of the varactor and the length and characteristic impedance of the transmission line. By using a high-impedance transmission line, a large phase control range can be achieved. A high-impedance transmission line, however, usually has a higher loss. As a trade-off between the phase-control range, insertion loss and return loss, the differential impedance of the transmission line is chosen to be equal to the system impedance (100Ω).

Figure 4 shows the performance of a differential MOS varactor at 60GHz in simulation. The DC bias voltages of the gates are set to 0.6V and the DC control voltage at the n-well is swept from 0 to 1.2V. The CV curve is almost flat when the control voltage is around 0 or 1.2V. By setting the control voltage digitally to either 0 or 1.2V, the varactor has a capacitance-control ratio of about 2 and a quality factor of more than 15 at 60GHz.

The transmission line used in this work is shown in Figure 5. It's a differential coplanar transmission line in ground-signal-ground-signal-ground (GSGSG) configuration with solid metal-1 ground underneath the signal lines. The signal lines are using metal-7 and the ground lines are using metal-7 down to metal-1 by vias. Here the width of the signal lines, ground lines and the gaps between them are all 4μm. The ground walls around the signal lines highly improve the isolation between lines, thus the transmission lines can be closely placed together in the layout to save area.

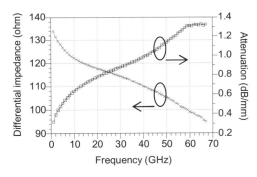

Figure 6. Measured differential impedance and attenuation of the transmission line.

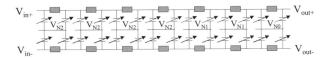

Figure 7. A schematic of 60GHz phase shifter, in which seven π sections are cascaded to realize a phase control range of 157.5°.

Figure 6 shows the measurement results of the transmission line. The measurement procedure is similar to that in [10]. The transmission line has a differential impedance of 100Ω and an attenuation of 1.3dB/mm at 60GHz.

Due to the limited capacitance-control ratio of a MOS varactor, the phase control range of each section is designed to be about 22.5° at 60GHz. The length of each transmission line is about 0.16 wavelengths at 60GHz. The insertion phase of each section is designed to be about either -101° or -79° when the control voltage is low or high respectively, in order to keep the impedance of each section relatively constant.

Seven π-sections are cascaded to achieve a total phase control range of 157.5° as shown in Figure 7. The DC bias voltages of the transmission lines are 0.6V. There are 8 different phase states by setting the control voltage of a certain number of π-sections to logic low or high according to 3 digital control bits (V_{N2}, V_{N1} and V_{N0} in Figure 7).

The phase shifter is implemented in the 65nm CMOS technology and occupies an active area of 0.2mm². Figure 8 shows the photograph of the phase shifter. Open and short de-embedding structures are used to correct for the bondpad and ESD parasitics. The total chip area is 1mm².

Open/short de-embedding structures

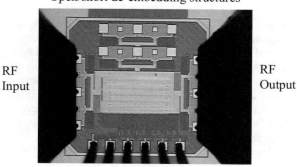

RF Input   RF Output

DC supply and 3-bit digital control

Figure 8.   The photograph of the phase shifter including open and short de-embedding structures.

III. MEASUREMENT RESULTS

Four-port on-wafer S-parameter measurements were conducted in a frequency range extending from 100MHz up to 67GHz using an Agilent E8361A combined with an N4421B H67 test-set together providing four-port measurement capability. The HP4155B parameter analyzer combined with a 41501B expander box was used for biasing of the test structures. Furthermore a 4-port probe-tip calibration was performed to place the measurement reference plane at the tips of the dual signal RF probes and finally on-wafer open and short structures were available for de-embedding purposes.

Two-port differential-mode S-parameters are derived from the four-port S-parameters [11]. The bondpad and ESD parasitics are de-embedded by the open and short de-embedding structures.

Figure 9 shows the insertion phase of the 8 different phase states over frequency. At 60GHz the phase resolution is 22° and the phase control range is 156°. The RMS phase error of the 8 phase states is less than 9.2°, as compared to an ideal

phase shifter with a phase resolution of 22.5°, for all the frequencies from 50 to 65GHz.

Figure 10 shows the relative phase shift of the 8 different phase states referred to state 000 ($N_2=N_1=N_0=0$). The phase shifter provides an almost linear phase shift from 1 to 67GHz.

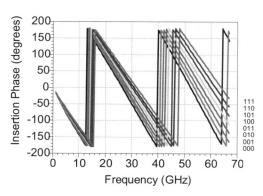

Figure 9.   The insertion phase of 8 different phase states over frequency.

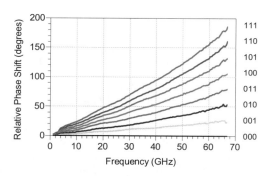

Figure 10. The relative phase shift of 8 different phase states over frequency.

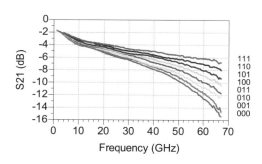

Figure 11. The insertion loss of 8 different phase states over frequency.

Figure 11 shows the insertion loss of the 8 different phase states over frequency. The insertion loss is 9.4±3.1dB over the 8 phase states at 60GHz. This loss variation is due to the low Q and large capacitance of a varactor when the DC control voltage is low (as shown in Figure 4). The average insertion loss is between 8.5dB and 10.3dB from 55 to 65GHz, and is between 1.7 to 11dB from 1 to 67GHz. Variable gain amplifiers could be used in each RF path to equalize the loss variation of the phase shifters and avoid array pattern degradation.

Figure 12 shows the input and output return loss of the phase shifter, which are better than 10dB from 55 to 65GHz and better than 9dB from 1 to 67GHz.

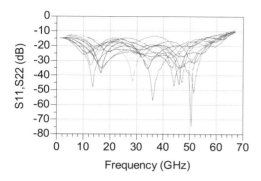

Figure 12. The return loss of 8 different phase states over frequency.

In Table 1, the key results of this work are summarized and compared with other passive [9], [12], [15] and active [13], [14], [16] phase shifters in compound semiconductors and silicon. The phase shifter presented in this work has a low insertion loss (among passive phase shifters) and a high phase resolution at 60GHz.

TABLE1. BENCHMARK OF PHASE SHIFTERS

Reference	Fre-quency (GHz)	Phase range / Resolution (degrees)	Gain (dB)	DC power (mW)	Tech-nology
This work	60	180 diff./22.5	-9.4	Passive ~0	65nm CMOS
Ellinger [9]	5.5	360/analog	-3.9	Passive ~0	0.6µm GaAs MESFET
Kang [12]	12	360/11.25	-14.5	Passive ~0	0.18µm CMOS
Maruhashi [15]	34	360/22.5	-13.1	Passive ~0	0.15µm GaAs HJFET
Kang [13]	12	360/22.5	3.5	Active 26.6	0.18µm CMOS
Koh [14]	26	360/22.5	-3	Active 12	0.13µm CMOS
MIN [16]	34	360/22.5	1	Active 5.4	0.12µm SiGe BiCMOS

IV. CONCLUSION

The phased array technique is highly beneficial to 60GHz wireless communication. Phase shifters are essential components in a phased array. This work presents the design of a 60GHz digitally controlled phase shifter in the 65nm CMOS technology. Using a differential varactor-loaded transmission-line architecture, the phase shifter has a phase resolution of 22.5°, an average insertion loss of between 8.5 to 10.3dB and a return loss of better than 10dB from 55 to 65GHz. The phase shifter occupies an area of only 0.2mm^2. Thanks to its low cost, simple design, low insertion loss and high phase resolution at 60GHz, the phase shifter is well suited for a 60GHz phased array.

ACKNOWLEDGMENT

The authors would like to thank Dr. Raf Roovers in the Research Department of NXP semiconductors for support in this work and Manel Collados in the same department for his help during the measurements.

REFERENCES

[1] P. Smulders, "Exploiting the 60 GHz Band for Local Wireless Multimedia Access," IEEE Communications Magazines, January 2002

[2] C. H. Doan, et al, "Design Considerations for 60 GHz CMOS Radio," IEEE Communications Magazines, December 2004

[3] B. Razavi, "A 60-GHz CMOS Receiver Front-End," IEEE JSSC, January 2006

[4] S. Reynolds, et al, "A Silicon 60-GHz Receiver and Transmitter Chipset for Broadband Communications," IEEE JSSC, December 2006

[5] K. Scheir, et al, "A 52GHz Phased-Array Receiver Front-end in 90nm Digital CMOS", ISSCC 2008

[6] A. Natarajan, et al, "A Bidirectional RF-Combining 60GHz Phased-Array Front-End", ISSCC2007

[7] S. Alalusi, et al, "A 60GHz Phased Array in CMOS," IEEE CICC, 2006

[8] A. Hajimiri, et al, "Integrated Phased Array Systems in Silicon," Proceedings of the IEEE, September 2005

[9] F. Ellinger, et al, "Varactor-Loaded Transmission-Line Phase Shifter at C-Band Using Lumped Elements," IEEE Trans. on MTT, April 2003

[10] L. Tiemeijer, et al, "Low-Loss Patterned Ground Shield Interconnect Transmission Lines in Advanced IC Processes," IEEE Trans. on MTT, April 2003

[11] D. Bockelman, et al, "Combined Differential and Common-Mode Scattering Parameters: Theory and Simulation", IEEE Trans. on MTT, July 1995

[12] D. Kang, et al, "Ku-band MMIC Phase Shifter Using a Parallel Resonator with 0.18-µm CMOS Technology", IEEE Trans. on MTT, January 2006

[13] D. Kang, et al, "A 4-bit CMOS Phase Shifter Using Distributed Active Switches", IEEE Trans. on MTT, July 2007

[14] K. Koh, et al, "A 0.13-µm CMOS Phase Shifters for X-, Ku-, and K-band Phased Arrays", IEEE JSSC, November 2007

[15] K. Maruhashi, et al, "Design and Performance of a Ka-band Monolithic Phase Shifter Utilizing Nonresonant FET Switches", IEEE Trans. on MTT, August 2000

[16] B. Min, et al, "Ka Band BiCMOS 4-bit Phase Shifter with Integrated LNA for Phased Array T/R Module", IEEE MTT-S 2007

[17] A. Nagra, et al, "Distributed Analog Phase Shifters with Low Insertion Loss", IEEE Trans. on MTT, September 1999

[18] R. Staszewski, et al, "A Digital Controlled Oscillator in a 90 nm Digital CMOS Process for Mobile Phones", IEEE JSSC, November 2005

A 71-73 GHz Voltage-Controlled Standing-Wave Oscillator in 90 nm CMOS Technology

Francesco M. De Paola, Raffaella Genesi and Danilo Manstretta
Electronics Department
University of Pavia
Via Ferrata 1, 27100 Pavia, Italy
francesco.depaola@unipv.it

Abstract— In this contribution we present a standing-wave voltage controlled oscillator that is suitable for operation in the lower licensed E-band (i.e., 71-73 GHz). Frequency tuning is achieved by periodically loading a shielded differential transmission with inversion-mode varactors. An output buffer is introduced to facilitate on-chip probing. The oscillator is implemented in 90 nm CMOS technology. The core power consumption is 19 mW from a 1.2 V supply and area occupation is $120 \times 80 \ \mu m^2$. For a 72 GHz frequency, the oscillator exhibits a measured phase noise of -112.2 dBc/Hz at 10 MHz. The resulting figure-of-merit is -176.5 dBc/Hz.

I. INTRODUCTION

In recent years, mainly because of the spectrum congestion below 10 GHz, the huge amount of bandwidth available millimeter-wave frequencies has captured the interest of researchers in the exploration for efficient architectures and circuit solutions for radio transceivers. The advantages of an increased operation frequency reside mainly in the increased available bandwidth, that means higher data rates, and in the reduction in size of the radiating antennas, that ultimately results into more compact and portable systems. Due to the different transmission properties of the atmosphere in the millimeter-wave region, several frequency bands have been targeted for the development of new applications. Among them, the unlicensed 57-64 GHz band has been dedicated to short-range high-data rate communications mainly for last-mile coverage or indoor networking while the 71-76, 81-86 and 92-95 GHz bands, also known as E-band, are used for point-to-point high-bandwidth communication links. The latter frequencies, as opposed to the 57-64 GHz band, require transmitting licenses from the FCC, though they do not suffer from the effects of oxygen absorption. However, there are plans for 10 Gbit/s links using these frequencies as well. In between, the 76-77 GHz band is allocated to vehicular radar applications. Traditionally millimeter-wave frequencies are considered the natural playground for III-V technologies. However, the continuous scaling of standard CMOS has recently achieved transistors with f_T and f_{MAX} that exceed 100 GHz [1]. This opportunity is opening the way for radio systems with an unprecedented level of integration: not only

This work has been carried out in the framework of the Italian National Research Program FIRB (contract nr. RBIP063L4L).

the analog and RF circuitry can be integrated together with the digital core on the same chip, but also the antenna has a reasonable size that theoretically allows it to be implemented on the same silicon die. In this perspective, while it has been demonstrated [1] that MOS transistors can still be used as active devices at such high frequencies, passive components still suffer from the loss of the silicon substrate and the metal interconnects that lower their quality factor when compared to III-V semi-insulating substrate technologies. A viable solution to this problem resides in the exploitation of the metal layers to implement shielded transmission lines at millimeter-wave. In this paper we describe a standing-wave voltage-controlled oscillator (SWO), based on a shielded quarter-wave transmission line, that operates in the 71-73 GHz band. In section II the transmission line-based resonator principle is described. Standing-wave oscillator design is addressed in section III. Finally, experimental results are given in section IV.

II. TRANSMISSION LINE RESONATOR

It is well known that a transmission line terminated with a short circuit or with an open circuit behaves like a resonator. For instance, a parallel type of resonance can be achieved using a short-circuited transmission line that has an electrical length of $\lambda/4$ at the desired oscillation frequency [2]. At the resonance, the line behaves as a parallel LC tank with

$$R_{\text{tank}} = \frac{4QZ_0}{\pi} \quad C_{\text{tank}} = \frac{\pi}{4\omega_0 Z_0} \quad L_{\text{tank}} = \frac{1}{\omega_0^2 C_{\text{tank}}} . (1)$$

The quality factor (Q) is a function of the propagation coefficient (β) and of the attenuation per unit-length (α)

$$Q = \frac{\beta}{2\alpha} \quad (2)$$

To overcome high-frequency limitations, a shielding technique has been proposed [3], [4] to prevent the electric field from penetrating into the semi-conducting substrate by means of floating metal bars located underneath the guiding structure. In this design, a shielded differential coplanar stripline (CPS) has been implemented (Fig. 1) using the top metal (M6) for signal propagation and the bottom metal (M1) for shielding. The distance between two consecutive bars has been set to 1 μm in order to minimize the field penetration. The shielding bars have also been exploited to control the resonant frequency.

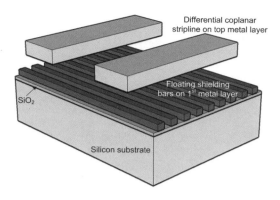

Fig. 1. Shielded CPS principle.

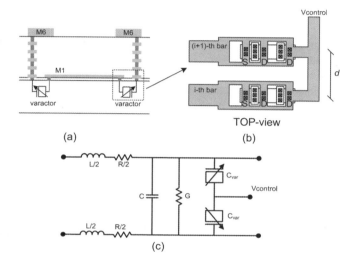

Fig. 2. (a) Cross-section of a shielded CPS periodically loaded with varactors. (b) Top view of the varactor area. (c) Equivalent circuit of a CPS unit cell.

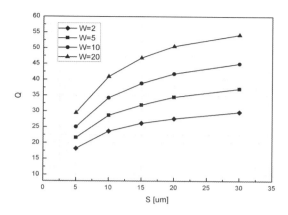

Fig. 3. Quality-factor of the coupled transmission line with shielding-bars as extracted from EM simulations at 70 GHz. The maximum Q (57.11) is achieved with W=40 μm and S=30 μm.

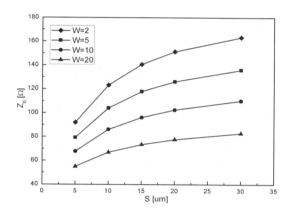

Fig. 4. Characteristic impedance of shielded CPSs.

MOS varactors have been periodically added to the original CPS: the gate of each varactor is connected to the signal line through a vertical metal via stack, while the source and drain are connected to each bar and to a control signal (2a-b). The equivalent circuit of a unit-cell of the CPS is shown in Fig. 2c, where R, L, C and G are the equivalent circuit elements of the unloaded ine and (C_{var}) represent the variable capacitors. The variable MOS capacitance alters the phase propagation velocity and hence the resonant frequency. The relation between resonance frequency and loading capacitance, for N cascaded unit-cells, is given by

$$f_{OSC} = \frac{v_p}{4l} = \frac{1}{4Nd\sqrt{L\left(C + C_{var}\right)}} \qquad (3)$$

where L and C are the inductance and capacitance per unit-length of the unloaded CPS, $l = N \cdot d$ is the total line length and d is the size of each cell, 2 μm in this design. The varactors were realized as NMOS transistors due to the unavailability of accumulation-mode varactors in the used technology at the time of design. Having the gate biased around VDD, the source and drain terminals tied together

to the control voltage and the bulk connected to ground, the NMOS transistors operate as inversion-mode varactors [5]. The width (W) and spacing (S) of the unloaded shielded CPS have been initially optimized by means of EMX [6] electromagnetic simulations of the unloaded structure aiming for the maximum Q. The attenuation (α) and the propagation constant (β) have been extracted from EM simulations according to [7]. In Fig. 3 the simulated quality factor (2) for different CPS geometries is reported. The quality factor increases as the lines separation and width increase. In fact, as the spacing increases, the magnetic quality factor increases due to higher inductance per unit-length, while resistive losses are reduced using wider lines. The presence of the shielding bars is essential to achieve this result since it strongly reduces substrate-related electric losses, that would be dominant at 70 GHz.

In Fig.4, the extracted differential characteristic impedance is reported. Increasing the lines separation, for a given width, will increase the line impedance until it will saturate when the two lines are far enough to neglect the mutual electric and magnetic coupling. When the line is loaded by MOS varactors, their finite Q will impact the overall quality factor of the resonator. This is because, while the magnetic quality

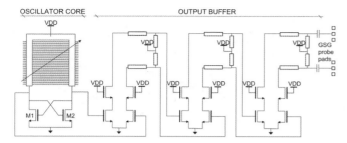

Fig. 5. Voltage-controlled standing-wave oscillator principle (a) and output-buffer schematic (b).

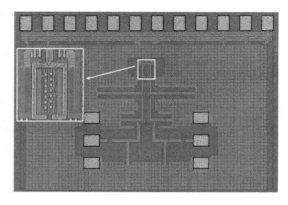

Fig. 6. Die photo of the test chip in 90nm CMOS. The oscillator core is magnified.

factor is not affected by the varactor loading, the electrical one is dominated by it, resulting into a lower quality factor of the overall structure.

Furthermore, the characteristic impedance of the loaded CPS descreases according to the following relation:

$$Z_L = \sqrt{\frac{L}{C + \frac{C_{\mathrm{var}}}{d}}} = \frac{Z_{unloaded}}{\sqrt{1 + \frac{C_{\mathrm{var}}}{C \cdot d}}} \qquad (4)$$

Hence, for a given desired characteristic impedance, a smaller line width must be selected, further reducing the overall Q, as evident from Fig. 3. The selected line dimensions, i.e., W=5 μm and S=30 μm, were chosen to obtain the desired loaded impedance and the optimum loaded Q. A higher quality factor is expected if accumulation-mode varactors are used instead of NMOS transistors.

III. STANDING-WAVE OSCILLATOR DESIGN

In Fig. 5a the oscillator schematic is reported. The resonator was implemented using the CPS described above. The necessary bias voltage for the oscillator is provided from the middle of the CPS short-circuit terminations, that is a differential zero-voltage point. Notice that the parasitic capacitance of the cross-connected couple and the non-zero length of the short-circuit termination effectively resulted into a shortening of the CPS with respect to the ideal length of $\lambda/4$. The circuit is operated with VDD=1.2 V and the control voltage varies between 0 and VDD. The transistor channel length is equal to the minimum allowed by the technology (i.e., 100 nm) while the width has been chosen from circuit simulation aiming for the maximum f_{MAX} and it has been found to correspond to 2 μm.

Circuit co-simulations in the Agilent ADS environment of the whole oscillator made of the CPS resonator, the varactors and the two cross-coupled connected MOS transistors (M1 and M2, in Fig.5a) have been used to size the varactors, the number of fingers of the transistors and the CPS length to meet center frequency and tuning range requirements. The final result of the analysis is 24 unit-cells (that gives an overall CPS length of only 48 μm), inversion-mode NMOS varactors with W=6 $\times$ 1 μm, L=0.165 μm and transistors with W=8 $\times$ 2 μm. In order to provide enough output power and to avoid loading the oscillator core directly with the RF probes, a buffer (Fig. 5b) consisting of three cascaded differential amplifiers with

transmission line inter-stage matching networks have also been included. The first stage of the buffer is sized aiming for a maximum capacitive load for the oscillator equal to 10 fF. The intermediate and the last stage dimensions are optimized for maximum output power.

IV. EXPERIMENTAL RESULTS

A test chip has been designed and implemented in TSMC 90 nm CMOS process with ultra-thick top metal. A die micrograph is given in Fig. 6. Bias and control pads are located on the top while the two outputs, that are suitable for on-chip measurement with coplanar GSG probes, are in the middle. The chip measures $1078 \times 780 \ \mu m^2$. A close-up view of the oscillator core is also given. It is evident that most of the chip area is due to the output buffer. Note that this buffer is only required for testing purposes and becomes not necessary when the oscillator is used as building block of a complete transceiver. The effective circuit area is then only $120 \times 80 \ \mu m^2$.

Achieving accurate phase noise measurements at such high frequencies is a rather difficult task due to unavoidable cable losses and environment disturbances. The measurement setup realized for the oscillator characterization is reported in Fig. 7. The outgoing signal from the probes is first down-converted by means of a Wisewave V-band mixer with a 70 GHz LO provided by an Agilent E8527D generator. Then, a second down-conversion feeds the signal to a low-frequency custom-made amplifying board that consists of two commercially available low-noise op-amps with bias and stabilization networks. The second board was found to be necessary since the output buffer did not provide the expected power for an accurate characterization due to cable and down-conversion mixer losses. The phase noise and the tuning curves are finally measured by an R&S FSUP signal analyzer. The oscillation frequency as a function of the control voltage is given in Fig. 8. Unfortunately, it was not possible to completely explore the overall tuning curve due to excessive and not predicted losses of the varactors when operated in maximum capacitance mode. This discrepancy is currently subject of further studies. For a center frequency of 72 GHz, the measured phase noise log plot

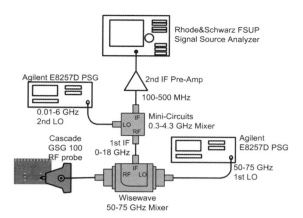

Fig. 7. Experimental setup for the VCO characterization.

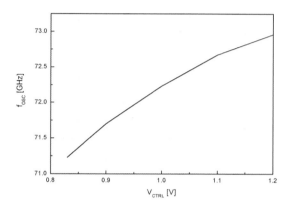

Fig. 8. Measured oscillation frequency versus tuning voltage.

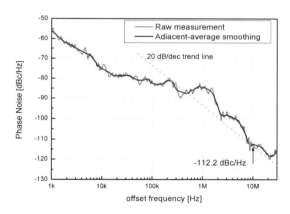

Fig. 9. Measured phase noise for 72 GHz oscillation.

TABLE I
COMPARISON WITH PUBLISHED E-BAND VCOS

VCO Technology [ref]	f_{osc} [GHz]	Tuning range [%]	PN [dBc/Hz]	offset [MHz]	P_{diss} [mW]	FOM [dBc/Hz]
65nm SOI-CMOS [8]	70.20	9.5	-106.1	10	5.4	-175.7
InP-DHBT [9]	74.00	6	-97	1	770	-165.5
SiGe 0.35μm [10]	72.00	n.a.	-102.5	1	290	-175.0
CMOS 90nm [this work]	**72.00**	**2.8**	**-112.2**	**10**	**19.2**	**-176.5**

The VCO core consumes 19 mW when operated with a 1.2 V supply and presents a FoM of -176.5 dBc/Hz.

V. CONCLUSIONS

The design and characterization of a CMOS voltage-controlled SWO suitable for operation in the 71-73 GHz range has been presented. Particular emphasis has been given to the design of the distributed resonator and some guidelines have been drawn. The measured phase noise at 72 GHz, -112.2 dBc/Hz and the FoM, -176.5 dBc/Hz, are comparable to state-of-the-art counterparts in different technologies.

ACKNOWLEDGMENT

The authors wish to thank R. Castello and Marvell for providing technology access and S. Shia (TSMC) for design kit support. The authors gratefully acknowledge Integrand Software and Agilent for providing simulation tools.

REFERENCES

[1] C. H. Doan, S. Emami, A. M. Niknejad and R. W. Brodersen, "Millimeter-Wave CMOS Design," *IEEE J. Solid-State Circuits*, vol. 40, pp. 144-154, Jan., 2005.
[2] D. M. Pozar, Microwave Engineering, 3rd ed. New York: Wiley.
[3] T. K. D. Cheung and J. R. Long, "Shielded Passive Devices for Silicon-Based Monolithic Microwave and Millimeter-Wave Integrated Circuits," *IEEE J. Solid-State Circuits*, vol. 41, pp. 1183-1200, May, 2006.
[4] D. Huang, W. Hant, N.-Y. Wang, T. W. Ku, Q. Gu, R. Wong and M.-C. F. Chang, "A 60 GHz CMOS VCO Using On-Chip Resonator with Embedded Artificial Dielectric for Size, Loss and Noise Reduction," *ISSCC Dig. Tech. Papers*, pp. 314-315, Feb., 2006.
[5] P. Andreani and S. Mattisson, "On the Use of MOS Varactors in RF VCO's," *IEEE J. Solid-State Circuits*, vol. 35, pp. 905-910, June, 2002.
[6] Integrand software Inc. *http://www.integrandsoftware.com*
[7] W. R. Eisenstad and Y. Eo, "S-parameter-based IC Interconnect Transmission Line Characterization," *IEEE Transaction on Components, Hybrids, and Manufacturing Technology*, vol. 15, no. 4, pp. 483-490, Aug. 1992.
[8] D. D. Kim, J. Kim, J. -O. Plouchart, C. Cho, W. Li, D. Lim, .Trzcinski, M. Kumar, C. Norris and D. Ahigren, "A 70GHz Manufacturable Complementary LC-VCO with 6.14GHz Tuning Range in 65nm SOI CMOS," *ISSCC Dig. Tech. Papers*, pp. 540-541, Feb., 2007.
[9] R.-E. Makon, I. Schneider, R. Driad, M. Lang, R. Aidam, R. Quay and G. Weimann, "Fundamental Low Phase Noise InP-Based DHBT VCOs With High Output Power Operating up to 75 GHz," *IEEE Compound Semiconductor Integrated Circuit Symposium*, pp159 - 162, Oct. 2004.
[10] H. Li, H.-M. Rein, R.-E. Makon, and M. Schwerd, "Wide-band VCOs in SiGe production technology operating up to about 70 GHz," *IEEE Microwave and Wireless Components Letters*, vol. 13, pp. 425 - 427, Oct. 2003.

is given in Fig. 9. In table I, the designed SWO is compared to some published VCO that operates in the similar frequency range by using as a metric the widespread used figure-of-merit:

$$FoM = PN\left(f_{off}\right) - 20\log\frac{f_{osc}}{f_{off}} + 10\log\frac{P_{diss}}{1mW} \quad (5)$$

On-chip leakage monitor circuit to scan optimal reverse bias voltage for adaptive body-bias circuit under gate induced drain leakage effect

M. Fujii, H. Suzuki, H. Notani, H. Makino and H. Shinohara
Renesas Technology Corp.
4-1, Mizuhara, Itami-shi, Hyogo, Japan
E-mail: fujii.masako@renesas.com

Abstract□ **This paper proposes on-chip leakage monitor circuit to scan optimal reversed body-biasing voltage (VBB) at which leakage current becomes minimal under gate induced drain leakage (GIDL) effect. The proposed circuit determines optimal VBB from the differential measurement of two replica circuit without absolute leakage current measurement. We fabricated this leakage monitor circuit in a 45nm-CMOS process. Measurement results shows 0.1 V resolution of VBB optimization.**

I. INTRODUCTION

Low power consumption design is one of the most important issues of LSI products. Reverse body biasing is a method to reduce leakage current between source and drain (Ioff_s)[1-2]. By the deep submicron technology, the stronger the reverse body biasing voltage (VBB), the smaller the leakage current (Ioff), depending on a linear line of semilogarithmic graph of Ioff vs. drive current (Ion). In the nano-scale technology, because gate-induced drain leakage (GIDL) current becomes more considerable, Ioff starts to increase at too strong VBB region. That is, minimal Ioff is given at an optimal VBB value. In addition recent years, there are many specifications which requires low leakage at room temperature under strong GIDL effect.

In this paper, we proposed a VBB controller to scan optimal VBB of a individual chip. The proposed VBB controller keeps optimal VBB on-the-fly. A test chip by 45nm CMOS technology outputs optimal VBB at 0.1V resolution.

II. OPTIMAL VBB SCAN UNDER GIDL EFFECT

GIDL effect increases Ioff at too strong VBB region. Fig. 1 shows Ioff/Ion characteristics at several VBB values. ▲ denotes fast transistor and ○ denotes slow transistor respectively. Both types of transistors were measured at several ΔVBB: 0V, -0.4V, -0.8V and -1.2V. As shown in Fig. 1(a), Ioff vs. Ion characters of fast transistor has minimal leakage current at VBB = -0.4V and 27C. The optimal VBB of the same transistor becomes -1.2V at high temperature, 125C as shown in Fig. 1(b). On the other hand, the optimal VBBs of slow transistor become 0 V at 27C and -0.4 V at 125C respectively. Likewise, Fig. 1(c) and 1(d) shows that PMOS's

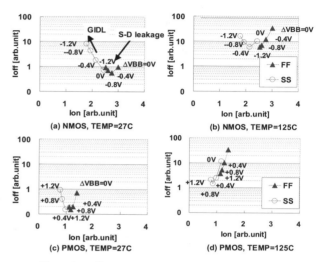

Figure 1. Ioff vs. Ion characteristics at several VBB values

optimal VBB also change. That is, the optimal VBB to minimize leakage current is variable on the temperature change and different among die-to-die variation. Hence, on-chip real-time monitoring circuit is needed to trace the optimal VBB under the device variation.

Some precedent works for monitoring and fixing die-to-die variation by body biasing are reported [3-5]. Most of them use drive current monitors, however. In the nano-scale generation, they have possibility to increase leakage current because of too strong VBB. Therefore, for optimizing VBB, we need to monitor leakage current directly.

Although there are some leakage monitors had been proposed already [6-8], they miss GIDL effect. For example, Ioff_s is enhanced by slight gate voltage to detection [6].

III. LEAKAGE CURRENT MONITOR CIRCUIT

We propose a leakage current monitor circuit for optimal body-biasing control. Fig. 2(a) shows the proposed leakage current monitor, which optimizes VBB of NMOS. In this paper, the VBB for NMOS is called VBBN, and the VBB for PMOS is called VBBP. The circuit of Fig. 2(a) contains a

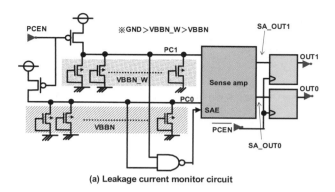

(a) Leakage current monitor circuit

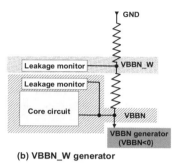

(b) VBBN_W generator

Figure 2. Proposed leakage monitor circuit for NMOS side.

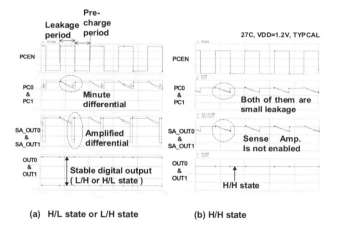

(a) H/L state or L/H state

(b) H/H state

Figure 3. Simulation results of the proposed leakage current monitor for NMOS side.

symmetric pair of off-NMOS cluster. Each cluster contains one hundred transistors to obtain enough leakage current at any operating conditions. One cluster connects to the same VBBN as the target chip. The other cluster biased by VBBN_W, which is slightly higher or weaker than VBBN. These off-transistors emulate the leakage characteristics of the target chip. Hence, they are replicated from a layout of a standard cell library. VBBN_W is generated by series resistors from VBBN as shown in Fig. 2(b). It has a characteristic that a stronger VBBN has larger difference from VBBN_W.

Fig. 3 shows simulation results of the proposed circuit. PC0 and PC1 is pre-charged to VDD during low state of PCEN. When PCEN becomes high, PC0 and PC1 start drop to low level by leakage current of off-NMOS cluster. A NMOS cluster of PC1 is biased weaker VBBN than that of PC0, leakage current driving to PC1 becomes smaller than that driving to PC0 for the GIDL device. It makes PC1 voltage higher than PC0 as shown in Fig. 3(a). A sense amplifier amplify the voltage difference between PC0 and PC1 at the timing of sense amp enable signal (SAE). The sensed results, SA_OUT0 and SA_OUT1, are captured in the following flip-flops, OUT0 and OUT1. Here, SAE is generated by the NAND of PC0 and PC1. Likewise, PC1 droops faster than PC0 for the non-GIDL device.

The proposed circuit determines VBB without absolute leakage measurement. Leakage of VBB is just compared to leakage of VBB_W. Only the results to relevant leakage are required for determine the output codes, which become the instruction signal to VBB generator.

If the leakage current is too small as shown in Fig. 3(b), both PC0 and PC1 do not reach to the logical threshold voltage of the NAND gate to generate SAE. Hence, high and high state of SA_OUT0 and SA_OUT1 is captured at OUT0 and OUT1. Here, the sense amp contains cross-coupled structure.

Fig. 4 shows four cases of leakage current state on the Ioff-VBB curves. At Case A, the leakage current at VBB is smaller than that of VBB_W. Then, the leakage current monitor outputs OUT0=H and OUT1=L. Table I(a) summarizes the output signal of the leakage monitor circuit for the other cases. Complement structure of Fig. 2 makes PMOS version of the leakage monitor circuit. The function of PMOS's leakage monitor is summarized in Table I(b).

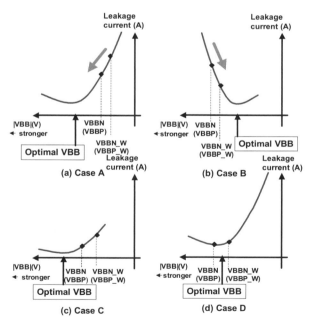

Figure 4. Each leakage state and activating leakage monitor

TABLE I.   SUMMARY OF LEAKAGE STATE AND OUTPUT SIGNALS
TO CONTROL VBB GENERATOR

(a) NMOS

Leakage condition (shown in Fig. 4)	OUT0	OUT1	Instructions to VBBN gen.
Case A	H	L	Stronger
Case B	L	H	Weaker
Case C&D	H	H	-
*not possible	L	L	-

(b) PMOS

Leakage condition (shown in Fig. 4)	OUT0	OUT1	Instructions to VBBP gen.
Case A	L	H	Stronger
Case B	H	L	Weaker
Case C&D	L	L	-
*not possible	H	H	-

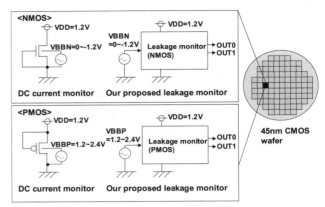

Figure. 6 Measured conditions and circuits

On real chip module, OUT0 and OUT1 become the functions to instruct VBB generator (VBBN gen. or VBBP gen.) By their instructions, VBBN or VBBP be stronger or weaker or keeping same potential. Measurement as described above is continued to run by PCEN input. Next determination starts by next leakage period as shown in Fig. 3(a). Each VBB comes closer optimal point to repeat above determination. If the any condition change, leakage monitor can follow up to determine without any special operations, and VBB optimized again.

The period of PCEN is decided by the trade-off of measurement resolution and response time. When the higher resolution, the response time becomes longer. In our technology, PCEN period was 240 uS for 0.1 V resolution of VBB. The proposed circuit consumes 30μW on time average in total at the maximum condition (FF, 125C).

IV.   IMPLEMENTATION AND MEASUREMENT RESULTS

We implemented leakage current monitor by using our 45nm CMOS process. Fig.5 shows the chip photograph of the leakage current monitor.

To confirm the functionality of leakage monitor, we also measured DC leakage current, which is fabricated near the leakage current monitor circuit (Fig. 6).

Fig. 7 shows the measurement results of DC leakage current. As shown in Fig. 7, we measured them at 25C, 55C, and 125C. Both of NMOS and PMOS have each optimal VBB. For example, Fig. 7(a) shows the minimum leakage VBBN or optimal VBBN of NMOS when 25C is -0.4V. VBB has limitation because of reliability limitation, therefore these measurements held on VBBN=0V~-1.2V, and VBBP=1.2V~2.4V and VDD=1.2V. Although the curve of NMOS when 125C has no bottom point in this graph, optimal

VBBN can be regard as -1.2V because of VBB range.

After DC leakage current measurements, we measured the output signal of leakage current monitor. Table II shows the results that measured at the same shot as shown in Fig. 7. The signals of OUT0 and OUT1 mean the same state as shown in Table I and Fig. 4.   For example, NMOS when the temperature is 25C and VBB is -0.3V shown in Table II(a), OUT0=H, and OUT1=L. Therefore the state of the leakage current is correspond to Case A of Table I and Fig. 4. In fact, as shown in Fig.7(a), the point of NMOS, 25C, VBB=-0.3V is slope to the left. It is the same slope as Case A.

The colored lines of Table II are turning point of output signal OUT0 and OUT1. In leakage current monitor measurement, we can regard the turning point voltage as the

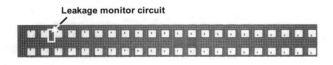

Leakage monitor circuit

Figure 5. Chip photogragh

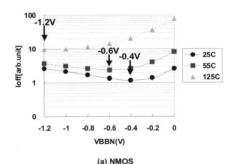

(a) NMOS

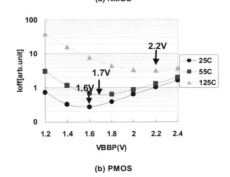

(b) PMOS

Figure 7. Measurement results of DC leakage current

TABLE II. Measurement results of leakage current monitor circuit

(a) NMOS

VBN(V)	25C OUT0	OUT1	55C OUT0	OUT1	125C OUT0	OUT1
-0.1	H	L	H	L	H	L
-0.2	H	L	H	L	H	L
-0.3	H	L	H	L	H	L
-0.4	H	L	H	L	H	L
-0.5	L	H	H	L	H	L
-0.6	L	H	H	L	H	L
-0.7	L	H	L	H	H	L
-0.8	L	H	L	H	H	L
-0.9	L	H	L	H	H	L
-1.0	L	H	L	H	H	L
-1.1	L	H	L	H	H	L
-1.2	L	H	L	H	H	L

(b) PMOS

VBP(V)	25C OUT0	OUT1	55C OUT0	OUT1	125C OUT0	OUT1
1.3	L	H	L	H	L	H
1.4	L	H	L	H	L	H
1.5	L	H	L	H	L	H
1.6	L	H	L	H	L	H
1.7	H	L	L	H	L	H
1.8	H	L	H	L	L	H
1.9	H	L	H	L	L	H
2.0	H	L	H	L	L	H
2.1	H	L	H	L	L	H
2.2	H	L	H	L	L	H
2.3	H	L	H	L	L	H
2.4	H	L	H	L	L	H

optimal VBB. For example, in Table II(a), OUT0 and OUT1 output H and L at -0.1 ~ -0.4V, and OUT0 and OUT1 output L and H from -0.6V to -1.2V. Therefore the optimum VBB is in -0.4V ~ -0.6V. Although at 125C, both of NMOS and PMOS has no turning point, their optimal VBB also regards as -1.2V and 2.4V because of VBB range.

Table III shows the summary of comparing the optimal VBB voltage indicated in Fig. 7 and Table II. Almost results of determined by leakage current monitor correspond to DC leakage current. Therefore leakage current monitors output correct answer expect 125C of PMOS. However, this mis-

TABLE III. The summary of measurement results and comparing each results.

(a) NMOS

NMOS	Minimum point of DC leakage	Turning point of OUT0/1	Minimum point indicated leakage monitor
25C	-0.4V	-0.4V~-0.5V	correct
55C	-0.6V	-0.6V~-0.7V	correct
125C	-1.2V	below -1.2V	correct

(b) PMOS

PMOS	Minimum point of DC leakage	Turning point of OUT0/1	Minimum point indicated leakage monitor
25C	1.6V	1.6~1.7V	correct
55C	1.7V	1.7~1.8V	correct
125C	2.2V	above 2.4V	incorrect (error of 0.2V)

sense is caused by the resolution of monitor circuit, which becomes rougher in stronger VBB region. It may be resolved by changing the design of series resistors of Fig 2(b). We measured DC leakage current and leakage current monitor on other shots. All of them indicated the same tendency. We proved our proposed new leakage current monitor to accurate mostly in any condition, under 0.1V step.

V. CONCLUSION

In the nano-scale processes, because of the trade-off of source-drain leakage and GIDL, leakage current is not linearly related to reverse body biasing voltage (VBB). Therefore, there is an optimal VBB to minimize leakage current. Each die has each optimal VBB in each condition. Measurement of absolute leakage current is difficult, therefore we proposed leakage current monitor, which search optimal VBB by comparing of relevant leakages. To establish the effects of leakage monitor circuit, we fabricated it in a 45nm CMOS process. To confirm the measurement results, we measured both of DC transistor's leakage current and leakage monitor circuit, and compared them. As a result, our proposed leakage monitor enables to determine the optimal VBB voltage accurately.

REFERENCES

[1] A.Keshavarzi et al. "Effectiveness of reverse body bias for leakage control in scaled dual vth CMOS Ics" *ISLPED, pp.207-211*, Aug. 2001.

[2] Y. Lin, et al. "Leakage scaling in deep submicron CMOS for SoC," *IEEE Transactions on electron devices, pp. 1034-1041, vol.49*, June 2002

[3] M. Sumita, S. Sakiyama, M. Kinoshita, Y. Araki, Y. Ikeda and K. Fukuoka, "Mixed body-biasing techniques with fixed Vt and Ids generation circuits" *ISSCC Digest, pp.158-159, Vol.1*, Febraty 2004.

[4] J. Tschanz et al. "Adaptive body bias to reducing impact of die-todie and within-die parameter variations on microprocessor frequency and leakage," *JSSC, pp.1396-1402, vol.37, Issue 11*, Nov. 2002.

[5] K. Arnim et al. "Efficiency of body biasing in 90-nm CMOS for low-Power digital circuits," *JSSC, pp.1549-1556, Vol.40, NO.7*, July 2005.

[6] C.Kim, K.Roy, S. Hsu, R. Krishnamurthy, S. Borkar, "An on-die CMOS leakage current sensor for measuring process variation in sub-90nm generations" *VLSI Circuit Digest, pp250-251*, June 2004.

[7] C. Kin, K. Roy, S. Hsu, R. Krishnamurthy and S. Borkar, "A process variation compensating technque with an on-die leakage current sensor for nanometer scale dynamic circuits" *VLSI Circ. pp.646-649, Vol.14, Issue 6*, June 2006.

[8] T. Kobayashi and T. Sakurai , "Self-adjusting threshold-voltage scheme for low-voltage high-speed operation" *CICC pp.271-274*,May 1994.

A 1.5V 13bit 130-300MS/s Self-calibrated DAC with Active Output Stage and 50MHz Signal Bandwidth in 0.13μm CMOS

Martin Clara, Wolfgang Klatzer, Daniel Gruber,
Arnold Marak, Berthold Seger
Infineon Technologies AG, Villach, Austria
email: martin.clara@infineon.com

Wolfgang Pribyl
Graz University of Technology
Graz, Austria
email: wolfgang.pribyl@tugraz.at

Abstract— **A high-performance 13bit current-steering DAC for analog subsystems is implemented in a standard 0.13μm CMOS technology. A novel dynamic background calibration scheme directly trims the unary DAC-elements in differently weighted segments of the current source array. Interleaved current cells implement an effective RZ-behavior with NRZ output current waveform, which improves the dynamic linearity of the converter by 20dB at 64MHz. Clocked at 130MHz, the converter draws 53mW from a 1.5V supply and achieves a SFDR>73dB for signal frequencies up to Nyquist. Operated at 300MS/s with a 3x interpolation filter, the converter consumes 73mW and achieves a SFDR>68dB within the signal bandwidth of 50MHz.**

I. INTRODUCTION

High-resolution and wide-bandwidth D/A-converters have found widespread use for signal synthesis in digital communication systems. Demanding applications require signal bandwidths up to 50MHz, at a resolution of 12 bits and beyond. Improving the linearity of the transmit-DAC, especially at higher signal frequencies, is often a key factor to optimize the overall system performance [1]. For System-on-Chip (SoC) integration the data converter module must be implemented in a deep-submicron CMOS-technology, along with linear analog signal processing circuits and complex digital circuitry. Moderate power consumption and small silicon area are mandatory requirements in this case.

In broadband applications single-polarity current-steering D/A-converters with resistive termination are the preferred architecture. Depending on the digital input data, current sources are selectively steered to a pair of resistors connected to the opposite supply rail. To meet the stringent silicon area limitations encountered in SoC-integration, calibration techniques are generally employed for a converter resolution larger than 11 bits.

In newer CMOS-technologies the decreasing supply voltage progressively limits the available output voltage swing of a passively terminated current-steering DAC, mainly because the required headroom for a high quality current source with a current switch in saturation does not scale accordingly. An attractive alternative in low-voltage designs is the introduction of an active output stage [2]. Since the current sources are isolated from the voltage output by the gain of the amplifier,

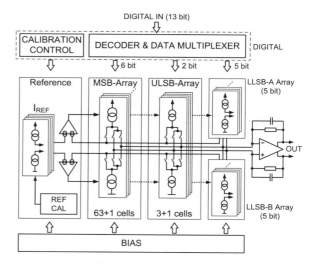

Fig. 1. Converter architecture

the linear full-scale range of the converter can be maximized. Because the current sources work into virtual ground nodes, the current switches can be fully overdriven. Besides, the amplifier provides a buffered output signal, centered at the correct common-mode voltage, for the subsequent on-chip circuit, which in most cases is an active reconstruction filter.

Nevertheless, the design of a D/A-converter with active output stage, able to process signals having a bandwidth in excess of 50MHz with high-linearity at moderate power drain poses various challenges. Subsequent sections of this paper address the architectural and circuit-level optimizations that were performed to approach this target.

II. CONVERTER ARCHITECTURE

Fig. 1 shows the architecture of the implemented self-calibrated DAC with active transimpedance output stage. The 13-bit converter core is split into three segments: A 6 bit unary MSB-array, a 2 bit unary Upper-LSB (ULSB) array and a binary 5 bit Lower-LSB (LLSB) array. The MSB and ULSB-array each include one redundant element to allow for uninterrupted data processing during the background calibration

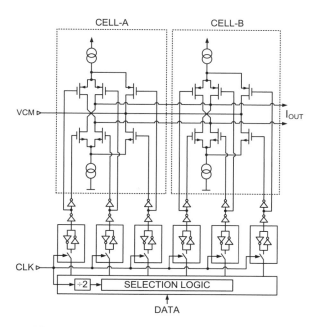

Fig. 2. Interleaved current cell (calibration not shown)

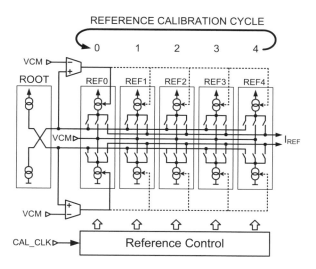

Fig. 3. Self-calibrated variable reference cell

of one of their elements. The segmented calibration requires a second, complete LLSB-array (LLSB-A and LLSB-B) for replacement during the trimming of one of the binary arrays.

The differential output current of the converter core is summed at the virtual ground nodes of the operational amplifier, configured as a transimpedance stage. The feedback resistors convert the signal current into the output voltage, providing a differential output swing of 1.5Vpp.

III. INTERLEAVED CURRENT CELL

Return-to-Zero (RZ) is an effective method to increase the dynamic linearity of a D/A-converter [1], [3]. However, the extreme slew-rate requirements for the active output stage make a standard RZ-implementation impractical for the converter architecture of fig. 1 [4]. Also, the inherent 6dB signal loss of the RZ-waveform is problematic in low-voltage designs.

By using an interleaved current-source array an effective RZ-scheme can be implemented for the individual current cells, while maintaining a NRZ output waveform [2]. Fig. 2 shows the architecture of the interleaved current cell. Each element in the MSB- and ULSB-array consists of two independently calibrated differential current cells (CELL-A and CELL-B). In normal operation one of the two cells is active for one clock cycle and the differential current is steered to the output (I_{OUT}), depending on the value of the input data bit. In the next clock cycle the other current cell becomes active, while the previously active cell is reset with both (P- and N-) currents connected to the common node VCM. Since P- and N-current are nominally equal, only their difference is flowing into the common node. A small single-ended buffer keeps VCM close to the common-mode potential seen at the virtual ground nodes of the output stage. A large bypass capacitor connected to VCM helps to absorb the switching spikes [2].

Given their reduced significance for the dynamic linearity of the D/A-converter, the LLSB-arrays do not employ interleaved current cells.

IV. DIRECT SEGMENT CALIBRATION

Dynamic current calibration repeatedly trims all elements in an array of equal-sized current sources [5]. Generally, only the currents of the MSB-segment are trimmed directly by comparison with a reference current of the same nominal size. The currents of the lower segments are then generated by dividing the trimmed current of an additional MSB-cell [5], [3]. Another approach consists in appropriately grouping together elements of the lower segments and compare their sum with the MSB-size reference current. In this way the array boundaries in a segmented architecture can be matched to each other without the need for geometric scaling [6].

In this design a variable reference cell directly calibrates the unary DAC-elements in different segments of the current source array with different weights. Fig. 3 shows the self-calibrated reference. It is split into five equal-sized cells that are appropriately combined to deliver the correct reference current for the calibration of the segmented main DAC-array. For a MSB-cell the sum of 4 reference currents is used, while the ULSB-cells and the sum of the LLSB-array (plus one extra LSB-current [6]) are each compared with a single reference current. The redundant fifth reference cell is included to always allow for one reference current to be calibrated in the background using the root cell for comparison. The reference currents are calibrated with the same timing as the current sources in the main DAC-array (CAL_CLK in fig. 3).

Fig. 4 shows the complete calibration cycle of the main DAC together with the simultaneous reference self-calibration. During ULSB- and LLSB-trimming, the unused reference currents are temporarily connected to the common node VCM (see fig. 3). The interleaved current cells A and B in the MSB- and ULSB-array are trimmed alternately in every second refresh cycle, as are the two LLSB-arrays.

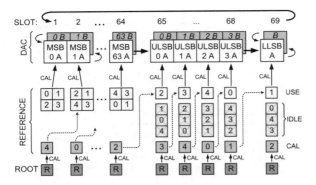

Fig. 4. Complete calibration cycle

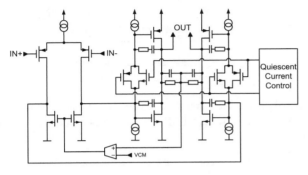

Fig. 5. Operational amplifier

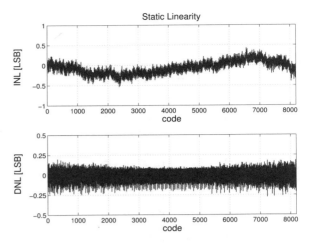

Fig. 6. Calibrated static linearity

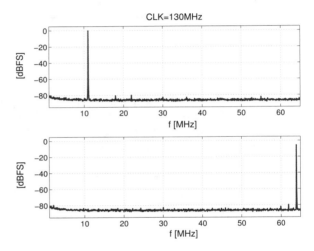

Fig. 7. 11MHz and 64MHz single-tone at 130MS/s

The periodicity of the dynamic current calibration process, in the main-DAC and in the reference, is eliminated by time-domain randomization of the calibration slot length [6]. In this way the energy residing in the calibration tones at multiples of the refresh rate is spectrally spread out and noise-like.

V. OUTPUT STAGE

The feedback capacitors in the transimpedance stage (see fig. 1) smooth out the steep current steps coming from the converter core and thus relax the slew-rate requirements of the amplifier. Since the capacitors also introduce a real LHP-pole into the overall transfer function, careful optimization of the pole location is required to keep the resulting in-band attenuation below an acceptable level. In this design the LHP-pole is trimmed to 100MHz, resulting in a 1dB loss at 50MHz.

The operational amplifier used in the transimpedance stage is shown in fig. 5. It is a two-stage Miller amplifier with push-pull output stage. The design is optimized for high slew-rate and large GBW. A replica loop stabilizes the quiescent current of the output stage transistors.

VI. MEASUREMENT RESULTS

Fig. 6 shows the static linearity of the converter with background calibration activated. The maximum INL and DNL are -0.53/+0.42 LSB and -0.27/+0.19 LSB, respectively.

Fig. 7 shows the output spectrum of a full-scale single-tone signal at 11MHz (top) and 64MHz (bottom), synthesized with 130MS/s. No spurious tones are visible above -79dBFS. The attenuation of the fundamental close to the Nyquist frequency

is 5.4dB, 1.5dB higher than given by the characteristic of the sinc-function. The SFDR with a sampling rate of 130MS/s and 300MS/s is shown in fig. 8. With interleaving enabled (RZ=ON), the SFDR at 130MS/s is 85dB for low-frequencies, remains above 80dB almost up to 20MHz and drops to 73.8dB near the Nyquist frequency. At 300MS/s an on-chip 3x interpolation filter is used and the SFDR is better than 68.7dB over the whole signal bandwidth of 50MHz. With the interleaving turned off (RZ=OFF), i.e. using only one half of the dual current cell in NRZ-mode, at 130MS/s the SFDR still approaches 85dB at low signal frequencies, but drops to 54dB close to the Nyquist frequency. The effective RZ thus improves the dynamic linearity of the converter by 20dB.

Of interest in a 2x time-interleaved architecture is the image tone at $\frac{1}{2}f_{CLK} - f_{SIG}$, generated by the aggregate gain and phase mismatch between the interleaved current cells. Fig. 9 shows the measured magnitude of the image tone for a full-scale sine wave synthesized at 130MS/s. Without calibration the in-band image appears between -65...-55dBc. Applying the background calibration without randomization pushes the

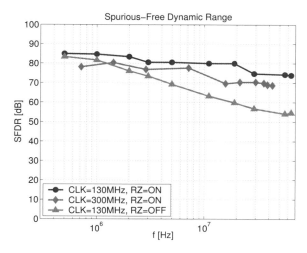

Fig. 8. SFDR at 130MS/s and 300MS/s

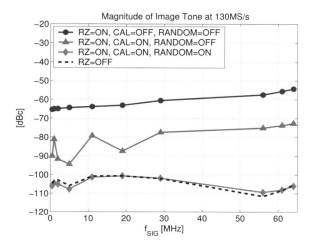

Fig. 9. Image tone magnitude at 130MS/s

image tone down by almost 20dB. Finally, with randomized calibration time slot the image tone is further suppressed and remains below -100dBc, very close to the level of the non-interleaved converter (RZ=OFF). With randomization the residual gain mismatch is no longer constant over time and the energy residing in the image tone is spectrally expanded into noise, like the calibration refresh tones.

A die micrograph of the converter prototype is shown in fig. 10. It is fabricated in a standard 1P6M 0.13μm CMOS technology. The converter runs from a 1.5V supply and dissipates in total 53mW at 130MS/s and 73mW at 300MS/s. The converter core consumes 21.5mW and 39.5mW, respectively. The output stage draws 30mW and is able to drive an on-chip load of 1kΩ. The module area is smaller than 1mm².

Table I summarizes the key performance parameters of the prototype D/A-converter.

VII. CONCLUSION

A 1.5V high-performance current-steering D/A-converter for analog subsystems implemented in a standard 0.13μm

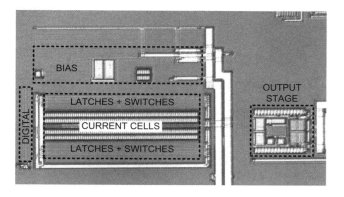

Fig. 10. Die micrograph of the D/A-converter

TABLE I
PERFORMANCE SUMMARY

Sampling Frequency	130MHz	300MHz
Signal Bandwidth	65MHz	50MHz (3x IP)
SFDR	>73dB	>68dB
Power (Analog/Digital)	51.5mW / 1.5mW	69.5mW / 3.5mW
INL, DNL	-0.53/+0.42 LSB, -0.27/+0.19 LSB	
Full-scale range	1.5Vpp differential	
Drive capability	1kΩ, single-ended, on-chip	
Technology	1P6M 0.13μm CMOS, 1.5V supply	

CMOS technology is presented. With a self-calibrated variable reference direct calibration of unary DAC-elements in segments with different weights is possible. Interleaving generates an effective RZ-scheme and improves the dynamic linearity of the converter by 20dB at 64MHz. The randomization of the calibration time slot, besides eliminating the calibration refresh tones, also suppresses the image tone at $\frac{1}{2}f_{CLK} - f_{SIG}$. An optimized transimpedance stage converts the signal current into a buffered output voltage with a swing of 1.5Vpp. The converter has 70dB+ linearity and only 1dB of additional in-band attenuation within a signal bandwidth of 50MHz.

REFERENCES

[1] A. Bugeja, Bang-Sup Song, P. Rakers, S. Gillig, *A 14-b, 100-MS/s CMOS DAC Designed for Spectral Performance*, IEEE Journal of Solid-State Circuits, Vol. 34, No. 12 ; pages 1719 - 1732; 1999.
[2] M. Clara, W. Klatzer, A. Wiesbauer, D. Straeussnigg, *A 350MHz low-OSR ΣΔ Current-Steering DAC with Active Termination in 0.13μm CMOS*, International Solid-State Circuits Conference 2005, Digest of Technical Papers: pp. 118-119.
[3] Q. Huang, P. Francese, C. Martelli, J. Nielsen, *A 200MS/s 14b 97mW DAC in 0.18μm CMOS*, IEEE International Solid-State Circuits Conference 2004, Digest of Technical Papers: pp. 364 - 532.
[4] R. Adams, K. Q. Nguyen, K. Sweetland, *A 113-dB SNR Oversampling DAC with Segmented Noise-Shaped Scrambling*, IEEE Journal of Solid-State Circuits, Vol. 33, No. 12, pp. 1871-1998, December 1998.
[5] D. Groeneveld, H. Schouwenaars, H. Termeer, *A Self-Calibration Technique for Monolithic High-Resolution D/A Converters*, IEEE J. Solid-State Circuits, vol. 24, pp. 1517-1522, December 1989.
[6] M. Clara, W. Klatzer, B. Seger, A. Di Giandomenico, L. Gori, *A 1.5V 200MS/s 13b 25mW DAC with Randomized Nested Background Calibration in 0.13μm CMOS*, IEEE International Solid-State Circuits Conference 2007, Digest of Technical Papers: pp. 250 - 251.

A 90nm 8b 120Ms/s-250Ms/s Pipeline ADC

L.Picolli[1], P.Malcovati[1], L.Crespi[2], F.Chaahoub[2], A.Baschirotto[3]

[1]University of Pavia – Italy - Department of Electrical Engineer
luca.picolli,piero.malcovati@unipv.it
[2]Conexant – USA - Newport Beach California
lorenzo.crespi,faouzi.chaahoub@conexant.com
[3]University of Milano-Bicocca – Italy – Department of Physics
andrea.baschirotto@unimib.it

Abstract— **A dual operating mode 8b, 1.1V, 120MHz/250MHz, 9.4mW/22.8mW pipeline ADC for Gb Ethernet applications is presented. Considering 60MHz of signal bandwidth in both operating modes, the ADC achieves a peak SNDR of 44.1dB/40.7dB (7b/6.5b ENOB), featuring a minimum FoM of 0.84pJ/conv at 120MHz and 2.2pJ/conv at 250MHz. A 90nm CMOS technology was used to integrate the ADC whose active area is 1.25x0.65mm^2.**

I. INTRODUCTION

Communication systems are nowadays requiring higher data conversion speed and lower power consumption, while technology scaling causes several disadvantages in analog circuit design, such as low voltage margin in cascode circuits and low switch linearity. In this paper we consider the implementation of an ADC for a Gb Ethernet link in a 90nm technology with 1.1V supply (as the worst case of the nominal 1.2V supply). In this application the signal bandwidth is about 60MHz and the system requires more than 6b ENOB, thus leading to the "safe" choice of an 8b ADC. The processing of a 60MHz-bandwidth signal can be done with an aggressive anti-aliasing filter (AAF) and a 120MHz ADC or by a relaxed AAF and a 250MHz ADC. The largest part of available solutions uses the first approach [1], [2]. In this paper a versatile ADC that can be used in both cases is presented. The proposed ADC is realized in a 90nm CMOS technology and guarantees the target 6b ENOB both with 120Ms/s and 250Ms/s sampling frequency.

II. A/D CONVERTER ARCHITECTURE

Figure 1 shows the proposed ADC architecture and timing diagram. It is a 4-stage pipeline structure, where the first three stages digitize 2.5b each, and the last stage digitizes 2b. In front of the ADC, a double-sampling sample-and-hold circuit (S/H) operates at half the ADC speed, to relax the op-amp bandwidth and power consumption requirements, while acquiring the input signal with low distortion. Transmission gates are used to implement the sampling switches, nevertheless featuring the required linearity for the target 800mV$_{ppdiff}$ signal swing. Finally, a digital block provides the proper timing and performs digital error correction, leading to an 8b digital output word. To cover the two possible data-rates introduced above, the ADC features two operating modes with different clock frequency (F_s) and power consumption values:

a low-power (LP) mode (9.4mW, F_s =120MHz) and a high-speed (HS) mode (22.8mW, F_s =250MHz).

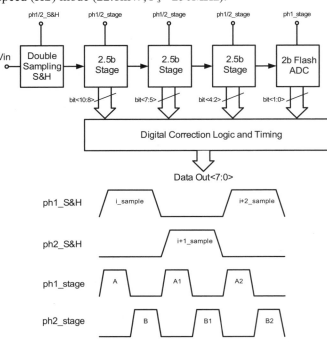

Figure 1 – Architecture and timing of the proposed A/D converter.

The proposed ADC structure peculiarity is that the MDAC block in the 2.5b stages, whose schematic is shown in Figure 2, includes an additional hold phase with respect to the conventional switched-capacitor structure, to maintain the residue available for the whole clock period. To this end, capacitor C_L in Figure 2 is added at the output of the op-amp. During *ph2_stage*, C_L, charged with the residue value previously calculated during *ph1_stage*, is connected in feedback around the op-amp, thus holding the output voltage until a new sample is ready. This additional hold phase in the MDAC relaxes the bandwidth and power consumption requirements of the 2.5b stages. Indeed, the flash ADC has half clock period available to produce the partial 2.5b conversion and to drive the MDAC switches, while the MDAC itself has half clock period available to settle to the next residue value. By using the conventional SC pipeline stage, both these operations would have to be carried out

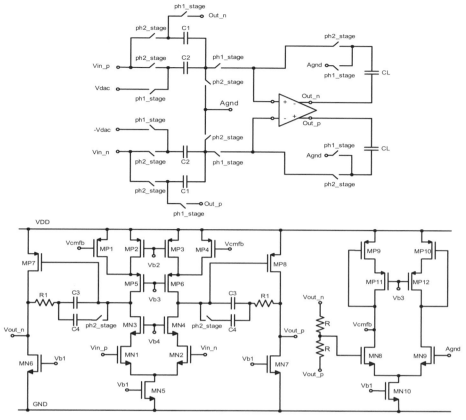

Figure 2 – MDAC structure and operational amplifier schematic.

within half clock period only.

The flash ADCs are based on a two-stage comparator: a preamplifier (to amplify the difference between signal and threshold voltage) and a clock-driven regenerative latch. On the negative edge of the clock, the latch determines the output bits, depending on the preamplifier output. The comparator structure will be discussed in the following section.

The ADC operates as explained in Figure 1: each sample of the input signal V_{in}, is held for an entire clock period by the double-sampling S/H. During phase $A1$ the input capacitances of the first-stage flash ADC are charged to the $(i+1)^{th}$-sample by the S/H. At the same time, the first-stage MDAC generates the ith-residue (based on the ith-sample) and charges the input capacitance of the second-stage flash ADC and the capacitor C_L. On the negative edge of $ph1\_stage$ both flash ADCs produce the output bits. During phase $B1$ the input capacitances of the first-stage MDAC are charged to the $(i+1)^{th}$-sample by the S/H, while C_L is holding the ith-residue, charging the input capacitors of the second stage MDAC. The third stage operates in the same way.

III. CIRCUIT DETAILS

Figure 2 shows the MDAC structure and the op-amp used in the MDAC. A sufficiently large DC-gain for 6b linearity (the first 2.5b stage has to be 6b linear) is achieved using a two-stage topology with a telescopic cascode first stage and a continuous-time common-mode feedback. A variable compensation network optimizes the op-amp settling performance. During $ph1\_stage$, when the MDAC is calculating the residue, C_3 and R_1 compensate the op-amp, while C_4 is added in parallel to C_3 to ensure stability during $ph2\_stage$, when C_L is closed in unitary feedback to hold the residue. MIM capacitors were used for C_L=100fF, C_1=100fF, C_2=300fF, C_3=280fF and C_4=80fF. The op-amp power consumption is scaled in the ADC chain: the 2nd and 3rd stage use a current 30% lower than the 1st stage.

The comparators of all the flash ADCs in the pipeline chain consist of a preamplifier stage (to amplify the difference between signal and threshold voltage) and a clock-driven regenerative latch. The structure of the comparator is shown in Figure 3. The continuous-time fully differential preamplifier.(on the left side in Figure 3) calculates the difference between the input signals, compares it with the difference between the threshold voltages and amplifies the result. The output common-mode voltage of the preamplifier is controlled by the MOS transistors circled in red, working in triode region. The amplified difference between the input signals and the threshold voltages (*Outp-Outn*) is then passed to the latch (on the right side in Figure 3), which, on the positive edge of the clock, determines the output bits, depending on its input. The continuous-time preamplifier reduces the comparator kick-back on the previous stage and guarantees a constant input capacitance, thus allowing the optimization of the previous stage bandwidth and power consumption. To ensure that the two differential input pairs work properly over the whole voltage swing, native MOS transistors were used where needed.

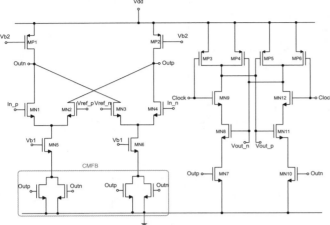

Figure 3 – Comparator structure.

IV. EXPERIMENTAL RESULTS

The ADC is realized in a 90nm CMOS technology. The chip operates at 120MHz/250MHz (LP/HS operating mode), and consumes 9.4mW/22.8mW (8.3mW/20.4mW for the analog part and 1.1mW/2.4mW for the digital part) from a 1.1V supply. Optimal ADC performance is achieved in LP mode, however, in the considered application (with 60MHz signal bandwidth), optimal system performance could be obtained with the 250MHz HS mode (relaxing the AAF). Indeed, the filter power consumption reduction in the receiving chain, allowed by the higher ADC sampling frequency, is much larger than the ADC power consumption increase in HS mode. Similarly, the linearity degradation, due to the stringent filtering specifications in LP mode, is worse than the linearity degradation due to the increased clock frequency in the ADC in HS mode. The measurement results (while satisfying the application specifications) are obtained using an external clock source with a significant jitter (>20ps). Better performance is expected when the device will operate embedded in the complete receiver with lower clock jitter. The power reduction between LP and HS operation mode was obtained by reducing the bias current of the first three conversion stages, leaving unchanged the S/H bias current.

Figure 4 shows the static DNL and INL measured in LP mode. The DNL is within +0.4LSB and –0.9LSB and the INL is within 0.8LSB and –1LSB (LSB referred to 8b). The ADC output signal spectrum obtained in LP mode with an input signal frequency of 10MHz is shown in Figure 5. The achieved SFDR is 50dB. Figure 5 shows also the ENOB vs. the input signal amplitude in both modes with signal frequency of 20MHz and 31.25MHz for the LP and HS mode, respectively. The curves showing the ENOB vs. the input signal frequency and the clock frequency are reported in Figure 6. The maximum ENOB achieved is 7b in LP mode and 6.5b in HS mode. The ADC features a minimum ENOB of 6.25b and 6.13b in LP and HS mode, respectively, corresponding to a FoM of 0.84pJ/conv (LP) and 2.21pJ/conv

(HS). For the HS mode no advantage in the bandwidth is taken in the FoM, since the 60MHz bandwidth is fixed by the application.

Table 1 summarizes the ADC performance. Figure 7 shows a photo of the chip, whose active area excluding pads is 1.25x0.65mm^2. Particular care was taken in separating analog and digital parts, to avoid crosstalk.

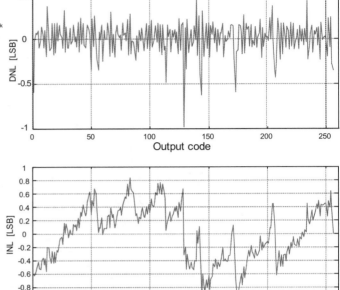

Figure 4 – Measured DNL and INL of the proposed ADC in LP operation mode.

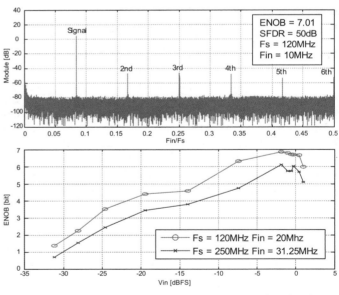

Figure 5 – Spectrum of the ADC in low-power operating mode and ENOB vs. input signal amplitude in both operating modes

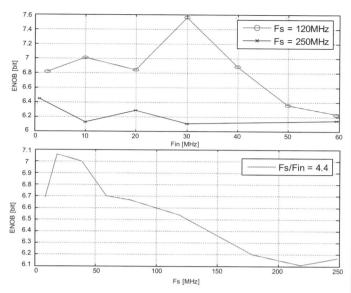

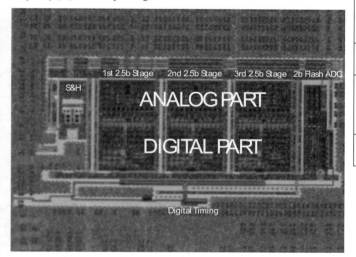

Figure 6 - ENOB vs. input signal frequency (Fin) and ENOB vs. sampling frequency (F_s) in both operating modes.

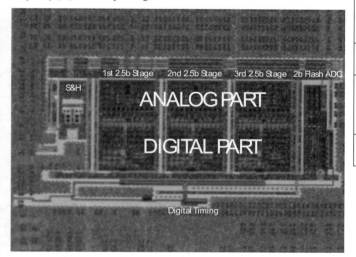

Figure 7 – Chip microphotograph

V. CONCLUSIONS

In this paper we presented an 8b pipeline ADC for Gb Ethernet applications. The proposed 0.8mm² 90nm CMOS chip features two operating modes with different sampling frequencies and power consumptions (120MHz/250MHz, 9.4mW/22.8mW). Over a bandwidth of 60MHz and with 1.1V power supply, the ADC achieves a peak SNDR of 44.1dB/40.7dB (7b/6.5b ENOB) with a minimum FoM of 0.84pJ/conv at 120MHz and 2.2pJ/conv at 250MHz. The achieved performance allows the Gb Ethernet specifications (6b ENOB over 60MHz bandwidth) to be fulfilled in both operating modes.

TABLE 1 – PERFORMANCE OF THE PROPOSED A/D CONVERTER

	Low Power Operation-Mode	High Speed Operation Mode
Technology	90nm CMOS	
Supply Voltage	1.1V	
Full-Scale	800mV$_{pp-diff}$	
Sampling Frequency	120MHz	250MHz
Resolution	8b	
SigSignal bandwith	60MHz	
Power Consumption	Analog=8.3mW Digital=1.1mW	Analog=20.4mW Digital=2.4mW
DNL	+0.4/-0.9 LSB	+1.2/-0.9 LSB
INL	+0.8/-0.9 LSB	+1.2/-1.4 LSB
ENOB	Max:7.04b Fin=30MHz Min: 6.25b Fin=59MHz	Max:6.47b Fin=1MHz Min: 6.13b Fin=30MHz
SNDR	Max:44.1dB Fin=30MHz Min: 39.4dB Fin=59MHz	Max:40.7dB Fin=1MHz Min: 38.7dB Fin=30MHz
SFDR	Max:54dB Fin=30MHz Min: 45dB Fin=59MHz	Max:50dB Fin=1MHz Min: 46dB Fin=30MHz
FoM	0.84pJ/conv ENOB=6.25b	2.21pJ/conv ENOB=6.13b
	$FoM = \dfrac{Power}{DR \cdot 2 \cdot Bandwidth} = \dfrac{Power}{10^{SNDR/20} \cdot 2 \cdot Bandwidth}$	
Active Area	1.25x0.65mm²	

REFERENCES

[1] Sotirios Limotyrakis, Scott D. Kulchycki, David K. Su and Bruce A. Wooley, *"A 150-MS/s 8-b 71-mW CMOS Time-Interleaved ADC"*, IEEE J. Solid-State Circ., vol. 40, n. 5, pp. 1057-1067, May 2005.

[2] Jan Mulder, Christopher M. Ward, Chi-Hung Lin, David Kruse, Jan R. Westra, Marcel Lugthart, Erol Arslan, Rudy J. van de Plassche, Klaas Bult and Frank M. L. van der Goes, *"A 21-mW 8-b 125-MSample/s ADC in 0.09-mm² 0.13-μm CMOS"*, IEEE J. Solid-State Circ., vol. 39, n. 12, pp. 2116-2124, May 2004.

[3] Dan J. Huber, Rodney J. Chandler and Asad A. Abidi, *"A 10b 160MS/s 84mW 1V Subranging ADC in 90nm CMOS"*, ISSCC 2007 Dig. Tech. Papers, pp. 454-455, Feb. 2007.

[4] Sanghoon Hwang, Junho Moon, Seunghwi Jung and Minkyu Song, *"Design of a 1.8V 6-bit 100MSPS 5mW CMOS A/D Converter with Low Power Folding-Interpolation Techniques"*, Proc. ESSCIRC 2006, pp. 548-551, Sept. 2006.

[5] Tomohiko Ito, Daisuke Kurose, Takeshi Ueno, Takafumi Yamaji and Tetsuro Itakura, *"55-mW 1.2-V 12-bit 100-MSPS Pipeline ADCs for Wireless Receivers"*, Proc. ESSCIRC 2006, pp. 540-543 Sept. 2006.

A 1.2V 56mW 10 bit 165Ms/s Pipeline-ADC for HD-Video Applications

Martin Trojer, Mauro Cleris, Ulrich Gaier,
Thomas Hebein, Peter Pridnig, Bernhard Kuttin,
Bernhard Tschuden, Christian Krassnitzer, Christian
Kuttin

Micronas Villach, Austria

Wolfgang Pribyl
University of Technology Graz
Graz, Austria

Abstract□ **A 10 bit 165MS/s pipelined ADC without a dedicated sample and hold is presented. Op-amp sharing and a single ended reference buffer loaded with a resistive divider are used. The ADC consumes 56mW and occupies 0.15 mm². It is fabricated in a 90nm 1.2V CMOS process and achieves 55 dB SNR for a 60 MHz input. A novel measurement technique called □pad noise suppression□ is introduced to prevent digital crosstalk from data outputs.**

I. INTRODUCTION

The demand on high-speed signal processing applications such as HDTV analog front-ends requires ADCs which meet the characteristics of low power consumption, 10 bit resolution and more than 160 MS/s sampling frequency. For RGB signals from graphic cards, where the pixel frequency can reach more than 60 MHz, the input bandwidth of the ADC must exceed more than 300 MHz. This means that the ADC should follow the pulses of a graphic card. For video signals the specification must be done taking the behavior of the human eye and brain into consideration.

Also digital crosstalk must be taken into account because of the integration of the ADC on a digital system (system on chip). Many approaches were proposed to reduce power and area e.g. op-amp sharing [6], no dedicated S&H, time interleaving. The power consumption is determined by the op-amp in the MDAC (Multiplying DAC) and the reference buffer. The ADC uses a 1.5 bit per stage with op-amp sharing topology. That is why the amount of op-amps is reduced to 4. Moreover two types of op-amps were used for simplicity in layout. Section II describes the architecture of the ADC and in section III circuits are introduced. Finally in section IV the measurement results are presented.

II. ADC ARCHITECTURE

The ADC consists of eight 1.5 bit stages with 4 shared op-amps plus a 2 bit Flash converter shown in Fig. 1. Each stage implies a sub-ADC where the sub-ADC of the first stage performs the decision at the same time as the first MDAC samples the input signal. This is necessary in order to have the

decision of the sub-ADC immediately after the sampling of the MDAC. Hence the sub-ADC samples the reference voltage during the amplification phase of the MDAC and follows the input signal during the sampling phase of the MDAC. In the MDAC the input is sampled on two capacitors where in the amplification phase one of these capacitors is flipped to the output of the op-amp. The matching of various control signals is difficult and requires a careful layout. At the end of this pipeline a two bit Flash ADC converts the residue into digital. In the first stage boosted switches are used for the input signal. After delaying the digital outputs of each stage by shift registers, error correction is used for compensating the offset of the sub-ADC. The maximum corrected sub-ADC offset at the first stage equals ¼ of the reference voltage vref after 8 stages. If the first stage samples the input signal the second will be in the amplification mode. The capacitors are chosen to fulfill the matching requirements. In the second stage they are scaled by a factor of two, so the load of the shared op-amp varies from phase to phase. Along with the third stage the capacitor values stay constant to simplify the layout. For noise considerations the amount of noise sources must be referred to the input of the pipeline and summed up.

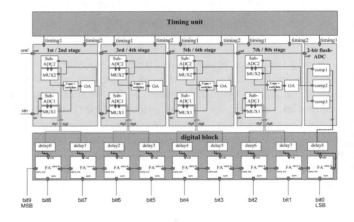

Figure 1. ADC structure without reference buffer

Noise contributors are kT/C, reference, op-amp and switching noise. For this 10 bit ADC the quantization noise corresponds to 280uVrms. Therefore the noise energy of the contributors should be lower than the quantization noise.

$$\text{Noise\_input} = 2\frac{k*T}{C} + \text{opamp\_noise}^2 + \text{ref\_noise}^2 + \text{switching\_noise}^2 \quad (1)$$

III. CIRCUIT DESCRIPTION

A. MDAC

Fig. 2 presents the MDAC where the input signal is sampled on Cin_1 and Cfeed_1. During amplification Cfeed_1 is flipped to the output and the charge of Cin_1 is transferred to Cfeed by activating the switch at the input of the op-amp with "samp inverted". Hence a gain of 2 is realized. This switch has to be optimized for op-amp settling and parasitics. Also in the amplification phase Cin_2 and Cfeed_2 are charged by the residue of the first stage. Because of using one op-amp for two stages the parasitics are pre-charged in the preceding phase. Further the decision of the sub-ADC needs several picoseconds to adjust the right reference voltage for subtraction.

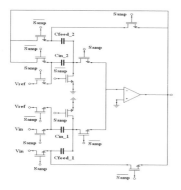

Figure 2. MDAC with shared op-amp

B. Sub-ADC Circuit Design

For the sub-ADC two charge distribution comparators are used. In Fig. 3 the dynamic latch stage of the comparator is presented where coupling capacitors are connected to the inputs. This topology shown in Fig. 3 is developed from the comparator published in [1]. The comparator requires a non overlapping two phase clock. During phase "samp inverted" the reference is sampled on Cref and vcm is sampled on Cin. When the signal samp is released the charge in Cref is redistributed (2) on both caps Cin and Cref and compared to the input voltage. With "samp inverted" M3 is active, M6 and M9 are off and the latch can perform the decision, whereby the load is an inverter working with positive feedback.

$$\text{Vin\_p} - \text{Vin\_n} = \frac{\text{Cref}}{\text{Cin} + \text{Cref}} * (\text{Vref\_p} - \text{Vref\_n}) \quad (2)$$

Fig. 4 illustrates the sampling network of the MDAC and sub-ADC. It demonstrates, that Cfeed and Cin must be charged by a current flowing through Rs_boost1 and Rs_boost2 after applying an input step. The voltage at R_vcm decreases to zero after some nanoseconds defined by the on-resistance of the switches. At the same time the comparator inputs are following the divided input voltage of the capacitors Cs_comp and Cpar_comp. In these capacitors too the reference voltage is stored and compared to the input. In that case little or no delay is generated because no current is flowing. Hence matching of the sample time is very difficult but could be reached by using a pre-amplifier in front of the comparator. Otherwise better matching could be achieved by sampling reference and input voltage at the same time in front of the comparator.

The advantage of this technique compared to other solutions is that the comparator decision is done immediately after sampling occurs. Therefore the available time for settling is enlarged.

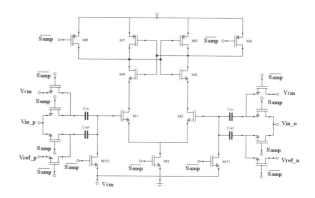

Figure 3. Comparator for sub-ADC

C. Folded Cascode Op-amp

The DC gain of the MDAC is determined by the resolution (N-bit). The total error ε_{tot} at the input of an N-bit converter should be less than LSB/2, which corresponds to the condition $\varepsilon_{tot} < 1 / 2^{N+1}$. So this translates for the open loop DC gain:

$$A_0 > 20 \cdot (N+1) \cdot \log2 \cong 66\text{dB} \quad (3)$$

For settling to N bit accuracy, it is necessary that the settling error $< 1/2^N$ is fulfilled. The output has to settle to N-bit accuracy in the time period $1/3f_{Clk}$ which leads to the following requirement for the GBW (4) where the feedback factor β is equal to 0.5.

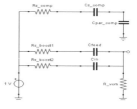

Figure 4. Sample network

$$GBW > \frac{3 \cdot (N) \cdot \ln(2)}{2\pi \cdot \beta} \cdot f_{CLK} \cong 1.22GHz \qquad (4)$$

The amplifier used is a folded cascode op-amp shown in Fig. 5 with gain boosting and a continuous time common mode loop. Due to the low supply voltage of 1.2V it is not possible to use more than 4 transistors in one branch to achieve enough headroom to stay in saturation. The currents in the cascode and input branches have the same values. The bias current for the common mode loop is mirrored by using the same drain source voltage on M17 and M15. This is realized by using vcm also for the cascode of the current source M17. Furthermore the common mode loop sees a higher load than the differential one where the bias current is in the range of the bias current for the input. The gain bandwidth GBW of the regulated cascode was calculated to be smaller than the overall GBW of the op-amp, but bigger than the 3dB bandwidth of the op-amp with fixed cascodes [2].

D. Reference Buffer

For the reference generation a simple single stage miller op-amp with cascode load of the differential pair M8 and M7 shown in Fig. 6 is used. In the output branch PMOS M1 drives the current to three low ohmic resistors R1, R2, R4. These are used for generating the reference voltages for the ADC. The resistor width is chosen by fulfilling the matching and gain error requirements of the ADC. Also vcm is produced by the same resistor string, so the references are always symmetrical to vcm. The open loop gain is up to 40 dB and is enough. The great benefit is the low noise contribution.

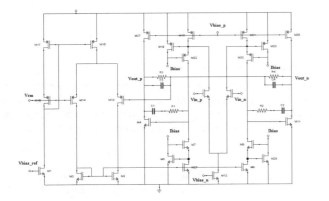

Figure 5.   Folded cascode op-amp

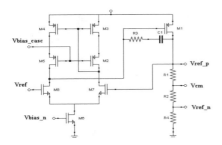

Figure 6.   Reference buffer

IV.   MEASUREMENTS

A. Pad Noise Supression

Although on IC and on test board level special care was taken to minimize the coupling of digital switching noise of the output pads into the sensitive analog input resulting in SNR degradation, further actions were taken in order to evaluate the ADC performance. The signal of the digital outputs was reduced from 3.3V to 1V and each ADC output signal was gated with a simple logic element shown in Fig. 7. As can be seen in Fig. 8, the stream of digital output words is disabled repetitively by applying the signal "disable_pad" which results in active and inactive time periods of the digital output pads spaced by D data words. Due to latency of the digital ADC logic, the actual sample time of each data word occurs some cycles before. If the suppressed time period is long enough, no disturbing pad rail action occurs at that time which leads to a stream of undisturbed data words. Storing only one sample out of D data words acquired in sequence leads to the concept of data decimation (1/D output decimation). The decimated sample rate now is a factor of D smaller (f_{str}/D, where f_{str} is the ADC strobe frequency). The overall time needed to sample the record of data now is a factor of D longer. This could lead to unwanted effects of additional SNR-degradation due to long-term jitter effects of the signal sources. By comparing data recorded with and without decimation, it should be ensured in advance that the test setup and the device under test are not prone to such kind of non-idealities. Notice that decimation involves loss of information which may hide relevant phenomena. In our case it was possible to ensure that the observed SNR degradation is truly related to digital pad noise as shown in Fig. 9.

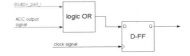

Figure 7.   ADC output signal gating

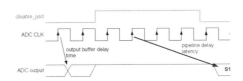

Figure 8.   Control sequence

B. Spectrum, DNL, INL

In Fig. 9 the signal to noise and distortion ratio depending on the sampling frequency can be seen. Unfortunately the clock input is located 8 pins away from the signal inputs. Also there was no extra supply available for the clock inputs to reduce the current loop on the board. For the 1V output driver two double bonded supply pins were used. This driver was developed to decrease the voltage swing and the switching noise impact. The ADC gets the reference from a 3.3V bandgap, which is also used for bias current generation. Moreover the input signal is amplified with a 1.2V buffer to drive the sample capacitors of the ADC to avoid distortion due to the parasitics of the input pins.

The figure of merit (5) of the introduced ADC with reference buffer equals 0.78pJ per conversion step. The power consumption can be further optimized by reducing the current in the cascode and output branch of the op-amp. This will be done in a future redesign.

$$FOM = \frac{P}{2 * BW * 2^{ENOB}} = 0.78pJ \ / \ step \quad (5)$$

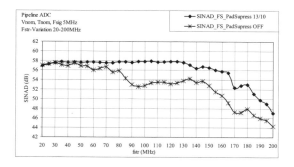

Figure 9. Signal to noise and distortion ratio with and without pad suppression

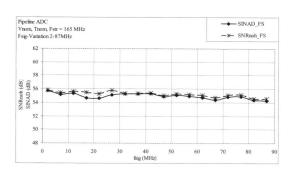

Figure 10. Signal to noise and distortion ratio depending on the signal frequency

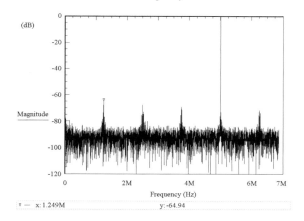

Figure 11. Decimated frequency spectrum @ fsig=60 MHz and -2dBFS

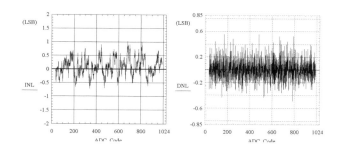

Figure 12. INL and DNL fsig=2MHz @ fs=165MS/s

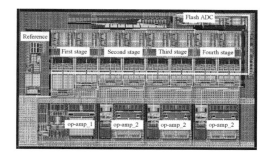

Figure 13. Pipeline ADC layout

V. CONCLUSION

A pipeline ADC with op-amp sharing, dynamic latch with capacitive inputs and single ended reference buffer has been presented. Due to two different sampling networks for MADC and sub-ADC the problem of matching of the sample point has been discussed. Furthermore it has been demonstrated that by using a 'pad noise suppression' technique the performance measurement has been improved by nearly 5 dB. The DNL corresponds to $^{+0.56}/_{-0.49}$ LSB10 and the INL equals $^{+1.03}/_{-0.72}$ LSB10. The effective number of bits is 9 @ 2 MHz input and 8.7 @ 87 MHz input measured with a strobe frequency of 165MHz. The ADC consumes 46mA at 1.2V and occupies an area of 0.15 mm^2 in a 90nm CMOS process.

REFERENCES

[1] L. Sumanen, M. Waltari, K. Halonen, "A Mismatch Insensitive CMOS Dynamic Comparator for Pipeline A/D converters", in Proc. ICECS'00, Dec. 2000, pp. I-32-35.

[2] Klaas Bult, Govert J. G. M Geelen, "A fast-settling CMOS opamp for SC circuits with 90 dB DC gain", IEEE J. Solid State Circuits, vol. 25, No. 6, pp. 1379-1384, December 1990.

[3] Iuri Mehr, Larry Singer, "A 55mW, 10-bit, 40-Msample/s Nyquist-Rate CMOS ADC", IEEE J. Solid State Circuits, vol. 35, No. 3, pp. 318-325, March 2000.

[4] Seung-Chul Lee, Young-Deuk Jeon, " A 10bit 205 MS/s 1.0mm^2 90nm CMOS Pipeline ADC for Flat Panel Display Applications", IEEE J. Solid State Circuits, vol. 42, No. 12, pp. 2688-2695, December 2007.

[5] D. W. Cline And P.R. Gray, "A power optimized 13-b 5-Msamples/s pipeline analog-to-digital converter in 1.2um CMOS", IEEE J. Solid State Circuits, vol. 31, No. 3, pp. 294-303, March 1996.

[6] H. Kim, D. Jeong, W. Kim, "A 30mW 8b 200 MS/s pipelined CMOS ADC using a switched-opamp technique", in IEEE Int. Solid-State Circuits Conf. (ISSCC 2005) Dig. Tech. Papers,pp. 284-285, 2000.

An 8-bit Flash Analog-to-Digital Converter in standard CMOS technology functional in Ultra Wide Temperature range from 4.2 K to 300 K

Y.Creten[1,2],P. Merken[1], R.Mertens[1,2]
[1]Integsys, IMEC
Leuven, Belgium
creten@imec.be

W.Sansen[2], C.Van Hoof[1,2]
[2]ESAT, Katholieke Universiteit Leuven
Leuven, Belgium

Abstract☐ **This paper presents the first standard CMOS Flash Analog-to-Digital Converter (ADC) operational over an Ultra Wide Temperature range (UWT) from room temperature (27☐C or 300 K) down to 4 K (-269☐C). To preserve the circuits performance over the UWT range in the presence of temperature induced transistor anomalies, dedicated architecture and switching schemes are employed.**

I. INTRODUCTION

Sensing very weak signals, e.g. in Space telescopes, requires a maximization of sensor detectivity which can only be achieved by cooling to temperatures as low as 100 mK. The associated pre-amplifiers, placed in close proximity to the sensors, operate at a temperature only slightly more elevated (4 to 40 K). Their output signal is typically transmitted over a few meters of cables to the "warm" or Room Temperature (RT) electronics. Conveyed as an analog signal, it is subjected to in-coupling of noise. To enable a more robust digital transmission of data between cold and warm electronics, the development of Analog-to-Digital Converters (ADC), operating in an Ultra Wide Temperature range (UWT) from Room Temperature down to deep cryogenic temperatures as Liquid Helium Temperature (LHT or 4.2 K) is required. At present, only one ADC appropriate for this temperature range is reported in literature [1], as most circuits suffer from carrier freeze out effects of the semiconductor material [2]. However, the reported Successive Approximation architecture is not well suited to read out large-scale sensor arrays (e.g. space telescopes). The Flash ADC architecture, presented in this paper, with a higher sampling rate, overcomes that problem and is a major step towards cryogenic digital sensor interfaces.

II. CMOS BEHAVIOR AT DEEP CRYOGENIC TEMPERATURES

The selection of an appropriate semiconductor technology is crucial to develop any circuit working in the UWT range. JFET transistors (minimum operating temperature of 40 K), Si Bipolar (minimum operating temperature of 100 K) and superconducting devices based on Josephson Junctions (maximum working temperature of 77 K) are immediately excluded. SiGe bipolar transistors are still operational down to

the lowest temperatures, but only at high base injection, requiring transistor currents of 10-100 µA As a consequence the thermal load of these circuits exceeds the tight power budget requirements for the actively cooled circuits targeted by this UWT ADC.

CMOS transistors function down to temperatures as low as LHT. Subthreshold leakage, thermal noise and mobility improve effectively with decreasing temperature, as one expects from theory, making cryogenic operating temperatures for CMOS transistors at first sight more favorable than RT. However, at temperatures below 100 K and particularly below 15 K, the behavior of transistors, especially of NMOS, is seriously disturbed due to carrier freeze out in the silicon [2-4]. The typical I_{DS} vs. V_{DS} curves of a standard NMOS transistor at 4.2 K are shown in Fig.1. The triangular shaped markers are measurements of a sweep from low to high V_{DS}, the spherical markers result from an inverse sweep from high to low. The dotted line indicates the room temperature measurements where no hysteresis was observed. The saturation current is lower at cryogenic temperature due to the increased threshold voltage (1 to 2 mV/K), not fully cancelled out by the carrier mobility increase at these temperatures.

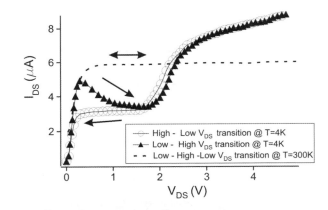

Figure 1. I_{DS} versus V_{DS} of a NMOS transistor in a standard 0.7µm CMOS technology at 4.2 K compared to room temperature characteristic.

Most prominent aberration is the kink with associated counter-clockwise hysteresis loop in the saturation region at a V_{DS} of about 2 V, where the NMOS transistor's noise can increase significantly. A second observation is the current overshoot in the linear region. The amplitude of the related clockwise hysteresis loop depends strongly on the speed of the sweep and temperature (below 15 K). This phenomenon is a result of temperature induced switching transients. When V_{DS} is swept from 0 V to positive value, non-ionized oxide-semiconductor interface states [4] cause a ΔV_T, which varies in time from an initial negative value to 0 V. As the value of V_{DS} is high enough, the electrical field stimulated ionization is sufficient to ionize the interface states. Therefore no overshoot is observed in high to low V_{DS} sweeps. The time constant associated with this transient depends strongly on the temperature, electrical field and doping profiles and is therefore difficult to describe in an analytical form. At LHT and small V_{DS} (linear region) this time constant can be equal to seconds.

Apart from these two most noticeable irregularities, or "cryo-effects", more secondary anomalies occur [2, 4]. These cryo-effects cause a substantial decrease in performance or even the failure of most classical analog circuits, hence require new approaches. Yet, from a circuit design point of view, no SPICE modeling of CMOS transistors down to LHT has been developed. In the next paragraphs it is demonstrated that by developing architectures minimizing the influence of cryo-effects, it is possible to design a Flash ADC functional from RT to LHT. Additionally it allows the extraction of room temperature a-like models enabling an adequate simulation of the circuits and prediction of their performance at LHT.

III. ARCHITECTURE

To meet the sample speed requirements over the broad temperature range, an 8 bit, 12.5 kHz Flash type ADC with mirrored Gray code output is developed. The 256 reference voltages, needed for an 8 bit Flash ADC, are implemented by a 256 taps on-chip poly-silicon resistor string. In order to optimize their resistance value, a trade-off between the circuit's speed (hence precision) and power consumption is made derived from [5]. A single-ended, three-phase comparator based on an Auto-Zeroed Sampled Data Converter equipped with a recirculating latch at the output is used in the design (Fig.2).

The advantage of single-ended circuit for cryogenic temperatures is that the inferior matching of CMOS devices at low temperatures does not influence the circuit's performance. To prevent the NMOS transistors from going into the kink region at high drain source voltages, a telescopic cascoded amplifier was used.

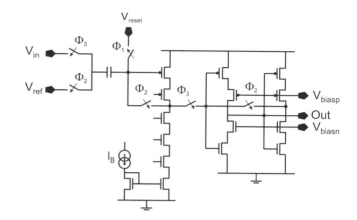

Figure 2. Schematic of comparator stage used in cryogenic Flash converter.

The comparison is performed in three non-overlapping phases, in which the switches Ph 1-3 are closed consecutively:

- "Cryo-reset" phase (Ph 1). To avoid hysteresis caused by low temperature induced current overshoots as will be explained below; the input of the amplifier, in an open loop configuration, is reset to an initial value;

- Auto-zeroing phase (Ph 2). The reference voltage is put onto the input node of the comparator stage, which is connected in feedback;

- Comparison phase (Ph 3). The input is sampled on the capacitor and the loop over the amplifier is opened. By the end of this phase, the result of the comparison is obtained at the output of the comparator stage.

Although superfluous at room temperature operation, the cryo-reset phase is essential to attain a low offset comparison at cryogenic temperatures. Consider the circuit without the cryo-reset phase and at a working temperature <15 K. If the previous output of the comparator stage was low, the NMOS transistors forming the current source of the amplifier are initially off (drain source voltage $V_{DS} = 0$). During the auto-zeroing phase, the in- and output of the amplifier will shift to the trip point of the amplifier which can be approximated by eq. (1), with I_{Bias}, the bias current generated in NMOS current source load, VDD the positive supply voltage, K_p a technology constant, V_T the threshold voltage and W and L respectively the channel width and length of the transistor.

$$V_{TripPoint} = V_{DD} - V_T - \sqrt{\frac{I_{Bias}}{K_p \frac{W}{L}}} \qquad (1)$$

During this transition, the drain source voltage V_{DS} of the NMOS transistors will increase to a value in weak saturation. The NMOS transistor will encounter large transient currents, $I \gg I_{bias}$ as can be seen on the NMOS current voltage-characteristics for low temperatures featured in Fig.1, contrary to the situation were previous output was high or RT conditions where $I = I_{bias}$.(bias point "B" in Fig3)

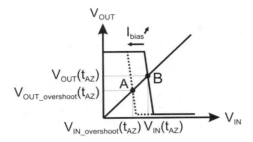

Figure 3. Transfer characteristic of the comparator stage. The solid line stands for I = IBias with bias point B. The doted line indicates input-output characteristic for I > IBias with bias point A.

In case of an initial transient in bias current, the trip point of the amplifier V_{TP} will increase slowly to its nominal value (from bias point "A" to bias point "B" in Fig.3), as the overshoot currents decrease in time.

However, at the switching frequencies of 10 kHz or faster, the nominal value will not be reached by the end of the reset phase but the trip point will be at an intermediate value. During the non-overlapping period between phase 2 and 3, the amplifier's characteristic is further reverting to its nominal value hence the output will drift to the positive supply voltage (bias point "A*" in Fig. 3). In the final comparison phase, the loop over the amplifier is opened. Due to the debiasing of the amplifier, large offsets will occur.

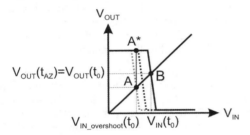

Figure 4. Transfer characteristic of the comparator stage. The solid line stands for I = I$_{Bias}$ with bias point B. the doted line indicates input-output characteristic for I > I$_{Bias}$ with bias point A*.

Therefore the cryo-reset phase in the comparison is added during which the input voltage is below the (steady-state) trip point of the amplifier, in order to set the output to the positive supply. On device level, the oxide-semiconductor interface states which are not ionized when transistors are off at T<15 K, are emptied by applying a large drain source voltages sweep for the NMOS transistors [4]. During the shift of the output to the trip point, the NMOS transistors cross the IV curves from high V_{DS} to low V_{DS}, without current overshoots. An extra advantage of the cryo-reset phase is that quasi-RT models, i.e. without taking low-temperature-induced hysteresis into account, could be used to design and accurately simulate the circuit.

At Room Temperature conditions, however, there is no overshoot with hysteresis in the transistor characteristics, hence the input-output characteristic is unambiguously defined, and the bias point remains stable, making the cryo-reset phase redundant at RT.

Tests on the comparator stage [7] have indicated a 7 mV input related offset at LHT in presence of a cryo-reset phase, increasing to 30 mV in absence of cryo-reset phase. At room temperature the offset is 2 mV for both conditions.

To make the ADC output, a binary thermometer code, more robust against bubble errors in the comparator output code, the thermometer code is converted to a mirrored-Gray code [6].

IV. IMPLEMENTATION AND MEASUREMENTS

An annotated layout of the test chip is shown in Fig.5. The die, occupying an area of 7400 x 5400 µm, has been processed in a conventional single-poly-layer, two-metal-layer 0.7 µm CMOS technology. The current consumption of the converter circuit, operated at 12.5 kHz is 200 µA for the core circuit and 900 µA for the resistor string at 5.5 V supply voltage and 200 pF output capacitance at LHT.

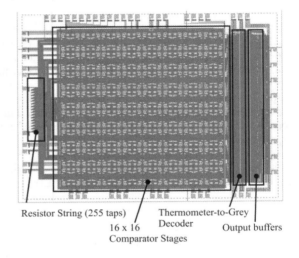

Resistor String (255 taps)   Thermometer-to-Grey
                        16 x 16   Decoder   Output buffers
                   Comparator Stages

Figure 5. Annotated layout of cryogenic Flash ADC implementation.

The DC reference voltages and bias currents are generated externally to enable optimization for the operating temperature within the UWT range. Clock signals are also generated off chip to allow omitting the cryo-reset phase of the comparator for room temperature conditions. The circuit has been packaged, mounted on a dedicated PCB attached to a cryogenic sample rod (Fig.6) and tested both at room temperature as well as at LHT in a Helium cooled cryostat.

Figure 6. Helium cooled cryostat containing dedicated test PCB.

Tests on the ADC test chip at RT confirm that the cryo-reset phase, crucial to the performance at cryogenic temperatures, in the comparison process is redundant to the functioning of the ADC. In Fig.7 showing the digital output versus the analog input of the ADC, the curves for measurements with and without proper cryo-reset phase virtually coincide.

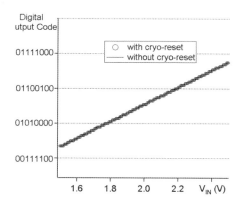

Figure 7. RT measurement of the Flash cryogenic ADC's digital output versus analog input, with and without cryo-reset phase.

However in LHT tests (<5 K), there is a clear distinction between the performance with and without proper cryo-reset phase (Fig.8) as was the case for the stand alone comparator stage.

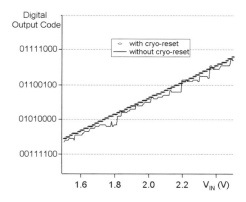

Figure 8. Cryogenic measurement of the Flash cryogenic ADC's transfer characteristic, with and without cryo-reset phase.

The DNL (Differential Non Linearity), calculated from the test results, increases up to 8 LSB (Least Significant Bit) when the cryo-reset stage is not performed correctly (Fig8). In case a proper cryo-reset phase is implemented, the DNL only increases from 0.5 LSB at RT to 1 LSB at LHT (Fig 9), which can be attributed to the increased mismatch between the poly-silicon resistors at these temperatures.

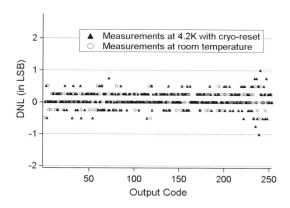

Figure 9. Differential Non Linearity of the cryogenic ADC for room temperature and cryogenic measurements with cryo-reset.

V. CONCLUSIONS

The first Flash ADC functional over an UWT range from room temperature down to 4.2 K has been demonstrated. By adding an extra cryo-reset phase, low temperature induced switching transients are diminished, resulting in a minimal loss of precision after cooling. This ADC is a proof of concept of the special design techniques and model extraction necessary for CMOS circuits at temperatures below Silicon carrier freeze out.

REFERENCES

[1] CRETEN, Y.; MERKEN, P.; SANSEN, W.; MERTENS, R.; VAN HOOF, C., 'A Cryogenic ADC operating Down to 4.2 K', Digest of Technical Papers of the IEEE Intern. Solid-State Circuits Conf., (ISSCC) 2007, pp 468 – 616.

[2] SIMOEN E., DIERICKX B., CLAEYS C., DECLERCK G., 'Transient response of silicon devices at 4.2 K: II. Application to the case of a metal-oxide-semiconductor transistor', Semicond., Science and Technology, 1991, vol. 6, pp 905- 911.

[3] CRETEN Y., CHARLIER O., MERKEN P., PUTZEYS J., VAN HOOF C., 'A 4.2 K readout channel in a standard 0.7 μ CMOS process for a photoconductor array camera', Journ. de Phys. IV, 2002, vol 12, pp 203-206.

[4] LYSENKO V.S., TYAGULSKI I.P., GOMENIUK Y.V., OSIYUK I.N., 'Effect of oxide-semiconductor interface traps on low temperature operation of MOSFETs', 2001, Semicond. Physics, Quantum Electronics & Optoelectronics, vol. 4, iss. 2, pp 75-81.

[5] UYTTENHOVE, K.; STEYAERT, M.S.J.; 'Speed-power-accuracy tradeoff in high-speed CMOS ADCs', 2002, IEEE Trans. Circuits Syst. II, vol. 49, Iss. 4, pp 280-287.

[6] CHUANG, Y.-J., OU, H.-H., LIU, B.-D. Liu, 'A novel bubble tolerant thermometer-to-binary encoder for Flash A/D converter', 2005, IEEE VLSI-TSA Intern. Symp. on VLSI Design, Automation and Test, pp 315-318.

[7] CRETEN, Y; PUTZEYS, J.; SOUVERIJNS, T.; MERKEN, P.; VAN HOOF, C.; SANSEN, W.; "Comparator stages for Analog-to-Digital Converters in a Standard CMOS Process Operational Down to 4.2 K", Proc. 7th European Workshop on Low Temp. Electronics (WOLTE7), pp 31-37, 2006.

A 3.6pJ/Access 480MHz, 128Kbit on-Chip SRAM with 850MHz Boost Mode in 90nm CMOS with Tunable Sense Amplifiers to Cope with Variability

Stefan Cosemans, Wim Dehaene

ESAT-MICAS Laboratory
K.U.Leuven, Leuven, Belgium
Stefan.Cosemans@esat.kuleuven.be

Francky Catthoor

IMEC
Leuven, Belgium

Abstract— An extremely low energy/operation, single cycle 32bit/word, 128Kbit SRAM is fabricated in 90nm CMOS. In the 850MHz boost mode, energy consumption is 8.4pJ/access. This reduces to 3.6pJ/access in the normal 480MHz mode and bottoms out at a very aggressive 2.7pJ/access in the 240MHz low power mode. This performance is obtained using novel, digitally tunable sense amplifiers and a tunable timing circuit that cope gracefully with the stochastic variations in the periphery.

I. Introduction

Small on-chip SRAMs are essential to enable low-power platforms that rely on distributed scratchpads. In technologies beyond 130nm, low power SRAM design is severely complicated by intra-die variations and leakage. For SRAM cells, leakage reduction has been obtained with low supply voltages [1][2] and high V_T transistors [3]. The cell stability issues and the increase in worst read delay due to intra-die variations have been mitigated with high cell supply voltages [4], with larger cells [1][2][6] or with more complex local peripherals [2][4][5][6]. For peripherals, the leakage problem has been addressed with dynamic voltage scaling (DVS) and supply gating. Less research effort has addressed two major issues related to stochastic intra-die variations: 1) replica-based timing is no longer applicable when large intra-die variations are present; 2) sense amplifier (SA) performance becomes restricted by intra-die variations. In [2], a very good first attempt was made to resolve this problem by introducing SA redundancy.

This work addresses the main power bottlenecks for small scratchpad memories. It reports an SRAM in a triple-VT 90nm CMOS process which targets an extremely low energy per operation at acceptable speed. Novel, digitally tunable SAs reduce energy and delay for data transmission from cell to memory output. All internal timing is derived from digitally tunable delay lines. This allows for a design without unnecessary safety margins, with optimal timing setting for each speed mode. At the same time, design-time risks are reduced.

This work was supported by IMEC and by Cadence Research Labs

II. Memory Organization and Operation

Fig. 1 shows the memory organization. The memory matrix is build up of local blocks, which each contain 32 words (1K cells). The top level matrix is subdivided in 8 columns by 16 rows of such local blocks. The memory is based on a fully subdivided word line (WL) architecture, so each word has its own local WL (LWL). The small, highly active stages in the decoder use low V_T transistors to improve performance at reduced supply voltages.

Fig. 2 shows a bit slice. The single-ended cell disables the pull down path and uses WL overdrive to improve write-ability. Short, buffered local bitlines (local BL, LBL), a write-after-read scheme and high cell and WL voltages are used to decrease the impact of cell variations on cell stability and memory speed. The read buffers allow a controlled swing on the global BL (GBL) from 100mV to 0mV. A SA restores the single-ended signal at the memory output. This GBL architecture is similar to the architecture in [5].

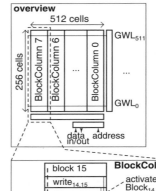

Technology	90nm ; 1P9M ; multi V_T
word length	32 bit
memory size	4K word ; 128Kbit
cell type	single-ended SRAM
cell size (logic DRC rules)	1.51μm x 1.3 μm 1.96 μm²
matrix size	772 μm x 634 μm 490 000 μm²
memory size	504 000 μm²

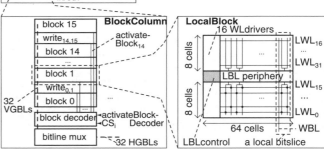

Figure 1. Memory organization and overview

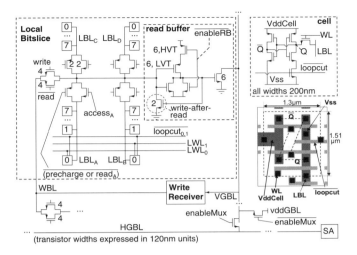

Figure 2. The cell and data transfer part of the memory

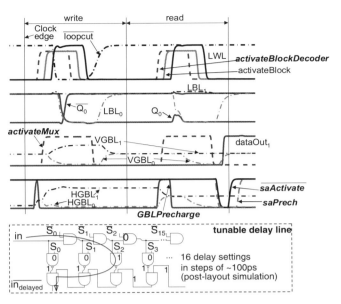

Figure 3. Simulated timing diagram and tunable delay line

Fig. 3 shows the timing diagram. All critical timing signals are derived from digitally tunable delay lines. The current implementation of the tunable delay elements is rather energy hungry, but given their relaxed constraints, it is easy to conceive low power tunable delay elements for future designs.

Tunable timing requires a calibration phase to obtain the optimal settings for the die and operation mode at hand. As the memory always functions correctly in the most relaxed timing setting, this calibration consists of a simple loop in which each timing delay is reduced until the memory stops working reliably. Then, margins are introduced to guard against time varying effects, such as power supply ripple and temperature variations. In the current implementation, this calibration loop is controlled externally.

The advantages of tunable timing are many. It avoids the need for replica-based timing, which is complicated and which fails in the context of the large, uncorrelated intra-die variations of current day technologies. Tunable timing can apply optimal delay settings to each operation mode of the memory individually, and can adjust this setting to the statistics of the die at hand. Compared to static timing approaches, this reduces both the required design margins and the design risks. An additional benefit is that a tunable timing circuit is almost universally applicable, which enables reuse. This reduces design cost, design time and design risk.

III. TUNED SENSE AMPLIFIERS

A. The Sense Amplifier Offset Problem

During a read operation, a small cell must develop a signal swing on a BL. Even when a subdivided bit line architecture is employed, the GBL is a huge capacitive load, especially when compared to the driving capability of the cell. If a large swing is required on this BL, both access time and energy consumption of the memory will increase significantly.

A good SA will reduce the required BL swing as much as possible. The ability of a SA to sense small input differences is limited by its input-referred offset. When the designed input swing is reduced, a traditional SA must be made larger and its dynamic energy consumption increases. Table I contains a lower bound on the size of the input transistors of a SA to obtain 6σ yield. The table also contains an estimate of the energy consumption associated with such a SA sizing, relative to the energy consumption of all other memory parts combined. These numbers take only threshold voltage mismatch of the input transistors into account. The energy numbers indicate that for traditional SAs, differential input swings below 50mV are not economic. For a SA, this is equivalent to a single-ended signal swing of 100mV

B. Tunable Sense Amplifier

A lower input swing can be obtained when circuit techniques are employed that solve the offset problem without transistor upsizing. In [2], SA redundancy was introduced. For each SA required, N (≥ 2) SAs are provided. During calibration, the best SA of the set is determined. Afterwards, only the best SAs will be used. The resulting SA offset distribution is the minimum of the N offset distributions of the individual SAs, which is much more favorable. However, the selection of the signal from the best SA must happen at run time. This introduces an overhead on access time and energy. As such, the scheme does not scale well to large values of N.

TABLE I. REQUIRED SIZE OF SENSE AMPLIFIER (SA) INPUT TRANSISTORS TO COPE WITH SA OFFSET

node	$A_{\Delta Vt}$ [mv μm] (estimated)	required SA upscaling[1] and SA energy contribution[2]		
		Vdiff[3]=100mV	Vdiff[3]=50mV	Vdiff[3]=25mV
90nm	4.5	6.8x (10%)	27x (40%)	108x (160%)
65nm	4	9.8x (15%)	39x (58%)	158x (233%)
45nm	2.5	7.7x (11%)	31x (46%)	123x (182%)
32nm	2.5	15.6x (23%)	63x (93%)	250x (380%)

[1] required size for the SA input transistors (for 6σ) [multiples of the technology's W_{min}]

[2] SA energy consumption [fraction of consumption of total memory, SAs excluded]

[3] voltage difference between inputs. Single-ended SAs require twice this as BL swing.

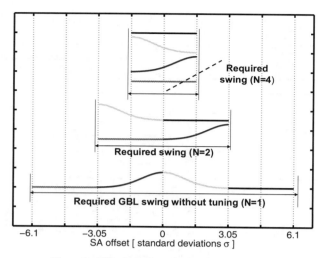

Figure 4. Effective offset of a tuned sense amplifier

SA tuning compared to SA redundancy		
# config bits	theoretical minimum single-ended input swing to overcome intra-die variations (1 failing SA in 10^9 SAs)	fraction of swing needed
	redundancy	tuning	
0	12.2 $\sigma_{Voffset}$	12.2 $\sigma_{Voffset}$	100%
1	8.32 $\sigma_{Voffset}$	6.10 $\sigma_{Voffset}$	73%
2	5.54 $\sigma_{Voffset}$	3.06 $\sigma_{Voffset}$	55%
3	3.56 $\sigma_{Voffset}$	1.52 $\sigma_{Voffset}$	43%
4	2.18 $\sigma_{Voffset}$	0.76 $\sigma_{Voffset}$	35%

This paper introduces a more versatile technique, tunable SAs. Each SA individually selects the most appropriate reference voltage to compensate for its offset. Fig. 4 indicates how such a scheme changes the effective offset distribution for the SA. As tuning does not require any selection in the critical logic path, it scales gracefully to large values of N. Table II compares tuning and redundancy based on a different metric: the theoretical remaining SA offset for a given yield target as function of $\log_2(N)$, the number of configuration bits. Tuning outperforms redundancy on this metric as well.

Fig. 5 discusses the SAs used in this design. Each SA has 4 configuration bits, which select one out of 16 reference voltages (N=16). In this prototype implementation, the reference voltages are generated on-chip with a simple resistive divider which consumes 13μA DC. The SA offset on a single die has a standard deviation of 19mV. To obtain a failure rate of less than 10^{-9}, an untuned SA of the size used, requires a single-ended input swing of at least 230mV. The novel design with tunable SAs employs a sufficient tuning range (300mV) and 16 levels, which in theory allows for an amazingly small single-ended input swing of just under 20mV. However, some margin is needed to guard against other noise sources and to obtain high speed operation. With relaxed timing settings (2ns memory access), no errors were observed when reading with 40mV single-ended GBL swing. In normal operation, 100mV swing is used and the SA reference voltages are chosen as to detect inputs below 70mV as a low logic input. This setting results in a faster access than the symmetric alternative, where this toggle point would be at 50mV. The area of the tuning circuitry per SA is rather large. However, as the employed GBL architecture requires only 32 SAs, the total area overhead is less than 1%.

C. Calibrating the Sense Amplifiers

The SAs can be calibrated by forcing all GBLs to the desired toggle voltage. The reference setting is swept. The highest setting for which a sense operation results in a high SA output is the best setting for this SA. In this design, this loop was controlled externally.

IV.   MEASUREMENT RESULTS

Table III shows the measured speed and energy consumption of the memory. Even though the WL and cell voltage are not scaled down, their energy consumption remains small. The limited currents make it feasible to generate these supplies with an on-chip converter in a future design. The memory covers a wide performance range, consuming between 8.4pJ/access at 850MHz and 2.7pJ/access at 240MHz. This greatly outperforms previous 90nm designs such as the 64Kbit, 16 bits/word memory that consumes 12.9pJ/access at 833MHz [6]. The measured total energy per access is comparable to the lowest values obtained with state-of-the-art 65nm subthreshold designs such as [2], even though the maximum speed of such designs is often below 10MHz.

Fig. 6 indicates that the cells operate reliably under intra-die variations, although the limited write margins suggest the use of a double-ended write for designs in future technology nodes. Such a change would have little impact on the reported performance.

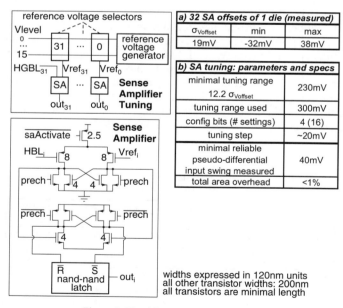

a) 32 SA offsets of 1 die (measured)		
$\sigma_{Voffset}$	min	max
19mV	-32mV	38mV

b) SA tuning: parameters and specs	
minimal tuning range 12.2 $\sigma_{Voffset}$	230mV
tuning range used	300mV
config bits (# settings)	4 (16)
tuning step	~20mV
minimal reliable pseudo-differential input swing measured	40mV
total area overhead	<1%

widths expressed in 120nm units
all other transistor widths: 200nm
all transistors are minimal length

Figure 5. Tunable sense amplifier system

TABLE III. MEASURED PERFORMANCE

	Measurement results [1]							
Maximum frequency [MHz]	850		780		480		240	
Main/Wordline/Cell Vdd [V]	1.2 / 1.2 / 1.2		1.0 / 1.2 /1.0		0.8 / 1.0 / 0.9		0.6 / 1.0 / 0.9	
	read	write	read	write	read	write	read	write
active energy / access [fJ]	6200	8935	3880	5833	2815	3686	1965	2074
Global decoder + GBL control	18%	24%	16%	19%	13%	19%	10%	18%
Sense amplifiers	14%	0%	15%	0%	14%	0%	16%	0%
cells	1%	2%	0%	3%	0%	2%	0%	2%
WL	1%	2%	2%	3%	2%	3%	4%	6%
local bitlines and readbuffer	12%	18%	11%	20%	9%	17%	8%	12%
global bitlines (100mV swing)	8%	13%	9%	17%	9%	21%	19%	25%
local control and decoder	14%	27%	15%	25%	13%	21%	10%	20%
timing	30%	14%	33%	14%	38%	17%	33%	17%
passive energy / access [fJ]	1322		801		457		674	
leakage power [uW]	1123		625		219		162	
Global decoder + GBL control [2]	18%		10%		-3%		-22%	
Sense amplifiers	0%		1%		0%		0%	
cells	25%		12%		22%		30%	
WL	31%		57%		56%		76%	
local bitlines and readbuffer	6%		6%		8%		5%	
global bitlines	0%		0%		1%		1%	
local control and decoder	19%		14%		15%		8%	
timing	0%		0%		0%		0%	
Total energy/access [fJ]	7522	10257	4681	6634	3272	4143	2638	2748
average[3] energy/access [fJ]	8433		5332		3562		2675	

[1] At room temperature. All energy values calculated as Q*VddMain, except for WL and cells.
[2] There is significant leakage from the WL supply to the global decoder supply
[3] 1/3 write, 2/3 read

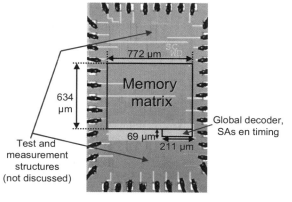

Figure 7. Die micrograph of 128Kbit SRAM

V. CONCLUSION

Variability-aware circuit techniques allow to cope with stochastic intra-die variations without introducing large margins. As an added benefit, they reduce design-time risks. The use of digitally tunable sense amplifiers and tunable timing circuitry resulted in an extremely low energy per operation single-cycle 32bit/word, 128Kbit SRAM design that was fabricated in 90nm CMOS. Measurements show that in the 850MHz boost mode, energy consumption is only 8.4pJ/access. In the normal 480MHz mode, the energy consumption reduces to 3.6pJ/access to bottom out at a very aggressive 2.7pJ/access in the 240MHz low power mode. The employed variability-aware techniques will scale very well to future technology nodes.

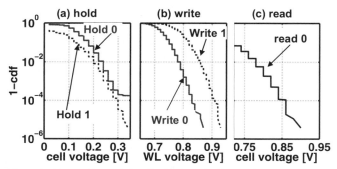

Figure 6. Measured cumulative distribution of cell operation margins for all 128K cells on a die. (a) Fraction of cells that fail to hold data at reduced V_{cell} [V_{WL}=0V] (b) Fraction of cells that can not be written correctly at reduced V_{WL} [V_{cell}=0.9V, V_{LBL}=0.6V]. C) fraction of cells that are not read correctly at reduced V_{cell} [V_{WL}=1.2V, V_{LBL}=1.0V]

REFERENCES

[1] B. Zhai, D. Blaauw, D. Sylvester, S. Hanson, "A Sub-200mV 6T SRAM in 0.13μm CMOS," ISSCC Digest of Technical Papers, pp 332-333, Feb. 2007

[2] N. Verma, A. Chandrakasan, 'A 256 kb 65 nm 8T Subthreshold SRAM employing Sense-Amplifier Redundancy," IEEE J. Solid-State Circuits, pp. 141-149, January 2008

[3] Y. Wang, H. Ahn, U. Bhattacharya, et al., "A 1.1GHz 12μA/Mb-Leakage SRAM design in 65nm Ultra-Low-Power CMOS with Integrated Leakage Reduction for Mobile Applications," ISSCC Digest of Technical Papers, pp 324-325, Feb. 2007

[4] J. Pille, C. Adams, T. Christensen, et al., "Implementation of the CELL Broadband Engine™ in a 65nm SOI Technology Featuring Dual-Supply SRAM Arrays Supporting 6GHz at 1.3V," ISSCC Digest of Technical Papers, pp 322-323, Feb. 2007

[5] S. Cosemans, W. Dehaene, F.Catthoor, "A Low-Power Embedded SRAM for Wireless Applications," IEEE J. Solid-State Circuits, Vol.42, pp. 1607-1617, July 2007

[6] K. Takeda, Y. Hagihara, Y. Aimoto, et al., "A Read-Static-Noise-Margin-Free SRAM Cell for Low-VDD and High-Speed Applications," IEEE J. Solid-State Circuits, Vol.41, pp. 1607-1617, January 2006

A Reconfigurable 65nm SRAM achieving Voltage Scalability from 0.25-1.2V and Performance Scalability from 20kHz-200MHz

Mahmut E. Sinangil*, Naveen Verma, Anantha P. Chandrakasan
Massachusetts Institute of Technology, Cambridge, MA
E-mail*: sinangil@mit.edu

Abstract—**A 64kb SRAM array fabricated in 65nm low-power CMOS operates from 250mV to 1.2V. This wide supply range is enabled by a combination of circuits optimized for both sub-V_t and above-V_t regimes. Reconfigurable circuits are used extensively, as low voltage assist circuits are required for functionality, but they must not limit performance during high voltage operation. The SRAM operates at 20kHz with a 250mV supply and 200MHz with a 1.2V supply. Over this range the leakage power scales by more than 50X.**

I. INTRODUCTION

Highly energy constrained applications, such as wireless sensor nodes and biomedical implants, preferentially operate at low voltage levels and at low frequencies to be close to the minimum energy point [1]. However these applications typically need to elevate their performance levels for short bursts of time to meet a certain system constraint. Thus, SRAMs for dynamic performance applications should operate efficiently over a large voltage and performance range. Also, since SRAMs account for a significant portion of the total area and power consumption of modern digital systems, Ultra-Dynamic Voltage Scalable (U-DVS) design should minimize the area and power overheads of achieving the large operating range.

The designs in [2], [3] and [4] demonstrate sub-V_t SRAMs. Because of the increased effect of variation due to random dopant fluctuation (RDF) and severely-degraded I_{on}/I_{off} ratio in sub-V_t region, these designs use different topologies and peripheral assist circuits to overcome these effects and enable functionality. For example, [2] and [4] uses 10T SRAM cells and [3] proposes an 8T cell. Although these designs achieve very low energy consumption, they cannot operate efficiently at higher voltages and consequently at higher frequencies since their circuits are designed to mainly target sub-V_t functionality. On the contrary, the design demonstrated in [5] works at high voltages and over a larger range but only in above-V_t . By restricting the voltage range as such, this design can employ static topologies with no reconfigurability and still support a large range since the trade-offs do not vary much within one region. However, more aggressive leakage power and active energy savings are required in highly energy constrained applications and therefore lowering the supply voltage into the sub-V_t region is crucial. Designing SRAMs for both sub-V_t and above-V_t regions is very challenging because of the fundamentally different trade-offs governing the circuit operation between these two regimes. In order to operate efficiently in both regions, circuits must be able to adapt themselves to the varying trade-offs over the voltage range. This adaptability is enabled by designing peripheral circuits with hardware reconfigurability.

This paper presents an SRAM that is designed for both sub-V_t and above-V_t operation. The design is operational from 250mV which is in deep sub-V_t region to 1.2V which is the nominal-V_{DD} for the process. An 8T bitcell is used to construct a high density array. Assist circuitry which is necessary for low-voltage functionality is designed with low overhead reconfigurability in mind. One of three different write-assist schemes are activated depending on the supply voltage level to prevent excess power. Multiplexed sense-amplifiers are used in the sensing network to minimize sensing delay. Lastly, bitcell and peripheral circuits are designed for optimal operation over the large voltage range.

II. DESIGN CONSIDERATIONS FOR U-DVS SRAM

A. Bitcell Design and Sizing

The traditional 6T SRAM cell fails to operate at low voltages because of read and write failures due to the degradation of Read Static-Noise-Margin (RSNM) and Write Margin. To limit the area overhead, an 8T bitcell is used in the design (Fig. 1) [3]. Two NMOS devices constitute the read-buffer and decouple the read and write ports of the cell. A write operation is done through WL, BL and BLB ports and a single-sided read operation is done through RDWL and RDBL ports. Decoupling of write and read ports gives designer more freedom to optimize the sizing of individual devices inside the cell for low-voltage functionality. Specifically, the 6T part of the cell can be sized for writability and the two read-buffer transistors can be sized for better read performance.

BVSS node is shared on each row, and it gets pulled-up if the row is not accessed. As a result, the voltage drop across the read-buffers of all un-accessed rows is brought to 0V. This causes the leakage from RDBL through un-accessed rows to be greatly reduced.

MCHd node is also shared on each row and connected to a gated driver. Since MCHd is the virtual supply node for the cross-coupled inverters inside the cell, bringing its voltage

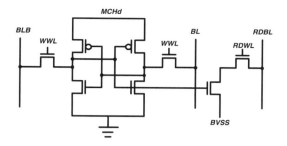

Fig. 1.   8T bitcell used in the design.

down is very effective to ease a write operation which will be discussed in the following sections.

Sizing of the read buffer devices inside the cell must be done by considering the entire voltage range. At voltage levels in or close to the sub-V_t region, using longer channel lengths increases the drive currents considerably. This is due to a decrease in the threshold voltage of the device with increasing gate length which is known as the reverse short channel effect (RSCE) [6]. However, in above-V_t regime, using longer channel length results in a decrease in the drive current.

Fig. 2 shows the 4σ drain current of a read-buffer with different gate lengths normalized to the minimum length read-buffer. There is a significant increase in 4σ current at low voltages which is due to RSCE. Larger channel area also improves 4σ current. The lengths of the read-buffer devices are chosen to be approximately 2 times the minimum length in order to increase performance at low voltages without degrading it too severely at high voltages.

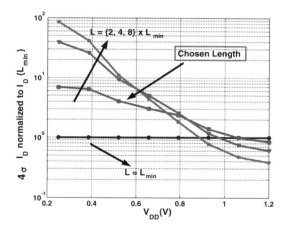

Fig. 2. 4σ drain current through a read-buffer for different gate lengths normalized to the minimum length read-buffer. Increasing the gate length results in a large current at low voltages but a smaller current at high voltages due to RSCE and a larger channel area.

B. BVSS Driver Design

As explained above, BVSS driver pulls the row-wise BVSS node up in order to mitigate the leakage through the RDBL when the row is not accessed. This structure employs a charge-pump circuit as shown in Fig. 3a. Doubling the gate drive of the NMOS pull-down device increases its drive strength by nearly 500X in sub-V_t so it can sink the aggregated current through all read-buffers in a row. The design in [3] exploits this exponential dependence of current to gate drive and uses a nearly minimum size pull-down NMOS at the output of the charge-pump.

For the U-DVS design, an interesting trade-off exists for the sizing of the pull-down transistor in the BVSS driver. The charge pump cannot be enabled beyond V_{DD} =0.6V due to reliability concerns. This causes a sudden drop in the performance vs. V_{DD} curve as shown in Fig. 3b. Up-sizing the NMOS transistor by nearly 10X makes the off-region smaller and ensures a nearly continuous performance improvement with increasing supply voltage.

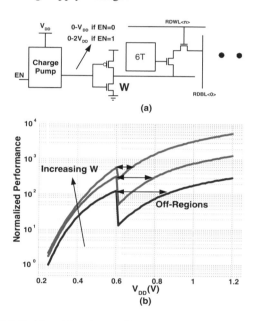

Fig. 3.   BVSS driver (a) and normalized read performance with different widths for the pull-down device in BVSS driver (b). Increasing the width is necessary for a continuous performance vs. V_{DD} curve beyond the voltage at which charge-pump cannot be activated.

C. MCHd Driver Design

Although the 8T cell can be sized for better writabilty, the effect of sizing is easily overcome by the variation as the supply voltage scales down. This causes the degradation of write margin of the cell. Fig. 4b shows the write margin distributions for the memory cell used in the design. A positive value shows a write failure. As the supply voltage goes down, the mean of the distribution becomes smaller. Additionally the distribution becomes wider which is due to the increased effect of variation at lower voltages. These two effects add up causing the tail of the distribution to get closer and closer to the point of failure as the supply voltage scales down. The distribution at 1.2V shows that there is enough write margin at this voltage. At 700mV, only the tail of write margin distribution fails whereas at 250mV, a significant portion of the memory cells are facing write failure. In order to maintain functionality at low voltages, peripheral assists should be employed to improve the write margin. However this peripheral assist circuits must be designed such that they introduce minimal power overhead to the design.

This motivates the concept of reconfigurability for write assists at different supply voltage levels. As mentioned above, MCHd node is connected to a gated driver as shown in Fig. 4a. MCHd driver is designed such that depending on the operating V_{DD}, MCHd voltage can be actively pulled-down, left floating or kept at V_{DD} during a write operation as shown in Fig. 4c. Reducing the supply node of the cell helps writability by degrading the strength of the internal feedback between the cross-coupled inverters. In *Keep at V_{DD}* mode, MCHd node is at V_{DD} all the times since no peripheral assist is required for functionality. In the *Float Header* mode, MCHd node is kept floating during a write access and the residual charge on this node is shared between the memory cells on the same row. This causes the MCHd node to droop to a slightly lower voltage during the write access. In the *Pull Header Down* mode, MCHd is pulled-down actively during the write cycle resulting in a better improvement in the write margin. Before the WL voltage goes down, MCHd node is actively pulled-up to V_{DD} in both modes. This programmable scheme prevents significant power overhead that would stem from keeping the write assists active at higher operating voltages.

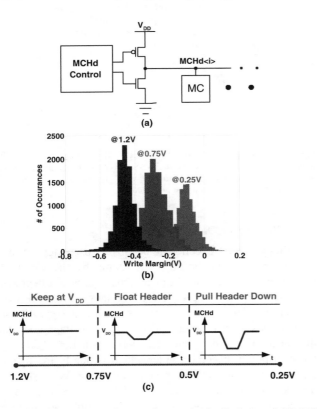

Fig. 4. MCHd driver circuit (a), write margin distributions at 1.2V, 0.7V and 0.25V (b) and three different writing schemes implemented in the design (c). One of the writing schemes is activated depending on the supply voltage level to prevent power overhead.

D. Sensing Network Design

Sense amplifier is in the critical path of a read access so the delay of this structure should also be considered very carefully. Since the U-DVS SRAM is intended to be operational in a very large voltage range, more than one sensing scheme should be employed to minimize the sensing delay.

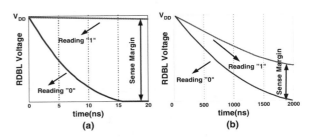

Fig. 5. Voltage waveforms in small-signal (a) and large-signal (b) sensing scenarios. Common-mode of the signals are close to V_{DD} for small-signal sensing whereas it is closer to ground level for large-signal sensing.

Small-signal and large-signal sensing schemes are widely used in SRAMs and both of these schemes have different design advantages over the other as explained in [7]. Fig. 5a and Fig. 5b show the RDBL voltage vs. time plots for two different scenarios. If the read access time is much faster than the parasitic droop on RDBL due to leakage (Fig. 5a), small-signal sensing scheme can be employed. However in the case of very long access times, which occurs at low voltage-performance modes, the increased effect of leakage results in severe degradation of the sensing margins (Fig. 5b). As a result, here, a large-signal sensing scheme must be employed.

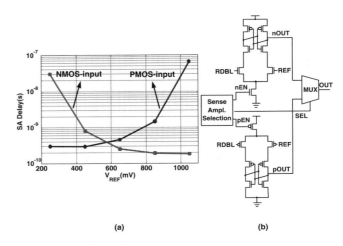

Fig. 6. Delay vs. REF for a sense-amplifier (a) and sensing network design (b). Devices for pre-charge/pre-discharge are omitted in the schematic for simplicity.

The sense-amplifier input voltages (i.e. RDBL and REF) are close to V_{DD} for small-signal sensing, whereas they are close to ground for large-signal sensing. Fig. 6a shows the delay vs. REF plots for NMOS-input and PMOS-input sense-amplifiers. The delay of this structure is shown to be highly dependent on the common-mode of the input voltages in [8]. Below a certain

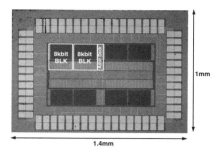

Fig. 7. Chip micrograph for the 64kbit SRAM implemented in 65nm CMOS process. The design consists of eight 8kbit sub-arrays.

level, as the common-mode input voltage decreases the delay of the sense amplifier increases. In order to keep the sensing delay low, two sense-amplifiers (one with NMOS-input and one with PMOS-input) are implemented along with a simple selection logic (Fig. 6b). At high voltage levels, the small-signal sensing scheme with the NMOS-input sense amplifier is activated. At low voltage levels large-signal sensing scheme is employed. Since the common-mode of the input signals is closer to ground level for large-signal sensing, PMOS-input sense amplifier is selected with this scheme.

III. MEASUREMENT RESULTS

A 64kbit SRAM is fabricated in a 65nm low-power process. The array consists of eight 8kbit sub-arrays and address decoder (Fig. 7). The memory performance scales from 20kHz to 200MHz over the 250mV to 1.2V operating range (Fig. 8). Due to test setup limitations, the performance measurements for 0.8V-1.2V are done by measuring access time. Leakage power scales down by more than 50X over the voltage range resulting in very significant power savings. Leakage, active and total energy curves are shown in Fig. 9. Active energy decreases quadratically as supply voltage decreases. Leakage energy, on the contrary, increases as the supply voltage decreases because of integrating leakage power over a larger access period. Total energy reaches a minimum around 400mV.

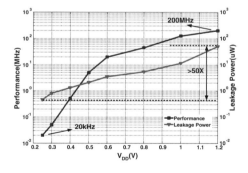

Fig. 8. Measured performance and power vs. V_{DD} plots. SRAM performance scales from 20kHz to 200MHz over the voltage range.

IV. CONCLUSION

An SRAM functional between 0.25V to 1.2V is presented in this paper. Sub-V_t operation requires additional circuitry

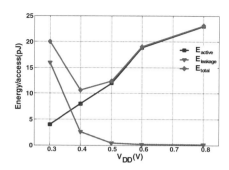

Fig. 9. Measured Energy/access vs. V_{DD} plot. Leakage and active components of the total energy is shown. Minimum energy point occurs around 400mV.

for correct functionality whereas standard techniques can be implemented for nominal V_{DD} levels. In order to maintain efficiency and prevent performance and power overheads, the SRAM features reconfigurable circuits to support this large voltage range and to manage different trade-offs associated with sub-V_t and above-V_t regions.

8T cell is sized for easy writability and good performance. One of the three write assist schemes are enabled depending on the supply voltage level to prevent power overhead. Multiplexed sense-amplifiers are used to minimize the sensing delay over the entire operating range. The design achieves 20kHz to 200MHz performance and more than 50X leakage power scaling.

ACKNOWLEDGMENT

This work is funded by DARPA and chip fabrication is provided by Texas Instruments. The authors thank Joyce Kwong and Masood Qazi for valuable discussions and support.

REFERENCES

[1] A. Wang and A. Chandrakasan, "A 180mV FFT Processor Using Sub-threshold Circuit Techniques," in *IEEE Int. Solid-State Circuits Conf. (ISSCC) Dig. Tech. Papers*, Feb. 2004, pp. 292–293.
[2] B. Calhoun and A. Chandrakasan, "A 256-kbit Sub-threshold SRAM in 65nm CMOS," in *IEEE Int. Solid-State Circuits Conf. (ISSCC) Dig. Tech. Papers*, Feb. 2006, pp. 628–629.
[3] N. Verma and A. Chandrakasan, "A 65nm 8T Sub-Vt SRAM Employing Sense-Amplifier Redundancy," in *IEEE Int. Solid-State Circuits Conf. (ISSCC) Dig. Tech. Papers*, Feb. 2006, pp. 328–329.
[4] T.-H. Kim, J. Liu, J. Keane, and C. H. Kim, "A High-Density Subthreshold SRAM with Data-Independent Bitline Leakage and Virtual Ground Replica Scheme," in *IEEE Int. Solid-State Circuits Conf. (ISSCC) Dig. Tech. Papers*, Feb. 2007, pp. 330–331.
[5] L. Chang, Y. Nakamura, R. K. Montoye, J. Sawada, A. K. Martin, K. Kinoshita, F. Gebara, K. Agarwal, D. Acharyya, W. Haensch, K. Hosokawa, and D. Jamsek, "A 5.3GHz 8T-SRAM with Operation Down to 0.41V in 65nm CMOS," in *Symp. on VLSI Circuits (VLSI) Dig. Tech. Papers*, June 2007, pp. 252–253.
[6] B. Yu, E. Nowak, K. Noda, and C. Hu, "Reverse Short-Channel Effects and Channel-Engineering in Deep-Submicron MOSFETs: Modeling and Optimization," in *Symp. on VLSI Technology (VLSI) Dig. Tech. Papers*, June 1996, pp. 162–163.
[7] K. Zhang, K. Hose, V. De, and B. Senyk, "The Scaling of Data Sensing Schemes for High Speed Cache Design in Sub-0.18μm," in *Symp. on VLSI Circuits (VLSI) Dig. Tech. Papers*, June 2000, pp. 226–227.
[8] B. Wicht, T. Nirschl, and D. S-Landsiedel, "Yield and Speed Optimization of a Latch-Type Voltage Sense Amplifier," *IEEE Journal of Solid-State Circuits*, vol. 39, pp. 1148–1158, July 2004.

A Cell-activation-time Controlled SRAM for Low-voltage Operation in DVFS SoCs Using Dynamic Stability Analysis

Masanao Yamaoka, Kenichi Osada, and Takayuki Kawahara
Central Research Laboratory, Hitachi, Ltd.,
1-280, Higashi-koigakubo, Kokubunji, Tokyo, 185-8601, Japan,
E-mail: masanao.yamaoka.ns@hitachi.com

Abstract— Increasing V_{th} variation leads to the deterioration of SRAM operating stability, and accurate stability analysis is required in today's SRAM design. For the first time, we defined SRAM dynamic operating margins, which is more accurate than conventional static operating margin. The dynamic operating margin analysis is applied to a low-voltage SRAM module design. The SRAM module uses a memory-cell-activation time control with short bit-line structure for both read and write stability improvement. The SRAM module also uses body-bias control by column for further low-voltage operation, which is suitable for DVFS operation. A prototype SRAM module with body-bias control achieved 0.6-V operation.

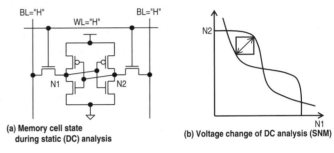

(a) Memory cell state during static (DC) analysis

(b) Voltage change of DC analysis (SNM)

Fig. 1. Conventional method to analyze read margin

I. INTRODUCTION

Today, process scaling increases the transistor's V_{th} variation. Increasing V_{th} variation deteriorates the circuit performance. Especially, V_{th} variation has a critical impact on SRAM stability. It has two reasons. First reason is that the SRAM is composed of small size transistor to achieve high density. The small-size transistor causes the increase of V_{th} variation. Second is that the SRAM is composed of six transistors and its operations are organized by their balance. The increasing V_{th} variation breaks the balance and SRAM operating stability is deteriorated. Therefore, the operating stability analysis is important at SRAM design to improve the SRAM performance. Conventionally, static operation analyses [1][2] were used to predict SRAM cell performance against V_{th} variation. However, the SRAM operates dynamically, and therefore, the static stability analysis is different from the real stability [3][4]. To avoid this situation, we defined a dynamic operating margin for the first time. When analyzing the operating stability by using the proposed dynamic operating margin, a combination of short bit lines and bit-line full-swing read can achieve both high read and write stability.

In low-power SoCs, the low-voltage SRAM is an indispensable component for a dynamic voltage and frequency scaling (DVFS) operation. We designed an SRAM module for DVFS SoCs. In the SRAM, the short local bit line and the back-gate bias control of SRAM cell [5] can improve operating stability and achieve low-voltage operation. The back-gate bias of the SRAM is controlled column by column only under lower V_{dd} conditions to maximize the body-bias effect to suitable for DVFS SoCs. This SRAM module achieved 0.6-V operation.

II. DYNAMIC STABILITY ANALYSIS

Today, the V_{th} variation causes the SRAM operation failure, and therefore, the SRAM operating margin analysis is indispensable in SRAM memory cell design phase. Conventionally, SRAM operating margin is statically analyzed as shown in Fig. 1(a) and (b). The bit-line (BL) and word-line (WL) voltages are fixed to the supply voltage (V_{dd}). However, in actual SRAM, the node voltages are not fixed. In Fig. 2(a) and (b), the state of the SRAM cell during a read operation is shown. After word-line activation, the data retention node N2 is driven to a higher voltage by a "H" precharged BL, and N1 is driven to a lower voltage by the rising N2 voltage. After WL inactivation, the N1 and N2 voltages are recovered and the read failure is prevented, if there is a voltage difference between N1 and N2 during read operation. We define the minimum voltage difference between N1 and N2 as a dynamic read margin. The dynamic read margin changes according to the bit and word structure, WL activating timing.

Fig. 3 plots the dynamic read margin when changing read time. The read time is, at most, 1.0 ns in today's multi-core SoCs [6]. By shortening the read time, the dynamic read margin is improved.

Just as with the dynamic read margin, a dynamic write margin is also defined by setting the memory cell state to a write operation (as shown in Fig. 4). When the dynamic write margin is in the negative range (solid lines in Fig. 4), the write operation completes correctly. Fig. 5 plots the dynamic write margin when changing write time. Contrary

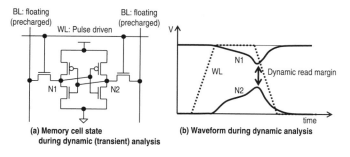

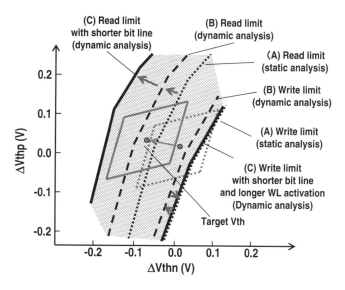

(a) Memory cell state during dynamic (transient) analysis

(b) Waveform during dynamic analysis

Fig. 2. Proposed method to analyze read margin

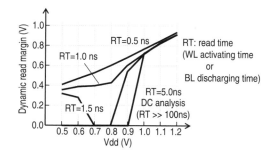

Fig. 3. Dynamic read margin vs. V_{dd}

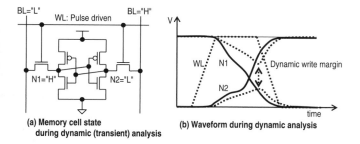

(a) Memory cell state during dynamic (transient) analysis

(b) Waveform during dynamic analysis

Fig. 4. Method to analyze write margin

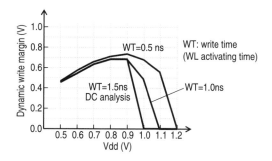

Fig. 5. Dynamic write margin vs. V_{dd}

Fig. 6. Dynamic operating V_{th} window under 0.8V V_{dd} supply voltage

to the dynamic read margin, the dynamic write margin is improved by extending the write time.

To confirm the evaluation of the dynamic operating margins, and to use them for SRAM cell design, a V_{th} window analysis is used. The graph in Fig. 6 plots the V_{th} window of SRAM operation. The horizontal and vertical axes indicate V_{th} values of nMOS and pMOS, which fluctuate due to systematic variations. The area bordered by the broken read and write

limit lines is the conventional static V_{th} window ((A) lines in Fig. 6). The diamond shape indicates the V_{th} fluctuation of manufactured SRAM, and this shape must be within the V_{th} window for correct SRAM operation. When using a dynamic operating margin, the read limit is improved, and the write limit deteriorates ((B) lines in Fig. 6). This area bordered by (B) lines is the dynamic V_{th} window.

III. SHORT LOCAL BIT LINE FOR HIGHER READ AND WRITE STABILITY

The read margin is influenced by the read time and is improved by reducing the read time as mentioned in Fig. 3. The read time is decided by a WL activating and a BL discharging time. On the contrary, the write is influenced by the write time and is improved by expanding the write time as mentioned in Fig. 5. The write time is decided by a WL activating time. Therefore, expanding the WL activating time and shortening the BL discharging time can improve both the dynamic read margin and the dynamic write margin at the same time. The BL discharging time can be easily controlled by short local bit lines and fully swinging the bit lines by the memory cell current, because the read operation is finished by the BL full discharging. The short bit line achieves short read time and contributes to the dynamic read margin improvement. The dynamic write margin can be maximized by expanding the WL activating time.

The circuit diagram of the read path of our SRAM module is indicated in Fig. 7. The memory module introduces hierarchical bit line structure and the local bit lines (LBL) are designed as short. The dynamic V_{th} window with the short local bit line is indicated as line (C) in Fig. 6. The read limit line is improved by using the short local bit lines, and the write limit line of dynamic analysis is also improved as that of DC analysis by deciding the WL activating time as enough length. At the memory cell design phase, the target V_{th} (central

287

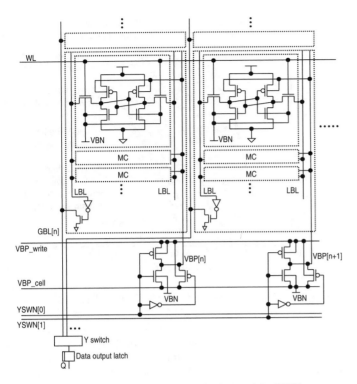

Fig. 7. Circuit diagram of body-bias control for DVFS

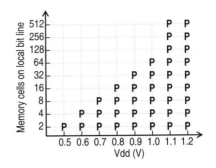

Fig. 8. Minimum V_{dd} vs. local bit-line length

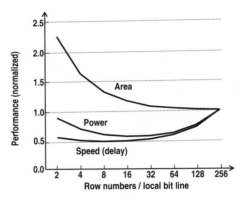

Fig. 9. Performance vs. local bit-line length

value of the diamond shape) is adjusted to place the diamond shape in Fig. 6 within the V_{th} window. Conventionally, a combination of a short local bit line and bit-line full-swing access is used for high speed operation [7]. When considering the read and write operation dynamically, the short bit lines also contribute to the high read and write stability.

Fig. 8 shows simulated shmoo plots when changing the V_{dd} and the number of memory cells on a local bit line. The shorter local bit line enables low-voltage operation. This shmoo can be plotted by using the dynamic read margin. Fig. 9 shows the SRAM performance when changing the local bit-line length. The shorter local bit line requires read circuit attached to the local bit line, and the area becomes larger. As to the power consumption and the operating speed, there are optimum points at the region that the memory cell numbers are 8 or 16.

IV. BODY-BIAS CONTROL BY COLUMN FOR LOW-VOLTAGE OPERATION IN DVFS SRAM

When using DVFS, the operating frequency is changed according to the V_{dd}; when using lower V_{dd}, the frequency is low and the SRAM has a longer operation time. Therefore, under lower V_{dd}, a body-bias control according to its operation is effective. Fig. 7 shows a circuit diagram of body-bias control for improving both read and write margins under lower voltage. The body nodes of the load pMOS of SRAM cell in the same column are connected through the n-well layer, and are controlled column by column according to the SRAM operation. The body nodes of the nMOS in the memory cells

are commonly connected in the same memory-cell array by a common p-substrate, and fixed to the p-substrate voltage. This well structure can be manufactured using only a double-well structure. The operating waveforms for lower and higher V_{dd} are shown in Fig. 10. At a write operation, the pMOS body nodes of data written column is reverse biased, and the write stability is enhanced. On the other hand, the pMOS body nodes in other columns are forward body biased, and the read stability is enhanced. In this circuit, less than 1.0-V body bias is applied, and only a thin gate oxide MOS is required. Furthermore, the body bias is only controlled when the operating speed is low, and the node voltage is sufficiently changed.

V. MEASUREMENT RESULTS

We manufactured prototype SRAM modules by a 90-nm G process. We chose 16-bit memory cells per local bit line by considering the SRAM performance acquired by Fig. 8 and Fig. 9. The 16-bit length achieves 0.8-V operation without body-bias and 40% power and 50% delay reduction with only 20% area penalty. Fig. 11 shows a micrograph of the prototype chip. Fig. 12 plots the failure rate with and without body-bias control. By using body-bias control, the minimum V_{dd} is reduced by more than 0.1 V, and achieved 0.6-V operation. Fig. 13 shows the power efficiency obtained by decreasing V_{dd}. A lower voltage operation achieves higher power efficiency and can be achieved by using body-bias

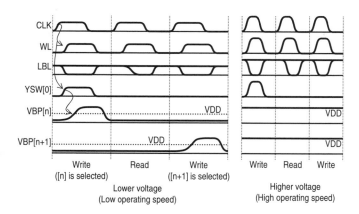

Fig. 10. Operating waveforms of higher and lower V_{dd}

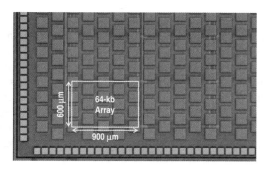

Fig. 11. Prototype chip micrograph

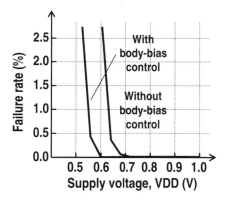

Fig. 12. Failure rate with and without body-bias control

control. This means the DVFS is effective to achieve high power efficiency in SRAM modules.

VI. SUMMARY

Due to the process scaling, the V_{th} variation becomes large, and the stability of SRAM operations are decreased. The accurate operating margin analysis is indispensable for SRAM cell design. We defined the dynamic operating margins to analyze SRAM cell performance. To improve the read and write stability dynamically, the read and write time have to be controlled to adequate level. We introduced the short bit line and bit-line full-swing read, and improved both the read and write stability. The proposed SRAM can operate under 0.8-V

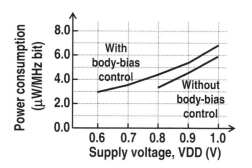

Fig. 13. Power efficiency under DVFS condition

supply voltage. Furthermore, we proposed an SRAM body-bias control column-by-column for low-voltage operation. The body-bias control of SRAM cells is changed according to its operating speed and voltage, and therefore, it is suitable for DVFS operation. The prototype chip achieved 0.6-V V_{dd} operation and higher power efficiency.

ACKNOWLEDGMENTS

The authors thank Prof. M. Takamiya and Prof. T. Sakurai from University of Tokyo for their valuable discussions, S. Yamaguchi for prototype management and testing, and N. Irie, K. Osada, K. Kasai, and M. Odaka for the project management. Part of this work was supported by the Ministry of Education, Culture, Sports, Science and Technology of the Japanese Government.

REFERENCES

[1] M. Yamaoka, K. Osada, R. Tsuchiya, M. Horiuchi, S. Kimura, and T. Kawahara, "Low Power SRAM Menu for SOC Application Using Yin-Yang-Feedback Memory Cell Technology," *Symp. VLSI Circuits Dig.*, pp. 288-291, June 2004.

[2] Y. Tsukamoto, K. Nii, S. Imaoka, Y. Oda, S. Ohbayashi, T. Yoshizawa, H. Makino, K. Ishibashi, and H. Shinohara, "Worst-Case Analysis to Obtain Stable Read/Write DC Margin of High Density 6T-SRAM-Array with Local Vth Variability," *Proc. ICCAD, pp. 394-405, November 2005.*

[3] M. Khellah, Y. Ye, N. S. Kim, D. Somasekhar, G. Pandya, A. Farhang, K. Zhang, C. Webb, and V. De, "Wordline & Bitline Pulsing Schemes for Improving SRAM Cell Stability in Low-Vcc 65nm CMOS Designs," *Symp. VLSI Circuits Dig. , pp. 9-10, June 2006.*

[4] H. Pilo, J. Barwin, G. Braceras, C. Browning, S. Burns, J. Gabric, S. Lamphier, M. Miller, A. Roberts, and F. Towler, "An SRAM Design in 65nm and 45nm Technology Nodes Featuring Read and Write-assist Circuits to Expand Operating Voltage," *Symp. VLSI Circuits Dig. , pp. 15-16, June 2006.*

[5] M. Yamaoka and T. Kawahara, "Operating-margin-improved SRAM with Column-at-a-time Body-bias Control Technique," *Proceedings of the 33rd European Solid-State Circuits Conference, pp. 396-399, September 2007.*

[6] H. Aoki et al., to be presented at 2008 VLSI circuits.

[7] J. Davis, D. Plass, P. Bunce, Y. Chan, A. Pelella, R. Joshi, A. Chen, W. Huott, T. Knips, P. Patel, K. Lo, and E. Fluhr, "A 5.6GHz 64kB dual-read data cache for the POWER6TM processor," *IEEE ISSCC Dig. Tech. Papers, pp. 622-623, February 2006.*

[8] M. Yamaoka, N. Maeda, Y. Shinozaki, Y. Shimazaki, K. Nii, S. Shimada, K. Yanagisawa, and T. Kawahara, "Low-Power Embedded SRAM Modules with Expanded Margins for Writing," *IEEE ISSCC Dig. Tech. Papers, pp. 480-481, February 2005.*

A Dual Port Dual Width 90nm SRAM with Guaranteed Data Retention at Minimal Standby Supply Voltage

Peter Geens and Wim Dehaene
K.U. Leuven, ESAT -MICAS
Kasteelpark Arenberg 10, B-3001 Heverlee, Belgium
Email: {Peter.Geens,Wim.Dehaene}@esat.kuleuven.be

Abstract—A 64kbit SRAM with dual port dual width was fabricated in a 1P9M 90nm CMOS technology. The narrow port has a width of 32bits, the wide port has 256bits. To minimise the leakage current a lowered secondary supply is applied to all inactive cells. The fine granular implementation allows the leakage currents to be reduced while the wake-up delay overhead is kept minimal. This system also includes a monitoring and regulation solution to minimise leakage currents while guaranteeing data retention on a die to die basis. Measurements show the SRAM is able to operate with a 2ns access time and is capable of a factor 2 leakage current reduction at a nominal 1V supply using a local series regulator.

I. INTRODUCTION

The evolution towards making systems more mobile, by increasing battery life and the simultaneous demand for more functionality, has made power consumption the key specification for digital electronics design. Not only is the active power consumption under close investigation, the stand-by consumption is the subject of research too. In the newly emerging bulk CMOS deep-submicron technologies needed to meet the functionality requirements, power consumption is dominated by leakage currents especially in SRAMs.

In the current state-of-the-art systems-on-chip, SRAMs are taking up the bulk of the area. This evolution makes that the power consumption is dominated by the SRAM and its interfacing. In stand-by mode the leakage currents originating in the SRAMs are the defining factors in the stand-by power consumption, due to the high number of leaking devices. It is imperative to control and reduce those leakage currents to be able to fulfil the stringent power consumption specifications for mobile communications.

With almost every new technology generation the number of metal layers increases. This in turn facilitates routing more signals and supplies across the chips.

The evolutions described above, have made introducing a secondary lower supply into the SRAM matrix an attractive and feasible option to reduce leakage currents during stand-by phases. Whether this second supply is referred to as a sleepy or drowsy supply[1]–[5] is of no consequence to the goal that is pursued: minimising the leakage currents through the exponential relation between supply and leakage[1] while maintaining the data in the matrix[2].

Due to the increased technological variability in current CMOS technologies, guaranteeing data retention on a die-to-die basis is not trivial. Process, Voltage,Temperature (*PVT*) and other time dependent variations need to be accommodated

for. While it is feasible to foresee margins during design time to compensate for these variations, those margins reduce possible power savings. In this paper a monitor with the same sensitivities towards PVT and other time dependent variations as the core SRAM cells is proposed. This monitor reduces the needed margins and allows to optimise power savings on a die-to-die basis.

This paper presents the implementation of a dual width dual port SRAM that unifies a monitoring and regulation system that guarantees data retention at minimal leakage current.

The different port widths of the memory enable the exploitation of the locality of access through wide loads. At the same time the data path is able to access the memories at smaller widths for actual computations. This architecture shows promise to reduce the power load of memories in embedded processors, as it lowers the decoder overhead. [10]

The paper is organised as follows. First the leakage reduction techniques as used in this design will be discussed. In the second part the monitoring solution to reliably retain data at minimal supply voltage will be proposed. The entire SRAM will be presented in the third section. In the next section the measurement results are shown and finally the conclusions will be drawn.

II. LEAKAGE REDUCTION

A. Leakage Mechanisms

In recent CMOS technology, there is a decrease of the bulk-effect and an increase of the Drain Induced Barrier Lowering (DIBL) effect on subthreshold leakage currents. The thinning of the gate oxides with every generation has also increased the gate-leakage currents [6], although the effect has been curbed by the introduction of high-K materials [9]. The relation between supply voltage and leakage currents has been reported earlier many times, e.g. in[1]–[5]. Both subthreshold and gate leakage currents depend exponentially on the supply voltage as both the voltage on the gate and across the transistor are linked closely to the supply voltage. This relationship can be exploited in circuits, including SRAM, to reduce the leakage currents by introducing a lower supply.

B. Dual Supply

The main leakage mechanisms in current CMOS technology are subthreshold and gate leakage. They both depend exponentially on the supply voltage in SRAMs [1] – [6]. This exponential relationship can be exploited to reduce the leakage

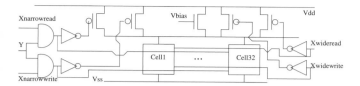

Fig. 1. Single word granularity stand-by control and supply generation

currents in SRAM cells that are in a non-active state, e.g. as in [1]–[5]. Due to the increasing number of metals available in current technologies the area increase, caused by introducing secondary supply lines into the core matrix, can be kept low.

C. Granularity

To be able to meet the speed requirements and static noise margin during read access, the addressed cells need to be brought to the higher nominal supply again. The granularity of this control varies from full memories [5] over row-by-row schemes [3] to single words [1]. The finest granularity combines the highest power savings with the lowest delay and power penalty to reactivate. All the cells, except those accessed during a read or write cycle, will be kept on a lower supply. This division also minimises the supply line capacitance that has to be charged every access cycle. The proposed solution follows this path.

Per word switching transistors are implemented that make the transition between the two supply voltages. To limit the total area overhead of the proposed system, a localised series regulator is implemented to generate the stand-by supply voltage. The series regulator per word merely consists of a biased transistor, with the bias voltage generated from the monitor and regulation system. This reduces the possible power savings as only the exponential lowering of the leakage currents will be taken into account. A small decoder section and wordline buffer are also implemented on a word by word basis to locally generate the needed signals. Despite the highly localised implementation, the total area overhead is estimated to be only 16%. Figure 1 shows the schematic of a word with the implemented local periphery.

III. DATA RETENTION

Although the viability of lowering the supply has been proven before [3]–[5], the question on the lower boundary for the "sleep" supply on die-to-die basis remains largely unanswered. In the high variability environments of today's technologies, guaranteeing data retention requires high margins on the "sleep" supply voltage to be taken into account to accommodate PVT and time dependent variations. Different environments and dies will require different supply voltages in order to preserve the data while maximising power savings. With an in situ monitor these margins can be minimised.

A. Bit Integrity

The Static Noise Margin (SNM) as defined by Seevinck [8] has been the standard bit integrity parameter for read conditions for many years. The SNM under hold (SNM_{hold})

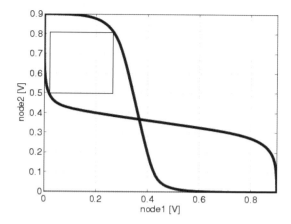

Fig. 2. SNM under hold

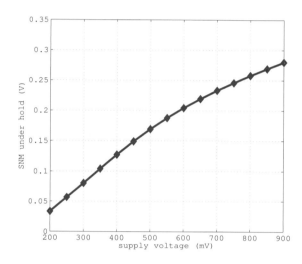

Fig. 3. Hold SNM as function of the cell supply voltage

is the logical extension of this definition to measure data retention capability under non-access conditions as depicted in figure 2. It can be measured with the same setup as the traditional SNM with the only difference being the off-state of the pass-transistors.

The bit integrity will diminish under lowered supplies, and as such also SNM_{hold}. As can be seen in figure 3 the relation between SNM_{hold} and supply voltage can be approximated over a large range, 200mV to 600mV, by a linear function.

B. SNM_{hold} Monitor

While it is feasible to foresee margins during design time to compensate for the above mentioned variations, those margins reduce possible power savings. To optimise the power savings feedback from the system over time is necessary. This feedback is based on in-situ monitoring of the SNM_{hold} parameter. However imperfections in the monitor will cause to need to take extra margins into account, which in turn lead to suboptimal leakage power savings. The proposed systems as

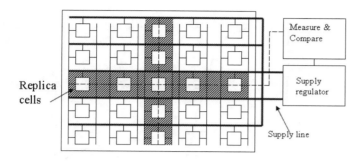

Fig. 4. monitor overview

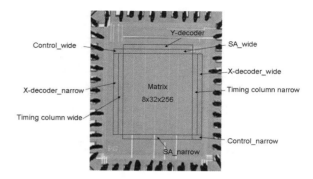

Fig. 5. SRAM annotated micrograph

Transistor	Length (nm)	Width (nm)
$M1_{a,b}$	160	360
$M2_{a,b}$	160	240
$M3_{a,b}$	80	360
$M4_{a,b}$	80	240
$M5_{a,b}$	80	240

TABLE I

TRANSISTOR DIMENSIONS OF THE 10T DUAL PORT SINGLE ENDED CELL

shown in figure 4 minimises this overhead by using monitor cells that share the same environment, including layout, with the core matrix cells. This means they match the behaviour of the core cell closely with regard to PVT variations

C. SNM_{hold} Monitor implementation

To have the best possible indicator of the actual behaviour the monitor has to mimic the behaviour of the SRAM cells as close as possible. This will decrease the margins that have to be taken to compensate for deviations in behaviour. To this end the monitor needs the same electrical and geometrical properties as the core cells. The environment of the monitor should also be identical, or as close as possible to the environment of the core cells.

The monitor can consist of a single SRAM cell, or multiple SRAM cells in parallel, where the internal nodes are accessible. As such the conditions of similar, if not identical, behaviour to the core cells can be guaranteed. In accordance with the law of large numbers [11] the mismatch influence of the transistors on the bit integrity parameter can be reduced with the square-root of the number of monitor cells, see also formula 1.

$$\sigma \sim 1/sqrt(N) \qquad (1)$$

The increased internal capacitance of the cells is not a hampering factor as the SNM_{hold} parameter is a static measure. However, the current needed to measure multiple cells in parallel is linearly depended on the number of cells. This creates a trade-off between leakage power savings and active power needed for the monitor measurements.

To determine the lower boundary of the stand-by voltage, the monitor is measured at low supply voltages. The current needed for those measurements is greatly reduced compared to the nominal case. This allows to put multiple cells in parallel and as such reduce the spread on the resulting monitor value. By having multiple replicated cells the placement of the monitor cells can be spread, see figure 4. This will eliminate the linear dependency of location on the mismatch even further reducing the spread σ of the monitor SNM distribution.

D. Control

Direct measurement of the SNM_{hold} parameter requires a control mechanism next to a monitor cell. As SRAMs are not

stand-alone applications a digital implementation was chosen. This implementation can run on the spare cycles of a neighbouring processor, or have it's own hardware. The algorithm will compare the measure SNM_{hold} value with an externally applied reference equal to the minimal desired SNM_{hold}. Based on this comparison the supply voltage will be regulated to meet the required minimum SNM_{hold} and as such guarantee data retention while maximising leakage current savings. A detailed description of the algorithm can be found in [2].

IV. SRAM

A. overview

The dual port and dual width specifications require the use of two decoders structures as the 2 ports can work independently and simultaneously. As a result the 32bit and 256bit wide access have separate decoders. The timing paths have also been split up to accommodate for differences in address. The matrix has an organisation of 256x256 core cells, with every bitcolumn having two sense-amplifiers, one for 32 bit and one for 256 bit access. The floorplan and chip micrograph are shown in figure 5. The unmarked areas contain not discussed auxiliary circuits to enable measurements.

B. cell

As shown in figure 6 a single ended cell was used for both ports. To increase the data retention and relax the destructive read conditions every cell was implemented with a read buffer. Read access is provided by the signals WLRW and WLRN, respectively for wide and narrow access. Direct write access is provided by the transistors M3a,b with the signals WLWW and WLWR for wide and narrow access. This results in a 10T cell that is read accessible on both ports simultaneously. The transistor dimensions are given in table I. All transistors used in the design have a low threshold voltage of 130mV.

292

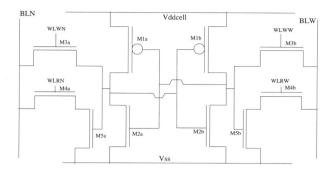

Fig. 6. Schematic of the single ended dual port SRAM cell

C. Timing

The most critical problem in the control of an SRAM system is the timing to enable the sense-amplifiers. If the sense-amplifiers are enabled too soon a false read out will be the result. Enabling the sense-amplifiers too late causes a larger swing and as such unneeded power dissipation while make the overall system slower.

This implementation uses a continuous time comparator (CTC) [7] on a dummy bitline for each port, as shown on figure 5 to ensure the sense-amplifiers are activated at the correct time. This CTC is enabled together with the decoders while also the read from the dummy word is started. When the CTC detects a large enough difference on the dummy bitline with regard to the reference voltage, it will activate the correct sense-amplifiers. This approach has the benefit of closely mimicking the behaviour of the core cells as the timing path has the same dependency on the address.

V. Measurements

Table II condenses the measurement results of the design for two modes and a reference simulation. The periphery voltages are in all cases kept identical. The decoders and sense amplifiers have the nominal 1V supply. The bitlines are precharged at 650mV. In low power mode the leakage current was reduced by a factor 2 to 530 μA with a total access delay of 2.5ns. In the nominal high speed setting the leakage current was reduced to 755 μA with an access delay of 2ns. Access delay measurements on both ports yielded identical results. The monitor system proved to be a reliable predictor of the actual retention voltage of the core cells on all tested dies, with the lower boundary being 200mV.

Mode	access time (ns)	matrix leakage (μA)	matrix supply voltage (mV)
low power	2.5	530	200
nominal	2	755	606
reference[a]	N/A	1100	1000

[a]simulated values

TABLE II
Measurement result overview

VI. Conclusion

A dual port dual width 64kbit SRAM was designed in 90nm CMOS technology. The SRAM combines actual noise margin monitoring with leakage reduction to assure minimal leakage with guaranteed data retention. The secondary lowered sleep supply is generated inside the system by a distributed series regulator. The fine granular structure of the control circuits results in a minimal reactivation delay while maximising the leakage reduction. The combination of the techniques result in an SRAM with up to a 2x leakage current reduction with a single cycle access time of 2.5ns or 25% leakage reduction for an access time of 2ns.

References

[1] P. Geens, W. Dehaene, "A small granular controlled leakage reduction system for SRAMs", *Journal of Solid-State Electronics*, no. 49, November 2005, pp 1776–1782
[2] P. Geens, W. Dehaene, "A Noise-margin monitor for SRAMs", *Proceedings of the International Conference on Memory Technology and Design*, May 2007
[3] F. R. Saliba, H. Kawaguchi, T. Sakurai, "Experimental verification of Row-by-Row Variable VDD Scheme Reducing 95% Active Leakage Power of SRAMs", *Symposium of VLSI Circuits Digest of Technical Papers*, 2005, pp. 162–165
[4] K. Nii, Y. Tsukamoto, T. Yoshizawa, S. Imaoka, Y. Tamagami, T. Suzuki, A. Shibayama, H. Makino and S. Iwade, "A 90-nm Low-Power 32-kB Embedded SRAM With Gate Leakage Suppression Circuit for Mobile Applications", *IEEE Journal of Solid-State Circuits*, vol. 39, no. 4,april 2004, pp. 684–693
[5] K. Roy, S. Mukhopadhyay, H. Mahmoodi-Meimand, "Leakage Current Mechanisms and Leakage Reduction Techniques in Deep-Submicrometer CMOS Circuits", *IEEE Proceedings of the IEEE*, vol 91, no. 2, February 2003, pp. 305–327
[6] R.W. Mann et al., "Ultralow-power SRAM technology", *IBM Journal on Research & Development*, VOL.47, NO. 5/6, September/November 2003
[7] J. R. Baker, H. W. Li, and D. E. Boyce, *CMOS, Circuit Design, Layout and Simulation, Ser. Series on Microelectronics.*, Piscataway, NJ: IEEEPress, 1998, ch. 26, pp. 685-717.
[8] E. Seevinck, F. List, J. Lohstroh, "Static Noise Margin Analysis of MOS SRAM cells", *IEEE Journal of Solid-State Circuits*, vol. sc-22, no. 5, October 1987, pp. 748–754
[9] K. Mistry et al., "A 45nm Logic Technology with High-k+Metal Gate Transistors, Strained Silicon, 9 Cu Interconnect Layers, 193nm Dry Patterning, and 100% Pb-free Packaging", *Proceedings of IEEE International Electron Devices Meeting*, 2007, pp. 247–250
[10] P.Raghavan, A.Lambrechts, M.Jayapala, F.Catthoor, D.Verkest, H.Corporaal,"Very wide register: an asymmetric register file organisation for low power embedded processors", *Proc. 10th ACM/IEEE Design and Test in Europe Conf.(DATE)*,Nice, France, April 2007, pp.1066–1071
[11] Jakob Bernoulli,*Ars Conjectandi: Usum & Applicationem Praecedentis Doctrinae in Civilibus, Moralibus & Oeconomicis*, 1713, Chapter 4.

Current reuse CMOS LNA for UWB applications

T. Taris, Y. Deval, J.B. Begueret
IMS laboratory
351 cours de la libération
33405 Talence Cedex, France
Thierry.taris@ims-bordeaux.fr

Abstract□ **To comply with the low power low voltage design constrains in modern RF CMOS technologies, a new LNA topology is here proposed. Implemented in a standard 130nm CMOS technology, two circuits operating under a 1.4V nominal voltage are reported. The first one dedicated to lower band of European UWB allocation ▯i.e. 3-5GHz- achieves a 13.8dB maximum gain for a 5.8mA current consumption. NF is so included in a 4.2 to 6.1 dB range. The second LNA addresses the 6-10GHz upper band. It performs a 12.2dB maximum gain and a 4.5dB NF_{min} for a 3 mA current consumption.**

Both circuits exhibit a more than -10dB input return loss over the considered bandwidth. S_{21} even reaches a 9dB and 11dB, respectively, when LNA core is supplied under 0.9V. Matching the input network order to the addressed bandwidth affords each circuit implementation to be included within a 1.8mm† silicon area.

I. INTRODUCTION

Approved by FCC, the Ultra Wide Band (UWB) technology using the unlicensed 3.1 to 10.6 GHz frequency band is capable to drive high data rate communications in short range applications at low cost with relatively low power consumption [1][2]. To support such system implementation, CMOS technology is a promising candidate not only because the digital circuitry benefits from Moore's law, but scaling of the CMOS devices with increasing f_T and f_{max} also facilitates the processing of large bandwidth analog signals with low power. Therefore, it is expected that single chip UWB solutions will appear in the near future.

Among the critical building blocks, brought into play in such broadband system architecture, is the Low Noise Amplifier. Conventional shunt resistive feedback topologies [3] likewise distributed amplifiers need a too large current consumption to cover the here considered frequency range. There are so not suited for low power purpose. Because of a direct correlation between noise and input matching common gate LNA design is basically limited and needs extra cost inductor to be optimized [4]. Transformer feedback [5][6][7] LNA are relevant architectures but they are also sensitive to technology modeling. In consequence their implementation and optimization are found to be very specific. LC cascode LNA [8][9], a wide spread and easy to design solution, achieves overall good broadband performances under acceptable power consumption.

Focusing on aggressive voltage scaling of CMOS technologies this work proposes a new UWB LNA topology based on LC ladder approach. To address the matter, both LC ladder filter synthesis and current reuse technique are first reviewed and illustrated with simulations of basic topologies. Section II presents the implementation of two LNA in a 130nm CMOS technology dedicated to 3-5GHz and 6-10GHz, respectively. The measurement results are then argued regarding to design considerations. At last a comparison with the state of the art points out the improvement of the here proposed architecture.

II. LC LADDER SYNTHESIS AND CURRENT REUSE CONSIDERATIONS

A. LC ladder wideband input matching

To cover the 7GHz bandwidth of UWB standard, LC ladder input matching is usually implemented by synthesizing a 6th order pass-band filter [8]. To do so 4 input inductors are required thus inducing an extra-cost silicon area. In Europe because of the 802.11a allocation, from 5.15 to 5.725 GHz, UWB is split in two bands: the lower band from 3.1 to 5.1GHz and the upper band from 6.4 to 10.6 GHz. Receivers generally address one of these two allocations. As a matter of consequence a 4th order pass-band filter would be sufficient to cover one of these two bandwidths. As proof of concept, the cascode LNA topology depicted in Fig. 1 has been simulated in 130nm CMOS technology for the two considered bandwidth.

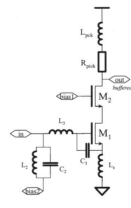

TABLE I. DEVICE SIZES FOR 3-5GHz AND 6-10GHz

	3-5 GHz	6-10 GHz
L_2/C_2	1.9nH/400fF	0.6nH/70fF
L_3/C_3	2.2nH/520fF	1.4nH/130fF
L_S	1.1nH	1.1nH
$(W/L)_{M1}$	40/0.13 □m	40/0.13 □m
$(W/L)_{M2}$	60/0.13 □m	50/0.13 □m
R_{pck}	50Ω	35Ω
L_{pck}	3nH	2nH

Figure 1. 4th order LC ladder LNA dedicated to 3-5GHz or 6-10GHz bands

Both configurations of this LNA whose sizing is reported in table I, operate under 1.6V and consume 4.8mA. Input matching and S_{21} parameter are exhibited in Fig. 2. These ones confirm the aforementioned LC filter order considerations: a 4th order network is enough to cover European UWB allocations in a conventional LC ladder synthesis.

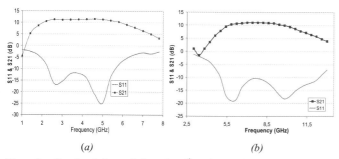

(a)   *(b)*

Figure 2.   Simulated S_{11} and S_{21} of a 4th order LC ladder cascode LNA dedicated to 3-5GHz *(a)* and 6-10GHz *(b)*

B. *The current reuse technique*

The cascode topology, proposed in Fig.1 and [8][9][10], has numerous benefits –i.e. good reverse isolation, quasi flat band large gain and low noise figure- which make it very popular. Nevertheless, stacking two NMOS transistors, it suffers from a nominal supply voltage which is not suited with aggressive scaling of modern CMOS technology. Combining a PMOS and a NMOS transistor between the two supply rails, current reuse topology, here reported in Fig. 3(a), allows LC ladder technique to be low voltage compatible.

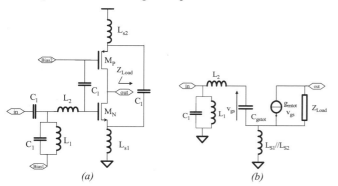

(a)   *(b)*

Figure 3.   LC ladder current reuse configuration *(a)* small signal equivalent circuit *(b)*

Assuming the small signal equivalent circuit presented in Fig. 3(b), F_{min} and voltage gain G_V can be expressed as it follows:

$$F_{min} = 1 + \frac{2}{\sqrt{5}} \frac{\omega}{g_{mtot}} C_{GStot} \sqrt{\gamma.\delta.(1 - |c^2|)} \quad (1)$$

$$G_v = \frac{g_{mtot}}{2R_S.j\omega C_{GS tot}}.Z_{load} \quad (2)$$

With $g_{mtot}=g_{mP}+g_{mN}$ and $C_{gstot}=C_{gsN}+C_{gsP}$

Based on conventional inductive degeneration, M_1 and M_2 are sized to perform the lowest noise figure at the geometry mean of the desired band-edge frequencies. F_{min} can be so estimated as reported in expression (1). L_1, L_2, L_{S1}, L_{S2} and C_1 are tuned with g_{mtot} and C_{gstot} to synthesize a 4th order passband filter according to [10]. Voltage gain derived in expression (2) figures out a frequency roll off. As well an inductive load, or stage, is expected to achieve a flat band

response. The minimum supply voltage, keeping both PMOS and NMOS transistors in saturation region, is:

$$VDD_{min} = \sqrt{\frac{2L_P I_D}{\Box_p C_{ox} W_P}} + |V_{TP}| \quad (3)$$

With L_p and W_p the PMOS transistor length and width respectively. μ_P is the hole mobility.

Expression (3), drawn in Fig. 4, exhibits that current reuse topology can so theoretically operate under very low voltage. W_p is here set to provide a 200fF gate to source capacitor thus fitting with a wide band LC filter synthesis.

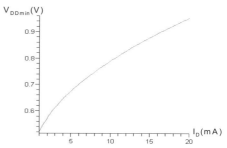

Figure 4.   Minimum supply voltage versus current consumption in a LC ladder current reuse topology. W_P=30µm, L_P=0.13µm, V_{TPMOS}=400mV

Though current reuse topology can support sub 1V operation, higher supply voltage than V_{DDmin} is required to address LNA design purpose.

III.   LNA IMPLEMENTATIONS AND MEASUREMENT RESULTS

Two UWB LNA dedicated to 3-5GHz and 6-10GHz bands respectively have been implemented in a 6 metal levels 130nm CMOS technology from STM. The full circuit design is reported in Fig. 6, the table 2 summarizes device sizing of each LNA. The first stage performs input matching, NF and gain as mentioned in section II. The second is a 50Ω output buffer whose picking load inductor L_{pck} compensates the frequency roll off of current reuse stage for flat band response. R_{pck} improves voltage gain at low frequency. A DC feedback loop is needed to keep both M_1 and M_2 in saturation region. To do so, V_{GS2} is controlled by Q_4 to Q_7 DC amplifier ensuring V_{DS1} equals to V_{REF} -i.e. a roughly $V_{DD}/2$-. V_{DS1} is collected through a large resistor which lessens loading effect.

The silicon area of each LNA, 1.8mm² and 1.2mm² including test PADs, are shown in Fig. 5. There are in good agreement with conventional LC ladder implementations [8] [10].

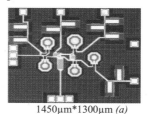 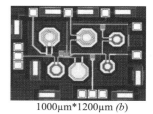

1450µm*1300µm *(a)*   1000µm*1200µm *(b)*

Figure 5.   chipmicrograph of 3-5GHz circuit *(a)* and 6-10GHz LNA *(b)*

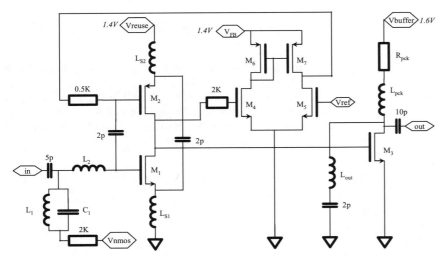

Figure 6.   UWB LC ladder current reuse LNA topology

TABLE II.   DEVICE SIZES FOR 3-5GHz AND 6-10GHz BANDS RESPECTIVELY

	3-5GHz	**6-10GHz**
M₁	$50/0.13\ \square m$	$25/0.13\ \square m$
M₂	$60/0.13\ \square m$	$30/0.13\ \square m$
M₃	$50/0.13\ \square m$	$50/0.13\ \square m$
L₁	$1.2\ nH$	$0.7\ nH$
C₁	$400\ fF$	$200\ fF$
L₂	$1.1\ nH$	$1.5\ nH$
L$_{S1}$	$1.6\ nH$	$0.35\ nH$
L$_{S2}$	$1.2\ nH$	$0.7\ nH$
L$_{pck}$	$1\ nH$	$1\ nH$
R$_{pck}$ (Ω)	$15\ \Omega$	$4\ \Omega$
L$_{out}$	removed	$1.2\ nH$

Measurements have been performed with a GSG probe bench combined with a HP 8510B network analyzer and a HP 8970 NF-meter. Nominal supply voltage is 1.4V for both circuits. The two LNA address input matching –i.e. S_{11}<-10dB- over the frequency bands of interest as depicted in Fig. 7(a) and (b).

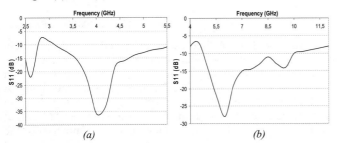

Figure 7. S_{11} parameter for 3-5GHz LNA *(a)* and 6-10GHz LNA *(b)*

Output matching, depicted in Fig. 8, is merely performed by the picking load inductor L_{pck} in the 3-5GHz LNA. In the 6-10GHz circuit, an additional L_{out} is needed to ensure S_{22} lower than -10dB.

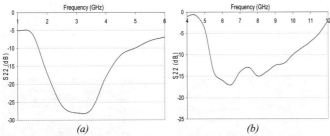

Figure 8. S_{22} parameter for 3-5GHz LNA *(a)* and 6-10GHz LNA *(b)*

S_{21} parameter reported in Fig. 9 (a) and (b) depicts a -3dB gain bandwidth from 2.8 to 4.8GHz and 5.6 to 8.8 GHz. A maximum 13.8dB@3.4GHz and 12.2dB@6.5GHz is observed for a 6mA and 3mA current consumption of current

reuse stage respectively. Bandwidths are found to be narrower than expected in both LNA because picking inductor L_{pck} does not fully compensate extra parasitic capacitors at output node.

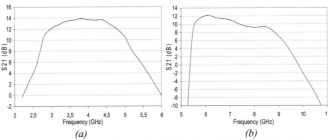

Figure 9. S_{21} parameter for 3-5GHz LNA *(a)* and 6-10GHz LNA *(b)*

Based on narrow band inductive degeneration approach, LC ladder technique allows a wideband low NF. Depicted in Fig. 10, it exhibits a 4.2dB minimum in the 3-5GHz range, and a 4.5dB minimum in the 6-10GHz range, and remains lower than 8dB for both circuits over the concerned bandwidth. The growth observed above 4.5GHz and 8.5GHz, respectively, are consistent with S_{21} cut off presented in Fig. 9.

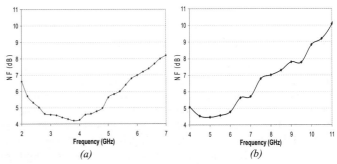

Figure 10. NF for 3-5GHz LNA *(a)* and 6-10GHz LNA *(b)*

The voltage gain versus V_{dd} is drawn in Fig. 11. To perform these measurements, both V_{REF} and V_{NMOS} have been tuned to keep M_1 and M_2 in saturation region during the V_{DD} sweep thus ensuring good NF and input matching. As well we observe that a 50% variation of V_{DD} –i.e. from 1.8V to 0.9V– induces no more than 3dB gain attenuation meaning a low dependency of such topology to supply voltage. Furthermore considering a sub 1V constrain, the circuits still achieve a 10dB and 12dB gain respectively, thus confirming current reuse ability for low voltage operation. ICP1 and IIP3 are found to be lowered in such case. Indeed V_{DD} lessening shifts the operating points of M_1 and M_2 closer to saturation region thus reducing the overall linearity of the LNA.

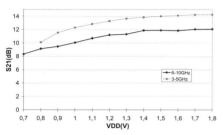

Figure 11. S_{21} versus supply voltage

Measurement results are summarized in table III. The Figure Of Merit (FOM) is defined as follows:

$$FOM = \frac{Gain_{Max/dB}.BW_{-3dB/GHz}}{NF_{min/dB}.P_{d/mW}}$$

TABLE III.   COMPARISON OF LNA PERFORMANCES

Ref	BW$_{-3dB}$ (GHz)	NF$_{min}$ (dB)	S$_{21max}$ (dB)	S$_{11}$ (dB)	IIP$_3$ (dBm)	P$_d$ (mW)	FOM
[TW$_1$]*	2.6-4.8	4.2	13.8	<-10	-5.8	8**	0.9
[11]	2-4.6	2.3	9.8	<-9	-7	12.6**	0.88
[12]	2-6.5	4.1	11.9	<-7.8	4	27	0.48
[TW$_2$]*	5.6-8.8	4.5	12	<-10	-3	4.8**	2
[13]	6-10	4.2	11.6	<-9	N/A	11**	1
[8]	2.4-9.5	4.2	10.4	<-9.4	-8.8	9**	1.95

[TW$_i$]*means This Work   **LNA core only

Relating the FOM to the bandwidth, the proposed LNA, [TW$_1$] and [TW$_2$], exhibit the best FOM compared to [11][12] in the 3-5GHz range and [8][13] in the 3/6-10GHz range, respectively. This feature relies on the low power low voltage operation allowed by current reuse configuration.

IV. CONCLUSION

Combining LC ladder network synthesis with current reuse configuration, a new CMOS LNA architecture matching low power low voltage constrains is here reported. As proof of concept, two circuits dedicated to 3-5GHz and 6-10GHz range have been implemented in a 130nm CMOS technology. Operating under 1.4V, both LNA exhibit a 13.8 and 12.2 dB gain for a 6 and 3 mA current consumption respectively. This work also demonstrates that a 4th order network can afford the circuits to perform a -10dB input return loss over the considered bandwidths. As a matter of consequence, this reduces the number of inductor compared to a conventional input matching synthesis [8]. Each LNA implementation is so included within a 1.8 and 1.2mm² silicon area thus addressing low silicon bulk, and by means low cost, purpose of UWB applications. NF increases from 4.2dB to 5.8dB in lower band and from 4.5dB to 8 dB in upper band.

At last a gain to supply voltage dependency is investigated highlighting that both circuits perform a 9dB and 11dB gain, respectively, when supplied under 0.9V. By means it depicts that current reuse configuration is well suited to challenge very low voltage operation in future CMOS technologies.

ACKNOWLEDGMENT

Authors would like to thanks ST Microelectronics for technology support.

Authors address special thanks to Mr Romaric TOUPE for measurements.

REFERENCES

[1] G. R. Aiello and G. D. Rogerson, "Ultra-wideband wirelesssystems," IEEE Microwave Mag., vol. 4, pp. 36-47, June2003.

[2] S. Roy, J. R. Foerster, V. S. Somayazulu, and D. G. Leeper,"Ultrawideband radio design: the promise of high-speed,short-range wireless connectivity," Proc. IEEE, vol. 92, pp.295-311, Feb. 2004.

[3] SC Blaakneer, DMW Leenaerts "An inductorless Wideband Balun-LNA in 65nm CMOS with balanced output", European Solid State Circuits Conference, ESSCIRC2007, pp.364-367, Munich, Germany

[4] R. Weng, P. Lin "A 1.5-V Low-Power Common-Gate Low Noise Amplifier for Ultrawideband Receivers". International Symposium on Circuit and System (ISCAS 2007), pp. 2618-2621, New Orlean, USA.

[5] Michael T. Reiha, John R. Long and John J. Pekarik, "A 1.2 V Reactive-Feedback 3.1-10.6 GHz Ultrawideband Low-Noise Amplifier in 0.13 µm CMOS", IEEE RadioFrequency Integrated Circuit, RFIC 2006, pp.384-385, San Franscisco, USA.

[6] Carlin H.J., Civalleri P.P. "Wideband Circuit Design" CRC Press LLC, 1998, chap. 6, pp289-295

[7] Chang-Tsung Fu and Chien-Nan Kuo, "3~11-GHz CMOS UWB LNA Using Dual Feedback for Broadband Matching", IEEE RadioFrequency Integrated Circuit, RFIC 2006, pp.67-70, San Franscisco, USA

[8] A. Bevilacqua, A. M Niknejad, "Ultra-Wideband CMOS LNA for 3.1 to 10.6 GHz Wireless Receivers", IEEE Integrated Solid State Circuit Conference, ISSCC 2004, pp. 382-383, San Francisco, USA

[9] T. Taris, O. Elgharniti, JB. Begueret, E. Kerhervé, "UWB LNAs using LC ladder and transformers for input matching networks", IEEE International Conference on Electronics, Circuits and Systems, ICECS2006, pp. 792-796, Nice, France.

[10] A. Ismail and Asad A. Abidi, "A 3–10-GHz Low-Noise Amplifier With Wideband LC-Ladder Matching Network » IEEE Journal of Solid-State Circuit (JSSC), vol. 39, n°12, Dec. 2004

[11] Kim, C.-W., et al.: "An ultra-widebnad CMOS low noise amplifier for 3-5 GHz UWB system," IEEE J. Solid-State Circuits, vol. 40, issue 2, pp. 544-547, Feb. 2005

[12] J.Jung,K. Chung,T.Yun,J. Choi and, "Ultra-Wideband Low Noise Amplifier Using a Cascode Feedback Topology," Silicon Monolithic Integrated Circuits in RF Systems, pp. 202-205, Jan. 2006

[13] Y. Chen; C. Kuo, " A 6-10-GHz ultra-wideband tunable LNA", IEEE International Symposium on Circuits and Systems, ISCAS 2005, pp. 5099 – 5102, Kobe, Japan

A UWB *Transformer-C* Orthonormal State Space Band-reject Filter in 0.13 μm CMOS

Sumit Bagga*, Zoubir Irahhauten*, Sandro A P Haddad†, Wouter A Serdijn*, John R Long* and John J Pekarik ‡

*ERL/DIMES, Delft University of Technology, 2628CD Delft, The Netherlands

Email: {s.bagga, w.a.serdijn and j.r.long}@tudelft.nl

†Freescale Semiconductores Brasil, Jaguariuna, SP 13820-000, Brazil

‡IBM Microelectronics, Essex Junction, Vermont 05452, USA

Abstract—An RF passive orthonormal ladder filter using transformers is presented, where the output is obtained from a linear, weighted combination of the voltages or currents at predetermined nodes or branches. With this topology, arbitrary rational transfer functions can be mapped onto silicon. Key features of this single-input, multiple-output (SIMO) topology include low-pass to band-pass/reject transformation without doubling the order of the filter and the realization of transmission zeros in the right-half-plane (RHP) (for superior approximations). As a proof of concept, a 7th order transformer-C filter implemented in CMOS 0.13 μm technology that can be used as a pulse shaping network (pulse width less than 0.5 ns) or band selection filter (offering a minimum of 20 dB attenuation at the IEEE802.11a WLAN band) for UWB transceivers is presented.

I. INTRODUCTION

Ultra-wideband (UWB) technology is viewed as a potential candidate for wireless short-range data communication in the unlicensed 3.1-10.6 GHz band allocated by the FCC. It promises high data-rate short-range communication at low-cost and low-power consumption due to its capability of sharing the bandwidth resources. One form of UWB communication is impulse radio, where short transient pulses (duration in the order of hundreds of picoseconds) are transmitted, which occupy a bandwidth of a few GHz [1].

As UWB systems transmitting at low spectral densities overlap with the bands of many other existing narrowband systems (e.g., IEEE 802.11a), this wide bandwidth cannot be exclusively assigned to UWB signals. To guarantee peaceful co-existence and to gain acceptance of UWB technology worldwide, interference from narrowband transceivers to UWB transceivers and vice versa must be avoided [2]. For example, the spectrum of a pulse shaping filter must not only adhere to the emissions mask of the UWB communication standard but also provide out-of-band attenuation in order to minimize aggregation. To this end, a band-reject filter can be employed.

In this paper, we demonstrate that *any* rational transfer function can be realized by a passive filter using transformers, where the output of the filter is obtained from a linear, weighted combination of the voltages or currents at predetermined nodes or branches. As a design example, a 7th order filter is chosen with a bandwidth from 3.1-10.6 GHz and a notch at 5.2 GHz offering the best compromise between roll-

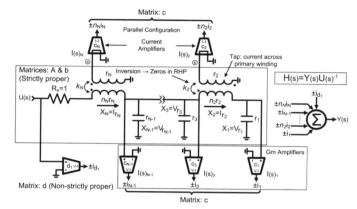

Fig. 1.   *Generic orthonormal* transformer-C *state space filter*

off, attenuation and hardware complexity. The notch depth complies with the U-NII criteria (notch depth $\geq$ 20 dB @ 5.15-5.25 GHz) to achieve the desired co-existence with WLAN. In order to map the desired transfer function onto a circuit realization, a state-space description is adopted.

II. ORTHONORMAL STATE SPACE FILTER

The proposed generic active/passive orthonormal ladder filter in Fig. 1 resembles that of a singly terminated low-pass LC ladder network, whose states are defined as the currents through the inductors and the voltages available across the capacitors. Note that the poles (i.e., the roots of denominator $D(s)$) of the filter are positioned in the left-half of the s-plane by the singly terminated *transformer-C* ladder and the zeros (i.e., the roots of numerator $N(s)$) are realized by the output summing stage, which implements the c vector.

To calculate the values of the reactive elements r_i (i.e., $([r_0; r_1, , r_n])$) we apply a continued fraction expansion on $D(s)$. Not only to realize the coefficients of the c matrix but also to compensate for the insertion loss of the filter, transconductance and current amplifiers can be employed to read out the output voltage and currents, respectively. The single element of matrix d is implemented using a transconductor for non-strictly proper (high-pass) transfer functions (i.e., order of $N(s) = D(s)$).

The salient features of this topology are,

1) Realization of arbitrary rational transfer functions (Butterworth, Elliptic, Chebyshev, InverseChebyshev, etc.)
2) Low-pass to band-pass/reject transformation without doubling the order of the filter
3) Realization of transmission zeros in the right-half-plane (RHP) (not feasible with common RLC ladder structure)
4) Single-input multiple-output (SIMO) topology allows for an output comprising two or more intermediate transfer responses

III. NUMERICAL FILTER APPROXIMATION AND ORTHONORMAL STATE SPACE SYNTHESIS

A filter is usually quantitatively described by its frequency domain magnitude response. The remaining specifications, such as the time domain (i.e., step and impulse) responses, phase and complexity are usually qualitatively defined and frequently neglected. Optimizing the performance characteristics on solely one criterion may result in an undesired performance in another (e.g., better magnitude response may result in a worse time domain response).

Because of fast, cheap computational methods, which effortlessly supply order-based coefficients for a normalized low-pass filter, engineers have become handicapped to a small set (e.g., Butterworth, Elliptic, Chebyshev, InverseChebyshev, Bessel, and a few others) of filter types based on conventional deterministic methods to synthesize a transfer function optimized only in the frequency domain. This results in a vast space of filter coefficients unexplored. We propose a generalized method of filter approximation optimizing both the time and/or frequency domain responses (see Fig. 2).

One of the most important aspects of analog filter synthesis is that the approximating transfer function or data set must lead to a physically realizable network which is dynamically stable. To achieve a good approximation to a given function $f(x)$ that is continuous in a given interval $a \leq x \leq b$, by some polynomial $g(x)$, there exist several mathematical techniques (e.g., *MiniMax*, Chebyshev Knots, Padé, Taylor, Splines, etc.) that are frequently used. An approximation that has proven to

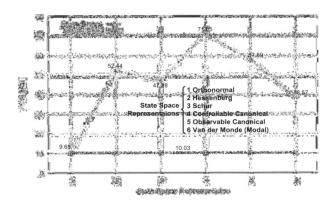

Fig. 3. *FDR comparison for different state-space descriptions of a 7th Daubechies' scaling function*

be successful for synthesizing arbitrary transfer functions and impulse responses is the Padé approximation of the Laplace transformed impulse response of the filter. By substituting $j\omega$ for s, the frequency domain characteristics are obtained and thus can be optimized, as the Laplace transform has a one-to-one mapping to the frequency domain.

Among the many possible state space descriptions for a transfer function, the orthonormal ladder form stands out, as it is semi-optimized for dynamic range (i.e., approximately 2 dB inferior to a fully optimized representation) [3] and thereby least sensitive with respect to mismatch and component variations [4]. In order to maximize the dynamic range of the system, one should minimize the objective functional (FDR), which represents the relative improvement of the dynamic range and contains all parameters which are subject to manipulation by the designer. The FDR comparison for different state-space descriptions of a 7th order Daubechies' scaling function is given in Fig. 3 [5].

Once the state space description (i.e., matrices A-D, where A is the state matrix, B is the input matrix, C is the output matrix and D is the feedforward matrix) of the desired transfer function is formulated, it can then be mapped onto a lumped element ladder structure.

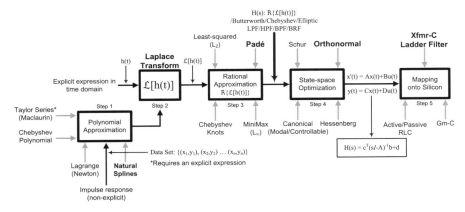

Fig. 2. *Analog filter synthesis*

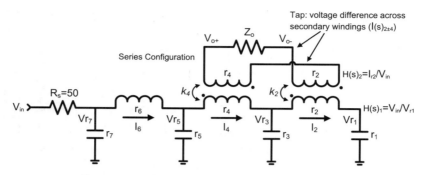

H(s)$_1$: Low-pass prototype (i.e., Daubechies' scaling function)
H(s)$_2$: Low-pass to band-pass transformation
H(s)$_{2\pm4}$: Composite band-pass/band-reject response (with notch @ ω$_0$)

Fig. 4. 7th order orthonormal transformer-C state space band-reject filter

IV. 7th ORDER ORTHONORMAL STATE SPACE BAND-REJECT FILTER

The actual design of the 7th order *transformer-C* band-reject filter to be implemented in CMOS technology is depicted in Fig. 4, where k and r_n denote the coupling coefficient of the transformers and the component reactances, respectively. The voltage across the capacitors and the current through the inductors or the primary windings of the transformers are given by V_n and I_n, respectively. The intermediate transfer functions are denoted by $H(s)_n$.

By taking the voltage difference of the secondary windings of transformers X_2 and X_4 and through proper component scaling (by their turns ratio (n) and coupling coefficient (k)), a low-pass to band-pass/band-reject transformation of a strictly proper (i.e., order of $N(s) < D(s)$) transfer function is realized. Upon calculating the input impedance, Z_{r7_1},

$$Z_{r7_1} = (((((((r_1 + r_2) \parallel r_3) + r_4) \parallel r_5) + r_6) \parallel r_7)$$

and (in our case, low-pass response) $H(s)_1$, any intermediate transfer function can be derived. The output of the proposed filter is a composite of two intermediate, band limited transfer responses resulting in a notch in the pass-band as given by the overall transfer function $((H(s)_5 - H(s)_3)/r_4) + ((H(s)_3 - H(s)_1)/r_2)$.

Process variations and mismatch will cause the notch to deviate from the desired frequency (ω_0). For frequency tuning, only the source and capacitive impedances can be scaled. First, in order to scale the source impedance to R and change the frequency of the notch from the normalized frequency ω_n to ω_0, we use the transformations, $L'_n = L_n R \omega_0$ and $C'_n = \frac{C_n}{R} \omega_0$ on the impedances of the lumped elements. Then, for frequency tuning of the notch, varactors can be employed instead of capacitors. The transformations now become, $R^T = \frac{R}{\alpha}$, $L'_n = L_n$ and $C'_n = \frac{C_n}{\alpha^2}$, where the frequency scaling factor $\alpha = \frac{\omega_0}{\omega_c}$ ($c = 1, 2, \ldots, \aleph$) with ω_c being the compensation frequency. Finally, for amplitude correction, current amplifiers can be employed at the output stage to compensate for any insertion loss in the pass-band.

V. MEASUREMENT RESULTS

Fig. 5 and Fig. 6 show the simulated and measured magnitude and phase response of the orthonormal *transformer-C* state-space filter realized in 0.13 μm CMOS IC technology. The desired U-NII co-existence criteria is satisfied, even though a 3 dB reduction in notch depth and a frequency shift of 100 MHz is observed. Measurements show a sharper roll-off at higher frequencies than required by the FCC frequency mask. Moreover, the insertion loss across the pass-band is inversely proportional to the notch depth, for both the band-stop filter of Daido Steel (i.e., fabricated using LTCC technology) and the CMOS based transformer-C state space filter.

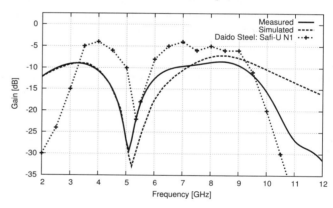

Fig. 5. Magnitude response of the 7th order orthonormal transformer-C state space band-reject filter (without de-embedding)

As a result, in the time domain, the measured and simulated impulse responses of the filter vary by a fraction of a nanosecond (see Fig. 7). Overall, the simulated results accurately predict the actual behavior of the proposed filter topology, as can be deduced from the measured data.

The chip microphotograph of the *transformer-C* band-reject filter is shown in Fig. 8. The key elements of this circuit are two high performance on-chip passive multi-layer stacked transformers that act as the voltage-difference sensing elements.

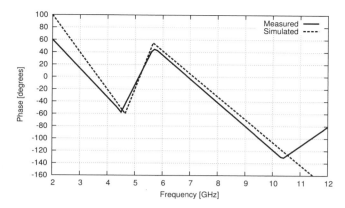

Fig. 6. *Phase response of the band-reject filter*

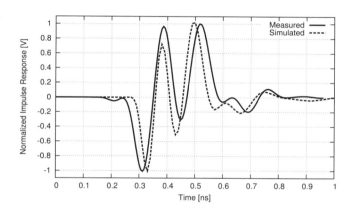

Fig. 7. *Impulse response of the band-reject filter*

TABLE I

***TRANSFORMER-C* FILTER SPECIFICATIONS**

Parameter	Simulated	Measured
Filter Type	Band-reject	
Order	7 (1-IND; 2-XFMR; 4-MIMCAP)	
Reactance Values (R_s =50 Ω)	r7=300; r5=825; r3=900; r1=350; (fF) r6=1; r4=2.2; r2=2.2; (nH)	
Insertion Loss	-8 (LB), -7.5 (UB) dB	-9 (LB), -8 (UB) dB
Bandwidth Lower-band (LB) Upper-band (UB)	(FCC Emissions Mask → ~ 3.1-10.6 GHz)	
	2.5-4.5 GHz	2-4 GHz
	7-10 GHz	6-9.5 GHz
Pulse width	≤ 0.5 ns (10-90 %)	
Notch Depth Frequency	(U-NII Criteria → ≥ 20 dB @ 5.2 GHz)	
	25 dB	22 dB
	5.2 GHz	5.10 GHz
Transformers (X_2/X_4) Dimensions	Turns ratio (n) ~ 1; Coupling coefficient (k): 0.75 150 x 150 μm²	
Termination Input Output	Single-ended (50 Ω) Differential (100 Ω)	
Physical size Chip Area (LxW) Active Area (LxW)	(1.0 x 0.75) mm; 0.75 mm2 (0.625 x 0.25) mm; 0.156 mm2	
Technology	0.13 μm CMOS IBM	

of approximately 0.5 nH. Finally, to guarantee that parasitic behavior does not influence the performance of the filter, at its input, multiple gold ball wire bond interconnects were placed in parallel during packaging.

VI. CONCLUSIONS

The proposed *transformer-C* filter methodology allows for the realization of (any) arbitrary rational transfer onto silicon. As a design example, a 7th order *transformer-C* orthonormal state-space band-reject filter in CMOS 0.13 μm technology is presented. Characteristics such as low-pass to band-pass/band-reject transformation without increasing the order of the filter, the realization of transmission zeros in the right-half-plane and the use of transformers, which allow for the weighted combination of the intermediate transfer functions are demonstrated with this topology.

Each transformer has 3.5 turns, metal width of 10 μm, coil spacing of 5 μm, inner dimension of 80 x 90 μm², an overall dimension of 150 x 150 μm² and a coupling coefficient of 0.75. The specifications of the 7th order orthonormal *transformer-C* band-reject filter are highlighted in Table I.

The interconnect length of the bond wire is about 500 μm, resulting in a series inductance to the RF input/output

REFERENCES

[1] M. Z. Win and R. A. Scholtz, "Impulse radio: How it works," *IEEE Communications Letters*, vol. 2, no. 2, pp. 36–38, Feb. 1998.
[2] A. V. Garcia, C. Mishra, F. Bahmani, J. S. Martinez, and E. S. Sinencio, "An 11-band 3-10 GHz receiver in SiGe BiCMOS for multiband OFDM UWB communication," *IEEE Journal of Solid-State Circuits*, vol. 42, no. 4, pp. 935–947, 2007.
[3] D. A. Johns, W. M. Snelgrove, and A. S. Sedra, "Orthonormal ladder filters," *IEEE Transactions on Circuits and Systems I: Fundamentals Theory and Applications*, vol. 36, pp. 337–343, 1989.
[4] G. Groenewold, "Optimal dynamic range integrators," *IEEE Transactions on Circuits and Systems I: Fundamentals Theory and Applications*, vol. 39, no. 8, pp. 614–627, 1992.
[5] S. A. P. Haddad, J. M. H. Karel, R. L. M. Peelers, R. L. Westra, and W. A. Serdijn, "Ultra low-power analog Morlet wavelet filter in 0.18 μm BiCMOS technology," *IEEE European Solid-State Circuits Conference*, pp. 323–326, Sept. 2005.

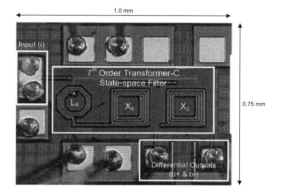

Fig. 8. *Chip microphotograph of the 7th order orthonormal transformer-C state-space filter in 0.13 μm CMOS technology; active area is 0.15 mm²; physical dimensions are (0.625 x 0.25) mm*

A 9mW High Band FM-UWB Receiver Front-end

Yunzhi Dong, Yi Zhao, John F.M. Gerrits, Gerrit van Veenendaal* and John R. Long
Electronics Research Laboratory/DIMES, Delft University of Technology, the Netherlands
*IC Lab, Innovation & Technology, NXP Semiconductors, Eindhoven, the Netherlands

Abstract— A low-power FM-UWB receiver front-end for low data rate (100 kbps) short-range (<10m) applications operating in the upper UWB band at 7.45GHz is described. The front-end comprises a 21 dB gain preamplifier and a 1GHz bandwidth FM demodulator. The measured receiver sensitivity is -86.8dBm while consuming 9mW from a 1.8V supply and -84.3dBm is achieved at 6mW power consumption. The 0.88mm^2 active area circuit is implemented in 0.25µm SiGe:C BiCMOS.

Index Terms: FM-UWB, FM demodulator, ultrawideband RF receiver front-end, bias current reuse.

I. INTRODUCTION

FM-ultrawideband (FM-UWB) radio is an analog implementation of a spread-spectrum system that targets short range (i.e., 1-10m) applications requiring bit-rates up to 100kbps. It offers the advantages of a simple and robust modulation scheme and a straightforward circuit implementation. Thus, FM-UWB radio presents a low-complexity, low-power and low-cost solution for robust UWB communications. Due to its flat power spectral density and steep spectral roll-off, the FM-UWB scheme optimizes exploitation of the available spectral mask approved for UWB transmission [1].

Fig. 1 presents the FM-UWB transceiver architecture. In the transmitter, a triangular frequency-shift keyed (FSK) sub-carrier signal generated by direct digital synthesis (DDS) modulates a RF VCO thereby yielding a constant-envelope FM-UWB signal. The complete FM-UWB receiver comprises a preamplifier, wideband FM demodulator, direct-conversion low-frequency sub-carrier filtering, amplification and FSK demodulation circuitry. In this paper, the design of a prototype FM-UWB receiver front-end (i.e., preamplifier and wideband FM demodulator) is described.

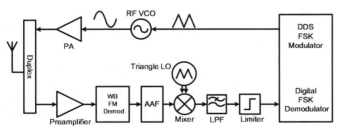

Fig. 1 FM-UWB radio transceiver architecture

Interference mitigation is one of the major challenges in today's UWB receivers. Strong in-band interference originating from WiMAX systems below 5GHz and 802.11a WLAN systems operating between 5-6GHz may be present. However, recent regulatory decisions in Europe also encourage use of the UWB spectrum above 6GHz. Therefore

this design targets a center frequency of 7.45GHz with 500MHz signal bandwidth.

The desired 10 meter link span corresponds to a sensitivity of at least -80dBm for the front-end. A previous demodulator implementation covering 3-5GHz [2] showed a modest sensitivity of -46dBm, so it is clear that an improved wideband demodulator is required. A more sensitive FM demodulator supports a wider dynamic range and lowers the preamplifier gain required in the receiver.

The QUBiC4X 0.25µm SiGe:C BiCMOS technology from NXP Semiconductors is used to implement the front-end circuits. Bias current reuse is applied to both the preamplifier and FM demodulator blocks in order to minimize power consumption from a fixed supply voltage.

The paper is organized as follows: Section II addresses the wideband FM demodulator; the design of a low-power high-gain preamplifier is discussed in Section III, and Section IV presents experimental results.

II. FM-UWB DEMODULATOR

A block diagram of the receiver front-end including the demodulator is shown in Fig. 2. In order to satisfy the requirements for sensitivity, multiple-access capability, and the low-power/low-cost constraints of the intended applications, a fixed time delay (FTD) demodulator is selected [4]. In this scheme, a group delay τ is added to input signal s(t), giving the delayed signal s(t-τ) with odd 90 degree phase shift at RF carrier frequency f_C. The original s(t) is then multiplied by the delayed signal s(t-τ) in order to produce the demodulated output [1]. The FTD demodulator output response is ideally given by equation (1), where K is the multiplication gain, A is the amplitude of input signal and K_D is the delay gain (i.e., phase shifter and gain block in Fig. 2).

$$V_{DEMOD}(f) = KK_D A^2 \sin(2\pi\tau(f - f_c)) \qquad (1)$$

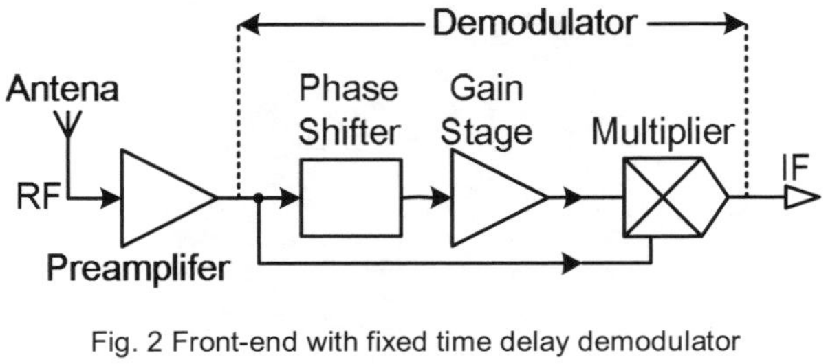

Fig. 2 Front-end with fixed time delay demodulator

It can be shown that the sensitivity and dynamic range (DR) of the demodulator, which is defined by the ratio of maximum RF input power to the minimum power required for a given SNR at the demodulator output, is given by the following equations

$$P_{Sensitivity} \approx \frac{1}{\pi\tau B_{RF}R} \sqrt{\frac{SNR_{SUB}B_{SUB}SN_{Gilbert}}{AV_{AMP}{}^4 K_D{}^2 K^2}} \qquad (2)$$

$$DR = \frac{P_{RFinMax}}{P_{Sensitivity}} \approx \frac{3V_T}{K_D} \frac{2\pi\tau B_{RF}K}{\sqrt{SNR_{SUB}B_{SUB}SN_{Noise}}} \qquad (3)$$

Here, SNR_{SUB} is the baseband SNR required for FSK demodulation, B_{SUB} is the baseband channel bandwidth and $SN_{Gilbert}$ is the noise spectral density at the demodulator output in V^2/Hz. Noise contributed by the preamplifier is assumed to be much smaller than $SN_{Gilbert}$ and is therefore neglected in eqs. (2) and (3). In practice, the noise figure of the receiver is dominated by the demodulator stage.

It can be seen from eq. (2) that increasing the voltage gain of the preamplifier or gain in the delay path, increasing the delay time τ, and minimizing the noise contributed by the multiplier are effective methods of improving the receiver sensitivity. However, as seen from eq. (3), gain in the delay path reduces the overall dynamic range, so the DR is optimized by minimizing noise arising from the multiplier and increasing the delay time. Also, once the sensitivity of demodulator is improved, the noise from preamplifier can not be neglected (see in eq. (2)).

Simulations of a balanced bipolar Gilbert multiplier in the technology used for implementation of the receiver show that the maximum input signal voltage is approximately 3 times the BJT thermal voltage (i.e., $3V_T$ or ~75mV at 25°C). Input greater than $3V_T$ drive the multiplier into the large-signal regime, which affects proper demodulation of subcarriers in a multi-access FM-UWB system [1].

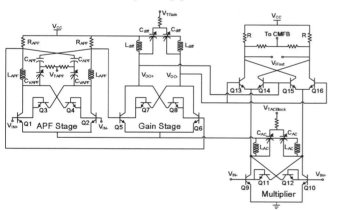

Fig. 3 Schematic of the FM-UWB demodulator

The demodulator implementation is shown in Fig. 3. The APF and gain stages drive a Gilbert multiplier consisting of input pair Q_9-Q_{10} (neutralized by diodes Q_{11}-Q_{12}) loaded by an LC tank (L_{AC} and C_{AC}) and transistor quad Q_{13}-Q_{16}. Current used to bias the APF and gain stages is fed via L_{AC} into Q_9-Q_{10} in order to boost its transconductance and the overall gain of the demodulator, K. This permits independent biasing of the input pair from the quad, which is used to optimize the multiplier's noise performance. Non-linear noise simulations predict that noise produced by the switching quad accounts for 93% of the

total noise at the demodulator output, and that collector shot noise (i.e., $2qI_{Bias}$) is the main source of noise in these devices. Therefore, as the bias current in the switching quad decreases, the output noise (i.e., $SN_{Gilbert}$) also decreases. Noise present at the quad inputs is rejected at the IF outputs by the balanced, cross-coupled circuit topology, whereas noise originating from the switching quad remains.

The emitter area of each transistor in the switching quad is chosen based on a trade-off between output noise, gain-bandwidth performance and the extrinsic base and emitter resistances, which affect the gain. In the final design, a voltage gain of 20 with a mid-band group delay in the delay path of 500ps is realized. Bias currents for the APF, gain and multiplier quad are set at 1.2mA, 1.7mA and 0.32mA, respectively. The sum of these bias currents flow into the input transconductor of the multiplier.

III. FM-UWB PREAMPLIFIER

The preamplifier in a radio receiver front-end suppresses the effect of noise contributed by other components (e.g., mixer and baseband circuitry) thereby increasing sensitivity. However, in the FM-UWB receiver design, emphasis is placed on voltage gain (~30dB) and minimizing power consumption from the 1.8V supply. In addition, a single-ended input and differential output are required in order to minimize implementation costs on the antenna side and interface to the demodulator, respectively. The overall sensitivity of the FM-UWB receiver is set by the demodulator, so noise figure on the order of 5dB can be tolerated.

A simple active circuit balun (see Fig. 4) consisting of parallel common-base (Q_1) and common-emitter (Q_2 ac grounded via C_P) amplifiers is adopted [3], because the relatively low input impedance forced by the common-base stage simplifies interfacing to a 50Ohm antenna. An input return loss of 10dB (including packaging parasitics) is expected.

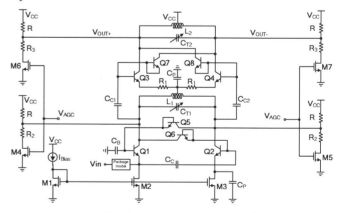

Fig. 4 Circuit schematic of the preamplifier

The Miller effect seen at the input of Q_2 is compensated by current feedback via diode-connected transistor Q_6. The input transistors drive a tunable resonant tank load formed by inductor L_1 and varactor C_{T1}. A second, differential common-emitter stage (Q_3, Q_4 driving tunable LC tank L_2 and varactor C_{T2}) increases the overall gain of the preamplifier to 30dB when loaded by the demodulator input impedance of 1.4kOhms. Bias current for the second stage is shared with the input stage as the tail current of pair Q_3, Q_4 flows through L_1. The neutrodyne formed by Q_3, Q_4 and diode-connected trransistors Q_5 and Q_6 suppresses the Miller effect in the second stage, further increasing the overall gain. An automatic gain control (AGC) function giving a gain range of 25 dB is realized by tuning the load impedance of both stages via MOSFETs M_4-M_7.

The bias current for Q_1 and Q_2 (I_{Bias}) is generated by a PTAT bias block (not shown in Fig. 4) which is then mirrored by NMOS transistors M_1 to M_3. A total 2mA current excluding emitter followers is consumed under 1.8V supply which fits the 4mW design specification. The pi-topology network formed by the input bondpad parasitic and ESD protection diode capacitance and bondwire and package lead inductance is absorbed in the RF input impedance matching network.

IV. EXPERIMENTAL RESULTS

The die photo of the receiver front-end (preamplifier and demodulator) fabricated in 0.25um BiCMOS technology is shown in Fig. 5. The preamplifier occupies an active area of $0.4mm^2$ while the demodulator occupies $0.4mm^2$ of the $1.62mm^2$ die. The testchip RF performance is characterized from measurement using on-wafer probing.

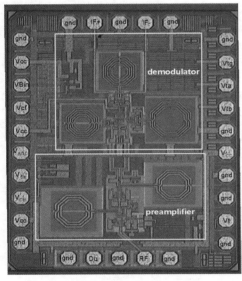

Fig. 5 Die photo of the front-end testchip

A stand-alone version of the preamplifier has been fully-characterized for S-parameters (see Fig. 6), noise figure (NF) and linearity from on-wafer probing. Emitter follower buffers are added to the stand-alone preamplifier to interface standard 50Ohm measurement equipment. However, these buffers degrade the amplifier linearity slightly (-16dBm P_{IIP3}, measured from a two-tone test) and are not used in the final receiver test chip. The measured input return loss is between 7 and 8dB over the 7.2-7.7GHz frequency range which is higher than intended because packaging parasitics are not included. The single-ended input to differential output power gain (S_{21}) is 21-22.5dB when the amplifier is biased at 2mA (excluding

emitter followers) from a 1.8V supply. Excellent isolation is seen as the measured S_{12} is better than -50dB up to 10GHz.

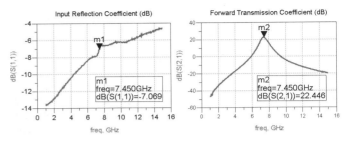

Fig. 6 Measured S_{11} and S_{21} for the preamplifier

The measured noise figure at different gain and bandwidth settings is shown in Fig. 7. Here V_{ctrl} and V_{ctrl_inter} are tuning voltages for varactor C_{T1} and C_{T2} in Fig. 4. Varying the tuning tanks to set the gain and bandwidth of the preamplifier has little effect on the noise figure. The average noise figure of 5.5dB measured across the 7-8GHz band is expected to be improved by 1dB when the amplifier input is impedance matched. The noise figure increases from 5.5 to 9 dB when the AGC voltage is used to tune the gain/bandwidth of the preamplifier. Tuning the resonant tanks via varactors C_{T1} and C_{T2} to set the tank gain/bandwidth has much less effect on the noise figure.

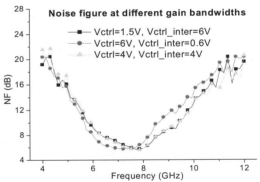

Fig. 7 Measured NF at different bandwidths

Evaluation of the demodulator and receiver performance focused on the measurement of sensitivity using the test set-up shown in Fig. 8. It is assumed that an SNR of 14dB is sufficient for FSK demodulation with a bit-error-rate less than 10^{-6}, and that the RF input power corresponding to this SNR at the demodulator output is defined as the sensitivity. The input power is measured with respect to the reference plane shown in Fig. 8. A high-speed oscilloscope is used to monitor the quality of the demodulated output signal in the time domain. The baseband (audio) amplifier increases the sensitivity of the spectrum analyzer when measuring very low RF input power levels. The 7.45GHz RF carrier has a bandwidth of 500MHz, and a 500kHz sub-carrier frequency is selected. Losses in the cables, connectors, balun, attenuators, input mismatch and the noise added by the baseband audio amplifier are calibrated and accounted for through the measurements.

The input balun (shown in Fig. 8) is only required for testing a stand-alone version of the demodulator (demod) IC. It is not needed when testing the complete receiver, which has only one single-ended RF input. Measured sensitivity curves from on-wafer probing of the stand-alone demodulator test chip are shown in Fig. 9. The IC remain function down to a voltage supply of 1.2V. RF signal bandwidth at 1GHz has also been tested and showed a response similar to the 500MHz case. The results are summarized in Table1 where the targets listed in the table were specified for the EU project Magnet-Beyond. It can be seen from the measured data that at one half of the target power consumption there is 7dB sensitivity margin.

SNR versus bias current in the quad is shown in Fig. 10. The optimum bias current for a given transistor size is a compromise between transistor ac performance (i.e., f_T of the BJT) and shot noise produced by the flow of bias current.

Sensitivity curves of the receiver front-end at different bias conditions are shown in Fig. 11. Measured receiver sensitivity is -86.8dBm (see Table 1), and at 6mW dissipation the measured sensitivity is still 4.3dB better than the initial target of -80dBm at 10mW dissipation. The above results imply possible trade-offs for other specifications such as even power consumption, smaller chip area or higher data-rate.

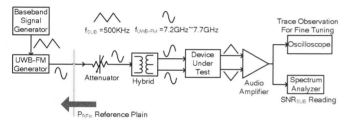

Fig. 8 Sensitivity measurement set-up

Table 1 Summary of measured results

Parameter	FM-UWB Demodulator		
	Target Spec	Measurements	
Sensitivity	-55dBm	-66.8dBm	-61.8dBm
Power Consumption	6mW	5.8mW	2.8mW
Power Supply	1.8V	1.8V	1.2V
Active Chip Area	-	0.4mm^2	0.4mm^2
	Receiver Front-End		
	Target Spec	Measurements	
Sensitivity	-80dBm	-86.8dBm	-84.3dBm
Power Consumption	10mW	9.1mW	6mW
Power Supply	1.8V	1.8V	1.5V
Active Chip Area	-	0.88mm^2	0.88mm^2

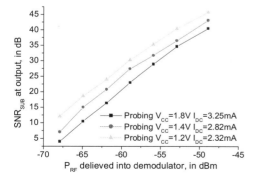

Fig. 9 Sensitivity of the demodulator vs. different DC Bias

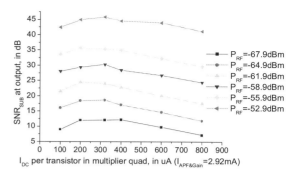

Fig. 10 SNR$_{OUT}$ vs. bias current for the multiplier quad

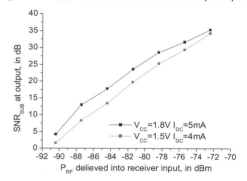

Fig. 11 Sensitivity of the RX vs. different DC bias

V. Conclusions

A complete FM-UWB receiver front-end has been demonstrated in the NXP Semiconductors QUBiC4x 0.25um BiCMOS technology. At 100kbit/s data rate, the measured receiver sensitivity is -86.8dBm consuming 9.1mW from a 1.8V supply. The receiver prototype demonstrates the advantages of low-complexity FM-UWB technology. FM-UWB promises to enable many new applications requiring robust low data-rate radios with power consumption on the order of a few milliwatts, and the potential for even lower power consumption in future.

VI. Acknowledgements

This work is supported by the 6th Framework European project 'Magnet Beyond' Implementation work was conducted within the IC Lab of NXP Semiconductors in collaboration with the Delft University of Technology.

Reference

[1] John F.M. Gerrits, John R. Farserotu, John R. Long, "Principles and Limitations of Ultra-Wideband FM Communication Systems", *EURASIP Journal on Applied Signal Processing,* 2005:3, 382-396.

[2] John F.M. Gerrits, John R. Farserotu, John R. Long, "A Wideband FM Demodulator for a Low-Complexity FM-UWB Receiver", *Proceedings of the 9th European Conference on Wireless Technology*, Sept. 2006.

[3] B. Nauta, "Single-to-differential converter", US patent no. 5,404,054 April 4, 1995.

[4] M.H.L. Kouwenhoven, *High-Performance Frequency-Demodulation Systems*, ISBN 90-407-1641-2, Delft University Press, 1998.

[5] P. Deixler, A. Rodriguez, W. De Boer, H. Sun, et al, "QUBIC4X: An f_T/fmax=130/140GHz SiGe:C-BiCMOS Manufacturing Technology with Elite Passives for Emerging Microwave Applications", *IEEE Bipolar/BiCMOS Circuits and Technology Meeting,* Sept. 2004.

A Low-Voltage Mobility-Based Frequency Reference for Crystal-Less ULP Radios

Fabio Sebastiano*, Lucien Breems*, Kofi Makinwa† Salvatore Drago*, Domine Leenaerts* and Bram Nauta‡

*NXP Semiconductors, Eindhoven, The Netherlands, Email: fabio.sebastiano@nxp.com
†Electronic Instrumentation Laboratory, Delft University of Technology, Delft, The Netherlands
‡IC Design Group, CTIT Research Institute, University of Twente, Enschede, The Netherlands

Abstract— The design of a 100 kHz frequency reference based on the electron mobility in a MOS transistor is presented. The proposed low-voltage low-power circuit requires no off-chip components, making it suitable for Wireless Sensor Networks (WSN) applications. After one-point calibration the spread of its output frequency is less than 1.1% (3σ) over the temperature range from -22 °C to 85 °C. Fabricated in a baseline 65-nm CMOS technology, the frequency reference occupies 0.11 mm^2 and draws 34 A from a 1.2-V supply at room temperature.

I. INTRODUCTION

Wireless Sensors Networks (WSN) need radios that are small, cheap and energy efficient. The largest fraction of the energy used in each node of a WSN is spent in idle listening to the channel [1]. If each node is equipped with an accurate time reference, synchronous networks can be employed to reduce the idle listening time. In that case, a higher accuracy of the time reference allows the receiver to predict the timeslot used by the transmitter with smaller error and to employ, consequently, a lower duty-cycle. Accuracy of a few ppm can be achieved by crystal-controlled oscillators (XCOs) but since such external components should be avoided in WSN nodes, accuracy can be given up for the sake of integration.

The tradeoff between integration and time/frequency accuracy is also present in the RF front-end. While commercial communication systems require high frequency accuracy, radios for WSN can be optimized to relax such specifications and so frequency accuracies of only a few percent are needed [1] [2]. In addition, the available power is limited to tens of μW, since the time reference is turned on continuously, and the supply voltage must be kept low to be compliant with typical WSN energy sources, such as batteries and energy scavengers.

Recently, much work has been devoted to implementing fully integrated frequency references in standard microelectronic technologies. The current state-of-the-art is illustrated in Fig. 1. *LC* oscillators [3] can provide accuracy and phase noise performances comparable to XCOs; however, it is impracticable to reduce their power consumption below 100 μW due to limited Q of integrated inductors and the possible need for high-speed frequency dividers. The accuracy of the compensated ring oscillator in [4] is high enough for WSN applications, but its power consumption is in the mW range. A very stable physical effect, i.e. the thermal diffusivity of bulk silicon, could be exploited for use in frequency references [5]; however, the silicon substrate needs to be heated to measure

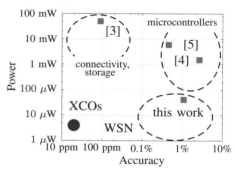

Fig. 1. Comparison among fully integrated oscillators that can replace XCOs in various applications; XCOs point is given as reference.

the diffusivity and this requires a few mW. The trimmed RC oscillator described in [6] also seems to achieve performances suitable for WSN, although the effect of process spread is not discussed.

An alternative way of realizing an accurate fully integrated oscillator is by employing charge mobility as a reference [7]. Mobility is less sensitive to process variations than other parameters, such as polysilicon resistance or oxide capacitance, and its standard deviation is less than 2% at room temperature for the adopted process. Although the temperature dependence of the mobility is large (approximately $T^{-1.5}$), it is well defined and can be compensated for. The effect of process spread can then be removed by a single room temperature calibration.

This paper presents a proof of concept of a fully integrated oscillator referenced to the mobility, which can cover the WSN application area in Fig. 1. The oscillator is based on a current-controlled relaxation oscillator, in which the current is proportional to the mobility. Experimental validation of such approach will be provided, demonstrating a frequency spread in the temperature range of interest of less than 1.1% after one-point calibration and a power consumption of 41 μW. The circuit is presented in section II; experimental results are shown in section III and conclusions are drawn in section IV.

II. CIRCUIT DESCRIPTION

A. Oscillator structure

A simplified schematic of the oscillator is shown in Fig. 2. It consists of a current reference, two current mirrors $M_1 - M_A$ and $M_1 - M_B$, two capacitors C_A and C_B and a comparator.

306

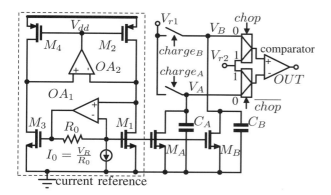

Fig. 2. Mobility-referenced oscillator.

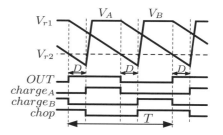

Fig. 3. Oscillator waveforms.

The drain current of M_1 is mirrored by M_A and M_B with a gain of four and, as explained in the next section, is given by

$$I_1 = \frac{I_A}{4} = \frac{I_B}{4} = \frac{\mu_n C_{ox}}{2} \frac{W_1}{L_1} k V_R^2 \qquad (1)$$

where μ_n is the electron mobility, C_{ox} the gate capacitance per unit area and k a constant determined by ratios of matched transistors sizes. As shown in the timing diagram in Fig. 3, C_A and C_B are alternatively precharged to V_{r1} and then linearly discharged by M_A and M_B. When the voltage on the discharging capacitor drops below V_{r2}, the output of the comparator switches and the linear discharge of the other capacitor starts immediately, while the recharge is delayed by D. The delay D ensures that non-idealities of the comparator do not affect the slope of the discharge at the crossing of V_{r2} and it is not critical, as it does not influence the period T. The delay D and the signals driving the switches are generated by a digital circuit not shown in Fig. 2.

By inspecting Fig. 2 and Fig. 3, the period and frequency of oscillation can be easily determined, and from (1):

$$T = \frac{2C}{I_A}(V_{r1} - V_{r2}) \Rightarrow f = \frac{1}{T} = \mu_n k \frac{C_{ox}\frac{W_1}{L_1}}{C} \frac{V_R^2}{V_{r1} - V_{r2}} \qquad (2)$$

where $C = C_A = C_B$. C_A and C_B are implemented with MOS capacitors operated in inversion and matched with transistor M_1, in order to obtain a process and temperature independent ratio $\frac{C_{ox} W_1/L_1}{C}$. If the reference voltages V_{r1} and V_{r2} are obtained from a bandgap reference, the residual frequency variations will be due to the spread and temperature dependence of the mobility and the voltage V_R. The latter can be used as a control voltage to compensate for the effects of temperature variations and process spread.

The two multiplexers at the input of the comparator are driven by the signal *chop*, shown in Fig. 3, to mitigate the effect of comparator offset. Thus, with an offset V_{os} at the comparator input, the output is switched when $V_A = V_{r2} - V_{os}$ or $V_B = V_{r2} + V_{os}$ and the total error in the period is given by

$$\frac{\Delta t}{T} \cong \frac{V_{os}}{2(V_{r1} - V_{r2})}\left(\frac{\Delta C}{C} - \frac{\Delta I}{I_A}\right) \qquad (3)$$

where $\Delta C = C_A - C_B$ and $\Delta I = I_A - I_B$. Hence, if the capacitors and current mirrors are well matched, the resulting error

is small. Since those components work at low frequency, good matching can be obtained by increasing device area and without significantly affecting oscillator's performances.

B. Current reference

The operation of the circuit in the dashed box in Fig. 2 can be understood by noting that M_2, M_4 and OA_2 constitute a low-voltage current mirror and that M_1 is effectively diode-connected through OA_1 and R. Using the square-law MOS model, it is possible to derive [8]

$$I_1 = \frac{\mu_n C_{ox}}{2} \frac{W_1}{L_1} \frac{V_R^2}{\left(\sqrt{\frac{n}{m}} - 1\right)^2} \qquad (4)$$

where $n = \frac{W_4/L_4}{W_2/L_2}$ and $m = \frac{W_3/L_3}{W_1/L_1}$.

The complete schematic is shown in Fig. 4. The current source I_0 is implemented by the unity-gain cascode current mirror $M_5 - M_8$. The value of I_0 is fixed by the current mirror $M_9 - M_{12}$ and by the external opamp[1], which forces a voltage drop V_R on R_1, so that $R_0 I_0 = \frac{R_0}{R_1}\frac{W_9/L_9}{W_{11}/L_{11}} V_R = V_R$. Resistance values ($R_0 = 200$ kΩ, $R_1 = 20$ kΩ) are chosen as a tradeoff between resistor area, current consumption and the contribution of the parasitic currents through R_1[2].

The start-up circuit and the implementation of the opamps are shown in the dashed boxes in the figure. A folded cascode structure is adopted for OA_2 to reduce its systematic input offset. Since OA_1 must provide an output quiescent current I_0, it is biased with $I_{17} = I_0/2$ and it is dimensioned such that $\frac{W_{13}}{L_{13}} = \frac{W_{14}}{L_{14}}$ and $5\frac{W_{15}}{L_{15}} = \frac{W_{16}}{L_{16}}$. The MOS capacitor M_{27} and the fringe metal capacitor C_c are compensation capacitors for the feedback loops involving respectively OA_1 and OA_2.

To avoid coupling digital noise to the gate of M_1 via the output mirrors $M_1 - M_{A,B}$ of Fig. 2, the current is mirrored to M_A and M_B using the node V_G and additional pMOS and nMOS mirrors (not shown in Fig. 4).

C. Comparator

The delay of the comparator must be negligible with respect to the oscillation period T. This requires high gain and large bandwidth in the case of an open-loop topology, or a very small hysteresis in the case of a Schmitt trigger implementation. To overcome this problem, within the constraints of

---

[1]An external opamp is used only for testing purpose.
[2]Note that a pad with large ESD protection diodes is connected to one end of R_1.

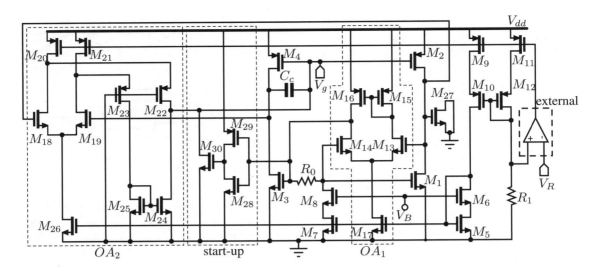

Fig. 4. Complete schematic of the current reference.

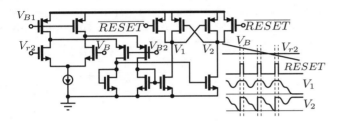

Fig. 5. Simplified schematic of autolatch comparator for $chop = 0$.

a very tight power budget, an *autolatch comparator* was introduced. Its schematic is shown in Fig. 5 for the case when $chop = 0$ together with some waveforms. The core of the circuit is a dynamic latch. When a comparison is needed, a digital circuit resets the latch and then enables it. As long as V_B has not crossed V_{r2}, V_1 goes periodically to V_{dd} and V_2 to ground. The signal on V_2 is inverted and delayed to generate the $RESET$ signal. V_1 and V_2 are then pulled up to V_{dd} and, after a delay, $RESET$ go low. This cycle is repeated until V_B crosses V_{r2} and V_1 go low. In this case the output is represented by the voltage on V_1. When $chop = 1$, the logic takes care of generating $RESET$ from the appropriate node and chooses the right output node. The latch is preceded by a folded preamplifier to prevent kickback noise appearing on oscillator's capacitors.

The delay of the comparator can be adjusted controlling the period of the described cycle. Simulations show that the delay is less than 13 ns in the worst case (process and temperature) with a total average current of 30 μA at 1.2 V supply. Low power is achieved by keeping the devices small, so as to minimize parasitic capacitance. Small devices have high flicker noise, but the offset compensation technique described by (3) also reduces the effect of flicker noise.

III. EXPERIMENTAL RESULTS

The oscillator has been realized in a baseline TSMC 65-nm CMOS process. The circuit occupies 0.11 mm^2 and uses only 2.5-V I/O thick oxide MOS devices. 1.2-V thin oxide devices were avoided because of their high gate current, which is not negligible in very low current circuits. Most of the area of the circuit is occupied by the current reference and by the oscillator capacitors[3] (Fig. 6). For flexibility in testing, all the reference voltages (V_{ref1}, V_{ref2}, V_R) were provided externally. For a nominal oscillation frequency of approximately 100 kHz, the reference current is I_1=125 nA for $C \cong 6$ pF, V_R=0.2 V, V_{ref1}=1 V and V_{ref2}=0.6 V. A low frequency was chosen to reduce the impact of parasitic effects, such as comparator delay. The total current consumption with 1.2 V supply voltage is 34.3 μA (18.9 μA for comparator ad logic; 14.4 μA for current reference; 1 μA through pin V_{r1}). Note that to reduce the effect of ESD leakage currents, the current in R_1 is relatively large (10 μA). If the reference voltage V_R were integrated on chip, this current would be negligible. Consumption can be strongly reduced with a less accurate or duty-cycled comparator. Since the aim is to prove the feasibility of the proposed concept, the testchip was not fully optimized for power consumption but for accuracy.

Long-term jitter measurements are reported in Fig. 7, together with lines showing the extrapolated thermal and flicker noise components. Period jitter is 52 ns (rms) and is dominated by comparator thermal noise. After a large number of periods, jitter is dominated by flicker noise from the current reference. Relative jitter is defined as the standard deviation of jitter divided by elapsed time; its value for a time period of the order of 1 s is an important parameter for time references used in WSN, since it limits duty-cycle of the receiver when synchronization is performed over a time scale of seconds [1]. It can be proven that for most oscillators, relative jitter becomes flat for increasing time, as observed in the measurements. The relative jitter is 0.1% after 1 s and is negligible compared to the temperature-induced frequency drift.

[3]The area labeled as "capacitors" in Fig. 6 contains also transistors M_1 ad M_3 of the current reference, which are required to match with MOS capacitor C_A and C_B.

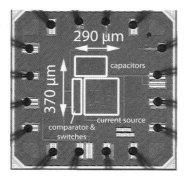

Fig. 6. Die micrograph of the test chip.

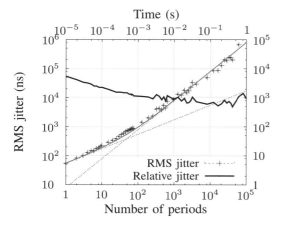

Fig. 7. Measured long-term jitter vs. time.

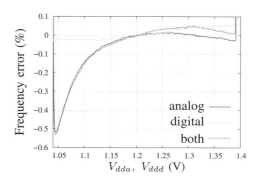

Fig. 8. Frequency error vs. variations of analog supply (V_{dda}), digital supply (V_{ddd}) or both.

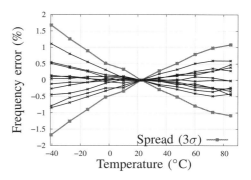

Fig. 9. Frequency error with respect to average frequency vs. temperature after one-point trimming at room temperature with $V_R = 0.25$ V for 11 samples; the average frequency (not shown) follows the temperature dependence of mobility ($\sim T^{-1.5}$).

Frequency pushing is shown in Fig. 8. The nominal supply voltage of the circuit should be 2.5 V (with pMOS and nMOS threshold voltages of 0.63 V and 0.57 V respectively) but the chosen topologies of the current reference and comparator allow functionality down to 1.05 V. The upper bound of the supply voltage is limited to 1.39 V by the start-up circuit in the current reference. With reference to Fig. 8, V_{dda} supplies the current reference, while V_{ddd} supplies the logic and the comparator. The increase of frequency with V_{ddd} is due to a decrease in the delay of the comparator, which is related to the period of $RESET$ in Fig. 5 and is fixed by logic circuitry.

Measurements on 11 samples from one batch show a frequency spread below 1.1% (3σ) over the range from -22 °C to 85 °C after one-point calibration (Fig. 9). For these measurements only, capacitors C_A and C_B were biased in deep inversion ($V_{ddd} = 1.5$ V, $V_{r1} = 1.6$ V, $V_{r2} = 1.2$ V) to ensure that the spread is only due to the core circuit.

IV. CONCLUSIONS

A fully integrated mobility-based frequency reference has been presented. Its frequency inaccuracy, due respectively to temperature, supply variations and noise, amounts to 1.1% (3σ) from -22 °C to 85 °C, 0.1% with 0.24 V supply variation and 0.1% (rms) over 1 s time span. This shows that, by adopting an appropriate temperature compensation scheme, mobility can be used to generate a reference frequency

accurate enough for WSN applications and that the proposed architecture is both low-voltage and low-power, as required by autonomous sensor nodes.

ACKNOWLEDGMENT

This work is funded by the European Commission in the Marie Curie project TRANDSSAT - 2005-020461.

REFERENCES

[1] F. Sebastiano, S. Drago, L. Breems, D. Leenaerts, K. Makinwa, and B. Nauta, "Impulse based scheme for crystal-less ULP radios," in *Proc. ISCAS*, May 2008, pp. 1508 – 1511.
[2] N. M. Pletcher and S. Gambini, "A 2 GHz 52μW wake-up receiver with -72 dBm sensitivity using uncertain-IF architecture," in *IEEE ISSCC Dig. of Tech. Papers*, Feb. 2008, pp. 524 – 525.
[3] M. S. McCorquodale, *et al.*, "A 0.5-to-480 MHz self-referenced CMOS clock generator with 90 ppm total frequency error and spread-spectrum capability," in *ISSCC Dig. of Tech. Papers*, Feb. 2008, pp. 524 – 525.
[4] K. Sundaresan, P. Allen, and F. Ayazi, "Process and temperature compensation in a 7-MHz CMOS clock oscillator," *IEEE J. Solid-State Circuits*, vol. 41, no. 2, pp. 433–442, Feb. 2006.
[5] C. Zhang and K. Makinwa, "Interface electronics for a CMOS electrothermal frequency-locked-loop," in *Proc. ESSCIRC*, Sept. 2007, pp. 292 – 295.
[6] M. Paavola, M. Laiho, M. Saukoski, and K. Halonen, "A 3 μW, 2 MHz CMOS frequency reference for capacitive sensor applications," in *Proc. ISCAS*, May 2006, pp. 4391–4394.
[7] R. Blauschild, "An integrated time reference," *IEEE ISSCC Dig. of Tech. Papers*, pp. 56–57, 1994.
[8] W. Sansen, F. Op't Eynde, and M. Steyaert, "A CMOS temperature-compensated current reference," *IEEE J. Solid-State Circuits*, vol. 23, no. 3, pp. 821–824, 1988.

A 36V Precision Programmable Gain Amplifier with CMRR Exceeding 120dB in all Gains

V. Schäffer, M. F. Snoeij, M. V. Ivanov

Texas Instruments GmbH
Erlangen, Germany

schaffer_viola@ti.com, m-snoeij@ti.com, ivanov_misha@ti.com

Abstract-A 36V programmable gain amplifier (PGA) is presented with sub-20 V offset and CMRR exceeding 120dB in all gains. It is the first 36V capable precision PGA that is implemented in a high-voltage CMOS process, allowing for several important additional functions, such as the detection of input and output fault conditions and an input switch network. This switch network in addition to acting as a 2-channel multiplexer also allows for various system-level diagnostic features. All opamps used in the PGA use chopper stabilization with a notch filter that removes chopping glitches, leading to very low offset for all gains and low 1/f noise. The input referred offset voltage is below 20 V (G=128). The PGA is implemented in a 0.35um CMOS process with a 36V extension, and has a total quiescent current of 2.7mA.

I. INTRODUCTION

While many application-specific sensor interface ICs [1] and integrated smart sensors [2] have been published in recent years, there is still a strong need for a more universal interface circuit for industrial applications. Here, apart from sensor outputs of a few millivolts, also larger signals of up to ±10V exist, such as those coming from remote transmitter outputs. These need to be processed and translated to the low voltage domain in which most A/D converters and microcontrollers operate. Moreover, these signals can have up to 10V of common mode voltage due to long signal lines, therefore common-mode rejection up to 100Hz is critical. Due to the variety of signal sources, high input impedance is essential, making systems based on resistor dividers at the input impractical.

The PGAs and instrumentation amplifiers (IA) that are currently available for use in such a signal acquisition system can generally be divided into two categories. Firstly, many IAs and PGAs exists that are capable of handling the high input voltages, such as ±15V, that are still commonplace in industrial applications. In order to be able to handle such voltages, they are made in bipolar technologies, and use laser-trimming to get the required DC precision [3].

A second class of PGAs is implemented in analog CMOS technologies [4]. This allows for the use of dynamic offset cancellation techniques to improve the DC precision of the PGA, thus eliminating the need for trimming. Moreover, the use of CMOS technologies allows for the addition of several digital functions. The most important of such additional functions is the ability of the PGA to detect internal fault conditions, such as an internal amplifier railing, that might otherwise not be directly noticeable in its analog output voltage. The detection of such a fault condition can then easily

be reported to the outside world via a digital output pin or digital bus. Since this can make the overall readout system much more robust against errors, there has been a considerable interest in PGAs with such additional functionality. However, until now, the supply voltage of such PGAs is relatively low, preventing their use in many industrial applications, where an input range of ±15V is required.

In this paper, we present the first precision PGA capable of handling up to 32V inputs that is implemented in a CMOS technology, and has many additional digital control and diagnostics functions required to create a flexible and robust system. Moreover, the PGA has an unprecedented CMRR of over 120dB in all gains, and a gain linearity better than 0.001%. In order to ensure low offsets for all gains, both the input and output amplifiers use chopper stabilization to reduce their offset to the microvolt level. In order to remove chopping glitches in the output of the amplifiers, a notch filter in the chopped high-gain path of the amplifier is used [5].

This paper is organized as follows. Section II presents the system-level design of the PGA, and discusses the overall topology, amplifier topology, and design approach to enable the 36V operation of the amplifier. In section III, the key additional functionality that the use of CMOS technology allows, such as error detection circuitry, is described. In section IV, measurement results are shown. Finally, conclusions are presented in section V.

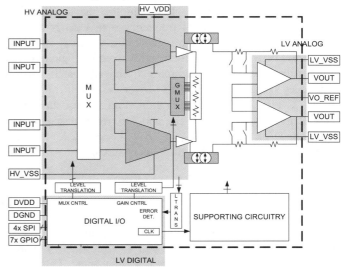

Fig. 1. Block diagram of the PGA presented.

II. SYSTEM LEVEL DESIGN

A. Device Architecture

Of the several possible instrumentation amplifier topologies, the 3-amp topology is the best-known approach [4,6]. However, it has two important drawbacks. Firstly, the use of voltage gain in the input amplifiers reduces the input common-mode voltage range for high gains, since the outputs of the input amplifiers can rail. Secondly, the common-mode rejection ratio (CMRR) of a 3-amp topology is limited to about 80dB in low gains by the degree of matching between the gain resistors around the output amplifier. Because of these limitations, a different approach was used, as shown in Fig. 1. The input amplifiers induce the input voltage across an adjustable resistor. The current through the resistor, and thus through the output stage of the input amplifiers, is mirrored and fed into the output amplifiers, where it is converted back into a differential output voltage. Through the use of this V-I and I-V conversion, the input CM range becomes independent of the gain, and the CMRR does not depend on resistor matching, but mainly on the CMRR of the individual amplifiers and the output impedance of the mirrors.

In order to ensure low overall offset for all gains, both input and output amplifiers use dynamic offset cancellation. Moreover, the DC precision of the current mirrors is critical for the overall offset, gain accuracy and linearity. Therefore, as shown on Fig. 2, these current mirrors are implemented with matched thin film resistors and amplifiers that also use dynamic offset cancellation.

B. Opamp topology

The PGA topology requires a total of 8 amplifiers, that all need dynamic offset correction. In all cases, a 3-stage amplifier with chopper stabilization is used (Fig. 3), in which a chopped high-gain path ensures low offset, while a parallel feed-forward stage ensures a wide bandwidth. A notch filter in the high gain path of the amplifier filters out the chopping glitches [5]. The resulting opamps have very low offset, no 1/f noise, low white noise, and no measurable chopping glitches at the output.

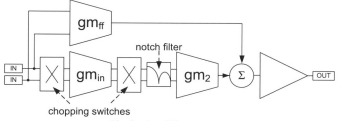

Fig. 3. Amplifier structure.

C. High-Voltage Design

The design goal for the PGA was to be able to operate on a ±18V supply, with an input common-mode range of ±16V. In order to achieve this specification, a CMOS process is used that has both 5V thin-oxide and 36V thick-oxide gate transistors, all with extended drains for high-voltage (HV) operation. However, all these HV-capable transistors have a degraded performance and matching, making them unsuitable for use in gain stages of amplifiers and other places where precision is required. However, the process also allowed for the use of the better performance low-voltage CMOS transistors that can be isolated from the substrate. Therefore, throughout the device, the approach was to use isolated low-voltage transistors in the signal path for circuit blocks that are driven by on-chip voltage regulators, V_{REG}, as illustrated in Fig. 4. A floating subregulator is used for the first stage of the input amplifier, which output voltage depends on input common mode. The output current of the input stage is cascoded, and passed to the 2nd stage current mirrors which operate at a supply voltage of 5V from the negative rail. Only the output stage of the input amplifier operates at the full 36V supply; the current mirrors again operate at 5V from either the positive or negative rail.

The output amplifiers operate at a separate supply voltage of 3 to 5V, which is essential to be able to drive a low-voltage ADC. This output supply voltage can be freely chosen to be anywhere within the high voltage supplies. Similarly, the digital support circuitry also operates at a low supply of 3 to 5V that can also be freely chosen within the high voltage supply range.

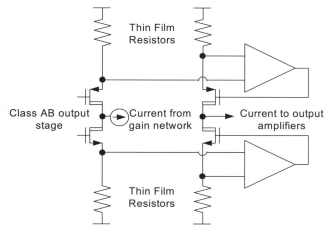

Fig. 2. Current mirror structure.

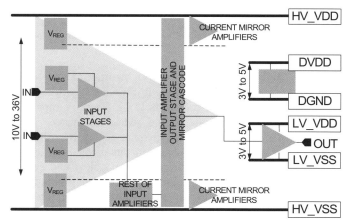

Fig. 4. On chip supply domains and regulators, V_{REG}.

311

III. KEY AUXILLARY FUNCTIONS

A. Detection of out-of-range conditions

A common problem in instrumentation amplifiers is detecting various conditions that can cause signal corruption while the amplifier output remains within its linear range. These can include input common-mode range violations, clipping or limiting in the intermediate stages and input faults. System-level indication and diagnostic capabilities are desired to alert the controller of a potentially invalid voltage at the amplifier output. A common way to implement this is to add comparators at the critical nodes (e.g. inputs and outputs of internal opamps) [4]. However, there are significant drawbacks: such comparators have a lot of circuitry, additional reference-generation is needed, and margins for mismatches, temperature and process variation reduce usable dynamic range.

Overload conditions can be detected within the amplifiers with minimal amount of additional circuits by detecting when an internal control loop is broken. This approach also maximizes the dynamic range and perfectly traces over temperature and process variation. Fig. 5 shows an example of indicating the negative opamp input common-mode range violation by detecting the railing of the amplifier that is driving the regulated cascode.

Similar functions were incorporated in internal opamps of the PGA to detect input common mode violation, input overload, output rail, output short and input clamp activation with corresponding digital flags and registers for system-level diagnostics.

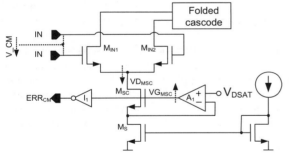

Fig. 5. Detection of the violation of the input common mode range. When the input common mode voltage V_CM approaches the negative rail, M_{SC} starts to triode until the amplifier can't correct for this at its gate and rails.

B. Improving system level settling time

Most high voltage amplifiers incorporate protection clamps to protect the precision input transistors from overload conditions and fast input transients [3,7]. These clamps draw current from the signal source when activated. In a multiplexed system, where each channel has an RC-filter, the input to the amplifier can change instantaneously when the channels are switched. During amplifier's slew and settling the input protection clamps are activated and drain charge from the input filter capacitor. Depending on the filter and source characteristics the capacitor re-charging can lead to a long settling time.

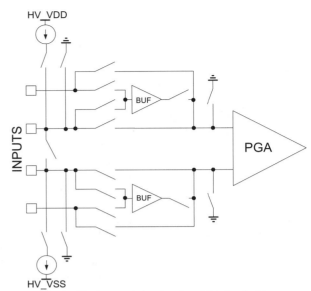

Fig. 6. The input switch network and the slew-buffer.

To avoid input current and thus improve system level settling time, a slew buffer was added (Fig 6). This low precision buffer contains thick 36V oxide MOS transistors that tolerate large differential voltages, and is switched into the signal path when an overload condition is anticipated. It supplies the current for the clamps of the precision stage thus preventing current drawn from the input. It is removed from the signal path after the clamp activating condition disappears and does not affect system accuracy and noise.

C. Input switch network

The use of the high voltage CMOS process enables unique functionality not previously integrated on precision industrial IAs. The integrated input switch network shown on Fig. 6. serves as a 2 channel multiplexer and provides means of reconfiguring the amplifier for system level trouble shooting and "housekeeping". For example the inputs can be shorted for calibration, an absolute voltage can be measured at either of the inputs or a wire-break at the input can be detected by connecting current sources to the input pins.

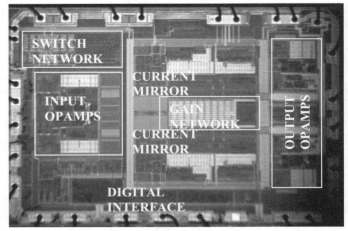

Fig. 7. Chip micrograph of the 36V precision PGA.

Table 1. Summary of the measured PGA performance.

Parameter		Mean	Std. dev.
Input Referred Offset Voltage (VOS) (G=128)		-0.4µV	6.3µV
VOS Temperature Drift		-0.01µV/C	0.06µV /C
Gain Non-linearity		0.0003%	0.0002%
Gain Error (GE) (G=128)		-0.036%	0.022%
GE Temperature Drift		-1.7ppm/C	0.1ppm/C
Common Mode Rejection (CMRR) (G=128)		-0.03µV/V	0.05 µV/V
(G=1)		-0.18µV/V	0.24 µV/V
Supply Current (High Voltage Input Supplies)		2.2mA	
(Low Voltage Output Supplies)		0.75mA	
Gain Range		1/8 to 128 in binary steps x (1 or 1.375)	
0.1-10Hz Input Referred Noise (G=128)		460nVp-p	
CMRR @ 1KHz		90dB	
Bandwidth (G<=4)		2MHz	

The statistical data is from 330 samples measured. The drift statistics are from 12 samples measured.

IV. MEASUREMENT RESULTS

A chip micrograph of the PGA fabricated in a 0.35um analog CMOS process with a 36V extension is shown in Fig. 7. The chip has an area of 3.6 x 2.4mm². The common mode rejection ratio (CMRR) distribution is shown on Fig. 8. The untrimmed CMRR exceeds 120dB (<1µV/V error) in all gains. The input offset voltage is better than 20µV (G=128). The 0.1Hz to 10Hz peak-to-peak input referred noise is measured to be 460nV$_{pp}$ (G=128). Since the noise spectral density is flat due to the chopped architecture, the total noise can be reduced by longer integration. Despite the V-I and I-V conversions and the multiple supply domains in the signal path the gain linearity is better than 0.001%. The PGA has a gain range of 0.125 to 128 in binary steps with an auxiliary gain of 1 or 1.375 in the output stage. The less than 0.1% gain error and less than 2ppm/°C gain error drift is determined by the matching of the untrimmed thin-film resistors. The total quiescent current is 2.2mA from the high voltage input supplies and 730uA from the low voltage output supplies. The 3dB bandwidth in G<4 is 2MHz. For gains larger than 4 the 3dB bandwidth is reduced by half for each 6dB gain step. Due to the notch filters used in the amplifiers the chopping glitches are practically invisible even in high gain. This is illustrated on the scope photo on Fig. 9.

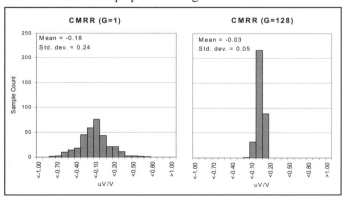

Fig. 8. The CMRR distribution (over 300 samples).

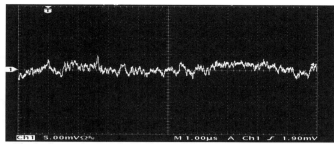

Fig. 9. Scope photograph showing no differential output glitch (G=128).

Table 2. Comparison to other similar High-Voltage PGAs.

Parameter	THIS PGA	PGA205	AD825x
Supply Voltage Range	10-36V	9-36V	10-30V
Input Referred Offset Voltage (high gain)	20µV	62µV	260µV
VOS Temperature Drift	0.1µV/C	0.6µV/C	1.7µV/C
Common Mode Rejection Ratio (G=1)	120dB	80dB	80dB
On Chip MUX and Diagnostic Functions	yes	no	no

V. CONCLUSIONS

A precision 36V programmable gain amplifier was presented targeted for industrial signal acquisition applications. By using an architecture that converts the input voltage to a current, mirrors this current by precision current mirrors and then converts the current back to voltage at the output stage an untrimmed common-mode rejection ratio over 120dB in all gains was achieved. Additionally, this architecture increases the input common-mode range and provides for level translation between the input and output supply domains. The offset voltage and 1/f noise were eliminated by the use of chopper stabilization in the internal amplifiers. Virtually no chopping glitches are visible at the output due to the utilization of notch-filters inside the amplifiers.

ACKNOWLEDGMENTS

The authors would like to thank J. Metzger, D. Trifonov, J. Doorenbos, S. Gulas, G. Haug and R. Burt for their design and characterization support and the layout team J. Graner, B. Young, R. Emrich, D. Bellemare, T. Lis.

REFERENCES

[1] M. Kämäräinen et al. , "A 1.5µW 1V 2nd-Order ΔΣ Sensor Front-End with Signal Boosting and Offset Compensation for a Capacitive 3-Axis Micro-Accelerometer", *ISSCC Digest Techn. Papers*, 2008, pp. 578-579

[2] C. Schott et al. , "CMOS Single-Chip Electronic Compass with Microcontroller", *IEEE J. Solid-State Circuits*, vol. 42, no. 12, pp. 2923-2933, Dec. 2007

[3] PGA205 Data Sheet, Texas Instruments Inc., Dallas, TX, 1993

[4] A.T.K. Tang, "Enhanced Programmable Instrumentation Amplifier", *Proceedings of IEEE Sensors*, 2005, pp. 955-958

[5] R. Burt and J. Zhang, "A Micropower Chopper-Stabilized Operational Amplifier Using a SC Notch Filter With Synchronous Integration Inside the Continuous-Time Signal Path", *IEEE J. Solid-State Circuits*, vol. 41, no. 12, pp. 2729-2736, Dec. 2006

[6] E. Nash, "A Practical Review of Common Mode Voltages and Instrumentation Amplifiers", Sensors Magazine, July 1998.

[7] AD8250 Data Sheet, Analog Devices Inc., Norwood, MA, 2007

A 65-nm 84-dB-gain 200-MHz-UGB CMOS Fully-Differential Three-Stage Amplifier with a Novel Common Mode Control

Ivonne Di Sancarlo[2], Dario Giotta[1], Andrea Baschirotto[2,3], Richard Gaggl[1]

[1]Infineon Technologies Austria AG, Siemensstrasse 2, A-9500 Villach, AUSTRIA
[2]Dept. of Innovation Engineering, University of Lecce, Via per Monteroni, 73100 Lecce, ITALY
[3]Dept. of Physics, University of Milano-Bicocca, Piazza della Scienza 3, 20126 Milano, ITALY

Abstract□ **A Single Miller capacitor FeedForward Compensation (SMFFC) technique with a novel Common Mode (CM) control circuitry for fully-differential multistage amplifiers is presented in this paper. The novel alternative to control the output common-mode voltage, adding a feed-forward path to a normal Common-Mode Feed-Back (CMFB) amplifier, allows to have a very stable and wide-band regulation. A fully-differential three-stage amplifier based on this approach has been implemented in 65-nm CMOS technology. A DC-gain of 84-dB and a bandwidth of 200-MHz are achieved, driving a 25-k&l/1-pF load. Thanks to the novel control circuitry, the CM path achieved 136-MHz bandwidth with 85-dB DC-gain. The power consumption is 10.17-mW with a 1-V power supply. It occupies 0.02-mm† of silicon area.**

I. INTRODUCTION

Scaled CMOS technologies are changing the scenario for the design of OpAmps. Scaled transistors feature wider bandwidth but poorer dc-gain. Thus multi-stage OpAmp structures have to be considered. On the other hand while transistor sizes are reduced, capacitance density is not reduced accordingly, or, in some cases (MIMCAP with few metal layers, etc…) is increased. In this scenario the frequency compensation required by the multistage topologies is facing an area issue, when the frequency compensation is implemented only with capacitors. For this reason some alternative compensation schemes using not only capacitor but also transistors have to be developed. In the literature several compensation schemes are reported to improve stability, frequency and transient responses of the multistage amplifiers, with Nested Miller Compensation (NMC) [1] typically taken as a reference. NMC is a well-established pole splitting technique for phase compensation but it has a major drawback, i.e. bandwidth reduction when using large number of stages. The undesired effect of right-half-plane (RHP) zero creation by the Miller capacitor requires a large output conductance in the last stage, to ensure stability, making it unsuitable for low-power applications. To improve stability by removing the RHP zero in the NMC, phase compensation schemes like Nested Gm-C Compensation (NGCC) [2] are reported. But the bandwidth improvement of this structure is not that significant while driving large capacitive loads. Many other structures have been developed and reported in literature [3,4,5] to further improve the bandwidth, but all of them use two capacitors for the compensation schemes. The single

Miller capacitor compensation approach is introduced to reduce the area and improve the small signal and large signal performance of the amplifiers. In multistage amplifiers with a large capacitive load, the pole at the output is located at low frequency and is very close to the dominant pole, which is the pole at the output of the first stage. The amplifiers have to be stabilized by removing the effect of the pole at the output. This can be done via pole-splitting using the Single Miller capacitor Compensation (SMC) or pole-zero cancellation using the Single Miller capacitor FeedForward Compensation (SMFFC) [6]. The latter approach, implemented in sub-micron technologies using low supply voltages (as usual with scaling) allows to provide high DC-gain and wide bandwidth. In a fully-differential realization of the SMFFC amplifier, a different CM regulation will be needed to overcome the drawbacks of a typical CMFB circuit [7].

In this paper a three-stage OpAmp realized in a 65-nm CMOS technology is presented. Different analysis for the differential path and the common mode path are needed. This is because some sign inversion introduced in the differential mode in the feedforward path by means of line-crossing are not active for the common mode and then instability for the common-mode signal would result. For this reason a novel compensation scheme for the common-mode control circuit is developed and here proposed.

The principle and the analysis of the fully-differential three-stage SMFFC amplifier are presented in Section II. The CM regulation for multistage amplifiers is introduced in Section III. In Section IV, the implementation of the circuit is described. The experimental results and performance comparison are given in Section V. The final conclusion is drawn in Section VI.

II. FULLY-DIFFERENTIAL SCHEME: SINGLE MILLER CAPACITOR FEEDFORWARD COMPENSATION

The proposed SMFFC approach, shown in Fig. 1, uses a feed-forward path to provide a left-half-plane (LHP) zero to compensate the second pole (first non-dominant pole). The feed-forward path adds current at the second stage output pushing the second non-dominant pole to higher frequencies. The LHP zero is placed near the second pole, and provides a positive phase shift which compensates for the negative phase shift due to the non-dominant poles.

The transconductance stages g_{m1}, g_{m2} and g_{m3} compose the three-stage amplifier. The output conductance and the lumped parasitic capacitance of each stage are represented by $g_{o(1,2,3)}$ and $C_{(1,2,3)}$ respectively. The feed-forward transconductance stage g_{mf1} provides the pole-zero cancellation. C_m is the Miller capacitor. The small signal model is based on the following assumptions: 1) the gains of all the stages are much bigger than 1; 2) the parasitic capacitances are much smaller than the Miller capacitor C_m and loading capacitor C_L.

The transfer function then is given [8] by:

$$A_{v(SMFFC)}(s) = \frac{A_{dc}\left(1 + s\frac{C_m g_{mf1}}{g_{m1}g_{m2}} - s^2\frac{C_m C_2}{g_{m2}g_{m3}}\right)}{\left(1 + \frac{s}{p_{-3dB}}\right)\left(1 + s\frac{C_L g_{o2}}{g_{m2}g_{m3}} + s^2\frac{C_2 C_L}{g_{m2}g_{m3}}\right)}.\quad (1)$$

where $A_{dc}=(g_{m1}g_{m2}g_{m3})/(g_{o1}g_{o2}g_{o3})$ is the OpAmp DC-gain and $p_{-3dB}=(g_{o1}g_{o2}g_{o3})/(C_m g_{m2}g_{m3})$ is the dominant pole. The gain bandwidth is given by $GBW = A_{dc} \cdot p_{-3dB} = g_{m1}/C_m$.

From (1), the amplifier has two non-dominant poles and two zeros. The position of the non-dominant poles depends on the parasitic capacitance of the second stage, C_2 that could be very small if the last stage transistor is not huge.

The stability analysis of the amplifier is done using the separate pole approach [9]. From (1) the zeros of the amplifier are obtained [8] as:

$$z_1 = \frac{g_{m1}g_{m2}}{g_{mf1}C_m}(LHP)\;;\; z_2 \cong \frac{g_{mf1}g_{m3}}{g_{m1}C_2}(C_m \gg C_2)(RHP).\quad (2)$$

As seen from the transfer function, the non-dominant poles are located on the left-hand plane and given [8] by:

$$p_2 = \frac{G_{meff}}{C_L}\;;\; p_3 = \frac{g_{o2}}{C_2} - \frac{G_{meff}}{C_L}\quad (3)$$

where $G_{meff} = (g_{m2}g_{m3})/g_{o2}$.

For stability of the circuit, the second and third poles need to satisfy the condition:

$$GBW \leq \frac{1}{2}p_2 \leq \frac{1}{4}p_3\quad (4)$$

$$\frac{g_{m1}}{C_m} \leq \frac{1}{2}\frac{G_{meff}}{C_L} \leq \frac{1}{4}\left(\frac{g_{o2}}{C_2} - \frac{G_{meff}}{C_L}\right).$$

The value of the compensation capacitor is given [8] by:

$$C_m = \frac{2g_{m1}C_L}{G_{meff}} = \frac{2g_{m1}g_{02}C_L}{g_{m2}g_{m3}} = \frac{1}{2A_{v2}}\left(4\frac{g_{m1}}{g_{m3}}C_L\right).\quad (5)$$

It can be seen that by appropriate choice of the second stage gain the compensation capacitor can be reduced.

Thus is no longer needed to have $g_{m3} \gg g_{m1}$. This helps reducing the power consumption of the amplifier.

Applying the Routh-Hurwitz stability criterion on the closed-loop transfer function of the SMFFC amplifier, the stability constraint can be expressed [8] by:

$$\frac{g_{o2}}{C_2} > \frac{g_{m1}}{C_m} \cdot \frac{1}{\left(1 + \frac{g_{mf1}}{g_{m2}}\right)}.\quad (6)$$

III. NOVEL COMMON-MODE REGULATION FOR MULTISTAGE AMPLIFIERS

The key point for compensation of the fully-differential mode is the use of a feedforward path through A' (Fig. 2). This path is not available for the common-feedback circuits and thus insufficient stability would be reached for the CM control circuit. Therefore an innovative alternative to control the output common-mode voltage of fully-differential amplifiers is presented in this section. The core of this novel approach is to add a feed-forward path to a conventional Common-Mode Feed-Back (CMFB) amplifier in order to improve its stability and increase its bandwidth. The structure is shown in Fig. 2.

The feed-back path works like a conventional CMFB amplifier, with its bandwidth related to the differential path compensation. Having a Miller compensation for the dominant pole, this part of the circuit provides the common-mode regulation for the low-mid frequency range, with a bandwidth limited by the differential path compensation. Anyway, the limit of the CMFB is that the CMFB path sees the same poles of the differential path plus an additional one at the control node. Additionally, the differential feed-forward has no impact on the CM transfer function. For this reason, the CMFB path alone is not enough, being at best poorly compensated by C_m, at worst totally unstable. The idea then is to add a feed-forward path for the CM regulation, like it has been done for the differential path.

This common mode feed-forward path also senses the output common-mode voltage and compares it with a reference, to inject a common-mode current in the second stage B, regulating the common-mode voltage. Having a zero in the transfer function, this path is intended to regulate the common-mode in the high frequency range. The combination of the two paths gives a very stable and wide-band regulation.

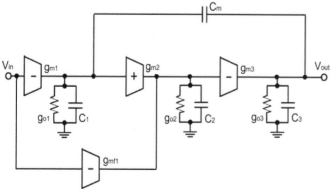

Figure 1. Structure of the three-stage SMFFC amplifier

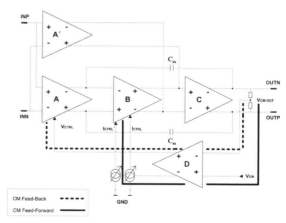

Figure 2. Structure of three-stage SMFFC amplifier with the CM-control

In practice, this is achieved placing the zero of the feed-forward path in such a way that it compensates the non dominant pole of the feed-back path.

Additionally, the bandwidth of the Common Mode regulation is not fully linked to the differential path bandwidth, but can be enlarged by increasing the power of the feed-forward path.

In general an amplifier would be necessary for each path (feed-back and feed-forward), a single amplifier can be used if both paths do not act on the same OpAmp stage.

IV. IMPLEMENTATION

The fully-differential three-stage SMFFC amplifier has been implemented in 65-nm CMOS technology with 1-V power supply. Only regular V_{TH} devices have been used. The schematic is shown in Fig. 7. The first stage is a folded cascode with a pMOS input differential pair, a cascode pair and an active load. The active load is also cascoded, in order to improve the output resistance of the stage. This stage provides a high gain, helping to create a dominant-pole system. The second stage is done with a pMOS in common source configuration. A simple current mirror provides the necessary phase inversion. Moreover, a compensation resistor ($R = 800\text{-}\Omega$) is connected to the gate of the reference side of this current mirror to enhance its speed and bandwidth [10]. The feed-forward path is a pMOS differential pair which provides the high frequency signal path from the OpAmp input to the output of the second stage. Thanks to it, no compensation capacitance is needed for the second stage. C_m is the Miller capacitor of 3.5-pF, connected between the output of the first stage and the output of the third one. Then, the third stage is a nMOS in common source configuration.

The feed-back path of the CM circuit senses the common-mode voltage at the output using an RC-summing network. Then it compares the output common-mode voltage $V_{CM\text{-}OUT}$ with a reference voltage ($V_{CM} = 0.5\text{-}V$) injecting the control signal into the folded cascode of the first stage. It provides a negative feed-back. The feed-forward path which provides a pole-zero cancellation, injects a common-mode current into the second stage, so regulating the common-mode voltage.

V. EXPERIMENTAL RESULTS AND COMPARISON

While designed for high-speed/high-gain on-chip operation (assumed load 1pF//25kΩ), for the measurement setup the OpAmp has been realized in closed-loop configuration with 0-dB gain (Fig. 3), with an effective capacitive load C_L of 10-pF and resistive load R_L of 200-kΩ (no buffer is used, the outputs are directly connected to pads).

Moreover, a capacitance C is needed in the feed-back path of this configuration, in order to avoid peaking in the frequency behaviour. This capacitance introduces a zero to cancel the pole due to the feedback resistors and the input capacitance of the amplifier, improving the stability. The realized test-chip includes, among other devices, a bandgap and a biasing circuit, to provide the V_{CM} and the biasing currents for the OpAmp.

The chip micrograph is shown in Fig. 4. The measured results, obtained using HP4395A network analyzer, Tektronix TDS7104 oscilloscope and Agilent E4440A spectrum analyzer, are summarized in Table I. The closed-loop response, the PSRR and the CMRR characteristics are shown

in Fig. 5 and Fig. 6 respectively. The high PSRR and amplifier's linearity prove that a high DC-gain is attained. Additionally, the stability over one order of magnitude of the load (designed for 1pF, measured with 10pF), proves the robustness of the implemented compensation techniques. A comparison table (Table II) shows the advantages and drawbacks of the proposed and previous three-stage amplifiers.

TABLE I.   MEASURED RESULTS

Load	10pF//200kΩ	SR	39.73V/μs
A_{dc}*	84dB	T_S	20.77ns
GBW*	200MHz	Rise time	10.97ns
PM*	76°	PSRR @ 1MHz	60.19dB
f_{-3dB}	16.8MHz	CMRR @ 1MHz	37.82dB
Power	10.17mW	HD₃ @ 5MHz	-82.3dBc
V_{DD}	1V	Output noise @ 1MHz	27.43nV/√Hz

*. simulated results, for 1pF//25kΩ

TABLE II.   PERFORMANCE COMPARISON OF THREE-STAGE AMPLIFIERS

Parameter	[11]	[4]	this work
DC-gain (dB)	~100	>100	84
GBW (MHz)	80	4.5	200
Load (pF//kΩ)	16//50	120//25	1//25
Phase margin	57°	65°	76°
Power (mW@Vdd)	7.8 @ 2.6	0.4 @ 2	10.17 @ 1
Capacitor Value (pF)	C_{m1}=7.7 C_{m2}=0.73	C_{m2}=3 C_a=7	C_m=3.5
Technology	0.35μm CMOS	0.8μm CMOS	65nm CMOS

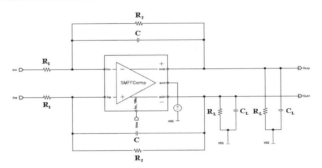

Figure 3.   SMFFC amplifier configured in closed-loop

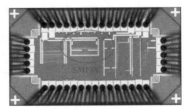

Figure 4.   Chip micrograph

VI. CONCLUSION

A fully-differential three-stage SMFFC amplifier with a novel CM-control, suitable for low-power application, has been realized and measured. A DC-gain of 84-dB and a bandwidth of 200-MHz have been achieved for the differential loop, driving a 25-kΩ//1-pF load. Thanks to the novel control circuitry, the CM-control achieved 136-MHz bandwidth with 85-dB DC-gain. Its bandwidth is comparable to the differential one, improving the stability of the CMFB loop.

Additionally, the OpAmp stability over one order of magnitude of the load proves the robustness of the implemented topology.

ACKNOWLEDGMENTS

The authors would like to thank Prof. W. Sansen for his helpful suggestions, and the lab guys who helped to measure amplifier performance.

REFERENCES

[1] R. G. H. Eschauzier, L. P. T. Kerklaan, and J. H. Huijsing, "A 100-MHz 100-dB operational amplifier with multipath nested Miller compensation structure," *IEEE Journal of Solid-State Circuits*, vol. 27, pp. 1709-1717, Dec. 1992.

[2] F. You, S. H. K. Embabi, and E. Sánchez-Sinencio, "Multistage amplifier topologies with nested Gm-C compensation," *IEEE Journal of Solid-State Circuits*, vol. 32, pp. 2000-2011, Dec. 1997.

[3] K. N. Leung, P. K. T. Mok, W. H. Ki, and J. K. O. Sin, "Three stage large capacitive load amplifier with damping-factor-control frequency compensation," *IEEE Journal of Solid-State Circuits*, vol. 35, pp. 221-230, Feb. 2000.

[4] H. Lee and P. K. T. Mok, "Active-feedback frequency-compensation technique for low-power multistage amplifiers," *IEEE Journal of Solid-State Circuits*, vol. 38, pp. 511-520, Mar. 2003.

[5] X. Peng and W. Sansen , "Transconductance With Capacitances Feedback Compensation for Multistage Amplifiers", *IEEE Journal of Solid-State Circuits*, vol. 40, pp. 1514-1520, Jul. 2005.

[6] X. Fan, C. Mishra, and E. Sánchez-Sinencio, "Single Miller capacitor compensated multistage amplifiers for large capacitive load applications", in *Proc. IEEE International Symposium on Circuits and Systems*, Vancouver, Canada, pp. 493-496, May 2004.

[7] D. Johns and K. Martin, Analog Integrated Circuit Design, chapter 6, pp. 287-291, John Wiley & Sons, Inc., 1997.

[8] X. Fan, C. Mishra and E. Sánchez-Sinencio, "Single miller capacitor frequency compensation technique for low-power multistage amplifiers," *IEEE Journal of Solid-State Circuits*, vol. 40, pp. 584–592, Mar. 2005.

[9] K. N. Leung and P. K. T. Mok, "Analysis of multistage amplifier-frequency compensation," *IEEE Transactions on Circuits and Systems-I: Fundamental Theory and Applications*, vol. 48, pp. 1041-1056, Sep. 2001.

[10] T. Voo and C. Toumazou, "High-speed current mirror resistive compensation technique," *Electronics Letters*, vol. 31, no. 4, pp. 248–250, Feb. 1995.

[11] X. Peng and W. Sansen , "Nested feed-forward Gm-stage and nulling Resistor plus Nested-Miller Compensation for Multistage Amplifiers", *IEEE Custom Integrated Circuits Conference*, pp. 329-332, May 2002.

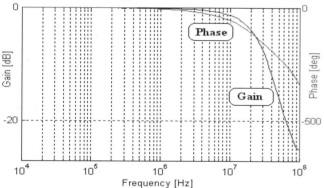

Figure 5.   Measured Closed-loop Response

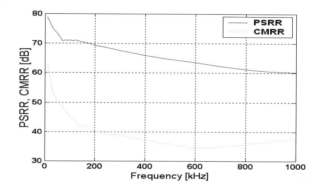

Figure 6.   Measured PSRR and CMRR

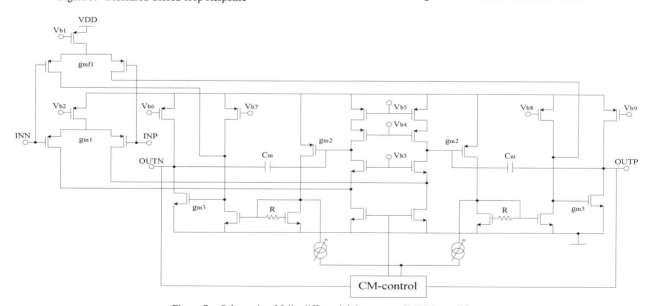

Figure 7.   Schematic of fully-differential three-stage SMFFC amplifier

A CMOS Source-Buffered Differential Input Stage with High EMI Suppression

Jean-Michel Redouté and Michiel Steyaert
Dept. ESAT - MICAS
Katholieke Universiteit Leuven
Heverlee, Belgium
Email: [jean-michel.redoute, michiel.steyaert]@esat.kuleuven.be

Abstract— This paper introduces a CMOS source-buffered differential input stage exhibiting a high degree of immunity against electromagnetic interferences (EMI) which are applied on its input pins. The measurements of a test-IC illustrate that the source-buffered differential pair generates a maximal EMI induced input offset voltage of 116 mV when a 750 mV RMS EMI signal is injected in its inputs, while a classic differential pair output is saturated with a maximal offset of 610 mV under the same circumstances.

I. INTRODUCTION

The electromagnetic compatibility (EMC) of integrated circuits is an important design parameter which is no longer excluded from any electronic product design flow. The dense integration level links the EMC issue of integrated circuits to the graceful coexistence between systems: as an example, Bluetooth, GSM and WiFi services have to coexist and operate in harmony within the close confinement of a modern mobile phone. Analog integrated circuits are particularly vulnerable to conducted electromagnetic interferences (EMI) which are transmitted via PCB tracks. This paper examines the electromagnetic susceptibility of a classic differential pair to EMI which is injected into its inputs. The EMI induced offset is evaluated mathematically, and a source-buffered differential pair generating a much smaller EMI induced offset voltage is introduced and described in detail. Measurements illustrate the superior electromagnetic immunity of the source-buffered differential pair opposed to the weak performance of the classic differential pair. When injecting an EMI signal of 750 mV RMS at the input, the measured maximal EMI induced input offset voltage corresponds to 116 mV for the source-buffered topology compared to 610 mV for the classical differential pair. Much more importantly, the output of the source-buffered differential pair remains in its operating region, while the output of the classic differential pair is completely saturated because of the large injected EMI voltage.

II. EMI INDUCED OFFSET IN A CLASSIC DIFFERENTIAL PAIR

When a classic differential pair is driven simultaneously by a common mode and and a differential mode EMI disturbance, an output offset current is generated owing to the parasitic bulk capacitance between the sources of M1-M2 and ground (represented by C_{T1} in Fig. 1) [1], [2]. This is now derived

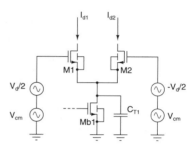

Fig. 1.   Classic differential pair, disturbed by a common mode and a differential mode EMI signal of the same frequency. Because of C_{T1}, $\overline{I_{d1}}$ is no longer equal to $\overline{I_{d2}}$ (offset current).

mathematically. Using the expression for a MOS transistor in saturation [3], and expressing V_{gsi} as the sum of a DC (V_{GSi}) and an AC component (v_{gsi}), the output offset current (I_{OS}) is expressed as:

$$
\begin{aligned}
I_{OS} &= \beta.\left(\overline{(V_{gs1} - V_t)^2} - \overline{(V_{gs2} - V_t)^2}\right) \\
&= \beta.(\overline{v_{gs1}^2} - \overline{v_{gs2}^2})
\end{aligned}
\tag{1}
$$

Where $\beta = \frac{\mu C_{ox}}{2}\frac{W}{L}$. The Parseval identity states that the total energy contained in a transient waveform is equal to the total energy of the waveform's Fourier transform summed across all of its frequency components [4]:

$$
\overline{v_{gsi}^2(t)} = \lim_{T\to\infty} \frac{1}{T}\int_{\frac{-T}{2}}^{\frac{T}{2}} v_{gsi}^2(t).dt = \int_{-\infty}^{\infty} |V_{gsi}(j\omega)|^2.d\omega
\tag{2}
$$

Expressing $V_{gsi}(j\omega)$ in terms of the common mode ($V_{cm}(j\omega)$) and the differential mode ($V_{dm}(j\omega)$) input voltage yields:

$$
\begin{cases}
V_{gs1}(j\omega) = H_{cm}(j\omega).V_{cm}(j\omega) + \frac{V_{dm}(j\omega)}{2} \\
V_{gs2}(j\omega) = H_{cm}(j\omega).V_{cm}(j\omega) - \frac{V_{dm}(j\omega)}{2}
\end{cases}
\tag{3}
$$

Where $H_{cm}(j\omega)$ is the transfer function for common mode signals. Provided that $g_{m1} = g_{m2}$, $C_{gs1}=C_{gs2}$:

$$
H_{cm}(j\omega) = \frac{j\omega.C_{T1}}{2.g_{m1} + j\omega.(C_{T1} + 2C_{gs1})}
\tag{4}
$$

Rewriting (1) using (2), (3), (4) in terms of the input offset voltage ($V_{OS} = I_{OS}/g_{m1}$) yields:

$$
V_{OS} = \frac{1}{V_{GS1} - V_t}\int_{-\infty}^{\infty} |H_{cm}(j\omega).V_{cm}(j\omega).
$$
$$
.V_{dm}(j\omega)|.cos\phi.d\omega
\tag{5}
$$

318

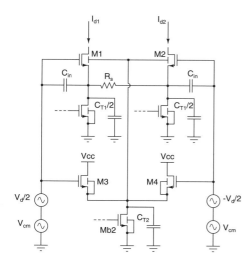

Fig. 2. Source-buffered differential pair with source resistance R_s.

Where:

$$\phi = atan\left(\frac{Im\{H_{cm}(j\omega).V_{cm}(j\omega).V_{dm}(j\omega)\}}{Re\{H_{cm}(j\omega).V_{cm}(j\omega).V_{dm}(j\omega)\}}\right) \quad (6)$$

Equation (5) lists the main contributing elements to the EMI induced input offset voltage of the classic differential pair. Firstly, the offset is proportional to the multiplication of the magnitudes of the common mode and differential mode EMI components, as well as to the phase between both. Secondly, the larger $V_{GS1} - V_t$, the smaller the input offset voltage: this is a controversial requirement, since the overdrive of an input differential pair must preferably be as small as possible in order to reduce the offset which is caused by mismatch [3]. It is therefore not possible to look for a convenient optimum using $V_{GS} - V_t$ as a design parameter. Thirdly, in order to decrease the offset current, $|H_{cm}(j\omega)|$ must be reduced as much as possible: this can be realized by decreasing C_{T1} (refer to (4)). It is however not possible to make the latter zero owing to parasitic effects.

III. EMI INDUCED OFFSET IN THE SOURCE-BUFFERED DIFFERENTIAL PAIR

Fig. 2 depicts the new developed source-buffered differential pair in which the nominal differential pair (M1-M2) is back-biased by an auxiliary differential pair (M3-M4). The latter bootstraps the bulk-source voltage of M1-M2 and keeps the average drain current of M1 and M2 at a constant value by forcing the common mode transfer function $H_{cm}(j\omega)$ to zero. This circuit is based on the EMI resisting differential pair which is presented in [5]: however, the major disadvantage of the latter is its high dependency on tightly specified tolerances of on-chip capacitors. This is overcome in the present circuit, as is shown later on. First observe that the output offset current is now expressed as a function of the gate-source voltage (analogous to (1)) and the bulk-source voltage:

$$I_{OS} = \beta.\left(\overline{\left(v_{gs1} - \gamma\sqrt{2\phi_f + V_{sb1}}\right)^2} \right. $$
$$\left. - \overline{\left(v_{gs2} - \gamma\sqrt{2\phi_f + V_{sb2}}\right)^2}\right) \quad (7)$$

Where $\beta = \frac{\mu C_{ox}}{2}\frac{W}{L}$. Using a small signal approximation, V_{sbi} is expressed as the sum of a DC component (V_{SBi}) and an AC component (v_{sbi}). As long as v_{sbi} is much smaller than $(2\phi_f + V_{SBi})$, a first order Taylor expansion can be used to simplify previous expression:

$$I_{OS} = \beta.\left(\overline{\left(v_{gs1} - \frac{\gamma}{\sqrt{2\phi_f + V_{SB1}}}v_{sb1}\right)^2}\right.$$
$$\left. -\overline{\left(v_{gs2} - \frac{\gamma}{\sqrt{2\phi_f + V_{SB2}}}v_{sb2}\right)^2}\right)$$
$$= \beta.\left(\overline{\left(v_{gs1} - \frac{g_{mb1}}{g_{m1}}v_{sb1}\right)^2} - \overline{\left(v_{gs2} - \frac{g_{mb2}}{g_{m2}}v_{sb2}\right)^2}\right)$$
$$= \beta.(\overline{v_{x1}^2} - \overline{v_{x2}^2}) \quad (8)$$

Where $v_{xi} = v_{gsi} - \frac{g_{mbi}}{g_{mi}}v_{sbi}$. $V_{xi}(j\omega)$ is expressed in terms of the common mode and the differential mode input voltage:

$$\begin{cases} V_{x1}(j\omega) = H_{cm}(j\omega).V_{cm}(j\omega) + H_{dm}(j\omega).\frac{V_{dm}(j\omega)}{2} \\ V_{x2}(j\omega) = H_{cm}(j\omega).V_{cm}(j\omega) - H_{dm}(j\omega).\frac{V_{dm}(j\omega)}{2} \end{cases} \quad (9)$$

$H_{cm}(j\omega)$ and $H_{dm}(j\omega)$ represent the common mode and the differential mode transfer function. Provided that $g_{m1} = g_{m2}$, $g_{mb1} = g_{mb2}$, $g_{m3} = g_{m4}$, $C_{gs1} = C_{gs2}$, $C_{gs3} = C_{gs4}$:

$$H_{dm}(j\omega) = \frac{(C_{T1}.R_s + 2.R_s.C_{bs1}).s + 2.R_s.g_{mb1} + 1}{\begin{array}{c}(2.C_{gs1}.R_s + 2.C_{bs1}.R_s + C_{T1}.R_s).s + \\ +2.R_s.(g_{m1} + g_{mb1}) + 1\end{array}} \quad (10)$$

$$H_{cm}(j\omega) = \frac{K.s\left(s + \frac{2.g_{m3}.C_{T1}.(g_{m1}+g_{mb1})}{K}\right)}{A.\left(s + \frac{2.g_{m3}}{C_{T2}+2.C_{gs3}}\right).\left(s + \frac{2.(g_{m1}+g_{mb1})}{C_{T1}+2.C_{gs1}}\right)} \quad (11)$$

Where A and K are respectively equal to:

$$A = g_{m1}.(C_{T1} + 2.C_{gs1})(C_{T2} + 2.C_{gs3}) \quad (12)$$

$$K = g_{m1}.C_{T1}.C_{T2} - 2.g_{mb1}.C_{gs1}.C_{T2} +$$
$$+2.(g_{m1} + g_{mb1}).C_{T1}.C_{gs3} + 2.g_{m1}.C_{bs1}.(C_{T1} + C_{T2}) \quad (13)$$

The input offset is now equal to:

$$V_{OS} = \frac{1}{V_{GS1} - V_t}\int_{-\infty}^{\infty} |H_{cm}(j\omega).V_{cm}(j\omega).$$
$$.H_{dm}(j\omega).V_{dm}(j\omega)|.cos\phi.d\omega \quad (14)$$

Where:

$$\phi = atan\left(\frac{Im\{H_{cm}(j\omega).V_{cm}(j\omega).H_{dm}(j\omega).V_{dm}(j\omega)\}}{Re\{H_{cm}(j\omega).V_{cm}(j\omega).H_{dm}(j\omega).V_{dm}(j\omega)\}}\right)$$

In order to minimize the input offset voltage, $|H_{cm}(j\omega)|$ must be reduced as much as possible, as was described in the previous paragraph (decreasing $|H_{dm}(j\omega)|$ is not an option, since this would equally reduce the differential voltage gain). This can be realized by setting K to zero, hereby warping the 2nd zero of $H_{cm}(j\omega)$ to very high frequencies. For K to be equal to zero, C_{gs1} must be equal to:

$$C_{gs1} = \frac{\begin{array}{c}g_{m1}.C_{T1}.C_{T2} + 2.g_{m1}.C_{bs1}.(C_{T1} + C_{T2}) \\ +2.C_{T1}.C_{gs3}.(g_{m1} + g_{mb1})\end{array}}{2.C_{T2}.g_{mb1}} \quad (15)$$

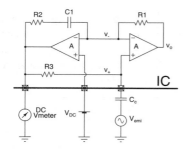

Fig. 3. Double-opamp measurement topology.

Two small on-chip gate-source capacitances are added between the gates and the sources of M1 and M2 in order to comply with relation (15) (C_{in} in Fig. 2). Unfortunately, integrated capacitors are subject to systematic offset, which typically introduces capacitance variations in the order of magnitude of +/-30%. This may significantly alter the total value of C_{gs1}, hereby increasing the offset voltage. For this reason, resistor R_s is connected between the sources of M1 and M2: this approach is widely used to linearize the input transconductance g_{m1}. Here, the main advantage of R_s is that the input offset voltage for high EMI frequencies is simplified to:

$$V_{OS} = \frac{1}{V_{GS1} - V_t} \int_{-\infty}^{\infty} | \frac{K}{A} \cdot \frac{C_{T1} + 2.C_{bs1}}{2.C_{gs1} + 2.C_{bs1} + C_{T1}} \cdot \\ .V_{cm}(j\omega).V_{dm}(j\omega)|.cos\phi.d\omega \quad (16)$$

Observe that since $H_{dm}(\infty)$ is small, the impact of the term K/A is heavily reduced at higher frequencies. Without R_s, $H_{dm}(j\omega)$ would be equal to 1, which would in turn increase the contribution K.

IV. MEASURING THE EMI INDUCED OFFSET

The EMI induced input offset voltage is maximal when the differential and common mode EMI components at the inputs are non-zero as well as in phase. Connecting the opamp as a voltage follower yields a differential input voltage which is close to zero for frequencies lying below or close to the gain-bandwidth (GBW) frequency, meaning that this setup can not be used to measure the EMI induced voltage for low EMI frequencies. The reason for this is situated in the negative feedback loop which is mandatory to preserve the correct DC biasing, but equally couples the EMI AC voltage. This shortcoming has been compensated by making the feedback loop DC only, as in the measurement structure which is depicted in Fig. 3 [6].

V. MEASUREMENTS

A test-IC containing four different circuits (Fig. 4) has been processed in the AMIS 0.35 μm CMOS technology (Fig. 5). The classic differential pair and the source-buffered differential pair have been used in the designs of two otherwise identical folded cascode opamps [3], labeled respectively A1 and A2: the design specifications are listed in Table I. The purpose of both opamps is to form a framework in which the EMI behavior of the classic differential pair versus the source-buffered differential pair is measured and compared.

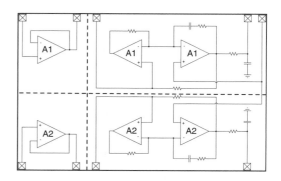

Fig. 4. Floorplan of the test-IC. A1 and A2 are folded cascode opamps, similar to each other except for the input differential pair: A1 contains the classic differential pair, A2 the source-buffered one. Both opamps are measured with the voltage follower configuration as well as with the double-opamp measurement setup.

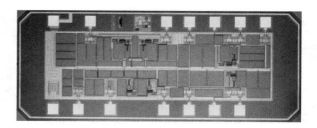

Fig. 5. Microphotograph of the test-IC.

a) for small EMI frequencies (below 200 MHz), the voltage follower measurement configuration can not be used to measure the correct EMI induced offset voltage (refer to section IV). Fig. 6 shows the EMI induced offset in function of the EMI frequency when an input EMI signal of 50 mV RMS in applied using the double opamp measurement setup: observe that the measured data fits the theoretical curve. Fig. 7 shows the EMI induced offset for an input EMI signal of 750 mV RMS using the double opamp measurement setup. This figure illustrates that the output of A1 (containing the classic differential pair) is heavily saturated, and confirms that the EMI induced offset progressively drops to zero for low EMI frequencies as predicted by the theoretical first order model.

b) for high EMI frequencies (above 200 MHz), the voltage follower measurement configuration is used. Fig. 8 shows the EMI induced offset for a small EMI signal of 50 mV RMS. Note the close correspondence between the theoretical curve and the measured curve starting from 200 MHz up to 800 MHz. For EMI frequencies lying below 200 MHz, the voltage follower configuration yields inaccurate results as predicted in section IV. For EMI frequencies exceeding 800 MHz, the parasitic effects of the PCB tracks, the bond wires and the ESD protections cause the measured curve to diverge from the theoretical first order model. Note that the offset of A2 is higher than what the theoretical model predicts: this stems from the approximations used in the first order model, as well as from inaccuracies in the modeling of the bulk capacitances. Fig. 9 shows the EMI induced offset for a large EMI input signal of 750 mV RMS. The maximal EMI induced input offset voltage corresponds to respectively 116 mV for A2

TABLE I
DESIGN SPECIFICATIONS

	A1 (classic diff. pair)	A2 (source-buff. diff. pair)
A_{DC}	54 dB	51 dB
GBW	36 MHz	24 MHz
g_{m1}	710 μS	710 μS
R_s	-	1.2 kΩ
P (including output buffers)	3.2 mW	3.5 mW

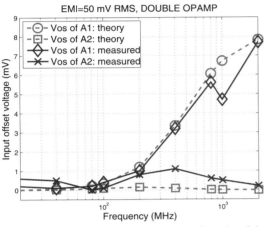

Fig. 6. Measurements using the double opamp configuration (injected EMI level = 50 mV RMS).

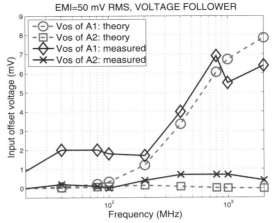

Fig. 8. Measurements using the voltage follower configuration (injected EMI level = 50 mV RMS).

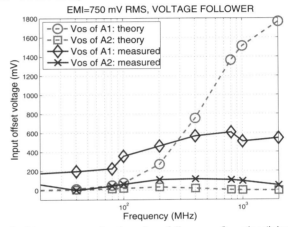

Fig. 9. Measurements using the voltage follower configuration (injected EMI level = 750 mV RMS).

(containing the proposed source-buffered topology) compared to 610 mV for A1 (with the classical differential pair). Observe that the measured EMI induced offset of A1 diverges from the theoretical curve because the output of the opamp is strongly saturated, meaning that the observed offset reduction achieved with the source-buffered differential pair is even higher than what the figures derived from Fig. 9 indicate.

VI. CONCLUSION

The EMI induced offset in a classic differential pair has been analyzed mathematically, and compared to the EMI induced offset in the source-buffered differential pair. The double-opamp measurement structure has been described, and has been shown to produce a much more correct offset measurement for low frequency EMI. The measurements of a test-IC presented in section V corroborate the mathematical deductions.

ACKNOWLEDGMENT

The authors wish to thank AMI Semiconductor Belgium for their cooperation, and the IWT (Institute for the Promotion of Innovation by Science and Technology) for partial funding.

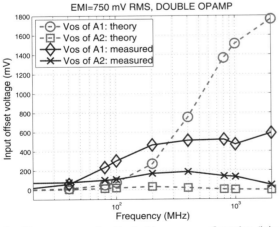

Fig. 7. Measurements using the double opamp configuration (injected EMI level = 750 mV RMS).

REFERENCES

[1] F. Fiori and P. S. Crovetti, "Nonlinear effects of radio-frequency interference in operational amplifiers", IEEE Trans. on Circuits and Systems I, vol. 49, no. 3, pp. 367-372, Mar. 2002.

[2] F. Fiori, "On the susceptibility of analog circuit to EMI", Proc. of Advances in Analog Circuit Design (AACD), Maastricht, the Netherlands, Apr. 2006.

[3] B. Razavi, Design of analog CMOS integrated circuits, McGraw-Hill, 2001.

[4] G. B. Arfken, H. J. Weber, Mathematical methods for physicists, international edition, 4th ed., Academic Press, ch. 14, 1995.

[5] J.-M. Redouté, M. Steyaert, "EMI resisting CMOS diff. pair structure", IEE Electronics Letters, vol. 42, no. 21, pp. 1217-1218, Oct. 2006.

[6] J.-M. Redouté, M. Steyaert, 'Active load for differential amplifier with high output impedance and reduced supply voltage', IEE Electronics Letters, vol. 44, no. 2, pp. 67-68, Jan. 2008.

Analog Signal Processing for a Class D Audio Amplifier in 65 nm CMOS Technology

Willem H. Groeneweg

NXP Semiconductors
BU Mobile & Personal, Cellular Systems
Zurich, CH-8048, Switzerland
Email: willem.groeneweg@nxp.com

Abstract☐ **Class D audio amplifiers provide high quality audio signals with very good efficiency. This makes them not only useful for high power home audio equipment and television, but also for battery powered portable devices. This paper shows details of an analog signal processor for a class D output stage which provides the audio output for a hands-free amplifier in mobile telephones. Two differential stages including output drivers have been successfully implemented on a combined baseband and audio chip using the thick oxide option of a 65 nm (gate width) CMOS process.**

I. INTRODUCTION

Class D amplifiers drive the loudspeaker with a pulse-width modulated (PWM) signal. The output stages are either switched on or off, with only a short transition in between. This switching mode provides a better efficiency than class AB analog output stages, which makes them useful in battery-powered systems. Hence, the lifetime of the batteries between charge cycles is increased.

The analog signal processing block described here is a part of a stereo class D audio amplifier integrated on a baseband- and audio chip for mobile telephone applications. The output stage for hands-free applications needs to provide considerable power (0.5 W_{RMS} or higher into 8 Ω load) at high efficiency.

The analog signal processor converts the analog input signal to a PWM signal for the class D output. The block consists of a second-order integrator loop which controls the output drivers to obtain lowest error residual with respect to the audio input signal. A second-order feedback loop is a straightforward implementation to obtain the required signal-to-noise and distortion performance. The building blocks of the analog signal processor are manufactured using the thick-oxide option (50 nm) of a 65 nm CMOS process.

The class D output stage itself consists of inverter stages with slew-rate control and transistor cascading, achieving an output swing which is twice the maximum drain-source voltage of the single elements. The output stage operates in differential ("BD", three-level) mode to achieve low dissipation and minimum electro-magnetic interference.

The goal of this paper is to show that specific requirements for IC designs in the mobile telephone market can be considered in the design. These requirements are: low supply current (for large stand-by time), small area (low cost, small package footprint), low-risk design (first time functionality, short time to market). The area of this signal processing part is equivalent to- or smaller than the area of the gain and feedback part of a class AB design.

In the next chapters, an overview of the system topology will be given, followed by more detailed descriptions of the building blocks. At the end of the paper, operation data and measurement results of the integrated chip will be given.

II. BLOCK DIAGRAM

A second-order integrator loop system is known from [1]. A study of several topologies led to a system with a feedback integrator at the input and a trans-conductance amplifier (OTA) as the second stage. The first integrator features a low impedance output stage which is able to drive the feedback capacitor. It was chosen because of its linearity and its high bandwidth. The second integrator offers high output impedance, low current consumption, simplicity and a small area.

The block diagram in Fig. 1 shows, that all circuits are operating in differential mode. A triangle clock waveform is used, which leads to "natural sampling" [2].

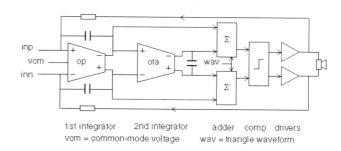

Figure 1. Block diagram of analog signal processing system for class D.

Here is an overview of the individual parts:

- The differential first integrator stage. The input signal enters via the pins "inp" and "inn" and can be applied as a current (from a DAC) or via series resistors. Input "vcm" is the common-mode reference voltage.

- The second stage is implemented as a C/gm integrator.

- The feed-forward analog adder stage secures the stability of the loop.

- Two comparators generate the PWM signal with the aid of a triangular clock waveform ("wav").

- The feedback path is implemented via resistors and an attenuator to the summing junctions of the first integrator.

III. CHOICE OF CAPACITOR TYPE

The first integrator needs a considerable amount of on-chip capacitance. Gate capacitors are chosen because of their high capacitance per area unit. Unfortunately, these capacitors are non-linear and would cause distortion.

To optimize linearity and sheet capacitance, three topologies were investigated. Fig. 2 shows the capacitance versus voltage across the gate. Each capacitor has the same area. The upper curve shows a single gate capacitor is named "gcap". Its capacitance reaches from 0.2 pF to 1.2 pF for a voltage range of -1.5 V to +1.5 V. This is inacceptable for our application.

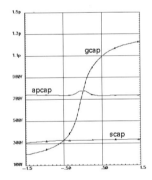

Figure 2. Capacitance versus gate voltage (+/- 1.5 V) for several configurations with the same area. The upper curve is a single gate-capacitor ("gcap"), the middle curve has two capacitors connected anti-parallel ("apcap") and the lower curve is a series connection ("scap").

The lower curve, "scap", shows two gate capacitors in series. The linearity is acceptable, but the drawback is the low capacitance of 0.3 pF.

The middle curve "apcap" shows two gate capacitors in anti-parallel configuration. The symmetry is good and the capacitance is 0.7 pF. The only drawback is the small "hump" in the middle of the curve. This means that the integration time-constant will be larger for a small (error) signal than for a large one. This has no consequences for the performance of the circuit. Hence, the "apcap" type was chosen to implement the integrator time-constants.

To optimize the chip area, a "fringe" (finger-type) metal capacitor was placed on top of each of the gate-capacitors and connected in parallel. This type of capacitor consists of a large number of adjacent narrow metal lines. The lines are alternately connected to the first- and the second node. With five metal layers, the "fringe" adds 20% to the capacitance per area.

IV. TIME CONSTANTS

The time-constants of the integrators determine the distortion, the supply rejection and the stability of the class D system.

For large-signal stability the slew rate of the first integrator must be lower than the slope of the triangle clock generator [1]. The time-constant (TC) is dimensioned for worst-case which means maximum supply voltage, minimum frequency, smallest capacitor and smallest resistor value.

Small-signal stability must be maintained by proper choice of the second integrator time-constant. The value is larger than for the first time-constant.

Equal (and large) signal amplitudes achieve the best signal-to noise ratio in a system. In system simulations, the signal at the output of the first integrator is about 3 times larger than that of the second integrator. In Fig. 3, a transformation is shown to equalize the adder input amplitudes.

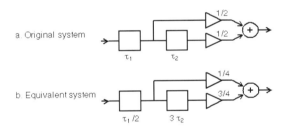

Figure 3. Time constant and gain transformation to achieve equal amplitude levels and lower first integrator timeconstant.

Fig. 3a shows the original system. Both adder inputs have the same "gain" of ½. To equalize the input signals, we need an adder gain of ¼ for the first input and ¾ for the second input. The gain changes can now be incorporated into the time-constants as in Fig. 3b. Gain is reversely proportional to the TC. We have now reduced the TC of the 1st integrator by a factor of two, which also reduces the chip area. The larger time-constant of the 2nd integrator can be solved by choosing a smaller gm, which reduces the current consumption.

V. FIRST INTEGRATOR

The gain block of the first integrator has differential inputs and differential outputs. Since the bidirectional type of class D modulation causes a large common-mode signal on the feedback to the first integrator input, the common-mode rejection of the stage shall be large. To achieve this, a number of points have to be considered:

- The bias current source for the PMOS input pair must be cascoded.

- The frequency range of the amplifier must be higher than the highest common-mode frequency.

- The DC working point shall be the most linear part of the input- and output range. Simulations showed that a DC point of 0.9 V and a range from 0.4 V to 1.4 V for the signal is optimum. The supply voltage is 2.65 V. We do not need elaborate rail-to-rail circuits.

- The common-mode feedback circuit must be very linear and accurate.

The simplified circuit schematic is shown in Fig. 4. The input pair is P1 and P2, the rest of the amplifier is formed by a folded cascode and a pair of complementary source-followers. These are necessary to give enough drive current into the capacitive (integrator) load and to the common-mode feedback resistors.

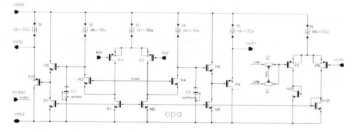

Figure 4. Circuit diagram of first integrator gain block.

The common-mode feedback circuit (CMF) uses a dedicated amplifier, at the right side of Fig. 4 (P5 and P6). Both the differential path and the common-mode path are one-stage circuits, and can both be compensated at the folded cascode output by capacitors to ground (C1 and C2).

The current consumption of the first integrator (208 µA) is the highest of all the blocks since it needs to operate at high frequencies.

The time-constant is programmed in parallel with the clock frequency as shown in Table I. The clock can be chosen for optimum overall efficiency. The resistors of the time-constants track with the resistor that determines the carrier frequency.

TABLE I.   GAIN-BANDWIDTH PRODUCT OF INTEGRATORS

Carrier frequency	1st Integrator GBP	2nd Integrator GBP
150 kHz	115 kHz	13.7 kHz
225 kHz	173 kHz	20.6 kHz
335 kHz (default)	258 kHz	30.6 kHz
500 kHz	384 kHz	45.7 kHz

VI. SECOND INTEGRATOR

The 2nd integrator is a differential C/gm type. The time-constant consists of the 1/gm output resistance with an anti-parallel gate-cap load. The advantages of this configuration

are small current consumption (11 µA), inherent stability (compensated by the TC) and high output resistance to get low capacitance area.

The circuit is shown in Fig. 5. The inputs are PMOS transistors (P1, P2) with degeneration (P3, P4) to achieve a linear gm range. The CMF circuit is a resistor chain that senses the average DC voltage and a feedback amplifier that controls the input PMOS current sources.

The time-constants are given in Table I. The tolerance is not affected too much by the gm, since gm tends to track with the gate capacitance via the oxide thickness.

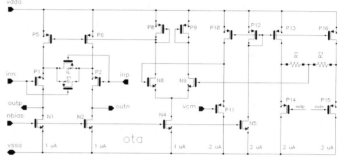

Figure 5. Circuit diagram of second integrator gain block.

VII. CLOCK GENERATOR

A symmetrical pulse-width modulation needs a triangle waveform as clock reference. A dedicated free-running triangle generator was chosen because it has accurate amplitude, a stable DC level and a frequency that tracks with the integrator TC. The tracking feature allows to design the time-constants with a smaller tolerance margin, which saves silicon area. An alternative system uses an integrated rectangle with the drawback that the amplitude depends on the TC.

The triangle generator is shown in Fig. 6. A cascoded current mirror (P3–P6) sources a stable current into a capacitor (C1) until an upper comparator threshold (1.3 V) is reached. From that moment on, another current mirror (N4, N5, N8, N9) with double current draws current out of the capacitor to ground until the lower threshold is reached. The cycle repeats.

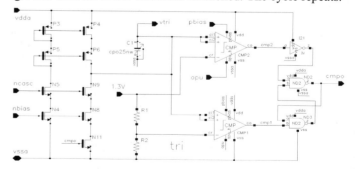

Figure 6. Triangle generator schematic.

VIII. ADDER AND COMPARATOR

To generate the PWM signal, two feed-forward adders drive two comparators which compare the adder signals with the triangle waveform. To save the adder stages, a comparator with three inputs was designed. Both feed-forward signals can be directly applied to the comparator inputs.

The circuit is shown in Fig. 7. The inputs are P1/P2 and P3/P4. One pair has a different size and current (factor 3) to provide the gain difference as described in chapter IV. The NMOS loads are current mirrors, which are cross-coupled to achieve voltage gain in the first stage. The second stage drives _____two cascaded inverters.

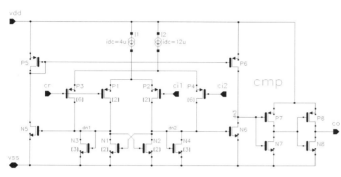

Figure 7.   Comparator and adder stage circuit diagram.

IX.   Gain Programming

A number of programmable gain settings are provided to adapt the input sensitivity to the signal source- and customer requirements. The gain range is from – 30 dB to +15 dB with a step size of 3 dB.

The circuit uses a number of programmable resistors around the class D block as shown in Fig. 8. R1a and R1b are in the input path, R3 is the feedback path. R4 and R5 serve to reduce the voltage swing from the class D output (5 Vpp) to a lower level. R3 must be fixed since it determines the first time-constant. With R2, the input voltage can be attenuated to achieve the low gain settings.

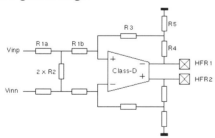

Figure 8.   Programmable gain resistor network.

X.   Test Chip Data

The class D amplifier has been placed on an audio and baseband chip. The first samples were functional. Measurement results are in Table II and mostly show pleasing results. Analysis has shown that we can take steps to improve the circuits further:

- Increase the output power above 600 mW and improve efficiency to 80% by reducing the metal resistance in power connections.

- Improve the power-supply rejection by 10 dB with better layout for matching of the input resistor network.

TABLE II.   Results and Data

Subject	Result	Unit
Power supply voltage (for analog signal processor)	2.65	V
Load resistance	8	Ω
Output power at THD = 1% and VDD = 3.6 V	530	mW
Efficiency at THD = 1%	76	%
Idle current consumption	430	μA
Input noise voltage (A-weighted)	33	μV
Signal to noise ratio (Pout = 0.5 W)	96.5	dB
Clock frequency (default value, used for measurements)	316	kHz
Harmonic distortion at Pout = 250 mW	0.025	%
Power supply rejection	63	dB
Signal processor area	0.157	mm^2
Class D output stage area	0.121	mm^2

XI.   Conclusions

An on-chip class D audio amplifier for hands-free applications in mobile telephones is feasible in the thick-oxide option of a 65 nm CMOS process.

The analog signal processing part has been described to some detail in this paper. For each block of the system, a low-power and/or area saving solution was found and implemented.

Measurements at the finished chip show encouraging results. Especially the distortion and signal-to-noise ratio have values, which are comparable to- or even better than comparable output stages for mobile telephones.

Acknowledgment

Thanks to Bernard Pilloud for the theory and measurements, to Marco Berkhout who gave valuable hints and to Bas Putter for the time-constant transformation.

References

[1]   Marco Berkhout, "An Integrated 200 W Class-D Audio Amplifier", IEEE Journal of Solid-State Circuits, Vol. 38, No. 7, July 2003.

[2]   B. Forejt, V. Rentala, J. D. Arteaga and G. Burra, "A 700+mW Class D Design with Direct Battery Hookup in a 90-nm Process", IEEE Journal of Solid-State Circuits, Vol. 40, No. 9, September 2005.

[3]   T. Ge, J. S. Chang, W. Shu and M. T. Tan, "Modeling and Analysis of PSRR in Analog PWM Class D Amplifiers", IEEE ISCAS 2006.

[4]   Ronan A. R. van der Zee and Ed van Tuijl, "A power-Efficient Audio Amplifier Combining Switching and Linear Techniques", IEEE Journal of Solid-State Circuits, Vol. 34, No. 7, July 1999.

Reduction of VCO Phase Noise through Forward Substrate Biasing of Switched MOSFETs

Domagoj Šiprak [1] , Marc Tiebout [2] and Peter Baumgartner [1]

[1] Infineon Technologies AG
Am Campeon 1-12, D-85779 Neubiberg, Germany
E-mail: domagoj.siprak@infineon.com

[2] Infineon Technologies Austria AG
Siemens Str. 2, A-9500 Villach, Austria
E-mail: marc.tiebout@infineon.com

Abstract□ **A reduction of close to carrier phase noise of a 14 GHz PMOS VCO is presented by forward substrate biasing the MOSFETs providing the oscillation in the VCO. This finding is explained by the physical effect of significantly reduced 1/f noise in transistors operated under large signal excitation and forward substrate bias. Measurements of MOSFET 1/f noise under switched gate bias condition and VCO phase noise are presented to explain the dependency between reduced 1/f noise and reduced VCO phase noise with forward substrate bias.**

I. INTRODUCTION

Recently advances in radio-frequency (RF) CMOS technology have opened the extensive use of CMOS for RF circuits. CMOS has replaced bipolar technologies in many RF applications due to its capability for system on chip integration. However, one main limitation of CMOS is the high 1/f noise compared to bipolar devices. 1/f noise limits area and power reduction of RF and analog circuits which is especially important for large volume and mobile applications. So methods for 1/f noise reduction are of special interest in CMOS RF and analog circuit design. Voltage controlled oscillators (VCO) are key building blocks of RF transceivers and the VCO phase noise affects strongly the system performance. Close to carrier phase noise is strongly influenced by the 1/f noise of CMOS devices. 1/f noise is known to be reduced in MOSFET operated under large signal excitation and was under extensive research in recent years [1]. These investigations did not include the effect of substrate biasing on 1/f noise in devices operated under large signal excitation but is described in companion paper [2]. In the following a reduction of close to carrier phase noise of a 14 GHz VCO will be reported by reducing the 1/f device noise of its PMOS core transistors operated under large signal excitation and forward substrate bias.

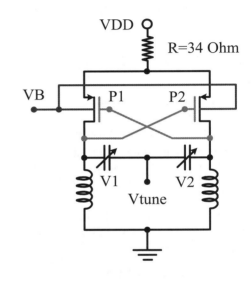

Fig. 1 VCO schematic.

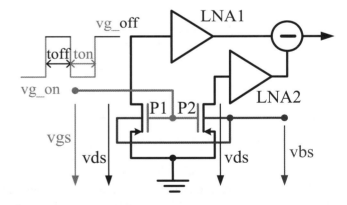

Fig. 2 1/f device noise measurement setup.

326

II. VCO DESIGN AND MEASUREMENT SETUP

VCO design has been performed in a 0.13 μm RF CMOS technology from Infineon Technologies AG with a top thick metal option [3]. Fig.1 shows the VCO schematic with PMOS core transistors P1&2 having an explicit bulk connection pad. The bulk pad is ac coupled on chip to ground by a blocking cap and 50Ω resistive termination. The tail current of the VCO is provided via a poly silicon resistor R instead of a transistor to avoid the 1/f noise contribution of the tail current source. VCO LC tank consist of a symmetrical coil and accumulation type varactors V1&2 (n-gate over n-substrate) for frequency tuning. Phase noise was measured using a down conversion mixer and Europtest PN9000 equipment (delay line method). For phase noise measurements the VCO was supplied with batteries. Fig. 3 shows the die photo of the VCO.

1/f device noise under switching gate bias excitation was measured with the setup shown in Fig. 2. The drain current noise of transistors in a differential pair (P1&2) having common gate, source and substrate connections is amplified by two low noise amplifiers and the out coming signals are subtracted. This arrangement cancels out the large signal perturbation due to the switching gate signal and adds the noise powers of the two transistors. The gate terminal of the test structure is terminated by a 50Ω resistor (not shown in Fig. 2) to avoid signal reflections at the gate.

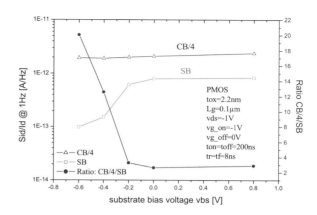

Fig. 4 Sid/Id @ 1Hz vs. substrate to source voltage vbs for constant (CB)and switched (SB) gate bias.
Sid/Id for CB is divided by 4 to be compared to SB [1, 2].

Reference of abbreviations:
Lg: transistor gate length, tox: gate oxide thickness,
vds, vgs, vbs: drain, gate and bulk to source voltage,
vg_on and vg_off: gate on- and off-voltage,
ton and toff: gate voltage on- and off-time,
tr and tf: rising and falling times of gate pulse

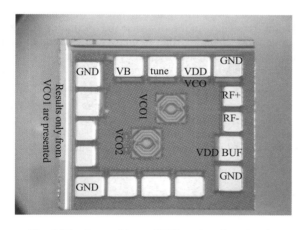

Fig. 3 Die photo with two VCOs using shared pads.

III. 1/f DEVICE NOISE MEASUREMENT RESULTS

Fig. 4 reports the measured 1/f device noise power spectral density Sid at 1Hz normalized to the drain current Id of the transistor in the on-state with respect to the substrate to source voltage vbs for constant (CB) and switched gate bias (SB) conditions. It can be clearly seen that 1/f noise is only weakly dependent on substrate bias under constant gate bias while a strong dependence exists for the noise measured under large signal switching excitation.

Fig.5 shows the frequency dependence of the normalized 1/f noise power spectral density Sid/Id for CB condition with zero substrate bias and with substrate forward back bias (FBB) as well as for switched gate bias (SB) condition with zero substrate bias and forward substrate back bias. The noise power as well as the slope of the curve is reduced in the case of forward substrate bias under switched gate bias condition.

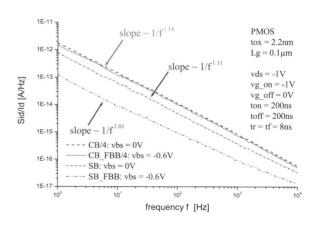

Fig.5 Sid/Id vs. frequency for constant and switched gate bias.

IV. VCO MEASUREMENT RESULTS

VCO key figures of merit like current consumption Idd, oscillation frequency and phase noise versus supply voltage VDD, bulk voltage VB and tuning voltage Vtune are summarized in Tab. 1.

Fig. 6 shows the measured VCO phase noise versus offset frequency from carrier for different VCO bulk pad voltages and zero volt tuning voltage. It can be seen that by changing the bulk voltage into the direction of forward bias phase noise in the 30 dBc/Hz region and corner frequency fc separating 30 and 20 dBc/Hz regions is reduced.

Fig. 7 shows the measured VCO phase noise versus offset frequency from carrier for a tuning voltage of 1.2V and two different VCO bulk pad voltages. The dependency of phase noise on bulk pad voltage is qualitatively the same for low and high tuning voltages.

TABLE I
MEASURED POWER, FREQUENCY AND PHASE NOISE
OF VCO VERSUS BIAS VOLTAGES

VDD [V]	VB [V]	Vtune [V]	Idd [mA]	Fre-quency [GHz]	Phase noise @ 10kHz Offset [dB]	Phase noise @ 5MHz Offset [dB]
1.55	1.5	0	10.5	14.1	-47.0	-123.4
1.55	1.5	1.2	9.6	15.43	-44.9	-122.6
1.55	0	0	18.3	13.67	-51.4	-115.7
1.55	0	1.2	18.1	15.08	-50.5	-118.8
1.55	0.2	1.2	13.6	15.16	-48	-121
1.55	0.4	1.2	11.2	15.23	-46.7	-122.6

Frequency dependence of VCO phase noise in Fig. 6/7 and 1/f device noise in Fig. 5 show both a smaller slope in direction towards a stronger forward substrate bias. The correlated behavior of phase noise on the one hand and 1/f device noise on the other hand could origin in both cases from the substrate bias influence on 1/f noise. But as the slope of 1/f noise vs. frequency of PMOS devices is also reduced for a reduced gate to source voltage the change in phase noise slope could be also explained by a reduced oscillation amplitude.

Fig. 8 reports the dependency of phase noise on oscillation frequency for two different methods of changing the oscillation frequency. In the first case the oscillation frequency is changed by changing the tuning voltage Vtune. In the second case the oscillation frequency is changed by changing the bulk voltage VB.

The measurement in Fig. 8 shows a significant sensitivity of phase noise on bulk voltage VB whereas the sensitivity of phase noise with respect to tuning voltage Vtune is much smaller. In particular, phase noise at same oscillation frequency is smaller for a stronger forward substrate bias.

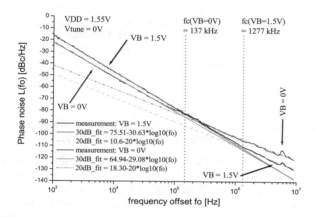

Fig. 6 VCO phase noise vs. offset frequency for a low tuning voltage of 0V.

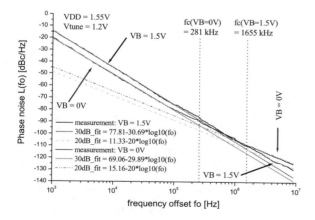

Fig. 7 VCO phase noise vs. offset frequency for a high tuning voltage of 1.2V.

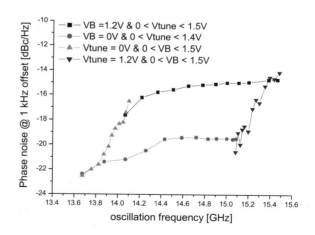

Fig. 8 VCO phase noise vs. oscillation frequency.

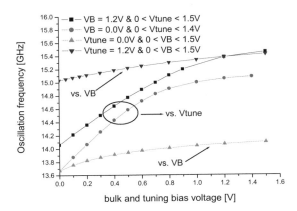

Fig. 9 Oscillation frequency vs. bulk and tuning voltage.

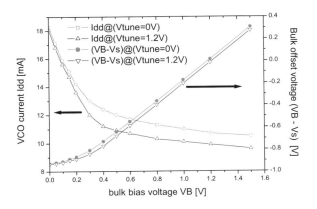

Fig. 10 VCO current Idd and offset voltage between bulk and source vs. bulk pad voltage VB.

Fig. 9 shows the dependency of the oscillation frequency on tuning voltage and bulk pad voltage. The bulk voltage has a smaller influence on the oscillation frequency compared to the tuning voltage. The sensitivity of the oscillation frequency on bulk voltage increases with lower bulk voltage due to the increased source and drain junction capacitance contribution to the total LC tank capacitance with a lower bulk bias.

Fig. 10 reports also the dependency of VCO current consumption Idd on the bulk voltage for two tuning voltages of 0V and 1.2V. The current consumption increases for a stronger forward substrate bias because the threshold voltage of the PMOS transistors is lowered and additionally the transistor junction diodes are forward biased.

Besides Fig. 10 reports on the right y-axis also the effective voltage difference (VB-Vs) between the bulk and the source of the transistor which can be calculated from the drain current Idd, the resistor R in Fig. 1 and the supply voltage VDD according the equation Vs=VDD-Idd*R. From these curves it can be seen that the effective bulk to source voltage changes only slightly when the transistor junction diodes get forward biased. By circuit simulation it is verified that the gate voltage at transistors P1 and P2 is always lower than the source voltage. So the effective gate to bulk voltage is even less than the reported source to bulk voltage. In [2] it is shown that the noise reduction is smaller with a reduced gate to forward bulk voltage during the transistor off-state. As the forward substrate bias lowers the threshold voltage also a smaller gate to source voltage is needed to switch the transistor off. For a quantitative comparison of 1/f noise reduction on device level and phase noise reduction in the VCO one needs to regard this voltage offsets in the VCO.

Another important aspect for a quantitative determination of the phase noise reduction through the forward substrate bias concurred switched bias noise effect is the duty cycle between the time when the transistors P1 and P2 are in inversion and the time when the transistors are switched off. The noise reduction will be the stronger the longer the off-time is compared to the on-time [4].

The increase in phase noise far from carrier for the extreme forward substrate bias condition (VB=0V) in the measurements of Fig. 6 and Fig. 7 can be explained by the operation of the MOS transistors P1 and P2 in Fig. 1 in triode region due to a reduced threshold voltage through forward substrate bias. Operation in triode region reduces the quality factor of the LC tank and leads to increased phase noise far and close to carrier [5]. The operation in triode region due to reduced threshold voltage through forward substrate bias could be mitigated by using a smaller transistor gate width. The increase in phase noise far from carrier can have its origin additionally also in the shot noise of the forward biased substrate diode of the parasitic bipolar transistor formed by the source, substrate and drain of the MOS transistor.

V. CONCLUSION

In this work it is clearly demonstrated that strong 1/f noise reduction in switched MOSFETS under forward substrate bias, observed on device level, can be exploited in circuits. In particular, the effect observed at low frequencies on device level is effective also in high frequency circuits like the 14 GHz VCO presented in this work. Good agreement between 1/f device noise under switched bias conditions and close to carrier phase noise of a 14 GHz VCO has been found.

REFERENCES

[1] A.P. van der Wel et al. , "Low-Frequency Noise Phenomena in Switched MOSFETs," IEEE J. Solid-State Circuits, vol. 42 (3), pp. 540-550, March 2007.

[2] D. Šiprak, N. Zanolla, M. Tiebout, P. Baumgartner, and C. Fiegna, "Reduction of Low-Frequency Noise in MOSFETs under Switched Gate and Substrate Bias," Proc. ESSDERC/ESSCIRC 2008, in press.

[3] T. Schiml et al. , "A 0.13μm CMOS Platform with Cu/Low-k Inter-conects for System On Chip Applications," VLSI 2001, pp. 101-102.

[4] J.S. Kolhatkar, Ph.D. thesis, University of Twente, 2005.

[5] D. Miyashita et al. , "A Phase Noise Minimization of CMOS VCOs over Wide Tuning Range and Large PVT Variations," Proc. CICC 2005, pp. 583-586, 2005.

A WiMedia UWB Receiver with a Synthesizer

Mikko Kaltiokallio, Ville Saari, Tapio Rapinoja, Kari Stadius, Jussi Ryynänen, Saska Lindfors, Kari Halonen

Department of Micro and Nano Sciences

Helsinki University of Technology

Espoo, Finland

Email: mka@ecdl.tkk.fi

Abstract—**This paper describes a direct-conversion receiver for WiMedia UWB applications. The receiver consists of separate BG1 and BG3 LNAs including a 2.4-GHz notch filter, quadrature mixers, a base-band gm-C low-pass filter with variable gain, and a fast-hopping synthesizer. The UWB receiver is targeted for a mobile handset and therefore special emphasis has been placed on the reduction of interferers. The receiver achieves 60-dB gain, noise figure less than 6.2 dB, LO settling time of less than 3 ns and DC current consumption of 137 mA from a 1.2-V supply for BG1 operation mode. The chip was fabricated using 65-nm standard CMOS process.**

I. INTRODUCTION

Ultra wideband (UWB) communications is targeted to provide short-range high data-rate communications for mobile and peripheral devices e.g. mobile multimedia terminals, laptops and digital cameras. This calls for low-cost, low-power single-chip CMOS solutions that can be easily integrated into the consumer devices.

The active research during the past few years has produced few implementations of UWB receivers that can be found from [1-3]. The latest ECMA-368 standard defines the frequency range of 3.1-10.6 GHz for ultra-wideband (UWB) devices [4]. According to the ECMA-368 this frequency range is further divided into 14 sub-bands each with bandwidth of 528 MHz. This paper describes a complete receiver design for a mobile terminal. The receiver includes a dual-band front-end, an active adjustable-gain 240-MHz base-band filter, and a fast-hopping synthesizer. Circuits are integrated on the same chip using 65-nm CMOS process. The receiver covers band groups (BG) 1 and 3 consisting of bands with center frequencies of 3432, 3960, 4488 MHz and 6600, 7128, 7656 MHz, respectively. Due to the wide operational band UWB receivers are susceptible to strong interferers caused by other radios within the same mobile terminal or by close-by radios. Therefore close attention has been paid on the possible interference scenarios for a mobile terminal. To suppress the most difficult interferers, a 2.4-GHz notch filter and a selective 5th-order base-band filter have been included in the receiver. A transmitter was also integrated on the same chip, but it is not reported here because the design was carried out by our partner.

The paper is organized as follows: in Section II the receiver topology is described. In Sections III-V are the RF front-end, the fast-hopping synthesizer and the gm-C base-band filter, respectively. Finally, in Section VI are the measurement results and in Section VII are the conclusions.

II. RECEIVER

The block diagram of the implemented direct-conversion receiver is shown in Fig. 1. The input of the receiver utilizes a dual-input scheme for the two band-groups covered by the receiver. With the dual-input, the matching and the gain responses of the two signal paths can be separately optimized and thus higher interferers can be tolerated. Moreover, with dual-input the functionality of at least one of the band groups

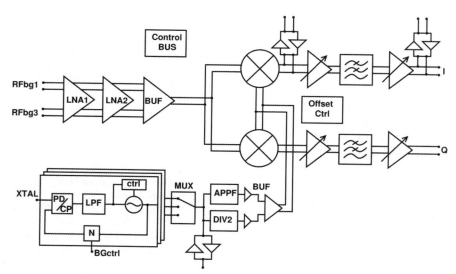

Figure 1. Receiver block diagram with test inputs and outputs.

is more likely to be guaranteed under difficult interference conditions. The RF front-end utilizes separate signal paths up to the buffer driving the mixers. Current-steering DACs at the base-band input control the DC offset injected into the base-band filter. The local oscillator (LO) architecture uses three parallel phase-locked loops (PLL) to generate the LO tones for the sub-sequent bands inside corresponding band group and a multiplexer (MUX) for selecting one of these tones for quadrature generation circuits. Additionally, there are test inputs and outputs for stand-alone measurements of different circuit blocks, as is depicted in Fig. 1. The LO quadrature generation circuits utilize a dual signal path where a divide-by-two (DIV2) circuit is used for BG1 and an active two-stage poly-phase filter (APPF), where the resistors are replaced by transconductance elements, is used for BG3. This quadrature generation scheme enables to cover both band groups 1 and 3 with only one VCO in each PLL. Additional buffering circuits are used to amplify and drive the LO signal to the mixers. The low quality passive components available in the process degrade passive PPF performance, therefore an aggressive design choise to use the APPF was made. Unfortunately the APPF did not perform as simulated and thus measurement results of BG3 are limited to a gain plot.

III. FRONT-END

The wide bandwidth of the UWB radio poses challenges in the front-end design. Wide input matching bandwidth is difficult to achieve without trading it to other performance metrics. Additionally, the wide reception band leads to degraded out-of-band filtering of the interfering signals and thus the linearity requirements of the receiver become more stringent. Despite pre-filtering, these interferers (GSM900, 2.4-GHz WLAN, etc.) can corrupt UWB reception due to intermodulation or desensitization. This situation is relaxed with BG3 because of the less congested spectrum.

The inductively degenerated common source LNA has been previously extensively used. However, in order to achieve appropriate matching for a UWB radio a feedback or a parallel common-gate stage are used as has been seen in previously published LNAs [2,3]. The topology we have chosen for the BG1 LNA relies on two feedbacks from the first stage and second stage loads to provide sufficient matching even with the additional parasitic capacitance introduced from packaging, as is depicted in Fig. 2. Furthermore, with the double feedback the degeneration inductor could be omitted from the LNA. This saves die area and enables compact layout in the dual-input configuration. Cascode configuration has been utilized in the amplifier stages to achieve higher gain. The differential signal paths are crossed in the LNA so that negative feedback is maintained, because both amplifier stages invert the signal phase. In the first stage a shunt-peeked load provides gain peaking while the feedback enables the use of only one inductor in this topology. There is also a LC-notch filter that is used to attenuate interferers around 2.4 GHz. The filter utilizes a cross-coupled pair to enhance the Q-value of the notch. All the resistors in the LNA were made tunable with

switches so that process variations could be tolerated. The BG3 LNA also uses a two-stage feedback topology.

Super source-follower buffers after the LNAs are used to drive the mixers [5]. The BG3 buffer uses an additional inductor in the load to provide additional gain peaking. The output signals of the buffers are directly connected to the sources of the double-balanced Gilbert-cell mixer switches. Compared to a typical high-impedance input this low-impedance node suffers less from the parasitic capacitance of the two signal paths resulting in near-flat frequency response. A current source and common-mode feedback circuitry is used to bias the switches and set the DC output voltage level of the mixer load for the base-band filter.

IV. SYNTHESIZER

Three parallel PLL units are used for generating the subsequent LO frequencies for BG1 and BG3. At a time, one of the bands, in the active band group, is selected with a multiplexer. Furthermore, we are also covering band group 6 (7656, 8184, 8712 MHz), which is a Japanese replacement of BG3. Compared to alternative methods, such as SSB mixing or ping-pong PLLs, this approach offers better spectral purity [6]. Inherently, multiplexer-based multi-tone frequency synthesizer offers very high hopping speed. The PLLs have large tuning range allowing us to cover band group three and six, as well as double frequency of band group one. For instance, the third PLL provides frequencies 7656 MHz (BG3), 8712 MHz (BG6), and 8976 MHz (2x BG1). In our preceding work [6] both bands BG1 and BG3 were covered with corresponding VCO. Therefore, prior work included six coils and occupied 1.9-mm^2 die area. Now, we have only

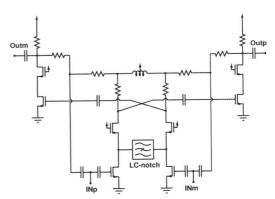

Figure 2. BG1 LNA1 & LNA2 schematic.

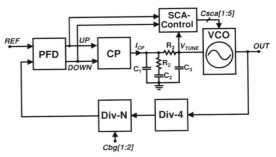

Figure 3. PLL schematic.

three small coils, and die area is reduced to 0.6 mm^2. The structure of a single PLL is depicted in Figure 3. A NMOS-core LC-VCO has 5-bit switched capacitor array (SCA) for coarse frequency tuning, and fine tuning is achieved with a differential accumulation-mode MOS-varactor. In order to lock the PLL properly, the right tuning curve has to be found by switching the capacitors in the SCA. An automated control loop compares VCO tuning voltage to high and low reference using two comparators. Comparator outputs provide signals for a state machine. A lock detector is used to disable curve switching when PLL is in locked condition. The PLL includes a third-order passive loop filter, and with nominal current setting (50 µA) in charge pump, the loop bandwidth is 500 kHz. We are using a 66-MHz reference frequency, and a divide-by-four prescaler. The programmable divider is based on an asynchronous counter, which provides high operation speed with low power consumption.

V. BASE-BAND FILTER

The implemented 5th-order low-pass filter, shown in Fig. 4, is designed to fulfill the performance requirements of the analog base-band circuit between the constant-gain RF front-end and a low resolution 5-bit analog-to-digital converter, similar as in [7]. The passband edge frequency of the filter is 240 MHz. A 5th-order Chebyshev prototype has been selected to suppress interference from concurrently operating radio transmitters in the vicinity or within the same terminal. The real pole of the selected odd-order prototype has been extracted from the filter transfer function and realized at the filter input with the passive load components of the preceding down-conversion mixer as shown in Fig. 4. Thus, the out-of-band linearity of the filter increases considerably. The complex pole pairs of the transfer function have been realized with a 4th-order continuous-time leapfrog filter, in which gm-C technique with pseudo-differential transconductors has been used.

The variable gain range of the filter is 34 dB to achieve the desired full-scale level of the ADC. For an accurate filter frequency response, the transconductances and the parasitic capacitances of the filter building blocks are not allowed to change with different gain settings. The transconductance of the first transconductor Gm1, in Fig. 4, is the only exception and therefore, Gm1 has five 6-dB gain steps. An output buffer designed to drive a 5-bit ADC has been implemented at the filter output, as shown in Fig. 4. The fine 1-dB gain steps from 0 dB to 5 dB are accomplished by switching the resistive load of the output buffer. The DC-offset of the receiver is compensated with a 6-bit current-steering digital-to-analog converter (IDAC) at the filter input.

The corner frequencies of the passive pole and the 4th-order leapfrog filter are controlled separately with 5-bit switched capacitor matrices. The separate controls are required, because the corner frequency of the passive pole is dependent on the source resistance, i.e. the load of the preceding mixer, while the corner frequency of the leapfrog

filter is proportional to the transconductance of the transconductors.

VI. MEASUREMENTS

The chip was fabricated using a standard 1.2-V 65-nm CMOS process and it was bonded directly onto a PCB. The active area of the design is 2.7 mm^2, which includes the reported blocks, control bus, decoupling capacitance and interconnect wiring. The chip photograph is shown in Fig. 5.

The measured frequency responses of the receiver in BG1 and BG3 mode are presented in Fig. 6. The gain has been measured from the base-band filter output and thus the effects of the RF front-end, base-band filter and LO generation are all visible in the figure. The gain level of the first sub-band in BG3 is already 10 dB lower than for BG1 which indicates that the LO signal amplitude is not sufficient for the mixers. This was also verified in the reception band where the operational band of the divider and the APFF overlap. Additionally, there is a 15 dB difference in gain of the three sub-bands which suggests that the frequency response of the LO path droops heavily. The BG1 gain of the RF front-end is 60±1 dB. The gain variation was slightly higher than expected on the basis of the simulation results. The most probable cause of this is the PCB board and modeling of the RF input. Matching of the BG1 input covers a frequency range from 2.6 to 4.9 GHz with the PCB board. The measured noise figures of the receiver are 6.2, 6.1 and 5.7 dB for sub-bands 1, 2 and 3, respectively. By excluding the noise from the active base-band the receiver noise figure decreases by 1 dB. The measured input compression point (ICP) of the receiver is -32.5 dBm (referred to a 100Ω source impedance) with a 4-GHz test tone and minimum base-band gain. The in-band IIP2 and IIP3 of the receiver are +15.5 and -19 dBm with maximum gain, respectively. The ICP with a

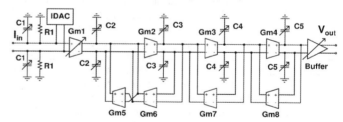

Figure 4. Base-band filter schematic.

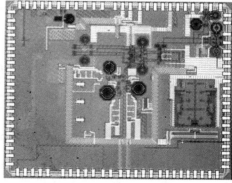

Figure 5. Chip photograph.

2.4-GHz blocker is -28 dBm measured with maximum base-band gain. The measured IIP3 for 880 and 2420 MHz interferers with 15 db power level difference is -9 dBm which is 10 dB better than without the notch filter. The total current consumption of the receiver in BG1 mode is 137 mA.

The frequency synthesizer is able to provide the BG1, BG3 and BG6 tones for the LO-generator circuitry. The measured settling time between the sub-sequent bands is less than 3 ns with a 3-MHz hopping rate. A typical measured phase noise of the PLL is depicted in Fig. 7. The in-band phase noise level is -86 dBc/Hz and correspondingly, the out-of-band level at 1 MHz is -94 dBc/Hz. As can be seen from the phase noise plot the noise floor of the measurement equipment limits the phase noise result at frequencies higher than 5 MHz offset from the carrier. The measurement results are collected in Table 1.

VII. CONCLUSIONS

A WiMedia UWB receiver with an active base-band filter and a synthesizer was described. The receiver operates in BG1 mode with 60-dB maximum gain and NF better than 6.2 dB. The settling time of the on-chip synthesizer is less than 3 ns with in-band phase noise of -86 dBc/Hz. The current consumption is 137 mA from a 1.2-V supply. The presented design cannot be easily compared to other UWB implementations because of different target applications and extent of realizations. However, comparing this design to recent papers [2, 3] it is observed that the performance metrics given by BG1 are comparable to existing ones.

ACKNOWLEDGEMENTS

The authors would like to thank Nokia, Finish Funding Agency for Technology and Innovation (TEKES), Nokia Foundation, Olli Viitala, Arttu Uusitalo and Janne Kukkonen for their contribution.

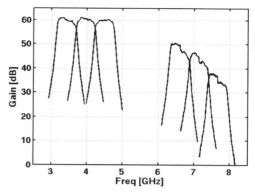

Figure 6. BG1 and BG3 gain response.

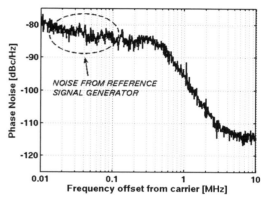

Figure 7. PLL phase noise.

TABLE I. MEASUREMENT RESULTS

	Band Group 1		
RF Band	3168-3696 MHz	3696-4224 MHz	4224-4752 MHz
Gain max/min	58.5/24.5 dB	59/25 dB	59/25 dB
NF	6.2 dB	6.1 dB	5.7 dB
S11 < -10dB	2.6…4.9 GHz		
ICP	-32.5 dBm@100Ω		
In-band IIP2	+15.5 dBm@100Ω		
In-band IIP3	-19 dBm@100Ω		
Blocker IIP3*	-9 dBm@100Ω		
Freq. Hopping	< 3 ns		
Phase Noise — In-band	-86 dBc/Hz		
Phase Noise — Out-of-band	-94 dBc/Hz @ 1 MHz		
Spurious Tones	-48 dBc @ 66 MHz		
Supply	1.2 V		
DC current	35 (RF) + 60 (BB) + 42 (LO) = 137 mA		
Technology	65 nm CMOS		
Active Area	2.7 mm²		

*Measured with 2420 and 880 MHz test signals at 15 dB power difference.

REFERENCES

[1] Razavi, B., et. al., "A 0.13 um CMOS UWB transceiver," IEEE Solid State Circuits Conference, pp. 216-217, 2005.

[2] Bergervoet, J., Harish, K., Lee, S., Leenaerts, D., van de Beek, R., van der Weide, R., Roovers, R., "A WiMedia-Complient UWB Tranceiver in 65nm CMOS," IEEE Solid State Circuits Conference, pp. 112-113, 2007.

[3] Sandner, C., et. al., "A WiMedia/MBOA-Compliant CMOS RF Transceiver for UWB," IEEE Journal of Solid-State Circuits, 41 (12), pp. 2787-2794, 2006.

[4] ECMA-368 Standard, "High Rate Ultra Wideband PHY and MAC Standard", www.ecma-international.org/publications/files/ECMA-ST/ECMA-368.pdf, 2007.

[5] Kaukovuori, J., Ryynänen, J., Halonen, K., "A dual-band direct-conversion RF front-end for WiMedia UWB receiver," IEEE Radio Frequency Integrated Circuits Symposium, pp. 211-214, June 2007.

[6] Stadius, K., Rapinoja, T., Kaukovuori, J., Ryynänen, J., Halonen, K., "Multi-Tone Fast Frequency Hopping Synthesizer for UWB Radio," IEEE Transactions on Microwave Theory and Techniques, 55 (8), pp. 1633-1641, 2007.

[7] Viitala, O., Lindfors, S., Halonen, K., "A 5-bit 1-GS/s Flash-ADC using active interpolation," IEEE European Solid-State Circuits Conference, pp. 412-415, Sept. 2006.

An Ultra Low Power and High Efficiency UWB Transmitter for WPAN applications

Shengxi Diao, Yuanjin Zheng

Institute of Microelectronics, A*STAR (Agency for Science, Technology and Research), Singapore

Abstract □ **This paper presents a single-chip transmitter for ultra wide band (UWB) wireless communication system based on impulse radio technology. It is implemented in a CMOS 0.18-□m technology with 3.3V voltage supply. The transmitter can generate UWB pulse with 2GHz bandwidth with 20-dB side-lobe rejection. The differential output swing is 7.2V under 100&!loads. The average current consumption of the transmitter is 224□A at 1Mbps with the highest energy efficiency of 10.5%.**

Index Terms □ **Ultra Wideband (UWB), transmitter, pulse generator, impulse radio, WPAN, CMOS, low power, low data rate.**

I. INTRODUCTION

Multi-band Ultra Wideband Impulse Radio (UWB-IR) is a promising technology for low data-rate communication (e.g. IEEE 802.15.4a) and offers new capabilities of precision location and positioning besides communication. Research on this technology is driven by emergence of applications like wireless sensor networks (WSN) and wireless personal area networks (WPAN). These applications require low-power and low-cost communication system.

So far several works have been published in developing UWB-IR transceivers. In [1], a coherent transceiver is reported, but a complex circuit is required. A burst mode pulse generator realized in HBT technology is presented in [2], while the process cost is quite high. A robust pulse generator is implemented in [3], but the output peak power is very low and the output swing is quite small, which limits the maximum communication distance. All those works reported so far are suitable for short range (< 10m) applications. It can be easily verified that a UWB pulse with high peak power (e.g. 18dBm) and low pulse repetition frequency (PRF) can meet the FCC mask while be able for longer range communication (e.g. > 20m) assuming same receiver sensitivity. On the other hand, efficiency improvement is also a key parameter for sustaining long battery life especially for WSN and WPAN etc. applications.

In this paper, a low-complexity, low cost and high efficiency transmitter is presented. It utilizes a fast start-up LC oscillator to achieve high output peak power while consuming low DC power, i.e. attain high efficiency.

II. UWB TRANSMITTER DESIGN AND ANALYSIS

As well known, all UWB systems' emission is required to meet FCC spectral mask [4]. For low data rate application, if taking full use of UWB FCC spectrum mask, it is capable to cover longer communication distance (> 20m) since the low pulse repetition frequency allows high output peak power. A switched LC oscillator is a good option for UWB-IR transmitter, because for a non-coherent receiver based on energy detection, the requirement of frequency accuracy and phase noise is greatly relaxed. If a phase locked loop is applied to lock the frequency, the power consumption will be increased and the circuit will become more complex. Moreover, the energy efficiency and peak power of the transmitter should be improved.

The proposed UWB-IR transmitter architecture is shown in Fig. 1 and the data flow of the transmitter is shown in Fig. 2.

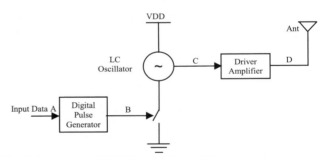

Fig. 1. Low data rate UWB-IR transmitter architecture

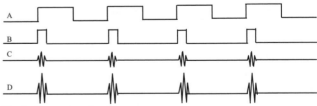

Fig. 2. Transmitter data flow

As shown in Fig. 1 and Fig. 2, the rising edge of input digital data A triggers a digital pulse generator to generate a nano-second wide digital pulse B. The pulse train B will control the tail current source of the LC oscillator, and consequently an UWB pulse train is generated at C. After amplification by the driver amplifier, the output pulses D will be sent to a matched antenna.

A. Start-up Analysis

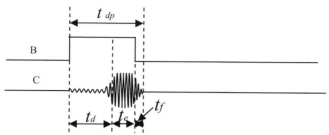

Fig. 3. Oscillation process of a switchable LC Oscillator

In the proposed UWB-IR transmitter, the LC oscillator will be switched on and off by a nano-second wide digital pulse as shown in Fig. 3. The oscillation of a switched LC VCO can be considered with three periods: start-up time duration of t_d, oscillation duration of t_e and oscillation decay period of t_f. Here rising edge and falling edge are assumed symmetrical. Only t_d will be analyzed here. The addition of the first two equals the whole duration time of t_{dp} of the digital control pulse. During t_d, LC oscillator and DA are turned on and consume a large amount of power, but have no contribution to the output UWB signal. Therefore, fast start-up is required to improve power efficiency and be helpful to control the digital pulse width accurately. In real case, instantaneous start-up is difficult to be achieved. However, it should be as short as possible; at least t_e should be the dominant period in t_{dp}.

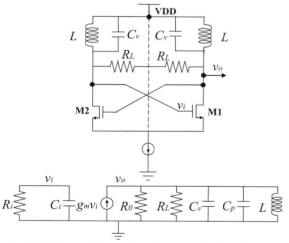

Fig. 4. LC VCO circuit (upper) and its small-signal equivalent circuit (lower)

A common LC VCO and its small-signal schematic are shown in Fig. 4. Here C_v is the varactor capacitance and C_p is the parasitic capacitance. R_L is the load resistance. R_i, C_i and R_o represent the input resistance, input capacitance and output resistance respectively. g_m represents the

transconductance of M1. The response of $Vo(t)$ due to $Vi(t)$ can be expressed as [5]:

$$V_o(t) = f[V_i(t)] + A_1 \cdot e^{\frac{\omega_0}{2Q}(1 - g_m R_L)t} \cos(\omega_0' t) \qquad (1)$$

where $\omega_0 = 1/\sqrt{L(C_v + C_p)}$ is the steady-state oscillation frequency, ω_0' is the frequency during oscillation build-up. Notice that $f[Vi(t)]$ represents input dependent DC item and A_1 depends on initial condition (noise) and mismatch. Q is the quality factor of the circuit.

In order to achieve fast start-up, two methods can be applied as seen from (1): 1) Setting large bias current and big transistor size to make g_m high and hence maximize the small signal loop gain. 2) Slight mismatch of the differential transistor will raise $f[Vi(t)]$ and A_1, then leads to a faster start-up. The drawback is that it makes the differential output asymmetric, but for energy detection non-coherent receiver it is acceptable. In this design both considerations are incorporated properly.

B. Pulse Shape

The output pulse envelope determines the pulse spectrum. The transmitter output pulses train can be characterized as follow:

$$V_{tx}(t) = \sum_{n=0}^{N} \{Cf[V_i(t - nT)]\}$$
$$+ \sum_{n=0}^{N} \left[CA_1 \cdot e^{\left(\frac{t - nT}{\tau}\right)^2} \cos(\omega_0'(t - nT)) \right] \qquad (2)$$

where $\tau = 1/\sqrt{\alpha \mu_n C_{ox}(W/L)R_L}$ and $nT < t < (nT + t_{dp})$. α is a constant value. μ_n and C_{ox} are process parameters. (W/L) is the aspect ratio of tail transistor (NM1 in Fig. 6). C is the buffer gain and T is the period of input data.

From (2), the output of UWB-IR transmitter is an UWB pulse modulated by a carrier with the frequency ω_0'.

C. Amplitude Analysis

Since the design is targeted for long communication range, high output peak power is desired and thus differential circuit configuration is utilized. As shown in Fig. 5, assuming antenna loading (100Ω) and receiver sensitivity (-60dBm), the distance is proportional to the output swing of the transmitter. The differential output amplitude A_{od} can be written as:

$$A_{od} = V_{max} \propto I_{max} \cdot R_L \qquad (3)$$

where I_{max} represents the maximum current through buffer and R_L represents the load resistance.

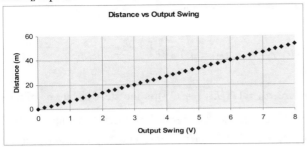

Fig. 5. Output swing vs communication distance in free space

III. UWB-IR TRANSMITTER CIRCUIT DESIGN

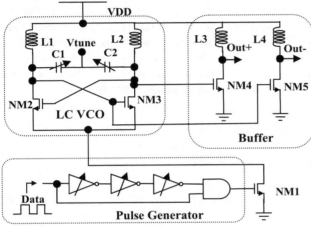

Fig. 6. Proposed UWB-IR Transmitter

Fig 6 shows the proposed transmitter circuit, which includes a pulse generator, a LC VCO and a buffer driver amplifier. Buffer is switched on and off simultaneously with the VCO through a gate bias (not shown here). The OOK modulation scheme is adopted. The pulse width is tunable by adjusting the current of delay elements. Cross-coupled NMOS pair NM2, NM3 (60μm/0.35μm) forms a VCO core. The LC tank consists of inductors L1, L2 (1nH) and varactors C1, C2 (1pF). Accumulation-MOS varactor is used here which can achieve 1GHz tuning range (3.59-4.6GHz) for calibration purpose. To facilitate fast start-up and high output peak power the sizing of transistors NM2-5 are big. Hence the parasitic capacitance is quite big around 0.6pF. L3, L4 (1.5nH) and NM4, NM5 (120μm/0.35μm) forms a buffer. It is used to drive 100Ω loading and stabilize the frequency of LC VCO. The digital data with certain duty cycle is used to trigger the pulse generator. A narrow pulse of about 1.2ns will be generated according to the rising edge of the input data. This pulse controls the gate of NM1 to turn on or off the VCO and buffer circuits. Large W/L ratio (120μm/0.35μm) for NM1 is chosen to minimize the

drain-source voltage and effectively present a short circuit directly to the ground.

Theoretical Gaussian pulse and simulation results of the UWB-IR transmitter are shown in Fig. 7. It can be shown that the simulation meets very well with the theoretical one. It is also evidenced that a Gaussian-Like UWB pulse is generated as exposed in frequency domain. The slight difference is due to slight asymmetric rising edge and falling edge of UWB pulse.

For this circuit, I_{max} is chosen as 86mA and R_L 42Ω. The output swing of differential pulse is around 7.2V, leading to a communication distance reaching 50m according to Fig. 5.

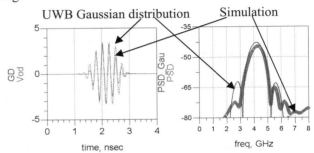

Fig. 7. Pulse generation results: theoretical vs simulation results

IV. MEASUREMENT RESULTS

The transmitter chip is realized in Chartered's 0.18-μm process and occupies an area of 0.8mm x 0.6mm (core circuit). A die photo is shown in Fig. 9. The chip is mounted on a Rogers Printed Circuit Board (PCB) and tested. With 1Mbps baseband input data, the circuit can generates a pulse with 2GHz bandwidth (-20dB). Fig. 8(a) shows the output pulse with 1.2ns width and peak swing of 7.2V. To our best knowledge, this is the highest output swing reported for the integrated UWB transmitters. As shown in Fig 8(b), the center frequency of the pulse is 4GHz and fits into the FCC spectrum mask. The current consumption is 224μA at 1Mbps for whole transmitter. Around 200ps start-up time is achieved. The performance is summarized in Table I. Furthermore, an energy

TABLE I
PERFORMANCE SUMMARY

	Measurement results
Process	CMOS 0.18μm
Supply Voltage	3.3V
Die Area	0.8mm x 0.6mm (core circuit)
Modulation	OOK
Maximum Data Rate	1Mbps
Input data duty cycle	0.1%
Current consumption(1Mbps)	224μA
Pulse width	~ 1.2ns (tunable)
Differential output swing (Vpp)	7.2V
Center frequency	4GHz
Frequency band	3-5GHz
Start-up	~ 200ps

efficiency is defined in (4) as the ratio between the emission energy and average power consumption per pulse. A comparison of the power efficiency is listed in Table II. It can be seen the best power efficiency is demonstrated for this design.

$$\eta = \frac{Output\ Peak\ Power \times Pulse\ Width\ (J)}{DC\ Energy\ Consumption\ Per\ Pulse\ (J/pulse)} \quad (4)$$

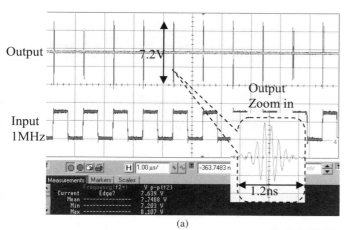

(a)

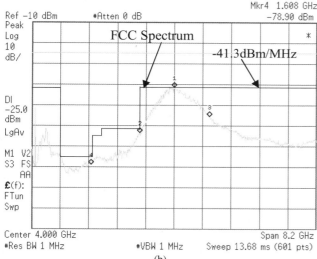

(b)

Fig. 8. (a) Measured time domain UWB pulse vs Input Data
(b) Measured UWB pulse PSD in compliance with FCC Mask

V. CONCLUSION

An UWB impulse transmitter based on a burst controlled LC VCO is presented in this paper. The chip has been implemented in a 0.18μm CMOS process and demonstrated UWB pulse generation with OOK modulation in low power consumption. The highest output swing and energy efficiency has been achieved. It is well suited for WSN and WPAN etc. applications.

TABLE II
PERFORMANCE COMPARISON ON UWB PULSE TRANSMITTERS

Reference	Technology	η (/pulse)
[3], 2007	CMOS 0.18μm	1.575%
[6], 2007	CMOS 90nm	5.745%
[7], 2007	CMOS 0.18μm	0.22%
[8], 2006	CMOS 0.13μm	0.67%
This Work	**CMOS 0.18μm**	**10.5%**

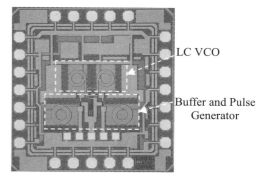

Fig. 9. Die photograph of the UWB Transmitter

ACKNOWLEDGMENT

The authors would like to thank M. Annamalai, Han Dong from Institute of Microelectronics and Fei Ting, Prof. Heng Chun Huat from National University of Singapore for their kind suggestions and helps on this circuit design and implementation.

REFERENCES

[1] Y. Zheng, Y. Zhang, Y. Tong, "A novel wireless interconnect technology using impulse radio for interchip communications", *IEEE Trans. Micro. Theory Tech.*, vol. 54, no. 4, Part II, pp. 1912-1920, April 2006.

[2] A. Cacciatori, L. Lorenzi, L. Colalongo, "A power efficient HBT pulse generator for UWB radars", *IEEE Int. Symp. on Circuits and Systems*, pp. 3916-3919, May 2007.

[3] T. A. Phan, J. Lee, V. Krizhanovskii, S. K. Han, S. G. Lee, "A 18-pJ/Pulse OOK CMOS transmitter for multiband UWB impulse radio", *IEEE Microwave and Wireless Components Letters*, vol. 17, issue 9, pp. 688-690, Sept. 2007.

[4] Federal Communications Commission, "Revision of part 15 of the commission's rules regarding ultra-wideband transmission systems: First report and order," Washington DC, ET-docket 98-153, FCC 02-48, pp. 1–118, Feb. 14, 2002.

[5] A. D. Berny, R. G. Meyer, A, Niknejad, "Analysis and design of wideband LC VCOs", a dissertation from UCB in May, 2006.

[6] Wentzloff, D.D. and Chandrakasan, A.P., "A 47pJ/pulse 3.1-to-5GHz all-digital UWB transmitter in 90nm CMOS," *IEEE Int. Solid-State Circuits Conf.*, pp. 118-119, Feb. 2007.

[7] T. Norimatsu, R. Fujiwara, M. Kokubo, M. Miyazaki, A. Maeki, Y. Ogata, S. Kobayashi, N. Koshizuka, and K. Sakamura, "A UWB-IR transmitter with digitally controlled pulse generator," *IEEE J.Solid-State Cicuits*, vol. 42, no. 6, pp.1300–1309, Jun. 2007.

[8] L. Smaini, C. Tinella, D. Helal, C. Stoecklin, L. Chabert, C. Devaucelle, R. Cattenoz, N. Rinaldi, and D. Belot, "Single-chip CMOS pulse generator for UWB systems," *IEEE J.Solid-State Cicuits*, vol. 41, no. 7, pp. 1551–1561, Jul. 2006.

A 3-10 GHz Flexible CMOS LO Generator for MB-OFDM UWB Application Using Wide Tunable VCOs

Eun-Chul Park, Inhyo Ryu, Jeongwook Koh, and Chun-Deok Suh

Connectivity Lab., System LSI Division, Samsung Electronics Co.

Yongin, Korea

Email: eunchul71.park@samsung.com

Abstract — A frequency synthesizer for MB-OFDM UWB system is implemented in CMOS RF process. The LO generator includes three wide tunable VCOs, PLLs, and quadrature generators. This synthesizer with three VCOs gives more flexible power management scheme and generates lower spurious tones than single side-band mixing method. This scheme supports all band groups except band group 2 which wireless LAN application occupies. Local oscillator including PLLs consumes 17.8 ~ 45.7 mA according to TFC code from 1.2V power supply. Phase noise has been measured less than -100 dBc/Hz over the operating frequency range.

I. INTRODUCTION

Ultra-wideband (UWB) technology has emerged as a steep growing market for short-range high data-rate wireless personal area networks (WPANs) system. This connectivity technology connects personal area information to neighboring networks and becomes a basic unit of overall network. The existing wireless solutions are hard to meet the driving force of customers for requiring higher data rate communication. The key issues in MB-OFDM UWB RF system are wideband matching in RF amplifiers and mixers from 3 to 10 GHz, wideband operation in analog baseband filters and amplifiers over 250 MHz. Frequency synthesizer is also one of tough parts in UWB system due to tone generation over a wide range of frequencies in conjunction with fast hopping time requirement within 9.5 ns. Single-side band (SSB) mixing methods have been widely researched as a solution for multi-tone generation and fast frequency hopping. SSB mixer generates either of the sum or difference frequency from two different signal sources [1]-[5]. Two different voltage controlled oscillators (VCO) [1]-[4] or single VCO and its divided signal [5] are used as the signal sources of SSB mixer. This approach intrinsically consumes much power from SSB mixer to gain enough power, which results in the shortened battery-driven operation time. Also, two signal sources and a SSB mixer should be always activated for single tone generation. For the same reason, the power consumption may not be saved even when the communication falls in sleep mode or time-frequency code (TFC) is set to fixed frequency mode. For 3 -10 GHz frequency band, at least two SSB mixers and multiple divider chains are required, which increases system complexity and chip area. Also, multiple signal-mixing

increases the number of spurious tones that introduce out of band signal or noise.

In this work, we introduce alternative approach using three wide tunable VCOs to deliver power, size and complexity issues. We integrated VCOs, phase locked loops (PLLs), switch, and quadrature generators in SAMSUNG 65 nm CMOS RF process.

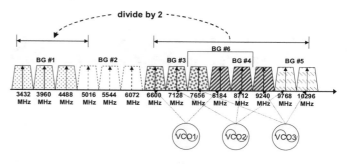

Figure 1. Frequency allocation of MB-OFDM and coverage of each VCOs

II. ARCHITECTURE

Fig. 1 shows the frequency allocation of MB-OFDM UWB system and depicts the frequency coverage of each VCO. The basic idea of this work is that three LO tones are generated from three separate VCOs at the same time and form a band group. For example, in Fig. 1, the first VCO produces the first sub-band tones in band group 3 and 4. The second VCO makes the second sub-bands in band group 3, 4 and the first sub-band in band group 5. The third VCO generates another tone in band group 3, 4 and 5. Three sub-band tones of the band group 1 are obtained by dividing sub-band tones in band group 3-6. Therefore, the tones in band group 1 are produced by dividing the output frequencies of VCOs whereas tones in other bands are directly derived from VCO output, which makes the VCO tuning range effectively extended. Considering frequency dividing for band group 1, around 30 % of VCO tuning range will be enough to generate all the sub-band tones except for band group 2. Tuning range of low frequency VCO (VCO1) should be from 6600 to 8184 MHz, VCO2 from 7128 to 9768 MHz, and VCO3 from 7656 to 10296 MHz. Fig.2 shows the block diagram of the proposed

LO scheme. A set of quadrature signals is selected from of three poly-phase filter outputs and the selected set is fed to the frequency divider or poly-phase filter buffer according to the selected band group. In three-band hopping mode, all VCOs, PLLs, and VCO buffers are activated and either poly-phase filter buffer or high frequency divider is activated. One or two VCO/PLL blocks are deactivated in the case of two-band hopping or fixed frequency mode, so that unnecessary power consumption can be reduced. The load pulling of VCO must be treated carefully as it may cause PLL to be unlocked at the switching instance. To avoid the phenomena and make a successful frequency hopping, the position of band switch has been chosen after PPF. Fig. 3 shows the block diagram of PLL. The output frequency of VCO is divided by 8 in high frequency prescaler. Programmable counter consists of an 8/9 dual-modulus prescaler followed by pulse swallow counters. Synchronous counter is used in dual-modulus prescaler whereas ripple counter is used in pulse swallow counter.

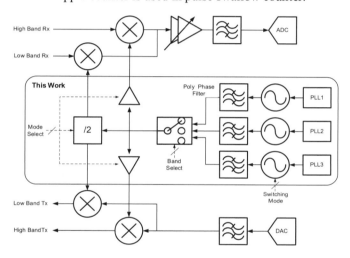

Figure 2.   Block diagram of proposed LO architecture

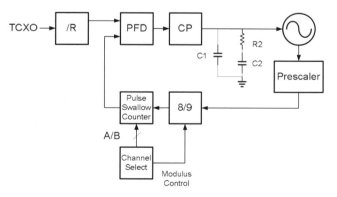

Figure 3.   Integer-N PLL block diagram

III.   PHASE NOISE ANALYSIS

As for phase noise, there are two aspects to consider. One is how much the phase noise degrades input SNR by mixing neighboring transmitter signal down on the band of interest. The other is how pure the transmitted signal is enough to meet the requirement for spectrum mask at transmitter output and

SNR at receiver input. The former is related to sensitivity, and the latter is related to error vector magnitude (EVM). For packet error rate of less than 8%, the sensitivity is -80.8 dBm for 53.3 Mbps and -70.4 dBm for 480 Mbps. From (1), minimum phase noise should be less than -95 dBc/Hz at 1 MHz offset frequency. Also, MB-OFDM specifies the different EVM requirements according to the data rates. -19.5 dB or less is required for over 320 Mbps transmission. As in (2), EVM can be obtained by integrating the phase noise over the frequency range. The loop bandwidth should be chosen carefully to minimize phase noise. PFD-referred noise is dominant within loop bandwidth and VCO phase noise is dominant out of loop bandwidth. Optimal bandwidth is where the two noise sources meet. In-band phase noise was empirically predicted by (3). In previous work [1], normalized phase noise was measured around -200 dBc. By using (2) and (3), EVM has been extracted and plotted in Fig. 4. From Fig. 4, loop bandwidth is chosen to minimize phase error.

$$P_{int} + 10\log(BW) + PN < P_{sig} - NF - SNR \qquad (1)$$

$$EVM = 10\log\int 2 \cdot L(f)\,df \quad [dB] \qquad (2)$$

$$\begin{aligned}\text{Phase Noise} = &(\text{Normalized Phase Noise Floor}) \\ &+ 10\log(f_{ref}) + 20\log(N_{div})\end{aligned} \qquad (3)$$

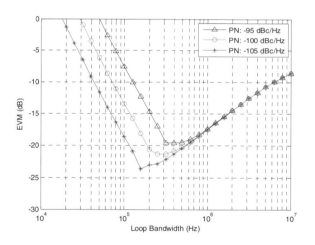

Figure 4.   EVM plot for different phase noise and loop bandwidth

IV.   QUADRATURE SIGNAL AND I/Q IMBALANCE

I/Q mismatch introduces a image signal within wanted channel, thus corrupts the signal. The degradation by I/Q impairment can be figured by image rejection ratio (IRR). The image rejection ratio is related to magnitude error (e) and phase error ($,$) by the simplified equation (4). In this work, output phase of LO signal is tunable in quadrature generator to compensate I/Q mismatch

$$IRR = \frac{\sqrt{1 - 2(1-e)\cdot\cos\theta + (1-e)^2}}{\sqrt{1 + 2(1-e)\cdot\cos\theta + (1-e)^2}} \qquad (4)$$

A. High Frequency Divider

High frequency divider is one of the key elements in integrated circuits for wide band communication. We exploited D flip-flop based divider which is known for wide-band and stable dividing characteristics. Fig. 5 shows schematic of high frequency latch, a half part of divider. For high speed dividing operation, it is required that load resistance of divider and parasitic capacitance at load should be minimized. To increase voltage headroom, we removed current source from the conventional design and biased clock receiving transistor directly. DC voltage from VCO output is blocked by capacitor. I/Q phase is controlled by changing the bias current of either of latches in D flip-flop. Roughly 10° of phase calibration has been simulated.

B. Phase Tunable Poly-Phase Filter

Fig. 6 shows the two-stage poly-phase filter with phase tuning scheme. Similar to frequency divider, designed poly-phase filter has I/Q calibration capability by adjusting control voltage of varactor in second stage. More than 10° of phase calibration was simulated.

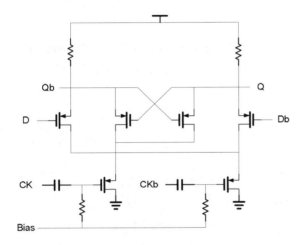

Figure 5.   High speed frequency divder latch cell

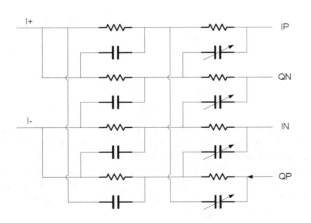

Figure 6.   Schematic of two-stage poly-phase filter with varactor tuning

V.   MEASUREMENT RESULTS

The fabricated VCO including buffers consumes 2 mA (0.8 mA in core) from a 1.2 V supply voltage. The oscillation frequency varies from 6.27 to 9.79 GHz in VCO1, 6.8 to 10.6 GHz in VCO2, and 7.23 to 11.34 GHz in VCO3, respectively. Overall tuning range of three VCOs is measured more than 40 %. The measured oscillation frequency of upper band VCO (VCO3) is shown in Fig. 7. We compared the measured phase noise over the tuning range and simulated one of lower band VCO in Fig. 8. Phase noise has been measured less than -100 dBc/Hz over the operating frequency range.

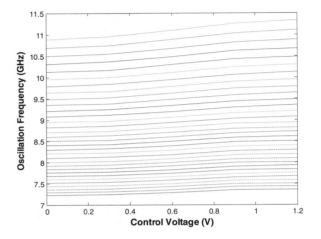

Figure 7.   Measured oscillation frequency of VCO3

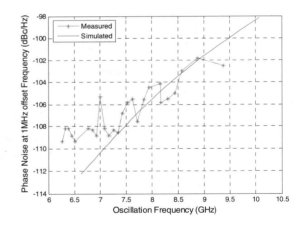

Figure 8.   Measured phase noise of VCO1

Fig. 9 shows the measured phase noise characteristics of the frequency synthesizer. In-band phase noise is ranges from -73 to -70 dBc/Hz over the tuning range and loop bandwidth is measured around 200 kHz. The EVM is about -20 dB for band group 1 and -17 dB for higher band.

For band group 1, high frequency quadrature divider provides required LO frequencies. This frequency divider operates up to 13.6 GHz input frequency with -12.5 dBm output power. The high frequency divider including output buffers dissipates 6.7 mA (2 mA in core DFFs) from 1.2 V

340

power supply. The measured sensitivity curve of the divider is shown in Fig. 10. Even if the bias current control voltage changes from 0.5 to 0.9 V, little movement from 8 GHz is observed. The output power variation is about 1.5 dB in band group 1 frequencies.

Local oscillator including PLL is integrated and consumes from 17.8 ~ 45.7 mA according to TFC code from 1.2V power supply. The output spectrum of LO generator in band group 1 is shown in Figure 11. At least 28.5 dB suppression of other band tones is achieved. The reference spurs are less than -40 dB. And, any spurious tones were not detected.

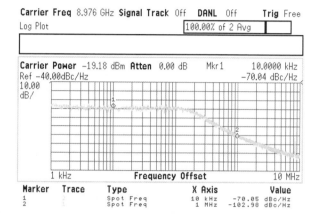

Figure 9.   Measured PLL phase noise performance

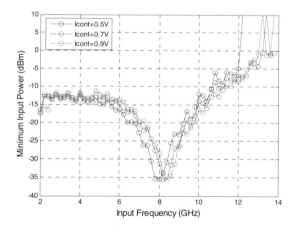

Figure 10. Sensitivity curve of freuency divider

VI.   CONCLUSIONS

A 3-10 GHz flexible LO generator for MB-OFDM UWB application was proposed for flexible power mamagement and low power cosumption. Phase noise was briefly reviewed to meet the specification on SNR and EVM. We have designed and integrated all the VCOs, PLLs including LPF, and quadrature generators in a small size of 1.25 mm² as shown in Fig. 12. Also, we demonstrated the proposed LO architecture with three VCOs gives more flexible power management scheme and generates less spurious tones than single side-band mixing method from spectrum measurement. The

proposed LO generator covers all band groups except band group 2.

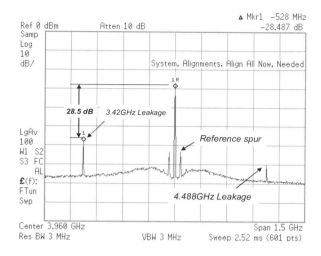

Figure 11. Output spectrum of LO generator in band group 1

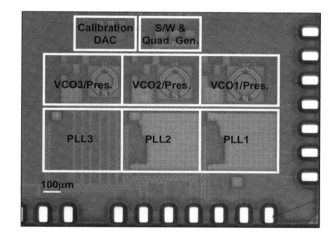

Figure 12. Fabricated LO generator using three wide tunable VCOs

REFERENCES

[1] J.-E. Lee, E.-C. Park, C.-Y. Cha, H.-S. Chae, C.-D. Suh, J. Koh, H. Lee, and H.-T. Kim, "A Frequency Synthesizer for UWB Transceiver in 0.13 μm CMOS Technology," Silicon Monolithic Integrated Circuits in RF Systems Dig. Tech. Papers, 2006, pp. 4.

[2] R. Roovers, et. al., "An Interference-Robust Receiver for Ultra-Wideband Radio in SiGe BiCMOS," IEEE J. Solid-State Circuits, Vol. 40, No. 12, pp. 2563-2572, Dec. 2005.

[3] C.-F. Liang, S.-I Liu, Y.-H. Chen, T.-Y. Yang, and G.-K. Ma, "A 14-Band Frequency Synthesizer for MB-OFDM UWB Application," IEEE Int. Solid-State Circuits Conf. Dig. Tech. Papers, pp. 437-438, 2006.

[4] J. Lee, "A 3-to-8-GHz Fast-Hopping Frequency Synthesizer in 0.18 μm CMOS Technology," IEEE J. Solid-State Circuits, Vol. 41, No. 3, pp. 566-573, 2006.

[5] Alverto Valdes-Garcia, et. al., "An 11-Band 3- 10 GHz Receiver in SiGe BiCMOS for Multiband OFDM UWB Communication," IEEE J. Solid-State Circuits, pp. 935-948, 2007.

[6] B. Razavi, T. Aytur, F.-R. Yang, R.-H. Yan, H.-C. Kang, C.-C. H, and C.-C. Lee, "A 0.13 μm CMOS UWB transceiver," IEEE Int. Solid-State Circuits Conf. Dig. Tech. Papers, pp. 216-217, 2005.

0.13 μm CMOS Cartesian loop transmitter IC with fast calibration and switching scheme from opened to closed loop

Shoji Otaka, Masahiro Hosoya, Hiroaki Ishihara
Corporate R&D Center
Toshiba Corporation
Kawasaki, Japan

Toru Hashimoto, Yuta Araki
Semiconductor Company
Toshiba Corporation
Yokohama, Japan

Abstract□ A 0.13 μm CMOS Cartesian loop transmitter IC with calibration and loop setting scheme of less than 5 μs is fabricated in order to keep high efficiency in wide output power range. The proposed scheme adjusts amplitude, phase, loop gain by using TX modulated signal for fast loop setting. Adjacent channel power leakage ratio (ACPR) is improved by 18 dB. The transmitter IC without PA consumes 62 mA, in which feedback path consumes 22 mA.

I. INTRODUCTION

The Cartesian loop transmitter (CLT) is a promising candidate for linearized transmitters because IM3 is highly suppressed by using a negative feedback technique [1-3]. When CLT is applied to wireless systems with wide transmission power control (TPC) such as CDMA, feedback path should be shut down at lower output power to avoid unnecessary power consumption in the feedback path. In FDD system such as WCDMA system, calibration and loop setting should be done during transition time in TPC or transport format combination (TFC) template, 25 μs, as shown in Fig. 1[4]. Therefore, CLT needs fast calibration time and fast switching time between opened and closed loop while satisfying stability of the loop. Furthermore, high accuracy gain setting is required for the whole gain range.

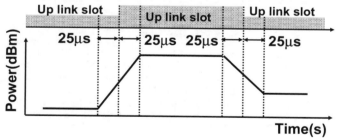

Figure 1. TPC or TFC template in WCDMA system

In recent work, a fast loop-switching scheme has been implemented for WLAN system; however, it takes over a few tens of μs for loop gain setting [5]. Moreover, gain resolution is generally a few dB in the previous works. For applying CLT to transmitter for WCDMA, our targets are to realize the calibration and loop switching time of less than 20 μs and gain resolution of less than 1 dB.

II. CARTESIAN LOOP TRANSMITTER

Figure 2 shows block diagrams of the Cartesian loop transmitter IC with external SiGe power amplifier. Forward path consists of I/Q variable gain of error amplifiers (VAMP), quadrature modulator (QMOD), variable gain driver (VDRV) and external PA. Feedback path is composed of directional coupler (CPL), variable gain amplifier (VGA) and quadrature demodulator (QDEM). Amplitude/phase detector (Adet/Pdet) detects amplitude/phase differences between I/Q and FI/FQ. Gain of VGA is controlled by the control signal V_A in accordance with the amplitude difference detected by Adet. Phases of FI/FQ are controlled by LO phase shifter ($\Delta\theta$) in accordance with the phase difference detected by Pdet. When the feedback loop is closed, feedback signal FI/FQ are subtracted from I/Q through polarity switch (PSW), where polarity signal of 0, π is applied from Pdet. An external controller including ADC, DAC and memory controls calibration sequence.

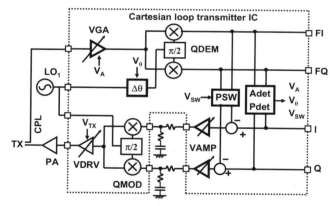

Figure 2. Block diagrams of the Cartesian loop transmitter IC

III. CALIBRATION SCHEME

Calibration is done with the opened loop by using modulated TX signal to reduce transition time caused by signal change from a training signal to the modulated TX signal. In this scheme, non-linearized TX signal is transmitted from PA at the calibration time. After calibration, TX signal is linearized by the feedback technique through the fast loop switching. For realizing short transition time from opened to closed loop, the amplitudes and the phases of FI/FQ are approached to those of I/Q before closing the feedback loop. The proposed sequence is as follows: 1) applying I/Q signal with VAMP gain setting of 0 dB, TX output level is set by V_{TX} of VDRV, 2) amplitude adjustment: after closing SW-A, the amplitudes of FI/FQ are adjusted to be equivalent to those of I/Q by applying the amplitude difference between I/Q and FI/FQ to VGA as the control signal V_A as shown in Fig.3, 3) a calibration controller samples V_A through ADC and saves it to memory and, after that, the amplitude adjustment feedback path of Adet-VGA-QDEM is opened by SW-A and the controller applies the saved V_A to VGA through DAC, 4) phase adjustment: after closing SW-θ, the phases of FI/FQ are adjusted to those of I/Q in phase or anti-phase by applying the phase difference between I/Q and FI/FQ to Δθ as the control signal $V_θ$ as shown in Fig.3, 5) the controller samples $V_θ$ through ADC and saves it to memory and, after that, the phase adjustment feedback path of Pdet-Δθ-QDEM is opened by SW-θ and the controller applies the saved $V_θ$ to Δθ through DAC, 6) FI/FQ are fedback to I/Q through PSW with the appropriate polarity and the gain of VAMP is changed from 0dB to 20dB, and then calibration mode is finished. The loop gain is increased to 20dB by the gain increase of VAMP in this case. In the proposed sequence, the transition time is very short, because RF amplitudes between before and after closing the loop are almost the same. Furthermore, PA delivers desired output during even transition time in TFC template and delivers linearized output in data transmission.

In amplitude detection, the amplitude difference $\Delta A=(FI^2+FQ^2)-(I^2+Q^2)$ is obtained. The amplitude adjustment feedback of Adet-VGA-QDEM makes ΔA to approach zero with setting k_1 large, and then V_A is sampled as shown in Fig.3. In phase detection, $\sin\Delta\theta= I \times FQ - Q\times FI$ [4] and $\cos\Delta\theta= I \times FI + Q\times FQ$ are obtained. The phase adjustment feedback of Pdet-Δθ–QDEM makes sinΔθ, approximately Δθ, to approach zero with setting k_2 large, and then $V_θ$ and a polarity of cosΔθ are sampled, where that of cosΔθ determines polarity of PSW.

IV. CIRCUIT CONSIDERATION AND DESIGN

This section describes implementation of circuits in Cartesian loop transmitter IC as shown in Fig. 2.

A. LO phase shifter (Δθ)

LO phase shifting for phase adjustment is adopted to keep high linearity. LO phase shifting after LO divider was avoided to keep high I/Q-phase accuracy with sacrificing power consumption, because I/Q phase accuracy of Cartesian loop transmitter is mainly determined by the phase accuracy in feedback path. Therefore, wide LO phase shifting per stage is required to lower power consumption. Figure 4 shows LO path with proposed LO phase shifters. The phase shifter is composed of passive RC bridges, M1-C1 and M2-C2, where R is implemented using MOSFET in linear region and is controlled by $V_θ$. In order to keep M1 and M2 in linear region, DC blocking capacitor C is inserted and voltages of both sources and drains are set to GND through resistors. The phase range of the phase shifter is ideally π per stage. In actual design, the phase range is about π/2 due to parasitics. Considering that the phase shift in f_{LO} becomes a half of that in a half f_{LO}, two stages of the phase shifters (PS1 and PS2) and polarity selection of FI/FQ (PSW in Fig.2) are equipped for 2π phase range. Furthermore, LO phase switching Pθ is implemented in PS1 as shown in Fig.4 in order to overcome the reduction of phase range in each PS due to parasitics.

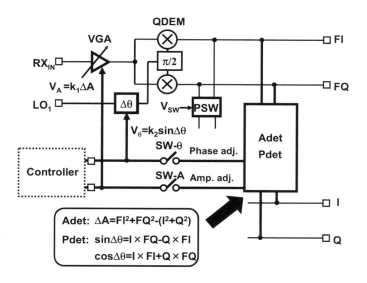

Figure 3.   Amplitude/Phase Adjustment

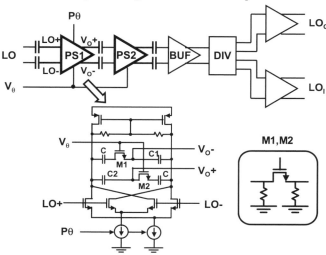

Figure 4.   LO phase shifter

B. Adet/Pdet

A basic circuit configuration for Adet/Pdet is A×B+C×D, where multipliers with Gilbert cell are used and subtraction or summation is implemented on current mode.

Figure 5 shows a block diagram of Adet/Pdet. The output of Adet is transferred to VGA as the gain control signal V_A in the amplitude calibration period. After the amplitude calibration, MOS switch, SW-A, is opened and memorized V_A is applied from controller. Pdet outputs the phase signal V_θ to the phase shifter $\Delta\theta$ and the phase polarity signal V_{SW} to PSW in the phase calibration period. After the phase calibration, SW-θ is opened and controller outputs V_θ. Controller also outputs V_{SW} after detecting the polarity.

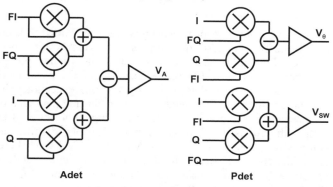

Figure 5.   Block diagram of Adet/Pdet

C. PSW and VAMP

Connection of feedback signal FI/FQ with right polarity to I/Q is controlled through MOS switches, PSW. The polarity is determined by the polarity of $\cos\Delta\theta$ detected in Pdet. When the Cartesian loop is active, FI/FQ signals are summed to I/Q signals through the MOS switches placed in virtual ground of inverting OPAMP.

VAMP with 0dB/20dB gain setting is also implemented by using inverting OPAMP, in which input resistance is changed by MOS switches placed at virtual ground.

D. Foward path

Forward path consists of Gilbert type QMOD and VDRV composed of linear-in-dB attenuator [6], class-A amplifier, and class-AB amplifier. Attenuation variation due to V_{TH} variation is compensated by using resistance-ratio based control scheme [7]. The compensation technique is also applied for the phase-shift control signal V_θ in Fig.4.

E. Feedback path

In feedback path, VGA consists of linear-in-dB attenuator and low-input-impedance current divider (CD) for QDEM. CD consists of parallel connection of common-gate MOSFETs M3-M6 and a current mirror M10-M11 in one polarity as shown in Fig.6. Differential input impedance is set to 100 Ω. No on-chip inductors are used for small chip area, because low NF is not required. Passive mixers are adopted for QDEM to obtain high linearity.

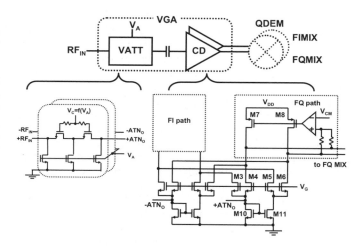

Figure 6.   Circuits for feedback path

V.   MEASURED RESULTS

The Cartesian loop transmitter IC is fabricated in 0.13um CMOS technology. Chip photo is shown in Fig.7. Active area is 2.8 mm^2 in forward path and 2.3 mm^2 in feedback path.

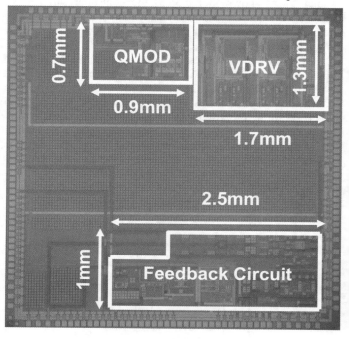

Figure 7.   Chip photo

Figure 8 shows measured results of variable attenuator and LO phase shifter in feedback path. Left side of graph indicates linear-in-dB gain range over 25 dB when measuring signal amplitude of FI/FQ at RF input of –30 dBm input for measurement. A range of control voltage V_A from 200 mV to 1 V is used for attenuation control. Input power over –5 dBm can be linearly received. Right side of graph shows LO phase characteristic after frequency divider (DIV). This indicates the phase range of over $\pi/2$ is achieved. Considering the polarity switches of baseband domain and LO frequency domain, the phase range of over 2π is achieved.

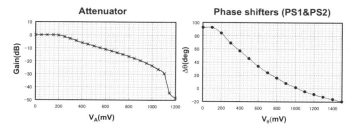

Figure 8. Measured results of Attenuator and Phase shifter

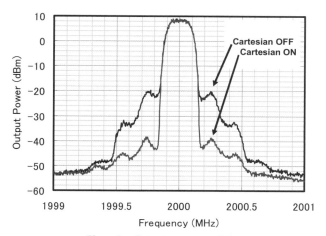

Figure 9. Output spectrum at PA

Figure 9 shows output spectra at 2 GHz with and without feedback loop, when π/4 shifted QPSK of 192 kHz is applied, where output power is 20 dBm. VDRV delivers -3dBm in this case. ACPR is suppressed by 18 dB compared to that without feedback loop. EVM of 6 % is improved to less than 2 % by applying the loop. Cascaded configuration of PSW and VAMP causes signal bandwidth to be reduced from 4 MHz to 192 kHz, because a phase delay in PSW was not estimated in design. However, signal bandwidth can be improved by combining VAMP with PSW. Forward path consumes 40 mA and feedback path consumes 22 mA from 1.5 V. PA consumes 120 mA from 2.5 V for both cases. Output power range is over 20 dB with gain resolution of less than 1 dB by using analog variable attenuator.

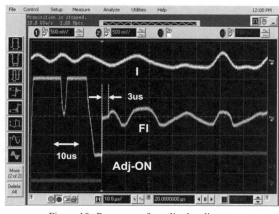

Figure 10. Response of amplitude adjustment

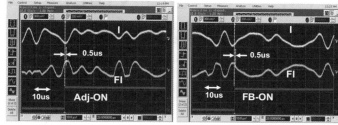

Phase adjustment   Feedback OFF/ON

Figure 11. Response of phase adjustment and loop switching

Figure 10 shows transitions of FI in amplitude adjustment. Transition time is within 3 μs, which is mainly determined by response time of the amplitude adjustment feedback path. Figure 11 shows phase adjustment (left), loop switch from open to close (right) when modulated I/Q are input. FI/FQ is controlled in anti-phase of I/Q in this case. Transition times are both within 0.5 μs. Figure 12 also shows response of phase adjustment and loop switching when applying single tone signal as I/Q signals to clarify the transient time. Considering that it takes less than 10 μs in total for digital control domain, this satisfies our target of 20 μs.

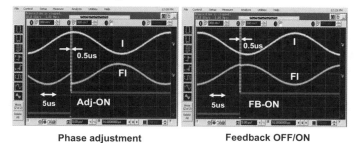

Phase adjustment   Feedback OFF/ON

Figure 12. Response of phase adjustment and loop switching

REFERENCES

[1] V. Petrovic, "Reduction of spurious emission from radio transmitters by means of modulation feedback", in Proc. Conf. on Radio Spectrum Conservation Techniques, Sept. 1983, pp.44-49.

[2] F. Carrara, A. Scuderi, and G. Palmisano, "Wide-Bandwidth Fully Integrated Cartesian Feedback Transmitter", in Proc. on IEEE 2003 Custom Integrated Circuits Conference, pp.451-454.

[3] J. L. Dawson and T. H. Lee, "Automatic Phase Alignment for a Fully Integrated Cartesian Feedback Power Amplifier System", in IEEE Journal of Solid-State Circuits, Dec., 2003, pp.2269-2279.

[4] 3rd Generation Partnership Project, "3GPP TS 25.101 V7.8.0," June 2007.

[5] N. Sornin, M. Massei, L. Perraud, and C. Pinatel, "A robust Cartesian feedback loop for a 802.11a/b/g CMOS transmitter", in proc. of 2004 IEEE Radio Frequency Integrated Circuits Symposium, pp.145-148.

[6] H. Dogan, R. G. Meyer, and A. M. Niknejad, "A DC-10 GHz linear-in-dB attenuator in 0.13 um CMOS technology", in proc. of 2004 Custom Integrated Circuits Conference, pp.609-612.

[7] Y. Araki, T. Hashimoto, and S. Otaka, "A 0.13um CMOS 90dB Variable Gain Pre-power Amplifier using Robust Linear-in-dB Attenuator", 2008 RFIC Symposium, to be published.

Low Drop-Out Voltage Regulator with Full On-Chip Capacitance for Slot-Based Operation

Wim Kruiskamp and René Beumer
SiTel Semiconductor
's-Hertogenbosch, The Netherlands
wim.kruiskamp@sitelsemi.com

Abstract□ **This paper presents a full on-chip low-dropout voltage regulator (LDO) for slot based applications like e.g. digital cordless telephones. The LDO uses a floating and charged capacitor to drive the gate of an nMOS pass transistor. The LDO has been integrated in a 0.18μm CMOS technology. The LDO is designed for 20mA output current with a 200mV dropout voltage and occupies 0.033mm^2 of die area. The output voltage varies only a few milli Volt when a 5mA load step or 500mV input step is applied to the circuit. The LDO is stable for output currents in the complete range from 0mA to 20mA and does not require an external load capacitor. The LDO can operate for tens of milli seconds without recharging the floating capacitor.**

I. INTRODUCTION

Low dropout voltage regulators (LDO) are widely used circuits in electronic systems. The purpose of an LDO is to provide a constant supply voltage to other circuits and to isolate circuits from each other to reduce cross talk via the supply lines. The optimal supply strategy, in terms of performance, is to supply each circuit by its own dedicated LDO. Such a supply strategy is only achievable with small and efficient LDOs that do not require external components.

An important application where LDOs are used is digital wireless communication like for instance GSM, DECT and Bluetooth. In these standards, communication only takes place in certain slots within a time frame. For power saving reasons, the transceiver is powered-down as much as possible. This means that during each frame, there is a period that the circuits are disabled and a constant supply voltage is not needed. The LDO presented in this paper exploits this time-discontinuous behavior.

II. BASIC PRINCIPLE OF THE PROPOSED LDO

A. Output stage

The output stage of the proposed LDO is shown in Fig. 1. It consists of an nMOS transistor M1 in a source-follower configuration, a gate decoupling capacitor C1 and a load capacitance Cload. Because the transistor behaves as a cascode device for the load Rload, it guarantees a good power

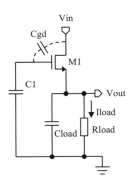

Figure 1. Output stage

supply rejection ratio (PSRR) for all frequencies as long as the transistor operates in saturation.

The smallest drain source voltage at which the transistor is in saturation is achieved when the transistor is biased close to weak inversion. With a minimum length transistor, this defines a minimum transistor width which is proportional to the load current.

The PSRR of the output stage is limited by the capacitive voltage divider of the parasitic gate-drain capacitance Cgd and C1. At frequencies higher than the output pole, defined by the transconductance gm of transistor M1 and the load capacitance Cload, the PSRR increases linear with the frequency. In a situation without the opportunity of an external capacitor, the PSRR is independent of the load capacitance Cload for frequencies up to several hundreds of mega Hertz. For a high PSRR at these frequencies, the capacitor C1 must be at least an order of magnitude larger than Cgd. As the width of the transistor, and therefore also Cgd, is proportional to the load, C1 is also proportional to the load current.

B. Feedback control loop

For good performance at low frequencies, the output stage is controlled by a feedback loop. This feedback loop consists of an OTA driving the gate of transistor M1. A problem however is that the gate of transistor M1 has to be driven at a

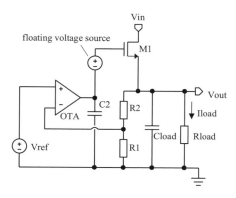

Figure 2. Feedback control loop

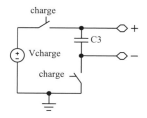

Figure 3. Floating voltage source

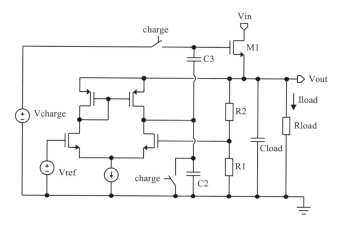

Figure 4. Simplified schematic of the proposed LDO

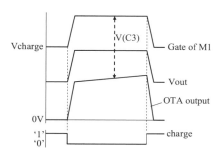

Figure 5. Typical waveforms

gate-source voltage higher than the output voltage and this might be higher than the input voltage of the LDO. In previously published regulators this is solved by supplying the OTA by a charge pump [1,2] or by supplying the gate of the nMOS transistor directly by a charge pump and add an LDO with a pMOS pass transistor in series [3]. In the proposed control loop as shown in Fig. 2 however, the problem is solved by adding a floating voltage source in series with the gate of the transistor. The output range of the OTA is now sufficient without the need of a high supply voltage.

This control loop is stable as long as the unity gain frequency (UGF) of the loop is smaller than the output pole. In a simplified calculation, the control loop has a phase margin of at least 60 degrees when the following condition is true:

$$2 \cdot \frac{R_1}{R_1 + R_2} \cdot \frac{gm_{OTA}}{C_2} < \frac{gm_1}{C_{load}} \qquad (1)$$

All variables of (1) are independent of the load current, except for the transconductance of M1 (gm1), which is proportional to the load current. The lowest phase margin therefore occurs at minimum load current.

C. Floating voltage source

The floating voltage source does not have to deliver any DC current, except for a small gate-leakage current of the pass transistor M1. Furthermore, the voltage source is only needed for a limited amount of time during each frame. It is therefore possible to implement the floating voltage source by a charged capacitor C3 as shown in Fig. 3. The capacitor is recharged during the idle time of each frame and operates as a floating voltage source during the active time of each frame.

D. Complete LDO

The complete circuit [4] is shown in Fig. 4. The OTA is an nMOS differential pair, loaded with a pMOS current mirror. The OTA is supplied by the output of the LDO itself. This configuration has two advantages: Improved stability and improved PSRR:

- The transconductance of M1 will always be higher than the transconductance of the OTA because the tail

current of the OTA is part of the current through M1. According to (1), it is then always possible to make the system stable for all load currents including the worst-case no load situation.

- The PSRR of the LDO is improved as the OTA is not connected to the input voltage.

The waveforms of the LDO are shown in Fig. 5. During the idle period, the OTA is powered down and the output of the OTA is grounded. The capacitor C3 is now recharged via a switch to Vcharge (~1.8V). The output voltage is a gate-source voltage lower than Vcharge and will typically be higher than 1V. When the switches are opened, the OTA will start to charge C2 until the LDO is in regulation. The charge on C3 will slowly leak away through the gate of M1, the switch and through the capacitor itself. The feedback loop compensates for this by increasing the voltage at the bottom of C3, keeping the output voltage Vout constant. The capacitor must be recharged before the output of the OTA start to clip. With careful design, the available time can be more than sufficient for digital communication applications like e.g. DECT.

E. Two stage LDO

In order to improve PSRR, a cascade of two LDOs can be used as shown in Fig. 6. The first LDO regulates the input voltage to an intermediate voltage and the second from that intermediate voltage to the output voltage. This strategy improves transient performance at the expense of increased die area and increased drop-out voltage.

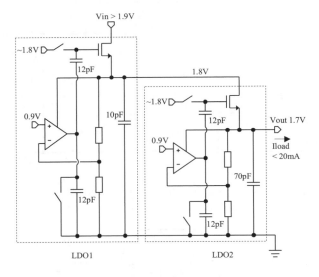

Figure 6. Two-stage LDO

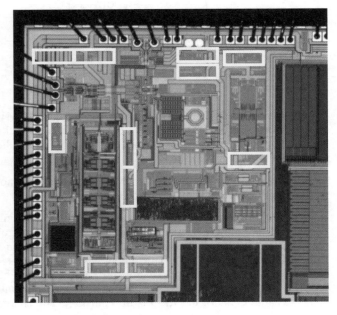

Figure 7. Microphotograph of part of the SoC

III. Experimental Results

The two-stage LDO as shown in Fig. 6 is used in the transceiver of a DECT cordless phone system-on-chip (SoC). The IC is processed in a 0.18μm standard CMOS technology. All transistors in the LDO are standard 1.8V devices. The die area of a two-stage LDO, without load capacitance, is 0.033mm². The measured LDO is designed for a maximum load current of 20mA and a drop-out voltage of 200mV.

The microphotograph of part of the SoC is shown in Fig. 7 and the LDOs are highlighted. Each circuit in the transceiver is supplied by its own dedicated LDO, resulting in eleven LDOs in total for the complete transceiver. The LDOs are placed close to the blocks they are supplying.

The start-up behavior of the LDO is shown in Fig. 8. In the idle state, the output voltage is about 1V. When the switches are opened, the output voltage rises to 1.7V. It takes less than two micro seconds for the output to become stable.

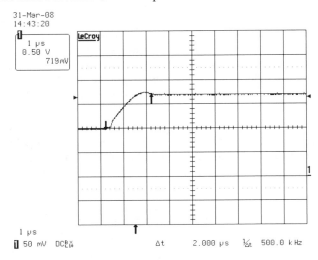

Figure 8. Measured start-up behavior

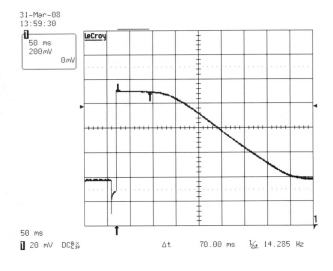

Figure 9. Measured output voltage droop rate

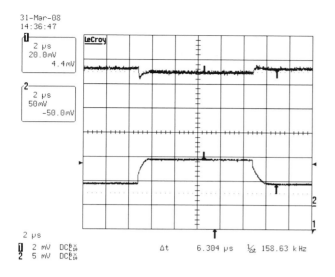

Figure 10. Measured load transient response; upper curve is Vout (20mV/div), lower curve is Iload (4.5mA → 9.5mA → 4.5mA).

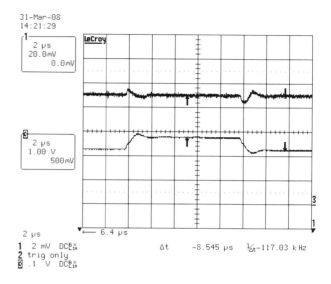

Figure 11. Measured input transient response; upper curve is Vout (20mV/div), lower curve is Vin (2.25V → 2.75V → 2.25V).

When the LDO is active for a long time without recharging the floating capacitors, the output voltage will eventually drop as shown in Fig. 9. The output voltage stays constant for 70ms. During that period the feedback loop compensates for the leakage of the floating capacitor. After 70ms, the output of the OTA clips at the supply voltage. The feedback loop can then no longer compensate the leakage anymore and the output voltage of the LDO drops. A DECT frame has a length of 10ms and consists of 24 receive or transmit slots with a length of only 417us each. The measured 70ms is therefore much more than required and provides a good margin for temperature and process variation.

The regulator was subjected to a load transient, as shown in Fig. 10. The 5mA load current step then causes an output voltage variation, in steady state, of 4mV. This variation is mainly due to parasitic resistance in the routing from the LDO to a pin of the IC. Close to the LDO, where the output voltage is used, the static variation is much smaller. The overshoot due to a load transient of 5mA is only a few milli Volt and the output voltage is stable within a micro second.

The regulator was also subjected to an input voltage transient, as shown in Fig. 11. The 500mV input variation then does not result in a steady state variation of the output voltage. The dynamic variation is only a few milli Volt and the output voltage is stable within a micro second.

IV. CONCLUSIONS

A full on-chip LDO, with an nMOS pass transistor, driven via a charged floating capacitor, has been presented. The LDO is stable for all load currents, including the no load current situation, and does not require a load capacitor for stability. The output voltage only varies a few milli Volt when a 5mA load step or a 500mV input step is applied to the LDO. The LDO can operate long enough, without recharging the floating capacitor, to be useful for slot-based digital communication applications like e.g. DECT. The simple structure and small die area are additional advantages for local voltage regulation in a SoC.

REFERENCES

[1] C.-H. Lee, K. McClellan and J. Choma, Jr., "A supply-Noise-Insensitive CMOS PLL With a Voltage Regulator Using DC-DC Capacitive Converter," IEEE J. Solid-State Circuits, vol. 36, pp. 1453 – 1463, Oct. 2001.

[2] G. Nebel, T. Baglin, I. San Sebastion, H. Sedlak and U. Weder, "A very low drop Voltage regulator Using an NMOS output Transistor," in Proc. ISCAS, 2005, pp 3857 – 3860.

[3] V. Gupta, G.A. Rincón-Mora, "A 5mA 0.6um CMOS Miller-Compensated LDO Regulator with -27dB Worst-Case Power-Supply Rejection Using 60pF of On-Chip Capacitance," in Proc. ISSCC, 2007, pp. 520 – 521.

[4] M. W. Kruiskamp and C. R. Beumer, "Low dropout voltage regulator for slot-based operation," EP1830238, patent pending, Sept. 2007

High-Performance Low-Dropout Regulator Achieved by Fast Transient Mechanism

Hong-Wei Huang[*], Chia-Hsiang Lin[+], Ke-Horng Chen[+]

[*] RichTek Technology Corporation, Hsinchu, Taiwan, R.O.C

[+] Department of Electrical and Control Engineering National Chiao Tung University, Hsinchu, Taiwan, R.O.C

Abstract—An adaptive reference control (ARC) technique is proposed for minimizing overshoot/undershoot voltage and settling time of low-dropout regulators (LDO). Linear operation provided by ARC technique can dynamically and smoothly adjust the reference voltage for increasing slew rate of error amplifier and forcing output voltage back to its steady-state value rapidly. The amount of transient revision is proportional to transient-state output voltage variation and load condition. In addition, dynamic push-pull technique is used to enhance transient response. Experimental results demonstrate the undershoot voltage, settling time and load regulation are improved 31%, 68.5% and 70% when load current changes between 1 mA and 100 mA.

I. INTRODUCTION

Low-dropout (LDO) regulators are widely used in portable electronic device because of only occupy small chip area and can convert a battery voltage to a low-noise, accurate voltages for noise-sensitive system-on-chip (SoC) applications. However, large parasitic capacitance at the gate of power transistor degrades the slew rate of error amplifier in case of load variations. Thus, several techniques are proposed for improving transient response time and transient voltage variations in order to maintain a reliable supply voltage for SoC applications.

The first technique named as non-linear control [1-3] speeds up the time of charging/discharging the large parasitic capacitor (C_g) at gate of power transistor as shown in figure 1. These techniques have the ability to provide large quiescent current for driving large parasitic capacitor at output of error amplifier in case of load variations. However, it may suffer from the oscillation problems.

Another technique is prediction control. The most famous prediction technique is adaptive voltage position (AVP) [4, 5], which continuously maintains constant output impedance of converters. This technique improves dynamic performance like transient response time and overshoot/undershoot voltage at the sacrifice of static performance like load regulation. Another one popular technique is end-point prediction (EPP) [6]. However, EPP technique, which is only suitable for the reference tracking, still suffers from large overshoot/undershoot output voltage and slow response time in case of large load variations.

According to the analysis of literatures, we can summarize that the fast transient technique must contain three important characteristics for providing a reliable

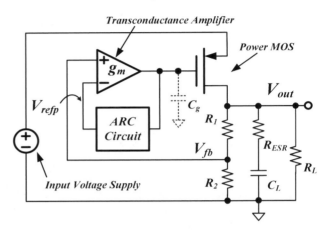

Figure 1. Low-dropout regulator with adaptive reference control (ARC) technique.

supplying voltage. Those are the system stability at full loads, small overshoot/undershoot output voltage, and good line/load regulation. In order to satisfy the aforementioned demands, adaptive reference control and dynamic push-pull techniques are proposed to provide these three fast transient characteristics at the same time for getting a regulated power supply.

The following section describes the analysis of ARC technique for LDO regulators. Section III introduces the architecture of ARC technique. Experimental results are shown in section IV. Finally, a conclusion is made in section V.

II. CONCEPT OF ADAPTIVE REFERENCE CONTROL OPERATION FOR LOW-DROPOUT REGULATOR

The block diagram of proposed LDO with ARC technique is shown in figure. 1. This LDO is composed of the transconductance amplifier, ARC circuit, power transistor, output capacitor C_L with equivalent series resistance (ESR) R_{ESR}, resistors R_1 and R_2.

In this design, ESR frequency compensation is used to introduce a pole-zero cancellation to ensure the closed-loop stability. It is a simple and popular method to compensate the phase margin of the system. However, ESR degenerates the overshoot/undershoot voltage and limits the performance of regulator in case of load variations. In order to overcome this issue, an adaptive reference control technique is proposed.

The concept of proposed ARC technique is shown in figure 2 (a) and (b). Reference voltage (V_{refp}) which is

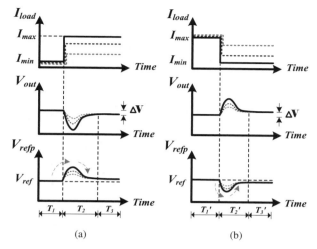

Figure 2. Concept of adaptive reference control. (a) Load current changes from light to heavy. (b) Load current changes from heavy to light.

close to voltage V_{ref} can be adaptively and smoothly adjusted according to the error voltage (V_{err}) between voltage V_{refp} and scaled output voltage V_{fb}. During load transient period, the reference voltage V_{refp} is increased (or decreased) to enhance slew rate of transconductance amplifier according to the quantity of the V_{err} when $V_{fb} < V_{ref}$ (or $V_{fb} > V_{ref}$). It means that this scheme is response to the overshoot/undershoot of output voltage instantly and creates an adaptive adjustment of reference voltage.

With the ARC technique, waveforms of V_{out} and V_{refp} are shown in figure 2 (a) and (b) when load current changes from light to heavy load, or vice versa. The main concept is that reference voltage V_{refp} only changes during load transient period (T_2 and T_2'). At steady state, V_{refp} is close to V_{ref} and the value of output voltage is not affected. That is the reason why the performance of the ARC technique is better than that of the AVP technique. Besides, load regulation can be enhanced if V_{refp} is directly proportional to load condition [7], i.e. voltage variation ΔV can be reduced. Hence, the value of voltage V_{refp} in T_3 region is larger than that in T_1 region. Similarly, the value of voltage V_{refp} in T_3' region is less than that in T_1' region when load current changes from heavy to light. Based on the aforementioned description, ARC technique can use the error voltage V_{err} and load condition to control V_{refp} signal for dynamically determining the reference voltage. The implementation of ARC circuit is described in the following section.

III. DESIGN OF PROPOSED CIRCUITS

The schematic of low-dropout regulator with adaptive reference control circuit is shown in figure 3. M_p is the power transistor, and M_{sen} is the sensing transistor for sensing load condition, i.e. I_c is a load sensing current. I_a is generated by reference controller and its value is proportional to error voltage V_{err}. In order to achieve ARC technique, an additional resistor R_f is serial to a fixed voltage V_{ref}. By using two revised current I_a and I_c to flow through the resistor R_f, the reference voltage V_{refp} can be dynamically adjusted for LDO regulator according to the output voltage variation and load condition.

A. Transconductance Amplifier

Transconductance amplifier is composed of transistors $M_1 \sim M_5$ and $M_{1a} \sim M_{5a}$. Two cascaded flipped voltage followers (CASFVF) [8, 9] composed of (M_1, M_2, and M_5) and (M_{1a}, M_{2a}, and M_{5a}) have small output impedances to improve the linearity of level shifters. Therefore, the voltage difference between V_{refp} and V_{fb}, is equal to the voltage difference between nodes N_1 and N_2. Using three current mirror pairs, which are (M_2, M_3), (M_{2a}, M_{3a}) and (M_4, M_{4a}), the transconductance can be determined as:

$$g_m = (V_{refp} - V_{fb})\frac{2K}{R_d} \qquad (1)$$

K is the ratio of current mirror. The structure of transconductance amplifier is with a broad bandwidth about MHz, and it is contributed to enhance the transient response time. However, the DC gain is slightly lower and not enough to support an excellent performance for load regulation. Hence, the load regulation compensator is used to retrieve it.

B. Reference Controller and Dynamic Push-Pull Circuit

As shown in figure 4, the reference controller uses the transistors M_{3b} and M_{4b} to mirror the small-signal current form M_{2a} and M_4, respectively. Based on current mirror pairs, (M_6, M_{6a}) and (M_7, M_{7a}), the revised current I_a can be generated and derived as:

$$I_a = (V_{refp} - V_{fb})\frac{2K}{R_d} \qquad (2)$$

According to (2), the revised current that is proportional to output error voltage can be used to adjust the reference voltage in case of large load variations.

Dynamic push-pull circuit is composed of transistors M_{6b}, M_{6c}, M_{7b}, M_{7c} and $M_8 \sim M_{11}$. Based on the appropriate design for the ratio of current mirror ($M>1$), voltages of node N_1 and N_2 are set to "1" and "0" to force transistors M_8 and M_{11} to be turned off at steady state. Assumed i_1 and i_2 are the sum of small-signal current of $M_{6b, 7b}$ and $M_{6c, 7c}$, respectively. They can be determined as:

$$i_1 = i_2 = \frac{1}{2}g_m(1+M) \qquad (3)$$

Once the load current changes and causes large output variations, the small-signal current i_1 (or i_2) is generated to pull the voltage of node N_1 (or N_2) down (or up). And then transistor M_8 (or M_{11}) is turned on to charge (or discharge) the voltage V_G. Hence, this dynamic push-pull scheme can effectively enhance the transient response time for regulating the output voltage of LDO regulator back to a stable voltage level. In addition, transistors M_9 and M_{10} are used to prevent the noise of N_1 and N_2 from coupling to the gate of power transistor when transistors M_8 and M_{11} are turned on.

Once load current rapidly changes from light to heavy, the gate-source voltage of power transistor can't be adjusted immediately owing to the slew rate of transconductance amplifier. Hence, the output capacitor C_L supplies the insufficient charge between load current and input supplying source. There is a undershoot voltage

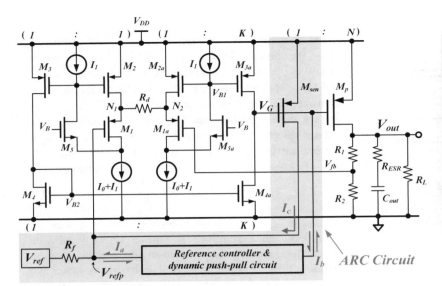

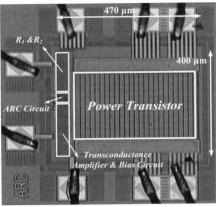

Figure 5. Chip micrograph.

Figure 3. The schematic of low-dropout regulator with adaptive reference control circuit.

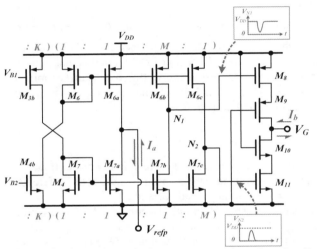

Figure 4. The schematic of reference controller and dynamic push-pull circuit. (M>1)

at output node. Thus, the reference controller converts the error voltage V_{err} to a revised current I_a and increases the value of reference voltage V_{refp}. Consequently, the slew rate of transconductance amplifier can be enhanced during transient period. Moreover, the dynamic push-pull circuit pulls up the voltage of node N_2 to discharge the node V_G through transistor M_{11}. The gate-source voltage of power transistor is rapidly increased and thus more energy is delivered to the load. When output voltage is regulated back to its expected voltage, i.e. V_{err} is small; the revised current becomes trickle current and is not large enough to affect the reference voltage. Besides, the voltage of node N_2 is smoothly reset to "0" to turn transistor M_{11} off. Finally, the voltage V_{refp} becomes constant again at steady state.

C. Load Regulation Compensator

According to [7], the output voltage of LDO regulator can be derived as:

$$V_{out} = V_{refp}\left(1+\frac{R_1}{R_2}\right) - I_{out}R_{load\_reg} \text{ where } R_{load\_reg} = \frac{R_o}{1+A_{EA}\beta} \quad (4)$$

R_{load_reg} is the load regulation, A_{EA} is the open-loop gain of the error amplifier, β is the feedback factor and R_o is the output resistance of power transistor. In order to reduce the voltage variation $\triangle V$ due to load variations, the ARC circuit uses a load sensing current I_c to solve this issue and we can obtain the following condition is:

$$\frac{R_f}{N}\left(1+\frac{R_1}{R_2}\right) = R_{load\_reg} \quad (5)$$

Hence, the sizes of R_f and the value of N are carefully designed to get a minimum voltage variation $\triangle V$.

Based on the reference controller and load regulation compensator, the adaptive reference voltage V_{refp} can be derived as following equation to satisfy the demands of different load condition during transient and steady periods.

$$V_{refp} = V_{ref} + \left((V_{refp} - V_{fb})\frac{2K}{R_d} + \frac{I_L}{N}\right)R_f \quad (6)$$

IV. EXPERIMENTAL RESULTS

The proposed LDO regulator with adaptive reference control technique was implemented in TSMC 0.35-μm CMOS technology. The chip micrograph is shown in figure 5 and chip area is 400 μm×470 μm. A summary of the LDO performance is shown in Table I.

The load current with rising time and falling time of 0.1 μs changes from 1 mA to 100 mA, or vice versa. Figure 6 (a) and (b) are the waveforms of LDO regulator without and with ARC technique, respectively. Obviously, the undershoot voltage and settling time are improved about 31% and 68.5%, respectively. Load regulation is improved about 70%. The enlarged waveforms are shown in figure 7 (a) and (b) which demonstrate that the ARC technique can smoothly adjust reference voltage to stabilize output voltage in case of load variations.

V. CONCLUSION

A LDO regulator with ARC technique is presented in this paper. ARC technique can dynamically and smoothly

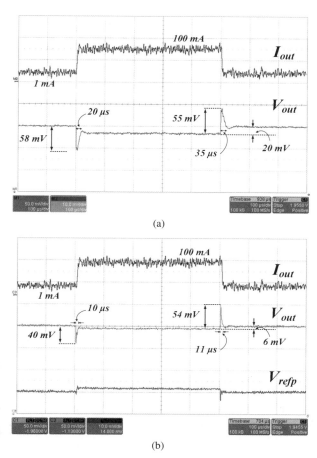

(a)

(b)

Figure 6. Transient response of a LDO regulator with load current step from 1 mA and 100 mA, or vice versa. (a) Without ARC technique. (b) With ARC technique. (V_{out} = 2V)

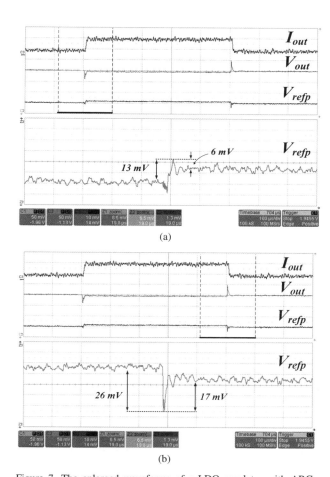

(a)

(b)

Figure 7. The enlarged waveforms of a LDO regulator with ARC technique. (a) Load current changes from 1 mA to 100 mA. (b) Load current changes from 100 mA to 1 mA.

TABLE I: SUMMARY OF THE LDO PERFORMANCE

Technology	0.35-μm CMOS
Supply Voltage	2.1 V to 5 V
Output Voltage	2 V
Maximum Load Current	100 mA
Line Regulation	5 mV/V
Load Regulation	w/o ARC: 0.2 mV/mA with ARC: 60 μV/mA
Quiescent Current	40 μA
Dropout Voltage (I_{out}=100 mA)	60 mV
Settling Time (C_L=4.7 μF, R_{ESR}=0.5 Ω) (100 mA→1 mA)	w/o ARC: 35 μs with ARC: 11 μs
Undershoot Voltage	w/o ARC: 58 mV with ARC: 40 mV
Overshoot Voltage	w/o ARC: 55 mV with ARC: 54 mV

adjust the reference voltage, which is proportional to the output error voltage and load condition, to enhance slew rate of error amplifier. Not only the undershoot/overshoot voltage can be improved, but also the settling time and load regulation can be enhanced significantly.

REFERENCES

[1] Hoi Lee, Philip K. T. Mok, and Ka Nang Leung, "Design of low-power analog drivers based on slew-rate enhancement circuits for CMOS low-dropout regulators," *IEEE Trans. Circuits and Systems II*, vol. 52, no. 9, pp. 563-567, Sept. 2005.

[2] Jeongjin Roh, "High-performance error amplifier for fast transient DC-DC converters," *IEEE Trans. Circuits and Systems II*, vol. 52, no. 9, pp. 591-595, Sept. 2005.

[3] Ke-Horng Chen, Hong-Wei Huang, and Sy-Yen Kuo, "Fast Transient DC-DC Converter with On-Chip Compensated Error Amplifier," *IEEE Trans. Circuits and Systems II*, vol. 54, no. 12, pp. 1150-1154, Dec. 2007.

[4] Kaiwei Yao, Kisun Lee, Ming Xu, and Fred C. Lee, "Optimal design of the active droop control method for the transient response," *Applied Power Electronics Conference and Exposition*, vol. 2, pp. 718-723, Feb. 2003.

[5] P. Hazucha, T. Karnik, Bradley A. Bloechel, C. Parsons, D. Finan, S. Borkar, "Area-Efficient Linear Regulator With Ultra-Fast Load Regulation," *IEEE J. Solid-State Circuits*, vol. 40, no. 4, pp. 933-940, April 2005.

[6] Man Siu, Philip K.T. Mok, Ka Nang Leung, Yat-Hei Lam, Wing-Hung Ki, "A voltage-mode PWM buck regulator with end-point prediction," *IEEE TCAS II*, vol. 53, no. 4, pp. 294-298, April 2006.

[7] R. K. Dokania and G. A. Rincon-Mora, "Cancellation of load regulation in low drop-out regulators," *Electronics Letters*, vol.38, no.22, pp.1300-1302, Oct. 2002.

[8] J. Ramirez-Angulo, S. G. Ivan Padilla, R. G. Carvajal, A. Torralba, M. Jimenez, F. Munoz, Antonio Lopez-Martin, "Comparison of Conventional and New Flipped Voltage Structures With Increased Input/output Signal Swing and Current Sourcing/Sinking Capabilities," *IEEE International Midwest Symposium on Circuits and Systems*, pp. 1151-1154, Aug. 2005.

[9] R. G. Carvajal, J. Ramirez-Angulo, A. J. Lopez-Martin, A. Torralba, J. A. G. Galan, A. Carlosena, F. M. Chavero, "The flipped voltage follower: a useful cell for low-voltage low-power circuit design," *IEEE Trans. Circuits and Systems I*, vol. 52, no. 7, pp. 1276-1291, July 2005.

A High-Power-LED Driver with Power-Efficient LED-Current Sensing Circuit

Wing Yan Leung, Tsz Yin Man, Mansun Chan
The Department of Electronic and Computer Engineering
Hong Kong University of Science & Technology
Hong Kong SAR, China
mchan@ece.ust.hk

Abstract☐ **For lighting application, high-power LED nowadays is driven at 350mA and a sensing resistor is used to provide feedback for LED-current regulation. This method adds an IR drop at the output branch, and limits power efficiency as LED-current is large and keeps increasing. In this paper, a power-efficient LED-current sensing circuit is proposed. The circuit does not use any sensing resistor but extracts LED-current information from the output capacitor of the driver. The sensing circuit is implemented in a Buck-boost LED driver and has been fabricated in AMS 0.35μm CMOS technology. Measurement results indicate a power-conversion efficiency of 92% and at least 90 times power reduction in sensing compared to existing approach.**

I. INTRODUCTION

High-power LED has been commonly adopted as flashlight for camera phones and is replacing traditional light-bulb in high-end flashlights. One of the most commonly used high-power LED is driven at 350mA, and LED manufacturers are constantly working on driving LED at higher output current so that it can provide sufficient light output for broader lighting applications. Commercial high-power LED can be driven at current as high as 1.5A nowadays [1].

This brings about the need for high-power LED driver that can deliver and regulate LED-current in a power-efficient manner. Switch Mode Power Converters (SMPCs) are common choices for high-power LED driver as they can deliver high output-current at high power-conversion efficiency. However, SMPCs are originally output-voltage-regulated, and thus have to be converted to an output-current-regulated driver. Commercial products use a sensing resistor placed in series to the high-power LED to sense the current and convert it to a feedback voltage for system control [2]-[8]. For applications like flashlights in camera phones or torches where only one high-power LED is used, power dissipation for sensing can take up to 26% of the total power delivered [4]. This seriously compromises power-conversion efficiency and shortens battery-life of those products.

Furthermore, sensing resistor approach has power dissipation that increases in square rate to LED-current. As driving current of high-power LED increases, this sensing

scheme will dissipate higher power and further limit power efficiency. Therefore, more power-efficient LED-current sensing circuit has to be developed to meet this challenge.

As Li-ion battery that has a voltage of 2.7V to 4.2V is commonly used as power source for handheld devices, a high-power LED driver has to step up or step down this supply voltage to drive a 350mA high-power LED of forward voltage of 3.4V to 3.7V. This makes Buck-boost converter one of the most suitable candidates. In this paper, an LED-current sensing circuit that is suitable for Buck-boost and Boost converter is presented. In the next section, existing approach to LED-current sensing and the operation principle of a buck-boost converter will be reviewed. The operation principle and implementation of the proposed LED-current sensing circuit will be presented in section three, and measurement results of the proposed LED-current sensing circuit will be discussed in section four.

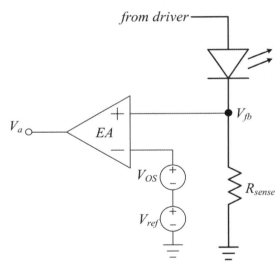

Figure 1. LED-current sensing with sensing resistor

As illustrated in figure 1, a common approach [2]-[8] to LED-current sensing in high-power LED driver is to use a sensing resistor placed in series to the high-power LED. The high-power LED to be driven and its sensing resistor form a feedback network that replaces the resistive feedback network used in conventional Buck-boost converter. LED-current is then defined by

$$I_{LED} = \frac{V_{ref}}{R_{sense}} \tag{1}$$

Existing commercial products use voltage references of values ranging from $110mV$ to $1.23V$ [2]-[8]. Hence, to drive a 350mA high-power LED, the required sensing resistors are between $314m\Omega$ to 3.5Ω. Power efficiency of such sensing circuit P_{snese} shows a square dependence on LED-current and can be calculated by the equation

$$P_{sense} = I_{LED}^{2} R_{sense} \tag{2}$$

This gives an estimation of power dissipation of a range between 38.5mW to 430mW. With LED-current increasing to increase light output, the power dissipated by such LED-current sensing circuit will be increasing at square rate at the same time.

One way to lower the power dissipation is to use a smaller sensing resistor but then sensing accuracy is compromised. For any amplifier design used as the error amplifier for LED-current sensing, the offset voltage V_{OS} of it can be reflected in the feedback voltage as

$$V_{fb} = V_{ref} + V_{OS} \tag{3}$$

When reference voltage V_{ref} becomes smaller, offset voltage V_{OS} becomes more significant in the expression thus degrades sensing accuracy. Therefore when a smaller reference voltage is used, the offset voltage of error amplifier has to be reduced proportionally to maintain accuracy. This posts a lower limit on possible reference voltage value as there is always random offset introduced by process variation.

II. PROPOSED CURRENT SENSING CIRCUIT

In fact, output current information can be extracted from the Buck-boost converter itself. Figure 2 illustrates a Buck-boost converter driving a high-power LED and figure 3 gives the sketches of a few important waveforms.

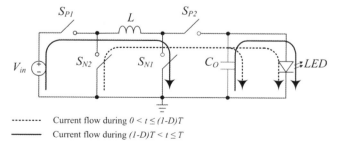

-------- Current flow during $0 < t \leq (1-D)T$
———— Current flow during $(1-D)T < t \leq T$

Figure 2. A Buck-boost High-power LED driver

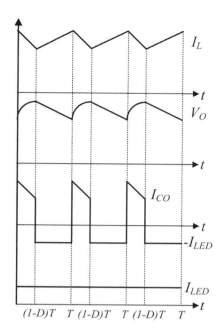

Figure 3. Sketches of waveforms of a Buck-boost high-power LED driver

In 'Reset' state ($0<t=(1-D)T$), switches S_{P1} and S_{N1} are off, and switches S_{P2} and S_{N2} are on. The driver is detached from voltage source V_{in}. Energy stored in inductor is delivered to output capacitor C_O and the high-power LED. In 'Set' state ($(1-D)T<t=T$), switches S_{P1} and S_{N1} are on and switches S_{P2} and S_{N2} are off. Current flows from voltage source V_{in} to inductor L and energy is stored. Meanwhile, the high power LED is disconnected from the inductor and output-current is solely provided by output capacitor C_O. Therefore, current flowing out of output capacitor is equal to the LED-current in this time period, and this information on LED-current is found in the slope of decreasing V_O based on equation 4.

$$I_{Co} = C_O \frac{dV_O}{dt} \tag{4}$$

The proposed LED-current sensing circuit makes use of this property and recovers LED-current information by using a resistive network, a differentiator and a sample and hold circuit.

System diagram of the proposed LED-current sensing circuit is shown in figure 3. A feedback voltage is generated by using a resistive potential divider. An error amplifier, differentiating resistor R_{diff} and capacitor C_{diff} form the differentiator that differentiates feedback voltage across time to give V_{diff}. As differentiator draws current from the input, a voltage buffer is required to provide the current required so that no current is drawn from potential divider. A sampling switch and capacitor C_{samp} form the sample and hold circuit that samples the output of the differentiator during 'set' period and hold it for the remaining time. Another error amplifier EA is used to compare the sampled voltage V_{samp} with reference voltage V_{ref} to define LED-current.

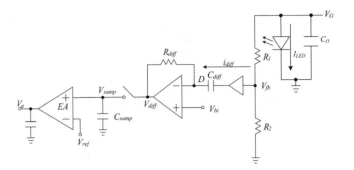

Figure 4. System diagram of the proposed LED-current sensing circuit

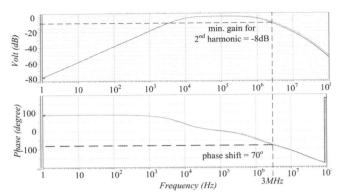

Figure 5. Frequency response of the proposed LED-current sensing circuit

Equation (5) gives the relationship between nodal voltage V_{diff} and feedback voltage V_{fb}.

$$V_{diff}(t) = V_{bi} - R_{diff}C_{diff}\frac{d}{dt}V_{fb}(t) \tag{5}$$

It can be seen that V_{bi} has to be set to a value high enough such that V_{diff} is larger than zero all the time. It should be noticed that there is a negative sign before the derivative term which means that V_{diff} decreases when the slope of V_{fb} is positive and vice versa.

As capacitor current represents LED-current only when $(1-D)T<t \le T$, hence only the differentiation result during that period is useful. A sample and hold circuit is needed to sample the value of V_{diff} during that time period and hold it in the remaining time. When sampling switch is close, value of V_{diff} is sampled by the capacitor C_{samp} to be V_{samp}, and when the switch is open, V_{samp} holds the value of V_{diff} to the instant right before the switch opens. An error amplifier is then used to compare V_{samp} with V_{ref} to provide voltage V_a for PWM control. The LED-current is defined in equation (6).

$$I_{LED} = \frac{V_{ref} - V_{bi}}{R_{diff}} \frac{C_O}{C_{diff}} \left(1 + \frac{R_1}{R_2}\right) \tag{6}$$

Bandwidth of the proposed sensing circuit is critical to its performance as it has to differentiate a fast-varying V_O accurately to recover LED-current information. Switching frequency of the proposed driver is 1MHz and the signal V_O is triangular during the period of interest. Hence the LED-current sensing circuit is designed to include two harmonics of signal V_O such that sensing can be more accurate. Transfer function of the LED-current sensing circuit is shown in figure 5. Transfer function of the LED-current sensing circuit from I_{LED} to V_{diff} is given as equation (7).

In the transfer function, R_1 and R_2 is the feedback resistors. G_{ma}, R_{oa} and C_{oa} are the trans-conductance, output resistance and parasitic output capacitance of the error amplifier used in differentiator respectively. R_O denotes the load, which is the resistance of the high-power LED.

For accurate sensing and high bandwidth, transconductance G_{ma} and output resistance R_{oa} have to be large. In the proposed design, $40\mu A$ is used to bias the differentiator and the voltage buffer to achieve high bandwidth. In addition to the $20\mu A$ that flows through resistor R_1 and R_2, the worst case total power dissipation in sensing circuit is $420\mu W$ when V_{in} is $4.2V$. This is 90 times less than the most power-cautious approach currently used.

III. MEASUREMENT

The proposed LED-current sensing scheme and the respective Buck-boost LED driver are fabricated in AMS $0.35\mu m$ process. The chip area is $2.4mm$ by $2.5mm$. Measurement is done on sensing accuracy, line and load regulation, and power efficiency of the chip.

Figure 6 shows the buffered output of differentiator V_{diff} and the buffered sampled voltage V_{samp} when supply voltage is $2.7V$ and an LED-current of $350mA$. Because of the switching noise coupled from switching nodes of the driver, there is switching noise in the waveform of the output of differentiator V_{diff}. However, as the value of V_{diff} is sampled in instants when the driver is not switching, and the value is held constant thereafter, the switching noise induced distortion that appears in V_{diff} node is not passed to V_{samp}, as shown in the figure.

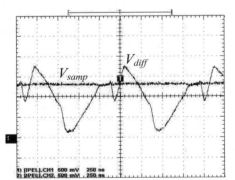

Figure 6. Buffered differentiator output V_{diff} and sampled voltage V_{samp}

$$\frac{\Delta V_{sample}}{\Delta I_{LED}} = \left(\frac{R_2}{R_1+R_2}\right)\left(\frac{G_{ma}R_{oa}}{1+G_{ma}R_{oa}}\right)\frac{R_O}{(1+sC_OR_O)}\frac{sC_{diff}R_{diff}}{\left(1+s\dfrac{C_{diff}R_{diff}}{1+G_{ma}R_{oa}}\right)(1+sR_{oa}C_{oa})} \tag{7}$$

356

A plot of output-current for different reference voltages V_{ref} is shown in figure 7. The measured feedback factor is linear with a scale V_{samp}/I_{LED} of $1.85mV/mA$. When supply voltage V_{in} is changed from 2.7V to 3.6V, the output current for the same reference voltage V_{ref} does not change significantly.

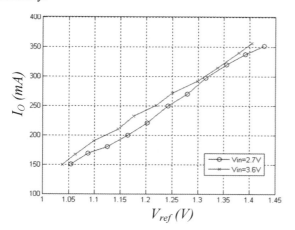

Figure 7.   Output current versus reference voltage at V_{DD} =2.7V and 3.6V

To test current regulation ability of the proposed LED driver under different loading resistance, two resistors of 10Ω and 4.7Ω are used. The preset output current is $350mA$, and input voltage V_{in} is swept from $2.7V$ to $3.6V$. Measurement result is shown in figure 8 and it proves that the driver provides a relatively constant output current under different loading resistances. The maximum difference in output current between a 10Ω load and a 4.7Ω load is $6mA$.

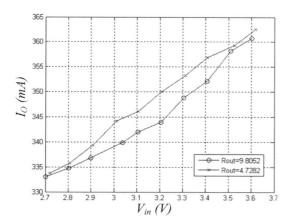

Figure 8.   Measured current regulation at different loading resistor values and input voltages

Figure 9 shows the plot of efficiency for output current between $150mA$ to $350mA$. Three curves are obtained under input voltages at $2.7V$, $3.3V$ and $3.6V$. The minimum efficiency is 87%, and is measured at an input voltage of 2.7V and an output current of 350mA. The maximum efficiency for 350mA output current is 92% and is measured at supply voltage of $3.6V$.

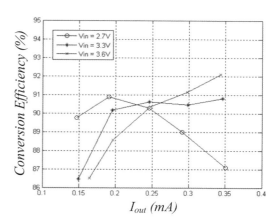

Figure 9.   Plot of efficiency at different output current

IV.   CONCLUSION

In this paper, an LED-current sensing circuit that uses 90 times less power than the most power efficient design existed is proposed. The proposed sensing circuit senses LED-current by differentiating the voltage of the output capacitor and uses only at maximum $420\mu W$ of power. It is implemented in a Buck-boost LED driver and the design is fabricated in AMS $0.35\mu m$ process. Measurement results confirm a reasonable sensing accuracy and line/load regulation. The maximum power efficiency is measured to be 92%. As the power consumption of the proposed LED-current sensing circuit does not increase proportionally to the LED-current, the circuit is particularly useful when LED-current continues to increase in the future.

ACKNOWLEDGMENT

This work is supported by an earmarked grant from the Research Grant Council under the contract number HKUST611205.

REFERENCES

[1]   "Philips Lumileds LED technology breakthrough fundamentally solves efficiency losses at high drive currents", Press Information, Philips Lumileds Lighting Company, 13 February 2007.

[2]   "1A Synchronous Buck-boost High Current LED Driver", datasheet LTC3454, Linear Technology Corporation, December 2005.

[3]   "Offline and DC-DC PWM controllers for High Brightness LED Drivers", datasheet MAX 16802, Maxim Integrated Products, January 2006.

[4]   "NCP5030: Buckboost Converter to Drive a Single LED from 1 Li-ion or 3 Alkaline Batteries", datasheet NCP 5030, Rev. 0, Semiconductor Components Industries, LLC, December 2006.

[5]   "1.5MHz, 30A, High-Efficiency LED-Driver with Rapid Current Pulsing", datasheet MAX 16818, Maxim Integrated Products, October 2006.

[6]   "Synchronous Boost Converter with Down Mode High Power White LED Driver", datasheet tps61058/tps61059, Texas Instrument Incorporated, December 2005.

[7]   "1.2A High Power White LED Driver, 2MHz Synchronous Boost Conveter with I2C compatible interface", datasheet tps61050, Texas Instrument Incorporated, March 2007.

"LM3402/LM3402HV Constant Current Buck Regulator for Driving High power LEDs", datasheet LM 3402, National Semiconductor, October 2006.

Boost DC-DC Converter with Charge-Recycling (CR) and Fast Reference Tracking (FRT) Techniques for High-Efficiency and Low-Cost LED Driver

Chun-Yu Hsieh and Ke-Horng Chen

Department of Electrical and Control Engineering

National Chiao Tung University

Hsinchu, Taiwan

Abstract—A charge-recycling (CR) technique and fast reference tracking (DRT) are proposed for implementing a high efficiency and low cost RGB backlight module in color sequential notebook computers' display. A RGB LED driver composed of an asynchronous 1.5MHz DC/DC boost converter with FRT and CR techniques was fabricated in TSMC 0.25μm BCD 40V to generate 17V for 6-series red LEDs or 21V for 6-series green, or blue LEDs. The CR technique stores extra energy at the output node when the output voltage is switched from low to high voltage level and releases the reserved energy back to the output node at next period. Furthermore, the output voltage can be rapidly switched between two different voltage levels by FRT technique without wasting much power owing to the CR technique.

I. INTRODUCTION

The most popular and power-efficiency backlight module is white LED backlight in LCD panels. The reason is that the power dissipation can be reduced about 40% compared to conventional CCFL backlight module. However, the color filter still is needed and thus generates about 70~80% NTSC color gamut. It is important to decrease to the power consumption in backlight module due to the color filter. Fortunately, without the requirement of color filter in LCD panels, the color-sequential (MCS) algorithm [1] in Fig. 1 that effectively reduced color breakup and motion blur effects can saves much power consumption of the backlight module. The color gamut can be raised to about 110% NTSC and the power dissipation can be further reduced to only 40% of that with CCFL backlight module. Therefore, the LCD panels without color filter need a low cost and high efficiency RGB backlight driver to achieve a high quality image display.

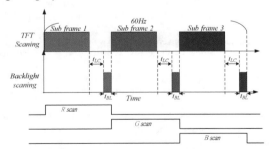

Fig. 1. (a) The timing diagram of color sequential technique for color-filter-less LCD panel.

The MCS method displays three different colors of backlight in sequence in a period (1/60s). That is all LEDs are not needed to be turned on at the same time. However, the different colors of LEDs have different forward voltages due to the difference of LEDs between material and process. Therefore, nine boost converters in a RGB backlight module are demanded for notebook's panel. Contrarily, if the output supplying voltage can be rapidly switched between 17V and 21V, we need only one DC-DC converter shown in Fig. 2 to drive RGB LEDs for implementing the modified MCS algorithm. For achieving high efficiency and low cost, charging recycling and fast reference tracking techniques are developed in this paper.

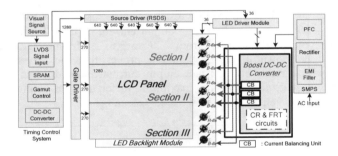

Fig. 2. The proposed LED driver with only one DC-DC converter in.

A charge-recycling (CR) technique is proposed for save much power dissipation during the transition between two different output supplying voltages. Furthermore, in order to rapidly switch between two output voltages, a fast reference tracking (FRT) technique is presented in Section II. The circuit implementation is presented in Section III. The chip was fabricated in TSMC 0.25μm BCD 40V and experimental results are shown in Section IV. Finally, a conclusion is made in Section V.

II. FAST REFERENCE TRACKING TECHNIQUE

The LED driver for mixed color sequential algorithm needs two characteristics to meet the requirements of the LCD response time. One is the fast reference voltage tracking [2] for rapidly switching two different voltages between three colors and the other one is the charge recycling technique for reducing power consumption and improving the efficiency. Thus, the total schematic of the proposed RGB driver is shown in Fig. 3 (a).

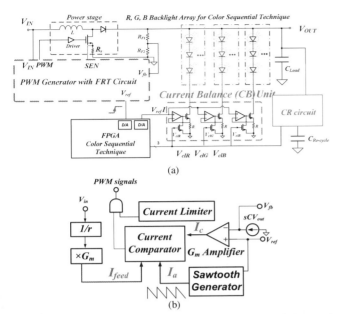

(a)

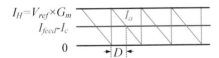

(b)

Fig. 3. (a) The proposed driver contains FRT, CR, and current balance unit (CB) circuits. (b) PWM generator with FRT technique.

A. Circuit of FRT technique

In Fig. 3 (b), the FRT technique for improving line transient speed needs a new current I_{feed} that stands for the input voltage information. The definition of the peak value $I_H=V_{ref}*G_m$ of the saw-tooth generates a larger duty cycle to increase the output voltage quickly for fast tracking the variations of the reference voltage V_{ref}. The duty cycle of a voltage-mode boost converter operated in continuous current mode (CCM) is defined as (1) and shown in Fig. 4. Ideally, the variation of I_c can be neglected compared to the variations of I_{feed}.

$$D = \frac{V_o - V_{in}}{V_0} = \frac{I_H - (I_{feed} - I_c)}{I_H} = \frac{V_{ref} \times G_m - I_{feed}}{V_{ref} \times G_m} \quad (1)$$

where $I_H = V_{ref} \times G_m$

Fig.4. The determination of duty waveform in the FRT technique.

At steady state, the feedback voltage V_{fb} is equal to the reference voltage V_{ref} is shown in (2) when the current I_{feed} is used to minimize the variation of error current I_c. From (1) and (2), the expression of the duty cycle is rewritten as (3).

$$V_{ref} = V_{fb} = \frac{R_{F2}}{R_{F1} + R_{F2}} V_o = rV_o \text{ where } r = \frac{R_{F2}}{R_{F1} + R_{F2}} \quad (2)$$

$$D = \frac{V_o - V_{in}}{V_o} = \frac{rV_o \times G_m - I_{feed}}{rV_o \times G_m} \text{ where } I_{feed} = rV_{in} \times G_m \quad (3)$$

Moreover, wideband G_m amplifier [3] is utilized to increase the system bandwidth. Besides, current limit circuit is also used to control peak current to make sure the correctly regulated output voltage. The circuit implementation is shown in Fig. 5.

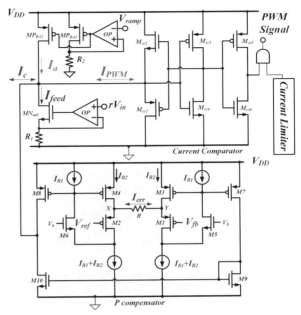

Fig. 5. The PWM generator with FRT technique consists of V-I converter, P compensator, and current comparator.

B. Analysis of FRT technique

The analysis of FRT operation is divided into four stages as follows and shown in Fig. 6.

Stage I: when the reference voltage V_{ref} steps from V_{ref1} to V_{ref2}, the peak value I_H of saw-tooth current I_a is increased instantly due to reference tracking mechanism. The error current I_c, which is the output of G_m amplifier, is also increased owing to a larger difference voltage between V_{ref} to V_{fb}. A feedforward current I_{feed} is determined by input voltage V_{in}. The difference current between I_{feed} and I_c is compared to saw-tooth current I_a for determining duty cycle. Therefore, the summation current of I_{feed}-I_c is decreased instantly as a result that reference voltage V_{ref} is increased. Thus, by comparing I_a and I_{feed} - I_c, the control signal V_{PWM} is switched to a high level and the turn-on time of power transistor MN_1 is limited to a predefined maximum duty that represents a peak current level. Thus, the boost converter is controlled by the peak current loop. The output voltage is raised to a high-supplying level for a forward conduction voltage of serial G or B LEDs within a short time [4-5].

Stage II: when the output voltage V_{out} approaches the high-supplying level, the error current I_c is gradually decrease by because the difference voltage between V_{fb} and V_{ref} is decreased. Owing to fast response of G_m amplifier, the current of I_{feed} - I_c is increased rapidly. Thus, the PWM generator can substitute for the peak current control to circuit regulate the output voltage.

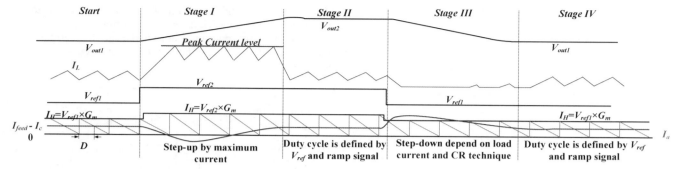

Fig. 6. The timing diagram of the proposed LED driver circuit with FRT technique.

Stage III: when the reference voltage V_{ref} is decreased instantly from V_{ref2} to V_{ref1}, the error current I_c by G_m amplifier is instantly decreased owing to a larger difference voltage between V_{ref} and V_{fb}. Besides, due to the reference tracking mechanism, the peak value of saw-tooth current I_a is decreased. Thus, the current I_a decreases and I_{feed}-I_c increases instantly as well. By comparing I_a and I_{feed}-I_c, the control signal V_{PWM} can be adjusted to a lowest level to turn off power transistor MN_1. Thus, the output voltage is decreased according to load current and the charge-recycling circuit as describe in Section III.

Stage IV: when the output voltage is decreased to the low-supplying level, the error current I_c is increased. Due to the fast response of G_m amplifier, the current of I_{feed}-I_c is decreased instantly. The fast and stable pulse width control is guaranteed.

III. CR TECHNIQUE FOR IMPROVING EFFICIENCY

The low-supplying level is quickly raised to the high-supplying voltage by the proposed FRT technique. However, the decreasing speed from high-supplying to low-supplying voltage depends on the output capacitor and load current. It is very hard to pull low the output voltage due to low load current. Therefore, the charge-recycling circuit redirects the extra charge from the output capacitor to the recycling capacitor $C_{Re-cycle}$ to maintain the high efficiency and rapidly pulls low the output voltage at the same time. When the mixed color sequential technique switch the different color LEDs, three signals (V_{clR}, V_{clG}, V_{clB}) in Fig. 3 (a) and Fig. 7 determine the one-shot signal. If the V_{out} drops from high to low-supplying voltage, it enables a one-shot signal to turn on power transistor M_{P1}. Thus, the charge-recycling circuit is activated and stores extra energy in the $C_{Re-cycle}$. Besides, when V_{out} increases from low to high-supplying level to turn

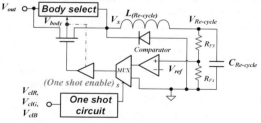

Fig. 7. the circuit of charge recycling technique

on the G- or B-LEDs, the charge-recycling circuit discharges the $C_{Re-cycle}$ and the stored energy is used to speed up the raising time. Moreover, because $V_{Re-cycle}$ switches between high or low supplying level, the body select circuit is needed to prevent the forward biasing current from decreasing efficiency. The charge recycling circuit effectively saves much power when the backlight module changes from R-LEDs to G- or B-LEDs.

The LEDs backlight module needs two different voltage in the different time, and the difference voltage V_{diff} is approximately 5V. Thus the charge-recycling circuit can transfer 5V energy from capacitor. Thus, the $C_{Re-cycle}$ is chosen a value like that of external of capacitor C_{load}. Owing to the laws of conservation of energy, the one-shot time is defined as (4).

$$T_{one-shot} = \frac{(C_{load} \text{ or } C_{Re-cycle}) \times V}{I_{tran}} \quad (4)$$

I_{tran} is an average current in the transmitted energy period. The slope of inductor current is defined as $V_{diff}/L_{Re-cycle}$. The peak value of inductor current I_{peak} is about $2 \times I_{tran}$. Thus, the value of inductor is defined as (5).

$$\frac{\Delta V}{L} \cdot t = I_{peak} \Rightarrow \frac{V_{diff}/2}{L_{Re-cycle}} \cdot \frac{T_{one-shot}}{2} = 2 \cdot I_{tran}$$

$$\Rightarrow L_{Re-cycle} \approx \frac{V_{diff} \cdot T_{one-shot}}{8 I_{tran}} \quad (4)$$

According to (4) and (5), the CR circuit is designed to smoothly transfer energy between two capacitors. The one shot signal is determined by V_{clR}, V_{clG}, and V_{clB}. When the backlight module changes from G- or B- LEDs to R- LEDs, it sends one shot signal to turn on the power transistor M_{P1}. At this time, the CR circuit is activated to transmit energy from C_{load} to $C_{Re-cycle}$. Contrarily, when the backlight module changes from R- LEDs to G- or B- LEDs, the stored energy is restored back to C_{load}. However, when G- LEDs changes to B- LEDs, the CR circuit is not activated.

IV. EXPERIMENTAL RESULTS

The proposed boost converter with charge recycling circuit was fabricated in 0.25μm TSMC BCD 40V process. When the output voltage changes from high-supplying level for G- or B- LEDs to low-supplying level for R- LEDs, a one-shot signal is sent to turn on the power transistor for transmitting energy from C_{load} to $C_{Re-cycle}$. The charge-recycling waveforms are shown in Fig. 8. In Fig. 8(a), the $I_{L(Re-cycle)}$ transmits energy from V_{out} to $V_{Re-cycle}$ and the energy stored in $C_{Re-cycle}$ at time T_1. The dropout voltage of V_{out} depends on the value of load capacitor C_{load} and load current at time T_2. When the low-supplying level steps to high-supplying level, a one-shot signal is sent to restore the recycling energy. The stored energy in the $C_{Re-cycle}$ is transferred back to V_{out} for rapidly raising the output voltage. Thus, Fig. 8(b) shows the reversing current $I_{L(Re-cycle)}$ from $V_{Re-cycle}$ to V_{out} at time T_3. The stored energy in $C_{Re-cycle}$ is released to speed up the transient time at the dynamic output voltage. The output voltage gets much energy from the CR circuit of boost converter at time T_4.

Thus, the extra energy stored at the $C_{Re-cycle}$ is efficiently used to drive the LED arrays. The micrograph of the chip is shown in Fig. 9. Performance summary is listed in Table I.

Table I: PERFORMANCE SUMMARY

Input Voltage	8~13.5V	Inductor	10 µH
Output Voltage	16~21V	Capacitor	C_{load}=4.7 µF, $C_{Re-cycle}$ =4.7 µF,
Switching frequency	1.5MHz	Load Regulation	0.5mV/mA@V_{IN}=12V, V_{OUT}=21V
Max. output current	300mA	Line Regulation	1.36mV/V@V_{OUT}=30V, I_{OUT}=80mA

V. CONCLUSIONS

A RGB LED backlight driver is proposed for rapidly switching between driving 6-series R (about 17V) and 6-series G/B LEDs (about 21V). Owing to voltage difference about 4V between driving series-R and series-G/B LEDs, the FRT technique is presented to enhance line and load regulations. Besides, extra energy can be stored in a charge re-cycling capacitor at the transition from high voltage (21V) to low voltage (17V) while it can be restored back to output node to speed up the raising of voltage back 21V at the stage of driving G/B LEDs. The proposed LED driver with charge recycling circuit was implemented in 0.25µm TSMC BCD 40V process. Experimental results show that the transition time can be reduced within 22µs and the power consumption of the backlight module is smaller than 3W in Fig. 10.

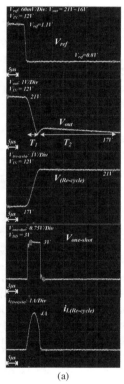 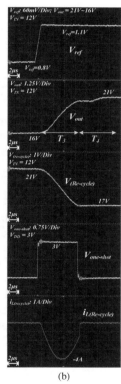

(a) (b)

Fig. 9. (a) When G- or B- LEDs switch to R-LEDs, the extra energy is stored in the auxiliary inductor $L_{(Re-cycle)}$ and capacitor $C_{Re-cycle}$, which is triggered by the one-shot signal. (b) When R-LEDs switch to G- or B- LEDs, the extra energy stored in the auxiliary inductor $L_{(Re-cycle)}$ and capacitor $C_{Re-cycle}$ is released to the output node V_{out}, which is triggered by the one-shot signal.

(a) (b)

Fig. 10. (a) The power consumption of LCD panel with color filter and CCFL backlight is larger than 5W. (b) The power consumption of the color filter-less LCD panel with the proposed RGB backlight driver is about 2-3W.

Fig. 9. Chip micrograph.

REFERENCES

[1] Yi-Fu Chen, Che-Chin Chen, and Ke-Horng Chen, "Mixed Color Sequential Technique for Reducing Color Breakup and Motion Blur Effects," *IEEE/OSA Journal of Display Technology*, pp. 377-385, Dec. 2007.

[2] Man Siu, Philip K.T. Mok, Ka Nang Leung, Yat-Hei Lam, Wing-Hung Ki, "A voltage-mode PWM buck regulator with end-point prediction," *IEEE TCAS II*, vol. 53, no. 4, pp. 294-298, April 2006.

[3] Werner Hollinger, Manfred Punzenberger, "An Asynchronous 1.8MHz DC/DC Boost Converter Implemented in the Current Domain for Cellular Phone Lighting Management," *IEEE European Solid-State Circuits Conference*, pp. 528-531, Sep. 2006.

[4] Ke-Horng Chen, Hong-Wei Huang, and Sy-Yen Kuo, "Fast Transient DC-DC Converter with On-Chip Compensated Error Amplifier," *in IEEE Transaction on Circuits and Systems II,* pp. 1150-1154, Dec. 2007.

[5] Hong-Wei Huang, Chun-Yu Hsieh, Ke-Horng Chen, and Sy-Yen Kuo, "Adaptive Frequency Control Technique for Enhancing Transient Performance of DC-DC Converters," *IEEE European Solid-State Circuits Conference,* pp. 174-177, Sep. 2007.

[6] Doshi, Montu; Zane, Regan, "Digital Architecture for Driving Large LED Arrays with Dynamic Bus Voltage Regulation and Phase Shifted PWM" *IEEE Applied Power Electronics Conference,* pp.287-393, Feb. 2007.

An 11-bit 8.6GHz Direct Digital Synthesizer MMIC with 10-bit Segmented Nonlinear DAC

Xueyang Geng, Xuefeng Yu, Fa Foster Dai, J. David Irwin and Richard C. Jaeger

Department of Electrical and Computer Engineering, Auburn University

Auburn, AL 36849-5201, USA

Email: {gengxue,yuxuefe,fosterdai,irwinjd,jaegerc}@auburn.edu

Abstract—This paper presents a low power, high speed and high resolution SiGe DDS MMIC with 11-bit phase and 10-bit amplitude resolutions. Using more than twenty thousand transistors, including an 11-bit pipeline accumulator, a 6-bit coarse DAC and seven 3-bit fine DACs, the core area of the DDS is $3 \times 2.5 \mathrm{mm}^2$. The maximum clock frequency was measured at 8.6GHz with 4.2958GHz output. The DDS consumes a power of 4.8W under a 3.3V power supply. It achieves the best reported phase and amplitude resolutions and the best power efficiency figure of merit (FOM) $182 \mathrm{GHz} \cdot 2^{\mathrm{ENOB}} / \mathrm{W}$. The measured SFDR is approximately 40dBc with 4.2958GHz Nyquist output and 48dBc with 4.2MHz output at the maximum clock frequency of 8.6GHz. The chip was measured using LCC-52 packages.

I. INTRODUCTION

Ultra high-speed heterojunction transistors (HBT) allow a direct digital synthesizer (DDS) to operate at mm-wave frequency, a preferable solution to synthesis of sine waveforms with fine frequency resolution, fast channel switching and versatile modulation capability. There are several high speed DDS designs reported with clock frequencies from 9GHz to 32GHz and DAC resolution from 5 bits to maximum of 8 bits [1]–[3]. The maximum achieved spurious-free dynamic range (SFDR) in previous DDS designs is approximately 30dBc, which is not sufficient for typical radar and wireless applications. These ultra-high speed DDSs have been implemented in indium phosphide (InP) (HBT) technology and only tested on wafer [1]–[3]. The DDS described in this paper employs a $0.13\mu m$ silicon germanium (SiGe) BiCMOS technology, which is less expensive, more robust and has higher yield than the InP devices. The design presented here achieves 11-bit phase and 10-bit amplitude resolutions with maximum clock frequency of 8.6GHz. It consumes 4.8W with the best reported power efficiency figure of merit (FOM) of $182GHz \cdot 2^{ENOB}/W$ and the best reported SFDR of 40dBc.

II. ROM-LESS DDS WITH SEGMENTED NONLINEAR DACs

The proposed DDS adopts a ROM-less architecture which combines both the sine/cosine mapping and digital-to-analog conversion together in a sine-weighted nonlinear digital-to-analog converter (DAC). The block diagram of the 11-bit 8.6GHz ROM-less DDS with nonlinear DAC is shown in Fig. 1. The major part of the ROM-less DDS is an 11-bit pipeline phase accumulator and a 10-bit segmented current-steering nonlinear DAC, which includes a 6-bit coarse DAC and seven 3-bit fine DACs.

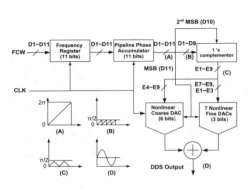

Fig. 1. Diagram of the 11-bit ROM-less DDS with 10-bit segmented DAC.

3-bit fine DACs. The 10-bit frequency control word (FCW) feeds the accumulator which controls the output frequency of the synthesized sine waveform. Since the output frequency cannot exceed the Nyquist rate, the MSB of the accumulator input is tied to zero. The two most significant bits (MSB) of the accumulator output are used to determine the quadrant of the sine waveform. The MSB output of the phase accumulator is used to provide the proper mirroring of the sine waveform about the π phase point. The 2nd MSB is used to invert the remaining 9 bits for the 2nd and 4th quadrants of the sine waveform by a complementor, and the outputs of the complementor are applied to the segmented nonlinear DAC to form a quarter of the sine waveform.

Under a 3.3V power supply and a SiGe HBT base-collector voltage of 0.85V∼0.9V, all the digital logic is implemented using 3 level current mode logic (CML) with differential output swings of 400mV. For an 11-bit DDS using CML logic, power consumption is the biggest issue. Each tail current in a CML gate is set to 0.3mA, close to 40% of peak f_T current instead of traditionally 70∼80%. Otherwise the power consumption will exceed 9.0W. A tradeoff has been made between operating speed and consumed power.

A. 11-bit Pipeline Accumulator

To achieve the maximum operating speed with a fixed FCW, a pipeline accumulator is used in this design. It uses the most hardware, but achieves the fastest speed. The total delay of the accumulator is one full adder (FA) propagation delay plus one D-flip-flop (DFF) propagation delay. Fig. 2 illustrates the

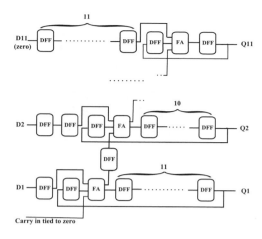

Fig. 2. 11-bit pipeline phase accumulator.

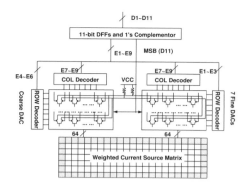

Fig. 3. Diagram of 10-bit segmented nonlinear DAC.

architecture of the 11-bit pipeline phase accumulator, which has a total of 11 pipelined rows. Each row has a total of 12 DFF delay stages placed at the input and output of a 1-bit FA. Eleven DFFs are needed for a pipeline accumulator. One more DFF for each row is used to retime the signal for layout consideration. It will retime the signal after the metal wire delay from the accumulator output to its input. Obviously, the pipeline accumulator has a propagation delay of 11 clock cycles, including a latency period equals to 10 clock cycles plus one retiming clock cycle. Note that an accumulator needs at least one delay stage even without any pipelined stages. The pipeline accumulator shown in Fig. 2 allows that the 11-bit accumulator to operate at the speed of a 1-bit accumulator consisting of an FA and a DFF.

B. 10-bit Segmented Nonlinear DAC

The structure of the nonlinear DAC is shown in Fig. 3. To reduce the complexity of the nonlinear DAC, segmentation has been employed. Since the quadrant of the sine waveform was determined by the two MSBs, a 9-bit segmented sine-weighted DAC is used to generate the amplitude for a quarter phase ($0 \sim \pi/2$) sine wave. The 9-bit sine-weighted DAC is divided into a 6-bit thermometer decoded coarse nonlinear DAC and seven 3-bit thermometer decoded fine nonlinear DACs. The first 6 bits of the complementor outputs control the coarse nonlinear DAC, and the highest 3 bits also address the selection of the fine DACs. The lowest 3 bits of the complementor outputs determinate the output value of each fine DACs.

There are several approaches on the DAC segmentation methods [1], [4]. If we quantize the phase word of a quarter sine wave to $a + b + c$ bits, we have:

$$
\sin\left(\frac{\pi}{2} \cdot \frac{\alpha + \beta + \gamma}{2^{a+b+c}}\right) = \sin\left(\frac{\pi}{2} \cdot \frac{\alpha + \beta}{2^{a+b+c}}\right)
$$
$$
+ \cos\left(\frac{\pi}{2} \cdot \frac{\alpha + \beta_{avg}}{2^{a+b+c}}\right) \cdot \sin\left(\frac{\pi}{2} \cdot \frac{\gamma}{2^{a+b+c}}\right) \quad (1)
$$

where $0 \leq \alpha \leq 2^{a-1}, 0 \leq \beta \leq 2^b,$ and $0 \leq \gamma \leq 2^c$. For a 3-level CML logic, setting $a = b = c = 3$ results in a segmentation with the best power efficiency, since 3-to-7

thermometer decoder circuit can be implement using one stage CML gate. With 11-bit phase and 10-bit amplitude resolutions, the equations below are used to generate the coarse and fine DAC current matrices shown in Fig. 4.

$$
I_k = \begin{cases} \lfloor (2^{10} - 1)\sin\left(\frac{2\pi(0.5)}{2^{11}}\right) \rfloor, (\alpha = \beta = 0) \\ \lfloor (2^{10} - 1)\sin\left(\frac{2\pi(\alpha+\beta+0.5)}{2^{11}}\right) - \sum_{n=0}^{k-1} I_n \rfloor, \\ \quad (1 \leq \alpha \leq 7, \ 1 \leq \beta \leq 7 \cdot 2^7) \end{cases} \quad (2)
$$

$$
I_{\alpha,m} = \begin{cases} \lfloor (2^{10} - 1)\cos\left(\frac{2\pi(\alpha+\beta_{avg})}{2^{11}}\right)\sin\left(\frac{2\pi(0.5)}{2^{11}}\right) \rfloor, \\ \quad (m = 0) \\ \lfloor (2^{10} - 1)\cos\left(\frac{2\pi(\alpha+\beta_{avg})}{2^{11}}\right)\sin\left(\frac{2\pi(m+0.5)}{2^{11}}\right) \\ \quad - \sum_{n=0}^{m-1} I_{\alpha,n} \rfloor, (1 \leq m \leq 7) \end{cases}
$$
$$(3)$$

The coarse DAC current source matrix provides 512 unit current sources. Each fine DAC has about 8 unit current sources used to interpolate the coarse DAC. The unit current of each current source is set at $26\mu A$. The largest current in the current source is $338\mu A$, which is composed of 13 unit current sources. The current switch contains two differential pairs with cascode current sources for better isolation and current mirror accuracy. The current outputs are converted to differential voltages by a pair of off-chip 15 Ω pull-up resistors. Fig. 4 shows that the currents from the cascode current sources are fed to outputs OUTp and OUTm by pairs of switches (M_{switch}). The MSB controls the selection between different half periods. The current switch contains two differential pairs with minimum size transistors and a cascode transistor to isolate the current sources from the switches, which improves the bandwidth of the switching circuits.

For the layout, considering the current source matching, each current source is split into four identical small current sources which carry a quarter of the required current. A quadrature layout style is adopted to improve the matching and linearity. To further improve their matching, all the current source transistors, including coarse DAC and fine DACs, are randomly distributed in the current source matrix and a

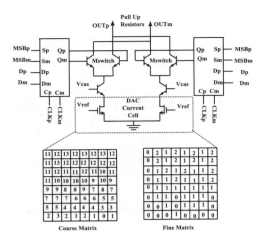

Fig. 4. Current switch circuit of the nonlinear DAC.

random-walk scheme [5] was used for the current switches. Two dummy rows and columns have been added around the current source array to avoid edge effects. In order to minimize the phase difference of the clock to the DFFs, an H-tree clock scheme is used to make the clock signal reach each block simultaneously.

III. EXPERIMENT RESULTS

The die photo of the SiGe DDS MMIC is shown in Fig. 5. This DDS design is quite compact with an active area of $3 \times 2.5mm^2$ and a total die area of $4 \times 3.5mm^2$. The DDS is tested in a 52 pin ceramic leadless package. Figs. 6-10 illustrate the measured DDS output spectra and waveforms for different outputs and clock frequencies. Fig. 6 presents a 4.2MHz DDS output spectrum with an 8.6GHz clock input, with the minimum FCW of 1. The measured output power is approximately -8.3dBm and the measured SFDR is about 48dBc. The tone at 91.7MHz comes from the nearby campus FM radio station. Fig. 7 shows the waveform for the spectrum of Fig. 6. Fig. 8 and Fig. 9 demonstrate the operation of the DDS at maximum clock of 8.6GHz with Nyquist output (i.e., FCW=1023). Thus, the output frequency is set as $\frac{2^{10}}{2^{11}} \times f_{clk} = 4.2958GHz$. The first order image tone due to mixing of the clock frequency and the DDS output frequency occurs at $8.6GHz - 4.2958GHz = 4.3042GHz$, as shown in Fig. 9. The measured SFDR of the device is approximately 40dBc. The tone at 91.7MHz appears again in the spectrum. Fig. 10 gives the measured DDS output waveform with 4.2958GHz Nyquist output and 8.6GHz clock. The enveloped signal frequency results from mixing output and its image, which is $\frac{2^{10}+1}{2^{11}} \times f_{clk} - \frac{2^{10}-1}{2^{11}} \times f_{clk} \approx 8.4MHz$. All measurements were done with packaged parts and without calibrating the losses of the cables and PCB tracks.

To evaluate the performance of mm-wave DDSs, a power efficiency figure of merit can be defined as

$$FOM = \frac{MaxClock\,(GHz) \times 2^{ENOB}}{Power\,(W)}. \qquad (4)$$

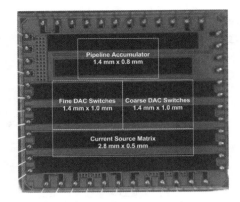

Fig. 5. Die photo of the 11-bit ROM-less DDS.

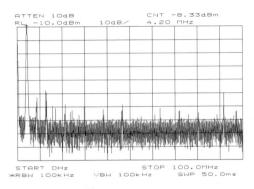

Fig. 6. Measured DDS output spectrum with 4.2MHz output and the maximum 8.6GHz clock (FCW=1), showing about 48dBc SFDR. The tone at 91.7MHz is from the nearby campus FM radio station.

Table I compares mm-wave DDS MMIC performances. Compared to the InP DDS MMICs, this SiGe DDS greatly improves the resolution and is the most complicated design with approximately twenty thousand transistors. Most of the InP DDS MMICs were measured using probe stations [2], [3], while this DDS RFIC was packaged. The package has a thermal resistance of approximately $30\,°C$. With 4.8W power consumption at room ambient temperature, the junction temperature of the SiGe devices can reach as high as $180\,°C$ theoretically. At such high temperature, the device performance is greatly degraded and the DAC current switches are no longer synchronized due to increased internal delays, which introduce noticeable distortion to the output waveform. When the device is cooled, the DDS can operate at the maximum clock frequency of 8.6GHz. At room temperature, the packaged DDS can operate at the maximum clock frequency of 7.2GHz. When compared with the 9-bit 9.6GHz DDS [6], this design achieves two more phase and amplitude bits. As a result, this DDS achieves 10 dB larger SFDR and one third more power efficiency FOM.

IV. CONCLUSION

Implemented in a $0.13\mu m$ SiGe BiCMOS technology with f_T/f_{max} of 200/250GHz, this paper presented an 11-bit 8.6GHz SiGe DDS MMIC design with a 10-bit segmented sine-weighted DAC. With Nyquist output, the DDS achieves a

TABLE I
MM-WAVE DDS MMIC PERFORMANCE COMPARISION

Technology f_T/f_{max} [GHz]	InP 137/267 [1]	InP 300/300 [2]	InP 300/300 [3]	SiGe 100/120 [6]	SiGe 200/250 [this work]
Phase resolution [bit]	8	8	8	9	11
Amplitude resolution [bit]	7	7	5	8	10
Max clock [GHz]	9.2	13	32	9.6	8.6
SFDR [dBc]	30	26.67	21.56	30	40
Power consumption [W]	15	5.42	9.45	1.9	4.8
Die area $[mm^2]$	8x5	2.7x1.45	2.7x1.45	3x3	4x3.5
FOM $[GHz \cdot 2^{ENOB}/W]$	16.0	42.6	34.8	131.9	182.0

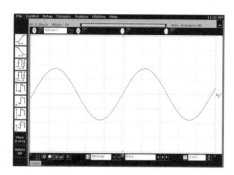

Fig. 7. Measured DDS output waveform with 4.2MHz output and 8.6GHz clock.

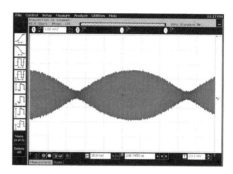

Fig. 10. Measured DDS output waveform with 4.2958GHz Nyquist output and 8.6GHz clock. The enveloped signal frequency is ther mixing of the output and its image, which is 8.4MHz.

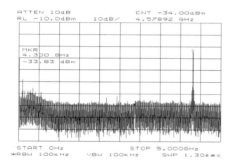

Fig. 8. Measured DDS Nyquist output spectrum with 4.2958GHz output and the maximum 8.6GHz clock (FCW=1023), showing about 40dBc SFDR. The tone at 91.7MHz is from the nearby campus FM radio station. The image tone locates at 4.3042GHz.

maximum clock frequency of 8.6GHz, and an SFDR of 40dBc. The Power consumption of the DDS is approximately 4.8W, and the power efficiency FOM is $182GHz \cdot 2^{ENOB}/W$. This DDS MMIC is the first mm-wave DDS with larger than 11-bit phase and 10-bit DAC amplitude resolutions and achieves the best power efficiency.

ACKNOWLEDGMENT

The authors would like to acknowledge Eric Adler and Geoffrey Goldman at U.S. Army Research Laboratory and Pete Kirkland and Rodney Robertson at U.S. Army Space and Missile Defense Command for funding this project.

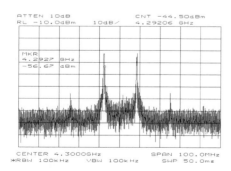

Fig. 9. Measured DDS Nyquist output spectra zoomed in to 100MHz span with 8.6GHz clock. The output frequency is 4.2958GHz and the alias image is 4.3042GHz.

REFERENCES

[1] A. Gutierrez-Aitken, J. Matsui, E. Kaneshiro, B. Oyama, A. Oki, and D. Streit, "Ultra high speed direct digital synthesizer using InP DHBT technology," *IEEE Journal of Solid-State Circuits*, vol. 37, no. 9, pp. 1115–1121, Oct. 2002.

[2] S. E. Turner and Kotecki, "Direct digital synthesizer with ROM-less architecture at 13-GHz clock frequency in InP DHBT technology," in *IEEE Microwave and Wireless Components Letters*, May 2006, pp. 296–298.

[3] S. E. Turner and D. E. Kotecki, "Direct digital synthesizer with sine-weighted DAC at 32-GHz clock frequency in InP DHBT technology," *IEEE Journal of Solid-State Circuits*, vol. 41, no. 10, pp. 2284–2290, Oct. 2006.

[4] J. Jiang and E. K.F.Lee, "A low-power segmented nonlinear DAC-based direct digital frequency synthesizer," *IEEE Journal of Solid-State Circuits*, vol. 37, no. 10, pp. 1326–1330, Oct. 2002.

[5] J. Vandenbussche, G. V. der Plas, and A. V. den Bosch, "A 14 bit 100 MSamples update rate 42 random walk CMOS D/A converter," in *Proceedings of ISSCC*, Feb. 1999, pp. 146–147.

[6] X. Yu, F. Dai, J. D. Irwin, , and R. C. Jaeger, "A 9-bit 9.6GHz 1.9W direct digital synthesizer implemented in 0.18μm SiGe BiCMOS technology," *IEEE Journal of Solid-State Circuits*, vol. 43, June 2008.

Fully integrated, high performance triple SD PLL (2.2Ghz to 4.4Ghz) with minimized interaction

Stefano Cipriani, Eric Duvivier, Gianni Puccio, Lorenzo Carpineto, Biagio Bisanti, Francesco Coppola, Martin Alderton*, Jeremy Goldblatt*

Entropic Communications, Sophia Antipolis France *San Diego, USA

Abstract — 3 Sigma delta PLLs covering an octave have been integrated on one BiCMOS 0.35um CSS (channel stacking switch) chip. The 3 PLLs can work simultaneously synthesizing the same frequencies or different frequencies. To minimize the dynamic coupling among the PLLs a complete calibration algorithm has been implemented while to avoid static coupling a large use of differential structure and other design techniques have been used. The maximum composite spurious (due to PLLs coupling, Xtal spurious and fractional spurs) is –35dBc (in +/-15MHz range). Each PLL has a frequency range from 2.2GHz to 4.4GHz with a worst-case (over process and temperature) integrated rms of 1.2deg at 3.8GHz. The frequency step (31.25KHz) is obtained with a 10bit SD clocked at 32MHz. The single PLL draw 35 mA from 3.8 Volt supply (regulated internally to 2.8 or 3.4 Volt) for 3.2 mm^2.

Index Terms — CSS, PLL, Sigma delta, Satellite communications, frequency coupling, Xtal, VCO, Charge pump, BiCMOS, calibration algorithm.

I. INTRODUCTION

In the actual multi media world, multi users and multi application concepts are becoming very popular. A typical example is an apartment with multiple TV DVR and different satellite dishes. Specifically the IC including the 3 SD-PLLs has been developed for a CSS chip enabling the possibility of connecting multiple viewers with a single cable to multiple LNB inputs instead of using as many cables as the users [1] (see Fig.1).

For this kind of application a single chip enabling multiple operations is very beneficial in terms of system simplicity and price. Clearly these kinds of applications require multiple independent frequency sources not interacting among themselves and this is the major technical challenge. In fact while a viewer is looking at a specific channel another viewer must be able to look at another independent channel, or change channels, without perturbation for the first viewer. These requirements make the design of the PLL very challenging because there are extra tradeoffs to take into account in addition to the ones existing for a single PLL design. This paper describes the PLL architecture choice in Section II and the most critical blocks' (VCO, Programmable divider, Regulators, CP and SD) design guidelines in section III.

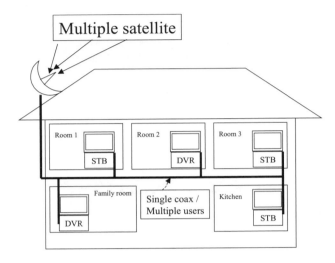

Fig. 1. CSS/BTS typical application scheme

In Sections IV and V the calibration algorithm and the related hardware are described. The Measurements are presented in Section V.

II. ARCHITECTURE

This design has to produce high performances PLLs (close in normalized phase noise= -215dBc/Hz) with some extra constraints linked to the presence of 3 PLLs on the same die. Some of these extra constraints are in contrast with the normal tradeoffs to produce a high performance PLL:

PLL loop bandwidth:
- "Large" (for the disturbed PLL) to have a fast response of the wanted PLL when a disturbing PLL is locking.
- "Optimal" for the noise performance (taking into account as well the presence of the SD).

Loop filter:
- "Integrated" to obtain a compact and low cost solution.
- "External" to be able to use higher charge pump current to minimize the noise.
- "with high overshoot" to allow filter integration.

- "with low overshoot " (for the disturbing PLL when locking) to minimize the perturbation on the disturbed PLL

After this preliminary analysis a SD PLL with a loop BW of around 200KHz with a differential opamp based CP and an integrated loop filter was selected (see Fig.2). In addition, to limit the interaction during the locking phase of the disturbing PLL, we implemented a "low overshoot mode" for the locking PLL. Nevertheless even using state of the art PLL blocks (VCO, CP and programmable divider) we faced some problems to maintain the PLL locked and performing in spec over temperature. In fact the temperature range is very large [-20°deg to 125°deg Tjunction] and the PLL is required for this application to remain locked "forever"

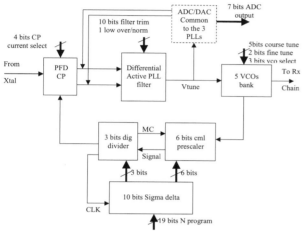

Fig. 2.   PLL top level block diagram

without performance degradation. For this reason a lot of effort has been put as well into the calibration algorithm to limit the PLL variation and to obtain the required pulling performance.

III. PLL BLOCKS DESIGN

As previously described the coupling [2] among the different PLLs is one of the major issues for this kind of design. For this reason all the PLL blocks have been designed not only driven by the specification requirement but also taking care of the immunity from coupling mechanisms and spurious emissions.

A. VCOs

The first structure analyzed was a ring oscillator [3] due to the "inductor free" structure (low coupling) but the overall performance was not suitable for the application. The chosen structure is an LC type of oscillator with a

cross-coupled PMOS (see Fig.3). The reason of this choice has been driven by the performance required from the VCO: low noise, low spurious emissions and low sensitivity to spurious coupling. To cover the needed frequency range [2.2GHz to 4.4GHz], 5 VCOs has been implemented for each PLL. To increase the isolation among the VCOs and between the VCOs and other circuits, each VCO bank uses a dedicated regulator with a dedicated Vbat and bypass external capacitor in addition to some internal filtering capacitors.

Another key feature of the required VCO is minimization of KV variation over temperature, process and Vtune voltage. For this reason each VCO has been divided into 32 sub-bands selectable via 5 coarse-tune bits and 2 fine-tune bits.

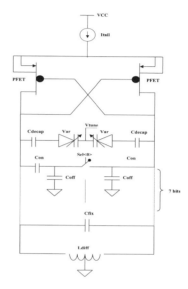

Fig. 3.   VCO schematic

B. Programmable divider

The programmable divider is a 9 bit divider, using 6 bits ECL followed by a 3 bits CMOS divider.

The number of ECL and CMOS divider bits has been chosen to reduce the frequency of the digital operation (64MHz=2*Fxtal). In this way we can reduce the current spike due to the ECL to CMOS converter and the CMOS divider operation itself.

The minimum divider ratio is theoretically 64 when all zeros are programmed but due to the SD divider the minimum divider ratio is 68 (Fout = 2176MHz) due to the N variation induced by the SD (+/- 4). When we are using a divider ratio around 127/128, we need to resynchronize the output divider signal due to different delays of the digital divider when working in bypass mode (below 127) rather than in divider mode (over 127).

C. Charge pump-filter

The CP generates currents through resistors controlled by the PFD sourcing or sinking current to a differential active filter based on a low noise OPAMP. The reason for this choice was the necessity to achieve a very low noise floor (the spec is –215dBc/Hz normalized) but with a low current CP to allow the filter integration.

We are able to achieve the wanted noise performance with low CP current (around 250u) enabling the integration of a differential filter.

D. SD

The SD is a 10bit 3rd order structure. To limit the interaction among the 3 PLLs, the 3-sigma deltas have been placed together in the middle of the chip supplied by a dedicated regulator and using a dedicated Vbat.

In addition the Vbat and GND lines have been completely shielded with a dedicated down bond to the paddle.

For the same reason the clocks for the 3-sigma deltas have been chosen out of phase (2 with 180 degrees phase difference and the third one with an asynchronous delay of around 10 ns) [4]

IV. CALIBRATION ALGORITHM

We find a fundamental requirement is the implementation in the IC of a calibration algorithm [5] mainly for 2 reasons:

1. Maintain over process and temperature the PLL locked without any performance degradation.

2. Minimize the phase pulling of a locked VCO while locking another VCO.

A. PLL parameter stabilization

The key factor to maintain the PLL performance constant over temperature and process is to keep as constant as possible the KV/N ratio. Without any specific calibration scheme the native overall variation is around 1:6. The strategy was to select the charge pump currents (8 values) based on the Vtune (lower or higher than 1.5Volt) and the calibration words (4 ranges). In addition to maintain the PLL locked in a limited Vtune range (0.3 Volt to 2.2 Volt) over temperature the calibration algorithm selects the acceptance locking window for the Vtune in accord with a linear temperature law. In this way we are able to limit the KV/N variation to 1:2.5.

B. Pulling minimization

During the calibration phase to select the right VCO and calibration words we faced a pulling problem for an already locked VCO. From some measurements (see Fig.3) we found that when a moving VCO was crossing an existing VCO with a frequency rate variation lower than 30 MHz/ms the pulling on the locked VCO was huge.

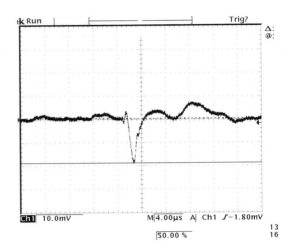

Fig. 3. Static VCO instantaneous phase: 25mV/rad on the scope display => Peak phase error due to VCO crossing a locked VCO (19.2mV peak => 44 deg)

The minimum frequency rate variation is guaranteed by the PLL loop bandwidth but when the disturbing VCO is locking close to an existing VCO this minimum slope can be reached during the PLL overshoot. For this reason the calibration scheme is quite complex. The first step is to create a look up table with the min and max frequency for each VCO with min and max calibration word. This table is used to calculate the first guess starting point (VCO number and calibration word) for the calibration scheme. When the landing frequency of calibrating VCO is closer than 6MHz to an existing VCO the algorithm will arrive at the final landing frequency in different steps and using the low overshoot mode for the PLL in order to avoid the calibrating VCO crossing the existing VCO with a freq rate variation lower than 30MHz/ms.

V. SERVO HARDWARE

As described in the previous paragraph the implemented algorithm required some extra hardware that is described here following.

A. ADC/DAC

In the chip there is a single 7 bit ADC/DAC used to measure the Vtune line of each PLLs (ADC function) or pre-charge the PLLs` filter to a wanted value (DAC function). In addition the ADC function is used to measure the chip temperature to choose the right CP current and the right Vtune window.

All of these ADC/DAC functions can run one at a time on one selected PLL.

B. Low overshoot mode filter

The selected PLL sizing is producing 35% overshoot in normal operation. For this reason a low overshoot mechanism has been studied to limit the number of steps needed without impacting the peak phase error performance.

The low overshoot is based on a Y-type architecture for the PLL filter (due to its low sensitivity to capacitor change) and a lower CP current. The CP current is fixed =45uA. In addition the R1 in the PLL filter is increased by 6 times and C2 reduced by 10 times during the low overshoot mode. The overshoot in "low overshoot mode" is reduced to 5%.

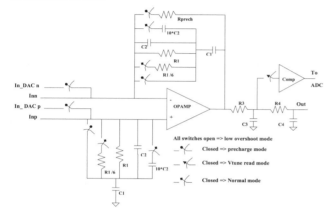

Fig. 4. Integrated loop filter diagram

VI. MEASUREMENTS

Here following are some performances measurements.

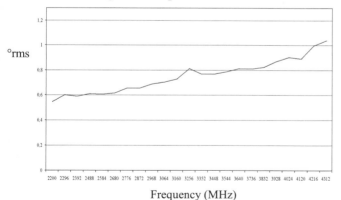

Fig.6 Int rms phase noise [3Khz to 15Mhz] for frac channels

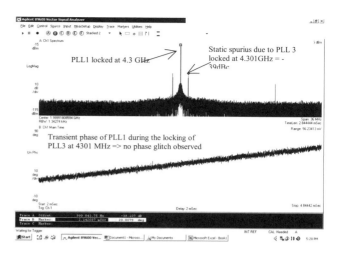

Fig. 7. Phase pulling during a PLL locking close (1MHz) to an already locked PLL

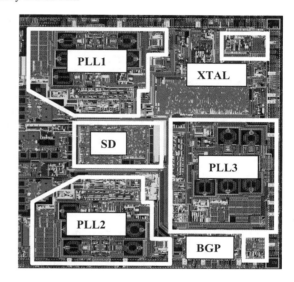

Fig.8 IC layout (PLLs section)

REFERENCES

[1] DBS Entropic white pages, http://www.entropic.com/pages/tech_DBSOutdoor.html
[2] B. Biswas and K. Ray "Discrimination of a second order injection synchronized oscillator against interfering tones" Transactions on circuits and systems, Vol.21 n°3, May,1974
[3] Liang Dai "Design of low noise CMOS ring oscillators" Transactions on circuits and systems Vol.49 n°5, May 2002
[4] B. Bisanti et al. "Offset signal phasing for a multiple frequency source system" US patent application 200070176663, August 2, 2007
[5] F. Coppola et al. "Multiple frequency source system and method of operation" US patent application 20070183014, August 9, 2007

A Low-Power Programmable Dynamic Frequency Divider

Jérémie Chabloz, David Ruffieux, Christian Enz
Swiss Center for Electronics and Microtechnology (CSEM)
Neuchâtel, Switzerland
Email: jeremie.chabloz@csem.ch

Abstract—In this paper, a solution to realize a low-power programmable frequency divider using dynamic logic is proposed. By cascading compact dual-modulus divider slice with recursive feedback mechanisms, any dividing ratio is easily implemented. A 5-stages 0.18μm CMOS implementation demonstrates a power consumption factor as low as 235 nW/MHz under 1.2 V supply for high dividing ratios.

Index Terms—Frequency dividers, Prescalers, Dynamic logic, Low-Power

I. INTRODUCTION

Frequency dividers are an essential component of frequency synthesizers. They are used as prescalers in the phase-locked loop (PLL) feed-back path and their dividing ratio also defines the ratio between the PLL output frequency and the reference clock frequency. Frequency generation blocks for multi-channel or even multi-standard compliant transceivers need to be reconfigurable and be able to generate several different frequencies. Hence the need for a multi-modulus programmable divider which could also be used in a fractional PLL with a $\Delta\Sigma$ modulator.

The presented divider has been designed to be used in a fractional PLL. This PLL generates the local oscillator for the intermediate frequency (IF) of a low-power super-heterodyne receiver operating in the 2.4 GHz ISM band [1], [2]. A simplified schematic of the receiver is shown in figure 1. The architecture chosen for the frequency synthesis is similar

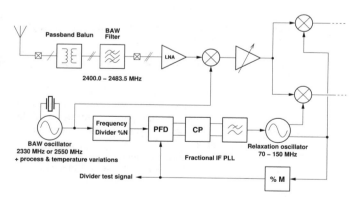

Fig. 1. Super-heterodyne receiver architecture

to the one presented in [3]. A bulk-acoustic wave (BAW) oscillator is used as a first local source and runs at a fixed frequency, determined by the physical dimensions of the BAW

resonator. The second downconversion uses a quadrature relaxation oscillator (IF oscillator) with a large tuning range. Since the second downconversion is of a direct conversion for the given application, the selected channel frequency is determined by the sum or the difference of both oscillators frequencies. Two frequency dividers are needed, the first one with a fixed division ratio generates a signal used as a reference by the fractional IF PLL. The second one is used as a multi-modulus prescaler for the IF PLL.

Basic principles for the dual-modulus dynamic divider cell will be presented in section II. In section III, it is explained how to realize and cascade several of those cells in a modular way, followed by some measurement results in section IV.

II. DYNAMIC DIVIDERS

The basic dual-modulus divider cell used in this work is presented in figure 2(a). It was originally introduced in a patent by the second author [4].

A. Basic principles

The modulus control signal div_val allows to switch between two modes; either the input frequency is divided by 2 (div_val = '0'), or it is divided by 3 (div_val = '1'). When in divide-by-2 mode, two of the clocked transistors are short-circuited and the circuit is equivalent to a well known true single-phase-clock (TSPC) flip-flop [5] looped on itself, save for an extra pMOS transistor. As can be seen on the time diagram of figure 2(b), in divide-by-3 mode, the circuit cycles through all possible internal states, except for the two impossible states where the internal nodes are all low ("000") or all high ("111"). The hatched regions in the time diagram of figure 2(b) correspond to the states which are "swallowed" in divide-by-2 mode, thus decreasing the cycle period by one input clock period. This also defines portions where falling transitions on the div_val signal would be forbidden if one wanted to avoid glitches and erratic behavior from the dual-modulus divider.

The theoretical maximal output frequency of the dividing cell can be approximated by the equivalent self-oscillating frequency of the corresponding three-inverters ring oscillator. This is heavily mitigated by the need for rail-to-rail signal, even though this requirement can be avoided by the use of differential clock signals, AC coupling capacitors and separate bias circuitry [3], [4]. In that case, the divider behaves as an injection-locked ring oscillator, whose locking range is

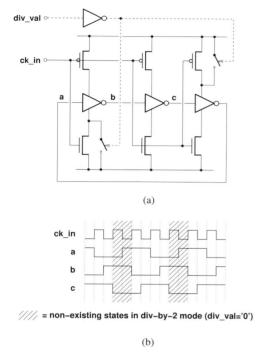

(a)

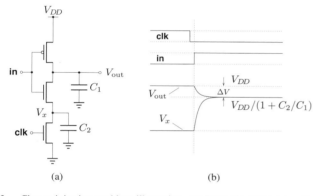

(b)

Fig. 2. Dynamic divider-by-2/3 implementation. (a) Basic schematic. The div_val signal allows to change the division mode. (b) Time diagram. The hatched part represent the swallowed cycle portion in divide-by-2 mode

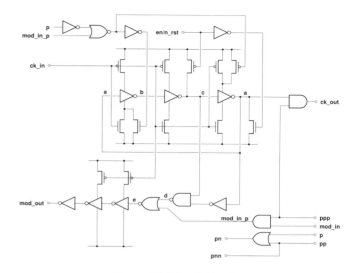

Fig. 4. Modular divider slice

the rising edge on the input in should not imply a falling edge on the output, since it is latched. Nonetheless, the rising edge on the input implies a new repartition of the charges contained in C_1 between C_1 and C_2. The latched output node is thus discharged from V_{DD} to its final value by an amount ΔV,

$$\Delta V = \frac{1}{1 + C_1/C_2} \cdot V_{DD}. \tag{1}$$

For example, it is straightforward to see that if $C_2 = C_1$, then after switching, the value of ΔV is as high as $V_{DD}/2$ and the high state of the latch is not guaranteed any more. This effect is still worsened by charges which are trapped in the channel of the inverter nMOS transistor when its gate is at V_{DD}, which increases the number of flowing charges [6]. It can be determined that during each cycle of the divider cell in figure 2(a), several such "dangerous" transitions occur, and therefore care has to be brought during design to ensure that no unwanted discharging takes place. It also emphasizes the absolute need for post-layout parasitic extraction and simulation. Should the divider not work due to charge injection, the obvious solution which does not require major changes would be to increase the ratio between the capacitances C_1/C_2 by artificially loading the internal nodes a, b and c. Of course, this would increase the power consumption and decrease the maximum attainable frequency as well.

III. MODULAR CHAIN

The proposed programmable divider is an adaptation of the clever idea introduced by C. S. Vaucher *et al.* in [7], with some minor changes and using the dynamic dividers presented in section II. One stage (or "slice") of the presented divider chain is described in figure 4. A divider chain is realized by cascading several stages according to figure 5.

In each stage, a once-per-cycle recursion signal mod_out is generated from the internal states and corresponding signal coming back from next stage mod_in. This signal is resynchronized on the falling edges of the input clock ck_in thanks

Fig. 3. Charge injection problem illustration. (a) Dynamic half latch with capacitances put in evidence. (b) Waveforms

determined by the input clock amplitude, supply voltage and bias current. This particular case will not be investigated in this paper.

B. Charge injection

One perverse effect of using dynamic logic arises from the charge injection phenomenon. This effect is similar to problems encountered in switched capacitors circuits, magnified by the need for low power and high speed which leads to trying to minimize capacitances at internal nodes. Let us illustrate this concept by a concrete example. Consider the dynamic half latch of figure 3(a) in which C_1 and C_2 represent the total capacitance on their nodes. Apply next at the inputs the waveforms found in the upper half of figure 3(b). The principle of the half-latch says that when the clk signal is down, then

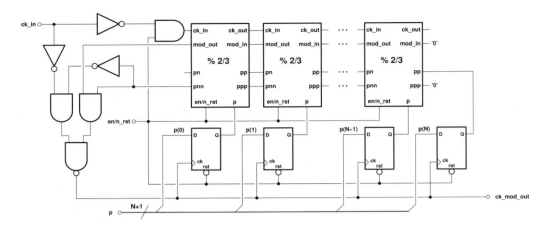

Fig. 5. Modular divider chain with N cascaded stages and maximal possible range.

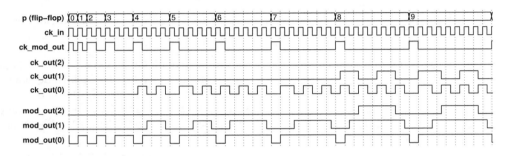

Fig. 6. Time diagram of divider chain simulated with behavioural HDL model and N=3. The division ratio is auto-incremented.

to a dynamic p²-latch. In each stage, the mod_in signal is used to validate the swallowing of one input clock period by putting temporarily the dual-modulus cell in divide-by-3 mode depending on the value on the stage modulus control p. Since each mod_out signal is recursively validated by all the previous mod_in signals, the signals on the bus p of width $N + 1$ are directly binary-coding the final division ratio, so that

$$K = \sum_{i=0}^{N} p_i \cdot 2^i. \tag{2}$$

This is a clear advantage over other schemes for programmable dividers requiring large look-up tables (LUT) or complicated combinatorial logic. It is also very advantageous to have the possible range extended toward lower ratios. Indeed, with N cascaded stages, the achievable division ratio K ranges from 2 to $2^{N+1} - 1$. For example, a 5 stages modular divider would achieve division ratios ranging from 2 to 63. D flip-flops are used to latch the division ratio control word and to ensure that every change occurs synchronously. Clock signals ck_in and mod_out(0) are multiplexed so that correct initialization is secured and so that cases with $K < 2$ are handled right.

An equivalent HDL model for the modular divider has been developed so that a better understanding of the chain functioning can be grasped from fast behavioural simulations. The results for such a simulation are shown in figure 6 for 3 cascaded stages and for division ratio control word p being

incremented at each step.

One definitive asset of the modular chain is that the mod_out signals are recursively resynchronized. This means that there is no jitter accumulation and the chain behaves as a synchronous divider without the associated power consumption penalty.

In order to save power when the latest stages in the chain are not needed, a clock gating strategy is used. Since a low state on the ppp signal exactly carries the information that every next stages are not used, it can be directly used with an *and* gate to validate the ck_out signal. This gating is also necessary to prevent the internal state of the unused stages to get de-synchronized, allowing smooth transitions between two consecutive division ratios.

One of the certain disadvantages of the chain as it is implemented in figure 5 is that the duty cycle D of the output clock is inversely proportional to the division ratio $D = 1/K$. This is not a problem for PLLs using classical phase detectors, since they are intrinsically sampled systems and use only the rising (or falling) edge of the divided controlled oscillator. Nonetheless, it has to be pointed out that the far spectral content of the divider signal is fastly growing with decreasing duty cycle. This is clearly an incentive to bring extra care during layout phase to minimize parasitic coupling, e.g. through power supply lines.

An example layout for one slice in a mainstream 1P6M $0.18\,\mu$m CMOS process is shown in figure 7. It can be seen that the modularity extends to the layout with direct

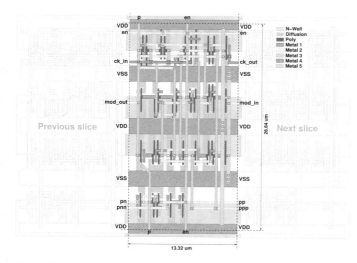

Fig. 7. Layout of one modular divider slice in a mainstream 0.18 μm CMOS process. The modularity extends to the layout with direct signal connections between adjacent slices.

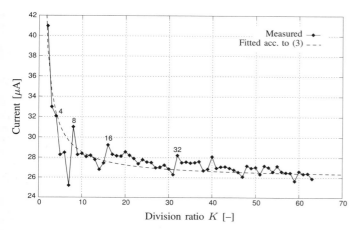

Fig. 8. Measured current consumption. $V_{DD} = 1.2$ V, $f_{clk} = 132.8$ MHz

signal connections between adjacent slices. Using dynamic dividers with minimal size transistors yields a very compact implementation, one slice being only 13.32μm $\times$ 26.64μm large. A complete 5-stages divider exactly as described in figure 5 is in turn 79.92μm $\times$ 33.3μm.

IV. MEASUREMENTS RESULTS

An implementation of the 2.4 GHz receiver presented in figure 1 has been realized in 0.18μm CMOS. Figure 8 shows the measured current consumption of the 5-stages IF PLL divider chain while varying its dividing ratio. As expected, small peaks in the measured curve are showing for values for which an additional stage has to be switched on, i.e. binary values "10", "100", "1000", etc. A very crudely approximated equation modeling the total current consumption I_{tot} using equivalent loading capacitors can be expressed as

$$I_{tot} \simeq f_{clk} \cdot V_{DD} \cdot \left[C_{eq} + \frac{C_{div}}{K} \right] \quad . \tag{3}$$

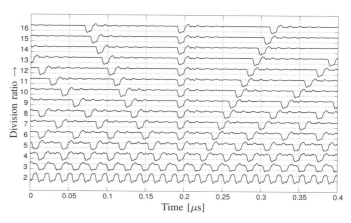

Fig. 9. Measured divided waveforms for several dividing ratios. The input clock frequency is $f_{clk} = 132.8$ MHz.

For the measured divider, fitting of the approximation (3) drawn with a dashed line in figure 8 yields $C_{eq} \simeq C_{div} \simeq$ 160 fF. For $K \gg 1$ the value of C_{eq} can be interpreted as a current consumption merit factor independent from supply voltage and frequency since $1\,\mathrm{fF} = 1\,\mathrm{nA} \cdot \mathrm{MHz}^{-1} \cdot \mathrm{V}^{-1}$. It is more usual to use a power consumption merit factor for dividers, which is dependent from supply voltage and would reach toward 235 nW/MHz for higher values of K.

Measured divided waveforms for several consecutive division ratios are shown in figure 9.

V. CONCLUSION

A novel modular low-power programmable frequency divider solution has been presented. Its basic building block is a compact dual-modulus divider cell whose functioning principles have been explained. The cascaded N stages divider allows division ratios from 2 to $2^{N+1} - 1$. A 5-stages divider implementation in 0.18μm CMOS demonstrate a power consumption factor as low as 235 nW/MHz under 1.2 V supply for high division ratios.

REFERENCES

[1] J. Chabloz, D. Ruffieux, A. Vouilloz, P. Tortori, F. Pengg, C. Müller, and C. Enz, "Frequency synthesis for a low-power 2.4GHz receiver using a BAW oscillator and a relaxation oscillator," in *Proceedings of the European Solid-State Circuits Conference, München, Germany*, 2007, pp. 492–495.

[2] C. Enz, J. Chabloz, J. Baborowski, C. Müller, and D. Ruffieux, "Building blocks for an ultra low-power MEMS-based radio," in *Proc. of the IEEE International Workshop on Radio-Frequence Integration Technology RFIT 2007, Singapore*, 2007.

[3] D. Ruffieux, J. Chabloz, C. Müller, F. X. Pengg, P. Tortori, and A. Vouilloz, "A 2.4GHz MEMS-based transceiver," in *IEEE Int. Solid-State Circuits Conference ISSCC 08 Tech. Digest, San Francisco*, 2008.

[4] D. Ruffieux, "Frequency divider with variable division rate," Worldwide Patent 2004/084 411, Sep. 30, 2004.

[5] J. Yuan and C. Svensson, "High-speed CMOS circuit technique," *IEEE Journal of Solid-State Circuits*, vol. 24, no. 1, pp. 62–70, Feb. 1989.

[6] G. Wegmann, E. A. Vittoz, and F. Rahali, "Charge injection in analog MOS switches," *IEEE Journal of Solid-State Circuits*, vol. 22, no. 6, pp. 1091–1097, Dec. 1987.

[7] C. S. Vaucher, I. Ferencic, M. Locher, S. Sedvallson, U. Voegeli, and Z. Wang, "A family of low-power truly modular programmable dividers in standard 0.35μm CMOS technology," *IEEE Journal of Solid-State Circuits*, vol. 35, no. 7, pp. 1039–1045, Jul. 2000.

Supply-Noise Mitigation Techniques in Phase-Locked Loops

Abhijith Arakali, Nema Talebbeydokthi[1], Srikanth Gondi[2], and Pavan Kumar Hanumolu

School of EECS, Oregon State University, Corvallis, OR 97331

[1]Intel Corporation, Folsom, CA 95630

[2]Kawasaki Microelectronics America, Inc., R&D Division, San Jose, CA 95131

Abstract—**Supply-noise significantly affects the jitter performance of ring oscillator-based phase-locked loops (PLLs). While the focus of much of the prior art is on supply-noise in oscillators, this paper illustrates that supply-noise in other building blocks also contribute significantly to PLL output jitter. The current design employs a split-tuned PLL architecture wherein the power supply of the building blocks is derived from the regulated power supply of the VCO. The prototype PLL fabricated in a 0.18μm digital CMOS process occupies 0.18mm² and consumes only 3.3mW, from a 1.8V supply, of which 0.54mW is consumed in the regulators, while operating at 1.5GHz. The PLL achieves 33ps and 41ps peak-to-peak jitter with no supply noise and with 100mV peak-to-peak supply noise, respectively.**

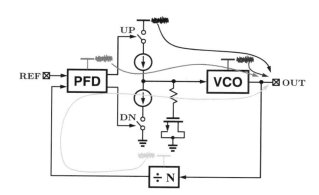

Fig. 1.   Effect of supply noise in PLLs.

I. Introduction

Phase-locked loops (PLLs) are essential building blocks of frequency synthesizers and clock generators and they are used in nearly all analog, digital, and radio-frequency integrated systems. Identifying the oscillator as the PLL circuit element that is most sensitive to supply noise, a low-dropout regulator that shields the oscillator from the supply noise is commonly employed [1]-[3]. This approach facilitates the use of simple inverter-based voltage controlled oscillators (VCOs) that have fast switching characteristics and can therefore achieve better phase noise. However, PLLs employing supply-regulated VCOs suffer from two conflicting requirements: (1) suppression of VCO phase noise with minimum power consumption mandates wide PLL bandwidth, and (2) a wide PLL bandwidth requires wider regulator bandwidth to maintain PLL stability, resulting in larger power dissipation. In this paper a PLL architecture wherein these tradeoffs do not exist is employed.

While it is true that VCO is most sensitive to supply noise, it is very important to realize that other building blocks of a PLL such as the phase-frequency detector (PFD), charge pump (CP), divider, and clock buffers are also susceptible to supply noise and hence can contribute significant amount of output jitter due to supply noise. To our knowledge, there has been little published literature on this aspect of the PLL design. The focus of this paper is on the qualitative analysis and mitigation techniques of supply noise effects on all the building blocks of a PLL.

Figure 1 illustrates all the important supply noise coupling paths that cause jitter on the PLL output clock. For simplicity, various clock buffers such as the reference buffer and the VCO buffer are not shown in the figure. In order to understand the effect of supply noise in each of the individual building blocks,

a transistor-level transient simulation of a conventional PLL is used and the results are shown in Fig. 2. The power-supply noise rejection (PSNR) for each of the building blocks at a particular noise frequency is evaluated as follows: A supply noise tone is injected into the supply of a given building block of interest (say charge-pump), and the resulting jitter at the output of the PLL is measured. The PSNR is then calculated using the following expression,

$$\text{PSNR[dB]} = 20\log10 \left(\frac{T_j/T}{\Delta V_{DD}} \right), \qquad (1)$$

where, T_j represents the peak jitter of the output clock having a period T, resulting from the sinusoidal perturbation of amplitude ΔV_{DD} on the supply voltage.

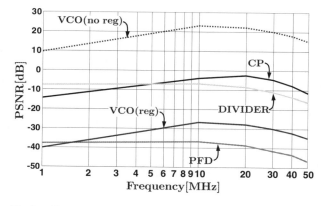

Fig. 2.   Simulated PSNR curves of each of the PLL building blocks.

The PSNR curves shown in Fig. 2 reveal many aspects of supply-noise coupling in PLLs that are very useful to implementing noise mitigation techniques. First, as is well known that the VCO supply noise, when its supply is unregulated, is by far the dominant source of output jitter. Consequently, much of the effort has been focussed on suppressing the detrimental effect of supply noise in VCOs [1]-[3]. Second, when the VCO is supply regulated, it is clear that charge-pump and divider limit the overall jitter performance in the presence of supply noise. It can be shown that reference clock buffer and VCO buffer exhibit similar sensitivity as the divider and therefore also contribute significantly to output jitter. In time-domain, a 100mV sinusoidal tone on the supply of the PLL using a supply-regulated VCO causes a peak-to-peak jitter of 40ps, a considerable fraction of the output clock period.

In this paper we have employed a PLL architecture that facilitates the use of simple low-dropout regulators that combat supply noise not only in the VCO but also in all the other building blocks. The prototype PLL achieves a supply-noise sensitivity of -20dB, thus confirming the effectiveness of the proposed design techniques. The rest of the paper is organized as follows. Brief analysis of supply noise in PLL building blocks is presented in Section II, Section III describes the proposed architecture while Section IV discusses the issues with regulator design and the experimental results are presented in Section V.

II. SUPPLY NOISE IN PLL BUILDING BLOCKS

A. Supply Noise in PFD and Charge-pump

The conceptual schematic of a commonly used phase frequency detector is shown in Fig. 3(a). Ideally, the up (UP) and

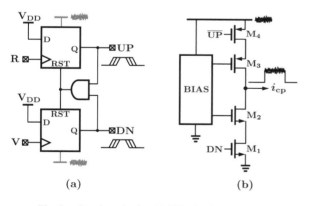

(a)   (b)

Fig. 3.   Supply noise in: (a) PFD (b) Charge-pump.

down (DN) paths are fully symmetric since they are made out of identical flip-flops and a symmetric AND gate. In practice, careful attention is paid to minimize the mismatches in the UP and DN paths to suppress reference spurs or equivalently in time-domain to minimize deterministic jitter. Under these conditions of symmetry the supply noise induced jitter in the UP and DN signals is cancelled resulting in excellent supply-noise immunity of the PFD. We note that the systematic mismatch between the UP and DN current sources in the charge pump causes imperfect cancellation of the supply noise

in UP and DN paths, resulting in the leakage of the PFD supply noise to the output of the PLL. As indicated by the simulated PFD PSNR curve in Fig. 2, even in the presence of some systematic mismatches, a supply-noise sensitivity better than -30dB is achievable.

While the PFD is intrinsically immune to supply-noise, commonly used single-ended source-switched charge-pumps such as the one shown in Fig. 3(b) are very sensitive to supply noise. The poor immunity is illustrated by the simulated charge-pump PSNR curve in Fig. 2. This susceptibility arises from: (i) finite output impedance of the current sources and (ii) asymmetric noise coupling into the UP and DN current sources through the bias circuitry. While it is possible to improve the supply immunity by using cascoded current sources and/or fully-differential architectures, they incur severe headroom and differential loop-filter area penalty, respectively. In view of these difficulties, in this work, a PLL architecture that allows a low-swing charge pump without compromising the tuning range of the VCO is combined with a low-dropout regulator to mitigate jitter degradation due to charge-pump supply noise.

B. Supply Noise in Divider and Clock Buffers

Supply noise in *digital* circuit elements of the PLL such as the divider and clock buffers also contribute significantly to the output jitter. A vast majority of the clock buffers and the dividers in the PLL are implemented either directly by CMOS inverters or structures derived from them (for e.g. true single phase clock flip-flop). Hence, the supply noise sensitivity of the *digital* building blocks can be understood simply by analyzing the CMOS inverter shown in Fig. 4. As

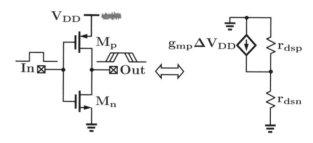

Fig. 4.   Supply noise in a CMOS inverter.

is well known, the changes in the supply voltage (ΔV_{DD}) directly modulate the delay of the inverter by injecting a noise current, $g_{mp}\Delta V_{DD}$, into the output. This noise current is proportional to the transconductance of the PMOS transistor g_{mp} and the supply perturbation ΔV_{DD}. The delay modulation of the inverter manifests itself as jitter at the output of the inverter. Since the capacitors in digital circuits are minimized, the supply-noise sensitivity is poor over a broad range of frequencies, typically into several hundred megahertz. In this work a regulator that shields all the *digital* circuits from wideband supply noise is employed.

III. PLL ARCHITECTURE

The PLL architecture which strives to minimize supply-noise induced output jitter is shown in Fig. 5. The PLL

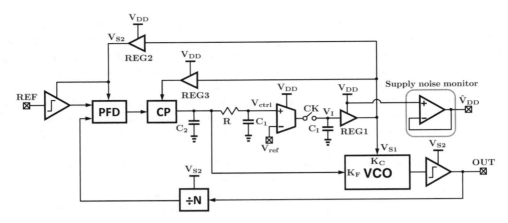

Fig. 5.   Proposed supply-regulated PLL architecture.

employs a split-tuned VCO that is controlled through a high-gain low-bandwidth coarse control path and a low-gain wide-bandwidth fine control path [4]. The frequency-tracking coarse control loop integrates the voltage across the loop-filter capacitor C_1 and produces an output voltage V_I. This voltage serves as an input to a low-dropout regulator (REG1) whose output serves as the supply (coarse control) voltage V_{s1} to the VCO. A novel regulator architecture that provides better than -40dB power supply noise rejection is employed to effectively shield the VCO from supply perturbations. The design of this regulator is not the focus of this paper, and therefore, its design details will be presented separately.

The supply noise sensitivity of charge-pump, divider, and reference/VCO clock buffers is reduced by employing specially designed low-dropout regulators (REG2, REG3). The VCO supply voltage V_{s1} serves as the input to both the regulators, thereby obviating the need for a bandgap reference circut. Note that the coarse-control loop biases the charge-pump to a known voltage V_{REF} in steady-state, thereby circumventing any voltage headroom issues even in the presence of few hundred milli-volt drop in the regulator (REG3). The possible start-up problems in this self-regulating architecture are avoided by a simple start-up circuitry that connects the inputs of regulators, REG2, REG3, to a known voltage at power-up. The design details of these regulators are discussed in the next section.

IV. REGULATOR DESIGN

Regulators used in the proposed architecture are co-designed along with the PLL, by accounting for the intrinsic supply-noise suppression provided by the PLL feedback itself. It is well known that the PLL feedback suppresses: (1) the high-frequency noise introduced into the PFD, charge-pump, and the divider and (2) the low-frequency noise introduced into the VCO buffer. Consequently, in order to improve wide-band supply noise immunity of the PLL, the regulators should provide excellent noise rejection at low frequencies, typically, at least up until the PLL bandwidth.

A commonly used low dropout regulator is shown in Fig. 6 where ω_i, ω_a, and ω_o represent the pole frequencies at the am-

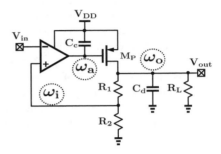

Fig. 6.   Low-dropout regulator.

plifier input, amplifier output, and the regulator output nodes, respectively. The amplifier input capacitance is relatively small in regulators designed for low-load currents, and hence is not considered as a design parameter. The location of ω_a, and ω_o plays a crucial role in determining the power supply rejection properties of the regulator. Consider the power-supply noise rejection curves shown for the two frequency compensation cases ($\omega_a < \omega_o$ and $\omega_a > \omega_o$) in Fig. 7. The regulator provides

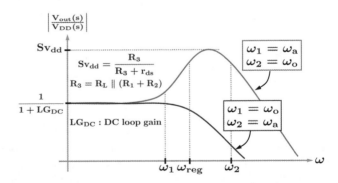

Fig. 7.   Regulator power supply noise rejection curves.

good low-frequency rejection in both cases. However, for the case when $\omega_a < \omega_o$, the noise rejection degrades beyond the amplifier pole at the same rate as the loop gain would reduce. Consequently, in order to achieve good supply rejection in the vicinity of the PLL bandwidth, the amplifier pole, ω_a, should be moved to high frequency, a design requirement that incurs severe power penalty. On the other hand, when $\omega_a > \omega_o$, the regulator provides excellent wide band supply noise rejection as illustrated in Fig. 7. This condition ($\omega_o < \omega_a$) is, however, difficult to meet in practice for the following two reasons: First, a low load resistance R_L, defined as the ratio of regulator output voltage to the average load current pushes the output pole, ω_o, to high frequencies. Second, the large gate capacitance of the pass transistor reduces the amplifier pole frequency. While it is possible to increase the size of the capacitor C_d, to make ω_o dominant, it incurs a large area penalty. In this work, a split-regulator architecture is employed to mitigate the aforementioned conflicting design tradeoffs.

The power to all the building blocks, excluding the VCO and the G_m cell, are provided using two separate regulators REG2, REG3 (see Fig. 5). The partitioning of power supplied by the two regulators is done in a way that allowed the regulator output pole to be dominant using a reasonably small decoupling capacitor of 30pF. In other words, the split-regulator approach increases the load resistance, R_L, and output impedance of the pass transistor and lowers the gate capacitance of the pass transistor, thereby, making it easier to make the output pole dominant. Simulation results indicate that this split-regulator approach, as opposed to using a single conventional regulator using 60pF of decoupling capacitor, provides more than 30dB supply noise rejection improvement.

V. EXPERIMENTAL RESULTS

The prototype IC fabricated in a $0.18\mu m$ digital CMOS process operates from 0.8GHz to 3GHz. A wide-bandwidth voltage follower circuit operating from a clean supply is also incorporated to directly monitor on-chip supply (see Fig. 5). Figure 8 shows the measured supply noise rejection curve with and without supply regulation when the PLL is operating at 1.5GHz. It can be seen that a significant improvement in supply noise rejection has been achieved. In time domain, this rejection translates to an increase of 2.6ps in peak-to-peak jitter when a sine wave of amplitude $200mV_{pk-pk}$ (measured with the supply noise monitor) is injected. The jitter histograms without and with supply noise are depicted in Fig. 9(a) and Fig. 9(b), respectively. The power consumption of the PLL is 3.3mW of which 1.2mW is consumed in the VCO and only $540\mu W$ in the regulators. More importantly, the regulator power dissipation is independent of the PLL bandwidth. The die photograph and the performance summary table are presented in Fig. 10.

VI. ACKNOWLEDGEMENTS

The authors would like to thank Satoru Suenaga, Masa Konishi, Kouichi Abe, Yoshinori Nishi, and Suyama Takashi of Kawasaki Microelectronics for fabrication support. This work was partly supported by SRC under contract 2007-HJ-1597.

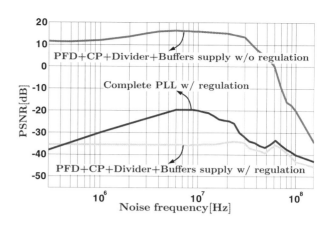

Fig. 8.   Measured power supply noise rejection (PSNR) performance.

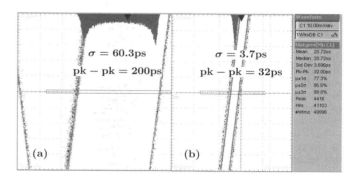

Fig. 9.   Jitter histograms with $50mV_{pk-pk}$ supply-noise: (a) Without regulator. (b) With regulator.

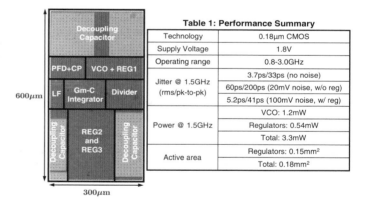

Table 1: Performance Summary

Technology	0.18μm CMOS
Supply Voltage	1.8V
Operating range	0.8-3.0GHz
Jitter @ 1.5GHz (rms/pk-to-pk)	3.7ps/33ps (no noise)
	60ps/200ps (20mV noise, w/o reg)
	5.2ps/41ps (100mV noise, w/ reg)
Power @ 1.5GHz	VCO: 1.2mW
	Regulators: 0.54mW
	Total: 3.3mW
Active area	Regulators: 0.15mm²
	Total: 0.18mm²

Fig. 10.   Die-photo and performance summary table.

REFERENCES

[1] V. von Kaenel et al., "A 320 MHz, 1.5 mW @ 1.35 V CMOS PLL for microprocessor clock generation," IEEE J. Solid-State Circuits, vol. 31, pp. 1715 - 1722, Nov. 1996.

[2] K. Chang et al., "A 0.44-Gb/s CMOS quad transceiver cell using on-chip regulated dual-loop PLLs," IEEE J. Solid-State Circuits, vol. 38, pp. 747 - 754, May 2003.

[3] S. Sidiropoulos et al., "Adaptive bandwidth DLLs and PLLs using regulated supply CMOS Buffers," Symp. VLSI Circuits Dig., pp. 124 - 127, June 2000.

[4] G. Wei et al., "A 500-MHz MP/DLL clock generator for a 5-Gb/s backplane transceiver in $0.25 - \mu m$ CMOS," ISSCC Dig. Tech. Papers, pp. 464-465, Feb. 2003.

A 46pJ/pulse analog front-end in 130nm CMOS for UWB impulse radio receivers

Nick Van Helleputte, Georges Gielen

Katholieke Universiteit Leuven, ESAT-MICAS
Kasteelpark Arenberg 10
3001 Heverlee, Belgium
+32 16 32 86 18, nvanhell@esat.kuleuven.be

Abstract— This paper presents an integrated ultra-low power analog frontend architecture for UWB impulse radio receivers. The receiver is targeted towards applications like wireless sensor networks and body-area networks typically requiring ultra energy-efficient, low data-rate communication over a relative short range. The proposed receiver implements pulse correlation in the analog domain to severely relax the power consumption of the ADC's and digital backend. Furthermore a fully integrated prototype of the analog front-end, containing an analog pulse correlator, a linear-in-dB variable gain amplifier and a 4-bit ADC, is demonstrated. Several design decisions and techniques, like correlation with a windowed LO instead of with a matched template, exploiting the duty-cycled nature of the system, operation in the sub-1GHz band as well as careful circuit design are employed to reach ultra-low power consumption. The analog front-end was manufactured in 130nm CMOS and the active circuit area measures only 600μm x 730μm. A maximum channel conversion gain of 50dB can be achieved. The AFE consumes 1.44mA at 1.2V power supply and operates at a pulse rate of 37.5Mpulses per second. This corresponds to an energy consumption of 46pJ/pulse which is by far best-in-class. A wireless link over more than 3.5m in an office-like environment has been demonstrated which makes the proposed receiver well suited for the targeted applications.

I. INTRODUCTION

Wireless sensor networks and body area networks have gained an increasing interest in the last few years. They provide a huge all-new myriad of application domains with very specific requirements for the communication. Often only modest data rates over short distances are required. The practical feasibility of such applications depends largely on the power consumption of the sensor nodes, which is dominated by the radio. For long-term battery-powered, or even autonomously scavenger-powered devices, ultra energy-efficient radios are required. The analog front-end presented meets the demands while only consuming the extremely low value of 46pJ/pulse.

Since the FCC defined ultra-wideband (UWB) communication in 2002 [1], a lot of research has been started on this topic. Impulse radio communication is a specific form of UWB where data is modulated on ultra-short pulses in time. This form of communication has a high robustness against fading and multipath channels and allows the use of fairly simple, low-power transmitter and receiver designs. Furthermore the use of short pulses allows to monitor the time-of-arrival of the signal, which results in accurate localization almost for free. As such, impulse radio communication becomes increasingly popular for energy-efficient low data-rate radios.

To achieve ultra-low power consumption, the proposed receiver architecture implements pulse correlation in the ana-

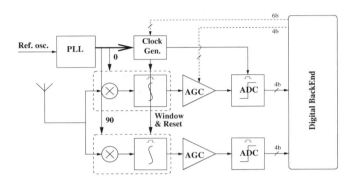

Fig. 1. Complex analog correlating receiver architecture.

log domain allowing the ADC's and the digital back-end to be clocked at the low pulse rate [2]. To overcome the problem of transmitter/receiver synchronization, I/Q reception is employed so that small clock offsets between transmitter and receiver can be tracked and corrected. The receiver architecture is discussed in more detail in section II.

Since the pulse correlation is shifted towards the analog domain, the feasibility of the proposed receiver depends on the possibility of an energy-efficient implementation of the analog front-end (AFE). One of the most power consuming functionalities of the AFE is typically the analog pulse correlation and template generation. To reduce the power consumption of this function, correlation with a windowed LO instead of with a matched locally generated template is performed. Furthermore, the duty-cycled nature of the pulsed input signal is exploited by only enabling the RF blocks when an input pulse is expected to arrive. Finally the receiver operates in the sub-1GHz band which provides sufficient bandwidth for the required data-rates. The design of the AFE is explained in section III. Experimental measurement results are shown in section IV.

II. RECEIVER ARCHITECTURE

With impulse radio communication, data is modulated onto several short pulses according to a certain modulation scheme and spreading code. BPSK modulation is employed since it poses the least strict requirements in terms of output SNR . The FCC defined two frequency bands for UWB, the 0-960MHz band (currently available for imaging and ranging) and the 3.1-10.6GHz band. Since the low band provides sufficient bandwidth for the targeted performance, this band was chosen

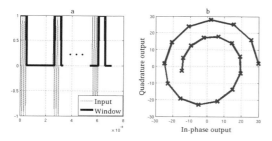

Fig. 2. a) Input pulses and RX window clock in the presence of clock offset. b) The corresponding constellation diagram resembles a spiral.

to keep the power consumption of the RF building blocks as low as possible. The bandwidth ranges from 300MHz to 900MHz with a center frequency of 600MHz. To recover the data, the receiver has to detect the pulse train and then recover the data by correlating the received pulse train with the proper spreading code. As is often the case, most of the power savings can be found at the highest design abstraction level. Thus designing an ultra-low power impulse radio receiver starts with an optimal architectural exploration.

There are several methods to implement impulse radio receivers. As was shown in [2], if power consumption is the main criterion, the most promising receiver architecture is the "complex analog correlating receiver" (see figure 1). In the analog correlating receiver, the pulse train is detected in the analog domain and the data is recovered in the digital domain. This has the benefit of only needing low-resolution ADC's at the low pulse rate (e.g. 37.5MHz). The consequence is that the whole digital back-end is only working on data at the same low pulse rate as well. The power consumption of the ADC's and the digital back-end can thus be very low compared to an all-digital design where the incoming pulse is immediately digitized requiring fast, high-resolution ADC's and fairly complex high-speed logic to recover the pulse train.

Of course the problem of recovering the pulse train is now shifted to the analog domain. To do this, the incoming signal needs to be correlated with a template waveform. Generating the proper template waveform including channel effects is not a trivial thing to do. It is however possible to use a windowed clock instead, as is explained in [2]. The windowed clock can be generated fairly easily in a power-efficient way [4] but constitutes a performance loss compared to the ideal template. This needs to be compensated for by modulating a single data bit onto sufficient pulses until the required SNR is achieved. The number of pulses needed depends on the application (required datarate, distance between transmitter and receiver, channel properties etc.). To generate the windowed clock, an LO with the same center frequency as the incoming pulse is generated with an ultra low-power PLL [4]. This LO is only passed to the mixer inputs when a window signal (see figure 1) is high, effectively generating the windowed clock. In our application, the window signal is a clock at pulse rate with an on-period of 5ns. For a Gaussian pulse with a center frequency of 600MHz, 99% of the pulse energy is contained in a 4ns

period. The 5ns window is thus sufficiently long to receive the pulse even if the window is slightly misaligned. On the other hand, it is short enough in order not to receive too much noise and interference without posing too strict requirements on the clock generator.

The output of the analog correlator is amplified and converted to digital. Since transmitter and receiver in a real application obviously are not synchronized, clock offset between the two needs to be addressed. A small clock offset results in a slowly but gradually increasing phase difference between incoming signal and the window. As a result, the incoming pulse signal will gradually move outside the window and eventually data is lost (see figure 2a). To overcome this problem, the digital back-end can reposition the window clock if it detects clock offset. To detect the clock offset and the direction, I/Q reception is employed. Clock offset will now result in a constellation diagram resembling a spiral towards the origin (see figure 2b). If the RX clock is faster than the TX clock, the constellation diagram will rotate clock-wise. The speed of rotation determines the value of the clock offset. The digital back-end is thus able to track the clock offset and correct for it. In the following section the design of each building block of the ultra low-power AFE is discussed.

III. RECEIVER DESIGN

Energy-efficient implementations for the PLL and for the complete digital back-end have been demonstrated previously [3], [4]. The final part of the receiver, the analog front-end, will be discussed in this section. The main building blocks are the programmable clock generator, the analog pulse correlator, the variable gain amplifier and the analog-to-digital converters. All the blocks are DC-coupled and the output stages properly bias the input stages of the next block. This eliminates the need for additional bias networks. Each of the building blocks will be discussed in detail.

A. Clock generator

A pulse reception cycle starts when the window clock goes high (see figure 1). When it goes down again, the ADC should sample after the internal amplifiers have settled. Finally the integrators should be reset after the ADC's have sampled. The positioning in time of all these clocks should be programmable, as was explained earlier, to counter the effects of clock offset. The receiver thus needs three internal clock signals derived from the LO: an ADC sample clock, a window clock and an integrator reset clock. All three clocks are clocks at pulse rate (e.g. 37.5MHz). Since the window is 1ns longer than the transmitted pulse, the precision of the clock positioning should be better than 1ns.

Four identical cascaded stages are employed to generate the clock at pulse rate. Each stage consists of a MUX and a negative edge-triggered divide-by-two with differential outputs. An extra MUX is placed behind the last divider (see figure 3). The first stage is driven by the 600MHz LO. Each MUX determines whether LO/OUT_i or $\overline{LO/OUT_i}$ is passed to the first/next divider. Using four of these stages it is possible to

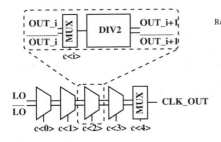

Fig. 3. First stage of the clock generator.

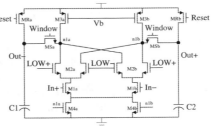

Fig. 4. Analog pulse correlator schematic.

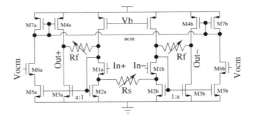

Fig. 5. Variable gain amplifier schematic.

derive from a 600MHz LO a 37.5MHz clock and position the rising edge with a precision of 833ps (= half the LO period). 5 bits, connected to the MUX's, are used to select the different clock positions. An edge-triggered glitch generator is then used to generate the proper window and reset pulses. With the proposed scheme a minimum number of gates are clocked at the high LO frequency compared to a more straightforward approach using a programmable counter. The clock generator, including clock buffering, consumes 350μW.

B. Analog pulse correlator

The analog pulse correlator is basically a mixer followed by an integration stage. The circuit is shown in figure 4. The mixing action itself is performed by a double balanced switching Gilbert cell. The benefit of using this topology, is that it provides an easy-to-implement means to duty-cycle the power consumption. As discussed before, the template waveform is a windowed version of the LO and is generated by an AND of the LO and the window signal, resulting in the signals LOW (see figure 4). The LO is thus passed to the mixer only when a pulse is expected to arrive. Any other time, LOW is low meaning that all transistors M2 are shut off. No direct path from vdd to vss remains, eliminating the mixer's power consumption when it is not needed.

The mixers output current is integrated and held onto capacitors C1 and C2. The pulse correlator thus also acts as a sample and hold, which means that no additional sample and hold is needed for the subsequent ADC. This provides a second major contribution to the overall low power consumption.

At the end of the pulse reception cycle, capacitors C1 and C2 should be reset. Instead of grounding the capacitors and thus discarding any charge present in them, they are reset by precharging them to vdd through transistors MR. The reset current is subsequently reused as part of the bias current. At the start of the integration interval, both capacitors are fully charged. They discharge at an almost constant rate to give the proper bias current together with bias transistors M3. At the same time they integrate the signal current. This current reuse provides a third contribution to reduce power consumption.

The mixer provides a 19dB voltage conversion gain and has an input-referred 1dB compression point of -12dBm. This guarantees linear operation in the presence of relative strong narrowband interferers. The average power consumption is 105μW at 1.2V with a window length of 5ns and a pulse repetition frequency of 37.5MHz (duty-cycle of 18.75%).

C. Variable gain amplifier

The correlators output signal must be amplified to the proper levels for A/D conversion. Depending on the distance between transmitter and receiver and the channel properties, the received signal levels can vary by as much as 30dB. A linear-in-dB variable gain amplifier is thus needed. This VGA is digitally controlled by the back-end.

The VGA is a two-stage amplifier similar to the one described in [5]. The schematic is shown in figure 5. The first stage, consisting from transistors M1-M2 is a source-degenerated fully differential transconductance amplifier. The second stage (transistors M3-M4) is a transimpedance amplifier. A common-mode feedforward structure consisting of transistors M4-7 is used for common-mode output control. The differential first-stage output current is sensed by transistors M5. Differential signals are canceled at node ncm. The second-stage output current is regulated with current mirrors M4-M7. Furthermore the desired output common-mode voltage can be regulated through the externally applied voltage Vocm.

The gain ranges between 31.27dB and 1.76dB while the bandwidth is larger than 60MHz. The maximum settling time is 11ns, which is sufficiently fast for receiving 37.5MPulses per second. The maximum total power consumption in the worst setting is 350μW.

D. Analog to digital converter

As shown in [2], a resolution of four bits for the ADC proves to be the most power-efficient solution. Given this rather low needed resolution and the modest conversion rate (37.5MHz), a flash ADC is the most suitable structure. Flash ADC's typically use a resistor ladder to generate the reference voltages. In order to minimize the effects of kickback noise, a rather large current needs to flow through the reference ladder. Therefore comparators with built-in reference voltages were employed as to eliminate the reference ladder [6]. Each comparator has four binary-weighted calibration capacitors in order to fine-tune the trip points of each comparator individually after manufacturing. Since the output impedance of the VGA is fairly high, a simple low-output-impedance buffer drives the ADC to eliminate the effect of kickback noise on the input. The comparator thermometer code goes through a bubble error correction stage and is subsequently converted to gray code using a ROM-based encoder. The complete ADC including input buffer consumes 200μW at 1.2V.

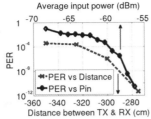

Fig. 6. Die photo.

Fig. 7. PER versus avg input power and TX-RX distance.

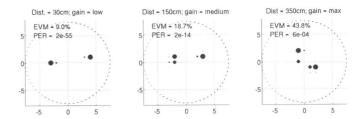

Fig. 8. Measured constellation diagrams.

IV. MEASUREMENT RESULTS

The analog front end was manufactured in 130nm CMOS technology. A die photograph is shown in figure 6. The chip contains two identical channels which are clearly visible at either side of the die photo. The clock generation circuitry can be found in the middle of the die. The active circuitry measures $600\mu m$ x $730\mu m$.

Figure 7 (diamond markers) shows the theoretical PER versus the average input signal power. The PER is calculated from the EVM's of the measured constellation diagrams. A sensitivity of $-61dBm$ is reached with a PER of 1E-3. An indoor experiment was performed where sinusoidal pulses with BPSK modulation were transmitted wirelessly with wideband bowtie antennas. The radiated signal had an EIRP below $-41dBm/MHz$. The PER as a function of the distance is shown in figure 7 (X markers). Figure 8 shows some constellation diagrams as measured at the output of the ADC's. Shown as well are the associated EVM's and corresponding theoretical PER. To give better visual feedback, the size of each dot is relative to the times it was measured and a unity circle is drawn. A PER better than 1E-3 can be reached at 3.5m distance which is about 3 times further than the results presented in [8].

The front-end has a total power consumption of 1.73mW (excluding LO generation) when receiving 37.5Mpps. The power consumption of the different building blocks is summarized in table I. A comparison with similar UWB transceivers is shown in table II. It is clear that the proposed receiver

achieves true energy-efficient communication. The energy consumption per pulse is about 5 times lower than the work in [7], [8] while it is 10 times lower than in [9]. With on-chip generation of the LO (using the PLL described in [4]) the energy-consumption is projected to rise to about 55pJ/pulse which still makes the proposed analog front-end by far best-in-class for low-range, low-datarate communication.

V. CONCLUSION

Impulse radio UWB communication is becoming increasingly popular for low data-rate, low range, ultra-low power communication. Typical applications include sensor networks and body area networks. A suitable architecture for a low-power impulse radio receiver is discussed and an ultra low-power integrated quadrature analog front-end is presented. The IC was manufactured in 130nm CMOS technology. A maximum total channel gain of 50dB can be achieved and a wireless link in excess of 3.5m has been demonstrated. The AFE consumes 1.73mW total from a 1.2V supply and is capable of receiving 37.5MPulses per second. The resulting energy-consumption of 46pJ/pulse is 5 to 10 times better than previous work.

ACKNOWLEDGMENT

The authors would like to thank the entire Pinballs team and the IWT-SBO who partially funded this research work.

TABLE I
POWER CONSUMPTION OF THE DIFFERENT BLOCKS.

Analog Pulse Correlator	Clock	VGA	ADC
2 x 105μW	350μW	2 x 350μW	2 x 200μW

TABLE II
PERFORMANCE COMPARISON

	This work	[7]	[8]	[9]
Band	sub-1GHz	6-8.5GHz	sub-1GHz	3-5GHz
Pulserate	37.5MHz	8MHz	1MHz	20MHz
Power	46pJ/p^a	250pJ/p	300pJ/p	640pJ/p^a

^{a}Doesn't include energy consumption of LO generation
(with the LO from [4], this would rise to about 55pJ/pulse for this work)

REFERENCES

[1] FCC, "First report and order," *FCC 02-48*, Feb. 2002.
[2] M. Verhelst, et al, "Design of an Energy-Efficient Pulsed UWB Receiver," *Proc. AACD*, April 2006.
[3] M. Verhelst, W. Dehaene, "A Flexible, Ultra-Low Power 35pJ/pulse Digital Back-end for QAC UWB Receiver," *Proc. ESSCIRC*, Sept. 2007.
[4] N. Van Helleputte, G. Gielen, "An Ultra-low-Power Quadrature PLL in 130nm CMOS for Impulse Radio Receivers," *Proc. BioCAS*, Nov. 2007.
[5] P. Naktongkul, A. Thanachayanont, "A 1V 25dB 100MHz CMOS variable gain amplifier cell," *ISCIT*, Oct 2004.
[6] P. Nuzzo, et al, "A 10.6mW/0.8pJ Power scalable 1GS/s 4b ADC in 0.18mm CMOS with 5.8GHz ERBW," *DAC*, July 2006.
[7] M. Anis, R. Tielert, "Low Power UWB Pulse Radio Transceiver Front-End," *Proc. ESSCIRC*, Sept. 2007.
[8] T. Terada, T. Kuroda, "A CMOS Ultra-Wideband Impulse Radio Transceiver for 1-Mb/s Data Communications and 2.5-cm Range Finding," *IEEE JSSC*, p891-898, Apr 2006.
[9] Ryckaert, J. et al, "A 16mA UWB 3-to-5GHz 20Mpulses/s Quadrature Analog Correlation Receiver in 0.18μm CMOS," *Proc. ISSCC*, Feb. 2006.

A 7.5mA 500 MHz UWB receiver based on Super-regenerative principle

Prakash.E.Thoppay,Catherine Dehollain and Michel J.Declercq
Electronics laboratory(LEG1)
Ecole Polytechnique Fédérale de Lausanne (EPFL)
CH-1015 Lausanne, Switzerland.
Email: prakash.thoppayegambaram@epfl.ch

Abstract— Low power impulse radio-ultra wide band(IR-UWB) receivers have potential application in the area of wireless sensor networks. In this paper the possibility of super-regenerative receivers for pulse detection is demonstrated. The super-regenerative receiver is implemented in a 0.18 μm CMOS process for a 500 MHz bandwidth (-3 dB) centered at 3.8 GHz. The receiver is operating at 1.5 V and consumes a peak current of 7.5 mA. The receiver shows a 16.5 mV amplitude difference between the presence and absence of a pulse at an average received power of -91.3 dBm at a pulse repetition rate of 1 MHz.

I. INTRODUCTION

Recently there has been an increase in the research interest for the design of low power consumption receivers. Such low power consumption receivers find a potential application in the area of wireless sensor networks. The need for such low power consumption receivers is also emphasized in the IEEE 802.15.4a task group. In the case where the communication across wireless nodes is achieved through impulse based UWB signals, a low power consumption for the receiver is achieved through aggressive duty cycling. Nevertheless the instantaneous power consumption is usually high due to the wide bandwidth nature of the received signals. The instantaneous power consumption for such receivers matters during the synchronization phase of such systems because ideally the receiver needs to be switched on for the whole of the synchronization phase. In this work an architecture based on super-regeneration is proposed for reducing the instantaneous power consumption.

In a non-coherent energy collection UWB receiver [1] the major power consuming blocks are the cascade of gain stages which are needed if a passive mixer is used and in the case of an analog correlation receiver [2] the major power consuming blocks are the LNA/mixer and the oscillator. In both the receiver architectures the RF stage amplifier is operated in the open loop. Whereas, in the case of a super-regenerative based impulse receiver the oscillator is used to achieve high gain for a given current. Due to the high gain for a given current the instantaneous power consumption is reduced.

II. SUPER-REGENERATIVE RECEIVER:THEORY

A. Principle of operation

The main building blocks of a super-regenerative receiver are the low noise/isolation amplifier, the oscillator, the en-velope detector, the baseband amplifier and the decision maker(Figure-1). The super-regenerative receiver is an ideal candidate for systems using an OOK modulation. In the forthcoming section, the principle to detect the presence or absence of a pulse is described. The presence of a pulse indicates a '1' and an absence indicates a '0'.

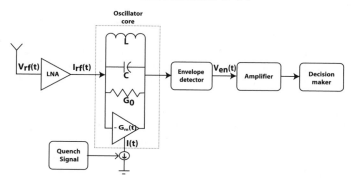

Fig. 1. Block diagram of the super-regenerative receiver

The low noise/isolation amplifier has dual purpose: 1)To amplify the received signal $V_{rf}(t)$ and injecting as current $I_{rf}(t)$ into the core oscillator resonant element. 2)It prevents the reradiation of the signal generated in the core oscillator through the antenna. The core oscillator bias current I(t) is periodically varied using the quench signal as shown in Figure-1. This in turn varies the negative conductance $G_m(t)$ as seen by the resonant element. The negative conductance $G_m(t)$ is varied periodically in such a way that the core oscillator is driven in and out of oscillation. Now, when a pulse $V_{rf}(t)$ centered around the oscillator resonant frequency arrives around the time when the core oscillator goes into oscillation, the oscillator is forced to start immediately due to the injected pulse current $I_{rf}(t)$ by the LNA. The difference in the start-up time is captured using an envelope detector.

The above concept is shown in Figure-2. The first row indicates the time varying bias current I(t) of the core oscillator. The peak current I_{bias} is greater than the critical current I_{cric} to start oscillation. The second row is the time varying effective conductance seen by the resonant circuit (LC). The G_0 indicates the loss in the resonant element. The third row indicates the incoming RF pulse centered around the

LC resonant frequency. The fourth row indicates the envelope variation $V_{en}(t)$. As seen in the fourth row due to the RF pulse, the core oscillator is forced to start immediately and reaches a higher amplitude in comparison to the state when the oscillator is allowed to start due to noise. The output of the envelope detector is further amplified using a baseband amplifier and the peak value is sampled. The sampled value V_{peak} is compared with a reference voltage to make a decision on the presence of a pulse.

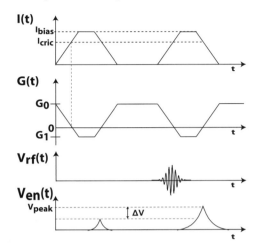

Fig. 2.   Graph showing the super-regeneration principle

B. Selectivity of Super-regenerative receivers

The influence of quench signal on the reception bandwidth is explained in this section. In the super-regenerative architecture shown in Figure-3 the gain of the LNA/isolation amplifier is determined by the g_m and the Q of the LC network. When the oscillator is biased below the critical current required to start oscillation, the effective conductance seen by the LC element is decreased thereby enhancing the output impedance of the LNA/isolation amplifier. Thus the LNA/isolation amplifier along with the oscillator core acts as a Q-enhanced amplifier [3], [4]. In the case where the bias current is time varying, the Q of the filter follows the current waveform and at a point where the loss of the resonant element is completely compensated by the regenerative circuit it becomes infinite. Now increasing the bias current further the critical current is particularly interesting because the oscillator core becomes unstable and starts oscillating. Due to the voltage build-up following an exponential curve a super-high gain is achieved for a given current. The presence of the input signal is detected by the forced oscillation imposed by the input signal on the oscillator core. Thus the selectivity of the super-regenerative system is determined by the time the oscillator core stays below the critical current and the gain of the super-regenerative system is dominated by the time the oscillator core stays above the critical current. Also an important conclusion from the above argument is: the bandwidth of the super-regenerative system is upper-bounded by the bandwidth of the LC resonant element.

Thus in order to receive a wide-band pulse, the Q of the filter should be low as dictated by the pulse bandwidth and secondly to achieve the maximum bandwidth of the filter the oscillator core should switch fast from the Q-enhanced mode to the super-regenerative mode [4], [5]. The latter can be achieved by having a very fast rise time of the bias current. Typically the quench signal rise time is of the order of the pulse duration. It is equally important that the start of the oscillation should be aligned with the incoming pulse for maximum gain. It is because in case when the pulse is before the start of the oscillation the pulse energy is dissipated in the resonator and if the pulse comes after the start of the oscillation then the envelope variation is smaller. This alignment problem is equivalent to the synchronization issue in other kind of UWB receivers.

III. SUPER-REGENERATIVE RECEIVER- CIRCUIT IMPLEMENTATION

In this work the super-regenerative receiver is implemented in a 0.18um CMOS process. The transistor level implementation is shown in Figure-3. The receiver is designed for a 500 MHz bandwidth (-3 dB) reception centered at 3.8 GHz. The main power consuming blocks in a super-regenerative system are the LNA/isolation amplifier and the oscillator.

A. Low noise/ Isolation amplifier

The LNA/isolation amplifier and the oscillator use the same resonant element, this helps in reducing the chip area and at the same time the amplifier injects the RF current into the resonant element. This is shown in Figure-3. In this implementation, a pseudo-differential amplifier is used, since a 500 MHz bandwidth at 3.8 GHz is targeted an inductive degenerated LNA configuration is used for input matching.

B. Core Oscillator

A cross-coupled differential pair is used as the regenerative core. Since the oscillation at high frequencies are limited by the parasitic elements, an on-chip inductor is used as a resonant element. The required Q is determined by the pulse bandwidth thus for a 500 MHz bandwidth at 3.8 GHz which is around 8. The bias current is controlled by the quench signal as shown in Figure-3. A reverse biased diode is used to vary the oscillation frequency.

C. Envelope detector

The envelope detection is mathematically modeled as a squaring operation followed by a low pass filter. The fact that in a differential amplifier the common source node moves at twice the signal frequency is used to achieve envelope detection. As shown in Figure-3, the transistors M7 and M8 form a differential pair and the output is taken at the common source node . The high frequencies are filtered by the parasitic capacitance across the bias transistor M19 and the transistor M11. The reference voltage is generated by having a same sized transistors M9 and M10. The envelope detector is operated in weak inversion for better quadratic gain [4].

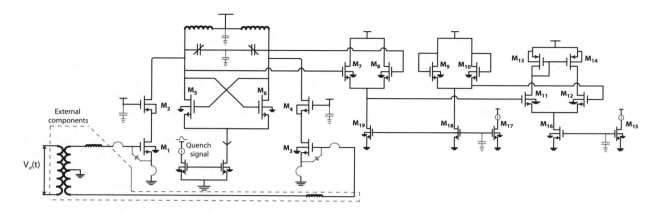

Fig. 3. Schematic of the proposed super-regenerative receiver

D. Baseband amplifier

The baseband amplifier amplifies the envelope difference between the presence and absence of a pulse. Due to the fact that the oscillator starts due to noise even when there is no incoming pulse, the difference in envelope variation is small when the received pulse strength is low. Therefore it is necessary to amplify this difference for proper detection thereby improving the receiver sensitivity.

IV. MEASUREMENTS

The wide-band signal is generated by up-converting the baseband pulse to the required frequency using a mixer and a local oscillator. The baseband pulse voltage and the center frequency signal strength are set in such a way to achieve -41.3 dBm/MHz. A 1 MHz pulse repetition rate is used for all the below measurements. For the measurements synchronization between the quench signal and the receiver pulse is achieved manually.

An external balun network as shown in Figure-3 is used for generating differential signals which are connected to the pseudo-differential amplifier. The LNA/isolation input is matched at 3.8 GHz for a 500 MHz bandwidth. The matching network is designed to have a $S_{11} < -10dB$ for a 500 MHz bandwidth centered around 3.8 GHz. Each arm consumes around 2.5 mA of current. A sufficient trans-conductance is needed in the LNA to force the immediate oscillation start-up.

The oscillator core consumes around 2.1 mA of current, the critical current required to start oscillation is around 1 mA. A high biasing current is used to start the oscillation immediately within the short duration of the quench signal. A trapezoidal shaped quench signal is used for the receiver. The quench slope which is critical for the selectivity of the receiver is of the same order as the pulse duration. For the measurements a total quench duration of 17 ns is used. The rise(fall) time is equal to 5 ns.

The average output envelope variation during the presence and absence of a pulse is usually small in comparison to the peak envelope amplitude. It is therefore better to sample the peak pulse amplitude to detect the presence or absence

of a pulse, thereby improving the sensitivity of the super-regenerative receiver [4]. At present for the measurements the value is noted through an oscilloscope, a sampling circuit synchronous with the quench signal is to be implemented in future. The sampled value is to be compared with a reference voltage and a decision is made whether it is '1' or '0'. The

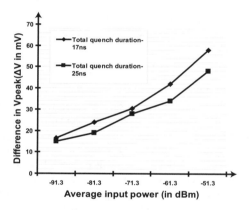

Fig. 4. Detected amplitude difference versus average input power

difference in sampled voltage during the presence and absence of a pulse is a direct indication of the sensitivity of the receiver. In Figure-4 the difference in peak voltage(V_{peak}) for different duration of quench is shown. The x-axis in Figure-4 indicates the average input power in dBm. Thus for an input power of -91.3 dBm averaged over 1 μs corresponding to a peak signal amplitude of $193\mu V$ in a 500 MHz bandwidth, the measured difference is 16.5 mV. Thus with a good reference voltage it is possible to detect the presence of a pulse. When the bias current $I_{bias}(> I_{cric})$ is applied for a longer duration the voltage difference decreases as shown in Figure-4. The reason is mainly due to the fact that if a very strong quench signal is applied the oscillator reaches the steady state value even when there is no pulse. Though there is a variation in the envelope it is small and therefore becomes difficult to detect leading to a decrease in the receiver sensitivity. So the total quench duration is critical in achieving better sensitivity.

The amplitude difference (in dB) for the received pulses

centered at different frequencies is plotted in Figure-5. It indicates the signal rejection by the super-regenerative receiver. The rejection is due to both the input selectivity of the LNA/isolation amplifier and also due to the resonant element in the oscillator circuit. The graph is normalized to the peak amplitude, since the oscillator circuitry is tuned to 3.8 GHz, the response is maximum at the oscillation frequency.

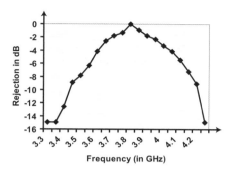

Fig. 5. Signal rejection of the super-regenerative receiver centered at 3.8 GHz

As mentioned earlier the maximum gain is achieved when the received pulse is synchronized to the point where the regenerative core goes into oscillation. In Figure-6 the variation in amplitude difference with respect to the time shift in the quench signal is shown. From Figure-6 it can be seen that the super-regenerative receivers have better performance when the quench is aligned with the incoming pulse to an order of 2 ns. It is possible to change the quench slope and collect energy from the multi-path components. Doing so, will decrease the sensitivity to the pulse alignment but the performance has not been measured in such a scenario.

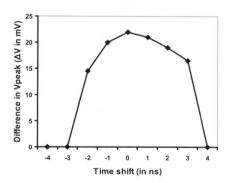

Fig. 6. Timing sensitivity of the super-regenerative receiver

The performance summary of the super-regenerative receiver performance is shown in Table-I. The chip microphotograph is shown in Figure-7.

V. CONCLUSION

In this paper the pulse detection using the super-regenerative principle is demonstrated. The super-regenerative receiver is implemented in a 0.18 μm CMOS process. The receiver consumes a peak current of 7.5 mA and is operated at 1.5 V. The receiver shows a -12 dB rejection at a frequency offset

TABLE I

PERFORMANCE SUMMARY OF THE WIDE-BAND SUPER-REGENERATIVE RECEIVER

Technology	CMOS 0.18 μm
Die surface(pads included)	2.25 mm^2
Resonator quality factor(Q)	8
Center frequency	3.8 GHz
Bandwidth (-3 dB)	500 MHz
Supply voltage	1.5 V
Power consumption	11.25 mW
Pulse repetition rate	1 MHz
LNA current	5.2 mA
Oscillator current	2.1 mA
Total current consumption	7.5 mA

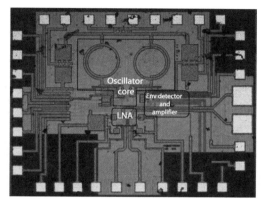

Fig. 7. Microphotograph of the super-regenerative receiver

of 400 MHz. Using the fact that the receiver blocks needs to be switched on only during the reception of the pulse, a very low average power consumption can be achieved. The receiver is sensitive to the alignment between the quench signal and the arrival of the incoming pulse. The next step will be to address the alignment of the quench signal with the pulse arrival.

VI. ACKNOWLEDGEMENT

This work was performed under MICS framework funded by the Swiss National Science Foundation.

REFERENCES

[1] Fred.S.Lee et al,*A 2.5 nJ/bit 0.65 V Pulsed UWB Receiver in 90 nm CMOS*,Solid state circuit IEEE Journal of , VOL. 42, NO. 12,pp. 2851-2859, December 2007.
[2] J.Ryckaert et al,*A CMOS Ultra-Wideband Receiver for Low Data-Rate Communication*,Solid state circuit IEEE Journal of,VOL. 42, NO. 11,pp. 2515-2527, November 2007.
[3] Jia-Yi Chen et al,*A Fully Integrated Auto-Calibrated Super- Regenerative Receiver in 0.13-μm CMOS*,Solid state circuit IEEE Journal of, VOL. 42, NO. 9,pp. 1976 - 1985, September 2007.
[4] A.Vouilloz et al, *A Low-Power CMOS Super-Regenerative Receiver at 1 GHz*, IEEE Journal of Solid State Circuits, VOL. 36, pp. 440-451, March 2001.
[5] F. Xavier Moncunill-Geniz et al, *A Generic Approach to the Theory of Superregenerative Reception*, IEEE Transactions on Circuits and Systems-I, VOL. 52, NO. 1,pp. 54-70., January 2005.

Low-Power CMOS RF Front-end for Non-Coherent IR-UWB Receiver

Yuan Gao, Yuanjin Zheng
Institute of Microelectronics
A-STAR, Singapore
yuanjin@ime.a-star.edu.sg

Chun-Huat Heng
Department of Electrical and Computer Engineering
National University of Singapore, Singapore
elehch@nus.edu.sg

Abstract□ **This paper presents a low-power CMOS front-end for 3-5 GHz non-coherent impulse-radio ultra-wideband (IR-UWB) receiver. The proposed front-end comprises a variable-gain low noise amplifier (VG-LNA), an active balun and an analog squarer. Current reuse topology has been adopted in both VG-LNA and active balun to reduce the power consumption. The squarer design is based on the quadratic law of MOSFET in saturation and the performance is optimized for 3-5 GHz UWB signal detection using cascode stage and active load. The VG-LNA has a measured maximum voltage gain of 33 dB/12 dB for high/low gain modes with minimum noise figure 3.7 dB/4.2 dB respectively. Measurements show that the proposed RF front-end achieves an input sensitivity of -91 dBm for UWB on-off keying (OOK) input signal at 1 Mbps pulse rate with an energy efficiency of 3.1 nJ/bit.**

I. INTRODUCTION

Ultra-wideband (UWB) technology is undergoing fast development in recent years as it is regarded as a promising technology for short-distance communication. For the high data-rate applications (> 100 Mbps) such as video streaming and high speed internet access, OFDM based UWB systems have been well reported [1-2]. However, there is also emerging demands for low-power, low data-rate communication system for various indoor applications such as automation/security, remote sensing and asset tracking. For such kind of applications, non-coherent impulse-radio UWB (IR-UWB) transceiver architecture is preferred for its low-complexity and low power consumption merits.

In a non-coherent IR-UWB receiver RF front-end, low noise amplifier (LNA) and energy detector (ED) are critical circuit blocks to identify the pulse signal from the noise floor. Rectifier and squarer are the two most often used ED structures. Conventional rectifier is usually implemented with Schottky diode. However, high performance Schotty diodes for high sensitivity RF application are not widely available in standard CMOS technology. Another often used solution is to utilize the existing four-quadrant multiplier (mixer) to implement a squarer by connecting both input ports together. But this method is inefficient since squarer only requires two-quadrant operation. A more efficient approach is to use

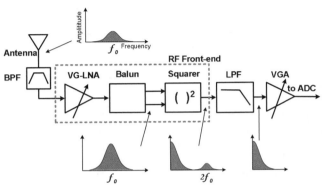

Fig. 1. The system diagram of the non-coherent IR-UWB receiver and the signal spectrum at each node.

circuits that directly realize the squaring function exploring the quadratic-law behavior of MOS transistors in saturation.

In this paper, a low-power CMOS RF front-end for non-coherent IR-UWB receiver energy detection is designed. The proposed front-end comprises a variable gain LNA (VG-LNA), active balun and analog squarer. Both VG-LNA and active balun utilize current reuse topology to reduce power consumption. The LNA gain switching function is implemented through shunt feedback variable resistor. The squarer is based on the quadratic law mentioned earlier.

II. RECEIVER STRUCTURE

The structure of the proposed non-coherent IR-UWB receiver is illustrated in Fig. 1. The received pulse signal from the UWB pulse generator can be approximated as a Gaussian pulse modulated by a carrier, which is expressed as:

$$S_{TX}(t) = Ae^{-\pi\left(\frac{t}{\tau}\right)^2} \cdot \cos(2\pi f_c t), \qquad (1)$$

where A is the amplitude of pulse, τ represents the duration of the pulse and f_c is the carrier frequency. After the amplification by VG-LNA, the pulse signal strength is enhanced. The input/output relationship of an ideal squarer circuit can be given as:

$$S_{RX}(t) = k\left[A_1 e^{-\pi\left(\frac{t}{\tau}\right)^2} \cdot \cos(2\pi f_c t)\right]^2 = \frac{kA_1^2}{2}e^{-2\pi\left(\frac{t}{\tau}\right)^2} + \frac{kA_1^2}{2}e^{-2\pi\left(\frac{t}{\tau}\right)^2}\cos(4\pi f_c t),\quad (2)$$

where k is the gain of the squarer and A_1 is the amplitude of the received signal after LNA. It can be observed from (2) that the received signal is splitted into two parts after the squaring operation. The first part is the down-converted Gaussian pulse envelop while the second part is the upconverted Gaussian pulse to the center frequency of $2f_c$. Energy detection through the processing of the low frequency component of the squarer output consumes less power and results in simpler circuit architecture. Therefore a low-pass filter is used to filter out the high frequency components before the VGA.

To achieve high sensitivity IR-UWB receiver, the LNA should provide high gain to the received weak RF signal and the squarer should be optimized to efficiently amplify the down-converted Gaussian pulse envelop signal to boost the output voltage swing.

III. CIRCUIT STRUCTURE

A. Low noise amplifier

The 3-5 GHz variable gain LNA is a four-stages cascaded resistive feedback amplifier as shown in Fig. 2. Current reuse topology is utilized to stack the four-stage amplifiers into two current-reuse cells [3]. The input impedance matching is achieved using the LC ladder matching network while resistor R_{f1} provides weak shunt feedback to increase the circuit stability without degrading the noise figure. All the source degeneration inductors are implemented with the bonding wires. The bonding wire and package parasitics in the input/output RF signal path have been absorbed into the matching network through extensive full-wave EM simulations in Ansoft HFSS. Unlike [3] which only provides fixed gain, variable gain function has been incorporated into this current reuse topology through varying the feedback resistors value in stage 2 and 3 to improve the linearity. The overall LNA noise figure and input/output impedance matching will not be significantly affected by the gain switching.

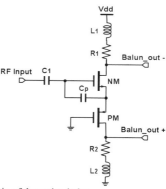

Fig. 3. The schematic of the active balun.

B. Balun

Fig. 3 shows the schematic of the active balun which can convert the single-ended LNA output to differential signals for squarer input. This active balun consists of a NMOS and PMOS pair [4]. The current sharing topology greatly reduces the power consumption. Resistor R_{1-2} and inductor L_{1-2} provide shunt peaking for the differential outputs in 3-5 GHz. The sizing ratio of the complementary transistor pair can be adjusted to minimize the output amplitude imbalance. Simulations show that this active balun can result in ± 0.6 dB and $\pm 5°$ amplitude and phase imbalance.

C. Squarer

The schematic of the proposed squarer is shown in Fig. 4. Transistors NM_{1-4} have the same sizes and they are biased in saturation region. The differential RF input signal is connected to NM_{1-2} to perform squaring function while NM_{3-4} are AC grounded so as to cancel the output DC offset. The total biasing current is set by the current source I_{total}. NM_{5-6} are cascode stages to enhance the squarer output impedance. PMOS transistors PM_{1-2} work as active loads, they are biased with a common-mode feedback (CMFB) circuit.

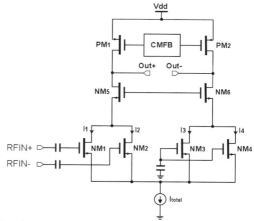

Fig. 4. The schematic of the squarer circuit.

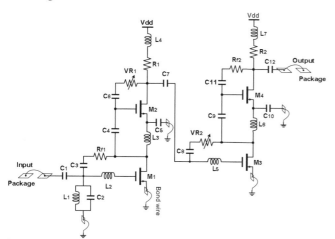

Fig. 2. The schematic of the variable gain LNA circuit.

Ignoring the channel length modulation and transistor body-effect, the drain current of NM_{1-4} can be given as:

$$I_1 = \frac{1}{2}\beta\left(\frac{W}{L}\right)\left(V_B + \frac{v_{in}}{2} - V_{TH}\right)^2, \qquad (3)$$

$$I_2 = \frac{1}{2}\beta\left(\frac{W}{L}\right)\left(V_B - \frac{v_{in}}{2} - V_{TH}\right)^2, \qquad (4)$$

$$I_3 = I_4 = \frac{1}{2}\beta\left(\frac{W}{L}\right)(V_B - V_{TH})^2, \qquad (5)$$

where β is the transistor constant, W/L is the size ratio of NM_{1-4}, V_B is the biasing voltage and V_{TH} is the transistor threshold voltage.

The squarer output voltage can be expressed as:

$$V_{out} = I_{out} \cdot R_{load} = (I_1 + I_2 - I_3 - I_4) \cdot R_{load} = \frac{\beta}{4}\frac{W}{L}v_{in}^2 R_{load}, \qquad (6)$$

where R_{load} represents the equivalent total loading resistance at the output of the squarer. From (6), it can be observed that, besides using larger transistors for the transconductance stage, increasing the squarer load resistance is another efficient way to boost the squarer output voltage. At low frequency, R_{load} is limited by the squarer output resistance since the squarer output is connected to the gate of next stage which has very high input impedance. The output resistance can be expressed as:

$$R_{load} \approx r_{o,PM1} \| \left[\left(1 + \frac{g_{m,NM5} \cdot r_{o,NM1}}{2}\right)r_{o,NM5}\right], \qquad (7)$$

where r_o is the transistor output resistance and g_m is the transistor transconductance. The large R_{load} together with the parasitic capacitance will provide the desired low-pass filtering to suppress the high frequency component resulting from the squaring action. The optimized R_{load} should be the one that maximizes the squarer output voltage without significantly filtering the down-converted low frequency Gaussian envelope component by the squarer.

IV. MEASUREMENT RESULTS

The fully integrated receiver RF front-end has been realized in a six-metal layers 0.18-μm CMOS process from CSM. The chip die microphotograph is shown in Fig. 5. The front-end has an active die area of 2.8 mm², including the ESD protected I/O pads. Two source followers connected to the output of squarer are integrated on-chip for testing purpose. The whole chip is mounted in a QFN32 package and soldered on a PCB board for measurement. The LNA, active balun and squarer draw 10.5 mA, 3 mA and 4 mA respectively under a 1.8V DC supply, and result in a total instantaneous power consumption of 31.5 mW. The average power consumption can be reduced significantly when the receiver on/off switching is triggered by a pulse with on duration of only 100 ns given the approximate 90 ns front-end startup time and 2 ns UWB pulse width. The average energy consumption is 3.1 nJ/bit at data rate of 1Mbps.

Fig. 6 shows the measured LNA voltage gain and noise figure. The maximum voltage gain in high/low gain mode is 33 dB/12 dB respectively with a corresponding measured minimum noise figure of 3.7 dB/4.2 dB at 3.4 GHz. The noise

figure is below 5 dB across 3-5 GHz band. The measured IIP3 of the LNA at 4 GHz is -38 dBm/-19 dBm for high/low gain mode. Fig. 7 presents the measured squarer output voltage versus squarer input UWB pulse (@1 Mbps) power. It can be observed that the squarer output voltage amplitude grows linearly with the increase of input RF power in the range of -55 dBm to -45 dBm until it get saturated at approximately 180 mV when the input power is above -45 dBm. The usage of cascode stage and active load in squarer limits the output voltage headroom. Nevertheless, the output saturation can be avoided by switching the gain of LNA to adjust the squarer input power.

Fig. 8 shows the measured RF front-end input and output pulse in time-domain. The LNA input UWB pulse width is 2 ns and when the pulse has a peak to peak voltage (V_{pp}) of 0.8 mV, the squarer output is 16mV, sufficient for the detection by the following stage. The equivalent sensitivity of the proposed receiver front-end is -91 dBm at 1Mbps pulse rate. It should be noted that the negative voltage in the squarer output is due to the decoupling capacitor between the squarer and the buffer. In the full integrated receiver, squarer and the following stages are DC coupled and this phenomenon will be eliminated.

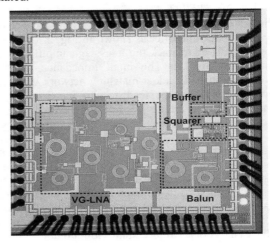

Fig. 5. The packaged die photo of the RF front-end.

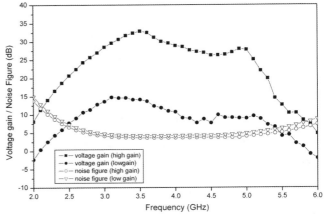

Fig. 6. Measured LNA voltage gain and noise figure in high/low gain modes.

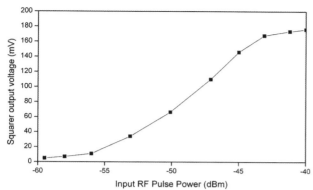

Fig. 7. Measured squarer output voltage versus input RF pulse power.

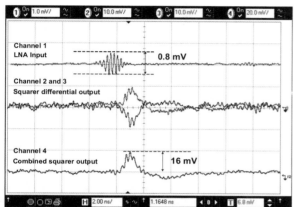

Fig. 8. Measured time domain pulse results.

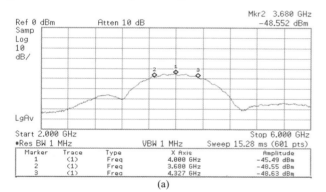

(a)

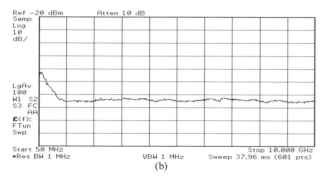

(b)

Fig. 9. Measured signal spectrum, (a) input UWB pulse, (b) Squarer output.

The measured spectrum of input pulse and squarer output are shown in Fig. 9 (a) and (b). The transmitting pulse has a 3-dB bandwidth of 640 MHz with the center frequency at 4.0 GHz. As shown in Fig. 9 (b), the squarer output spectrum is concentrated in the low frequency range. No high frequency component in 6-10 GHz can be observed due to the low-pass output bandwidth of squarer. The measured performance of the proposed receiver RF-front-end is listed in Table I and compared with other recently reported energy detection based receiver. Although the power consumption is slightly higher compared to other UWB IR receiver, the sensitivity is actually higher given the same data rate for our proposed UWB receiver.

TABLE I.   PERFORMANCE SUMMARY

Paper	Modulation	Sensitivity	Rate	nJ/bit	Tech.
[5]	PPM	N/A	20 Mbps	1.44	180 nm
[6]	PPM	-99 dBm	100 Kbps	2.5	90 nm
[7]	OOK	-65 dBm	1 Mbps	2.6	180 nm
This work	OOK	-91 dBm	1 Mbps	3.1	180 nm

V.   CONCLUSIONS

A fully integrated CMOS RF front-end for non-coherent IR-UWB receiver is presented. Implemented in 0.18-μm CMOS process, the whole receiver front-end has a chip size of 2.8 mm^2 and consumes DC current of 17.5 mA with a 1.8 V power supply. By exploiting the duty cycle of the UWB transmitted pulse, the receiver can achieve 3.1nJ/bit energy consumption and -91 dBm sensitivity for a 1Mbps pulse rate. The proposed receiver is proved to be well suited for low-cost, low-power IR-UWB applications like WPAN and sensor networks.

ACKNOWLEDGMENT

The authors would like to thank all the staff of Integrated Circuits and Systems Laboratory in Institute of Microelectronics for their assistance and support.

REFERENCES

[1] R. Roovers, et al., "An interference-robust receiver for ultra-wideband radio in SiGe BiCMOS technology," IEEE J. Solid-State Circuits, vol. 40, no. 12, pp. 2787-2794, Dec. 2005.

[2] C. Sander, et al., "A WiMedia/MBOA-compliant CMOS RF transceiver for UWB," IEEE J. Solid-State Circuits, vol. 41, no. 12, pp. 2787-2794, Dec. 2006.

[3] Cha C.Y. and Lee. S.G., "A 5.2-GHz LNA in 0.35-μm CMOS utilizing inter-stage series resonance and optimizing the substrate resistance," IEEE J. Solid-State Circuits, vol. 38, no. 4, pp. 669-672, Feb. 2003.

[4] T. Hsu and C-N. Kuo, "Low power 8-GHz ultra-wideband active balun", in Proc. IEEE SiRF 07, 2006, pp.365-368.

[5] J. Ryckaert, et al., "A CMOS ultra-wideband receiver for low data-rate communication," IEEE J. Solid-State Circuits, vol. 42, no. 11, pp. 2515-2525, Nov. 2007.

[6] F.S. Lee and A.P. Chandrakasan, "A 2.5 nJ/bit 0.65V pulsed UWB receiver in 90nm CMOS," IEEE J. Solid-State Circuits, vol. 42, no. 12, pp. 2851-2859, Dec. 2007.

[7] D.C. Daly and A.P. Chandrakasan, "An energy-efficient OOK transceiver for wireless sensor networks," IEEE J. Solid-State Circuits, vol. 42, no. 5, pp. 1003-1011, May. 2007.

Super-regenerative UWB Impulse Detector with Synchronized Quenching Mechanism

M. Anis
Institute of Microelectronic Systems
University of Kaiserslautern, Germany
Email: anis@eit.uni-kl.de

R. Tielert
Institute of Microelectronic Systems
University of Kaiserslautern, Germany

N. Wehn
Institute of Microelectronic Systems
University of Kaiserslautern, Germany
Email: wehn@eit.uni-kl.de

Abstract— This paper presents low power fully integrated super-regenerative UWB impulse detector with automatic adjustment of incoming pulses at highly sensitive region by using synchronized voltage controlled quenching mechanism. In-band and out-of-band interferences are eliminated by logic comparison and redundancy check between the outputs of multiple super-regenerators tuned within UWB spectrum. The test structure has been implemented on 0.18μm CMOS technology, active area of $1.4mm^2$. The UWB signal to in-band interferer ratio of -36dB is achieved with sensitivity of -95dBm at data rate of 20Mb/s and power consumption of 5mW at 1.5V.

I. INTRODUCTION

The ultra wideband impulse radio (UWB-IR) is a rapidly developing wireless technology that promises low power and low cost short range communication for low to medium data rate applications, like radio frequency identification (RFID) tags and wireless body area networks. The most of the complexity and power consumption of UWB-IR system is in receiver design. There are some technical challenges and open issues in receiver design that remain to be solved, such as achieving high sensitivity, high RF gain, large bandwidth and interference mitigation while maintaining low power consumption. Many research papers have been published but no test chip currently offers all the functionality together. Multiple number of amplifiers and mixer stages with high speed ADCs are required in previous implementation of UWB receivers, presented in [1][2][3], consume large amount of power without the support of narrow band interference mitigation techniques. The UWB impulse radio technology is seeking for new design concept to support high sensitivity, high RF gain, large bandwidth and while maintaining low power consumption with narrow band interference suppression abilities. This paper presents a new design architecture of UWB impulse detector by using an old super-regenerative technique, presented first in 1922 by E.H. Armstrong [5]. The super-regenerator has been used in recent years to demodulate narrow band signals rather than ultra-wideband signals [6][7][8]. This is due to its low power and low cost implementation for short range wireless applications. The inherent drawback of large bandwidth of super-regenerator is beneficial for UWB impulse detector, in which large bandwidth is required to obtain high performance. Previously reported super-regenerative UWB receiver requires multiple UWB impulses to detect single data bit [9][10]. This work presents super-regenerative UWB impulse detector to collect energy of single impulse per bit. This is achieved by

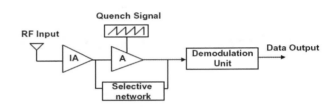

Fig. 1. The conceptual diagram of super-regenerator

locating the position of impulse on highly sensitive region of quenching pattern at zero crossing of the equivalent conductance by fully integrated synchronized quenching mechanism. The in-band interference mitigation technique is based on logic comparison and redundancy check between the outputs of multiple super-regenerators.

II. PRINCIPLE OF SUPER-REGENERATION

The super-regenerative circuit consists of isolation amplifier, an amplifier with time varying gain and bandpass selective feedback network forming an oscillator and demodulation unit, as shown in figure 1. The isolation amplifier between the antenna and oscillator is used to inject the RF input signal into the oscillator tank and reduce the leakage of the oscillation signal back to the antenna. The central frequency of an oscillator is determined by LC resonant tank. The oscillator is turned on and off by periodic signal called quench signal. The principle of super-regeneration is based on detection of variation in start up time of tuned oscillator in each quench cycle. The start-up time is inversely proportional to the bias current of oscillator, and the amplitude and frequency gap between the tuned frequency of oscillator and frequency of input RF signal. Without any external signal, the building up of the oscillations depends on the feedback gain and thermal noise, which is relatively slow process. The super-regenerative approach can be summarized by equivalent parallel resonant tank of oscillator, as shown in figure 2. The resonant tank consists of inductor L, capacitor C, and conductance $G_P - G_N$. Here G_P represents the parasitic losses of LC resonator and $-G_N$ represents the negative conductance due to active devices. The equivalent conductance G_T, placed in parallel with the inductor and the capacitor, is equal to the sum of negative and positive conductances. The RF input signal is represented

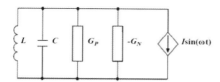

Fig. 2. Equivalent resonant circuit representation of an oscillator.

by sinusoidal current source $I \sin(\omega t)$. The transient behavior of the circuit can be described by summing the current, given by

$$\frac{C dV_{LC}}{dt} + \frac{1}{L} \int V_{LC} dt + G_{LC} V_{LC} = I \sin(\omega t)$$

The complete solution for voltage V_{LC} across the tank is presented in [4]. When G_T is positive, the active devices do not provide enough energy to compensate all the tank losses. This means that the free oscillation is damped and forced response is dominant and circuit works in filtering mode. When G_T is negative, the active devices provide more energy to build up the free oscillation from the input RF signal . This means that the free oscillation is dominant and circuit works in super-regeneration mode. The circuit works first in filtering mode to capture an initial RF signal then in super-regenerative mode by changing the equivalent conductance G_T in negative region to amplify the selected signals. The RF signal is mainly selected at critical level of quench signal close to the zero crossing of equivalent conductance ($G_T = 0$). The exact alignment of this critical level is not required for OOK modulated narrow band signals because several zero crossings of equivalent conductance occur during single data bit. But, the perfect alignment of UWB impulse close to the zero crossing of equivalent conductance is mainly required to maximize the sensitivity of UWB impulse detector [11]. Voltage controlled phase and frequency tracking loop are implemented to adjust the zero crossing of equivalent conductance close to the position of UWB received impulse pattern.

III. SUPER-REGENERATIVE UWB IMPULSE DETECTOR

The system architecture of super-regenerative UWB impulse detector is shown in figure 3. The tuned frequency of an oscillator is adjusted by integrated LC tank. The transistor M_1 is required to quench the oscillations periodically. An envelope detector senses the magnitude of the oscillations and the clocked comparator is used to compare its output V_{ENV} with reference voltage V_{REF}, just before the end of quenching cycle. The transconductance amplifier is used to adjust the oscillator current by comparing the average of digital received pattern to the VDD/2. DC-free on-off keying modulated pattern is required to adjust the bias current of oscillator at the critical level by automatic current control loop. Initially the transconductance amplifier provides large current which causes the oscillation in each quench cycle and high level voltage is received at the demodulated digital output of receivers. The output of low pass filter starts to increase, which causes the decrease in bias current of an

oscillator and adjusted on critical level. The output of the VCO is applied to the quench shaper to select the shape and extreme levels of quench signal at the gate terminal of transistor M_1. The sawtooth shape of the quench pattern is selected to control the bandwidth and sensitivity in efficient manner [12]. The automatic adjustment of incoming pulses in highly sensitive region ($G_T = 0$) is implemented by voltage controlled quenching mechanism with phase and frequency tracking loop. The shape and frequency of quench pattern, bias current of oscillator and threshold level of comparator are adjusted to shut down the oscillation before its amplitude reaches the saturation level. The bias current of oscillator is adjusted according to the quench rate. If the quenching frequency is high, short time duration is available for the oscillation amplitude to reach the reference level and requires high DC-bias current of oscillator. If the quenching frequency is low, long time duration is available for the oscillation amplitude to reach the reference level and requires low DC-bias current of oscillator. In this architecture, quenching of super-regenerative oscillator is made by changing the channel conductance of transistor M_1 across the critical level. The gate of the transistor M_1 is connected to the output of quench shaper and the source is connected to the common mode voltage level of oscillator in filtering mode. The equivalent conductance G_T can be represented as

$$G_T = g_{LC} + g_{ds1} - g_m/2$$

Here g_{LC} represents the parasitic losses of LC resonator, g_{ds1} represents the transistor channel conductance and $-g_m/2$ represents the negative conductance due to active devices. The equivalent conductance G_T is equal to the sum of negative and positive conductances. When the gate voltage V_{G1} is at high level and V_{GS1} is higher than the threshold voltage V_{TH} of transistor M_1, the oscillator shuts off rapidly due to very high conductance g_{ds1}. When the gate voltage V_{G1} starts to decrease slowly, the V_{GS1} also starts to decrease which results in the decrease in conductance g_{ds1} and G_T. The super-regenerator is highly sensitive at the quench voltage level for $V_{GS1} \approx V_{TH}$ due to zero crossing of equivalent conductance ($G_T = 0$) in the vicinity of this quench level. Figure 4 shows the simulation results for detection of UWB impulse close to the location where the difference between the gate voltage of transistor M_1 and the common mode level of oscillations is equal to the threshold of transistor M_1, $V_{GS1} \approx V_{TH}$. The UWB impulse detection can only be achieved if its location is inside the sensitive region. The amplitude of oscillations reaches the saturation level quickly in the presence of UWB impulse within sensitive region and slowly in the absence of impulse. When the gate voltage is further decreased and $V_{GS} < V_{TH}$, the transistor channel conductance g_{ds1} will also decrease to zero level and oscillator shifts from filtering mode to super-regeneration mode. In this condition, circuit is not sensitive to the incoming UWB impulse. The simulation results in figure 5 shows that the circuit is not sensitive to the UWB impulse during $V_{GS} < V_{TH}$ at similar quench rate and bias current. Figure 6 shows the measured output at the

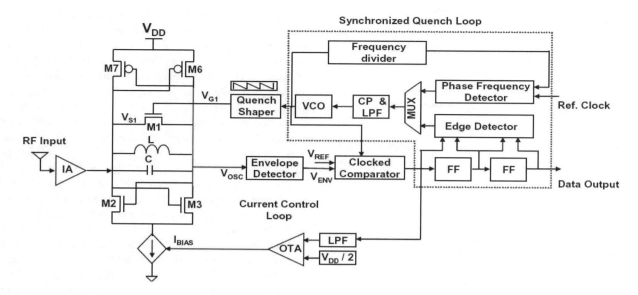

Fig. 3. The design architecture of super-regenerative UWB Impulse detector with synchronized quenching mechanism

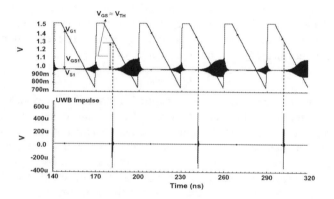

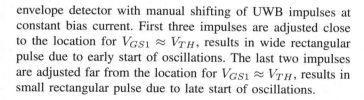

Fig. 4. The simulation results for the position of UWB impulses close to the sensitive region

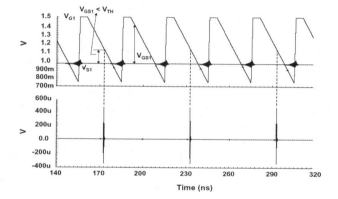

Fig. 5. The simulation results for the position of UWB impulses outside the sensitive region

envelope detector with manual shifting of UWB impulses at constant bias current. First three impulses are adjusted close to the location for $V_{GS1} \approx V_{TH}$, results in wide rectangular pulse due to early start of oscillations. The last two impulses are adjusted far from the location for $V_{GS1} \approx V_{TH}$, results in small rectangular pulse due to late start of oscillations.

IV. INTERFERENCE MITIGATION TECHNIQUE

The interference mitigation technique is based on logic comparison and redundancy checks between five super regenerative detectors (SRD) which are tuned at central frequencies of 6.4, 7.2, 8.0, 8.8, 9.6 GHz, as shown in figure 7. These detectors can extract the energy of UWB pulses, noise and interfering channels. The Manchester coding scheme is the most effective DC-free on-off keying modulation scheme to eliminate the effect of narrow band interferences by logic comparison and redundancy check between the digital demodulated outputs of all super-regenerators. The control unit is

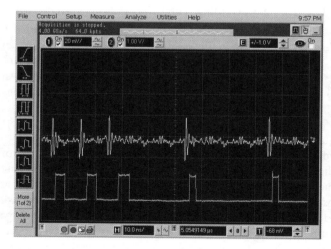

Fig. 6. The measured output of the envelope detector with manual shifting of UWB impulses at constant bias current

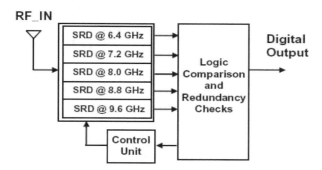

Fig. 7. The system overview of UWB impulse detector with interference mitigation technique

Fig. 8. The die photograph of test structure

responsible to enable and disable the corresponding detector according to the results of logic comparison and redundancy check. If the digital demodulated outputs of all detectors are same, it means no interfering channel exists within transmission. In this case, only one detector is enough to extract the transmitted data and remaining detectors can be turned off to reduce the power consumption. If the digital demodulated output of enable detector is disturbed from Manchester coding scheme during the operation by interfering channels, the control unit enables all detectors to make logic comparison and redundancy check of all detector outputs and selects the detector which is unaffected by interfering channels.

V. EXPERIMENTAL RESULTS

The bandwidth and sensitivity of all super-regenerative detectors are measured by injecting the on-off keying modulated pattern of variable frequency and amplitude of sinusoidal signals, generated by discrete colpitts oscillators made by using BFP-540 transistors. The measured bandwidth at quench rate of 40Mb/s varies from 500MHz to 800MHz for -95dBm to -40dBm signals, respectively. The performance of impulse detector is measured by injecting the 40dB attenuated output of UWB impulses generator, reported in [9], mixed with sinusoidal interfering channel to measure the signal to interference ratio. The measured UWB signal-to-sinusoidal interferer ratio is -36dB for $BER < 10^{-3}$ at 20Mb/s data rate with maximum sensitivity of -95dBm and power consumption of 5mW at 1.5V. The test structure is implemented on 0.18μm CMOS technology having active area of 1.4mm^2. The die photograph of test structure is shown in figure 8.

VI. CONCLUSION

The super-regenerative circuit cannot recover all of the energy transmitted by sinusoidal carrier. It is sensitive to only a portion of that energy in which the oscillator is at limit of instability. This property is mainly beneficial for detecting UWB impulse signals in which energy is concentrated over the small period in discrete time intervals. It means that the super-regenerative technique is more efficient in UWB systems than in narrow band systems. The alignment of incoming received impulse to the zero crossing of the equivalent conductance

is required to maximize the sensitivity. Voltage controlled quenching mechanism with synchronized phase and frequency control loop along with automatic current control loop is presented in this paper to adjust the position of received impulses in highly sensitive region of quench pattern. The logic redundancy and redundancy check between multiple super-regenerative detectors are proposed for mitigating the effect of narrow band interfering channels.

ACKNOWLEDGMENT

This work is funded by the Research Center Ambient Intelligence (AmI).

REFERENCES

[1] Y. Zheng, Y. Tong, C. W. Ang, Y.-P. Xu, W. G. Yeoh, F. Lin, and R. Singh. A CMOS carrierless UWB transceiver for WPAN applications. Solid-State Circuits Conference. ISSCC 2006. Digest of Technical Papers. IEEE International, pages 378-387, Feb. 6-9, 2006.
[2] F. Lee and A. Chandrakasan. A 2.5nJ/b 0.65v 3-to-5GHz subbanded UWB receiver in 90nm CMOS. Solid-State Circuits Conference, 2007. ISSCC 2007. Digest of Technical Papers. IEEE International, pages 116-590, 11-15 Feb. 2007.
[3] I. ODonnell and R. Brodersen. An ultra-wideband transceiver architecture for low power, low rate, wireless systems. Vehicular Technology, IEEE Transactions on, 54(5):1623-1631, Sept. 2005.
[4] J.-Y. Chen, M. Flynn, and J. Hayes. A fully integrated auto-calibrated super-regenerative receiver in 0.13-mu CMOS. Solid-State Circuits, IEEE Journal of, 42(9):1976-1985, Sept. 2007.
[5] E.H. Armstrong, Some recent developments of regenerative circuits, Proc. IRE, vol. 10, pp. 244-260, Aug. 1922
[6] F. Moncunill-Geniz, P. Pala-Schonwalder, and O. Mas-Casals. A generic approach to the theory of superregenerative reception. IEEE Transactions on Circuits and Systems , 52(1):54-70, Jan. 2005
[7] B. Otis, Y. Chee, and J. Rabaey. A 400 muw-rx, 1.6mw-tx super-regenerative transceiver for wireless sensor networks. Solid-State Circuits Conference, 2005. Digest of Technical Papers. ISSCC. 2005 IEEE International, pages 396-606 Vol. 1, 10-10 Feb. 2005.
[8] J.-Y. Chen, M. Flynn, and J. Hayes. A fully integrated auto-calibrated super-regenerative receiver in 0.13-muhboxm CMOS. Solid-State Circuits, IEEE Journal of, 42(9):1976-1985, Sept. 2007.
[9] M. Anis and R. Tielert. Low power UWB pulse radio transceiver front-end. 33rd European Solid State Circuits Conference, 2007. ESSCIRC, pages 131-134, 11-13 Sept. 2007.
[10] M. Anis and N. Wehn. Fully Integrated Multi-channel UWB Impulse Generator and Detector. ISSCC 2008 Student Forum.
[11] P. E. Thoppay, C. Dehollain, and M. J. Declercq. An automatic pulse alignment method for slope controlled super-regenerative receiver systems. Microelectronics and Electronics Conference, 2007. RME. Ph.D. Research in, pages 125-128, 2-5 July 2007.
[12] P. Favre, N. Joehl, P. Deval, M. Declercq, and C. Dehollain. A low-power 1ghz superregenerative transceiver with time-shared PLL control. Solid-State Circuits Conference, ESSCIRC 2000. Proceedings of the 26th European, pages 45-48, 19-21 Sept. 2000.

A fully-integrated Wienbridge topology for ultra-low-power 86ppm/°C 65nm CMOS 6MHz clock reference with amplitude regulation

Valentijn De Smedt, Pieter De Wit, Wim Vereecken and Michiel Steyaert
Katholieke Universiteit Leuven, Dept. Elektrotechniek, afd. ESAT-MICAS
Kasteelpark Arenberg 10, B-3001 Heverlee, Belgium
Email: valentijn.desmedt@esat.kuleuven.be

Abstract—Fully integrated Systems-On-Chip demand very accurate, low power, temperature independent clock references. In this paper, an improved Wienbridge topology is presented, meeting the specifications of this problem. Measurements show a temperature dependence of $86ppm/°C$ and absolute accuracy of 0.9% at an oscillation frequency of 6MHz. The circuit consumes $66\mu W$ and is realized in a 65nm technology measuring $150\mu m$ by $200\mu m$. A remarkable similarity between simulation and measurement results has been observed.

I. INTRODUCTION

Integration of complete systems on a single chip is one of the most important evolutions in modern micro-electronics. Fully integrated Systems-On-Chip, including both analog and digital circuits, are necessary to obtain high performance, power-efficient and low cost systems. To eliminate the off-chip components, the need for a very stable, precise, fully integrated, low-power clock references arises to eliminate the usage of an external crystal.

In this paper, a solution to this problem will be described using a well known oscillator structure: the Wienbridge oscillator. The usage of an improved topology allows to use this RC-structure to obtain an oscillator with the wanted specifications.

This paper is organized as follows. Section II describes the problem with the common Wienbridge topology in nanometer CMOS. Afterwards, Section III discusses the alternative Wienbridge oscillator topology. The amplitude regulator incorporated in the oscillator is investigated in Section IV. Simulation and measurement results are presented in Section V. Finally, some conclusions are drawn in Section VI.

II. THE WIENBRIDGE OSCILLATOR

A. Ideal Wienbridge Oscillator

The Wienbridge oscillator is an harmonic oscillator consisting of 2 building blocks: an amplifier and a passive RC-feedback network (see figure 1). The oscillation frequency can be calculated using the Barkhausen criterion on the feedback network:

$$\begin{cases} |H(s)| = 1 \\ \angle H(s) = 0 \end{cases} \tag{1}$$

These conditions are fulfilled if the amplifier has a gain of 3 and zero phase shift, resulting in the following oscillation

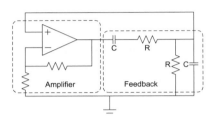

Fig. 1. Conventional Wienbridge topology using a passive feedback network and an opamp.

frequency:

$$f = \frac{1}{2 \cdot \pi \cdot R \cdot C} \tag{2}$$

It is clear that in this ideal implementation, the oscillation frequency is only dependent on the passive RC network. If a temperature independent oscillation is required, this network should consist of temperature stable passive elements. In the technology used, this network consists of N- and P-poly resistors and MIM-capacitors. The temperature dependency of the capacitors is negligible. Since the used N- and P-poly resistors respectively have a positive and negative first-order temperature dependency, a combined resistor with the remaining second-order temperature dependence can be obtained.

B. Implementation Non-idealities

Using an non-ideal opamp introduces its finite output impedance and phase shift in the circuit. The output impedance becomes part of the feedback circuit, thereby becoming an oscillation frequency determining parameter. Since the output resistance of the transistors changes strongly with temperature and the pole frequencies in the amplifier (controlling the phase shift of the amplifier) are also very temperature dependent, this poses a large problem to temperature-stable oscillation: the opamp becomes the critical part of the oscillator circuit. A temperature stable oscillator using the conventional Wienbridge topology can thus only be made using a very high performance opamp. This in his turn severely limits the low-power operation capabilities of such a circuit. The impact of process variability increases the mentioned problem. The gain, output impedance and phase shift will have wide

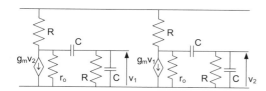

Fig. 2.   Improved Wienbridge Oscillator Topology

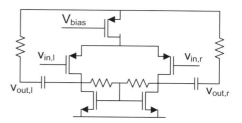

Fig. 3.   Gainboosting amplifier for the lower cascode transistors.

distributions, having a large impact on the absolute accuracy of the oscillation frequency.

To avoid this trade-off between power consumption, temperature stability and absolute accuracy, a new topology has been developed.

III. IMPROVED WIENBRIDGE TOPOLOGY

A. Basic structure

As explained in the previous section, the amplifier is the critical part in the Wienbridge oscillator. The required specifications can be summarized as follows: (1) a high output impedance, (2) no phase shift at $f = f_{osc}$ and (3) a non-inverting voltage gain of 3. It can be seen that these conditions have to be preserved under changing temperature and process variability.

The amplifier needed can be easily realized using a simple common source amplifier with drain resistor. As can be seen, the drain resistor R becomes, together with the output resistance of the transistor r_o part of the feedback network. Since this resistance $R /\!/ r_o$ determines the oscillation frequency and the output resistance of a MOST strongly varies with temperature, it should only be determined by the temperature stable, resistor R. This is achieved by maximizing the output resistance of the amplifier r_o by adding two cascode transistors. In this way the output resistance is mainly determined by the drain resistor R and almost independent of r_0, the resistance of the transistor-branch.

The phase shift of the amplifier should be minimized at the oscillation frequency. This can be realized by limiting the size of the cascode transistors.

A solution to the inverting behavior of the amplifier, can be found in cascading two (inverting) amplifiers with feedback network, see figure 2. The resulting structure is a loop of two Wienbridge oscillators. A differential signal will be found between the output nodes of the two amplifiers.

B. Stability of the voltage gain: Source degeneration

In a Wienbridge oscillator, a voltage gain of 3 is required. The gain of the common source amplifier can be described as:

$$A = g_m \cdot (R /\!/ r_o) \quad (3)$$

As said before, the output resistance of the transistor branch r_o is maximized, resulting in an amplifier output resistance, determined by resistor R, which is strongly temperature independent. Contrary, the transconductance of the transistor g_m varies as much as 35% over a temperature range of -40 to 100°C, resulting in a large fluctuation of the gain.

In order to stabilize this gain, source degeneration is used. Using this technique, the transconductance of the amplifier becomes:

$$g_{m,deg} = \frac{g_m}{1 + g_m \cdot R_{deg}} \approx \frac{1}{R_{deg}} \quad (4)$$

which is largely determined by the source resistor R_{deg}, a very temperature independent component. This source degeneration also results in an increase of output resistance by a factor $(1 + g_m \cdot R_{deg})$, which is favorable indeed. As can be seen, a trade-off exists between the magnitude and the temperature stability of the transconductance. A solution to this problem can't be found in increasing the current through the amplifier given a certain DC-biasing, since the lowered output impedance would compensate the increase in g_m.

C. Increase of the gain: Current bleeding

A solution to the previous problem can be found in current bleeding. Using this technique, extra current can be delivered to the common source transistor, without increasing the current through the cascodes and output resistor R. To minimize the impedance reduction at the current bleeding node, two cascode transistors are added to the inserted current sources. The resulting amplifier has a temperature-stable voltage gain of 3 and high output impedance.

D. Controlling the output resistance: Gain boosting

To increase the output resistance of the amplifier even more, gain boosting has been applied to both cascode transistors. This results in an additional output resistance increase with a factor approximately equal to A, being the voltage gain of the gain-boosting amplifier. The gain boosting also has a positive effect on the phase shift of the amplifier: since the impedance at the source of the gain-boosted cascode transistor will lower, its pole will shift towards a higher frequency, which will reduce the phase shift of the amplifier at the oscillation frequency. Because of the differential nature of the oscillator, the gain-boosting amplifiers have been implemented as fully differential amplifiers. The gain-boosting amplifier used on the lower cascode is shown in figure 3, the gain-boosting amplifier used on the upper cascode is similar, but uses a NMOS-differential pair. Since the supply voltage in the 65nm process is rather small, a capacitive coupling between the output of the gain-boosting amplifiers and the gate terminals of the cascode transistors is used.

The resulting amplifier is shown in figure 4. It has a phase shift < 0.4° until a frequency of 24MHz.

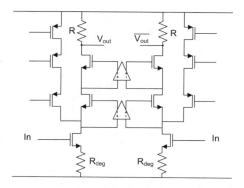

Fig. 4. Completed amplifier used in the Wienbridge Oscillator

E. Guaranteeing the absolute accuracy

A lot of design decisions have been made to reduce to influence of the transistor branch on the oscillation frequency. This also has serious advantages concerning the absolute accuracy of the oscillation frequency. Since this frequency is purely dependent on the passive components of the feedback network, the accuracy of f_{osc} will depend on the spread on the value of these components. In a CMOS technology, the spread on passive components typically is significantly smaller compared to active components. As stated before, the temperature dependency of these components can be made much lower compared to that of the active components.

IV. THE AMPLITUDE REGULATOR

A. Purpose and stability problem

To make sure the output impedance of the transistor branch remains high, the transistors have to operate in the saturation region. This means that the output amplitude has to be limited prior to the deformation of the output signal. This is only possible with a non-linear circuit which influences the gain of the Wienbridge amplifier. Typically an amplitude regulation circuit consists of three parts: (1) measurement of the amplitude by peak detection, (2) integration of the peak signal on a capacitor and (3) feedback to the gain of the amplifier. As described in [1] one of the main problems of amplitude regulation with peak detection is its instability. A first pole in the feedback network can be found in the integrator. The second pole appears due to the delay between the gain adaptation and the amplitude change. This is, in an harmonic oscillator, a consequence of the finite Q-factor [2].

B. Proposed Solution and Implementation

One solution to cope with this instability problem is by making a shortcut around the second pole for high amplitudes. By measuring the signal peaks at the source of the transistor (see figure 7), there is an immediate influence from the peak detection circuit on the amplitude. For high signal levels the signal will leak through the source of peak-detecting transistors. When the regulator network is in stable operation, only a very small peak current is running through these sources which makes the input impedance of the measuring circuit

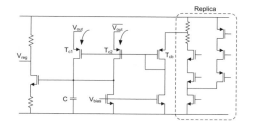

Fig. 5. Schematic of the amplitude regulator

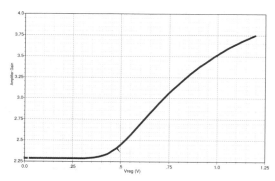

Fig. 6. Gain of the amplifier as function of the voltage applied to the bridge transistor

very high. The increased leakage current over temperature causes a small linear temperature coefficient of the input impedance. In section V, a solution to this problem will be described.

The adaptation of the gain can be done by a transistor between the to amplifier branches. This transistor controls the impedance at the source of the input transistors, which also controls the gain. One very beneficial property of this technique is that it doesn't influence the DC-operating point of the circuit, only the AC-gain is altered in this way. The influence on the output resistance is negligible due to the shielding by the gain-boosted cascode transistors. Figure 6 shows the voltage gain as a function of the gate voltage on the 'bridge' transistor. The complete regulation circuit with peak detection transistors $T_{c,1}$ and $T_{c,2}$, integration capacitor C and feedback amplifier is shown in figure 5. To determine the wanted level of the detected signal, a replica of the amplifier is used.

C. Complete Circuit

Using the different components discussed in the previous sections, the complete amplifier can be constructed. The full schematic can be seen in figure 7, in which the gainboosting amplifiers and the amplitude regulator circuit have been left out, to increase clarity. The current by the input transistor is $10\mu A$, of which 60% is conducted through the cascode transistors. The remaining 40% is supplied through the current bleeding. The total power consumption, biasing included, is $66\mu W$ at a supply voltage of $1.2V$. The feedback circuit is designed to obtain an oscillation frequency of 6 MHz.

396

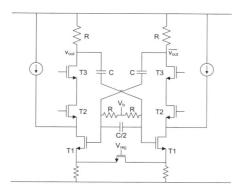

Fig. 7. Complete schematic of the Wienbridge Oscillator.

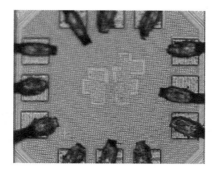

Fig. 8. Chip photograph

TABLE I
OVERVIEW OF SOME KEY PROPERTIES

Technology	$65nm$ CMOS
Frequency	$5.998MHz$
Power consumption	$66\mu W$
Temperature Coefficient	$86, 1ppm/°C$
Absolute Accuracy	$53kHz$ (0.88%)
Area	$200\mu m$ by $150\mu m$

TABLE II
COMPARISON TO THE STATE-OF-THE-ART

Ref.	Tech.	f (MHz)	T Sens. ($ppm/°C$)	P (μW)	Trimming/ Calibration?
This Work	$65nm$	6	86	$66\mu W$	No
[3]	$0.5\mu m$	$4-22$	460	$400\mu W$	Yes
[4]	$0.6\mu m$	0.68	106	$400\mu W$	No
[5]	$0.25\mu m$	7	400	$1.5mW$	No

Since the simulated temperature behavior corresponds very well to the measured behavior, an improvement to the measured circuit is simulated. In this circuit, the temperature coefficient of the amplitude regulator is compensated by adding an opposite, first-order temperature coefficient in the resistors of the feedback network. This results in a simulated temperature dependence of $28 - 33ppm/°C$, which corresponds to the remaining second-order temperature coefficient of the resistors ($36ppm/°C$).

In table II, a comparison is made between the presented circuit and some recently published temperature stable oscillators. As can be seen, the proposed topology performs very well in a deep-sub-micron CMOS technology.

VI. CONCLUSION

An improved Wienbridge topology has been developed, realizing a fully-integrated, low-power, precise, temperature-independent oscillator. Advanced design techniques have been used to obtain a high-performant oscillator, of which the specifications are listed in table I.

ACKNOWLEDGMENT

The authors would like to thank John van den Homberg, Kathleen Philips and Ed van Tuijl for their continous support during this work. We would also like to thank Philips for the processing of the samples and AnSem for the temperature-controlled measurement setup.

V. MEASUREMENT RESULTS

The complete circuit has been designed and processed in a 65nm Mixed Signal/RF CMOS technology. The capacitors used are MIM-capacitors. Resistors are implemented as a combination of N- and P-poly resistors. Note that no trimming or calibration is used. The active area of the chip measures $200\mu m$ by $150\mu m$ and is shown in figure 8.

During measurements, 7 samples have been measured. The oscillation frequency at room temperature is 5.998MHz with a standard deviation of 53kHz (0.88%). Figure 9 shows the temperature dependency of the oscillation frequency in a temperature range from 0 to 100°C. A linear frequency dependency of $86.1ppm/°C$ exists, which corresponds very well to the simulated value of $81 - 92ppm/°C$, including process corners. The amplitude of the output signal remains constant, proving good operation of the amplitude regulator. An overview of the most important properties of the circuit, are listed in table I.

REFERENCES

[1] E. Vannerson and K. Smith, "Fast amplitude stabilization of an RC oscillator," *JSSC*, vol. 9, no. 4, pp. 176–179, 1974.
[2] V. De Smedt and P. De Wit, "An Accurate Integrated Frequency Reference," Master's thesis, Katholieke Universiteit Leuven, ESAT-MICAS, Leuven, Belgium, June 2007.
[3] A.L.V. Boas et al, "A 1.8 V supply multi-frequency digitally trimmable on-chip IC oscillator with low-voltage detection capability," *SBCCI*, pp. 44–48, 2004.
[4] Y.S. Shyu et al, "A process and temperature compensated ring oscillator," *AP-ASIC*, pp. 283–286, 1999.
[5] K. Sundaresan et al, "Process and temperature compensation in a 7-MHz CMOS clock oscillator," *JSSC*, vol. 41, no. 2, pp. 433–442, 2006.

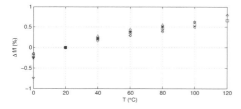

Fig. 9. Measured frequency deviation as a function of temperature

A 0.3-μW, 7 ppm/°C CMOS Voltage Reference Circuit for On-Chip Process Monitoring in Analog Circuits

Ken Ueno[†], Tetsuya Hirose[††], Tetsuya Asai[†], and Yoshihito Amemiya[†]

[†]Department of Electrical Engineering, Hokkaido University, 060-0814, Japan
[††]Department of Electrical and Electronics Engineering, Kobe University, 657-8501, Japan
E-mail: k_ueno@sapiens-ei.eng.hokudai.ac.jp

Abstract—A CMOS voltage reference circuit for on-chip process compensation in analog circuits has been developed in 0.35-μm CMOS process. The circuit generates a reference voltage based on threshold voltage of a MOSFET at absolute zero temperature. Theoretical analyses and experimental results showed that the circuit generates a quite stable reference voltage of 745 mV on average. The temperature coefficient and line sensitivity of the circuit were 7 ppm/°C and 0.002%/V, respectively. The circuit consists of subthreshold MOSFETs with a low-power dissipation of 0.3 μW or less. By utilizing the nature of the reference voltage, which changes with the process conditions of threshold voltage in each LSI chip, the circuit can be used as an elementary circuit block for on-chip process compensation systems.

I. INTRODUCTION

Progress in CMOS technology by device and voltage scaling has made it possible to integrate large scale analog and digital circuit systems for high performance and low power dissipation on a single chip. On the other hand, process variations in an LSI chip have become a significant issue in state-of-the-art CMOS technology. This is because process variations cause degradation of circuit performance and low fabrication yield in low power circuits. Therefore, it is becoming highly important for LSI designers to compensate for process variations. In CMOS process parameters, variation of threshold voltage of a MOSFET is one of the serious problems because threshold voltage has a significant impact on its drain current.

The variation of threshold voltage can be classified broadly into two categories: within-die (WID) (intra-die) variation and die-to-die (D2D) (inter-die) variation [1], [2]. The former affects the relative accuracy of transistors placed closely within a chip, and can be reduced in analog circuits by using large-sized transistors [3] and careful layout techniques [4]. However, the latter affects the absolute accuracy of the chip and could not be compensated in conventional circuit techniques. Therefore, a design method providing sufficient circuit performance even at the worst case corners is required. As a result, it has not been possible to optimize the performance, power dissipation, operating frequency, and area overhead of LSIs.

To solve these problems, in this paper, we propose a CMOS voltage reference circuit to monitor the D2D variation of threshold voltage. The circuit generates a voltage based on the threshold voltage of a MOSFET in an LSI chip. Because the output voltage changes with the process conditions of threshold voltage in each LSI chip, the circuit can be used as an elementary circuit block for on-chip process compensation systems. The following sections describe this reference circuit.

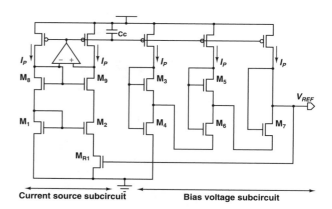

Fig. 1.   Schematic of the proposed voltage reference circuit.

II. CIRCUIT CONFIGURATION

Figure 1 shows voltage reference circuit we proposed. The circuit consists of a current source subcircuit, a bias-voltage subcircuit, and an operational amplifier. The current source subcircuit is based on a β multiplier self-biasing circuit and uses a MOS resistor M_{R1} instead of an ordinary passive resistor. The bias-voltage subcircuit accepts the current through pMOS current mirrors and generates the reference voltage. The bias-voltage subcircuit consists of a diode-connected transistor (M_4) and two differential pairs (M_3-M_6, M_5-M_7), and is based on the translinear principle. We operate all MOSFETs in the subthreshold region except for MOS resistor M_{R1}, which is operated in the strong-inversion and deep triode region. An operational amplifier and nMOS current mirror (M_8, M_9) are used to improve the power supply rejection ratio (PSRR) and line sensitivity of the circuit.

The circuit generates negative and positive temperature dependent voltages and combines these voltages to produce a reference voltage with a zero temperature coefficient. The following sections describe the circuit operation in detail.

A. Operation Principle

The subthreshold MOS current I_D can be expressed as

$$I_D = KI_0 \exp\left(\frac{V_{GS} - V_{TH}}{\eta V_T}\right), \quad (1)$$

where K is the aspect ratio (=W/L) of transistors, $I_0(= \beta(\eta - 1)V_T^2)$ is the process-dependent parameter, $V_T(=k_BT/q)$ is the thermal voltage, V_{TH} is the threshold voltage of a MOSFET, and η is the subthreshold slope factor [5]. In the circuit in

Fig.1, the current flowing in the circuit I_P is determined by the ratio of M_1 and M_2 and the resistance of MOS resistor M_{R1}, and is given by

$$I_P = \beta(V_{REF} - V_{TH})\eta V_T \ln(K_2/K_1), \qquad (2)$$

where β is the current gain factor.

In the bias-voltage subcircuit, gate-source voltages of transistors (V_{GS3} through V_{GS7}) form a closed loop with the reference voltage V_{REF}, so we find that

$$\begin{aligned}
V_{REF} &= V_{GS4} - V_{GS3} + V_{GS6} - V_{GS5} + V_{GS7} \\
&= V_{GS4} + \eta V_T \ln\left(\frac{2K_3 K_5}{K_6 K_7}\right) \\
&= V_{TH} + \eta V_T \ln\left(\frac{3I_P}{K_4 I_0}\right) + \eta V_T \ln\left(\frac{2K_3 K_5}{K_6 K_7}\right).
\end{aligned} \qquad (3)$$

The reference voltage can be expressed by the sum of gate-source voltage V_{GS4} and thermal voltage V_T scaled by the transistor sizes. Because these voltages have negative and positive temperature dependence, respectively, a constant voltage reference circuit with little temperature dependence can be constructed by adjusting the size of the transistors. Note that the threshold voltages of transistors in source-coupled pairs (M_3-M_6, M_5-M_7) are canceled each other by source-coupled circuit configuration.

B. Temperature Dependence

The temperature dependence of the threshold voltage can be given by

$$V_{TH} = V_{TH0} - \kappa T, \qquad (4)$$

where V_{TH0} is the threshold voltage at absolute zero, and κ is the temperature coefficient of the threshold voltage [6]. From Eqs. (2) and (4), the output voltage in Eq. (3) can be rewritten as

$$\begin{aligned}
V_{REF} &= V_{TH0} - \kappa T \\
&+ \eta V_T \ln\left\{\frac{6\eta K_{R1} K_3 K_5 (V_{REF} - V_{TH})}{K_4 K_6 K_7 (\eta - 1) V_T}\ln\left(\frac{K_2}{K_1}\right)\right\}.
\end{aligned} \qquad (5)$$

The temperature coefficient of the reference voltage V_{REF} in Eq. (5) is given by

$$\begin{aligned}
\frac{dV_{REF}}{dT} &= -\kappa + \frac{\eta k_B}{q}\ln\left\{\frac{6\eta K_{R1} K_3 K_5 (V_{REF} - V_{TH})}{K_4 K_6 K_7 (\eta - 1) V_T}\ln\left(\frac{K_2}{K_1}\right)\right\} \\
&+ \eta V_T \left\{\frac{1}{V_{REF} - V_{TH}}\left(\frac{dV_{REF}}{dT} + \kappa\right) - \frac{1}{T}\right\}.
\end{aligned} \qquad (6)$$

On the condition where $V_{REF} - V_{TH0} \ll \kappa T$ and $\eta V_T \ll \kappa T$, the temperature coefficient of the reference voltage V_{REF} in Eq. (6) is rewritten as

$$\frac{dV_{REF}}{dT} = -\kappa + \frac{\eta k_B}{q}\ln\left\{\frac{6q\eta\kappa}{k_B(\eta-1)}\frac{K_{R1} K_3 K_5}{K_4 K_6 K_7}\ln\left(\frac{K_2}{K_1}\right)\right\}. \qquad (7)$$

Therefore, the condition for a zero temperature coefficient can be given by

$$-\kappa + \frac{\eta k_B}{q}\ln\left\{\frac{6q\eta\kappa}{k_B(\eta-1)}\frac{K_{R1} K_3 K_5}{K_4 K_6 K_7}\ln\left(\frac{K_2}{K_1}\right)\right\} = 0. \qquad (8)$$

By setting the aspect ratios K in accordance with Eq. (8), a constant reference voltage of a zero temperature coefficient can be obtained. From Eqs. (5) and (8), the output voltage V_{REF} is given by

$$V_{REF} = V_{TH0}. \qquad (9)$$

Therefore, the circuit generates the threshold voltage of MOSFET at absolute zero temperature.

C. Temperature stability of the reference voltage V_{REF}

As discussed in previous sections, the circuit generates a reference voltage with little temperature dependence. However, because the output voltage refers to the threshold voltage of a MOSFET at absolute zero temperature, it is assumed that process variations have a significant impact on the output voltage. Temperature characteristics of the reference voltage depend on both the temperature coefficient of the threshold voltage κ and the aspect ratios of transistors K, as shown in Eq. (7). Therefore, the temperature coefficient of threshold voltage κ is the key parameter for temperature independent operation. The following discusses the temperature stability of κ with process variation.

The physical expression of threshold voltage in Eq. (4) can be expressed as

$$V_{TH} = -\frac{E_g}{2q} + \psi_B + \frac{\sqrt{4\varepsilon_{si} q N_A \psi_B}}{C_{OX}}, \quad \psi_B = V_T \ln\left(\frac{N_A}{n_i}\right), \quad (10)$$

where ψ_B is the difference between fermi level and intrinsic level, ε_{si} is the silicon permittivity, N_A is the channel doping concentration, n_i is the intrinsic carrier density, and E_g is the bandgap energy of silicon [5]. From Eq. (10), the temperature coefficient of the threshold voltage ($\frac{dV_{TH}}{dT} = \kappa$) is given by

$$\frac{dV_{TH}}{dT} = -(2\eta - 1)\frac{k_B}{q}\left\{\ln\left(\frac{\sqrt{N_c N_v}}{N_A}\right) + \frac{3}{2}\right\} + \frac{\eta - 1}{q}\frac{dE_g}{dT}, \quad (11)$$

where N_c and N_v are the effective densities of states in the conduction and valence bands, respectively. From Eqs. (10) and (11), we find that the threshold voltage V_{TH} and the temperature coefficient of the threshold voltage κ depend on the channel doping concentration N_A. The temperature coefficient of the threshold voltage contains N_A as a process variation parameter, but the effect of the variation on the temperature coefficient κ can be ignored because N_A is contained in a logarithmic function.

To verify the effect of the process variations on the threshold voltage and the temperature coefficient of the threshold voltage, Eqs. (10) and (11) were calculated considering 0.35-μm CMOS parameters. Figure 2 shows a plot of the calculated threshold voltage V_{TH} and the temperature coefficient of threshold voltage κ as a function of the channel doping concentration N_A. In the doping concentration around 2×10^{17} cm^{-3}, which is the typical concentration in the CMOS process we used, the threshold voltage of a MOSFET changes significantly, about $\pm20\%$, with N_A, while the temperature coefficient of the threshold voltage changes little, about $\pm2\%$. This is because doping concentration N_A in Eq. (11) is

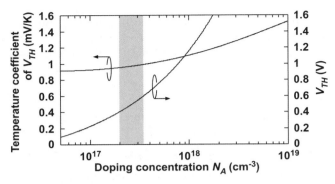

Fig. 2. Calculated TC of threshold voltage $(dV_{TH}/dT = \kappa)$ (left axis) and threshold voltage (V_{TH}) (right axis) as a function of channel doping concentration (N_A).

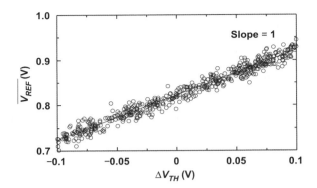

Fig. 3. Scatter plot of the output voltage as a function of D2D threshold voltage variation ΔV_{TH} from 500-point Monte Carlo simulations. The output voltage shows a linear dependence on threshold voltage $\left(\Delta \overline{V_{REF}}/\Delta V_{TH} \approx 1 \right)$.

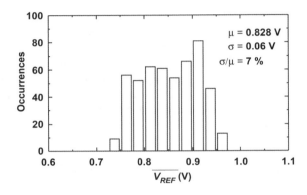

Fig. 4. Distribution of the output voltage with 500-point Monte Carlo simulations assuming both D2D and WID variations.

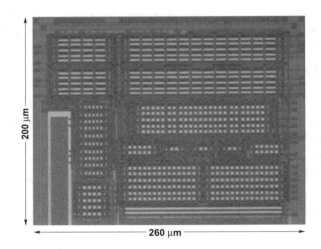

Fig. 5. Chip micrograph.

contained in a logarithmic function. Therefore, the variation of N_A is compressed, and the temperature coefficient of the threshold voltage κ has little process dependence. By setting the aspect ratios K in Eq. (8), a constant voltage of a zero temperature coefficient can be obtained.

III. SIMULATION RESULTS

We confirmed the operation of the circuit by a SPICE simulation with a set of 0.35-μm standard CMOS parameters and a 1.5-V power supply. To verify the stability of the circuit operation with process variations, Monte Carlo analysis assuming both D2D variations (uniform distribution: –0.1 V $< \Delta V_{TH} <$ 0.1 V) and WID mismatch variations (Gaussian distribution: $3\sigma_{V_{TH}}$) in all MOSFETs were considered.

Figure 3 shows the scatter plot of the average output voltage $\overline{V_{REF}}$ in the temperature range of –20 to 80℃ as a function of the D2D variation in threshold voltage ΔV_{TH}. The output voltage shows a linear dependence on the variation of threshold voltage, because the circuit monitors the threshold voltage of MOSFET as shown in Eq. (9). Figure 4 shows the distribution of average output voltage $\overline{V_{REF}}$. The average voltage $\overline{V_{REF}}$ was about 828 mV in this simulations. The coefficient of variation (σ/μ) in 500 runs, which include D2D and WID variations, was 7%.

IV. EXPERIMENTAL RESULTS

We fabricated a prototype chip with a 0.35-μm, 2-poly, 4-metal standard CMOS process. Figure 5 shows a chip micrograph of our prototype chip. The chip area was 0.052 mm^2(=200 μm $\times$ 260 μm). Figure 6 shows measured output voltage V_{REF} as a function of temperature from –20 to 80℃ with different power supply V_{DD}: 1.4, 1.5, 2, 2.5, and 3 V. An almost constant output voltage can be obtained. The average output voltage was about 745 mV. The temperature variation and temperature coefficient were 0.48 mV and 7 ppm/℃, respectively. Figure 7 shows output voltage V_{REF} as a function of power supply from 0 to 3 V at room temperature. The circuit operated correctly with more than 1.4 V power supply. The line sensitivity was 0.002%/V in the supply range of 1.4 to 3 V. A constant reference voltage with little temperature and power supply dependence can be obtained. The current I_P was extremely low, about 36 nA at room temperature, and the maximum current I_P was 39 nA at 80℃. The total power dissipation of the circuit was 0.3 μW at a 1.5-V power supply and at room temperature.

Table I summarizes the performance of the proposed circuits and compares the performance of reported CMOS voltage

400

TABLE I

COMPARISON OF REPORTED CMOS VOLTAGE REFERENCE CIRCUITS

	This work	De Vita [7]	Leung [8]	Giustolisi [9]	Huang [10]
Process	0.35-μm, CMOS	0.35-μm, CMOS	0.6-μm, CMOS	1.2-μm, CMOS	0.18-μm, CMOS
Temperature range	−20 - 80℃	0 - 80℃	0 - 100℃	−25 - 125℃	20 - 120℃
V_{DD}	1.4 - 3 V	0.9 - 4 V	1.4 - 3 V	1.2 V	0.85 - 2.5 V
V_{REF}	745 mV	670 mV	309.3 mV	295 mV	221 mV
Power	0.3 μW(@1.5 V) Room temp.	0.036 μW(@0.9 V) Room temp.	29.1 μW(@3 V) Max. temp	4.3 μW(@1.2 V) N.A.	3.3 μW(@0.85 V) Average
TC	7 ppm/℃	10 ppm/℃	36.9 ppm/℃	119 ppm/℃	271 ppm/℃
Line sensitivity	0.002%/V	0.27%/V	0.08%/V	N.A.	0.9%/V
Chip area	0.052 mm^2	0.045 mm^2	0.055 mm^2	0.23 mm^2	0.0238 mm^2

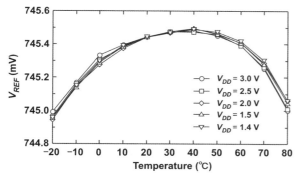

Fig. 6. Measured results of the output voltage V_{REF} as a function of temperature with different power supply.

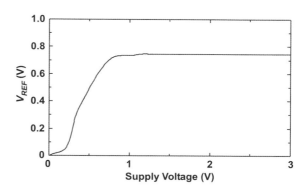

Fig. 7. Measured results of the output voltage V_{REF} as a function of power supply.

reference circuits [7]-[10]. The proposed voltage reference circuit shows the best temperature coefficient and line sensitivity performance compared to the other CMOS voltage reference circuits.

The simulation and measurement results have showed that the effect of the WID mismatch variation can be made small, but that the effect of the D2D process variation of threshold voltage directly affects the output voltage. Therefore, the absolute value of the output voltage changes significantly with process variations. In general, the change in reference voltage is fatal in LSI systems. However, we assume the reference voltage of the circuit as a D2D process variation signal in each LSI chip and, by using the on-chip signal, the reference voltage circuit can be used as an elementary circuit block for on-chip compensation systems such as a robust reference current generator, slew rate compensation techniques in analog buffers, frequency compensation in VCO, and so on.

V. CONCLUSION

A CMOS voltage reference circuit to monitor the process variation in each LSI chip was developed. A prototype chip with a 0.35-μm CMOS process was fabricated and its operation was demonstrated in this paper. The temperature coefficient and line sensitivity were 7 ppm/℃ and 0.002%/V, respectively. The power consumption was extremely low, about 0.3 μW. Because the output voltage changes with the process conditions of threshold voltage in each LSI chip, the circuit can be used as an elementary circuit block for on-chip process

compensation systems. The output voltage of the proposed circuit enables us to monitor the D2D variation of each LSI chip.

ACKNOWLEDGMENTS

This work is supported by VLSI Design and Education Center (VDEC), the University of Tokyo in collaboration with Cadence Design Systems, Inc.

REFERENCES

[1] K. A. Bowman, S. G. Duvall, J. D. Meindl, "Impact of Die-to-die and Within-die Parameter Fluctuations on the Maximum Clock Frequency Distribution for Gigascale Integration," IEEE JSSC, pp. 183 - 190, 2002.
[2] H. Onodera, "Variability: Modeling and Its Impact on Design," IEICE Trans. Electron., Vol.E89-C, pp. 342 - 348, 2006.
[3] M. J. M. Pelgrom, A. C. J. Duinmaijer, A. P. G. Welbers, "Matching properties of MOS transistors," IEEE JSSC, pp. 1433 - 1439, 1989.
[4] A. Hastings, The Art of Analog Layout, Prentice Hall, 2001.
[5] Y. Taur, T.H. Ning, Fundamentals of Modern VLSI Devices, Cambridge University Press, 2002.
[6] I. M. Filanovsky, A. Allam, "Mutual Compensation of Mobility and Threshold Voltage Temperature Effects with Applications in CMOS Circuits," IEEE Trans. Circuits Syst. I, Fundam. Theory Appl, pp. 876-884, 2001.
[7] G. De Vita, G. Iannaccone, "A Sub-1-V, 10 ppm/℃, Nanopower Voltage Reference Generator" IEEE JSSC, pp. 1536 - 1542, 2007.
[8] K. N. Leung, P. K. T. Mok, "A CMOS Voltage Reference Based on Weighted ΔV for CMOS Low-dropout Linear Regulators," IEEE JSSC, pp. 146 - 150, 2003.
[9] G. Giustolisi, G. Palumbo, M. Criscione, F. Cutri, "A Low-Voltage Low-Power Voltage Reference Based on Subthreshold MOSFETs," IEEE JSSC, pp. 151 - 154, 2003.
[10] P-H. Huang, H. Lin, Y-T. Lin, "A Simple Subthreshold CMOS Voltage Reference Circuit With Channel- Length Modulation Compensation," IEEE Trans. Circuits Syst. II, Exp. Briefs, pp. 882 - 885, 2006.

Electronic Interface for Piezoelectric Energy Scavenging System

E. Dallago, D. Miatton, G. Venchi
Department of Electrical Engineering
University of Pavia, 27100 Pavia, Italy

V. Bottarel, G. Frattini[1], G. Ricotti, M. Schipani
STMicroelectronics
20010 Cornaredo, Milan, Italy

Abstract- **The paper focuses on an electronic interface for systems, called Piezoelectric Energy Scavenging Systems (PESS), which convert the energy of mechanical vibrations into electrical energy using a piezoelectric transducer. The output of the transducer is a strong and irregular function of time hence, to obtain a suitable supply source, an AC-DC conversion is needed. Classical rectifiers (half/full bridge or voltage doubler) with an output storage capacitor do not fit very well, since they work as peak detectors, converting only input voltages which are higher than their output voltage.**
The paper shows an electronic interface which is able to efficiently harvest the energy associated to the randomic voltage waveform delivered by a piezoelectric transducer. Its working principle is based on an inductive step-up converter; an active driving circuit is used to set the phases of the converter. The energy is stored into a capacitor which is also used to supply the active elements of the step-up converter, realizing a completely autonomous energy scavenging system. For this reason the whole circuitry has been designed with a very low-power consumptions, about 700 nA. A prototype was diffused in 5V CMOS STMicroelectronics technology and measurements showed its effectiveness.

I. INTRODUCTION

Energy scavenging systems are used to harvest the normally lost environmental energy and to convert it into electrical energy. This approach can be attractive where batteries are a bottleneck for the whole system (e.g. they have a finite life time and their replacement or recharge is not feasible or too expensive). An energy scavenging system, instead, is a theoretically endless energy source. In literature many papers describe methodologies to realize the energy-scavenger [1], [6], [8]. A lot of them focus on the conversion of the energy associated to mechanical vibrations since they can be easily found in many environments [1], [7]. This paper focuses on a piezoelectric transducer since it is one of the more efficient systems to convert the energy of mechanical vibrations [1]-[2].

The electrical output of the transducer is a strong and irregular function of time [1]-[4], [9] thus an AC-DC conversion is needed to realize a DC power supply. In literature many solutions are presented to realize this function, mainly based on classical topologies of AC-DC converters [1], [3]-[4], [9]-[11] (e.g. half/full bridge, voltage doubler) with a capacitance C_O connected at their

[1]Now he is with National Semiconductor s.r.l., Strada 7, R3,20089, Rozzano (MI), Italy

output to store the harvested energy. The main limitation is that the energy associated to transducer output voltages lower than the voltage stored on C_O can not be harvested. This is a big drawback because in a real environment the mechanical vibrations and, consequently, the transducer output voltage, are often an irregular function of time. For example, Fig. 1 shows the measured voltage given by a piezoelectric transducer placed onto a car dashboard: there are few chances that the peaks following the one at 5 seconds could be harvested.

Anyway, even if the source is sinusoidal, after a transient a condition is reached when energy is no longer transfered from the transducer to the output. To realize an efficient energy scavenging system it is necessary to harvest the energy of the entire waveform.

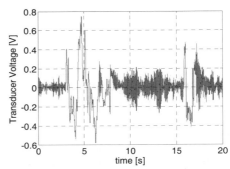

Fig. 1 Voltage supplied by a piezoelectric transducer, working in 31-mode, placed onto a dashboard.

The proposed solution is aimed at improving the efficiency of a PESS based on a cantilever-like piezoelectric transducer working in 31-mode. The front-end circuitry allows positive peaks of any amplitude to be harvested indipendently of the voltage across the storage capacitor C_O; while, for negative peaks, the behaviour of the circuit is the same as the standard voltage doubler.

A test chip was diffused in 5V CMOS STMicroelectronics technology and the measurements are presented.

II. WORKING PRINCIPLE OF THE PROPOSED SOLUTION

A piezoelectric transducer can be modeled as a current source, i_P, whose current is proportional to the derivative of cantilever strain, with a capacitor C_P in parallel [12]. Fig. 2a shows the block scheme of the proposed electronic interface while Fig. 2b is the working cycle obtained with an appropriate driving of the switches. Let us assume the cantilever starts from rest condition (no strain and no charge on plates) and it is then deflected from *a* to *b* (ref. Fig. 2b). If no load is connected to C_P, voltage v_P is the integral of current i_P and it reaches a local maximum V_{PMax} when the cantilever is at its maximum strain. At this point, C_P has collected the maximum charge, Q_{Pmax}, onto its plates and it stores an electrical energy equal to:

$$E = \frac{1}{2} \frac{Q^2_{Pmax}}{C_P} \qquad (1)$$

Energy harvesting is maximally efficient if all of this energy is extracted. A classical rectifier does not comply to this requirement because it connects the transducer to the output storage capacitance as soon as the voltage v_P is higher than V_O [4, 10]. In this way the transducer has to produce a charge $C_P V_O$ to reach the voltage V_O and from this moment on all of the extra generated charge is shared between C_P and C_O. Hence, all the cantilever deflections which produce a voltage lower than V_O do not transfer energy to C_O.

On the contrary the proposed solution is able to extract all the energy defined in (1) and to store it into storage capacitance C_O. This can be obtained in four phases. During phase 1 the transducer is strained (path *a-b* of Fig. 2b) and all the switches of Fig. 2a are open. In this way the whole interface circuit is not loading the transducer. When the maximum strain is reached, the transducer has generated the energy defined in (1), C_P stores it and voltage on node l_{x+} has reached the maximum. Driving circuitry senses this condition and starts phase 2: switch S2 is closed and a resonance between C_P and L takes place (path *b-c* of Fig. 2b). When the voltage on node l_{x+} reaches zero all the energy of the piezoelectric transducer has been transfered into inductance L. Driving circuitry senses this new condition and phase 3 starts: switch S2 is opened while switches S1 and S3 are closed (point *c* of Fig. 2b). When the current into L reaches zero the energy of L will be completely transfered to C_O and phase 3 ends. At this time switches S2 and S3 are opened.

If phases 2 and 3 are faster than the variation of the cantilever strain during these phases, in a first approximation the transducer can be considered motionless at the maximum deflection reached at the end of phase 1.

When phase 3 ends the cantilever starts to be deflected in the opposite direction and phase 4 can be started. Switch S1 is closed and path *c-d* of Fig. 2b is covered: current supplied by piezoelectric transducer recirculates through S1 and no charge is collected onto capacitor C_P, as in the standard voltage doubler topology. When the maximum deflection is reached (point *d*) phase 1 takes place again: differently from point *a* the cantilever is at a negative strain but still has no charges on its plates. Hence during the motion from *d* to *e* a positive charge is already collected on C_P corresponding to an energy that the circuit will be able to harvest. At the end of phase 1, when new maximum deflection is reached (point *f*), the charge increases further because of the positive deflection.

This demonstrates that this circuit recovers not only the energy of positive voltage peaks, but it is able to harvest

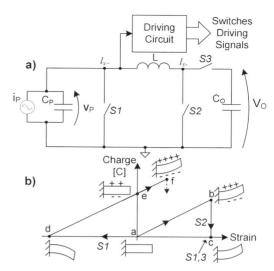

Fig. 2 a) Principle scheme of the proposed front-end circuit. b) Working cycle realized by the front-end circuit.

the energy corresponding to a whole deflection from negative peak to positive peak. This holds even if the amplitude of each deflection is different from the previous one.

III. DESIGN OF THE AC-DC CONVERTER

Fig. 3a shows the circuitry designed to implement the conceptual scheme of Fig. 2a.

The driving circuitry has to be supplied only by the output voltage V_O, i.e. by the harvested energy, hence its power consumption should be as low as possible. Furthermore, since voltage V_O is variable in time, a supply independent bias circuitry [5] has been designed so to make the whole current consumption independent on the supply variations. Some modifications have been introduced with respect to [5]; in particular, to implement the start-up function, the leakage of two p-channel MOSFETs has been exploited. This solution allows us to avoid additional start-up circuitry, reducing the total power consumption.

Switch S1 has been splitted in two switches: S1' and S1" which are used during phase 4 and phase 3 respectively. In fact, the purpose of the prototype is to check the validity of this new approach and an attempt was made to keep the driving circuitry as simple as possible. In particular, switch S1" can be simply driven inverting phase 3, while a dedicated circuit drives switch S1' by sensing the voltage across it.

Inductance L is an external component and its value has to be chosen so to obtain a resonant frequency with capacitor C_P faster than the dynamics of the mechanical strain. As it was said, this guarantees that during phase 2 and 3 the cantilever is almost motionless at its maximum deflection, thus the energy transfer from the piezoelectric transducer to the inductance is more efficient. In our case a value of 2200 µH was chosen while C_P was set to 220 nF (typical value for a practical piezoelectric transducer): this gives rise to a resonant frequency f_R of about 7.23 kHz. This frequency is significantly higher than the frequencies of typical environmental vibrations which are in the order of some tens of hertz [1].

During the start-up phase no energy is stored into C_O and its voltage is not enough to supply the actives elements, hence a passive path from the transducer to C_O has to be guaranteed. This function has been realized exploiting the parassitic body-drain diodes of switches S1', S1" and S3: they implement a passive AC-DC voltage doubler which works during the start-up. Inductor L does not interfere during the passive rectification.

Driving circuitry is presented in Fig. 3a as a block scheme, while Fig. 3b shows a picture of the diffused prototype; its area is equal to 320 x 360 μm^2.

During phase 1 driving circuit keeps all switches open.

Phase 2 has to start when v_P reaches its maximum value and it ends when v_P reaches zero. The first condition is detected by the Peak Detector while the second by comparator CMP1. The output signals of these blocks are routed to the SET (S) and RESET (R) input of a NAND based flip-flop which was designed to avoid the undetermined state.

Phase 3 has to start when the inductance current reaches its maximum value; since it is caused by the resonance between L and C_P, the current peak is reached when v_P is zero. This condition is detected by CMP1 which turns S2 off leaving node l_{x-} floating until the voltage v_2 gets higher than V_O. At this time CMP2 switches S3 and S1" on. The same comparator switches S3 and S1" off when the current which flows into inductance and into S3 crosses to zero.

Finally phase 4 has to start when i_P becomes negative. Solution described in [11] has been used: the loop implemented by operational amplifier OA1 and S1' forces the drain to source voltage of this switch to the input offset voltage of the operational amplifier, which was designed to be 20 mV.

An enable signal is used to improve the response speed of comparators CMP1 and CMP2 because they have to react to signals whose speed is in the order of f_R. The enable signal increases the bias current of CMP1 during phase 2 and of CMP2 during phase 3. This signal has the purpose to prevent an useless power consumption out of these phases. The average current consumption of the whole driving circuit is equal about 700 nA.

IV. EXPERIMENTAL RESULTS

Experimental characterization of the proposed circuit have been done with a function generator and a capacitance so to emulate the behaviour of the piezoelectric transducer. With respect to the equivalent circuit shown in Fig. 2a its Thevenin equivalent has been implemented. This was composed of a cascade of a function generator, which gives the equivalent output voltage of the transducer at no load condition, and of a capacitance which is the equivalent capacitance C_P of the transducer itself.

Fig. 4 shows the comparison of the output voltages obtained with the proposed front-end circuit and with a passive voltage doubler; this was realized with BAT86 Schottky diodes. Function generator supplied a sinusoidal input waveform with a peak amplitude equal to 1.5 V and frequency equal to 50 Hz. A load resistance equal to 650 kΩ has been connected in parallel with storage capacitance C_O.

It is possible to see that the proposed circuit works as a passive one until the energy stored into C_O is enough to supply the active elements, this condition is reached at t_1. From this moment on, an interval is needed to switch the bias circuit on. At time t_2 driving circuit is fully on and the output voltage reaches a value which is higher than the input voltage and is a function of the whole power consumption.

Fig. 5 shows a detail of the voltages V_O (blue trace), v_P (green trace) and v_2 (red trace): these were measured with the same input conditions defined in Fig. 4.

In particular it is possible to see that along phase 2 the voltage v_P is sinusoidal and it is due to the resonance between C_P and L. In the same phase switch S2 is closed and node l_{x-} is clamped at a voltage near to zero. It is possible to see also when S2 is opened because voltage on node l_{x-} gets higher than V_O: from this moment on CMP2 closes the switches S3 and S1". At the beginning of phase 4 an oscillation of v_P takes place: this is due to a resonance of the inductance L (which has not completely discharged into C_O) with parassitic capacitances. Fig. 5 shows that CMP1 was designed to open S2 before v_P reaches zero: in particular S2 is switched off when v_P is 400mV. This was done to prevent a delayed switching off of S2, due to the delay of the comparator.

Finally, Fig. 6a and Fig. 6b show the behaviour of the proposed solution and of the passive voltage doubler when the function generator delivers a variable amplitude signal. It is possible to see that the proposed solution is able to harvest the energy of peaks with amplitude lower than the output voltage stored into C_O.

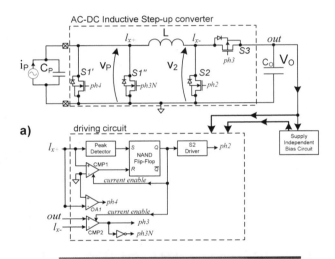

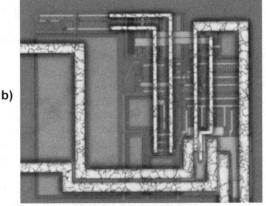

Fig. 3 a) Block scheme of the implemented front-end circuit. b) Picture of the diffused prototype.

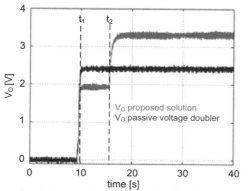

Fig. 4 Comparison between output voltages when function generator gives a sinusoidal signal.

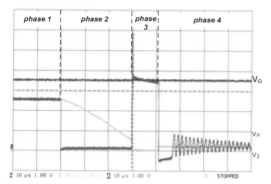

Fig. 5 Detail of the voltages V_O, v_P and v_2 during the four phases. Time scale: 10 μs/div; voltage scale for all traces 1 V/div.

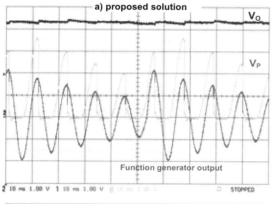

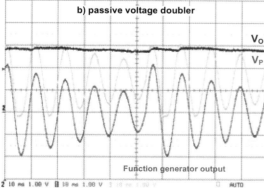

Fig. 6 a) V_O, v_P obtained with the proposed interface circuit; b) V_O, v_P obtained with a passive voltage doubler. Red traces are the function generator output. Time scale: 10 ms/div; voltage scale for all traces 1 V/div.

V. CONCLUSIONS

A novel front-end circuit for piezoelectric energy scavenging systems is presented. It is able to harvest the energy supplied by these transducers also when they are excited with randomic vibrations.

The main advantage of this solution, with respect a classical AC-DC converter, is that it is able to recover the energy associated to transducer output voltages lower than the voltage on storage capacitance C_O. It exploits the working principle of the inductive step-up converter.

A test chip was diffused using 5V CMOS STMicroelectronics technology. Experimental results show the effectiveness of this solution with respect to a classical AC-DC converter both when the mechanical vibration is sinusoidal and when it is randomic.

V. References

[1] S. Roundy, "Energy Scavenging for Wireless Sensor Nodes with a focus on Vibration to Electricity Conversion", PhD Thesis, The University of California Berkeley, Spring 2003.

[2] S. Roundy et al., "Improving Power Output for Vibration-Based Energy Scavengers", Pervasive Computing January-March 2005, pp. 28-36, Published by the IEEE and IEEE ComSoc.

[3] T. T. Le, Jifeng Han, A. von Jouanne, K. Mayaram, T. S. Fiez, "Piezoelectric Micro-Power Generation Interface Circuits" IEEE Journal of Solid State Circuits, pp. 1411-1420, Vol. 41, NO. 6, June 2006.

[4] E. Dallago, G. Frattini, D. Miatton, G. Ricotti, G. Venchi, "Self-Supplied Integrable High Efficiency AC-DC Converter for Piezoelectric Energy Scavenging Systems", International Symposium on Circuits and Systems ISCAS 2007, New Orleans LO, 27-30 May 2007, pp. 1633-1636.

[5] Z. Dong, P. E. Allen, "Low-Voltage, Supply Independent CMOS Bias Circuit", The 2002 45th Midwest Symposium on Circuits and Systems, 4-7 Aug 2002, pp. 568-570, Vol. 3.

[6] F. Peano, T. Tambosso, "Design and Optimization of a MEMS Electret-Based Capacitive Energy-Scavenger", Journal of Microelectromechanical Systems, pp. 429-435Vol. 14, NO. 3, June 2005.

[7] M. Renaud, T. Sterken, P. Fiorini, R. Puers, C. Baert, C. van Hoof, "Scavenging Energy from Human Body, Design of a Piezoelectric Transducer", The 13th International Conference on Solid-State Sensors, Actuators and Microsystems, Seoul, Korea, June 5-9, 2005, pp. 784-787.

[8] I. Stark, "Thermal Energy Harvesting with Thermo Life®", Proceedings of the International Workshop on Wearable and Implantable Body Sensor Networks, BSN 2006, pp. 19-22, IEEE Computer Society.

[9] J. Han, A. von Jouanne, T. Le, K. Mayaram, T. S. Fiez, "Novel power conditioning Circuits for Piezoelectric Micro Power Generators", APEC 2004, , February 2004, Vol. 3, pp. 1541-1546.

[10] E. Dallago, G. Frattini, D. Miatton, G. Ricotti, G. Venchi, "Integrable High-Efficiency AC-DC Converter for Piezoelectric Energy Scavenging System", IEEE Conference on Portable Devices, Orlando (FL), March, 2007.

[11] V. Bottarel, E. Dallago, G. Frattini, D. Miatton, G. Ricotti, G. Venchi, "Active Self Supplied AC-DC Converter for Piezoelectric Energy Scavenging Systems With Supply Independent Bias", Accepted for Lecture at IEEE International Symposium on Circuits and Systems, ISCAS 2008, Seattle, May 18-22, 2008.

[12] G. K. Ottman, H. F. Hofmann, G. A. Lesieutre "Optimized Piezoelectric Energy Harvesting Circuit Using Step-Down Converter in Discontinuous Conduction Mode", IEEE Transaction on Power Electronics, VOL. 18, NO. 2, March 2003, pp. 696-702.

A 0.2V-1.2V Converter for Power Harvesting Applications

Anna Richelli, Luigi Colalongo, Silvia Tonoli and Zsolt Kovács
Dept. of Electronics
University of Brescia
Brescia, Italy 25123
Email: anna.richelli@ing.unibs.it

Abstract— A DC/DC boost converter to power integrated circuits is presented. It can boost extremely low voltages, starting from about 150mV. The converter is based on a new hybrid inductive and capacitive architecture and it is suitable for power harvesting applications. A test chip was designed and fabricated using a UMC 180nm low threshold CMOS process. Measurements on the chip confirm the validity of the design.

I. INTRODUCTION

Nowadays, autonomous devices self-powered over a full lifetime by *harvesting* the energy coming from the surrounding environment (solar energy, temperature gradients, vibrations and so on) are very attractive for many applications as, for instance, smart sensors, ambient intelligence and smart cards active security [1]-[4]. On the other hand, energy harvesting exploits the external environment as a source of energy, and thus, due to its row quality (low voltages, low currents, or both), it is often unsuitable for supply standard integrated devices. By the way of example, thermopiles, which are very attractive for a wide range of applications, when exposed to low temperature gradients can deliver high currents at low voltages, much lower than the threshold of standard electronic devices.

In this paper we present a DC/DC boost converter designed in the UMC 180nm CMOS process that can supply 1.2V converting an input voltage of 200mV delivered, in our prototype, by a thermopile of 127 miniaturized Peltier cells exposed to a temperature gradient of 5°C.

In section 2 the state-of-art charge pumps will be shortly outlined, in section 3 the basic idea of the hybrid inductive-capacitive converter is introduced, in section 4 the measurement results are provided.

II. STATE-OF-ART

The classical charge pump proposed by Dickson [5] is based on a diode-connected MOS as charge transfer device and it provides approximately an output voltage: $V_{OUT} = (N+1)\cdot(V_{DD}-V_T)$ where N is the number of stages, V_{DD} is the supply voltage and V_T is the threshold voltage of the diode-connected MOS. Unfortunately, as the voltage is increased by charge pumping, the threshold voltage of the MOS transistors increases due to the body effect, the voltage step $V_{DD} - V_T$ of each stage is reduced and the overall efficiency decreases. Moreover, since the threshold voltage cannot be scaled as

much as the scaling trend of the supply voltage, the impact of the threshold voltage becomes more and more appreciable as the technology scales down. Therefore, several attempts were made to reduce the threshold voltage loss [6]-[7],[8]-[12] and a lot of work was devoted to investigate the power consumption of charge pumps [13].

The great effort to improve the performances of charge pumps has produced many efficient architectures. Unfortunately, due to the extremely low voltages, these architectures are unsuitable for power harvesting applications, as, for example, thermopile power sources. The main limitations come from from the threshold voltages of diodes and pass-transistors and from the low transistor channel conductivity due to low supply voltages. Furthermore, capacitive converters exhibit an intrinsic drawback when they are used in ultra-low voltage applications: a large number of pumping stages are required to boost very low supply voltages and the overall efficiency decreases drammatically.

On the other hand, DC/DC converters based on inductive components are widely used in power electronics and recently they were integrated in a CMOS standard process too [14]. The main limitations of a fully integrated inductive converter come from its low power efficiency at very low input voltages. In order to reach a reasonably large output voltage, these converters should be driven by almost ideal clock signals, large currents and almost lossless devices.

It is worth adding that several DC/DC converter ICs are fabricated in fully depleted SOI (Silicon On Insulator) technology to enable ultra-low voltage operations [15]. These circuits show good overall performances, thanks to the low leakage currents, but the technology is still expensive compared to the standard CMOS technologies.

III. DC/DC CONVERTER ARCHITECTURE

In this section a new DC/DC converter compatible with ultra-low voltage power harvesting applications will be described. It is based on a hybrid inductive and capacitive architecture and may be fabricated in standard low voltage low threshold CMOS processes.

In Fig. 1 the block diagram of the overall DC/DC converter architecture is shown. It is driven by an internal low voltage clock generator directly connected to the 200mV input voltage source. Two inductive step-up converters are used to boost the

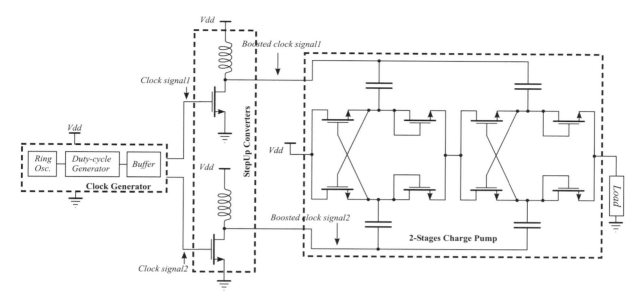

Fig. 3. Schematic of the proposed converter

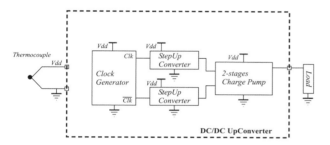

Fig. 1. Block diagram of the hybride inductive-capacitive converter

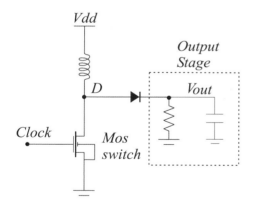

Fig. 2. Basic inductive step-up converter

low voltage clock signal followed by a 2-stage CMOS charge pump which rectifies and multiplies the boosted clock.

In order to better understand the circuit behavior, first the basic operation of an inductive step-up circuit will be explained. As shown in Fig. 2, a typical step-up is formed by a switch, an inductor and a diode connected MOS. When the MOS switch is on, the current flows from the power supply through the inductor and energy is stored in the inductor itself. In this first phase, the diode is reverse biased, the output stage is isolated and the output current is supplied by the charge stored in the load capacitor. When the MOS switch is abruptly turned off, since the current in the inductor cannot change instantaneously, an inductive voltage spike appears across the inductor, forcing the bottom end of the inductor (D) to a high positive voltage larger than the supply. The diode is forward biased and the current, initially flowing from the inductor through the MOS to ground, starts flowing through the diode to the load capacitor. In order to reach large voltage spikes the step-up converter usually operates in discontinuous conduction mode. The voltage spikes are strictly related to the inductance of the inductor, to the duty-cycle, to the conductivity of the MOS switches and to the clock edges. The larger the inductance and the current through the inductor, the larger the voltage spikes.

In the proposed overall architecture, two step-up converters driven by two non-overlapping clock signals are exploited to boost the low voltage clock produced by a ring oscillator powered directly by the 200mV voltage supply. After this stage, depending on the device sizing, the clock is boosted three or four times and can drive the following charge pump stages, pushing up the bottom plate voltages of the capacitors. The inductors were sized to optimize the voltage spikes at the operating frequency, that in turn depends on the maximum frequency achievable by the clock generator. The clock generator is a simple 9 stage CMOS ring oscillator followed by a 75% duty-cycle generator and by a buffer chain that drives the large capacitive load of the MOS inductor switches. Circuit simulations have shown that the operating frequency of the clock generator is in the range of several MHz, and that reasonable inductances are in the range of 33-47μH. It is worth noting that the two inductors (33μH) of our prototype are external SMD components whose physical dimensions are

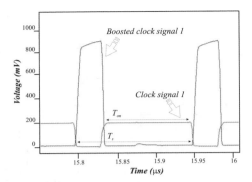

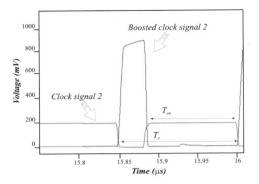

Fig. 4. Clock signal and boosted clock signal generated by the first step-up stage

Fig. 5. Clock signal and boosted clock signal generated by the second step-up stage

comparable with the IC size and much smaller if compared to the thermopile itself (it ranges from 1cm X 1cm X 0.2cm to 4cm X 4cm X 0.2cm).

Furthermore, the two MOS switches were sized as a tradeoff between conductance and parasitic capacitance: larger devices are desirable in order to force high currents on the inductors, on the other hand the drain capacitance grows linearly with the device width, clamping the voltage spikes of the inductor. In order to achieve large inductor voltages, the duty cycle T_{on}/T_s of the switches is an important parameter as well: large duty cycle forces a large current through the inductors and leads to large output voltages. On the other hand, more current through the switches leads to high power consumption; a tradeoff between maximum current and power consumption has to be reached. After an optimization process a duty-cycle of 75% was adopted. The duty-cycle generator has been designed using a flip-flop chain and logic gates. Hence, the overall clock generator is based on a simple 9-stage ring oscillator, followed by a 75% duty-cycle generator and by a buffer that drives the high capacitive load of the MOS switches.

The switches, as in the conventional step-up converters, are used to generate large voltage spikes when the inductors current is abruptly turned off. In the classical step-up converters, however, the inductor current is rectified by a diode which is directly connected to the output load. In our converter, the voltage spikes generated by the two inductors are used as the clock to push up the bottom plate voltage of the charge pump capacitors. In Figs. 4 and 5 the 75%-duty-cycle *clock signals* are plotted along with the inductors *boosted clock signals*. It is worth stressing that in the proposed converter the inductive step-ups generate two non-overlapping boosted clock signals exploited by the following charge pump.

The charge pump is based on a 2-stages modified Favrat architecture similar to that of [12] and suitable for very low voltage applications. In particular, only NMOS transistors are used as pass-transistors due to their low V_T compared to that of the PMOS ones: the NMOS threshold of the UMC process is slightly less than 100mV, depending both on the biasing conditions and on the transistor channel lenght. Therefore, the PMOS pass-transistors of [12] are replaced by diode-

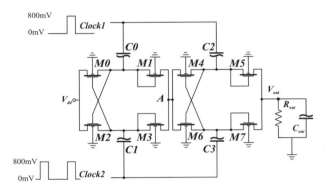

Fig. 6. Schematic of the 2-stage charge pump

connected NMOS devices, as shown in Fig. 6. The first stage of the charge pump is directly connected to the low voltage input source (through the transistors M0 and M2) while the bottom plate of the boost capacitors (of about 400pF) are biased by the 800mV rectangular clock waves generated by the inductive converters. After the initial transient, when $Clock1 = 800mV$, $Clock2 = 0$, M1 and M2 are on, while M0 and M3 are off; C1 is charged to Vdd through M1, while C0 is discharged through M2 and the voltage at node A reaches the value of about $800mV + Vdd$. Similarly when $Clock1 = 0$, $Clock2 = 800mV$, M0 and M3 are on, M1 and M2 are off; C0 is charged to Vdd through M0, while C1 is discharged through M3. Same considerations hold for the second stage as well and the output voltage Vout, neglecting the load current and the parasitics, may reach $2 \cdot 800mV + Vdd$.

The main features of the hybrid inductive-capacitive architecture comes both from the optimal use of the step-up converters, that drive only small capacitive loads, and from the large clock voltages that drive each stage of the charge pump.

IV. MEASUREMENTS

In order to test the validity of the proposed converter, a test chip was fabricated using a UMC 180nm CMOS process. The core area of the circuit is of about $900\mu m$ X $450\mu m$.
The measurement setup is based on a Peltier cell (which acts in reverse mode, as a thermopile), a heater and a heatsink which force a temperature gradient between the hot and the cold plate

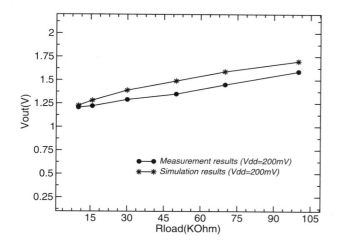

Fig. 7.   Comparison between Measurement results and Simulations

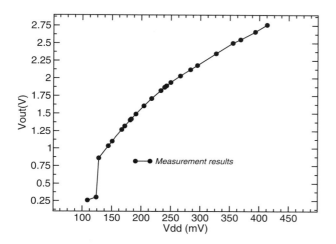

Fig. 8.   Measurement results varying the Voltage Supply, in the case of capacitive load

of the Peltier cell and, eventually, a board with the converter itself. The thermopile size is about 3cm X 3cm X 0.2cm, while the integrated converter is a 28pin CSOIC standard package; the two external inductors are very small SMD devices.

Several cycles of measurements on many chips were performed, using the nominal working conditions (0.2V voltage supply), with a resistive load ranging from 10KΩ to 100 KΩ. The output voltage is plotted in Fig. 7 and it is compared to the simulation results; a fair agreement between simulations and measurements is reported. The DC/DC converter can boost very low voltage supplies reaching about 1.2V output voltage at 10KΩ resistive load.

In order to investigate the converter behavior at very low input voltages and its suitability for power harvesting applications, measurements were performed reducing the voltage supply as low as 100mV. In Fig. 8 the output voltage is shown with

a voltage supply ranging from 100mV to 450mV, in the case of a capacitive load: the DC/DC converter can boost 140mV as well.

V. CONCLUSIONS

In this paper the feasibility of a DC/DC converter for very low voltage supplies is demonstrated, in the author knowledge, for the first time. The converter, supplied by an input voltage of about 200mV, generates a boosted output in the range of the typical voltages that power current integrated circuits (1.2V-1.5V). It is based on an hybrid inductive-capacitive architecture, it can be fabricated in a standard CMOS process and it is suitable for power harvesting applications. A test chip was designed and fabricated. It can supply 1.2V converting the input voltage given by a thermopile exposed to a 5°C thermal gradient.

ACKNOWLEDGMENT

The authors wish thank Europractice for the prototyping service and Proff. V. Ferrari and D. Marioli for the interesting discussions about possible applications of the converter.

REFERENCES

[1] A. Paradiso et Al., *Energy Scavanging for Mobil and Wireless Electronics*, IEEE Pervasive Computing, Mar. 2005.
[2] H. Lhermet et Al., *Efficient Power Management Circuit: Thermal Energy Harvesting to Above-IC Microbattery Energy Storage*, Proc. of ISSCC 2007, Feb. 2007.
[3] P. D. Mitcheson et Al., *Architectures for Vibration Driven Micropower Generators*, IEEE JMEMS, vol. 13, Jun. 2004.
[4] R. Amirtharajah et Al., *Self-Powered Signal Processing Using Vibration-Based Power Generation*, IEEE JSSCC, vol. 33, May 1998.
[5] J. Dickson et Al., *On-chip High-voltage Generation in NMOS Integrated Circuits Using an Improved Voltage Multiplier Technique*, IEEE JSSC, vol. 11, Jun. 1976.
[6] R. Pelliconi et Al., *Power Efficiency Charge Pump in Deep Submicron Standard CMOS Technology*, IEEE JSSC, vol. 38, Jun. 2003.
[7] A. Richelli et Al, *A 1.2 to 8V Charge Pump with Improved Power Efficiency for Non-Volatile Memories*, Proc. of ISSCC, Feb. 2007.
[8] J. T. Wu et Al., *Low Supply CMOS Charge Pump*, Symp. VLSI Circuits Dig. Tech. Papers, 1997.
[9] K. H. Cheng et Al., *A CMOS Charge Pump for sub-2.0V Operation*, Proc. of ISCAS, May 2003.
[10] J. Shin et Al., *A New Charge Pump without Degradation in Threshold Voltage due to Body Effect*, IEEE JSSC, vol. 35, Aug. 2000.
[11] L. Mensi et Al, *A New Integrated Charge Pump Architecture using Dynamic Biasing of Pass-Transistors*, Proc. of ESSCIRC 2005, Sep. 2005.
[12] M. D. Ker et Al, *Design of Charge Pump with Consideration of gate-oxide reliability in low-voltage CMOS processes*, IEEE JSSC, vol. 41, May 2006.
[13] G. Palumbo et Al, *A CMOS Charge Pump Circuits: Power Consumption Optimization*, IEEE TCAS-I, vol. 49, Nov. 2002.
[14] A. Richelli et Al, *A Fully-Integrated Inductor Based 1.8V-6V Step-Up Converter*, IEEE JSSC, vol. 39, Jan. 2004.
[15] Seiko Instruments Inc., *Ultra-Low Voltage Operation Charge Pump IC for Step-Up DC-DC Converter Startup*, Datasheet S-882Z Series.

A Low-Complexity, Low Phase Noise, Low-Voltage Phase-Aligned Ring Oscillator in 90 nm Digital CMOS

J. Borremans[1,2], J. Ryckaert[1], P. Wambacq[1,2], M. Kuijk[2], J. Craninckx[1]

[1] IMEC, Leuven, Belgium
[2] Vrije Universiteit Brussel, Brussels, Belgium

Abstract□ **An 8-phase phase-aligned ring oscillator in 90 nm digital CMOS is presented that operates up to 2 GHz. The low-complexity circuit consumes 13 mW at 2 GHz and 1.2 mW at 400 MHz, while a flat in-band phase noise below -120 dBc/Hz is achieved, in close agreement with the presented theory. The circuit occupies an area of 0.008 mm².**

I. INTRODUCTION

Encouraged by their appealing low-area, flexibility and scaling-friendly properties, all-digital transceiver ICs emerge in low-cost digital CMOS. Unfortunately, these systems are hampered by the VCO inductor, often required to meet the stringent phase noise requirements, for example in wireless applications. As a result, an RF top layer is required for the area-greedy inductor, and the concept of a true all-digital transceiver is obstructed.

Interestingly, techniques have been suggested mainly for wireline applications, to lower the phase noise of inductorless ring oscillators by injection locking them to a clean reference frequency [1]-[3].

In this work, we demonstrate a low-complexity low-power 8-phase Phase-Aligned Ring Oscillator (PARO) operating up to 2 GHz. At this frequency, it achieves a flat in-band phase noise lower than -120 dBc/Hz at offset frequencies down from 1 MHz, while consuming 13 mW. Similar performance is achieved operating at 400 MHz with a power consumption of 1.8 mW. The proposed oscillator is sub-1 V compatible. Quantitative theory on the impact of realignment on phase noise is presented.

II. PHASE-ALIGNED OSCILLATORS

Jitter in a free-running oscillator accumulates over time, resulting in a phase that drifts, expressed as phase noise (Fig. 1). The driving idea of phase-aligned oscillators is to truncate this accumulating jitter process by realigning the phase to a clean clock edge with period T_{RA}. At each such edge, the phase of the oscillator is reset, after which jitter starts building up again. As an illustration, a measurement of such an event is shown in Fig. 2, on a digitizing scope with long persistency. At a reference edge (and some delay), the oscillation is restarted. While a lot of jitter is present before realignment, after realignment, the flanks are clean. Due to

this repetitive correction, the phase deviation over time remains limited in a reference clock period, and so does the average jitter.

A key advantage of the technique is that the reference frequency can be chosen much higher than for a typical PLL. Therefore, the phase noise can be lowered downwards from much higher offset frequencies. However, since the realignment is a repetitive process in nature, the spectrum suffers from spurious tones at multiples of the reference frequency offset.

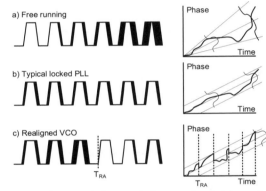

Fig. 1   Conceptual phase evolution over time in (a) an unlocked oscillator, (b) an oscillator in a typical PLL, and (c) a realigned VCO.

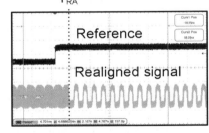

Fig. 2   Illustration of jitter truncation on a measurement of a phase-realigned oscillator. At the reference flank (and some delay), the oscillator is reset, and so is the jitter.

Different implementations have been proposed for realigned oscillators, more generically called clock multipliers. A basic solution, injection locking (Fig. 3a - [1]) benefits simplicity, but suffers incomplete realignment. As a result, phase noise is only moderately lowered. A more elaborate technique (Fig. 3c - [3]) injects a clean flank by multiplexing the oscillator's flank with the clean one, at each reference time. Complete realignment is achieved, but the timing and circuit complexity is increased, including loops, counters, multiplexers, etc. Especially at high frequencies, the timing of these loops is complicated and challenging [5]. A yet different technique consists of an open loop delay chain, where edges are combined to form the high frequency clock (Fig. 3b - [2]). This solution requires increased care and power consumption with regard to matching requirements.

In this work, we propose a simple modified architecture (Fig. 3d) that alleviates timing issues. A reference flank is converted into a pulse that briefly disables and restarts the oscillator to reset it. We exploit the property that a ring oscillator starts up immediately when an edge is injected. This solution requires no loops, nor complex circuitry. Therefore, this limits the sources for noise, jitter, power and area consumption.

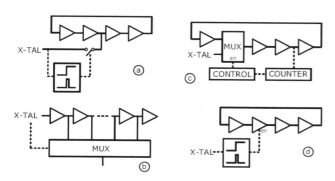

Fig. 3   Typical implementations of aligned oscillators (a)-(c), and proposed implementation (d).

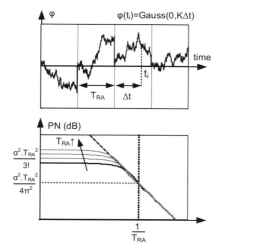

Fig. 4   Illustratrion of jitter truncation over time and offset frequency

III.   PHASE NOISE OF ALIGNED OSCILLATORS

It is instructive to catch the influence of the realignment on the phase noise of an oscillator quantitatively. Because of the repetitive nature of the realignment, we can treat the phase error in the system as a cyclostationary process with period T_{RA}. The phase error at time t_i, $\varphi(t_i)$, can be modeled as a random variable with a zero-mean Gaussian distribution with variance $K \cdot \Delta t = \sigma^2$ where Δt is the time interval between t_i and the previous realignment instance (Fig. 4). The phase noise power spectral density (PSD) can be calculated as the Fourier transform of the autocorrelation function $R_{ff}(\Delta t)$ of this process. The autocorrelation can be found as:

$$R_{\varphi\varphi}(\Delta t) = T_{RA} \int_0^{T_{RA}} E[\varphi(t), \varphi(t+\Delta t)] dt \qquad (1)$$

where $E[x]$ is the expectance value of x. We can find the expectance value as:

$$E[\varphi(t), \varphi(t+\Delta t)] = E[\varphi^2(t)] = K \cdot t = \sigma^2 \qquad (2)$$

for $t + \Delta t < T_{RA}$, or thus before realignment, with σ^2 the variance of the phase error. For $t + \Delta t \geq T_{RA}$, we find:

$$E[\varphi(t), \varphi(t+\Delta t)] = 0 \qquad (3)$$

since after realigning the oscillator, there is no more correlation with the phase error at a previous instance.

We can now find the autocorrelation as:

$$R_{\varphi\varphi}(\Delta t) = \frac{K}{T_{RA}} \cdot \frac{(T_{RA} - |\Delta t|)^2}{2} \qquad (4)$$

which is illustrated in Fig. 5. The phase noise power spectral density (PSD) can now be calculated:

$$PN(\omega) = \mathcal{F}[R_{\varphi\varphi}(\tau)] = \left(\frac{\alpha}{\omega}\right)^2 \cdot \left[1 - \frac{\sin(\omega T_{RA})}{\omega T_{RA}}\right] \qquad (5)$$

where $\mathcal{F}$ denotes the Fourier transform and ω is the offset frequency from the carrier. In this equation, we recognize $(\alpha/f)^2$ as the PSD of a free running VCO, which is achieved when the realignment frequency goes to zero (no realignment, $T_{RA} \rightarrow \infty$). For a fixed realignment frequency, the phase noise flattens towards low offset frequencies ($\omega \rightarrow 0$) with a corner frequency around $(3/2\pi^2) T_{RA}^{-1}$ (Fig. 4).

It follows from Taylor expansion of Eq. 5 that the level of the phase noise plateau is proportional to T_{RA}^2 revealing a 20 dB roll-off per decade of increase in the realignment frequency. Practically, when a flat phase noise of for example -120 dBc/Hz is desired up to at least 10 MHz, this could be achieved with a ring oscillator with -128 dBc/Hz phase noise at a 100 MHz offset, realigned at this last frequency. Doubling the reference frequency, halves the phase noise.

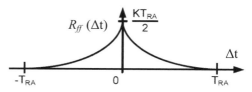

Fig. 5   Illustratrion of the autocorrelation funtion of the phase during the realignment process

IV. A LOW-COMPLEXITY PHASE-ALIGNED OSCILLATOR

The core oscillator (Fig. 6) consists of four stages elegantly making four differential 45-degree phase-shifted signals available. These can be particularly useful in linearized-LO mixers that reduce the spurious response [4].

The alignment is achieved exploiting the property that a ring oscillator starts up immediately when an edge is injected. At the reference flank, a pulse P of width ΔT_P is created that disables one stage, opening the loop to prevent a flank from being propagated (Fig. 6). This pulse should be wider than the jitter, and narrower than half of the oscillator's period T_{OSC}. By disabling the stage as such, we avoid a disruptive flank propagating through the loop, which may cause racing effects. Delayed by a time ΔT_{PD} a pulse P_D forces the output of the cell to the differential supply rails, which restarts the oscillation.

Once the clean flank is injected in the loop, the falling edges of P and P_D re-enable the delay cell and release its output. The alignment control signals are thus merely two delayed pulses P and P_D created at the reference flank.

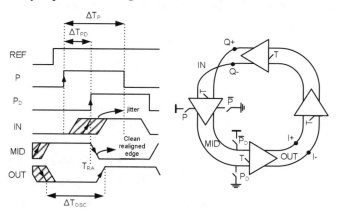

Fig. 6   Phase-aligned ring oscillator block diagram and timing scheme

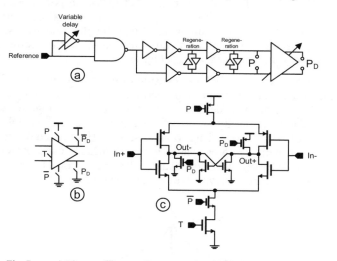

Fig. 7   a) Ring oscillator realignment pulser block diagram, b) delay cell, and c) transistor-level implementation of the delay cell

The pulses should only be narrower than $T_{OSC}/2$ (250 ps @ 2 GHz) and can fairly easily be created in contemporary

CMOS as depicted in Fig. 7a. A single-ended reference flank is converted into a pulse, using a variable delay cell and a NAND operation. Next, the single-ended pulse is converted into a differential one using an additional delay stage. Two-stage regeneration removes the delay between both signals to turn the pulse in a pure differential one. The output serves as the control voltage P, while an additional delay stage delivers P_D. In the generation of these control pulses, only a few delay cells are used, which limits the jitter added to the reference. In our design, both the pulse's slew rate and width are tunable to adapt the realignment strength and open-loop duration.

In this design the oscillator is completely stopped and restarted rather than being steered through injection locking (e.g. [1]). Therefore we achieve complete realignment. In contrast with solutions in literature (e.g. [3]), the proposed timing scheme is simpler (inherently no feedback) and compliant with sub-1 V operation (see measurements).

V. IMPLEMENTATION AND MEASUREMENT

The circuit has been realized in a 90 nm digital CMOS process, at a 1 V supply voltage. As there is a direct correlation between voltage swing and phase noise, a lowered supply voltage requires more current to retrieve low phase noise. The chip, with an active area of only 0.008 mm^2 (Fig. 10) has been measured mounted on a PCB.

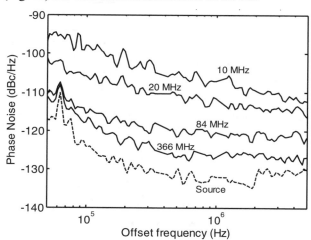

Fig. 8   Measured phase noise of the PARO running at 2 GHz for different realignment frequencies (noted next to the curve), as well as the measured phase noise of the reference source. Towards lower offset frequencies, the reference source limits the phase noise.

Fig. 8 shows the shaped phase noise spectrum for different realignment frequencies, at 2 GHz operation. For 2 GHz and 950 MHz operation, Fig. 9 plots the phase noise vs. the realignment frequency. The 20 dB/decade roll-off confirms the expected theoretical improvement from equation (5). At low frequency offsets, the noise hits the noise floor of the source used in this experiment (-120 dBc at 100 kHz offset on the HP83712B). Overall, the measured spur level is independent of the reference or oscillation frequency, and varies around -40 dBc.

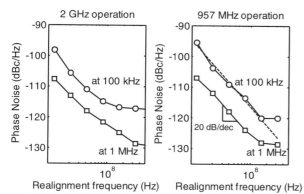

Fig. 9   Measured phase noise vs. the realignment frequency operating at 2 GHz and 957 MHz. The phase noise at 100 kHz is limited by the reference source.

At a supply of 0.5 V, the performance of the oscillator, now running at a lower frequency, is not deteriorated. Its phase noise is similar as at a 1 V supply, while the circuit consumes very low power (1.8 mW). This demonstrates that the technique is robust and is compatible with low voltage and low power applications. Fig. 2 illustrates the jitter truncation by realignment on a real-time capture around the realignment instance, on a high-frequency digitizing oscilloscope with high persistency, running at a 0.5 V supply.

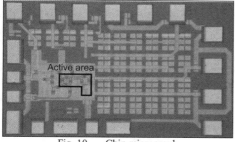

Fig. 10   Chip micrograph

The free-running VCO has a tuning range of 0.96 to 2 GHz at 1 V, and 210 to 400 MHz at 0.5 V. The measured I-Q imbalance is around 2° over the whole tuning range. Fig. 6 lists a performance summary.

The proposed PARO achieves a combination of the lowest phase noise at the highest frequency, for the lowest complexity and a low power consumption (although other solutions include a PLL), on the lowest area, with the most phases available. Further, the PARO needs a lower reference frequency than other solutions that achieve similar phase noise. It should be noted that at 100 kHz offset, the phase noise is limited by the reference source available to the authors. A reference source with higher spectral purity will lower phase noise at these offset frequencies.

VI.   CONCLUSIONS

A low-complexity, low-phase noise, low-voltage reference-aligned ring oscillator has been presented, along with theory. While the circuit is readily compatible with the applications of [1]-[3], it may also be a possible step on the path towards a true all-digital wireless transceiver in plain digital CMOS.

ACKNOWLEDGMENT

The authors would like to thank Claude Desset and Geert Van der Plas for the technical discussions.

REFERENCES

[1]   S. Ye, L. Jansson, I. Galton, "A Multiple-Crystal Interface PLL with VCO Realignment to Reduce Phase Noise", Dig. of Tech. Papers, ISSCC 2002, pp. 78-447, Feb. 2002.

[2]   G. Chien, P. R. Gray, "A 900 MHz local oscillator using a DLL-based frequency multiplier technique for PCS applications", Dig. of Tech. Papers, ISSCC 2000, pp. 202-203, Feb. 2000.

[3]   R. Farjad-Rad, W. Dally, Ng Hiok-Tiag, et. al, "A low-power multiplying DLL for low-jitter multigigahertz clock generation in highly integrated digital chips", IEEE J. Solid State Circuits, Vol. 37, No. 12, Dec. 2002.

[4]   R. Bagueri, A. Mirzaei, S. Chehrazi, et al., "An 800-MHz–6-GHz Software-Defined Wireless Receiver in 90-nm CMOS", IEEE J. Solid State Circuits, Vol. 41, No. 12, Dec. 2006.

[5]   P. C. Maulik, D. A. Mercer, "A DLL-Based Programmable Clock Multiplier in 0.18μm CMOS With -70 dBc Reference Spur", IEEE J. Solid State Circuits, Vol. 42, No. 8, Aug. 2007.

[6]   S. Giekink, "An 800MHz -122dBc/Hz-at-200kHz Clock Multiplier based on a Combination of PLL and Recirculating DLL", Dig. of Tech. Papers, ISSCC 2008, pp. 454-455, Feb. 2008.

TABLE I.   PERFORMANCE COMPARISON (* INCLUDE A PLL, ** INCLUDES OUTPUT BUFFERS, *** MEASURED AT THE FLAT PHASE-NOISE REGION OF THE SOURCE)

	[1] ISSCC02 *	[5] JSSC 07 *	[6] ISSCC 08 *	[2] ISSCC00 *	[3] JSSC 02 *	This work		
Technology	0.35um BiCMOS SOI	0.18um CMOS	90nm CMOS	0.35um CMOS	0.18um CMOS	90 nm digital CMOS		
Supply voltage	2.7-3.3V	1.8V	1V	3.3V	1.8V	1V		0.5 V
Osc. Freq.	96 MHz	176 MHz	800 MHz	900 MHz	2 GHz	2 GHz	950 MHz	400 MHz
Spot noise [dBc/Hz]	-102.5 @ 20 kHz	-110 @ 50kHz	-121 @ 200 kHz	-120 @ 30 kHz	-110 @ 50kHz	-120 @ 200 kHz (***)		-119 @ 200 kHz
Reference frequency	480 kHz	8 MHz	100 MHz	100 MHz	250 MHz	87 MHz	87 MHz	50 MHz
Reference spur power	-34 dBc	-70 dBc	-48 dBc	-30 dBc	-30 dBc	-39 dBc	-41 dBc	-38 dBc
Tuning range	-	250 MHz	-	-	1.8 GHz	1.1 GHz		210 MHz
Available phases	7-phase	Differential	Single-ended	Differential (Quadr. Possible)	3-phase	Quadrature (8-phase possible)		
Power consumption	6.8 mW	16 mW	15 mW	130 mW	12 mW **	13 mW	5.3 mW	1.8 mW
Actve area	0.22 mm²	0.5 mm²	0.048 mm²	1.2 mm²	0.05 mm²	0.008 mm²		

A 1.2V Receiver Front-End for Multi-Standard Wireless Applications in 65 nm CMOS LP

M. Vidojkovic[1], M.A.T. Sanduleanu[2], V. Vidojkovic[3], J. van der Tang[4], P. Baltus[1] and A.H.M van Roermund[1]

[1]Technical University of Eindhoven, Mixed-signal Microelectronics Group,
Eindhoven, The Netherlands, (now with Holst Centre/IMEC, Eindhoven),
[2]IMEC, Leuven, Belgium,
[3] Philips Research, Eindhoven, The Netherlands (now with Sitel Semiconductor, 's-Hertogenbosch), The Netherlands,
[4]Broadcom, Bunnik, The Netherlands

Abstract A low-power low-voltage wide-band inductor-less multi-standard receiver RF front-end in a digital CMOS 65nm Low Power (LP) process is described. S11 less than -10 dB is measured in the frequency range from 10MHz up to 5GHz. The front-end featuring two gain modes, achieves a voltage gain of 29dB in the high voltage gain mode, and a voltage gain of 23dB in the low voltage gain mode. The 3dB bandwidth of the RF front-end is 2.5GHz. The measured NF at 1GHz is 5.5dB in the high gain mode and 7.7dB in the low gain mode. The front-end achieves an IIP3 of 13.5dBm and 7.5dBm in the high and the low gain mode, respectively. It consumes 13 mA from a 1.2V supply in both gain modes. The implemented front-end occupies a chip area of 670um x 860um.

I. INTRODUCTION

The proliferation of wireless standards has motivated the wireless industry to look for multiple radio devices. The integration of multiple functions on-chip enables connectivity with different systems at various locations. In order to increase hardware flexibility and functionality, RF designers are trying to design and implement cost-effective, multi-standard RF transceivers. It is a challenge to stretch the design space of an RF front-end in such a way that it satisfies simultaneously the requirements of as many standards as possible. One possibility is the use of tuned RF front-ends based on narrow-band, tunable LNAs [1]. As performance and frequency control in the narrow band LNA are inter-related, the complexity and the occupied chip area of the tuned multi-standard RF front-end grow rapidly as the number of covered standards increases. Another approach is a single wide-band RF front-end that can satisfy the requirements of any standard in a wide frequency range [2], [3]. In combination with a tunable RF filter after the antenna, this seems to be a straightforward and a cost-effective solution for a multi-standard RF front-end. The assumption here is that MEMS devices capable of tunable RF selectivity will be available in a near future.

The aim of this paper is the realization of a multi-standard receiver capable of low voltage operation (1.2V) and low power consumption. It is based on a wide-band inductor-less RF front-end. The design is realized in a baseline 65nm Low-Power (LP) process. Section II of this paper presents the operation of the multi-band receiver front-end, the measurement results are discussed in Section III and conclusions are given in Section IV.

II. MULTI-BAND RECEIVER FRONT-END

The wide-band RF front-end is shown in Fig.1. The first building block in the RF front-end is the inductor-less wide-band LNA. The LNA has single-ended input and differential output. Thanks to the single-ended input an external passive balun for the input matching is not required, and an increase in NF of 1dB to 2dB that is given by available passive baluns is prevented. Therefore, the noise requirements of the wide-band RF front-end can be relaxed. However, since the LNA does not have a balanced input extra attention has to be paid in achieving a high IIP2. The output of the LNA is differential and AC coupled to a source follower, which isolates the LNA from the passive mixer. The passive mixer switches a current and requires a voltage-to-current conversion at the input. This is performed by the resistor R_1. Both the source follower and the voltage-to-current conversion are linear functions.

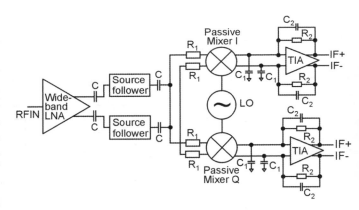

Figure 1.   Wide-band receiver front-end

Therefore, the linearity of the RF receiver front-end is maximized. The current at the output of the passive mixer is converted in a voltage by the transimpedance amplifier (TIA) with the R_2-C_2 feedback, performing at the same time a low-pass filtering.

A. Wide-Band Active Balun LNA

A simplified schematic of the wide-band LNA is shown in Fig. 2. The LNA provides a single-ended-to-differential conversion. It consists of a non-inverting common gate amplifier in parallel with an inverting common source amplifier. For the input matching, the input signal is first attenuated by the amplifier input resistance. Then, the common gate stage amplifies the input signal by a voltage gain $g_{m1}R_1$, and the common source stage amplifies the input signal by a voltage gain $-g_{m2}R_2$. Such a configuration cancels the noise associated with g_{m1} [4] when the input resistance of the LNA $1/g_{m1}$ matches exactly the source impedance $R_s = 50ohm$, the noise associated with g_{m1} will cancel out. Moreover, in this case the amplified output signal is balanced. For this condition, the noise is determined by the noise of M_{n2}, and it decreases by increasing g_{m2}. The transconductance g_{m2} can be adjusted as long as the load resistor R_2 is adjusted for the balance, as well. In practice, the noise cancellation and the output signal balance are not ideal. At higher frequencies, the parasitic capacitances of the transistors affect the input matching. Inductance from the bond-wire is used to compensate for the parasitic capacitances. By adjusting the components values the input matching can improve in a wide frequency range. Extra load resistors R_1 and R_2 in series with the PMOS transistors M_{p1} are used for programming the LNA in a low gain mode.

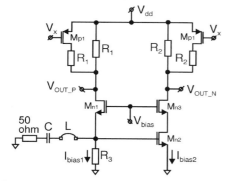

Figure 2. Simplified schematic of the wide-band LNA

B. Source Follower

A simplified schematic of the source follower is shown in Fig. 3. Together with the resistance $R_1 + R_{on,mixer}$ ($R_{on,mixer}$ is the resistance of the mixer when the mixer is ON) performs a voltage-to-current conversion in the following way. The voltage at the drain of M_{n2} is converted in a current through

the resistance $R_1+R_{on,mixer}$. The capacitor C plays a role of a DC blocker. The current fluctuations on the resistance $R_1+R_{on,mixer}$ are passed through M_{n1} and sensed on the output impedance of the current source implemented by M_{p1}. The feedback circuit consisting of M_{p2} and R_{p2}, follows these fluctuations by modulating the current source M_{n2}. The capacitor C_{p2} is used to control the peaking of the source follower.

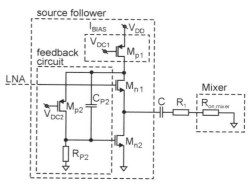

Figure 3. Simplified schematic of the source follower

Assuming that the source follower is perfect then $V_{g1} \approx V_{s1}$ (V_{g1} and V_{s1} are the voltage at the gate and the source of M_{n1}, respectively). The current through $R_1+R_{on,mixer}$ can be approximated by $i=i_1+i_2$, (i_1 is the current through M_{n1}, and i_2 is the current through M_{n2}). Thus, for $i_1 \ll i_2$, $i_2 \approx i$ □ $V_{g1}/(R_1+R_{on,mixer})$. The noise figure of the source follower can be improved by increasing the transconductance of M_{n1} and M_{n2}, and/or decreasing $R_1+R_{on,mixer}$.

C. Passive mixer and transimpedance amplifier (TIA)

The passive mixer is AC coupled to the source follower, (see Fig. 4). It commutates the current obtained through the $R_1+R_{on,mixer}$ resistance, and passes it to the transimpedance amplifier (TIA) and the R_2-C_2 feedback, which perform the current-to-voltage conversion. The capacitor C_1 is used to suppress the noise at the higher frequencies. The passive mixer can achieve high gain, moderate noise and high linearity.

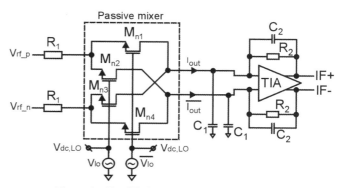

Figure 4. Simplified schematic of the passive mixer

A simplified schematic of the transimpedance amplifier used in this implementation, is shown in Fig.5. It is a simple differential amplifier that consists of a differential pair M_{n1}-M_{n2} loaded with the PMOS transistors M_{p1}-M_{p2}. The OTA insures biasing of the PMOS transistors in such a way that the output voltage of the differential pair achieves maximal swing. The voltage gain of the TIA can be approximated by $A_{TIA,v}=-g_{m1,2}r_{on1,2}\|r_{op1,2}$. Approximately, the variable $g_{m1,2}=g_{m1}=g_{m2}$, where g_{m1} and g_{m2} are the transconductances of M_{n1} and M_{n2}, respectively. Approximately, the variable $r_{on1,2}=r_{on1}=r_{on2}$, where r_{on1} and r_{on2} are the output resistances of M_{n1} and M_{n2}, respectively. And by approximating the variable $r_{op1,2}=r_{op1}=r_{op2}$, where r_{op1} and r_{op2} are the output resistances of M_{p1} and M_{p2}, respectively.

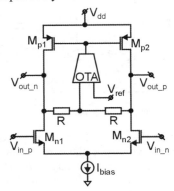

Figure 5.   Simplified schematic of the TIA

The conversion gain of the passive mixer together with the transimpedance amplifier (TIA) and the R_2-C_2 feedback can be approximated by $G \approx (2/\pi)(R_2/(R_1 + R_{on,mix}))$. The noise figure can be reduced by decreasing $R_1+R_{on,mixer}$, increasing R_2, and by increasing the transconductances of M_{n1} and M_{n2}, and decreasing the transconductances of M_{p1} and M_{p2} in the TIA.

III.   MEASUREMENT RESULTS

Based on the qualitative description of the building blocks and using the insights related to operation of those, the RF front-end is designed and implemented in a baseline CMOS 65nm LP process. Fig. 6 shows the die photomicrograph.

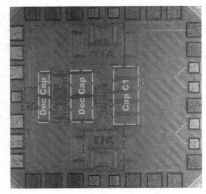

Figure 6.   Die photomicrograph

The chip area together with the bond pads is 1mm^2, and the active chip area is approximately 670um x 860um. The power dissipation of the receiver RF front-end is 15.6 mW at 1.2V supply.

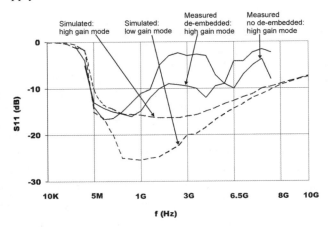

Figure 7.   S11 of the receiver RF front-end

In Fig. 7 the S11 of the RF receiver is presented. The dashed lines present the simulated S11 in the low and high voltage gain mode with parasitic extraction including the estimated parasitic of the bond pad and the bond-wire. The solid lines show the measured S11 in the high gain mode with and without de-embedding the transmission line and the SMA connector on the PCB that are connected to the LNA input. First, the characteristic impedance of the transmission line deviates from 50 ohm. Second, the SMA connector is connected to the transmission line in such a way that it introduces discontinuity. Therefore, after the de-embedding of the transmission line and the SMA connector from the measured S11, the obtained results are much closer to the simulated values of S11.

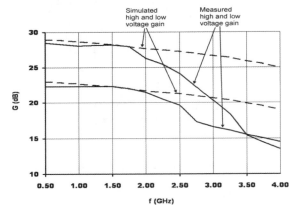

Figure 8.   Voltage gain of the receiver RF front-end as a function of RF frequencies

Fig. 8 shows the voltage gain of the RF receiver as a function of the RF frequencies. The dashed lines represent the simulated high and low voltage gain with parasitic extraction.

416

The solid lines are the measured high and low voltage gain of the RF receiver. The simulated high voltage gain is 29dB, whereas the simulated low voltage gain is 23dB. In both cases the 3dB bandwidth is around 3.5GHz. The measured high voltage gain is close to 29 dB, and the measured low voltage gain is close to 23dB. However, the measured 3dB bandwidth for both cases is around 2.5GHz. The differences between the simulated and measured voltage gain can be explained by discrepancies in S11. The 3dB bandwidth can be further improved by adding an additional amplifier stage before the source follower.

Figure 9 shows the achieved NF of the receiver RF front-end. The dashed lines represent the simulated NF with parasitic extraction. The simulated NF is 4.9-5.5dB in the high gain mode, and 7.4-7.9dB the low gain mode of the RF receiver. The solid lines show the measured NF. The measured NF is 5.5-7.5dB in the high gain mode, and 7.7-9.9dB in the low gain mode of the RF receiver. At the lower frequencies, the measured NF matches the simulated NF. The differences between the simulated and measured NF at the higher frequencies can be explained by discrepancies in S11 and the voltage gain. Since the implemented receiver RF front-end has a single-ended input, it does not require a BALUN when connected to the antenna. Therefore, the NF impairment of typically 1.5 to 2dB is prevented, and a higher NF of the implemented receiver front-end is accepted.

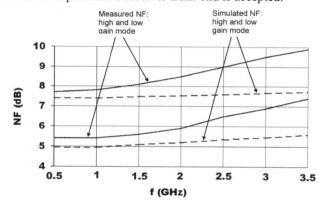

Figure 9.   NF of the receiver RF front-end

Figure 10 illustrates the measured IIP3 of the implemented RF front-end in the high gain mode. The two test tones are chosen at 1GHz and 1.001GHz. The frequency of the LO signal is 998MHz. The output fundamental signals are at 2MHz and 3MHz, while the third order intermodulation products are located at 1MHz and 4MHz. The measured IIP3 is -13.5dBm in the high gain mode and -7.5dBm in the low gain mode of the RF front-end.

Analyzing the measured results the following features of the implemented front-end can be highlighted: low power consumption, high voltage gain and small chip area. Apart from this, it operates at a low supply voltage of 1.2V. The front-end has a moderate noise figure and a high *IIP3*.

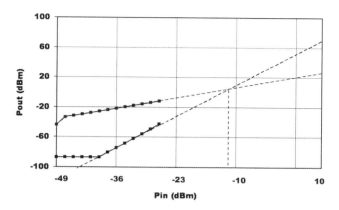

Figure 10.   Measured IIP3 in the high gain mode

IV.   CONCLUSIONS

In this paper the realization of a wide-band inductor-less RF front-end capable of low voltage operation (1.2V) and low power consumption (15.6mW), is presented. This is an important requirement for modern baseline deep sub-micron CMOS processes and one of the most difficult to fulfill in the RF part of the front-end. In a combination with a tunable RF filter after the antenna it represents a cost-effective solution for a multi-standard RF front-end. S11 lower than -10 dB, is measured in the frequency range from 10MHz up to 5GHz. The front-end achieves a voltage gain of 29dB in a high voltage gain mode, and a voltage gain of 23dB in a low voltage gain mode. The 3dB bandwidth of the RF front-end is 2.5GHz. The measured NF at 1GHz is 5.5dB in the high gain mode and 7.7dB in the low gain mode. The front-end achieves an IIP3 of −13.5dBm and −7.5dBm in the high and the low gain mode, respectively. The front end occupies 670um x 860um of real-estate on chip.

ACKNOWLEDGMENT

The author would like to thank Philips Research from Eindhoven for the technical support during the design and processing of the test chip.

REFERENCES

[1]   F. Agnelli, G. Albasini, I. Bietti, A. Gnudi, A. Lacaita, D. Manstretta, R. Rovatti, E. Sacchi, P. Savazzi, F. Svelto, E. Temporiti, S. Vitali and R. Castello, "Wireless multi-standard terminals: system analysis and design of a reconfigurable RF front-end," *IEEE Circuits and Systems Magazine*, vol. 6, no. 1, pp. 38-59, First quarter 2006.

[2]   M.Vidojkovic, V.Vidojkovic, M.T.Sanduleanu, J.v.Tang, P.Baltus and A.v.Roermund, "A 1.2V Inductorless Receiver Front-End for Multi-Standard Wireless Applications", IEEE Radio and Wireless Symposium, January 2008, pp.41-44.

[3]   R. Bagheri, A. Mirzaei, S. Chehrazi, M. E. Heidari, M. Lee, M. Mikhemar, W. Tang and A. A. Abidi, "An 800-MHz - 6-GHz software-defined wireless receiver in 90-nm CMOS," *IEEE Journal of Solid-State Circuits*, vol. 41, no. 12, pp. 2860 – 2876, December 2006.

[4]   F. Bruccoleri, E. M. Klumpernik, and B. Nauta, "Noise Cancelling in Wideband CMOS LNAs" ISSCC Dig. Tech. Papers, Feb., 2002, pp. 406-07.

A 1.2 GHz Semi-Digital Reconfigurable FIR Bandpass Filter with Passive Power Combiner

Axel Flament, Antoine Frappé,
Andreas Kaiser, Bruno Stefanelli
IEMN – ISEN
Lille, France
E-mail: axel.flament@isen.fr

Andreia Cathelin
STMicroelectronics
Crolles, France
andreia.cathelin@st.com

Hilal Ezzeddine
STMicroelectronics
Tours, France
hilal.ezzeddine@st.com

Abstract□ **This paper presents a reconfigurable semi-digital RF-FIR filter suitable for digital transmitters using 1-bit "£ signal generation. A transmission line based 5-channel power combiner allows both increase of output power and programmable filtering of the signal. A prototype has been built with 65nm CMOS and Integrated Passive Devices (IPD) technologies. The system exhibits a 14dB power gain for a peak power of 17dBm at 1.2GHz and an attenuation of out-of band noise of up to 15dB. CMOS and IPD chip size are respectively 2.05mm† and 17.78mm‡.**

I. INTRODUCTION

In SDR wireless transmitters, the trend is to digitize the transmission chain targeting a high level of integration and re-configurability. Reference [1] proposes a Digital-to-RF Converter (DRFC), merging a DAC and mixer into a single bloc. Delta-Sigma ($\Delta\Sigma$) modulation can be used to reduce the numbers of bits required in the converter. Reference [2] first demonstrated a 3-bit $\Delta\Sigma$ modulator with DRFC aimed at OFDM signals at 5GHz. More recently, direct digital generation of the RF signal by a 1-bit modulator has been reported in [3]. This architecture is presented on Fig.1. The up-conversion of the signal is done in the digital domain, and a simple CMOS inverter can act as a power DAC to convert the signal to the analog domain. One of the drawbacks of $\Delta\Sigma$ modulation is the need for a passive RF filter to attenuate the out-of-band noise generated by the modulator. This filter limits the re-configurability of the system. Also, the simple CMOS inverter DAC has a limited output power at low supply voltages. The circuit presented in this paper allows alleviating both constraints by introducing reconfigurable semi-digital FIR RF filtering through a passive power combiner with transmission line architecture.

Section II describes the multi-channel power DAC and power combiner architecture. Section III introduces the semi-digital FIR filter based on the multi-channel power combiner. Section IV describes the System in Package (SiP) co-integration between a CMOS 65nm and IPD technology, and finally measurement results are presented in section V.

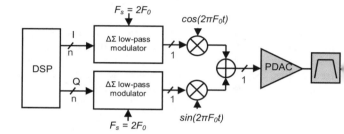

Figure 1. 1-bit digital transmitter architecture [3]

II. POWER DAC AND POWER COMBINING

A. Voltage-mode Power DAC

Either voltage or current switching can be used to convert a 1-bit digital RF signal to analog. If an ideal filter is inserted between the DAC output and the load, voltage-switching has very high efficiency, as actually no out-of-band power is generated at the converter output. Voltage switching can be implemented by a CMOS inverter. The devices need to be scaled to reach a very low on-resistance of both the NMOS and PMOS transistor. Fig.2 shows the circuit used for 1 output channel. It consists of a chain of scaled CMOS inverters. The relative sizes are indicated (1 stands for the minimum size, 0.06 μm in this technology). The estimated on-resistance r_s of the output stage is approximately equal to 0.56Ω.

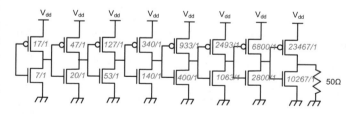

Figure 2. Voltage-switching power-DAC implemented with scaled CMOS inverters

B. Power combining with transmission lines

At low voltage, output power is usually increased by inserting an impedance matching network between the power amplifier and the load impedance. An alternative approach is to use several power amplifiers in parallel and to combine the outputs in some way. In this work, a transmission line network is used to combine the outputs of several PDACs.

The power combiner is built with 5 channels driving a real load impedance R_L, representing e.g. the antenna. This number of channels is not restricted and can be extended to an N-channel configuration. In each channel a CMOS inverter drives a quarter wavelength transmission line with characteristic impedance Z_0. Fig.3 shows the topology of the 5-channel power combiner.

In the case of ideal transmission lines, i.e. without losses, the power gain, defined as the ratio between the output power for N channels activated and for 1 channel activated, equals to:

$$G_{P \ (f=f0)} = N^2 \ (Z_0^2 \ / \ R_L + r_s)^2 \ / \ (Z_0^2 \ /.R_L + Nr_s)^2 \qquad (1)$$

where N stands for the number of activated channels.

Z_0 is chosen large enough (50Ω here) to provide a good power transfer at the expense of output power. In this case, power transfer tends towards unity while power gain is a function of N^2, N representing the number of active channels.

III. FIR FILTERING

The principle of a semi-digital FIR-DAC using the output of a 1-bit $\Delta\Sigma$ modulator has been reported in [5]. The $\Delta\Sigma$ output stream feeds a digital delay line. Selected taps are summed in the analog domain by means of weighted current sources.

The power combiner architecture offers the possibility to implement such a semi-digital filter at RF frequencies. The shift register is made with fast flip-flops using True Single Phase Clock (TSPC) dynamic logic. As PDACs operate in the voltage-mode, all of the coefficients are equal to +/-1. It is indeed impossible to weight voltage sources in an inverter array. Fig.4 shows the global architecture including both power combiner and digital delay line.

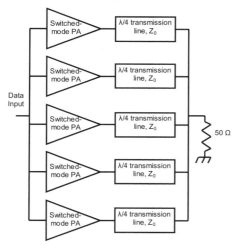

Figure 3. Architecture of the 5 channel power combiner

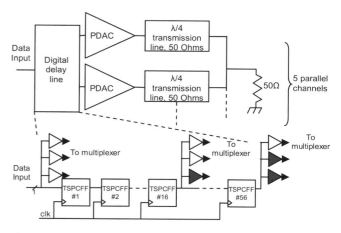

Figure 4. Implementation of digital delay line and RF FIR filter

FIR filtering is implemented in a reconfigurable way. The different delayed samples are selected thanks to a multiplexing circuit, allowing different filtering transfer functions. Three combinations of delay taps are available:

$$H_1(z^{-1}) = 1 + z^{-8} + z^{-16} + z^{-24} + z^{-32} \qquad (2)$$

$$H_2(z^{-1}) = 1 - z^{-14} + z^{-28} - z^{-42} + z^{-56} \qquad (3)$$

$$H_3(z^{-1}) = 1 + z^{-16} + z^{-24} + z^{-32} + z^{-48} \qquad (4)$$

The FIR transfer functions are periodic in the frequency domain with periodicity of 1/T, where T is the delay between taps of the delay line (in our case 8 or 14 clock periods).

We see e.g. that the 8th delayed sampled is taken once in (2) while the 16th delayed sample is used twice in (2) and (4). As those samples feed the multiplexing circuit through a CMOS inverter, the capacitive load on node "16" is twice higher that on node "8". In order to ensure the same capacitive load on each node, dummy inverters are added on these nodes as shown on Fig.4. Finally, each channel can be individually activated and the sign of each tap can be inverted. Programming is done through a serial interface.

IV. IMPLEMENTATION

A. Complete architecture

The complete system architecture is shown in Fig.5. A differential 5-channel power combiner is implemented in a 2-chip approach. Digital delay lines and PDACs are implemented in 65nm CMOS technology, whereas the passive power combiner is implemented on an Integrated Passive Devices (IPD) technology, both from STMicroelectronics.

B. Driver chip

The 65nm CMOS silicon chip includes a digital delay line made with fast flip-flops and 10 PDACs. Three different signal sources can be selected through a multiplexer. The first is a square wave at ¼ of the clock frequency. Then, a pseudo-random sequence (PRS) can be generated on-chip using the Built-in Self Test (BIST) technique. The generator is made with 20 flip-flops and an XOR gate. The PRS sequence is close to white noise and will be used to evaluate the power gain of the structure. Finally, a high-speed differential 1-bit digital input can be used. This is particularly useful to feed the 1-bit output of a digital ΔΣ modulator (such as [3]) to the circuit. Fig.6 shows the block diagram of the 65nm CMOS chip. The die is pad-limited, which explains the quite large area of 2.05 mm² (Fig.7).

C. Passive power combiner

Quarter wavelength transmission lines in the 1-2 GHz frequency range are a few centimeters long. For this reason they have been replaced by a π lumped-element equivalent circuit, resulting in a significant area gain. A 50Ω quarter wavelength TL at 1.95GHz can be modeled by two 1.6pF capacitors and a 4.1nH inductance (Fig.8).

As the transmission line is directly connected to an inverter output, which exhibits a capacitive behavior, we decided to use this capacitance as a part of the lumped element model. This capacitance is non linear and we sized the inverter in order to present an average output capacitance of the required value.

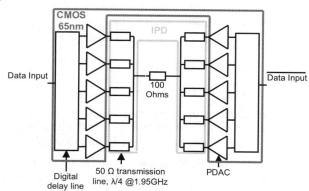

Figure 5. Implementation of the global architecture in CMOS 65nm and IPD technologies

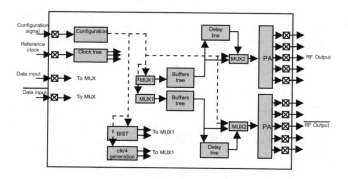

Figure 6. Block diagram of the 65nm CMOS test chip

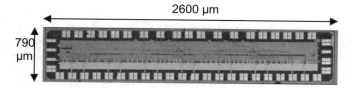

Figure 7. Photomicrograph of the CMOS 65nm chip

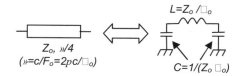

Figure 8. Transmission line lumped element equivalent

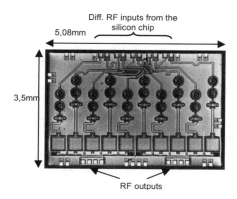

Figure 9. Photomicrograph of the IPD chip

Finally, the silicium and IPD chips are wire-bonded together. These wires can be modeled by a 1nH/mm inductance, leading to a decrease of the inductance value implemented on the IPD chip. The IPD chip occupies a 17.78 mm² area (Fig.9).

V. MEASUREMENT RESULTS

A first set of measurements has been made using the on-chip PRS generator. The output spectrum of the PRS generator is approximately white. The measured pass-band of the transmission lines is lower than the targeted UMTS TX band (1920-1980MHz). Fig.10 shows the power-spectral density measured at the output of the system with 5 channels activated and no FIR filtering function. The PSD peaks around 1.2GHz. By retro-fitting simulations, this appears to be due to the bond-wires in series with the IPD inputs, as well parasitic capacitances in the on-chip routing scheme. Consequently, measurements presented hereafter are all in the 1 to 1.4 GHz band.

The various FIR transfer functions can be demonstrated using the PRS generator. Fig.11 shows transfer function H_1 for a 2.4GHz clock, Fig.12 transfer function H_3 for a 1.6 GHz clock. The shape of the measured noise spectrum is very close to the theoretical transfer function. Both examples have a center lobe at 1.2 GHz, but periodicity changes with the clock frequency.

The circuit has also been tested in conjunction with digital ΔΣ RF signal generator of [3]. Because of synchronization issues, results for a 436MHz main clock are presented here. The 6th image is centered on 1.199GHz and falls into the pass band of the power combiner. Fig.13 shows the measured output spectrum of the power combiner with one and five channels activated, demonstrating the power gain of 14dB of the 5 channel combiner. Fig.14 shows the same spectrum when activating the H_1 FIR filter function. Table I sums up the measurement results and current consumption.

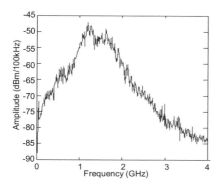

Figure 10. Mesured output spectrum with PRS input at 2.4 Gs/s

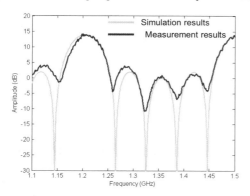

Figure 11. FIR filtered pseudo-random sequence
$(H_1(z^{-1}) = 1 + z^{-8} + z^{-16} + z^{-24} + z^{-32})$ at 2.4Gs/s

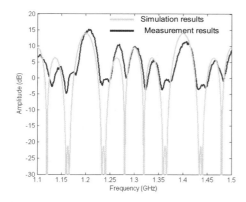

Figure 12. FIR filtered pseudo-random sequence
$(H_3(z^{-1}) = 1 + z^{-16} + z^{-24} + z^{-32} + z^{-48})$ at 1.6Gs/s

TABLE I.   SUMMARY OF MEASUREMENT RESULTS

	Measurement results @436MHz clock
Voltage supply	1.2V
Max. Peak Output Power (estimated)	18dBm
Power Gain @1.2GHz	14dB
Silicon chip size	2.05mm²
IPD chip size	17.78mm²
Current consumption 1 channel without FIR filter	15mA
Current consumption 5channels without FIR filter	29mA
Current consumption 5 channels with FIR filter	38mA

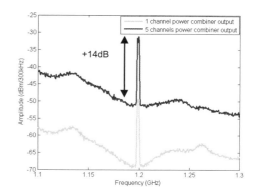

Figure 13. Output spectra with Δ–Σ modultated input signal

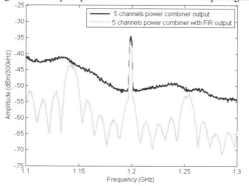

Figure 14. FIR filter applied to Δ–Σ modultated signal

VI.   CONCLUSION

This work demonstrates a RF power combiner using lumped-element transmission lines in 65nm CMOS and IPD processes. Power gain increases with a quadratic function of the number channels. It also allows implementing a programmable RF FIR band-pass filter suitable for SDR.

REFERENCES

[1] P. Eloranta, P. Seppinen, S. Kallioinen, T. Saarela, A. Parssinen, "A WCDMA transmitter in 0.13μm CMOS using direct-digital RF modulator," IEEE International Solid-State Circuits Conference, 2007, pp.340-607, 11-15 Feb. 2007

[2] A. Jerng, C.G. Sodini, "A wideband delta-sigma digital-RF modulator for high data rate transmitters," IEEE Journal of Solid-State Circuits, vol. 42, pp. 1710-1722, Aug. 2007

[3] A. Frappé, B. Stefanelli, A. Flament, A. Kaiser, A. Cathelin, "A digital ΔΣ RF signal generator for mobile communication transmitters in 90nm CMOS," IEEE 2008 Radio Frequency Integrated Circuit Symposium, Atlanta, Georgia, June 2008, in press

[4] N. Srirattana, A. Raghavan, D. Heo, P.H. Allen, J. Laskar, "Analysis and Design of a High-Efficiency Multistage Doherty Power Amplifier for Wireless Communications", IEEE Transactions on Microwave Theory and Techniques, Vol.53, N°3, pp. 852-860, Mar. 2005

[5] D.K. Su, B.A. Wooley, "A CMOS oversampling D/A converter with a current-mode semidigital reconstruction filter," IEEE Journal of Solid-State Circuits, Vol.28, N°12, pp.1224-1233, Dec. 1993

A Fractional Spur Reduction Technique for RF TDC-Based All Digital PLLs

Ping-Ying Wang, Hsiang-Hui Chang and Jing-Hong Conan Zhan

MediaTek Inc. HsinChu, Taiwan

ABSTRACT

In this paper, a technique is proposed to suppress the fractional spur induced by non-linearity of the loop in all digital PLLs (ADPLLs).

The measurement results show that the fractional spurs are reduced by at least 9dB, to below -75dBc, when the technique is applied to a conventional all digital PLL (ADPLL) at 3.6GHz. The extra silicon area needed for technique is only 0.02mm^2

Keywords: ADPLL, Spur, Time-to-Digital Converter (TDC), Digital Controlled Oscillator (DCO)

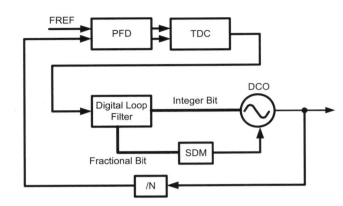

Fig. 1 Block diagram of the conventional ADPLLs

I. INTRODUCTION

All digital PLL has been reported to have superior performance at lower cost [1][2]. However its fractional-N operation induces high fractional spurs [3][4][5] when compared to a conventional charge pump-based fraction-N PLL [6], which is still most popular architecture used in synthesizer of mobile communication, thus limiting the applications of ADPLLs in high-end products. The reason is described below.

In a conventional fractional-N PLL [6], a high order sigma-delta modulator is used to eliminate idle tones induced by the fractional-N operation. However, the fractional spur is still sensitive to the linearity of the loop. For a conventional analog PLL [7], the non-linearity of the loop includes the charge pump current mismatch and the clock feed-through. They can be suppressed by the passive loop filter because the resolution of the loop filter and voltage controlled oscillator is infinite in analog domain.

For ADPLLs as shown in Fig. 1, non-linearity of the loop could be introduced by quantization error, non-linearity and meta-stability of digital phase detector and /or the digital controlled oscillator (DCO). Since the output of the digital loop filter is converted into time domain by the DCO, the timing error induced by quantization error is determined by the resolution of the DCO rather than the digital loop filter. As a result, unlike in charge pump PLLs, the spurs caused by non-linearity cannot be eliminated by a digital loop filter or a digital algorithm [5] because the resolution of the digital loop filter is limited by the quantization error of the DCO. Furthermore, the DCO quantization error cannot be filtered by the loop due to its high-pass transfer function. The short-term quantization error of the DCO will be sampled back to the loop and amplified due to gain variation of the TDC [9], resulting in spurs.

From the arguments above, DCO quantization error must be reduced to suppress spur in fractional-N ADPLLs. In a conventional DCO [8], the frequency is controlled by

switching capacitors in a LC tank and the resolution is determined by the minimum capacitance of switching unit capacitor in LC tank. With progress of the process technology, the fine feature size of the MOS indeed improve the minimum capacitance of MOS capacitor, however, the gate oxide capacitance is also increased due to decrease of the gate oxide thickness so the frequency resolution determined by the minimum capacitance is limited by the conflict between the feature size of MOS and gate oxide thickness. Besides, the minimum capacitance requirement for higher output frequency is also increased in order to achieve the same frequency resolution. For example, comparing 3.6GHz with 36GHz, the minimum capacitance requirement is grown up 10 times which exceeds the progress of the process technology so the minimum capacitance used in switching capacitor array of DCO cannot be improved arbitrarily since advanced process technology still set a limit on the minimum achievable capacitance as mentioned above.

The conventional technique to improve DCO resolution is to apply frequency average technique, as suggested in [1][8]. The frequency resolution indeed reduces accumulated phase errors induced by frequency quantization error. However, this technique cannot eliminate the fractional spur induced by short term phase error because the short-term phase error induced by DCO quantization error remains the same while using the frequency average technique [8].

Another problem induce by the frequency average is the non-monotonic DCO gain induced by the device mismatch between the integer and fractional capacitor so the dynamic element matching (DEM) is needed to minimize the mismatch, however, the switching noise is also increased by the DEM, thus the possibility of the noise coupling in DCO is also increased to degrade the spur/noise performance.

To alleviate all problems mentioned above, we propose a fractional spur reduction technique for ADPLLs to improve the short-term frequency resolution of DCO by using capacitance average technique instead of the frequency average technique [8]. The DEM is also replaced by the dynamic fractional bit tracking circuit to eliminate switching noise. The measurement results verify the validation of the technique.

The technique is also low cost and low complexity because it only requires addition of a simple analog low pass filter and rearranging switches in a conventional DCO [8]. In the next section, we will explain the frequency average, DEM technique and associated problem in the conventional ADPLLs.

II. CONVENTIONAL ARCHITECTURE

A. Frequency Average

The architecture of a generic ADPLL [1][2][3][4][5][8] is shown in Fig.1. The phase error is digitized and then a digital loop filter processes these values. The output of the digital loop filter is converted into time domain by the DCO. In conventional DCO, the switching capacitor array in the DCO is used digitally to control the frequency of the LC oscillator as shown in Fig. 2. The capacitor array is separated into an integer part and a fractional part with the same device size. A high speed dithering signal generated by a digital SDM modulates the unit capacitor to achieve a higher DCO average frequency resolution [8], as shown in Fig. 3(a). The desired high resolution is achieved by toggling the DCO between frequencies f1 and f1+Δf by turning on/off MOS capacitor with a dithering signal. The frequency resolution with long-term average is smaller than the quantization errorΔf so the accumulated phase error induced by the quantization error Δf is eliminated.

Because the short-term phase error is proportional to Δf multiplied by the period of the DCO as shown in Fig. 3 (a), which is still limited by the minimum capacitance available in the specified process technology, the spur performance of fractional-N ADPLLs is worse [3][4][5][8].

B. Dynamic Element Matching

Another problem of the architecture is non-monotonic DCO gain induced by the device mismatch between capacitors used in the integer and fractional bit. When the digital fractional code of the digital loop filter is changed from full code to zero and the integer bit is also changed due to the carry of the fractional bit. In this case, the capacitor in the integer array is turned on and the capacitor of the fractional bit is off, if there is mismatch between two capacitors, it will induce a discontinue frequency drift to result in the non-monotonic DCO gain. The non-monotonic DCO gain will cause positive feedback to increase noise of a loop so it is important to keep the monotonic DCO gain.

To suppress the non-monotonic DCO gain, dynamic element match (DEM) technique is proposed in [4]. The capacitors used in integer bits and fractional bit are dynamic swapped digitally with random sequence so the n-

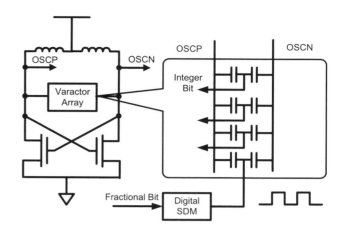

Fig. 2 Functional blocks of the conventional DCO

oise and harmonic distortion is suppressed. Due to all digital implementation the digital signal with large swing are toggled to increase the switching noise of the DCO and the possibility of noise coupling in RF circuits.

III. PROPOSED ARCHITECTURE

A. Capacitance Average

The proposed technique to suppress the DCO quantization error is illustrated in Fig. 3(b). A passive low pass filter is added at the output of the digital sigma-delta modulator to produce an analog output control signal which controls the unit MOS capacitor. The capacitance is averaged due to analog control voltage under large signal DCO swing. The Fig. 4 is the DCO frequency as the function of analog control voltage by simulation. The frequency of DCO is continuous with 40KHz/V VCO gain.

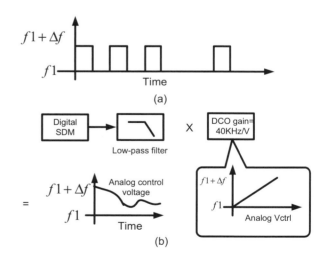

Fig. 3 (a) The DCO frequency is toggled between two discrete levels in the conventional architecture (b) The DCO frequency is continuous in our proposed architecture.

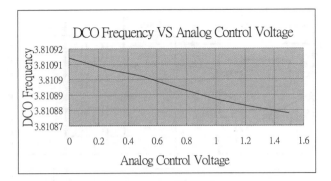

Fig. 4 The frequency of the DCO as function of the analog control voltage

Because of linearization of capacitance, the frequency variation is continuous as shown in Fig. 3(b). The short-term quantization of the DCO is therefore nonexistent. Although the digital nature of the dithering signal is converted into analog, the DCO still preserves its immunity against resistor rthermal, substrate and switching noise due to its low gain (40KHz/V) which is approximately only 1/1000 of the values for conventional VCO used in analog PLL.

B. Fractional bit tracking

Because the analog signal in the fractional bit and the digital signal in the integer bit can not be exchanged digitally in this architecture, the DEM technique [8] can not be used for capacitance average technique. To maintain monotonic frequency curve without resorting to DEM technique, we re-arrange the connection of the varactor

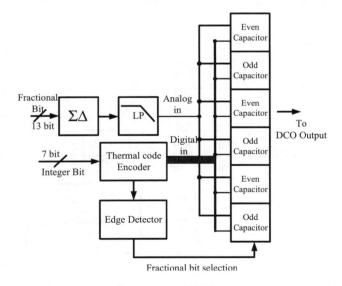

Fig. 5 The function blocks of our proposed architecture

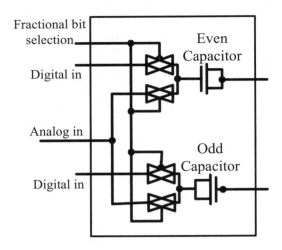

Fig. 6 Schematic of the unit capacitor

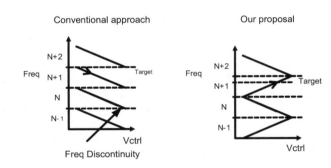

Fig. 7 The voltage-to-frequency transfer curve for conventional and our proposal technique

bank as show in Fig. 5. The detail schematic of unit capacitors is shown in Fig. 6. The analog low pass filter is shared by all capacitors and connected to one of the capacitors dynamically by edge decoder to reduce silicon area and phase noise induced by thermal noise of the resistor in the analog low pass filter which is 189KHz R-C filter in this design. The edge detector detects the transient bit of the thermal code and determines which capacitor should be connected to the analog low pass filter and serve as a fractional bit of the DCO.

Thermal codes guarantees the monotonicity of the capacitance in the integer capacitor array. Since the fractional bit is tracking the latest integer bit, there is no discontinuity of capacitance compared to the conventional approach [8]. However, the switching noise still exists when the fractional bit is changed because the sigma-delta modulated voltage should be charged to the zero first then charged to the desired value as shown in Fig. 7.

The noise induced by this discontinuity will cause undesired spurs and noise. The voltage-to-frequency transfer curve of the proposed capacitor array is folded to alleviate the problem, as illustrated in Figure 4b. The folded transfer curve results from the opposite polarity of the even and odd capacitors as shown in Fig 7. Assume the current tracking tank selects the N-th capacitor, and the fractional bit is changed to the N+1-th capacitor. For the proposed tracking tanks design, the sigma-delta modulated voltage doesn't need to approach zero first, the tracking bit control toggles digitally from N to N+1, and the sigma-delta modulated voltage then charges to the desired value directly. The two frequency tracking processes are highlighted in Figure 7.

IV. SILCON RESULTS

The silicon prototype was implemented in a 0.13um CMOS technology. Measured phase noise performance with and without the proposed spur reduction technique are shown in Fig. 8. It shows that the fractional spur still exists even when high order digital low-pass filter and a digital algorithm such as phase cancellation technique is used. When the proposed technique is applied, the fractional spur is under phase noise floor, implying a more than 9 dB spur reduction. The noise floor at 400 KHz is the same no matter if the spur reduction technique is applied. This means the frequency dithering and digital low pass filter used in the conventional DCO [8] indeed reduces phase noise but it cannot eliminate

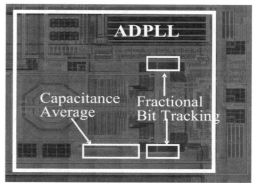

Fig. 9 The photograph of the proposed architecture

fractional spurs. Table I is the brief comparison of fractional spurs for TDC based all digital fractional-N PLLs, our design has the lowest spur with the largest quantization error of TDC which should result in largest spur, thus proving the spur is greatly reduced by the proposed technique.

Fig. 9 is the die photo of the chip. Comparing to the conventional DCO, the extra silicon area needed for implementing the passive low-pass filter and MOS switches is only 0.02mm^2.

ACKNOWLEDGEMENT

The authors would like to thank Lin-We Ke, Rickey Yue and the support from colleagues of MediaTek RF and product division.

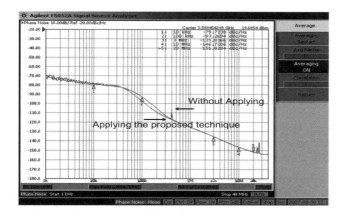

Fig. 8 Measured phase noise with spur measurement mode

Table I A summary of fractional spurs for all digital fractional PLL

	ESSCIRC 2008 [3]	ISSCC 2008[4]	ISSCC 2008[5]	Our Design
Fractional Spur	-42dBc @1MHz Channel Space	-53dBc@ 1MHz Channel Space	-45dBc@ 100KHz Channel Space	-75dBc@ 400KHz Channel Space
TDC Resolution	12ps	Noise-shaping	8ps	20ps

REFERENCES

[1] A. V. Rylyakov et. al., " A wide power-supply range (0.5V-to-1.3V) wide tunning range (500MHz-to-8GHz) all static CMOS ADPLL in 65nm SOI," ISSCC Dig. Tech. Papers, Feb 2007, pp.172–173.

[2] J. Zhuang, Q. Du and T. Kwasniewski,"A 4GHz Low Complexity ADPLL-based Frequency Synthesizer in 90nm CMOS", *CICC Dig Tech Papers*, Sept. 2007

[3] Tonietto R., Zuffetti E., Castello R. and Bietti I., "A 3MHz bandwidth low noise RF all digtial PLL with 12 ps time to digtial converter," *ESSCIRC Dig. Tech. Papers,* pp. 150 - 153, Sept 2006.

[4] Chun-Ming Hsu, M. Z. Straayer, M. H. Perrott., " A Low-Noise Wide-BW 3.6GHz digital sigma-delta Fractional-N Frequency Synthesizer with a Noise-Shaping Time-to-Digital Converter and Quantization Noise Cancellation," *ISSCC Dig. Tech. Papers.*, Feb 2008, pp.340–341

[5] Colin Weltin-Wu, Enrico Temporiti, D. Baldi, F. Svelto., " A 3GHz Fractional-N All-Digital PLL with Precise Time-to-Digital Converter Calibration and Mismatch Correction," *ISSCC Dig. Tech. Papers.*,Feb 2008, pp.344–345

[6] Riley T.A.D., Copeland M.A., and Kwasniewski T.A., "Delta-sigma modulation in fractiona-N synthesizer," *IEEE J. Solid-States Circuits*, vol. 28, pp. 553 - 559, May 1993

[7] F. M. Gardner, "Charge-pump Phase-Lock Loops," *IEEE Trans. on Commun.,* vol. COM-28, no. 11, pp. 1849 - 1858, Nov. 1980

[8] R. B. Staszewski et al., N. Barton, M. –C. Lee and D. Leipold, ''ALL-Digital PLL and Transmitter for Mobile Phone,'' *IEEE Journal of Solid-State Circuits*, vol. 401, No. 125, pp. 2469 - 2482, Dec 2005

[9] Vamvakos S.D., B.ogdan Staszewski R., Dheba M., Waheed K., "Noise analysis of time-to-digital converter in all digtial PLL," *IEEE workshop on Design, Applications, Integration and Software*, pp. 87 - 90, Oct 2006.

An Ultra Low Power SoC for 2.4GHz IEEE802.15.4 Wireless Communications

C. Bernier, F. Hameau, G. Billiot, E. de Foucauld, S. Robinet, D. Lattard, J. Durupt, F. Dehmas, L. Ouvry, P. Vincent

CEA-LETI, MINATEC

Grenoble, France

Abstract—**An Ultra-Low Power (ULP) SoC including an IEEE802.15.4 2.4GHz transceiver designed in 130nm CMOS technology is presented. Power consumption was minimized by using a concurrent system and design optimization to avoid the over-specification of blocks. A novel minimum complexity partial correlation algorithm is used in the digital baseband receiver and drains an average of 480µA (packet PSDU=20 bytes). At 1.2V, the transceiver drains 5.4mW and 8.1mW in RX and TX active modes, respectively, and achieves 1% PER for a -81 dBm input power. For a 250kbit/s data rate, the transceiver attains an energy efficiency of 21.5nJ/bit RX and 32.5nJ/bit TX.**

I. INTRODUCTION

Reducing the power consumption of RF links is essential to increase the lifetime of wireless sensor (WSN) and personal area networks (WPAN) [1]. To this end, several approaches are pursued by current research.

A first approach consists in taking advantage of the reduced specifications permitted by low-rate, short-range communication standards to propose new topologies for standard RF functions. These structures attempt to make the best use of available current, generally by using current reuse techniques, for RF front-ends, LO buffers, frequency doublers, etc. [2][3][4]. As a logical extension, other authors propose the use of passive structures for RX and/or TX mixers [5][6], LNA [7], or quadrature phase generation [8]. Finally, other approaches propose novel architectures including direct sampling architectures [9][10].

In this work, a different approach was used which consisted in using complete system modeling in order to specify an ultra-low power (ULP) direct conversion transceiver. Then, each elementary function was optimized for minimum power. In particular, a novel digital baseband demodulation algorithm was defined which resulted in a very efficient design in terms of power and area. Our challenging objective consisted in attempting to reach an energy efficiency close to 20nJ/bit in both TX and RX modes while complying with the IEEE802.15.4 standard.

The transceiver is integrated on a SoC which also includes an 8051 micro-controller clocked at 8MHz (Fig. 1). The transceiver can either be controlled by the 8051 or by an SPI bus which is also used to load the application code in the 32kbyte memory (SRAM). 4kbytes are available for user

This work was supported in part by the e-SENSE (FP6 IST-4-027227-IP) and Medea+ SWANS projects as well as STMicroelectronics.

data. All internal clocks (including the 5MHz PLL reference) are derived from a single 40MHz external clock.

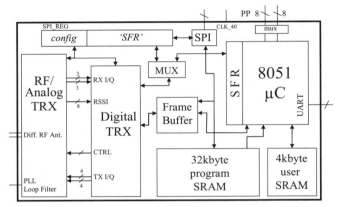

Figure 1. SoC Architecture

II. SYSTEM DESIGN FOR ULTRA-LOW POWER

The PHY modulation defined for the 2.4GHz band by the IEEE802.15.4 standard consists in a preliminary spreading of the 250kbps data stream into a 2Mchip/s stream by mapping each 4-bit symbol onto one of 16 quasi-orthogonal 32-chip pseudo-random sequences. The chip stream is then modulated using O-QPSK with half-sine pulse shaping. As will be shown, these choices offer considerable opportunities for both analog and digital ULP design.

For example, in the digital part of the receiver, the fact that half of the spreading codes are complex conjugates of the other ($c_{n+8}=c_n{}^*$, n=0,1,..,7) means that the correlation algorithm can be greatly simplified. Also, in our implementation, the receiver uses a novel algorithm which realizes eight non-coherent 4-chip partial correlations rather than a single 32 chip correlation. Indeed, even if, in the ideal case, partial correlations show a 3dB loss of performance compared to a 32-chip correlation, partial correlations perform better in the presence of RF frequency offsets as shown in Fig. 2. Thanks to this better performance, it is relatively simple to implement a compensation algorithm to withstand the worst case specified offset (±40ppm). The partial correlation algorithm is well suited to a ULP implementation since the most complex calculation is a square operation and most multiplications are simple multiply by ±1.

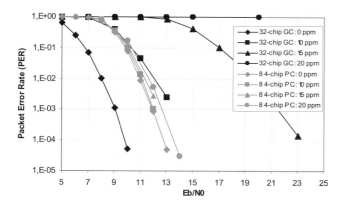

Figure 2. Comparison of the impact of sampling frequency offsets for 32-chip global correlation (GC) vs 8 4-chip partial correlations (PC) (assuming no compensation algorithm)

The IEEE802.15.4 modulation also offers opportunities for ULP design in the analog part of the transceiver. For example, since in a constant envelope modulation the information is contained in the sign of the baseband I and Q signals, non-linear amplification can be used in the analog RX chain with reduced resolution and low sampling rate ADC. Indeed, system simulations (Fig. 3) based on an accurate model of RF/analog imperfections showed that ADC's of low sampling rate (4 MS/s) and reduced dynamic range (3 bit) on the I/Q RX paths are sufficient, in turn allowing a drastic reduction of the consumption of the transceiver's digital operators.

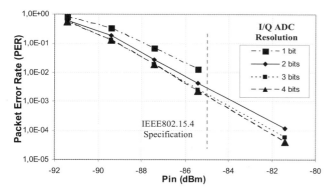

Figure 3. Simulated Packet Error Rate (PER) vs. input power

Generally speaking, high-level system modeling and simulation are essential to the specification of an ULP system since it is at the architectural level that most power savings can be realized by avoiding the over-specification of power-hungry analog and digital blocks. In addition, it is only through high-level simulations that the impact of each specification on overall performance can be analyzed and the interactions between the different imperfections can be understood.

III.   DIGITAL DESIGN FOR ULTRA-LOW POWER

The IEE802.15.4 2.4-GHz PHY packet format is given in Fig. 4 [11]. The preamble consists of 8 consecutive 0 symbols and is followed by the Start of Frame Delimiter (SFD) and PHY Header (PHR) which contains the length of the following PSDU (PHY payload).

Bytes:	4	1	1	Max: 127	2
	preamble	SFD	PHR	PSDU	CRC

Figure 4.   Packet format for IEEE802.15.4 2.4GHz PHY

The architecture of the digital receiver is given in Fig. 5. The 4 MS/s 3-bit I/Q streams are half-sine filtered before being fed to the synchronization block and the decoding module. The synchronization block recovers the symbol clock using a code-0 sliding matched filter implemented by eight 4-sample partial correlations and a recursive channel filter that increases the SNR by averaging samples over several symbol periods. If the output exceeds a programmable threshold (SYNCH_TH), the maximum peak is used to define a temporary symbol clock. The decoding structure is then turned on to search for the SFD which, when detected, locks the symbol clock definitely. The synchronization structure is then turned off.

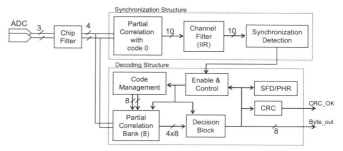

Figure 5.   Digital RX Architecture

Once the symbol clock is found, sliding correlations are no longer required and only the required symbol correlations are performed each symbol period. The sample stream is decimated by a factor of 2, meaning that a single complex sample per chip is retained. The partial correlation algorithm functions as follows: for each symbol period, the received symbol is:

$$\max(corr\_out(n)), \; n=0,..,15 \qquad (1)$$

with

$$corr\_out(n) = \sum_{p=0}^{7} \left(\left| \sum_{k=0}^{3} s_{4p+k} \times \left(c_{4p+k}^{n}\right)^{*} \right|^{2} \right) \qquad (2)$$

where s_m is the mth complex signal sample (of 32) and c_m^n is the mth complex chip (of 32) of the nth spreading code (of 16). To implement this algorithm, the following architecture is used:

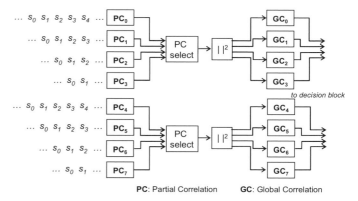

Figure 6.   Architecture of the partial correlations bank

427

If we consider the inner summation of (2), we may write down the 4-sample partial correlation, for a given n and p, as follows:

$$
\begin{aligned}
&s_{i0}c_{i0} + s_{q0}c_{q0} - js_{i0}c_{q0} + js_{q0}c_{i0} + \\
&s_{i1}c_{i1} + s_{q1}c_{q1} - js_{i1}c_{q1} + js_{q1}c_{i1} + \\
&s_{i2}c_{i2} + s_{q2}c_{q2} - js_{i2}c_{q2} + js_{q2}c_{i2} + \\
&s_{i3}c_{i3} + s_{q3}c_{q3} - js_{i3}c_{q3} + js_{q3}c_{i3}
\end{aligned}
\tag{3}
$$

where $c_{4p+k}^n = c_{ik} + j \cdot c_{qk}$ and $s_{4p+k} = s_{ik} + j \cdot s_{qk}$.
Since the even code chips are purely real (e.g. c_{q0}=0) and the odd code chips are purely imaginary (e.g. c_{i1}=0), the above equation can be simplified and rewritten as the sum of the following four terms:

$$
\begin{aligned}
&s_{i0}c_{i0} + s_{i2}c_{i2} \\
&j(s_{q0}c_{i0} + s_{q2}c_{i2}) \\
&- j(s_{i1}c_{q1} + s_{i3}c_{q3}) \\
&s_{q1}c_{q1} + s_{q3}c_{q3}
\end{aligned}
$$

As illustrated in Fig. 6, the complex sample stream is shifted and fed in series to two parallel banks of four partial correlation blocks (PC_n). Block PC_n calculates and outputs the above four terms for code n, n=0,..,7. The actual sum is performed directly in the $| \ |^2$ operator which calculates, for code n:

$$(s_{i0}c_{i0} + s_{i2}c_{i2} + s_{q1}c_{q1} + s_{q3}c_{q3})^2 + (s_{q0}c_{i0} + s_{q2}c_{i2} - s_{i1}c_{q1} - s_{i3}c_{q3})^2$$

and then for code n+8, since code n and n+8 are complex conjugates:

$$(s_{i0}c_{i0} + s_{i2}c_{i2} - s_{q1}c_{q1} - s_{q3}c_{q3})^2 + (s_{q0}c_{i0} + s_{q2}c_{i2} + s_{i1}c_{q1} + s_{i3}c_{q3})^2$$

Since the input samples of the four parallel PC blocks are time shifted by one sample, a single power operator is required since it alternately takes as input the output of one of the four PC blocks. Finally, the result of the eight partial correlations for code n (and n+8) is summed in the global correlation (GC_n) block. The decision block (Fig. 5) compares the values of the 16 correlations.

Spreading code n+1 is obtained from spreading code n thanks to a circular shift of 4 chips. This applies for the eight first codes necessary for the calculation of the partial correlations described above. This property means that the eight coefficients are obtained with only one circular shift register as described in Fig. 7. The shift is done at the chip rate (2 MHz).

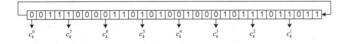

Figure 7.   Generation of spreading codes

As shown, this innovative implementation of the partial correlation algorithm minimizes complexity, operator size and power. Further dynamic power savings are obtained at the RTL level by using clock-gating techniques for preventing unnecessary clock edges from reaching momentarily unused registers, logic functions and their associated clock trees. Finally, power savings are obtained at the system level by defining the "reception_end" signal as

an interruption used to wake up the micro-controller from sleep mode.

IV.   RF/ANALOG DESIGN FOR ULTRA-LOW POWER

The RF/analog part of the transceiver is described in detail in [12] and its block diagram is given in Fig. 8. The direct conversion receiver architecture is ideal for an ULP analog design since the bandwidth of the baseband chain is minimized. This not only means that an amplifier's output impedance can be increased while its bias current is decreased without sacrificing gain, but also that transistors can be biased in weak and medium inversion where the gm/Ids ratio is highest, even if the design is more challenging. The RF front-end is here comprised of I/Q low-noise mixers whose >30dB gain is obtained thanks to its high output impedance. High-pass filtering is needed to eliminate the RX mixer output 1/f noise in order to conserve a reasonable NF. Simulations show that a cut-off frequency lower than 100kHz is necessary to avoid signal loss. The saturating amplifying and filtering chain consists of 6 identical limiting stages for a total gain of 58dB chosen so that the signal reaches the full-scale ADC input even for low input power. Part of each limiter output current is rectified and summed with the rectified output of the other stages of both I and Q paths, providing a practically 'free' received signal strength indicator (RSSI). An 8kHz 8-bit successive approximation ADC digitizes this signal. Each limiting amplifier/filtering chain with RSSI function drains less than 69μA. A digital RSSI measurement would have required higher I/Q ADC resolution or AGC on the baseband amplifiers. The 3-bit I/Q, 4MS/s ADC's are based on a single ladder FLASH architecture. Even without an LNA, the receiver has a 1% packet error rate (PER) for an input power of -81dBm.

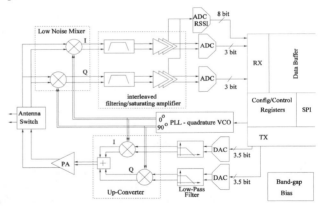

Figure 8.   Block diagram of 2.4-GHz transceiver

For the frequency synthesizer, the reduced phase noise specification means that a low current quadrature VCO can be used. Digital-like LO buffers increase the VCO signal swing and conversion gain of the TX mixers. The 16/17 prescaler draws less than 176μA at 2.5GHz thanks to minimal transistor sizing in the flip-flops and a layout-driven design to identify critical nets and counter unavoidable layout parasitics.

The transmitter uses direct up-conversion with LC-tank loaded mixers to reduce the power buffering requirements. The up-converter + AB-class buffer has a theoretical efficiency of 28% for 0dBm output power. The relaxed IEEE802.15.4 transmission mask and EVM specification (35%) make it possible to use 4-bit, 8MS/s I/Q DAC with

1st order low-pass filters. A differential TRX switch feeds a 100Ω differential antenna port.

V. Measurement Results

The SoC circuit core (Fig. 9) covers 9mm2 (4mm2 digital, 5mm2 analog). The digital baseband including both transceiver and micro-controller is implemented using only 30Kgates. As well, 37kbyte of embedded RAM is included for program data (32kbyte), CPU, user data (4kbyte) and frame buffer. The die is mounted in a 56-pin QFN package.

The current consumption per transceiver function is given in Table 2. (The 1.4mA required by biasing and design-for-test blocks are not included in the table.) In RX mode, the transceiver drains 4.5mA (analog: 650μA, PLL: 2mA, digital: 480μA) and 6.7mA in TX (analog: 3.1mA, PLL: 2mA, digital: 250μA). Fig. 10 shows the digital current drain during the reception of a 20 byte PSDU packet. Even without an LNA, the receiver exhibits a -81dBm sensitivity for 1% PER.

VI. Conclusions

This work presents a complete ULP transceiver based on the IEEE802.15.4 specification. The transceiver has been integrated on a WSN demonstration board (Fig. 11) and the communication compatibility with a commercially available transceiver has been demonstrated. Compared to state of the art (Table 1), this chip proves that globally addressing the system specifications can result in a radio with near to 20nJ/bit energy efficiency at 250kbps.

Acknowledgments

The authors would like to thank Y. Dubois, M. Gary, C. Bour, S. Dumas, J. Prouvée, and E. Mercier.

TABLE I.   STATE OF THE ART IEEE802.15.4 TRANSCEIVERS (250KBIT/S)

	L_{min} (nm)	RX Arch.	P_{RX} (dBm)	RX Power[1]	RX Eff.	TX Power	TX Eff.
[9]	90	Direct sampling	-73	4.5mW (1V)	18nJ/bit w/o PLL	–	–
This work	130	DCR	-81	5.4mW (1.2V)	21.5nJ/bit	8.1mW (1.2V)	32.5nJ/bit
[8]	180	Low-IF	-101	26.5mW (1.8V)	106nJ/bit	28.3mW (1.8V)	113nJ/bit

1The RX power consumption is given for the stated PRX input power level.

TABLE II.   MEASURED CONSUMPTION PER BLOCK

RX blocks	1.12mA	TX blocks	3.38mA
RF Front-end	440μA	Up-converter	2.73mA
Limiter	150μA	I/Q DAC	400μA
I/Q ADC	50μA	Digital	250μA
RSSI ADC	250nA	**PLL total**	**2mA**
Digital	480μA	Quad. VCO	400μA

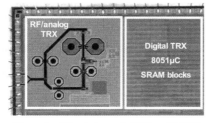

Figure 9.   Die photograph (130nm CMOS)

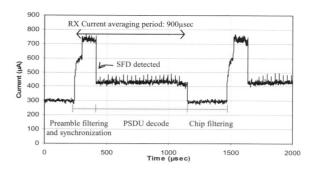

Figure 10. Measured digital RX current consumption (PSDU = 20 bytes)

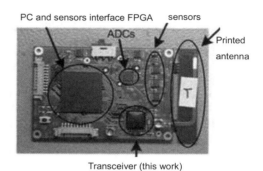

Figure 11. Picture of the WSN demonstration board

References

[1] C. Enz, A. El-Hoiydi, J.-D. Decotignie, V. Peiris, "WiseNET: An ultralow-power wireless sensor network solution," IEEE Computer, vol 37, no. 8, Aug 2004, pp.62-72

[2] J. A. M. Järvinen et al, "2.4-GHz receiver for sensor applications," IEEE Journal of Solid-State Circuits, Vol. 40, No. 7, July 2005.

[3] S.-S. Yoo, S.-O. Yun, S.-H. Shin, H.-J. Yoo, "A CMOS current-reused transceiver with stacked LNA and mixer for WPAN," IEEE 2006 Asia Pacific Conference on Circuits and Systems (APCCAS).

[4] T. Song, H.-S. Oh, E Yoon, S. Hong, "A low-power 2.4GHz current-reused receiver front-end and frequency source for wireless sensor network," IEEE Journal of Solid-State Circuits, Vol. 42, No. 5, May 2007.

[5] T.-K. Nguyen et al, "A low-power RF direct-conversion receiver/transmitter for 2.4-GHz-band IEEE 802.15.4 standard in 0.18-μm CMOS technology," IEEE Transactions on Microwave Theory and Techniques, Vol. 54, No. 12, December 2006.

[6] E. Sacchi et al, "A 15 mW, 70 kHz 1/f corner direct conversion CMOS receiver," Proceedings of the IEEE 2003 Custom Integrated Circuits Conference (CICC).

[7] B. W. Cook, A. Berny, A. Molnar, S. Lanzisera, K. Pster, "Low-power 2.4-GHz transceiver with passive RX front-end and 400-mV supply," IEEE JSSC, Vol. 41, No. 12, December 2006.

[8] W. Kluge et al., "A Fully Integrated 2.4-GHz IEEE802.15.4-Compliant Transceiver for ZigBee™ Applications," IEEE JSSC, Vol. 41, NO. 12, Dec. 2006, pp 2767-2775.

[9] H. Ishizaki, K. Nose, M. Mizuno, "A 2.4GHz ISM-band digital wireless transceiver with an intra-symbol adaptively intermittent RX," 2007 IEEE Symposium on VLSI Circuits Dig. Tech. Papers, pp. 84-85.

[10] K. Muhammad, R. B. Staszewski, "Direct RF sampling mixer with recusive filtering in charge domain," Proceedings of the 2004 International Symposium on Circuits and Systems (ISCAS).

[11] "Part 15.4: Wireless Meidum Access Control (MAC) and Physical Layer (PHY) Specifications for Low-Rate Wireless Personal Area Networks (WPANs)," IEEE Std 802.15.4TH-2006.

[12] C. Bernier et al., "An Ultra low power 130nm CMOS direct conversion transceiver for IEEE802.15.4", IEEE 2008 Radio Frequency Integrated Circuit (RFIC) Symposium, 15-17 June 2008, in press.

A 0.23mm² free coil ZigBee receiver based on a bond-wire self-oscillating mixer

Marika Tedeschi , Antonio Liscidini and Rinaldo Castello

Electronic Department, University of Pavia
via Ferrata 1, Pavia, Italy
marika.tedeschi @ unipv.it, antonio.liscidini @ unipv.it, rinaldo.castello @ unipv.it

Abstract— **A low-IF very compact low power quadrature receiver for ZigBee applications is presented. The receiver saves area and power with a quadrature self oscillating mixer based on high Q bond-wire inductors. The prototype, integrated in CMOS 90nm, provides 76dB of maximum voltage gain, with a 10dB noise figure, an IIP3 of -13dBm and a phase noise of -124dBc/Hz @ 3.5MHz with an active area of only 0.23mm² and a power consumption of 3.6mW (including the baseband complex filter).**

I. INTRODUCTION

Wireless sensor networks and ZigBee systems consist in a spatial distribution of autonomous short-range transceivers to monitor and control environment and/or devices. The large number of units present in the network relaxes the sensitivity of the single receiver but, at the same time, demands a low cost solution to increase the density of elements and thus the system flexibility [1-3]. According to this, the performance of the single transceiver are exchanged with the possibility of designing a long-lasting and cheap device.

In RF front-ends power and area-saving requirements trade-off with each other, since an inductor-free approach results in a cheaper design, while the use of resonant loads can guarantee high power efficiency. This trade-off disappears when integrated inductors are replaced by bond-wires, which guarantee at the same time a high quality factor and a small area. Although bond-wire inductors are not extensively used in large-volume product, due to concerns about their reproducibility, in some case this technique leads to commercially viable solutions (especially in the case of LC oscillators where the inductance spread can be compensated electronically with a sufficient varactor tuning range [4]).

In this work, bond-wire inductors were used in a quadrature self oscillating mixer derived from the LMV cell [5-6], thereby minimizing the active area of the receiver. It will be shown that a very high quality factor offers a more efficient current distribution among the RF building blocks but can increase losses or amplitude/phase mismatches in the front-end transfer function. An analytical description of the phenomenon was developed, resulting in new design optimization to minimize these effects.

II. RX ARCHITECTURE AND BOND-WIRE SELF OSCILLATING MIXER

The starting point for the receiver design is the LMV cell in Fig.1. Low power consumption and small area are obtained sharing the bias current between LNA, Mixer and VCO [5]. The power efficiency of this structure is paid in

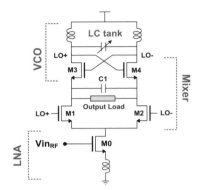

Fig. 1. Current sharing in the LMV cell (bias circuits not shown)

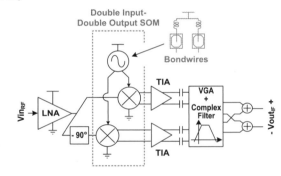

Fig. 2. Proposed receiver with bond-wire double input- double output SOM

terms of flexibility since the stacking limits the possibility to optimize the performance of each block. However, when the optimal bias currents of the VCO and the LNA are comparable, this technique is extremely advantageous because matching, RF signal amplification and down-conversion can be realized without any extra power consumption [5].

When bond-wire inductances are used in the LMV cell instead of integrated coils, there is an immediate reduction of the active area. On the contrary, the total power consumption remains approximately the same, since the bias current cannot be reduced without degrading the LNA performance. In this case the stacking of the LNA appears as a limit in the minimum current consumption, without taking advantages of the use of high-Q inductances in the oscillator tank.

For this reason, the receiver architecture reported in Fig.2 was adopted, where the LNA does not share the bias current with the mixers and the VCO. In this case, the

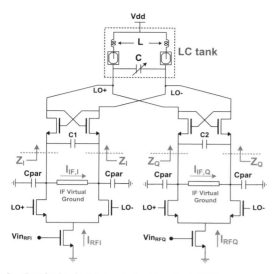

Fig. 3. Bond-wire double input- double output SOM

quadrature is realized on the RF signal path, while the down conversion is performed using the double input-double output self oscillating mixer (SOM) reported in Fig.3. The working principle of this SOM is the same of the LMV cell [5-6] where the oscillation is sustained through a positive feedback closed at RF by capacitor C1 and C2. The RF quadrature signals are injected in the mixer by two transconductors, down-converted and collected into the virtual grounds of two trans-impedance amplifiers (TIA).

The SOM in Fig.3 is particularly suitable to be used with bond-wires because requires only a couple of inductors and the capacitive load at the tank is minimal (merging mixers and VCO), maximizing the tuning range for a given varactor.

III. EFFECT OF HIGH Q TANK ON SOM TRANSFER FUNCTION

The tank sharing realized in the double input-double output SOM reported in Fig.3, introduces an amplitude/phase error between the I and Q paths, proportional to the quality factor of the inductors used. This phenomenon was investigated in order to minimize its effects maximizing the benefits provided by the use of bond-wires.

A. Origin of Mismatches and Losses

The working principle of the double input-double output SOM is identical to the current-mode LMV cell. The main losses derive from the current division at RF between the common mode capacitors C_{par} and the LC tank impedance reflected at the IF outputs (Z_I and Z_Q in Fig.3) [5]. As for the single LMV cell in [5], the Z_I and Z_Q of the double input-double output SOM were evaluated as a function of the common mode and of the differential parts of the tank impedances (Z_{tankCM} and $Z_{tankDIFF}$ in Fig.4):

$$\begin{cases} Z_I(\omega) = \frac{Z_{tankCM}(\omega)}{2}(1-j) \\ Z_Q(\omega) = \frac{Z_{tankCM}(\omega)}{2}(1+j) \end{cases} \quad (1)$$

Since the tank is shared between I and Q paths, the two impedances Z_I and Z_Q are complex conjugated and thus, in addition to a current loss, they produce a phase/amplitude mismatch. However this effect can be minimized

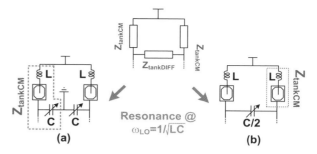

Fig. 4. VCO tank configurations: (a) resonance for common mode and differential signals, (b) resonance only for differential signal

considering that only the common mode component Z_{tankCM} appears at the IF outputs of the SOM.

B. Tank design strategy

In the previous solutions reported in literature [5-6], the use of integrated coils (with relative low Q) has limited to a negligible level the impact of the tank impedance reflection on the LMV cell transfer function. In this case, the use of bond-wires requires a more careful design of the resonant tank to minimize the losses in the presence of such a high Q resonator.

The VCO load has to guarantee a DC path for the bias of the SOM and a differential resonant impedance to set the proper oscillation frequency. Two different configuration, reported in Fig.4, were considered. In the solution of Fig.4.a the tank resonates both for common mode and differential signals and from (1) it has

$$\begin{cases} Z_I(\omega_{LO}) = \frac{\omega_{LO}LQ}{2}(1-j) \\ Z_Q(\omega_{LO}) = \frac{\omega_{LO}LQ}{2}(1+j) \end{cases} \quad (2)$$

where ω_{LO} and Q are the resonance frequency and the quality factor of the resonator.

The configuration in Fig.4.b resonates only for differential components while the common mode impedance at ω_{LO} is given by $Z_{tankCM} \approx j\omega_{LO}L$ leading to

$$\begin{cases} Z_I(\omega_{LO}) = \frac{\omega_{LO}L}{2}(1+j) \\ Z_Q(\omega_{LO}) = \frac{\omega_{LO}L}{2}(j-1) \end{cases} \quad (3)$$

Notice that in this case, the impedances reflected are smaller than (2) and independent from the quality factor.

C. Amplitude and Phase Errors

The two load configurations where compared in terms of amplitude/phase errors introduced in the double input-double output SOM. This was realized evaluating the transfer function for both cases using the same approach proposed in [5]. The down-converted current becomes:

$$\begin{cases} I_{IF,I} = \frac{1}{\pi} \frac{2+(1+j)\omega_{RF}C_{par}Z_{tankCM}(\omega_{RF})}{1+(1+j)\omega_{RF}C_{par}Z_{tankCM}(\omega_{RF})} I_{RFI}(\omega_{RF}-\omega_{LO}) \\ I_{IF,Q} = \frac{1}{\pi} \frac{2+(j-1)\omega_{RF}C_{par}Z_{tankCM}(\omega_{RF})}{1+(j-1)\omega_{RF}C_{par}Z_{tankCM}(\omega_{RF})} I_{RFQ}(\omega_{RF}-\omega_{LO}) \end{cases} \quad (4)$$

where Z_{tankCM} depends on the load configuration used. In particular in the case of a differential resonator, (4) becomes

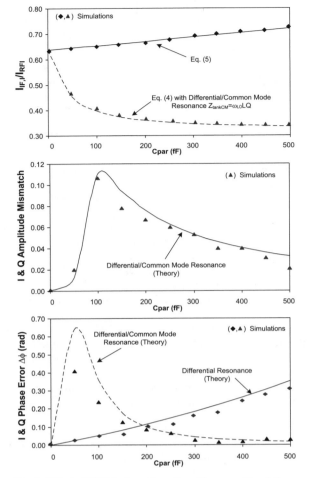

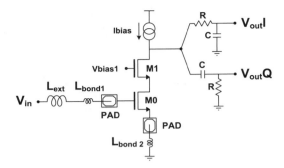

Fig.6 LNA input matching and quadrature generation

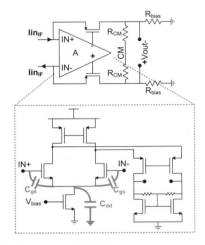

Fig.7 Virtual ground circuit details

Fig. 5. Effect of VCO tank configuration. Theory vs. Simulations (f_{LO}=2.45GHz, Q=40, L=2nH).

$$\begin{cases} I_{IF,I} = \frac{1}{\pi} \frac{2+(j-1)\omega_{LO}^2 C_{par}L}{1+(j-1)\omega_{LO}^2 C_{par}L} I_{RFI}(\omega_{RF} - \omega_{LO}) \\ I_{IF,Q} = \frac{1}{\pi} \frac{2-(j+1)\omega_{LO}^2 C_{par}L}{1-(j+1)\omega_{LO}^2 C_{par}L} I_{RFQ}(\omega_{RF} - \omega_{LO}) \end{cases} \quad (5)$$

where the dependency on the quality factor disappears and the amplitude mismatch between the IF outputs is zero. Notice that, since the conversion gain of the single LMV cell in current mode depends on the tank impedance reflection too, it can be improved compared to the solution reported in [5] adopting the differential mode resonator here proposed.

The simulated and calculated gain and amplitude/phase error for input frequencies close to ω_{LO} are reported in Fig.5 and confirm the superior immunity to C_{par} when the tank resonates only differentially. For the differential configuration, the gain can be even greater than $2/\pi$ due to the reactive nature of the impedance reflected at the IF outputs.

IV. RECEIVER DESIGN

The receiver in Fig.2 was tailored to ZigBee application and for this reason a low-IF architecture at 2 MHz was chosen. This approach is particularly suitable for a low-power, low-cost solution, and can guarantee a greater immunity to flicker noise than a direct-conversion one.

After the down-conversion and the first voltage amplification, the signal is AC coupled and filtered by a fully differential three-stage variable gain complex gm-C filter [6]. At the output of the 3rd stage the two paths are finally combined for image rejection.

A. Quadrature Generation and LNA input matching

The low noise amplifier schematic is reported in Fig.6. The input matching is realized through a series resonance and a real impedance synthesized by a bond-wire inductive degeneration (L_{bond2}). Even if a moderate deviation of the real part from the nominal value can guarantee a S11 below -10dB, the high Q resonant network requires an external inductor L_{ext} to center the frequency of operation and to compensate the variation of $L_{bond1,2}$. Moreover, the narrow-band input matching network filters out blockers close to the double of the VCO oscillation frequency, avoiding any injection locking phenomena [5].

Contrary to the previous work [6], the LNA removal from the stack allows to realize a less noisy impedance matching since the quadrature is generated at its output over an RC-CR load. This simple way to generate quadrature is suitable just for narrow band applications, since the 90° phase difference and the amplitude matching are assured only around the cut-off frequency $1/(2\pi RC)$. Due to the relaxed specs of the ZigBee, the amplitude/phase mismatches remain acceptable in all the frequency range required by the standard. The network has to be finally dimensioned trading off between minimum noise contribution and area occupation.

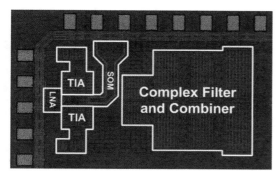

Fig.8. Chip Micrograph

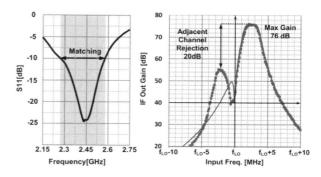

Fig.9. S11 and IF Gain Profile Measurements (f_{LO}=2.45 GHz)

B. Virtual ground design details

The virtual ground is provided by a trans-impedance-amplifier in a gain boosted cascode configuration (Fig.7). The differential low impedance, synthesized over a large bandwidth (around 10MHz), limits current losses and ensures high linearity in the presence of large interferers.

In the amplifier design, the most critical element is the input differential pair since its input capacitance contributes to the C_{par} and affects the conversion gain. In particular, using a differential pair input stage, the common mode capacitance is minimized being the series of $2C_{gs}$ and C_{dd} (Fig.7).

V. MEASUREMENTS RESULTS

The ZigBee receiver has been realized in a 90nm CMOS technology. Fig.8 shows the chip micrograph. The use of bond-wire inductors has minimized the area of the RF part (only 0.03 mm^2) making the baseband section dominant (0.20mm^2). The circuits draws 3mA from a power supply of 1.2V.

The external inductor L_{ext} (Fig.6) allows to centre the input resonance, resulting in a good S11 (Fig.9), while the varactor in the tank sets the proper oscillating frequency of the SOM (f_{LO}=2.45 GHz). Fig.9 shows also the IF gain profile with a maximum in band gain of 76dB (from 1MHz to 3MHz). A 20dB image rejection, is obtained without any calibration, giving a safe margin from a target spec of 4dB [2]. The spurious energy at the image frequency is due primarily to the error in the quadrature generation in the RC-CR filter, while the phase shift introduced in the I & Q SOMs was minimized through the use of a differential resonant tank.

In Table I the prototype is compared to the complete ZigBee receivers present in literature. The noise figure averaged over the band from 1MHz to 3MHz is around 10dB while the IIP3 is -13dBm. This results in a spurious free dynamic range of 54.5dB that is comparable to the state of art. Furthermore, compared to the previous solution reported in [6], the total area is 45% less thanks to a reduction of 80% of the RF Front-End part, keeping constant the power consumption.

VI. CONCLUSIONS

In this work bond-wires inductors were successfully introduced in the LMV cell producing very compact self oscillating mixer. A deep analysis on the mechanisms of loss and amplitude/phase mismatches has shown that the use of a differential VCO tank makes the cell conversion gain independent from the resonator quality factor. As a result a very compact receiver for ZigBee application based on bond-wires inductors has been designed minimizing the active area.

TABLE I
MEASUREMENTS AND COMPARISON

	This work	[1]	[2]	[6]
Gain (dB)	76	-	-	75
NF (dB)	10	24.7	5.7	9
IIP3 (dBm)	-13	-4.5	-16	-12.5
SFDR (dB)	**54.5**	50.3	55.3	55.5
PN @ 3.5MHz (dBc/Hz)	-124	-	-	-116
Power diss. (mW)	**3.6**	15	17	3.6
Integrated inductors	**0**	6	4	1
Area (mm^2)	**0.23**	2.1	0.8	0.35
Vdd (V)	1.2	1.8	1.8	1.2
Technology (μm)	0.09	0.18	0.18	0.09

ACKNOWLEDGEMENTS

This project has been supported by the Italian National Research Program FIRB (Contract Nr. RBAP06L4S5).
The authors want to thank Francesco De Paola for the support in the setup of test equipment and measurements, Marvell for technology access and Steve Shia (TSMC) for design kit support.

REFERENCES

[1] T.K. Nguyen, at al., "A Low-Power RF Direct-Conversion Receiver/Transmitter for 2.4-GHz-Band IEEE 802.15.4 Standard in 0.18-um CMOS Technology", *IEEE Trans. on Microwave Theory and Techniques*, vol. 54, No. 12, Dec 2006, pp. 4062-4071.

[2] W. Kluge, F. Poegel, H. Roller, M. Lange, T. Ferchland, L. Dathe and D. Eggert "A fully integrated 2.4GHz IEEE 802.15.4 compliant transceiver for ZigBee applications," *IEEE ISSCC Dig. Tech. Papers*, Feb. 2006, p. 1470.

[3] M. Camus et al.,"A 5.4mW 0.07mm^2 2.4GHz Front End Receiver in 90nm CMOS for IEEE 802.15.4 WPAN" *IEEE ISSCC Dig. Tech. Papers*, Feb. 2008, pp. 368-369.

[4] F. Svelto, R. Castello, "A Bond-Wire Inductor-MOS Varactor VCO Tunable From 1.8 to 2.4 GHz" *IEEE Trans. on Microwave Theory and Techniques*, vol. 50, No. 1, Jan 2002, pp. 403-407.

[5] A. Liscidini, et al., "Single-Stage Low-Power Quadrature RF Receiver Front-End: The LMV Cell," *IEEE J. Solid-State Circuits*, vol. 41, no. 12, pp. 2832-2841, Dec. 2006.

[6] A. Liscidini, M. Tedeschi, R. Castello," A 2.4 GHz 3.6mW 0.35mm^2 Quadrature Front-End RX for ZigBee and WPAN Applications" *IEEE ISSCC Dig. Tech. Papers*, Feb. 2008, pp.370-371.

An Ultra Low Power GFSK Demodulator for Wireless Body Area Network

Dong Han and Yuanjin Zheng

Institute of Microelectronics

A*STAR (Agency for Science, Technology and Research), Singapore

Abstract☐ **This paper presents a novel ultra low power Gaussian frequency shift keying (GFSK) demodulator with efficient input DC offset cancellation and frequency offset cancellation for wireless body area network (WBAN) application. The proposed demodulator uses a new multi-threshold phase domain analog to digital converter (PDADC) to improve the phase accuracy of the zero crossing detection, hence can achieve smaller modulation index and robust demodulation performance. Measured results show that the minimum detectable modulation index for the demodulator is 0.2. The demodulator symbol rate is up to 1.17Mbps and the carrier frequency is from 1MHz to 4MHz. The measured signal to noise ratio (SNR) for 0.1% bit error rate (BER) with 250kbps symbol rate and 0.28 modulation index is 16.7dB. The demodulator is implemented in a 0.18☐m digital CMOS process with only 0.11mm^2 chip area. The demodulator only drains 350☐A current from a 1.8V power supply.**

I. INTRODUCTION

Wireless body area network (WBAN) has received an increasing interest for personal healthcare and biomedical signal processing. In order to extend the battery life, the node devices of WBAN require low power and relatively low symbol rate wireless communication link. Low-IF wireless receiver and Gaussian frequency shift keying (GFSK) are widely used for the wireless link of low power communication system. Some FSK modulators [1], [2], and demodulators [3]-[5], have been reported with good performance, but the power consumption is still high for WBAN application. This paper introduces a low power mixed signal GFSK demodulator for WBAN for monitoring and processing electrocardiogram (ECG) and electroencephalogram (EEG) signals. The proposed demodulator uses a new phase domain analog to digital converter (PDADC) to improve the phase accuracy of the zero crossing detection. It achieves smaller modulation index and can overcome larger input DC and frequency offset with ultra low power consumption and ultra small chip area.

II. DESIGN OF THE GFSK DEMODULATOR

Fig. 1 shows the block diagram of the low-IF wireless receiver front end and the proposed GFSK demodulator. With properly setting the IF frequency, the low-IF wireless receiver can achieve high level integration without the flicker noise and DC offset issue. Hence it is very suitable for the low power low cost WBAN application. The proposed GFSK demodulator is a new kind of zero crossing based demodulator (e.g. [3]), which has four main building blocks: the input PDADC, one shot, low pass filter (LPF) and dynamic

threshold slicer. The input PDADC performs the input DC offset cancellation and high accuracy zero crossing detection, and then converts the input differential analog FSK signal into high frequency FSK pulse. The one shot circuit regulates the width of the FSK pulse to a fixed value, and the LPF averages the fixed width FSK pulse over the equal symbol period to produce the output voltage which presents the frequency information of the carrier signal. Finally the dynamic threshold slicer makes a binary decision on the LPF output to produce the demodulated data. Since the threshold of the slicer is dynamically generated and is in the middle of the LPF output swing, the slicer has very good immunity to the DC offset of the LPF output.

A. The Phase Domain Analog to Digital Converter

Fig. 2 presents the circuit implementation and operation concept of the single ended phase domain analog to digital converter (SPADC). As shown in Fig. 2(a), the general *m*-threshold SPADC uses a pair of maximum and minimum peak detectors to sense the peak and valley values of the input signal. These peak and valley values are stored at the holding capacitors C_1 and C_2 respectively with 10µs holding time. The current sources I_{B1}, I_{B2} and the transistors M_{1a} and M_{2a} form a constant biased source follower, which is used to isolate the holding capacitors and the resistive voltage divider network. Once the peak detectors sense the peak and valley values of the input signal, the resistive voltage divider will generate the *m* threshold voltages ($V_{th,1}$, $V_{th,2}$, ..., $V_{th,m}$).

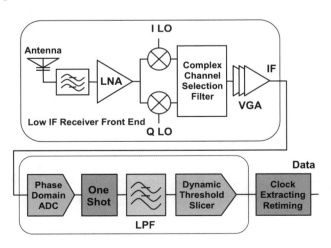

Figure 1.   The low-IF receiver front end and the GFSK demodulator.

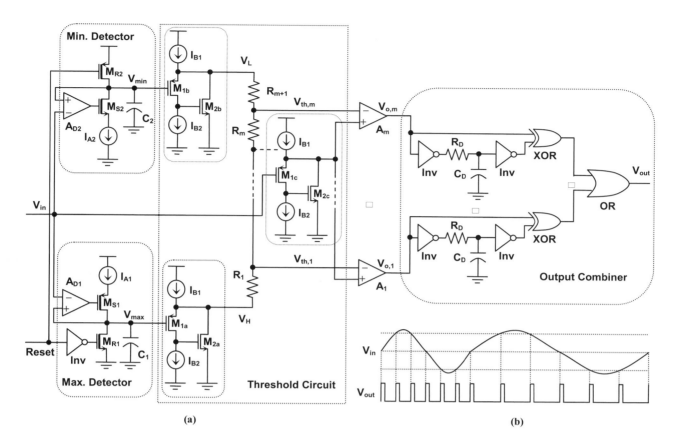

Figure 2.   Circuit implementation (a), and operation cencept (b) of the SPADC.

In order to achieve an equal comparison step in phase domain, the values of the m thresholds are defined by (1).

$$V_{th,i} = A \sin\left[\frac{90°}{m}(m - 2i + 1)\right] + B, \ i = 1, 2, ..., m ,(1)$$

where A is the amplitude of the input signal, B is the average of V_H and V_L, and $V_{th,i}$ is the i-th threshold. The input signal V_{in} is compensated by the same constant biased source follower and then compared with the m thresholds. The m comparison results ($V_{o,1}$, $V_{o,2}$, ..., $V_{o,m}$) are converted into m narrow pulse trains by the edge recorder, which is formed by the R_D, C_D, the inverter gates and the XOR gate, and then combined by the output OR gate. The output pulse train records all the $2m$ comparison events which are distributed evenly within any 360 degree phase window. Comparing with the conventional comparators, the SPADC achieves an improved phase accuracy with LSB(φ)=180°/m.

Fig. 2(b) shows the operation concept of the proposed SPADC with three thresholds. The peak detectors and the resistive voltage divider dynamically generate three thresholds for the following comparators. The input signal is shifted by the same voltage amount as the peak and valley values, and then compared with the three thresholds to produce the final combined output pulse train. It is clear that by using the

thresholds defined in (1), the output pulse train is distributed evenly within one cycle of the input signal regardless the input frequency variation. The frequency of the output pulse train is six times of the input carrier frequency, which relaxes much the following LPF selectivity, especially when the symbol rate is high.

B.   The Frequency to Voltage Converter

The PDADC, one shot, and LPF form the frequency to voltage converter (FVC). Fig. 3 shows the simplified circuit implementation and operation concept of the FVC with 60 degree phase accuracy. The input PDADC uses two SPADCs to perform zero crossing detection of the input differential GFSK signal with high phase accuracy. Since the input differential signal always has 180 degree phase difference, it is unnecessary for both SPADCs to use three thresholds. As shown in Fig. 3(b), the SPADC+ uses two thresholds ($V_{th,1+}$, $V_{th,2+}$) for zero crossing detection and the SPADC– uses only one threshold ($V_{th,1-}$), and then the combined output is same as the output in Fig. 2(b). Here the $V_{th,1+}$, $V_{th,2+}$ and $V_{th,1-}$ are calculated by applying (1) on the positive and negative input signals (V_{in+} and V_{in-}) respectively, and the total threshold number m is 3. Since the two SPADCs process the positive and negative input signals individually, the input PDADC has the naturally high immunity to the input DC offset. Besides, the sensed peak and valley values of the positive and negative input signals can be used to control the DC offset cancellation loop of the previous amplifier chain.

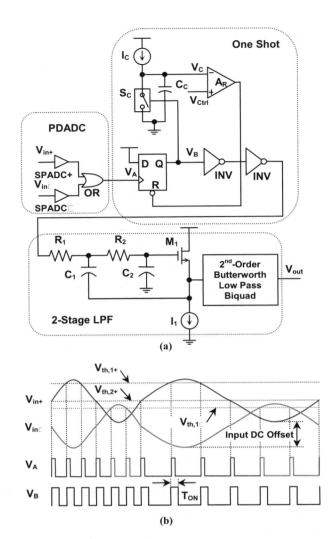

Figure 3. Simplified circuit implementation (a), and operation concept (b) of the FVC under the input differential analog FSK signal with DC offset.

To a summary, the PDADC has three thresholds and 60 degree phase accuracy. In this design, the input carrier frequency is 2MHz, thus the frequency of the PDADC output pulse train is 12MHz. The PDADC has a wide input voltage range from 0.3V to 1.5V, and can efficiently cancel input DC offset of up to 550mV with 600mV peak to peak input signal swing.

As shown in Fig. 3(a), the one shot circuit is a rising edge triggered pulse generator. Once V_A presents a rising edge, V_B is set to high level to turn off S_C, V_C is disconnected with ground, and I_C starts to charge C_C. When V_C exceeds V_{ctrl}, the reset amplifier A_R outputs low level to reset V_B. The pulse width T_{ON} can be tuned by V_{ctrl} from 5ns to 400ns. For 2MHz input carrier frequency, T_{ON} is set to 50ns.

As shown in Fig. 3(a), the LPF is a 2-stage 4th-order filter. The first stage is a 2nd-order passive RC LPF with a feedback path (transistor M_1 and current source I_1). The feedback path can improve the quality factor of the filter and achieve 9dB more attenuation at 10MHz. The second stage of the filter is a single ended 2nd-order Gm-C Butterworth low pass biquad.

The LPF is designed with in band gain of 0dB and -3dB bandwidth of 800kHz.

C. The Dynamic Threshold Slicer

The dynamic threshold slicer is a single threshold SPADC without the output combiner. Since the demodulator may process a low symbol rate GFSK signal, the transistors M_{R1}, M_{R2}, M_{S1}, and M_{S2} are replaced by the high threshold transistors to extend the holding time to 50μs. This dynamic threshold slicer has a wide input range from 0.2V to 1.6V which fully covers the LPF output range. Hence it can handle large DC offset of the LPF output, which is mainly caused by the input frequency offset.

III. MEASUREMENT RESULTS

The proposed GFSK demodulator has been implemented in a commercial 0.18μm digital CMOS process. Fig. 4 shows the chip photo of the GFSK demodulator. The active area of the demodulator is only 380μm by 290μm. Comparing with other implementations, this design achieves an ultra small chip area.

A clock extracting and retiming logic circuit has been also implemented into this demodulator chip for testing purpose. The continuous phase GFSK carrier signal with adjustable modulation index is generated in single ended from a signal generator. An operational amplifier based single ended to differential converter has been implemented on the testing board for the signal condition purpose. The additive white Gaussian noise (AWGN), which is generated from Labview®, and the input DC offset are injected into the differential GFSK carrier signal through the on board single ended to differential converter for BER and input DC offset cancellation testing.

Fig. 5 shows the measured 2MHz GFSK carrier signal with minimum detectable modulation index 0.2 and the demodulated 500kbps data. With three thresholds, the ideal noiseless minimum detectable modulation index of the demodulator is 0.167. The slight degradation of the minimum detectable modulation index is caused by the process variation and the white noise of the test setup.

Fig. 6 presents the measured results for a 2MHz GFSK carrier signal modulated at 500kbps symbol rate with modulation index 0.28. The maximum symbol rate of the demodulator is 1.17MHz which is achieved under a 2MHz GFSK carrier signal with 600mV peak to peak swing and

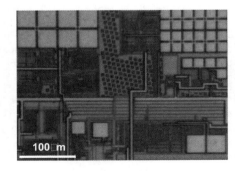

Figure 4. Chip photo of the GFSK demodulator.

436

modulation index 0.32. Fig. 7 shows the measured BER performance of the demodulator for a GFSK signal with 2MHz carrier frequency, 250kbps symbol rate, and modulation index 0.28. The measured SNR for 0.1% BER is 16.7dB. The demodulator consumes 350μA current from a 1.8V power supply.

The measured performance of the demodulator is summarized and compared with other state-of-the-art demodulators. As shown in Table I, this design achieves the lowest power consumption and smallest chip area with comparable BER performance and large input DC offset cancellation.

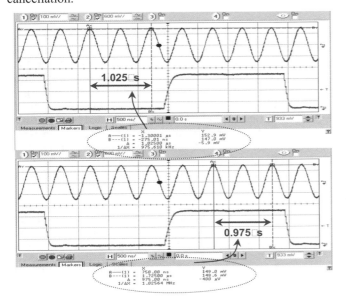

Figure 5. Measured carrier signal and the demodulated data from the dynamic threshold slicer output with 500kbps symbol rate, 2MHz carrier frequency and 0.2 modulation index (The top figure shows the measured lower frequency of the carrier signal is 1.95MHz, the bottom figure shows the measured higher frequency of the carrier signal is 2.05MHz).

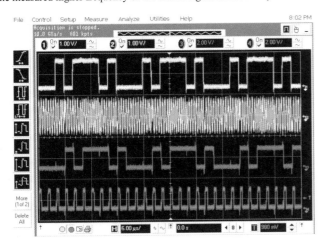

Figure 6. Measured baseband data (top), carrier signal, demodulated and resampled data, and the extracted symbol rate clock (bottom) with 500kbps symbol rate, 2MHz carrier frequency, 0.28 modulation index and "0101110100" baseband data.

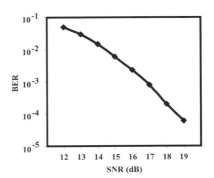

Figure 7. Measured BER of the demodulator with 0.28 modulation index.

TABLE I.   COMPARISON OF THE DEMODULATOR PERFORMANCE.

Parameters	This Design	[3]	[4]***	[5]	Unit
Technology	0.18	0.35	0.25	0.18	μm
Supply Voltage	1.8	3	2	1.8	V
Power Consumption	0.63	9	6	3.6	mW
Chip Area	0.11*	0.7	0.3	0.26	mm²
Modulation Index	0.28	0.32	0.28	0.32	-
Symbol Rate	0.25	1	1	1	Mbps
Carrier Frequency	2	2	2	5	MHz
Max. Input DC Offset	550**	-	-	-	mV
SNR (for 0.1% BER)	16.7	16.2	16.5	14.9	dB

*Including the clock extracting and retiming circuit.

**Measured with 600mV peak to peak input signal swing.

***Simulation performance only.

IV.   CONCLUSION

A novel zero crossing based GFSK demodulator CMOS IC has been presented. The proposed robust multi-threshold PDADC improves the zero crossing detection accuracy, enhances the input DC offset cancellation, and relaxes the LPF selectivity requirement. It makes the demodulator achieve smaller modulation index, ultra low power and ultra small chip area. Measurements show that the demodulator can achieve 16.7dB SNR for 0.1% BER with 0.28 modulation index and 0.63mW power consumption. It is very suitable for WBAN or other low power low cost applications.

REFERENCES

[1] Han Shuguang, Chi Baoyong, and Wang Zhihua, "A mixed-loop CMOS analog GFSK modulator with tunable modulation index," IEEE Transactions on Circuits and Systems–II, vol. 54, No. 6, Jun 2007, pp. 547-551.

[2] Hooman Darabi, Brima Ibrahim, and Ahmadreza Rofougaran, "An analog GFSK modulator in 0.35-μm CMOS," IEEE Journal of Solid-State Circuits, vol. 39, Dec. 2004, pp. 2292-2296.

[3] Bo Xia, Chunyu Xin, Wenjun Sheng, Valero-Lopez A.Y., and Sanchez-Sinencio E., "A GFSK demodulator for low-IF Bluetooth receiver," IEEE Journal of Solid-State Circuits, vol. 38, Aug. 2003, pp. 1397-1400.

[4] Tai-Cheng Lee, and Chin-Chi Chen, "A mixed-signal GFSK demodulator for Bluetooth," IEEE Transactions on Circuits and Systems–II, vol. 53, No. 3, Jun 2006, pp. 197-201.

[5] Hong-Sing Kao, Ming-Jen Yang, and Tai-Cheng Lee, "A delay-line-based GFSK demodulator for low-IF receivers," IEEE International Solid-State Circuits Conference, 2007, pp. 88, 589.

A 3-5 GHz Low-Complexity Ultra-Wideband CMOS RF Front-End for Low Data-Rate WPANs

Marco Cavallaro, Alessandro Italia, Giuseppina Sapone, and Giuseppe Palmisano

DIEES, Facoltà di Ingegneria
Università di Catania
Viale Andrea Doria 6, 95125, Catania, Italy

Abstract□ **This paper presents a 3-5 GHz ultra-wideband radio front-end for low data-rate wireless personal area network applications. The circuit, implemented in a 90-nm CMOS technology, includes a carried-based ultra-wideband transmitter, a sub-optimal coherent down-converter and a low-power LO signal generator. Thanks to a pseudo-Gaussian pulse generator, the transmitter is able to run up to 500 Mpps satisfying the FCC mask requirements with no filter and high spectral efficiency. The down-converter exploits a single-ended low-noise amplifier to minimize power consumption. It also performs on-chip single-ended-to-differential conversion of the RF signal by using an integrated transformer. The down-converter exhibits a 23-dB conversion gain and a double-sideband noise figure of 3.4 dB. The LO signal is generated by a low-power wideband *LC* VCO, which draws only 1.5 mA. The current consumption of the radio front-end is 15 mA in receive mode and 24 mA in transmit mode.**

I. INTRODUCTION

In the near future an outstanding spread of low data-rate wireless personal area networks (LR-WPANs) is expected to comply with the growing demand for industrial, vehicular, residential and medical applications. The IEEE 802.15.4a standard [1] recognizes ultra-wideband technology (UWB) as the best candidate for such short-range wireless applications. Indeed, UWB signaling is based on short pulse allowing elevated capacity/range, high robustness on multi-path environment and location capability.

The IEEE 802.15.4a standard defines a UWB physical layer, which operates in the 3-5 GHz and 6-10 GHz frequency bands. The protocol exploits an impulse radio based signaling scheme and the data bits are represented by a sequence of pulses (burst), which have a maximum repetition rate of 499.2 MHz. The signal bandwidth is approximately 500 MHz. A wider bandwidth can be provided by some optional channels. The data modulation is a combination of both PPM and BPSK. The time hopping technique is employed to provide interference rejection for multi-user access.

The development of wideband low-power, low-cost transceiver for new generation of LR-WPAN systems

represents a key-point for the spread of mass-market equipment. To this purpose, a proper choice of the transceiver architecture is of primary importance. All digital architectures [2] [3] ensure low complexity and power consumption. However, the digital approach usually provides a single operating frequency. The duration and the shape of the digitally generated impulse are greatly affected by the process tolerances. Moreover, an off-chip RF filter is typically required to fulfill the FCC mask requirements. On the other hand, carrier-based architectures guarantee high flexibility [4] [5] and the spectrum efficiency can be optimized by implementing a suitably shaped envelope [3]. In addition, bandwidth of the generated impulse can be accurately controlled. However, this approach requires analog wideband RF circuits and a strong design effort must be carried out to implement low-power and low-complexity circuit solutions.

In this paper, a 3-5 GHz UWB RF front-end for low-data rate communication and localization systems is presented. The circuit is mainly composed of a carrier-based UWB transmitter [5], a sub-optimal coherent down-converter and a low-power local oscillator (LO). Thanks to the adopted architecture and circuit solutions, the RF front-end, which was initially targeted for the IEEE 802.15.4a standard, is also suitable for various UWB standards. Moreover, it allows high spectral efficiency, high side-lobe rejection and low power consumption to be achieved without requiring external filters or baluns.

II. CIRCUIT DESCRIPTION AND DESIGN

The simplified block diagram of the proposed RF front-end is shown in Fig. 1. The circuit includes a UWB carrier-based transmitter, a sub-optimal coherent down-converter and a LO signal generator. The transmitter is composed of a BPSK modulator, a ramp generator, an UWB pseudo-Gaussian pulse generator and an output buffer. The ramp generator accepts the base-band PPM stream and produces a trapezoidal-wave, which drives the pulse generator. As shown in timing diagram of Fig. 2, during each rising and falling times of the trapezoidal-wave the pulse generator produces a pseudo-Gaussian envelope impulse. This

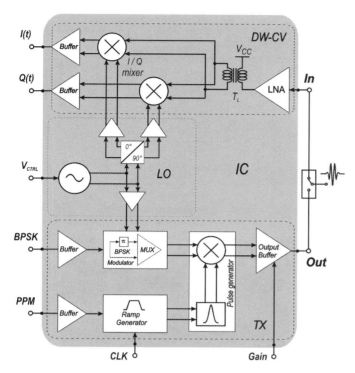

Figure 1. Block diagram of the proposed RF front-end.

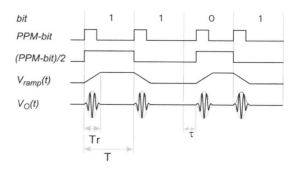

Figure 2. Generation of Gaussian-like envelope UWB impulses.

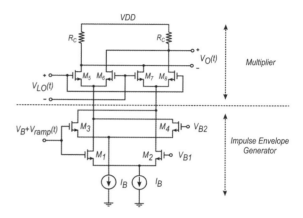

Figure 3. Schematic of the UWB pulse generator.

features a well-defined bandwidth since the ramp generator exploits a reference clock signal (CLK) to accurately control the rising and falling times of its output. The pulse generator includes a multiplier, which up-converts the pseudo-Gaussian envelope impulse to the desired center frequency. The phase modulation of the produced impulse is achieved by BPSK modulator, which is driven by the sine-wave signal produced by the LO. Finally, the output buffer enhances the signal power level and provides the differential-to-single-ended conversion along with broadband 50-Ω load matching. The down-converter comprises a single-ended 3-5 GHz low-noise amplifier (LNA) and a double-balanced I/Q demodulator. The monolithic transformer T_L loads the LNA and performs on-chip single-ended-to-differential conversion of the RF signal. The output buffers have been included for testing purpose. The LO signal is generated by exploiting a wideband LC voltage-controlled oscillator (VCO). A 2°order poly-phase filter has been adopted to produce the I/Q signals for the down-converter. LO buffers drive the LO port of the down-converter and transmitter.

Fig. 3 shows the schematic of UWB pulse generator, which is composed of a pulse envelope generator and an analog multiplier. The Gaussian-like pulse envelope generator consists of two cross-coupled differential pairs (M_1-M_2, M_3-M_4) differently biased by two voltages V_{B1}, V_{B2}, and current sources I_B. This circuit is driven into large signal condition by the linear rising/falling edge of the trapezoidal-wave generated by the ramp generator (V_{ramp}). The pulse envelope generator produces an impulse every rising/falling edge of the input signal. The multiplier, i.e. Gilbert Cell (M_5-M_8), performs the multiplication between the sinusoidal carrier V_{LO} and the Gaussian-like impulse train produced by the pulse envelope generator. In this way, a

carrier modulated impulse with a Gaussian-like envelope is generated. Therefore, the proposed UWB pulse generator results high flexible allowing both single-band and multi-band applications to be covered. Moreover, the accurate envelope of the generated impulses allows a high spectral efficiency to be achieved.

The schematic of the down-converter is shown in Fig. 4. For the sake of simplicity, only one of the two double-balanced mixers has been sketched. The LNA adopts a single-ended cascode topology, which allows high input/output isolation to be achieved. The implementation of a single-ended LNA represents a fundamental advantage for the application of interest. Indeed, it saves power consumption and avoids the use of an external balun that inevitably introduces high losses due to the required wideband characteristic. Inductors L_S and L_G perform the LNA input matching as in the classical narrow-band design, while C_F and R_F implement an AC resistive feedback to obtain wideband input matching along with adequate noise performance. A lower value for R_F results in better input matching but degrades noise performance. Therefore, R_F has been set as high as possible according to the input matching requirements. The primary winding of T_L, capacitor C_P, and resistor R_P represent an RLC shunt resonator, which loads the LNA. The capacitor C_P and the primary winding of T_L have been designed to resonate at the frequency of 4 GHz, while the shunt resistance R_P reduces the quality factor of the resonator to guarantee gain spectral-flatness. The two double-balanced mixers make use of a voltage-to-current (V-I) converter and a Gilbert quad. The transformer T_L conveys the LNA output

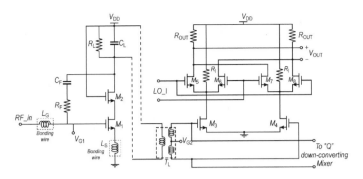

Figure 4. Transistor–level schematic of the down-converter.

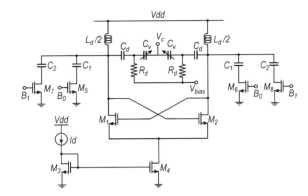

Figure 5. Shematic of the *LC* VCO.

Figure 6. RF front-end die micrograph.

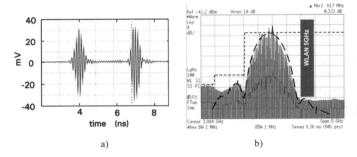

a)   b)

Figure 7. Transmitter output signal(160-MHz PPM-BPSK data, 1.5-GHz clock signal, 4-GHz LO). a) Time-domain measurement. b) Spectrum measurement.

signal to the differential pair M_3-M_4 and provides the DC-bias to the transconductor through the secondary-winding center-tap, as well. The Gilbert quad is resistively loaded. Resistors R_I have been inserted to optimize the current in the switching transistors and in the *V-I* converter independently. This technique also comes in advantage of the output voltage swing, since the voltage drop across the load resistances R_L is reduced allowing the use of higher-value resistors. The schematic of the adopted *LC* VCO is sketched in Fig. 5. The VCO employs a fully-differential NMOS cross-coupled topology. The *LC* tank consists of an integrated differential spiral inductor (L_D), N+POLY/N-WELL MOS varactors (C_V), and two switched metal-insulator-metal (MIM) capacitors (C_1, C_2). The switched capacitors, controlled by the two-bit channel-select digital word (B0, B1) provide coarse tuning steps allowing the channel selection. The N+POLY/N-WELL MOS varactors provide continuous frequency tuning and guarantee the desired frequency by compensating for the fabrication tolerances. To maximize the capacitance tuning range (C_{max}/C_{min}), the varactors have been decoupled using MIM capacitors (C_d) and proper biasing. The VCO tank inductor has a differential inductance value of 1.5 nH and a quality factor ranging from 24 to 28 all over the frequency range. The receiver LO interface includes a 2°order poly-phase filter, which generates the I/Q LO signals. Each quadrature path comprises a cascade of two differential pairs, which amplify the LO signal. On the other hand, the LO interface of the UWB transmitter consists of a simple differential pair.

III. EXPERIMENTAL RESULTS

The die micrograph of the proposed RF front-end is shown in Fig. 6. It was fabricated in a 90-nm CMOS technology and its die area is 2.9×2.2 mm^2, including bond pads. Fig. 7 shows the measured output signal of the transmitter with base-band 160-MHz PPM-BPSK data, 1.5-GHz clock signal and 4-GHz LO frequency. The output signal is reported in the time domain in Fig. 7a. Due to BPSK modulation, the output pulses are 180° phase shifted one to each other. The pulse duration is around 2 ns with a 60-mV peak-to-peak amplitude. Fig. 7b reports the simulated (dashed line) and measured spectrum of the generated impulse with a resolution bandwidth of 1 MHz. A 22-dB side lobe rejection has been obtained with an excellent agreement between the simulated and measured Gaussian-like envelope. 2.5-V thick oxide MOS devices have been adopted for the transmitter to ensure a high dynamic range for the pulse generator. Nevertheless, the

transmitter maintains low the power consumption since it draws only 21 mA.

In Fig. 8 the double-sideband noise figure (DSB-NF) and the conversion gain of the down-converter is reported as a function of the base-band frequency for the 500-MHz lower band channels. The circuit exhibits a 23.3 dB conversion gain and a 3.4 double-side-band noise figure (DBS-NF). The measured 1-dB input referred compression point (IP1dB) is -20 dBm at 4 GHz. An input third-order interception point (IIP3) of -8 dBm was measured using two 10-MHz-spaced tones centered at 4.1 GHz. The down-converter draws only 9 mA from a 1.2 V supply. Fig. 9 shows the VCO tuning range. The circuit achieves a wide tuning range of 40% from

3.2 GHz to 4.8 GHz with a tuning voltage ranging from 0 to 1.2 V. The measured phase noise at 1-MHz offset frequency is −114 dBc/Hz at 4 GHz (B_0=1, B_1=0, channel 2), −112 dBc/Hz, and −112.2 dBc/Hz at 3.5 GHz (B_0=0, B_1=1, channel 1) and 4.5 GHz (B_0=0, B_1=0, channel 3), respectively. The VCO core has a current consumption as low as 1.5 mA from 1.2 V supply. The receiver and pulse generator LO buffers draw 4.5 mA and 1.5 mA, respectively.

IV. CONCLUSIONS

A 3-5 GHz UWB RF front-end for LR-WPAN applications has been presented in this paper. The circuit has been designed and implemented using a 90-nm CMOS technology and includes a UWB carrier-based transmitter, a sub-optimal coherent down-converter and a low power LO signal generator. The RF front-end demonstrates excellent performance in terms of spectral efficiency and power consumption along with high flexibility and low complexity. In Table I, the performance of the proposed circuit is summarized and compared with recently published works.

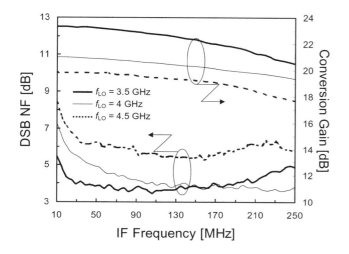

Figure 8.   Down-converter DBS noise figure and conversion gain.

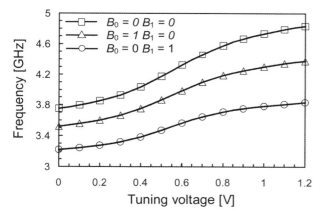

Figure 9.   VCO tuning range.

TABLE I.   SUMMARY OF RF FRONT-END PERFORMANCE AND COMPARISON WITH RECENTLY PUBLISHED WORKS

	Ref. [7]	Ref. TX [2] Ref. RX [6]	This work
Technology	CMOS 0.18 ☐m	CMOS 0.18 ☐m	CMOS 90 nm
Conversion gain [dB]	15	20	23.3
Noise figure [dB]	–	>11	3.4
IP$_{1dB}$ [dBm]	–	-15	-20
Power Consumption Rx [mW]	30.6	–	10.5^a@1.2V
-10 dB bandwidth [GHz]	–	1.4	1.1
Pulse width [ns]	–	1.75	2
Power Consumption Tx [mW]^a	73.8^a@1.8V	13.7@2.2V	14.4^a@2.5V
Chip die area [mm^2]	2.4 × 1.2	–	1.9 × 2.2

a. without output buffer

ACKNOWLEDGMENT

The authors wish to thank the support of Alessandro Castorina for measurements.

REFERENCES

[1]   Wireless Medium Acces Control (MAC) and Phisycal Layer (PHY) Specifications for Low-Rate Wireless Personal Area Networks (WPANs), Add Alternate PHYs, IEEE Standard 802.15.4a, 2007

[2]   T. Norimatsu et al. "A UWB-IR transmitter with digitally controlled pulse generator," IEEE J. Solid-State Circuits, vol. 42,no. 6, pp.1300–1309, Jul. 2007.

[3]   M. Fujishima, W. Badalawa, A. Oncu, T. Wang, "22-29 GHz CMOS pulse generator for ultra-wideband radar applications," IEEE J. Solid-State Circuits, vol. 42, no. 7, pp. 1464–1471, Jul. 2007.

[4]   J. Ryckaert, G. Van der Plans, V. De Heyn, C. Desset, B. Van Poucke, J. Craninckx, "A 0.65-to-1.4 nJ/burst 3-to-10 GHz UWB all-digital TX in 90 nm CMOS for IEEE 802.15.4a,☐ IEEE J. Solid-State Circuits, vol. 42, no.12, pp. 2860–2869, Dec. 2007.

[5]   M. Cavallaro, T. Copani, G. Girlando and G. Palmisano, "A novel pulse Generator for Ultra-Wideband Modulation Systems and Modulation using it", ST patent pending 2005.

[6]   J. Ryckaert, M. Verhelst, M. Badaroglu, S. D'Amico, V. De Heyn, C. Desset, P. Nuzzo, B, Van Poucke, P. Wambacq, A. baschirotto, W. Dehaene, and, G. Van der Plas, "A CMOS ultra-wideband receiver for low-data-rate communication," IEEE J. Solid-State Circuits, vol. 42, no. 11, pp. 2515–2527, Nov. 2007.

[7]   M-I. Jeong, J-H. Moon, C-S. Lee "Design of a transceiver RFIC for UWB chaotic OOK system in 018µm CMOS technology" in Proc. IEEE European Microwave Integrated Circuit Conf., pp. 275-278, Oct. 2007

A 828μW 1.8V 80dB Dynamic-Range Readout Interface for a MEMS Capacitive Microphone

S. A. Jawed[1], D. Cattin[2], M. Gottardi[1], N. Massari[1]
[1]MIS Division, Fondazione Bruno Kessler, Trento, Italy.
[2]DISI, University of Trento, Trento, Italy.
{jawed , gottardi , massari }@fbk.eu , cattin@disi.unitn.it

A. Baschirotto[3], A. Simoni[1]
[3]University of Milano, Bicocca, Milano, Italy.
andrea.baschirotto@unimib.it
simoni@fbk.eu

Abstract□ **A CMOS interface for a piston-type MEMS capacitive microphone is presented. It performs a capacitance-to-voltage conversion by bootstrapping the sensor through a voltage pre-amplifier, feeding a third-order sigma-delta modulator. The bootstrapping performs active parasitic compensation, improving the readout sensitivity by ~12dB. The total current consumption is 460uA at 1.8V-supply. The digital output achieves 80dBA-DR, with 63dBA peak-SNR, using 0.35um 2P/4M CMOS technology. The paper includes electrical and acoustic measurement results for the interface.**

I. INTRODUCTION

MEMS microphones are the new-generation high-accuracy and low-cost acoustic sensors and are one of the rapidly maturing areas of MEMS sensors owing to their improved aspects over the conventional Electret-Condenser-Microphones (ECM) [1]. These sensors are compatible with standard fabrication assembly procedures, have a reduced size, higher immunity to mechanical shocks and low-temperature coefficient. However, interfacing to this generation of sensors requires a challenging high-sensitivity and low-power capacitive readout interface. The interface has to minimize the large electrode-to-substrate parasitic capacitances that degrade the readout sensitivity and cause distortion due to the dielectric dispersion [2]. The capacitive variations of the microphone, resulting due to the incident acoustic pressure, are residing over a fixed bias capacitance. The front-end of the interface has to reject this bias capacitance while performing capacitance-to-voltage conversion for optimal utilization of the interface's dynamic range. Furthermore, the interface has to provide integrated biasing for the MEMS, which is typically higher than the supply-voltage.

The presented readout interface for a piston-type MEMS capacitive microphone with a maximum sensitivity of 10fF/Pa [2] is shown in figure 1. The interface performs a capacitance-to-voltage conversion by boot-strapping the sensor through a voltage pre-amplifier [3]. The resulting voltage is then fed to a third-order sigma-delta modulator (SDM). All the biases and reference voltages for the interface are generated internally, including the power-down logic and a charge-pump for the sensor bias voltage. The total current consumption of the interface is 460uA for a supply voltage of 1.8V. The digital

output achieves 80dBA dynamic-range, with 60dBA peak-SNR, the OSR is 60 with a sampling frequency of 2.4MHz, with an FoM of 2.07pJ/conversion-level (where FoM=Power/(2*DR*BW)), using 0.35um 2P/4M CMOS technology. Section II presents the design details of the readout interface. Section III presents the measurements results. Section IV concludes the work.

II. THE READOUT INTERFACE

The readout interface is shown in figure 1, which highlights the major functional blocks. The following text discusses these blocks in detail.

A. The Pre-Amplifier

The pre-amplifier is based on a source-follower buffer as shown in figure 2. A typical microphone pre-amplifier for audio applications might be required to readout acoustic signals down to 33dB-SPL (1mPa) [4]. The capacitive variation of the MEMS microphone for a 1mPa signal can be in sub-fF range and the injected charge to be readout is very small. The sensor's parasitic capacitances (C_0, C_{p1} and C_{p2}) also attenuate the signal by absorbing some of the injected charge. To readout this relatively weaker signal, a low-noise pre-amplifier is required. For this interface, a continuous-time (CT) pre-amplifier is preferred since it achieves low-noise for a certain power budget as compared to discrete-time (DT) pre-amplifiers [5]. The source-follower has one-current leg, therefore, low noise can be achieved for lower bias current. However, the pre-amplifier has to drive the SDM sampling capacitances, which sets the lower limit for the bias current of the pre-amplifier.

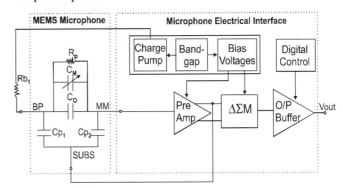

Figure 1. Major Functional Blocks of the Readout Interface

Large dimensions for the input PMOS M1 (1200um/1.5um) and the PMOS current-load M2 (500um/40um) are used to reduce their flicker noise. The bias current is set to 40μA. The large size of the input PMOS increases the parasitic capacitance at the input of the pre-amplifier and can reduce the sensitivity of the readout. Therefore, an optimal size of M1 exists where the sensitivity is maximized [5]. With the above-mentioned dimensions and bias current, the pre-amplifier achieves total in-band noise of 27dBA-SPL, where 1Pa of acoustic signal is assumed to give rise to a voltage signal of ~40mVpp at input of source-follower.

A dc-bias path should be established at the high-impedance input of the source-follower through a high-value resistor R_{b2}. This resistor, along with the capacitances of the sensor, gives rise to a low frequency pole, which should be kept out of the acoustic band. Expecting the fixed bias capacitance of the sensor in the order of tens-of-pF, the value of this resistor should be above 10 GΩ. Junction diodes are used to implement this resistor [6]. Using diodes as the bias resistor makes the initial settling faster and very large signals are automatically clipped, which avoids the saturation of the following SDM. There is a parasitic resistance R_p between the backplate (BP) and the moving-membrane (MM) of the sensor, which is estimated to be above TΩ [2]. R_p continuously sources a current into the high impedance node MM, the biasing diodes are sized so that this current does not pull-up the node.

When the sensor capacitance changes due to the incident acoustic wave, charge redistribution takes place among the sensor capacitances, which is translated into a voltage signal by the pre-amplifier. The fixed bias capacitance of the sensor (C_0) and the parasitic at MM (C_{p2}) reduce the redistribution sensitivity ($\Delta V/\Delta C$) since the redistribution occurs over the total capacitance of the structure, which can be several orders of magnitude higher than the actual capacitive variation. The pre-amplifier performs an active compensation of these parasitic capacitances C_{p2} and C_0 by bootstrapping the sensor's substrate (SUBS) to the output of the pre-amplifier [3]. This bootstrapping reduces the signal swing across these capacitors and minimizes their impact on the charge-redistribution sensitivity. BP of the sensor is connected to the charge-pump through a high value resistor R_{b1}, implemented using junction diodes, which forces the sensor to operate in charge-controlled mode, reducing the possibility of pull-in. This resistor also allows C_{p1} to participate in the bootstrapping hence reducing the signal swing across C_0. Therefore, using this two-terminal bootstrapping [3], both parasitics are effectively removed.

The MEMS microphone is a single-ended sensor while the SDM that follows the pre-amplifier expects a differential input. The pre-amplifier uses a dummy branch to provide a pseudo-differential output, which replicates the MEMS sensor capacitive structure, biased and bootstrapped just like the actual sensor. To provide good matching in drive-strength and variations with process, same device sizes and bias current are used for the dummy as the active branch. MIM capacitors are used to mimic the capacitances of the MEMS in the dummy branch.

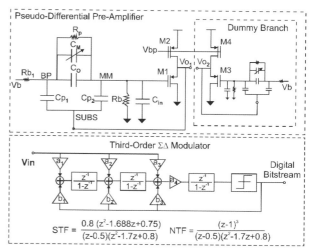

$$STF = \frac{0.8\,(z^2-1.688z+0.75)}{(z-0.5)(z^2-1.7z+0.8)} \qquad NTF = \frac{(z-1)^3}{(z-0.5)(z^2-1.7z+0.8)}$$

Figure 2.   Pseudo-differential Pre-amplifier and the third-order SDM

B. The Sigma-Delta Modulator

The pseudo-differential output of the pre-amplifier is fed to the third-order single-loop feed-forward sigma-delta modulator. The topology of the modulator is shown in figure 2 along with its STF and NTF. The feed-forward path from input to the quantizer is removed to avoid the use of another analog adder. This reduces the power consumption but alters the STF of the SDM. However, the STF is very close to unity inside the audio band. A gain factor of seven is provided at the input of the first integrator to translate the output of pre-amplifier to the dynamic range of the modulator, i.e. placing 1Pa (94dB-SPL) to -26dBFS of the modulator, the maximum readable signal is thus 20Pa (120dB-SPL).

The coefficients around the first integrator of the modulator are small, however, its sampling capacitance is large to lower its KTC noise. The second and the third integrators have relaxed capacitance sizes since their KTC noise is filtered by the first integrator, however, the signal swing around second and the third integrator is relatively larger. Therefore, opamps in all the integrators approximately face the same settling requirements. A fully-differential telescopic Opamp with 1.8V supply biased at 20uA is used for all the integrators. A telescopic topology is preferred because it can achieve low-noise for low bias current since there are no extra current legs and it can also meet the swing, gain and the slew-rate requirements [7]. The feedback reference voltages, centered at mid-rail are normalized to ±900mV by adjusting the feedback coefficients. Separate capacitors for the feedback are used, which relaxes the slew-rate of the integrators' opamps because the large input-sampling capacitors do not have to (dis)charge to the reference voltages [8].

The targeted application requires a single-bit digital output. At 1.8V supply with V_{th}=600mV, the modulator has sufficient linear range for the sampling switches and a switched-capacitor (SC) implementation guarantees stable filter coefficients, thus boot-strapped switches, switched RC integrators or switched-opamp techniques are not employed. The low-bandwidth requirement of the application (~20kHz) favors a DT implementation, moreover, a DT modulator is more tolerant to clock-jitters and does not suffer from excess loop delay as compared to a CT implementation. The behavioral simulations of the modulator were performed in Simulink using the $\Sigma\Delta$-Toolbox [9]. The simulated performance of the modulator is plotted against the measured performance in figure 4 and discussed in the next section.

C. Bandgap Reference and Bias Network

The bandgap (BG) reference is based on error-amplifier closed-loop topology and the center-point is placed at 40^0C taking it as the default internal temperature of the chip. This generates a temperature insensitive voltage bias which is fed to the bias generation block, which ultimately generates all the reference-biases for the SDM. A buffered resistor ladder with a 60uA current is used to generate these reference-biases. The biases for the opamps are mirrored using MOS transistors and are loaded with 100pF capacitors inside the chip to filter-out high-frequency glitches.

D. Chargepump, Powerdown Logic and Output Buffer

The charge-pump (CP) comprises of five cascaded stages based on static charge-transfer-switches and it is clocked at a rate four-time lower than the SDM frequency. This is done to avoid overlapping of the sampling phase of SDM with the CP switching, keeping the switching noise from entering the signal path. The power-down logic is implemented by sensing if the clock frequency goes below 50kHz. In the sleep mode, the whole interface is turned-off except the BG. This reduces the total current consumption to 30uA in sleep-mode. The digital output buffer is designed to drive a capacitive load of 100pF, with tri-state output for single line multiplexing. It is controlled externally to drive at the corresponding clock-polarity for the left/right channel selection.

III. MEASUREMENT RESULTS

A. Electrical Results

The interface is designed in 0.35um CMOS 2P/4M CMOS technology. The dimensions are $1400\times750\mu m^2$, the microphotograph is shown in figure 3. For the electrical measurements on a PCB, power-supply and the clock signal are provided by on-board batteries and oscillator, and the board is placed inside an electrostatically shielded box. The output digital bitstream of the modulator is sampled by a logic analyzer from Agilent and is post-processed in Matlab. The analog output of the pre-amplifier is analyzed by SpectraLab

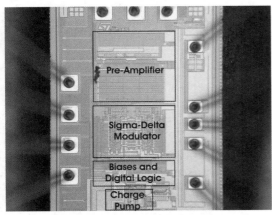

Figure 3.   Microphotograph of the Interface

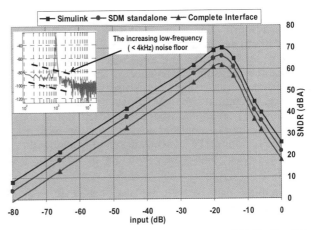

Figure 4.   SNDR v/s input amplitude for three cases: SDM in Simulink, SDM stand-alone measurement, complete interface measurment

software through the soundcard of a PC. The bias voltages of the interface, which are taken outside the chip for debugging, are filtered using external capacitors.

Figure 4 plots the SNDR versus input-amplitude for three different set of results: simulation of the SDM in Simulink, stand-alone electrical measurements of the SDM (the pre-amplifier is turned off and the input is applied directly to SDM) and the measured SNDR when the input is applied to the pre-amplifier. The figure plots the A-weighted SNDR versus the input amplitude for all three cases.

It can be observed from figure 3 that the SDM falls by ~4dB below the simulated value in Simulink. To track the reason for this lapse, the current in the opamps of the modulator is increased by externally adjusting their current bias. This is done to check whether it is the drive strength of the opamps and the settling inaccuracy that is causing the performance lapse. However, increasing the bias current by 50% does not alter the performance much. Inspection of the spectrum of output bitstream reveals that the noise floor is higher for low-frequencies (<4kHz) when compared to the Simulink results. This points to higher flicker noise in the opamp of the first integrator (the Simulink simulations did not include flicker noise effect).

Figure 3 shows that if the signal is fed to the pre-amplifier, further 4dB in the SNDR is lost. This could be due to noise of the pre-amplifier or low drive strength. The bias current of the pre-amplifier is increased by externally adjusting its bias, however, this does not alter the results. It seems that increased bias current improves the drive strength, but it also increases the thermal noise of the pre-amplifier, hence no considerable change in the results.

There is a slight offset in the dc-levels of the active and dummy branch output of the pre-amplifier. This can be attributed to the fact that the dummy branch is internally bootstrapped using MIM capacitors and the leakage through the MIM capacitors can cause this mismatch.

To test bootstrapping, on-board discrete capacitors are used to emulate the MEMS sensor. To minimize the impact of board parasitics on the bootstrapping, the external capacitors are kept ten-times higher than the values in the original sensor,

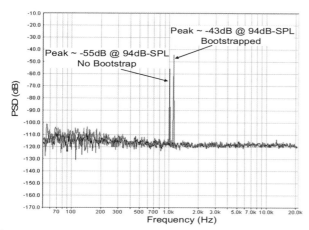

Figure 5. The effect of two-terminal bootstrapping at the analog output of the pre-amplifier, the signal amplitude is boosted by ~12dB

however, maintaining the same ratio among the capacitors. Figure 5 shows the effect of two-terminal bootstrapping, where a 12dB boost in the signal amplitude is achieved, at the analog output of the pre-amplifier. This boosted output corresponds to the signal-amplitude if there was only the signal capacitance C_M on the board, therefore, it implies that bootstrapping removed the absorption of signal in the parasitics C_{p2} and C_0. The results shown in figure 5 correspond to an electric input equivalent to 1Pa@1kHz of acoustic input.

B. Acoustic Results

The acoustic tests are performed using Knowles-SiSonic analog MEMS microphone. This test is not performed in an anechoic room, however, an adequate degree of acoustic shielding is achieved by enclosing the setup in a box. The acoustic input is provided through a speaker driven by Audio Precision instrument. The audio signal is calibrated using a reference microphone from Bruel&Kjaer, which is attached close to the MEMS. Figure 6 shows the PSD (65536 points) of the interface's digital output for a input signal of 1Pa@1kHz for acoustic and electric results.

First observation is that the signal amplitude of the acoustic results is 6dB lower. The interface is designed for a MEMS microphone which achieves a sensitivity of -34 dBFS/Pa with parasitic-compensation. Whereas, the under-test

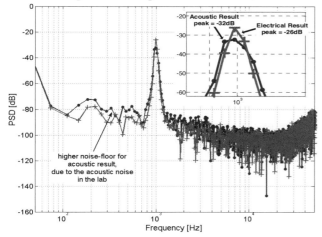

Figure 6. Electrical and Acoustic Results for 1Pa acoustic input

SiSonic microphone has a sensitivity of -42 dBFS/Pa, hence the loss of 6dB. Nevertheless, the close resemblance between electrical and acoustic results validates the compatibility of the interface with standard microphone specs. Second observation is the increased low-frequency noise floor, which can be attributed to higher acoustic noise around the test-setup because the sensor is not fully shielded, for instance, there are fans of lab instruments around the setup. The speaker cannot send more than 3Pa of acoustic signal so we were unable to test the interface for high acoustic inputs when the sensor is overloaded and introduces excessive distortion. Table I summarizes the characteristics of the designed interface.

TABLE I.   SUMMARY OF THE DESIGNED INTERFACE

Sampling Frequency	2.4 MHz
Oversampling Ratio	60
Signal Bandwidth	20 kHz
Peak SNDR / Dynamic Range	63 dBA / 80dBA
Power Consumption	Total Device : 828µW @ 1.8V Pre-Amp : 198 µW SDM : 180µW Bandgap : 198µW Biases : 252 µW
Power Supply	1.8V – 2.5V
Active Area	1400 x 750 µm²
Technology	

IV.   CONCLUSION

A CMOS interface for a piston-type MEMS capacitive microphone is presented. Electrical and Acoustic testing results are presented demonstrating 80dBA-DR, with 63dBA peak-SNR, using 0.35um 2P/4M CMOS technology. The total current consumption is 460uA at 1.8V-supply.

ACKNOWLEDGMENTS

The authors are grateful to STM-Milano, MEMS Business Unit for their valuable support.

REFERENCES

[1] Report from Yole Development, "SIMM'05 : Silicon Microphone Market 2005 – From Si microphone to acoustic modules", Sept. 2005.

[2] B. Margesin, A. Faes, F. Giacomozzi, A. Bagolini, M. Zen,"Fabrication of Piston-type Condenser Microphone with structured polysilicon diaphragm", 8th Italian Conf. on Sensors and Microsystems, 2003.

[3] S. A. Jawed, M. Gottardi, N. Massari, A. Baschirotto, "A low-voltage bootstrapping technique for capacitive MEMS sensors interface", IEEE-IMTC07, May 1-3 2007, Poland.

[4] J. H. Nielsen, C. Furst, "Toward More-Compact Digital Microphones", Analog-Dialogue, vol. 41, Sept 2007.

[5] J. Wu, G. K. Fedder, L. R. Carley, "A Low-Noise Low-Offset Capacitive Sensing Amplifier for a 50ug/√Hz Monolithic CMOS MEMS Accelerometer", IEEE JSSC, Vol. 39, No. 5, May 2004.

[6] C. E. Furst, "A low-noise/low-power preamplifier for capacitive microphones", Circuits and Systems, 1996. ISCAS '96., Volume 1, 12-15 May 1996 Page(s):477 - 480 vol. 1.

[7] S. Rabii, Bruce A. Wooley, "A 1.8-V Digital-Audio Sigma-Delta Modulator in 0.8-um CMOS", IEEE JSSC, June 1997.

[8] Libin Yao, M. S. J. Steyaert et al. "A 1-V 140-uW 88-dB Audio Sigma-Delta Modulator in 90nm CMOS", IEEE JSSC, November 2004.

[9] S. Brigati et al., "Modeling Sigma-Delta Modulator Non-idealities in Simulink", ISCAS 99.

A low-power capacitance to pulse width converter for MEMS interfacing

P. Bruschi, N. Nizza, M. Dei

Dipartimento di Ingegneria dell'Informazione, Università di Pisa
I-56122 Pisa, Italy
p.bruschi@iet.unipi.it

Abstract□ **A compact converter from capacitance to pulse width, suitable for interfacing integrated capacitive sensors is described. The circuit has been designed and fabricated using 0.32 μm/ 3.3 V CMOS devices from the BCD6s process of STMicroelectroncs and occupies an area of 1025 × 515 μm². Measurements performed on the test chip showed an excellent linearity, a temperature drift of 300 ppm/°C, and power consumption as low as 84 μW for continuous operation.**

I. INTRODUCTION

Integrated accelerometers and pressure sensors are probably the most successful examples of MEMS (Micro Electro Mechanical Systems). Practically the totality of integrated accelerometers and a large fraction of pressure sensors are based on capacitive sensing of either a seismic mass or a membrane. Capacitive sensors offer high relative sensitivity, small temperature dependence and virtually negligible power consumption. On the other hand, the small capacitance variations that have to be detected, typically in the fF range, require that the readout interface is placed in the same chip or the same package of the integrated sensor, in order to minimize parasitic capacitance and coupling with external noise sources. Then, the interface needs to be developed together with the sensor and should be carefully designed in order not to degrade the sensor advantages mentioned above. The most common approach is converting the capacitance to be measured into a voltage (C-to-V) by means of switched capacitor charge amplifiers [1]. This approach, combined with a sigma-delta ADC, is probably the optimum choice when the target is the maximum resolution [2]. On the down side, the discrete nature of the system makes it prone to thermal noise fold-over. Reduction of the effects of noise on the overall resolution is obtained at the cost of high current consumption or bandwidth reduction. The typical topological complexity required to manage charge injection and kT/C noise, contributes to further increase the power consumption.

On the other hand, capacitance-to-frequency converters are much simpler, less power demanding circuits [3]. However, the high sensitivity to temperature and process parameters of most practical implementations limits the achievable accuracy. Recently, a fully integrated interface capable to produce a pulse width modulated (PWM) signal with pulse duration linearly proportional to a capacitance has been presented [4]. Pulse width modulated (PWM) signals can be transmitted over moderately noisy or non linear channels, such as RF or optical links. Furthermore, a PWM signal can be easily read by a low cost microcontroller or converted into an analog signal using only a low pass filter. In spite of these advantages, very few examples of capacitance to PWM converters are currently present in the literature. The circuit proposed in [4] exhibits intrinsically low temperature drift and low dependence to parasitic capacitance, but requires a relatively high supply current (nearly 5 mA). In [5], a capacitance-to-PWM converter that combines the mentioned features of [4] with two orders of magnitude lower power consumption is presented. The result is obtained by means a chopper modulation technique to reduce the effect of low frequency noise, in place of the more current demanding OTA-based feedback loop of [4].

In this work we describe the design and experimental characterization of a prototype inspired to the idea of [5], fabricated using 0.32 μm CMOS devices from the process BCD6s (Bipolar-DMOS-CMOS) of STMicroelectronics.

II. PRINCIPLE OF OPERATION

The block diagram of the system is shown in Fig. 1(a) where the sensor is represented by the two capacitors C_R and C_X having a common terminal, while ck is a clock signal with 50 % duty cycle. The quantity to be acquired is the difference $\Delta C = C_X - C_R$ which depends on the physical or chemical quantity to be sensed. For correct operation of the interface, ΔC should be positive. The output signal, indicated with p in Fig. 1(a), consists in a sequence of pulses with the same frequency of the clock and duration τ proportional to ΔC. Block RG (ramp generator) produces a triangular waveform $V_S(t)$, synchronous with the clock signal, while CA is a differential current amplifier with gain 1/2. Blocks SA1 and SA2 are switch arrays, schematically shown in Fig. 1(b), connecting their input port to the output port in a straight or crossed fashion, depending on whether the control signal s is a logical "1" or "0", respectively. CMP is a low hysteresis comparator.

Capacitor C, is charged by currents I_{CA}, I_D and ΔI_B, with a sign depending on SA1 and SA2 state. Currents I_D and ΔI_B, are constant and chosen to satisfy the following conditions:

$$I_D > \max|I_{CA}|; \qquad \Delta I_B > I_D + \max|I_{CA}| \qquad (1)$$

Clearly, for the waveform V_C to be stationary, the net charge accumulated on C over a clock period (T_{ck}) should be zero. To simplify the comprehension of the measurement cycle, the ideal waveforms in the circuit are shown in Fig.1(c). In the following analysis, the input resistance of CA will be considered zero; this point is important to achieve low temperature dependence and will be addressed in next section. The expression of current I_{CA} is then:

$$I_{CA} = \frac{1}{2}(I_x - I_r) = \frac{1}{2}\frac{dV_S}{dt}\Delta C. \qquad (2)$$

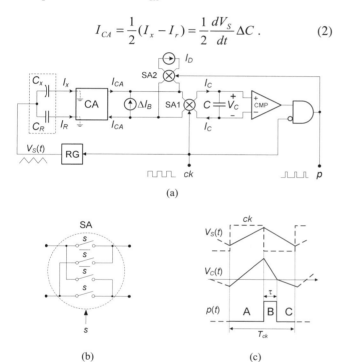

(a)

(b)   (c)

Figure 1. Schematic block diagram (a); functional view of the switch arrays SA1, SA2 (b); ideal waveforms in the circuit (c).

Note that I_{CA}, which is proportional to ΔC, changes sign at half the clock cycle due to the slope inversion of V_S. However, SA1 produces another sign reversal at the same time, so that the charge contribution of I_{CA} is always positive and given by:

$$Q_{CA} = \frac{\Delta C}{2}\int_0^{\frac{T_{ck}}{2}} \frac{dV_s}{dt}dt - \frac{\Delta C}{2}\int_{\frac{T_{ck}}{2}}^{T_{ck}} \frac{dV_s}{dt}dt = \Delta C \cdot \Delta V_S, \quad (3)$$

where ΔV_S is the peak-to-peak amplitude of V_S. On the other hand, the contribution of ΔI_B changes sign at half the clock cycle, so that, the net charge accumulated over a whole clock period is zero. The role of this current is to make V_C increase on the first half clock cycle and decrease on the second one, regardless of the value and sign of I_D and I_{CA}. This is guaranteed by the second of conditions (1). For this reason,

V_C reaches its maximum at the end of the first half clock cycle. As represented in Fig.1(c) we will assume now that the maximum is positive and discuss this point at the end of this section. Considering the effect of CMP and of the NAND gate, the output signal (p) turns on at the beginning of the second clock half cycle, as shown in Fig.1(c).

The contribution of I_D is negative in the first half clock period, due to the sign reversal operated by SA2. At the end of this period, both SA2 and SA1 change state, so that the contribution continues to be negative. Finally, when V_C crosses the zero and CMP changes state, the contribution of I_D becomes positive. Summing up the contributions over the three phases indicated with A, B and C in Fig.1(c), the net charge contribution of I_D is then:

$$Q_D = -2\tau I_D \qquad (4)$$

Equating to zero the total charge accumulated over a period, (i.e $Q_D + Q_{CA}$) we obtain the pulse duration:

$$\tau = \Delta C \cdot \frac{\Delta V_S}{2I_D}, \qquad (5)$$

It is easy to show that the system reaches the steady condition regardless of the initial state. Indeed, if the maximum of V_C is negative, SA2 stays in inverted state and, similarly to ΔI_B, I_D gives no charge contribution. Therefore, the unbalanced positive contribution of I_{CA} progressively raises the V_C waveform reaching the situation in Fig.1(c). On the opposite side, if V_C was always positive, the I_D contribution would be negative over the whole clock period and, due to the first of (1), V_C would progressively decrease reaching again the steady situation.

III. TOPOLOGY OF MAIN BLOCKS

The RG simplified schematic view is shown in Fig. 2. The circuit is composed of a Miller inverting integrator, made up of M_{3M}-M_{6M}, and two current sources M_{1M}, and M_{2M} that can be connected to the integrator input through M_{1S} and M_{2S} respectively.

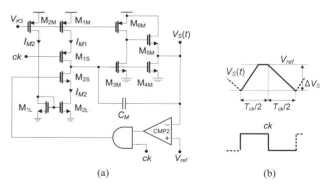

(a)   (b)

Figure 2. Schematic view of the RG block (a) and output waveform (b).

In the first clock half cycle ($ck = 1$), M_{2L} draws the current I_{M2} from the integrator, so that V_S increases at a constant rate. Let us suppose that V_S reach V_{ref} before the clock changes state. From this point, CMP2 keeps M_{2S} off and V_S is constant. In the second half period ($ck = 0$), M_{1S} turns on feeding the current I_{M1} to the integrator. V_S decrease during the whole second half clock period. The V_S decreasing slope is made slightly smaller than the increasing one ($I_{M1} < I_{M2}$, by design), so that Vs really reaches V_{ref} in the following increasing phase, as supposed above. The resulting waveform is reliably synchronous with the clock but not perfectly triangular. However, it can be easily shown that Eqns. (3) and (5) are still perfectly valid and that:

$$\Delta V_S = \frac{T_{ck} I_{M1}}{2 C_M} \Rightarrow \tau = \frac{\Delta C}{C_M} \frac{I_{M1}}{4 I_D} T_{ck} . \qquad (6)$$

In this way, we have obtained that the pulse width τ is proportional to the clock period and to ΔC, as desired. Note that only current and capacitance ratios appear in (6), so that a very small sensitivity to temperature is expected.

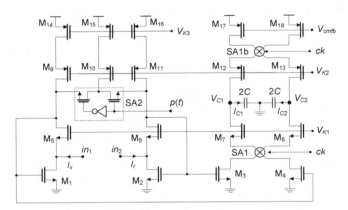

Figure 3. Schematic view of the current amplifier CA including also the function of I_D and ΔI_B current sources and switch arrays SA1, SA2.

Figure 3 shows the circuit designed to include the functions of blocks CA, SA1, SA2, and of current sources I_D and ΔI_B. M_{14}, M_{16} and M_{15} are constant current sources that set M_5 and M_6 drain currents. In particular, I_{D15} can be conveyed to M_6 or M_5 depending on the value of the digital signal p. Currents I_X and I_R enter the CA at the points indicated in the figure with in_1 and in_2. Thanks to the M_1-M_5 and M_2-M_6 feedback loops, the d. c. input resistance is of the order of $1/g_m^2 r_d$. Clearly, due to the finite bandwidth of the loop gain, the input impedance at the operating frequency ($f_{ck}=1/T_{ck}$) is higher than the d.c. value. However, as confirmed by simulations, the resistance is low enough to make the input voltage variations negligible with respect to the V_S swing. This condition is important to keep the input currents independent of the device parameters and temperature. The currents in M_1 and M_2 are mirrored to M_4 and M_3, respectively. Therefore:

$$\begin{aligned} I_{D3} &= I_r + I_{D16} + p \cdot I_{D15} \\ I_{D4} &= I_x + I_{D14} + \bar{p} \cdot I_{D15} \end{aligned} \qquad (7)$$

The integrating capacitor, C in Fig. 1(a), is replaced by two grounded capacitors of value $2C$. The equivalence is guaranteed by the stabilization of the common mode voltage

of nodes V_{C1} and V_{C2}, operated by a conventional feedback loop acting on M_{17} and M_{18}. Since M_{17} and M_{18} are nominally identical:

$$I_{C1} - I_{C2} = 2 I_{C1} = I_{D8} - I_{D7} \Rightarrow I_{C1} = \frac{I_{D8} - I_{D7}}{2}$$

Finally, considering that $I_{D8} - I_{D7}$ is equal to $\pm(I_{D4} - I_{D3})$, depending on the configuration of switch SA1, i.e. on the clock value, we can substitute Eqns. (7) into (8), obtaining:

$$I_{C1} = I_C = m_1 \cdot \left(\frac{I_x - I_R}{2} + \Delta I_B + m_2 \cdot I_D \right) \qquad (9)$$

where m_1 is -1 or 1 when ck is a logical "0" or "1", respectively, while m_2 is -1 or 1 when p is "0" or "1", respectively. Furthermore, the following substitutions have been operated: $2\Delta I_B = I_{D14} - I_{D16}$, and $2I_D = I_{D15}$. It is easy to show that (9) represents also the behaviour of the block diagram in Fig. 1(a), proving that the circuit in Fig.3 actually implements the required function.

It is worth noting that ΔI_B is obtained by making M_{14} and M_{16} (i.e. I_{D14} and I_{D16}) different by design. Similarly to this intentional current mismatch, casual offset currents in the CA are modulated by SA1 and produce no effects on the charge balance over a clock period, i.e. on the pulse width. Modulator SA1b has been added to extend this beneficial effect to possible mismatch of the M_{17} - M_{18} pair. Noise current components at frequency much lower than f_{ck} are also strongly rejected by this mechanism.

IV. EXPERIMENTAL RESULTS

A prototype has been designed using the $0.32\,\mu m\,/\,3.3$ V CMOS device subset of the STMicroelectronics process BCD6s. Table I shows the main component values for blocks RG and CA. The circuit was designed to work with an external 30 kHz clock. Currents I_D and ΔI_B were set to 20 nA and 53 nA, respectively. Switch arrays SA1 and SA1b are implemented by means of n and p MOSFET, respectively.

TABLE I.   PROTOTYPE DESIGN DATA (MOSFET ASPECT RATIOS: W/L)

Ramp Generator (SG)		Current Amplifier (CA)			
M_{1M}	14/50	M_{1-4}	4/12	M_{14}	54/50
M_{2M}	14/50	M_{5-8}	2/2.5	M_{15}	7.5/100
M_{3M}	2.5/8	M_9	43.2/10	M_{16}	46/50
M_{4M}	5/8	M_{10}	7.5/20	M_{17}, M_{18}	4/4
M_{5M}	4/2	M_{11}	36.8/10	C	0.5 pF
M_{6M}	50/50	M_{12}, M_{13}	4/1	C_M	3 pF

Polysilicon/n^+implant capacitors have been used for components C and C_M. To facilitate characterization of the device, a dummy sensor was included on the test chip. C_R was a constant capacitor of 500 fF, while C_X was the sum of a constant capacitance, identical to C_R, and a variable capacitor made up of four binary weighted capacitors that could be selectively connected in parallel. The total differential capacitance ΔC could be varied from 16 to 256 fF with step 16 fF through four configuration bits. Due to the required small capacitance values, non-standard capacitors were designed using overlaps of the three available metal layers. To maximize linearity, all capacitance values were obtained by parallel connection of a single elementary capacitor. Blocks CMP1 and CMP2 are conventional low hysteresis comparators. All the constant current sources indicated in the circuit have been derived from a single low power, low temperature drift current source (CS). An *ad hoc* three wire serial interface has been included in order to set various configuration bits used to vary the internal dummy sensor and trim selected currents. The main waveforms have been routed to diagnostic pads through low input capacitance buffers. A separate power supply line has been used for the buffers and the serial interface. An optical micrograph of the chip, with the main parts labeled, is shown in Fig. 4; the total dimensions of the circuit are 1025×515 μm^2.

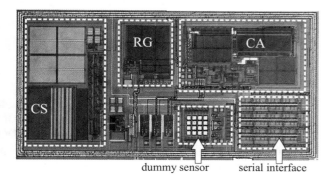

dummy sensor   serial interface

Figure 4. Layout of the prototype chip with the main blocks indicated. CS: current source; RG: ramp generator; CA: current amplifier.

For all measurements shown in this work, the 30 kHz clock was provided by a HP 33120A signal generator while the waveforms have been acquired with a Tektronix TDS220 digital oscilloscope. The chip temperature was varied by means of a Peltier cell cryostat with 0.1 °C precision. The power supply was set to 3 V. The main waveform in the circuit are shown in Fig. 5 for $\Delta C=160$ pF.

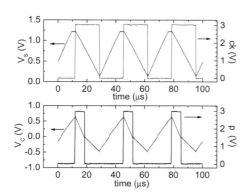

Figure 5. Experimental waveform measured on the test chip with $\Delta C=160$ fF.

Comparison with the ideal waveform in Fig. 1(c) proves the correct operation of the circuit.

The dependence of the pulse width on the differential capacitance ΔC is shown in Fig. 6 for two different

temperatures (0 °C and 80 °C). Curves at intermediate temperatures fall in between. It is possible to observe a satisfactorily linear response, with only local deviations that can be ascribed to parasitic capacitances of the dummy sensor.

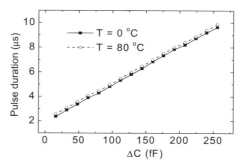

Figure 6. Measured dependence of the ouput pulse duration as a function of the sensor differential capacitance for two different temperatures.

The low sensitivity to temperature predicted by (6) is confirmed. The residual temperature drift over the whole temperature range is less than 2.5 % of full scale, corresponding to 300 ppm/°C. As far as noise is concerned, the visible effect is the jitter on the output pulse trailing edge. The resulting standard deviation of the pulse duration, estimated over a set of 50 randomly taken measurements, was $\sigma_\tau = 0.4$ % of full scale. The total supply current (diagnostic buffers excluded) is only 28 μA.

V. CONCLUSIONS

An original approach for converting small capacitance differences into pulse width has been described. Preliminary measurements demonstrate that the proposed circuit offers characteristics of good linearity and low temperature drift equivalent to those of the previous version [4], but with a power consumption two orders of magnitude lower.

ACKNOWLEDGMENT

The authors would like to thank the R & D group of the STMicroelectronics of Cornaredo (MI, Italy) for fabrication of the prototype chip described in this work.

REFERENCES

[1] M. Lemkin and B. E. Boser, "A Three-Axis Micromachined Accelerometer with a CMOS Position-Sense Interface and Digital Offset-Trim Electronics" IEEE J. of Solid State Circuits, vol. 34 1999, pp. 456-468.

[2] A. Gola, P. Bendiscioli, E. Chiesa, E. Lasalandra, A. Baschirotto, "A 80dB-SNR ±1g fully-integrated biaxial linear accelerometer in a standard 0.5μm CMOS technology for high-sensitivity applications", proc. of ESSCIRC 2002, Florence, Italy, Sept. 2002, pp.631-634

[3] A. D. DeHennis, K. D. Wise, "A Wireless Microsystem for the Remote Sensing of Pressure, Temperature, and Relative Humidity", IEEE J. Microelecromechanical Systems, vol. 14, 2005 pp. 12-22.

[4] P. Bruschi, N. Nizza and M. Piotto, "A Current-Mode, Dual Slope, Integrated Capacitance-to-Pulse Duration Converter", IEEE J. of Solid State Circuits, vol. 42, 2007, pp. 1884-1891.

[5] P. Bruschi, N. Nizza, M. Dei, G. Barillaro, "A low power capacitance to pulse width converter for integrated sensors" proc. of ECCTD 07, Seivilla, Spain, Aug. 2007, pp. 108-111.

A $14-bit$ Micro-Watt Power Scalable Automotive MEMS Pressure Sensor Interface

Akram O. Nafee
Electrical and Computer Engineering
University of Toronto
Toronto, Ontario, Canada
Email: nafee@eecg.toronto.edu

David A. Johns
Electrical and Computer Engineering
University of Toronto
Toronto, Ontario, Canada
Email: johns@eecg.toronto.edu

Abstract—**A technique to improve power scaling efficiency of MEMS interfaces over previous approaches is presented. Power scaling with respect to amplitude is achieved by cascading gain stages through an input gain-select mux, and power scaling with respect to input bandwidth of the sensor is achieved through periodic power-down of the interface. A prototype of the interface was fabricated in $1.8V$, $0.18\mu m$ CMOS process. Its power consumption scales between $4\mu W - 5.33mW$, while maintaining an SFDR of approx. $80dB$, a THD of $78dB$, and an input referred noise of $170.0nV/\sqrt{Hz}$.**

I. INTRODUCTION

The use of electronic systems in cars have increased rapidly over the last decade. Some of the most important developments in the field of automotive electronics have been in the field of automotive MEMS sensors. Currently, there are over 100 different kinds of MEMS sensors in automobiles, which serve a variety of different functions: safety, comfort, and drivetrain. Table I lists the different applications of automotive pressure sensors in cars, as well as their operating ranges. As cost pressure on all automotive components is high, low-cost, high-volume processes are pre-requisites for automotive electronics [1].

TABLE I
AUTOMOTIVE PRESSURE SENSOR'S OPERATING RANGES

Application	Full Scale Pressure (kPa)	Temperature Range (°C)
Gasoline vapor leakage	5.0	-30 to 120
Suspension	2,000	-30 to 120
Air-conditioning	3,500	-30 to 135
Gasoline/Diesel injection	20,000	-30 to 120
Common-rail	200,000	-30 to 120

For the different applications above, automotive MEMS pressure sensor output voltages can range from $40mV_{pp}$ to $400mV_{pp}$ differential. Moreover, the MEMS output bandwidth ranges from $0.5Hz$ to $0.5kHz$ [2]. The accuracy requirements for the pressure sensor is 14-bits in the voltage domain. To reduce cost of producing customized electronics for each sensor application, several reconfigurable sensor interface architectures have been proposed. An example of a typical interface system is shown in fig. 1, which uses a Programmable Gain Amplifier (PGA) at the front-end.

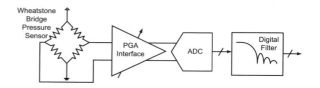

Fig. 1. The Sensor Interface System

The PGA amplifies the MEMS output signal to a reasonable voltage before it goes into the low power oversampling ADC. This maintains a constant input dynamic range to the ADC, thereby allowing a single ADC to be used for different applications with different sensor output voltages. Of the blocks shown in figure 1, the PGA is the most power consuming, thus the power efficiency overall system is limited by the PGA's power efficiency. In order to make the interface power efficient, its power has to scale inversely with the power of the sensor output, and directly with the sensor output bandwidth. This means that when the application changes so that the sensor output voltage goes from $40mV_{pp}$ to $400mV_{pp}$, the interface power reduces by $10^2 = 100$ times. Moreover, when the sensor output bandwidth changes from $0.5kHz$ to $0.5Hz$, the interface power reduces by $1,000$ times.

Previously proposed PGA architectures make use of scaling input and feedback impedances in an inverting amplifier configuration, while scaling the current and size of the amplifiers [3] [4]. Other architectures make use of a cascaded gain stage, where the gain is adjusted by selecting the desired output in the cascade, and the unused amplifiers are powered down [5]. These architectures are limited in their power scaling properties with respect to sensor output amplitude.

In this paper, a novel method of implementing power scaling with respect to amplitude in PGAs is proposed. The architecture is based on the cascaded gain topology, with the gain-select performed at the input rather than the output, in order to achieve an output voltage swing of at least $400mV_{pp}$. This allows 80% improvement in power scaling with respect to sensor output. Power scaling with respect to frequency can be achieved by periodically powering down the interface, in a similar manner as was done with power-scalable pipelined ADC's [6]. Measured results from a $1.8V$, $0.18\mu m$ CMOS

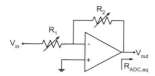

Fig. 2.   Single Stage PGA

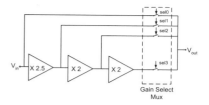

Fig. 3.   Cascaded Gain stage with output gain select mux

prototype show that the PGA interface has programmable gain ranging from $0dB$ to $20dB$ at $6dB$ intervals. It achieves an average SFDR $80dB$ and a THD of $78dB$ across all amplitudes and frequencies. The power consumption scales from $4\mu W$ to $5.2mW$, while maintaining 14 bit linearity.

II. PROGRAMMABLE GAIN AMPLIFIER ARCHITECTURES

A. Variable Input and Feedback

A typical PGA is shown in fig. 2. Most published topologies vary either the R_1 or R_2 to vary the gain [3] [4]. By varying only R_2, the input resistor R_1 is under-designed for the worst case thermal noise. By varying only R_1, the output resistance seen by the opamp remains constant. Since the opamp power is a strong function of the output resistance, the opamp is cannot be scaled in power. Alternatively, R_1 can be designed for thermal noise according to $4KTR$, to achieve 14 bit noise floor relative to the signal power. R_2 is then programmed to achieve the necessary gain to amplify the input signal to at least $400mV_{pp}$. In the subsequent analysis, "R" is defined as the resistor value required to achieve 14 bits thermal noise when the sensor output voltage is $40mV_{pp}$ signal, thus "$100R$", is the resistor value required to achieve a 14 bit thermal noise floor when the sensor output voltage is $400mV_{pp}$, i.e. $100\times$ the power. To model the noise of the ADC driven by the PGA, an equivalent resistance, $R_{ADC,eq}$, was added at the output of the PGA. Since the input of the ADC is a $400mVpp$ signal, $R_{ADC,eq} = 100R$.

The closed-loop gain accuracy of the opamp in fig.2 is given by $1/A\beta$. Since sensor applications require quantities to be measured to absolute accuracy, the closed-loop gain accuracy is critical. Thus, it is important that when the PGA gain scales, the gain accuracy remains constant. The inverse of the gain accuracy is equal to $A \times \beta = g_m R_o \times \frac{R_1}{R_1+R_2}$. In the two cases, a gain setting of 10 ($V_{in} = 40mV_{pp}$) and a gain setting of 2 ($V_{in} = 200mV_{pp}$), $A\beta_{10}$ and $A\beta_2$ are given by:

$$A\beta_{10} = g_{m10} \times 100R // (10R + R) \cdot \frac{1}{11} \approx 0.9g_{m10} \times R$$

$$A\beta_2 = g_{m2} \times 100R // (25R + 50R) \cdot \frac{1}{3} \approx 14g_{m2} \times R$$

$$(1)$$

Equating $A\beta_2 = A\beta_{10}$ yields $g_{m2} = g_{m10}/15.5$, which is less than the factor of signal power increase $(200mV_{pp}/40mV_{pp})^2 = 25$.

B. Cascaded Gain with Output Gain Select

Fig. 3 shows a block diagram of a cascaded gain amplifier with an output gain-select mux. The gain is set by selecting

which amplifier **output** is taken to be the PGA output [5]. Although this is the most commonly used cascaded gain amplifier, it has many disadvantages. Since the sensor output passes through the first amplifier for all gain settings (with the exception of "Gain 1" setting which bypasses all gain stages), the input resistance is sized for worst case thermal noise. Thus, the opamp is also sized for the worst case. To maintain the same gain accuracy for all amplifiers, the first stage opamp must be sized larger than the later stages. This means that this topology power inefficient, and thus has restricted flexibility for multiple sensor applications.

C. Proposed Design: Cascaded Gain with Input Gain Select

Instead of programming which amplifier **output** should be selected to achieve different gain, this work proposes programming which amplifier **input** should be selected. Figure 4 shows the cascaded gain PGA with input gain-select. The first amplifier is optimally designed for signals ranging from $40mV_{pp} - 100mV_{pp}$, the second stage $100mV_{pp} - 200mV_{pp}$, and the last stage $200mV_{pp} - 400mV_{pp}$. Any signal greater than $400mV_{pp}$ would bypass all the stages and feed directly into the ADC.

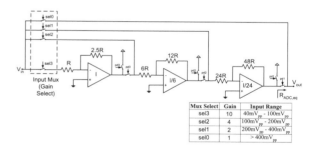

Mux Select	Gain	Input Range
sel3	10	$40mV_{pp} - 100mV_{pp}$
sel2	4	$100mV_{pp} - 200mV_{pp}$
sel1	2	$200mV_{pp} - 400mV_{pp}$
sel0	1	$> 400mV_{pp}$

Fig. 4.   Cascaded Gain stage with input gain select

Resistor values are calculated according to $4KTR$. Examining the amplifier gain accuracy of this topology yields:

$$A\beta_{10} = 0.6g_{m10} \times R$$
$$A\beta_4 = 3.5g_{m4} \times R$$
$$A\beta_2 = 14g_{m2} \times R$$
$$(2)$$

Equating $A\beta_{10} = A\beta_4 = A\beta_2$ yields $g_{m2} = g_{m4}/4$, which is exactly equal to the signal power scaling, $(200mV/100mV)^2 = 4$. Similarly, $g_{m4} = g_{m10}/5.8$, which is almost equal to the signal power scaling, $(100mV/40mV)^2 = 6.25$. With that, assuming that the first stage opamp is designed

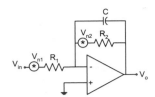

Fig. 5.   Noise model of active RC amplifier

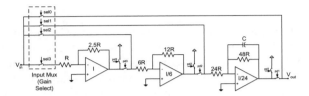

Fig. 6.   Cascaded Gain stage with final active RC stage

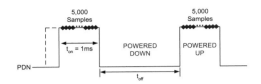

Fig. 7.   Power Down cycle of the interface

to consume current "I", then the second stage opamp can be designed to consume current "$I/6$" to maintain the same V_{eff} on the output transistors, and the third stage to consumes "$I/24$", as indicated in the figure.

Since the sensor in fig. 1 has a large output resistance (R_{sensor}), the effective gain of the first amplifier is $G = \frac{R_f}{R_{in}+R_{sensor}}$. One disadvantage of the above topology, is that, because the input resistor has to be sized according to thermal noise, its value may be too low compared to the sensor's output resistance, thus affecting the gain of the PGA.

Alternatively, the RC-stage shown in fig. 5 has a transfer function $H_1(s) = \frac{R_2/R_1}{1+R_2Cs}$.

The output noise power of the circuit in fig. 5 is:

$$V_{out,n}^2 = 4KTR_1 \times \left(\frac{R_2}{R_1}\right)^2 \times \frac{1}{4R_2C} + 4KTR_2 \times \frac{1}{4R_2C}$$

$$= \left(1 + \frac{R_2}{R_1}\right) \times \frac{KT}{C} \tag{3}$$

which is independent of absolute value of R_1, but on the ratio of R_2/R_1, and the value of C. Since this topology allows us to choose a high value for R_1, the gain of the amplifier in fig. 5 is not affected by the output impedance of the sensor.

Fig. 6 shows the final implementation of the cascaded gain amplifier with an RC final stage. Using the same noise analysis as equation 3, yields an output noise power $V_{out,n}^2 = 10KT/C$ for a "Gain = 10" setting, which represents the worst case. This configuration is also independent on the absolute value of "R", which can be arbitrarily chose to be large. The advantage of having the RC stage as the last stage is that the capacitor size can be made smaller, without affecting power scalability.

D. Power Scaling with respect to Frequency

The basic principle of power scaling with input frequency used in this work, is that the entire interface is powered down for a period of time [6]. This technique allows transistors to be designed for one operating point as opposed to current

scaling which could drive transistors in weak inversion. That effectively reduces the average power consumption by the same amount as the Power Down (PD) factor. Figure 7 illustrates the power down cycle of our design. If the interface was 'on' for t_{ON}, and 'off' for t_{OFF}, then the power down factor would be

$$PD = \frac{t_{OFF} + t_{ON}}{t_{ON}} \tag{4}$$

and the average power would be:

$$P_{avg} = P_{ON} \cdot \frac{t_{ON}}{t_{ON} + t_{OFF}} = \frac{P_{ON}}{PD} \tag{5}$$

The interface was designed so that when the output is $0.5kHz$, the system is never powered down, and in the $0.5Hz$ case, the interface has a PD factor of 1000. The ADC driven by the PGA can achieve power scaling with respect to frequency in a similar manner [6].

III. CIRCUIT IMPLEMENTATION

A. Operational Amplifier

Fig. 8 shows the circuit implementation of the fully differential two-stage chopped opamp. The architecture presented is based the Rapid Power-On Opamp shown in [6]. The switches allow the opamp to be powered on and off, and are programmed by a finite state machine. Chopping was also implemented to modulate the $1/F$ noise and offset out of band [7].

Large transistor lengths were used ($L = 0.5\mu m$) to reduce the $1/F$ noise effect by increasing the area. Moreover, PMOS input transistors are often used in sensor applications because they exhibit better $1/F$ noise performance. Although the analysis in the previous section was presented assuming a

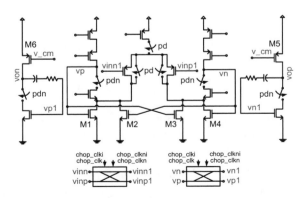

Fig. 8.   Two-stage Power Resettable chopped opamp

452

single stage opamp, the same analysis can be used for a two-stage opamp, as the total gain (A) is increased by the gain of the first stage.

B. Common Mode Feedback

Transistors $M1-M4$ in figure 8 form the inherent common-mode feedback for the first stage of the opamp. Due to stability considerations, a two-stage fully differential opamp is usually designed with two common-mode feedback stages, one for each stage. This is increases power consumption, which is undesirable in a low power system. The inherent common mode feedback structure eliminates the need for a specialized CMFB circuit. The N-cascoded current source is split into two equally sized sources, and the gates are cross coupled at the differential output of the first stage to form a negative feedback. Analysis for this CMFB configuration is shown in [8]. A continuous-time CMFB circuit was designed for the was designed for the class A output stage of the opamp.

IV. EXPERIMENTAL RESULTS

A prototype of the PGA architecture was fabricated in a $1.8V$ $0.18\mu m$ CMOS process with a PGA area of $0.617mm^2$ as shown in Fig. 9. The input of the PGA is applied from a low noise, low distortion signal generator. The PGA output is connected to an external commercial ADC. An output buffer was implement for testing purposes to drive the capacitance of the pads and PCB traces, in addition to the external ADC's input capacitance. The linearity of the output signal was measured using both a spectrum analyzer, as well as by analyzing the digital data coming out of the external ADC through a logic analyzer. The sampling frequency of the ADC was $5MHz$, and the chopping frequency was $625kHz$.

Fig. 10 shows the plot of THD Vs. input amplitude with different gain settings at an input frequency of $0.5kHz$. The same experiment was run with different frequencies of $50Hz$, $5Hz$, and $0.5Hz$. over the entire range of output amplitudes, THD varies between $70dB-90dB$, and the SFDR between $72-92dB$. The input referred noise of the PGA is $170.0nV/\sqrt{Hz}$. Fig. 11 shows how the average power of the PGA scales across different frequencies and amplitude ranges. As predicted, the power scales inversely with the input signal power, and directly with the input bandwidth, yielding an overall power consumption range of $4\mu W - 5.33mW$.

V. CONCLUSION

A technique to achieve efficient power scaling of MEMS interfaces is presented. The interface's power consumption

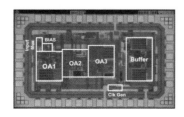

Fig. 9. Die Photo

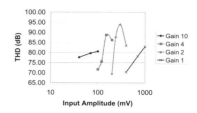

Fig. 10. THD Vs Input Amplitude with different Gain settings

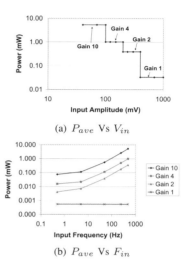

(a) P_{ave} Vs V_{in}

(b) P_{ave} Vs F_{in}

Fig. 11. PGA Power consumption Vs Input Amplitude and Frequency

scales from $4\mu W - 5.33mW$, while maintaining an SFDR of approx. $80dB$, a THD of $78dB$, and an input referred noise of $170.0nV/\sqrt{Hz}$.

ACKNOWLEDGMENT

The authors would like to thank The Bosch Research and Technology Center (RTC) for their collaboration and work in automotive MEMs pressure sensors.

REFERENCES

[1] I. Yokomori and Y. Suzuki, *Sensors for Automotive Technology*. Wiley-VCH, 2003, ch. 7, pp. 314–342.
[2] C. Lang and J. Vanderhaegen, "Kickoff meeting: Sacalable ADC," Bosch RTC, Meeting Presentation, 2006.
[3] S. C. D. Roy, "Digitally programmable gain amplifiers," vol. 33, no. 4, pp. 329–332, Dec. 1984.
[4] C.-C. Hsu and J.-T. Wu, "A highly linear 125-MHz CMOS switched-resistor programmable-gain amplifier," vol. 38, no. 10, pp. 1663–1670, Oct. 2003.
[5] S. Spiridon and F. Op't Eynde, "Low power CMOS fully differential variable-gain amplifier," in *Proc. International Semiconductor Conference CAS 2005*, vol. 2, 3–5 Oct. 2005, pp. 383–386.
[6] I. Ahmed and D. Johns, "A 50 MS/s (35 mW) to 1 kS/s (15 μ W) power scaleable 10b pipelined ADC with minimal bias current variation," in *Proc. Digest of Technical Papers Solid-State Circuits Conference ISSCC. 2005 IEEE International*, 6–10 Feb. 2005, pp. 280–598.
[7] A. Bakker and J. Huijsing, "A CMOS chopper opamp with integrated low-pass filter," in *Proc. 23rd European Solid-State Circuits Conference ESSCIRC '97*, 16–18 Sept. 1997, pp. 200–203.
[8] M. Dessouky and A. Kaiser, "Very low-voltage fully differential amplifier for switched-capacitor applications," in *Proc. ISCAS 2000 Geneva Circuits and Systems The 2000 IEEE International Symposium on*, vol. 5, 28–31 May 2000, pp. 441–444.

A High Gain-Bandwidth Product Transimpedance Amplifier for MEMS-Based Oscillators

F. Nabki and M. N. El-Gamal

McGill University, Montreal, Canada

Abstract- **A variable gain differential transimpedance amplifier (TIA) optimized for MEMS-based oscillator applications is presented. The TIA achieves a variable gain of 17 kΩ to 290 kΩ, i.e. a gain range of 25 dB. The 3-dB bandwidths corresponding to these gains are 256 MHz and 103 MHz, respectively. The suitability of the TIA for the targeted application is demonstrated by combining it with a MEMS resonator to create an oscillator at the frequency of 8.29 MHz, with a phase noise of -89 dBc/Hz at a 1 kHz offset frequency.**

I. INTRODUCTION

The wireless industry strives to constantly increase levels of integration, both from form factor and assembly cost perspectives. Most electronic systems require some type of timing circuitry, often considered to be a major bottleneck to high levels of integration. For example, the generation of high quality frequency references usually involves quartz crystals which cannot be fabricated on an integrated circuit (IC). At the same time, the quality (Q) factors of on-chip tanks built using passive inductors and capacitors in a modern CMOS technology are too low to generate a good frequency reference. Recent research has led to alternate technologies such as the above IC bulk acoustic wave (BAW) resonators [1]. Another promising technology suitable for integration is micro-electromechanical systems (MEMS). MEMS resonators have Q-factors which are close to those of crystals [2]. This work will focus on implementing an oscillator using clamped-clamped beam MEMS resonators.

As shown in Fig. 1, clamped-clamped resonators are vibrating beams fabricated on a silicon wafer, using the same manufacturing equipment used for traditional IC fabrication. Consequently, MEMS resonators are small enough to fit in the same packages as CMOS circuits, and can potentially be monolithically integrated [3]. Due to the electrostatic transducer gaps used to drive them into resonance, resonators possess very high motional resistances, typically in the order

of several tens of kilo-Ohms. To compensate for this loss, and to create a high performance MEMS-based oscillator, a transimpedance amplifier (TIA) having the following characteristics is needed: **i)** a very high gain (greater than 60 dBΩ), **ii)** a very high bandwidth to ensure a small phase shift around the feedback loop for optimal oscillation, **iii)** small input and output impedances to avoid loading the resonator's Q-factor, and **iv)** an automatic gain control (AGC) feature to prevent large oscillations from exerting the resonator's non-linearity. These are challenging specifications to fulfill simultaneously.

This paper presents a TIA that meets all of the requirements stated above. Its functionality and suitability for the targeted application is demonstrated by implementing a MEMS-based oscillator. First, the characteristics and equivalent model of the MEMS resonator will be presented, to outline the required TIA specifications. The TIA circuit will then be presented, followed by open-loop measurements. Finally, measurement results of an oscillator created by combining the TIA and a MEMS resonator in a closed-loop will be presented and discussed.

II. RESONATOR CHARACTERISTICS AND MODELING

A MEMS resonator can be modeled by a simple RLC circuit, as shown in Fig. 2. This model accurately describes the linear behavior of the resonator as a series-resonant system with a motional resistance, R_x, at resonance; however, since an oscillator is a large-signal system, a non-linear model will eventually be needed for high accuracy [4].

Devices used in this work are fabricated in a surface micromachining process as described in [3], and can have parameters that vary greatly depending on their geometries. For example, the motional resistance is proportional to the efficiency of the electrostatic transducer, which in turn depends on the electrode overlap area and the DC bias voltage, and is also heavily dependant on the size of the transducer gap. A bias voltage, V_{DC}, is usually applied across the electrodes, enabling electrostatic transduction of an input voltage, v_i, to excite the beam in its first flexural mode, and to generate a bandpass filtered output current, i_o.

To sustain oscillation in a positive feedback loop, a high

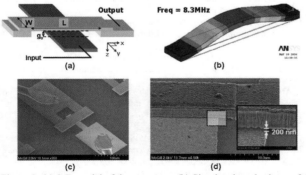

Figure 1: (a) 3-D model of the resonator. (b) Simulated mode shape of the resonator. (c) Micrograph of the resonator with wire bonds. (d) Close-up SEM picture of the resonator showing a 200 nm gap spacing.

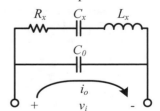

Figure 2: Typical linear model of MEMS resonators.

gain-bandwidth TIA is required to compensate for the high losses in the resonator device, and to allow for the low phase shift ($<10°$) required at the resonant frequency. The Q-factor of the resonator (Q_{ul}) can be easily loaded by the series resistances of the TIA, resulting in a loaded Q-factor:

$$Q_l = \frac{Q_{ul}}{1 + \left(\frac{R_i + R_o}{R_x}\right)}, \quad (1)$$

where R_i and R_o are the TIA's input and output impedances, respectively. These resistances must be much smaller than the motional resistance of the resonator, and also be small enough to allow for wide bandwidth operation, despite of the unavoidable interconnect parasitics. Input powers that are too large may force the resonator into non-linear excitation or, worse, cause a catastrophic failure. Therefore, the control of the oscillation power with an AGC is required to ensure optimal operation with the resonator.

In this work, the MEMS resonator used in conjunction with the TIA has a motional resistance of around 26 kΩ, a Q-factor of 1040, and a resonant frequency of 8.29 MHz.

III. CIRCUIT DESCRIPTION

The amplifier was designed and fabricated in a 0.18 μm CMOS process, and consumes 8.7 mW from a 2 V supply. The blocks making up the differential TIA are shown in Fig. 3. In closed-loop, the TIA amplifies the resonator output current, i_o, and supplies a voltage, $V_{OUT,RES}$, which is fed back into the resonator to sustain oscillation. An AGC regulates the oscillation amplitude to reduce the amount of non-linearity exerted in the resonator, thus mitigating noise folding [5]. The implementation and functionality of each block will be described in the following sections.

A. Input Stage

The input stage of the TIA is based on the g_m-boosted common-gate amplifier shown in Fig. 4 (a). Its purpose is to provide a fairly large initial gain, while having a small input resistance to minimize resonator Q-loading, and to maximize the high frequency input pole in the presence of sizable interconnect parasitics.

In this circuit, M_1 and R_1 form the main signal path, M_2 and R_2 provide negative feedback to boost the transconductance of M_1, and R_3 is a biasing resistor. This

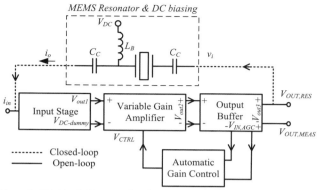

Figure 3: TIA block diagram, showing a resonator connected in closed-loop.

circuit is reproduced to form a matched dummy circuit to generate the DC voltage at the opposite input of the differential variable gain amplifier.

Assuming R_3 is large enough so that the signal current through it can be neglected, the low-frequency input impedance of this stage can be derived as:

$$R_{in} \approx \frac{1}{g_{m1}(1 + g_{m2}(R_2 \| r_{o2}))} \approx \frac{1}{g_{m1}A_{fb}}, \quad (2)$$

where A_{fb} is the gain of the feedback path created by M_2 and R_2. It can be seen that the gain of the feedback loop increases the transconductance of transistor M_1, and therefore lowers the input impedance of the amplifier beyond that of a traditional common-gate configuration biased at the same current. The simulated input resistance of this stage is 140 Ω, and its low-frequency transimpedance gain can be derived as:

$$\frac{v_{out1}}{i_{in}} = \frac{R_3 R_1 g_{m1}(A_{fb} + 1)}{1 + g_{m1}R_3(A_{fb} + 1)} \approx R_1, \quad (3)$$

where it has again been assumed that R_3 is large. This shows that the transimpedance of the input stage is simply equal to the load resistance R_1. To achieve a large gain, the size of R_1 must be maximized, but the voltage drop across it must be small enough to keep M_1 in saturation mode. This reveals the main advantage of the g_m-boosted topology, compared to a simple common-gate amplifier. A small bias current can flow through M_1 and R_1, allowing for a large transimpedance gain, while the feedback provided by M_2 and R_2 boosts the transconductance of M_1 such that the input impedance remains small.

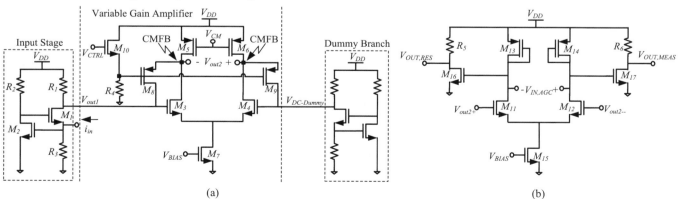

(a)   (b)

Figure 4: (a) g_m-boosted common-gate input stage with a variable gain amplifier stage, and (b) output buffer.

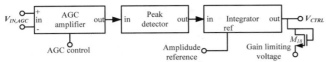

Figure 5: AGC block diagram.

B. Variable Gain Amplifier

The variable gain amplifier is shown in Fig. 4 (a), and is responsible for tuning the TIA's transimpedance gain. It is based on the differential pair amplifier M_3 to M_7, where the bias voltage V_{CM} is set by an on-chip common-mode feedback (CMFB) circuit (not shown) to stabilize the output at mid-rail. Transistors M_8 and M_9 act as variable resistors which alter the gain. Their resistances are set by the source follower composed of M_{10} and R_4, depending on the control voltage, V_{CTRL}.

C. Output Buffer

The output buffer is shown in Fig. 4 (b). The differential pair formed by M_{11} and M_{12} is loaded by the diode connected transistors M_{13} and M_{14}, which provide small impedances at their drains. This minimizes the bandwidth reduction resulting from driving the large transistors M_{16} and M_{17}. These transistors must be large in order to drive the interconnect parasitics: the amplifier formed by M_{16} and R_5 drives the interconnect, to the MEMS resonator, while the amplifier formed by M_{17} and R_6 drives the measurement equipment. Both of these common-source amplifiers have small output resistances (~60Ω) - for the first to avoid loading the resonator's Q-factor, and for the second to drive the 50 Ω input impedance of the measurement equipment. The outputs of the differential pair (M_{11} and M_{12}) are connected to the AGC circuit for oscillation amplitude control.

D. Automatic Gain Control Circuit

The block diagram of the AGC is shown in Fig. 5. The first stage senses the output of the TIA, and can have its own gain tuned to control the sensitivity of the AGC. The amplified signal is then fed into an opamp-based peak detector [6]. The peak of the signal is then compared to an amplitude reference, and the resulting difference is integrated to control the TIA's gain. The integrator's bandwidth is low enough to reject high-frequency ripples from the peak detector. To prevent oscillation through the resonator's feed-through capacitance, C_0 (see Fig. 2), the maximal gain set by the AGC during oscillation buildup is limited by M_{18}, depending on the value of a voltage at its source terminal. Simulations show that the AGC can limit oscillations at the resonator's input to amplitudes as small as -35 dBm.

IV. SIMULATION AND EXPERIMENTAL RESULTS

The TIA and MEMS resonator were tested in a 1 mTorr vacuum chamber to mitigate the reduction of the resonator's Q-factor by squeeze film damping [7].

A. Simulation

Figure 6 shows the simulated transimpedance gain and the bandwidth of the TIA, versus the amplitude control signal, V_{CTRL}. Shunt capacitances of 4 pF each were connected to the input and the output, to account for the interconnects attached

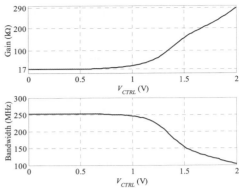

Figure 6: Simulated TIA gain and bandwidth for different values of V_{CTRL}.

to these ports. The bandwidth is 103 MHz for the highest gain setting, and extends to 256 MHz for the lowest gain setting. The gain is variable from 17 kΩ to 293 kΩ. This is sufficient to compensate for the losses in the MEMS resonator, and can allow for even more lossy, or higher frequency resonators to be used in the oscillator loop. The highest frequency resonator which could be accomodated by this TIA would have a resonant frequency of 25.6 MHz, with a maximum motional resistance of 17 kΩ. The highest loss resonator could have a 293 kΩ motional resistance, with a maximum resonant frequency of 10.3 MHz.

B. Open-Loop Measurements

The TIA was designed to handle very small input signal currents. The very low power levels (-70dBm) needed to measure the transfer function without gain saturation yielded inconsistent results. Furthermore, a vector network analyzer (VNA) is not well suited for this type of measurements, because S-parameters do not reflect an input current or the loading of an actual resonator.

To confirm that sufficient loop gain was present for oscillation, the resonator was connected to the input of the TIA, and the open-loop response was measured using an HP 8753D VNA. The VNA's input and output ports were connected to the resonator's input and the TIA's output, $V_{OUT,RES}$, respectively. These are both voltage ports and, consequently, the S_{21} transmission plot represents the loop gain, loaded by the VNA impedance. It can be observed from Fig. 7 that the loaded open-loop gain at the resonant frequency of the resonator is higher than 0 dB, thus ensuring that oscillation could be sustained in closed-loop. Interestingly, the resonator's Q-factor is measured from the open-loop gain bandwidth to be Q=1040.

C. Closed-Loop Measurements

The TIA was connected to the MEMS resonator as depicted in Fig. 3, and an Agilent E4440A performance spectrum analyzer (PSA) was connected to the TIA's $V_{OUT, MEAS}$ output to monitor the oscillator's spectrum, without loading the loop. Figure 8 (a) shows the resulting output spectrum. No spurs or excessive drift were observed, and the TIA was able to sustain a good oscillation.

The phase noise of the oscillator was also measured with the PSA for three different amplitudes of oscillation, as shown in Fig. 9. The phase noise plot for an optimal

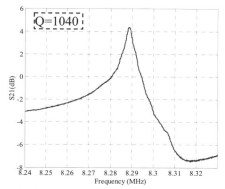

Figure 7: Open-loop transfer function of resonator with TIA.

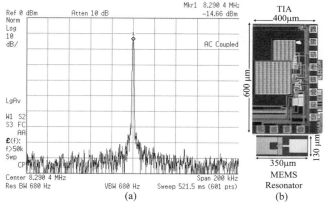

Figure 8: MEMS Oscillator (a) output spectrum, and (b) chips micrographs.

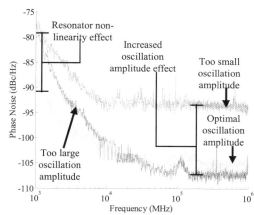

Figure 9: Phase noise of the MEMS oscillator at different oscillation powers.

Table 1: Comparison of noise performance with a similar MEMS oscillator.

MEMS Oscillator	This work	[8]
Resonator Q-factor	1040	3600
Frequency (MHz)	8.29	9.65
Phase noise @1 kHz (dBc/Hz)	-89	-80
Phase noise @ 1 MHz (dBc/Hz)	-106	-118

amplitude is -89 dBc/Hz and -106 dBc/Hz at 1 kHz and 1 MHz offset, respectively. When the amplitude of oscillation is too small, the overall phase noise performance is deteriorated due to the low carrier power relative to the noise floor. When the amplitude is too large, the exerted non-linearity of the resonator results in excessive noise-folding, and causes an increase of the close-in phase noise, offsetting the far-out phase noise improvement. This is consistent with simulations based on non-linear resonator models, as described in [4], where it is suggested that there exists an optimal amplitude of oscillation to minimize the close-in phase noise performance.

Table 1 compares the performance of the oscillator here with that in [8]. The close-in performance of the oscillator here is 9 dB better, while the far-out performance is worse by 12 dB. The better close-in performance is attributed to the optimal amplitude control. The lower far-out performance may be explained by the Q-factor of the resonator used here, which is 3.6 times smaller than that reported in [8]. The reduced Q-factor results in a theoretical phase noise reduction of around 11.1dB, which is close to what measurements indicate. It is therefore expected that, with a MEMS resonator having a similar Q-factor as in [8], the far-out phase noise performance of the TIA in a loop would be similar, with the added benefit of even further improved close-in phase noise.

CONCLUSION

A variable gain differential TIA optimized for MEMS-based oscillators was presented, with a power consumption of 8.7 mW and a chip area of 600x400 μm, as depicted next to a 370x130 μm MEMS resonator in Fig. 8 (b). The TIA was successfully demonstrated by interfacing it to a MEMS resonator to achieve an oscillator at the frequency of 8.29 MHz, with a phase noise of -89 dBc/Hz at a 1 kHz offset. An optimal amplitude of oscillation for close-in phase-noise performance was observed, and tests with higher-Q resonators are expected to yield improved far-out phase noise. The oscillator was recently integrated in [9] with a high resolution phase-locked loop to implement a compact, digitally programmable, and very stable signal source.

REFERENCES

[1] A. Dubois, et al., "Integration of high-Q BAW resonators and filters above IC," *Digest of Technical Papers of the IEEE International Solid-State Circuits Conference*, pp. 392-393, February 2005.

[2] J. Wang, J. E. Butler, T. Feygelson, and C. T. C. Nguyen, "1.51-GHz nanocrystalline diamond micromechanical disk resonator with material-mismatched isolating support," *IEEE International Conference on Micro Electro Mechanical Systems*, pp. 641-644, 2004.

[3] F. Nabki, T. Dusatko, M. N. El-Gamal, and S. Vengallatore, "Low temperature ceramic microelectromechanical structures," US Patent Application, December 2007.

[4] F. Nabki and M. N. El-Gamal, "Modeling and simulation of micro electromechanical (MEM) beam resonator-based oscillators," *Proceedings of the International Symposium on Circuits and Systems*, pp. 1324-1327, May 2008.

[5] C. Samori, A. L. Lacaita, F. Villa, and F. Zappa, "Spectrum folding and phase noise in LC tuned oscillators," *IEEE Transactions on Circuits and Systems,* vol. 45, no. 7, pp. 781-790, July 1998.

[6] D. A. Johns and K. Martin, "*Analog Integrated Circuit Design.*" New York, John Wiley & Sons, 1997.

[7] C. Zhang , G. Xu, and Q. Jiang, "Characterization of the squeeze film damping effect on the quality factor of a microbeam resonator," *Journal of Micromechanics and Microengineering,* vol. 14, pp. 1302-1306, July 2004.

[8] S. Lee, M. U. Demirci, and C. T.-C. Nguyen, "A 10-MHz micromechanical resonator Pierce reference oscillator for communications," *International Conference on Solid State Sensors, Actuators and Microsystems*, pp. 1094-1097, June 2001.

[9] F. Nabki, F. Ahmad, K. Allidina, and M. N. El-Gamal, "A compact and programmable high-frequency oscillator based on a MEMS resonator," *Proceedings of the IEEE Custom Integrated Circuits Conference*, September 2008.

A Synchronous Chopping Technique and Implementation for High-Frequency Precision Sensing

Mohamad Rahal and Andreas Demosthenous
Department of Electronic and Electrical Engineering
University College London
Torrington Place, London WC1E 7JE, UK
e-mail: {m.rahal; a.demosthenous}@ee.ucl.ac.uk

Abstract — A new architecture front-end for high-frequency electronic sensing is introduced. The architecture combines synchronous detection with chopping in a fully-differential topology. The proposed technique does not require the offset to be measured before a measurement is taken as in the prior art through the use of a microcontroller. An integrated circuit was designed in a 0.35-μm CMOS technology and tested with high-frequency inductive position sensors. The typical input-referred offset is 87 μV at a chopping frequency of 500 kHz.

I. INTRODUCTION

In industrial applications, there is a demand for measuring the linear or angular positions of objects. Ideally, this should be done without any mechanical contact. Various industrial sensors have been reported [1]-[4]. These sensors have to meet certain criteria such as reliability, small size, wide temperature range, insensitivity to moisture, dust and mechanical offsets, and long life. Contactless inductive sensors [3] are prime candidates to meet these demanding requirements.

One particular type of sensor is the high-frequency inductive position sensor [5], which utilizes the physical phenomenon of mutual inductance between an antenna and a target to determine the target position along a measurement axis. The sensor is shown in Fig. 1. An antenna containing transmitter and receiver coils on a printed circuit board (PCB) is supplied with an AC signal from an electronics module to drive a transmitter coil. Further analysis of the signals from the receiver coils by the electronics module determines the exact position of the target. However, due to the inherent errors and offsets of the existing readout system, a microcontroller is employed to measure this offset before every measurement is taken in order to increase resolution. This is particularly disadvantageous in fast sensing applications, such as when detecting from multiple targets, thus making the current approach impractical. In addition, the current synchronous detection architectures [6] are not optimal to reject the unwanted capacitive coupling between the transmitter and receiver coils, which occurs since both share the same PCB. All of these factors limit the speed and

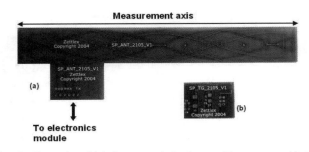

Fig. 1. Contactless high-frequency inductive position sensor. (a) The antenna/ receiver PCB; (b) the target. Twisted cables connect the transmitter (T_X) and the receiver coils (R_{XA} and R_{XB}) to the electronics module.

resolution of the sensor. The aim is to reduce the input-referred offset for these sensors below 100 μV.

Various techniques have been introduced to reduce the effects of errors and offsets in electronic sensing. One method is the use of synchronous detection [7], which involves the sampling of the input signal with a signal of the same frequency. This method is phase sensitive and gives a maximum output when the phase difference between the input and the modulating signal is zero and a minimum when the phase difference is 90 degrees. Other methods used to minimize the effect of amplifier offset include auto-zeroing and chopping [8]. Unlike the auto-zeroing method, which is based on sampling the offset, the chopping scheme modulates this offset into a higher frequency which can be removed by the use of a low-pass filter. In addition, it has an advantage over sampled based systems as it can be used in continuous-time applications. Recently, an offset stabilized operational amplifier design [9] was introduced that can achieve less than 1.5 μV input-referred offset at a chopping frequency of 16 kHz. In another study, an improved chopper stabilization technique [10] was theoretically introduced that suppressed the replicas of the $1/f$ noise at the chopping frequencies. An input-referred offset of 100 nV was achieved in [11] using nested chopper technique but the bandwidth was limited to a few tens of hertz.

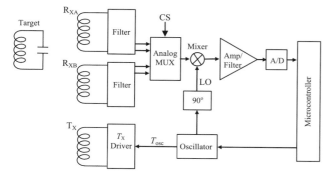

Fig. 2. Basic block diagram of the electronic acquisition system.

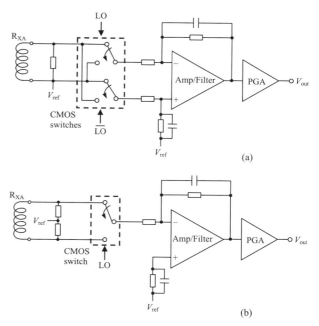

Fig. 3. Current system front-end with two different mixer configurations [6]. Only receiver channel A (R_{XA}) is shown here for simplicity. (a) One end of the receiving coil is fixed to a reference voltage. (b) Using a resistive divider with the mid-point fixed to a reference. A programmable gain amplifier is used to boost the signal.

In this paper a new method for measuring the displacement is introduced[1], which contrary to prior art [6] has significantly less offset and therefore, does not require a microcontroller to measure the offset before a position measurement is taken. In addition, the fully-differential architecture employed significantly reduces the effect of coupling between the transmitter and receiver coils. After this introductory part, Section II describes the basic theory of operation and the current front-end architectures employed with these sensors. In Section III, the new architecture is introduced and Section IV describes its circuit design and implementation. Section V presents measured results that show the performance of the new technique. Finally, conclusions are drawn in Section VI.

II. THEORY AND BASIC OPERATION

A. Theory of Sensor Operation

The target shown in Fig. 1 is a passive circuit formed by a simple winding or a set of tracks on a PCB. Each of the circuits is electrically insulated from each other and arranged along the measurement axis of the antenna. Usually, the vertical distance between target and antenna PCB is about 2 mm. In normal operation, at least two receiver coils are used to determine the target position. Due to the specific layout of the receiver coils on the PCB, the signals picked up by the coils are in-phase with each other in the time domain but in-quadrature as a function of distance along the PCB. Fig. 2 shows the basic outline of the measurement system for this type of sensor. The transmitter coil is driven by a buffer via an oscillator, which is capable of generating multiple frequencies. The received signals picked up by the coils are synchronously demodulated through a mixer by a signal whose frequency is equal to the resonant frequency of the target. A multiplexer is used to read from the two receiver coils. The oscillator provides the signal to the mixer (LO), which is in quadrature-phase with the signal provided to the buffer driver. The phase shifter provides the 90 degrees phase difference. The demodulated signals are amplified and filtered by an amplifier/filter sub-system to obtain the DC value. An analog-to-digital (A/D) converter is used to digitize this DC value for further processing by the microcontroller where the ratio of the two channels (DC output) is computed to obtain the position of the target.

B. Current Techniques

Two variants of a synchronous detection scheme are used in the current designs [6]. In the configuration shown in Fig. 3(a), one end of the receiver coil is fixed to a voltage reference (V_{ref}) and the signals are synchronously demodulated in a differential mode by switches using two signals, which are equal and opposite and having the same frequency at which the target resonates and being in-phase with the received signal. In a different configuration shown in Fig. 3(b), a resistive divider is used to fix the voltage at the middle point to a fixed reference. A local oscillator (LO) signal with the same frequency as the resonant frequency and in-phase with the received signal picked up by the coil is used to synchronously demodulate the signals at the ends of the resistive divider with a switch. Similarly, to the previous configuration [Fig. 3(a)] the output of the synchronous demodulator is connected to an amplifier/low-pass filter and a programmable amplification stage (PGA).

A significant problem of these circuits is that they suffer from inherent input offsets requiring the microcontroller to measure the offset before every measurement is taken. One type of offset is due to the inherent amplifier offset. This is a static offset which varies between chips. Another type of offset is due to capacitive transmitter signal breakthrough as the transmitter and receiver coils share the same PCB. Furthermore, the transmitter breakthrough consists of a series of odd frequencies of the fundamental frequency of the signal driving the transmitter coil. As a result, using synchronous detection as the case in the configuration shown in Fig. 3(a), would cause a DC offset at the output since the coupling would appear at the floating end of the resistor whereas the other end is connected to a fixed reference. Although the

---

[1] UK Patent Application No. 0724733.1; filed Dec. 2007.

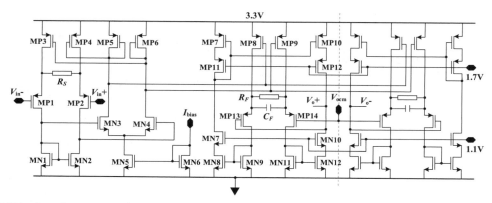

Fig. 5. Fully-differential IA schematic.

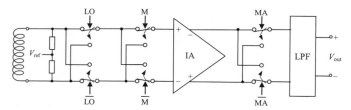

Fig. 4. Basic outline of the new architecture front-end.

configuration in Fig. 3(b) significantly suppresses this dynamic offset as the coupling appears as a common-mode signal at the two ends of the resistive divider [6], the microcontroller is still required to deal with the static offset due to the amplifier. This is a significant problem in high-speed applications where multiple targets are employed and measuring both the static and dynamic offset is not an option.

III. NEW CONFIGURATION

Fig. 4 shows the new configuration which replaces the mixer + amplifier/filter in Fig. 2. The recorded signal is converted into a differential one by the use of a resistive divider with the centre connected to a fixed reference [as in Fig. 3(b)]. A synchronous detection circuit (LO and $\overline{\text{LO}}$) is employed to select which target is selected by using a different synchronous demodulation frequency for each resonant target. In addition, two chopping mechanisms (M and $\overline{\text{M}}$) and (MA and $\overline{\text{MA}}$) are employed to remove the offset of the instrumentation amplifier. The average output is obtained through the use of a low-pass filter (LPF). If the phase difference between the received and the synchronous signal is zero, the outputs of the synchronous demodulator are in the form of fully-rectified signals. The difference between these two outputs is always fixed irrespective of the mismatch of the resistors of the divider. The outputs of the second chopping scheme are similar to the outputs of the synchronous detector but the effect of the imbalance has been removed by the differential nature of the synchronous detector and the amplifier. The LPF acts on the difference between the signals. As the offset is modulated into a much higher frequency, it can be easily removed by the LPF action.

IV. CIRCUIT IMPLEMENTATION

Fig. 5 shows the fully-differential instrumentation amplifier (IA) design used in the new architecture. The current

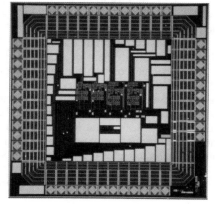

Fig. 6. Chip microphotograph including test structures.

feedback architecture has been developed based on the designs in [12], [13]. Any voltage difference at the input pair (MP1, MP2) will generate a voltage at the inputs of the operational transconductane amplifier (OTA), which consists of transistors MN3-MN5 and MP5-MP6. The outputs of this OTA are fed back to the input stage in such a way to make the drain currents of MP1 and MP2 equal. The currents flowing in MP5 and MP6 are mirrored to MP8, MP9, MP3 and MP4, respectively. If the differential current flowing in MP8 and MP9 is equal to zero (i.e., $V_{\text{in}}+ = V_{\text{in}}-$) and because of the cascode current mirrors MN7-MN12 and MP7-MP12, $V_{\text{o}}+$ is equal to V_{ocm} (output common-mode voltage). Since the ratios of MP3, MP4, MP8, and MP9 are the same, the currents in R_S and R_F are equal. Thus, the gain of the IA can be shown to be:

$$\frac{V_{\text{o}+} - V_{\text{o}-}}{V_{\text{in}+} - V_{\text{in}-}} \approx 2\frac{R_F}{R_S} . \tag{1}$$

The values of R_S and R_F were set to 766 Ω and 20 kΩ, respectively, giving a DC gain of 52 (34 dB). The simulated bandwidth of the IA with no load was about 20 MHz. In order to test the IA, on-chip source followers were inserted at its outputs to drive external loads (up to 10 pF). In this case the simulated gain dropped to 44 (33 dB) and the bandwidth to 3.7 MHz. The resistive divider was constructed using poly-2 resistors with value each of 500 Ω. The resistors were inter-digitized to improve their matching. The synchronous detector and chopping blocks were made up of transmission gates with on-resistance of 8 Ω. The synchronous and the chopping

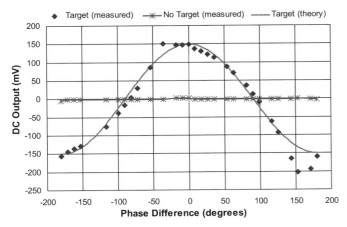

Fig. 7. DC output as a function of phase between excited signal of the transmitter and the synchronous signal when the transmitter is excited with 1 MHz signal. The chopping frequency was set to 500 kHz. Measurements were carried out with and without the resonant target at 1 MHz. In addition the theoretical cosine profile is plotted.

TABLE I
SUMMARY OF MEASURED PERFORMANCE

Parameter	Value
Process technology	0.35-μm
Power consumption	< 1 mW
Core area	240 μm × 150 μm
IA DC gain with buffers	32.3 dB
IA bandwidth @ 10 pF load	3.5 MHz
CMRR @ 1 MHz	58 dB
Input-referred offset + coupling	
@ 500 kHz chopping	87 μV
@ 1 MHz chopping	99 μV
Total integrated input noise (1.5 kHz BW)	1 μV rms

signals were applied externally. In this design we have implemented the LPF external to the chip in order to evaluate the performance of the new architecture. In a commercial implementation this block will be integrated on-chip.

V. MEASURED RESULTS

The integrated circuit was designed using a 5 V, 0.35-μm CMOS process technology. The chip microphotograph is shown in Fig. 6. Various samples were tested and the yield was 100%. Fig. 7 shows the effect of the phase difference between the transmitted and the synchronous signal. The transmitter and the synchronous detector were both excited with a 1 MHz signal and a 1 MHz resonant target was placed about 2 mm above the antenna PCB. The chopping frequency was set to 500 kHz. When the target was placed, the demodulated output changed with the phase difference as expected from the synchronous detection action following a cosine profile. When the target was removed and the transmitter and the synchronous signal were on, the demodulated output was constant against phase. In this case, the demodulated output was mainly due to the transmitter coupling, in addition to the amplifier offset. The typical measured input-referred offsets for 500 kHz chopping frequency were 69 μV and 87 μV when the transmitter was off and on, respectively. Increasing the chopping frequency to 1 MHz increases the offset due to the switches [11] and therefore, it was decided that 500 kHz is adequate for this application. Table I summarizes the measured performance.

VI. CONCLUSIONS

We have presented a new architecture front-end for high-frequency planar inductive position sensors. The new method offers considerable advantages compared to traditional techniques employed with these sensors. Measured results have been presented from a test chip to validate the performance of the new architecture. The proposed method in addition to improving system resolution, allows these high-frequency position sensors to work with multiple targets thus increasing speed and functionality.

ACKNOWLEDGMENT

The authors would like to thank the DTI (UK) for the financial support under grant TP/4/MHP/6/I/22071 and Zettlex Ltd. (UK) for providing the sensor sample.

REFERENCES

[1] X. Li and G.M. Meijer, "A novel smart resistive-capacitive position sensor," IEEE Trans. Instrum. Meas., vol. 44, no. 3, pp. 768-770, Jun. 1995.

[2] Y. Kano, S. Hasebe, C. Huang, and T. Yamada, "New type linear variable differential transformer position transducer," IEEE. Trans. Instru. Meas., vol. 38, no. 2, pp. 407-409, Apr. 1989.

[3] M. Jagiella and S. Fericean, "Miniaturized inductive sensors for industrial applications," Proc. IEEE Sensors, vol. II, pp. 771-778, Jun. 2002.

[4] A. Drumea, A. Vasile, M. Comes, and M. Blejan, "System on chip signal conditioner for LVDT sensors," Proc. 1st IEEE Electronics Systemintegration Technol. Conf. (ESTC 06), Dresden, Germany, vol. 1, pp. 629-634, Sep. 2006.

[5] R. P. Jones, R. A. Doyle, M. A. Howard, D. A. James, D. Kreit, and C. S. Sills, "Sensing Apparatus and Methods", US patent No. 7,208,945 B2, Apr. 24, 2007.

[6] M. Rahal and A. Demosthenous, "A readout system for inductive position sensors," Proc. IEEE European Conf. Circuit Theory and Design (ECCTD 07), pp. 958-961, 2007.

[7] R. Casanella, O. Casas, M. Ferrari, V. Ferrari, and R. Pallas-Areny, "Synchronous demodulator for autonomous sensors," IEEE Trans. Instrum. Meas., vol. 56, no. 4, pp. 1219-1223, Aug. 2007.

[8] C. Enz and G. Temes, " Circuit techniques for reducing the effects of op-amp imperfections: autozeroing, correlated double sampling, and chopper stabilization," Proc. IEEE, vol. 84, no. 11, pp. 1584-1614, Nov. 1996.

[9] J. Witte, K. Makinwa, and J. Huijsing, "A CMOS chopper offset-stabilized opamp," IEEE J. Solid-State Circuits, vol. 42, no. 7, pp. 1529-1535, Jul. 2007.

[10] A. Agnes, A. Cabrini, F. Maloberti, and G. Martini, "Cancellation of amplifier offset and 1/f noise: an improved chopper stabilized technique," IEEE Trans. Circuits and Systems-II: Express Briefs, vol. 54, no. 6, pp. 469-473, Jun. 2007.

[11] A. Bakker, K. Thiele, and J. Huijsing, "A CMOS nested-chopper instrumentation amplifier with 100nV offset," IEEE J. Solid-State Circuits, vol. 35, no. 12, pp. 1877-1883, Dec. 2000.

[12] R. Martins, S. Selberherr, and A. Vaz, "A CMOS IC for portable EEG acquisition systems," IEEE. Trans. Instru. Meas., vol. 47, no. 5, pp. 1191-1196, Oct. 1998.

[13] A. Brokaw and M. Timko, "An improved monolithic instrumentation amplifier," IEEE J. Solid-State Circuits, vol. 10, pp. 417-423, 1975.

A 211 GOPS/W Dual-Mode Real-time Object Recognition Processor with Network-on-Chip

Kwanho Kim, Joo-Young Kim, Seungjin Lee, Minsu Kim, and Hoi-Jun Yoo
Department of Electrical Engineering and Computer Science
Korea Advanced Institute of Science and Technology (KAIST)
Daejeon, Republic of Korea
kkh82@eeinfo.kaist.ac.kr

Abstract□ **This paper presents a 211 GOPS/W real-time object recognition processor with network-on-chip (NoC). The chip integrates 8 linearly connected SIMD clusters with 8 4-way VLIW processing elements (PEs) per cluster. The SIMD/MIMD dual-mode object recognition processor exploits both data-level and object-level parallelism based on the NoC configuration. The 8-way SIMD PE cluster is optimized for data-intensive object recognition tasks. Packet-based power management scheme is employed for low power consumption. The proposed processor takes 36mm² in 0.13□m CMOS process and achieves a peak performance of 96GOPS at 200MHz with 392mW power consumption.**

I. INTRODUCTION

Recently, intelligent vision processing such as object recognition and video analysis has been widely used in various applications such as mobile robot navigation, automotive vehicle control, video surveillance, and natural human-machine interfaces. Such vision applications require huge computational power and real-time response under the low power constraint, especially for mobile devices. Programmability is also needed to cope with a wide variety of applications and recognition targets.

Object recognition involves complex image processing tasks which can be classified into several stages of processing with different computational characteristics. In low-level processing (e.g. image filtering, feature extraction), simple arithmetic operations are performed on a 2-D image array of pixels. On the contrary, processing at higher levels is irregular and performed on objects that are groups of features extracted at the lower level. Because object recognition requires huge computation power on each stage, general-purpose processor cannot achieve a real-time performance due to its sequential processing. Many vision processors were previously reported based on massively parallel SIMD paradigm with a number of processing elements (PEs) for data-level parallelism [1-2]. However, these processors focus on only the low-level image processing operations like image filtering and thus they are not suitable for object-level parallelism, which occupies a relatively large portion on higher level vision applications such as object recognition. A multiple-instruction multiple-data (MIMD) multi-processor

was presented with Network-on-Chip (NoC) to exploit task-level parallelism [3]. However, it cannot reach a real-time performance due to its limited computing power and required complex data synchronization mechanism.

To overcome the computational complexity of the object recognition, visual attention based object recognition algorithm has been developed as shown in Fig. 1 [4]. Visual attention is the ability of the human visual system to rapidly select the most salient part of the image [5]. By the visual attention mechanism, the image region of interests is selected in a pre-attentive phase. Then, next visual processing such as key-point extraction, feature vector generation and matching focus on only the pre-selected image in a post-attentive phase. Therefore, computation cost reduction can be obtained by drastically reducing the amount of the image data to be processed on higher-level image processing tasks.

In this paper, a power efficient dual-mode real-time object recognition processor is presented for the attention-based object recognition applications. The proposed processor which integrates 8 linearly connected SIMD PE clusters can be configured into a SIMD or MIMD mode by adaptively selecting circuit or packet switching of the NoC in order to exploit both data-level and object-level parallelism. The 8-way SIMD PE cluster with 8 4-way very long instruction word (VLIW) PEs is specialized for object recognition tasks. A packet-based power management is employed for low power consumption. As a result, the object recognition processor achieves a peak performance of 96GOPS at 200MHz with 392mW power consumption while object recognition is running at 22 frames/sec.

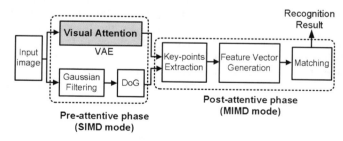

Figure 1.   Attention-based object recognition

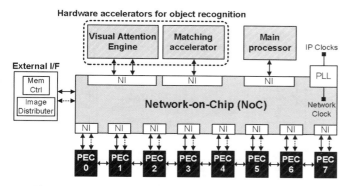

Figure 2. System architecture of the object recognition processor

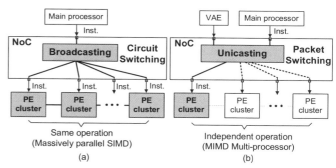

Figure 3. Dual-mode operations based on the NoC configuration

II. SYSTEM ARCHITECTURE

A. System Operation

Fig. 2 shows the overall architecture of the proposed NoC-based object recognition processor, which consists of a main processor, a visual attention engine (VAE), a matching accelerator (MA), 8 PE Clusters (PECs) and an external interface. The ARM10-compatible 32-bit main processor controls the overall system operations. The VAE, an 80x60 digital cellular neural network, rapidly detects the salient image regions on the sub-sampled image (80x60 pixels) by neural network algorithms like contour and saliency map extraction [4]. The 8 linearly connected PECs perform data-intensive image processing applications such as image gradients and histogram calculations for further analysis of the salient image parts (i.e., the objects) provided by the VAE. The MA boosts nearest neighbor search to obtain a final recognition result in real-time. The DMA-like external interface distributes automatically the corresponding image data to each PEC to reduce system overhead. Initially, 2-D image plane is equally divided into 8 PECs according to the image size specified by the main processor. Each core is connected to the NoC via a network interface (NI).

B. Dual-mode Configuration

The attention-based object recognition applications require a wide range of parallelism: data-level parallelism for the entire image as a pre-attentive phase and object-level parallelism for only salient image regions selected by the VAE as a post-attentive phase (See Fig. 1). To address the above requirements, the proposed object recognition processor has dual-mode configuration. According to the NoC configuration, the system has two different operation modes as shown in Fig. 3: SIMD and MIMD mode. In a circuit switching NoC, the main processor broadcasts instruction and data to all PE array. In this mode, the system exploits massively parallel SIMD operation for image pre-processing, achieving the peak performance of 96 GOPS at 200 MHz. On the contrary, in a packet switching NoC, each PEC is responsible for the objects, each of which contains image data around the extracted key-points. In the MIMD mode, the 8 PECs operate independently in parallel for object-parallel processing.

It takes about a few tens of cycles to change the NoC configuration depending on the network traffic status due to

circuit establishment and release time overhead for the circuit switching NoC. For object recognition application, however, the operation mode conversion occurs only twice during the recognition period of 1-frame image: SIMD to MIMD conversion after the pre-processing stage and MIMD to SIMD conversion after completing the recognition. Therefore, such a dual-mode architecture is suitable for object recognition with negligible impact on the overall system performance.

III. PE CLUSTER DESIGN

A. Overall Architecture

The PEC is a SIMD processor array designed to accelerate image processing tasks. Fig. 4 shows the block diagram of the PEC. It contains 8 linearly-connected PEs controlled by a cluster controller, a cluster processing unit (CLPU), 20 kB local shared memory (LSM), a LSM controller, and a PE load/store unit. The 8 PEs operate in a SIMD fashion and perform image processing operations in a column-parallel (or row-parallel) manner. The CLPU, which consists of an accumulator and an 8-input comparator, generates a single scalar result from the parallel output processed by the PE array. The LSM is used as on-chip frame memory or local memory for each PEC to store the input or processed image data and objects. A single-port 128-bit wide SRAM is used for the LSM to reduce area overhead. The LSM provides a single-cycle access and is shared between the PE load/store unit, the LSM controller and the CLPU. Arbitration for the LSM is performed on a cycle-by-cycle basis to improve the LSM utilization. The LSM controller is

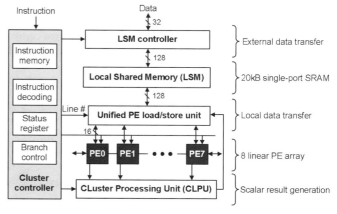

Figure 4. Block diagram of the PEC

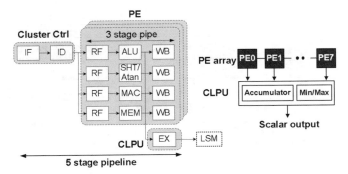

Figure 5.   Tightly coupled 5-stage pipeline of the PEC

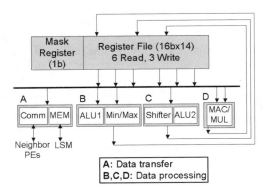

Figure 6.   Block diagram of 4-way VLIW PE

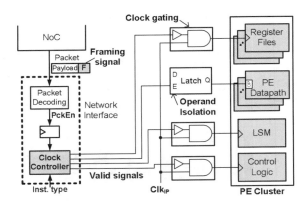

Figure 7.   Packet-based power management

responsible for data transfer between external memory or other PECs and the LSM while the PE load/store unit can access the LSM only for local data transfer. The LSM controller, which is an independent processing unit optimized for data transfer like the DMA engine, enables the data transfers in parallel with PE execution to hide excessive external memory latency. In addition, due to the simple control circuit in the SIMD architecture, the cluster controller including 2 KB instruction memory occupies only 6% of the total PEC area, which results in high computation efficiency.

B.   Tightly coupled Pipeline Structure

Fig. 5 shows the 5-stage pipeline architecture of the PEC. The cluster controller, the 3-stage pipelined PE array, and the CLPU are tightly coupled to maintain 1-cycle throughput for all operations. Especially, the tightly coupled PE array and CLPU architecture achieves single-cycle execution for statistical image processing tasks (e.g. histogram calculations) where an input image is transformed into a scalar or vector data, while the massively parallel SIMD processors [1,2] require sequential operations on a line-by-line basis to obtain the same result due to the absence of the CLPU-like vector-to-scalar processing unit. Such an architecture is suitable for object recognition because histogram calculations is the essential operation for key-point descriptor generation in the object recognition task [6].

C.   4-WAY VLIW PE

Each PE utilizes 4-way VLIW architecture to execute up to 4 instructions in a single cycle as shown in Fig. 6: three instructions for data processing (B,C,D) and one instruction for data transfer (A). It consists of two 16-bit ALUs, a shifter,

a multiplier, a 16-bit 9-port register file and a 1-bit mask register for supporting a conditional execution in a SIMD PE array. All PE instructions have single-cycle execution except 16-bit multiply-accumulate (MAC) operation, which has a two-cycle latency. The 16-bit datapath units of the PE can be configured to execute two 8-bit operations in parallel for gray-scale image processing. The resulting peak performance is 89.6 GOPS (8-bit fixed point) for 64 PE array and 6.4 GOPS for 8 CLPUs at 200MHz. The left and right neighbor PE registers can be directly accessed in a single-cycle using the linearly connected PE array for efficient inter-PE communication, which is one of the most frequently used operations for neighborhood image processing tasks such as image filtering. Meanwhile, memory access patterns are well predictable for such low-level image processing tasks due to the characteristics of regular and pre-defined data accesses. The 4-way VLIW PEs allow PEC software to pre-fetch the needed data in advance without performance loss by executing data transfer and processing instructions concurrently.

IV.   PACKET-BASED POWER MANAGEMENT

The modular and point-to-point NoC approach makes it easy to manage the overall system by decoupling computation of IPs from inter-IP communication, which enables efficient power management techniques compared to the bus-based system. For low power consumption, our chip performs packet-based power management at the IP level as shown in Fig. 7. Each PE cluster is individually enabled or disabled according to the framing signal of the packet to cut the power of inactive IPs. The valid signals generated by the network interface wake up the appropriate blocks within the IP only when incoming packet arrives. 4 clock domains of the PE cluster are individually controlled based on the issued instruction type. During the image data transfer phase for which only the LSM controller needs to be activated, the clock signals of the PE register files are gated-off and operand isolation to the PE datapath prevents unnecessary signal transitions to reduce power consumption. Since the PE datapath and register files occupy about 62% of the total power consumption, the power reduction up to 27% is achieved when the object recognition application is running. The packet-based power management scheme can be generally extended to a NoC-based multi-core system for the IP-level power control.

V. IMPLEMENTATION RESULT

The proposed object recognition processor is fabricated in a 0.13 μm 1-poly 8-metal standard CMOS logic process, and its die area takes 6 x 6 mm² including 1.9M gate count and 228kB on-chip SRAM. The chip micrograph and evaluation board are shown in Fig. 8 and Table I summarizes the chip features. Operating frequency of the chip is 200MHz for the IPs and 400MHz for the NoC. The power consumption is about 392mW (excluding the VAE and MA) at 1.2V power supply while object recognition application is running at 22 frames/sec.

Fig. 9 shows the comparison with the previously reported vision processors in terms of power efficiency [1-3,7]. To normalize the value, GOPS/W and nJ/W are adopted as a performance index. As a result, the chip achieves up to 4.3 times higher GOPS/W in case of 8-bit fixed-point operation and energy per pixel reduction up to 70% is obtained for object recognition task. Fig. 10 shows the performance evaluation when the object recognition application is running on the chip. In this example, the VAE performs a saliency map extraction as attention cues and 50 objects are used as a database for matching. In the SIMD mode, the VAE and 8 PECs take 14.4 ms to complete saliency map extraction and difference-of-Gaussian filtering while exploiting data-level parallelism of the 64 PE array. In the MIMD mode, higher-level vision tasks such as feature vector generation and matching are performed on objects extracted at the lower level stage while exploiting object-level parallelism. As a result, the chip achieves 22 frames/sec recognition speed without degradation of recognition rate, which is sufficient for real-time operation.

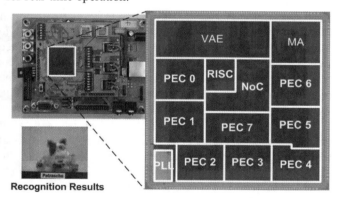

Figure 8. Chip micrograph and evaluation board

TABLE I. Chip features

Process	0.13um 1P 8M CMOS technology
Die Size	6mm x 6mm
Power Supply	1.2V for core, 2.5V for I/O
Operating Frequency	400MHz for NoC 200MHz for IPs
# of TRs (gates, memory)	1.9M gates, 228kB SRAM
Power Consumption	< 392mW (for full applications)
Peak Performance	96GOPS (for 8 PE clusters)
Object Recognition Rate	22 frame/sec @ 320x240 image

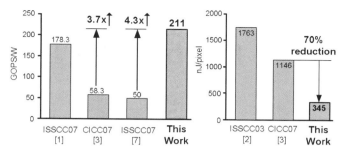

Figure 9. Power efficiency comparison

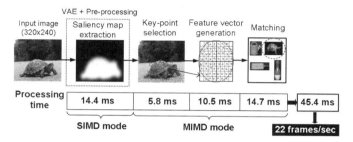

Figure 10. Performance evaluation

VI. CONCLUSION

A high performance and power efficient real-time object recognition processor is proposed for intelligent vision applications. The processor supports both the SIMD and MIMD computing modes based on the NoC configuration. The 8 linearly connected PE clusters optimized for object recognition tasks enable high performance image processing while achieving the low power consumption with the help of the packet-based power management. The chip achieves a peak performance of 96GOPS at 200MHz while dissipating 392mW from 1.2V power supply. The evaluation board with the fabricated chip demonstrates the real-time object recognition for intelligent mobile robot vision system.

REFERENCE

[1] A. Abbo, et al., "XETAL-II: A 107 GOPS, 600mW Massively-Parallel Processor for Video Scene Analysis," *ISSCC Dig. of Tech. Papers*, pp. 270-271, 2007.

[2] S. Kyo, et al., "A 51.2-GOPS Scalable Video Recognition Processor for Intelligent Cruise Control Based on a Linear Array of 128 Four-Way VLIW Processing Elements", *IEEE J. Solid-State Circuits*, vol. 38, no. 11, pp. 1992-2000, Nov. 2003.

[3] D. Kim, et al., "An 81.6 GOPS Object Recognition Processor Based on NoC and Visual Image Processing Memory," *Proc. of CICC*, pp. 443-446, 2007.

[4] K. Kim, et al., "A 125GOPS 583mW Network-on-Chip Based Parallel Processor with Bio-inspired Visual Attention Engine," *ISSCC Dig. of Tech. Papers*, pp. 523-524, 2008.

[5] L. Itti, et al., "A Model of Saliency-Based Visual Attention for Rapid Scene Analysis", *IEEE Trans. Pattern Analysis and Machine Intelligence*, vol. 20, no. 11, Nov. 1998.

[6] D. Lowe, "Distinctive image features from scale-invariant keypoints", *Int. J. Comput. Vis.*, vol. 60, no. 2, pp.91-110, Nov. 2004.

[7] B. Khailany, et al., "A Programmable 512 GOPS Stream Processor for Signal, Image, and Video Processing," *ISSCC Dig. of Tech. Papers*, pp. 272-273, 2007.

A Fully Programmable 40 GOPS SDR Single Chip Baseband for LTE/WiMAX Terminals

Torsten Limberg, Markus Winter, Marcel Bimberg, Reimund Klemm, Emil Matúš
Marcos B.S. Tavares, Gerhard Fettweis, Hendrik Ahlendorf, Pablo Robelly
Technische Universität Dresden
Vodafone Chair Mobile Communications Systems
01062 Dresden, Germany
Email: limberg@ifn.et.tu-dresden.de

Abstract— The increasing number of radio protocols along with the need for multimedia support in mobile communication devices call for heterogeneous, programmable multi-core processors. In this paper, we present a fully programmable, heterogeneous single chip SDR platform with multimedia support, fabricated in a 0.13 m CMOS process. Running at 175 MHz, a peak performance of 40 GOPS is delivered while dissipating 1.5 W. The typical MPSoC programmability problem is solved with a dedicated hardware unit which performs dynamic spatial and temporal mapping of tasks onto processing elements.

I. INTRODUCTION

Emerging next generation cellular standards like 3GPP LTE and WiMAX require a vast amount of modem signal processing. Both standards represent high data rate, low latency, packet optimized technologies, incorporating OFDMA/MIMO, adaptive modulation and coding techniques. In such systems, the dynamic variability of configurations due to user resource allocation in conjunction with high computational demand as well as low latency requirements call for programmable distributed baseband architectures. On the other hand, broadband media applications (e.g. H.264) will be running in handsets as well. Their data dependent control flow does not allow effective scheduling at compile time. Thus, a run-time solution of this problem is also required. Multi-core architectures, e.g. from Icera, Coresonic, PicoChip, Infineon's MuSIC [1] or Sandbridge's SB3011 platform [2], are acknowledged to be power efficient [3], [4] in such scenarios. However, the MPSoC programmability/scheduling problem is still one of the main obstacles to be overcome.

In this paper, we present the Tomahawk MPSoC which has a dedicated run-time scheduler hardware unit for solving the programmability/scheduling problem. We call this dedicated scheduling unit CoreManager and its purpose is to reduce the context switching overhead in the control code processor, which traditionally places major efficiency penalties on MPSoCs [5]. The Tomahawk is a low-power, C-programmable software defined radio platform with multimedia support, based on embedded software written as modular tasks according to the synchronous data flow model [6].

II. MPSoC ARCHITECTURE

The Tomahawk MPSoC exploits instruction, data and task level parallelism in order to meet stringent performance requirements with low energy consumption. Figure 1 shows a schematic of the Tomahawk. Below, we briefly discuss the components building this architecture.

The platform for the operating system and control code execution consists of two Tensilica DC212GP RISC processors. The signal processing block of the Tomahawk is composed by six fixed-point vector DSPs (VDSP), two scalar floating-point DSPs (SDSP), an LDPC decoder ASIP, a deblocking filter ASIP and an entropy decoder ASIC. Additionally, the CoreManager performs the scheduling of data transfers and signal processing tasks issued from the control code onto the VDSPs and SDSPs.

In the Tomahawk, local and global memories can be found. The local memories are part of the signal processing elements, which do not have direct access to the global memories. On the other hand, the global memories are accessible from all NoC master components (see Fig. 1) and consist of external DDR-SDRAMs and I^2C as well as an internal 256 KByte SRAM, which is used as scratchpad memory. Moreover, three independently (and parallel) accessible DDR RAM controllers provide large memory bandwidth in order to supply the processing elements (PE) and the control processors (CP) with data.

The peripheral part of the Tomahawk consist of the following components: an FPGA bridge that enables additional functionalities by the mapping of off-chip components into the address space of the Tomahawk, a single lane PCI Express interface that realizes communication links of 2GBit/s to a host computer, a VGA/Streaming interface that allows interfacing AD or DA converters, a freely programmable DMA controller, a general purpose I/O and an UART interface.

All components in the chip are connected by two low latency, high bandwidth, crossbar-like networks-on-chip (NoC) [7]. The FPGA bridge supports the same protocol and bandwidth of the NoC, and it can be seen by the NoC as a master or a slave depending on the function of component attached to it.

In order to achieve low power consumption, the data locality principle is used at multiple levels. For instance, within the STA (synchronous transfer architecture) processors [8] explicit register file bypassing is used. In contrast to the traditional approach, the STA functional units hold and exchange data

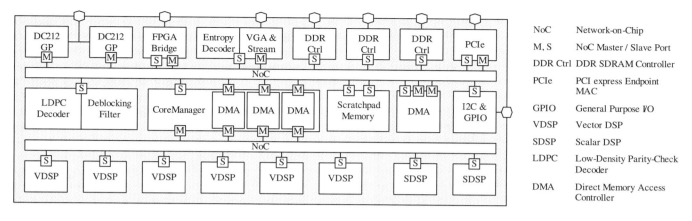

Fig. 1.   Tomahawk Schematic

NoC	Network-on-Chip
M, S	NoC Master / Slave Port
DDR Ctrl	DDR SDRAM Controller
PCIe	PCI express Endpoint MAC
GPIO	General Purpose I/O
VDSP	Vector DSP
SDSP	Scalar DSP
LDPC	Low-Density Parity-Check Decoder
DMA	Direct Memory Access Controller

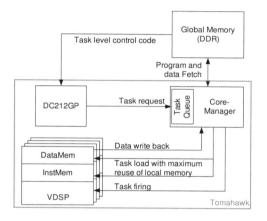

Fig. 2.   Task level data locality principle

maximize the local reuse of program memories, thus reducing the need for reloading (Fig. 2). This allows to reduce the required local and global memories and also the NoC bandwidth. Besides linear memory regions, the CoreManager and DMA controllers support two-dimensional memories. This allows for more effective implementation of multimedia and MIMO algorithms. Figure 3 shows how 2-D dependency checking on the memories is performed.

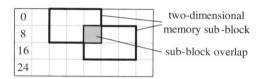

Fig. 3.   Dependency checking between two 2-D sub-blocks of a 2-D memory which is stored line after line in memory (numbers are line start addresses)

directly with each other. This significantly reduces the I/O bandwidth, size and power consumption of the register file. The VDSPs, SDSPs, LDPC decoder and the deblocking filter are all based on the STA principle.

III. PROGRAMMING MODEL

The C-based programming model of the Tomahawk, which is similar to the CellSS [9] programming model for the Cell processor [10], hides scheduling details from the programmer completely. However, in contrast to the CellSS software based scheduling, the CoreManager [11] computes the schedule of tasks issued from the control code with a dedicated hardware, and thus, it achieves a significantly better performance and energy efficiency. The programmer is merely required to identify all C-functions which shall be executed as tasks on one of the processing elements controlled by the CoreManager. The calls to these tasks are converted to so-called *task descriptions* [11] at compile time. At run-time, these task descriptions are sent to the CoreManager instead of calling the tasks explicitly. The spatial and temporal mapping of the tasks onto the PEs is then done automatically under consideration of data dependencies. Simultaneously, the control processor can continue execution and send further task descriptions to the CoreManager as long as a queue length of 16 tasks is not exceeded.

Concerning the data transfers, the CoreManager tries to

IV. IMPLEMENTATION AND RESULTS

The Tomahawk chip was designed using a UMC 130 nm, 8 metal layer CMOS standard cell design flow. The 57M transistor chip occupies 10×10 mm^2 (including all 480 I/O cells) and runs at 175 MHz. The typical case core supply voltage is 1.2 V, the I/O voltage is 3.3 V and 2.5 V for the high speed SSTL2 I/Os.

Figure 4 shows the setup of the measurement station. All presented results have been measured at this place. For the core power measurements, the PCB provides an independent power supply for the Tomahawk core. The core supply voltage can be adjusted from 0.9 to 1.35 V and has been set to 1.3 V for all measurements. Since the Tomahawk has only one single power domain for all components, obtaining exact power numbers for single components is impossible. Therefore, we approximately determined power numbers by ensuring that only the component under observation is running during the measurement. Static power for single components was neglected, what is acceptable for 0.13 μm. We could observe that all measurements results have been in the same range as power simulations on back annotated place and route netlists. Table I summarizes the power and area results of the core components.

467

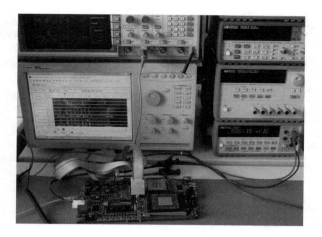

Fig. 4. Tomahawk Reference Board at Measuring Station

TABLE I
PROGRAMMABLE FUNCTIONAL UNITS AND COREMANAGER OVERVIEW

Unit	Power/mW	Area/mm^2	Memory portion (area)
SDSP	27	3.33	91.1 %
VDSP	85	3.80	79.5 %
CoreManager	282	5.95	24.3 %
DC212GP	30	2.50	15.8 %
LDPC	354	7.89	64.0 %
Deblocker	86	4.54	86.0 %

A. Scalar and Vector Processors

The VDSPs are 16 bit fixed-point, 4 way SIMD VLIW processors, issuing up to 5 instructions per cycle. To support H.264 video decoding, the VDSPs can be switched from fractional to integer arithmetic. The achieved performance of all VDSPs is 120 MOPS/MHz resulting in 21 GOPS at 175 MHz clock. The average power consumption is 85 mW for an FFT computation. Each VDSP occupies 3.8 mm^2 and has 32 KByte instruction and 16 KByte data memory. The use of dual port memories enables concurrent computation and data pre-fetching for pending tasks.

The SDSP has 3.33 mm^2 including 32 KByte instruction and 32 KByte data memory. Each SDSP has a dual cycle single precision floating point unit required for algorithms with large dynamic range like matrix inversion for MIMO processing. Additionally, all instructions can be executed conditionally, thus, enabling low overhead control structures for scalar operations like bit-stream processing. Each SDSP allows to issue up to 3 instructions per cycle, thus, a compute power of 0.7 GOPS is achieved for both SDSPs at 175 MHz clock frequency. For floating point FIR filter computations,each SDSP consumes 27 mW.

B. CoreManager

The CoreManager occupies 5.95 mm^2 (including 1.7 mm^2 for the 3 DMA controllers and 1 mm^2 for a debugging unit) and consumes 282 mW when fully loaded. The average time to schedule one task is about 60 clock cycles. At a clock rate of 175 MHz, this results in about 100 nJ energy dissipation per scheduled task. Compared to about 500 nJ/task that would be required if the scheduling algorithm would run 3000 cycles on a standard RISC processor like the Tensilica DC212GP core, this is an significant improvement. In order to save power, the CoreManager explicitly switches off the clock for PEs which are not in use. This is done in addition to the clock gates which are available for all registers in the PEs. The CoreManager itself is not clock gated. This leaves room for significant power reduction in future designs.

The presented CoreManager power numbers are simulated on back annotated place and route netlist. Measuring the real power consumption is practically impossible, because the CoreManager is not able to run without running at least one DC212GP and the DSPs. Furthermore, both NoCs are under load.

C. LDPC Decoder

The LDPC decoder ASIP [12] is dedicated to the decoding of low-density parity-check convolutional codes (LDPCCC) achieving 12 GOPS at 175 MHz. The decoder is able to decode variable block lengths at throughputs of several hundred MBit/s. It is a 64 way parallel, fixed-point SIMD-VLIW architecture with an area of 7.89 mm^2 and an average power consumption of 354 mW. 611 pJ are consumed per decoded bit when running 10 decoding iterations of a (128,5,13)-LDPCCC [12].

D. Deblocking Filter

One ASIP with 4.54 mm^2 has been added for acceleration of deblocking filtering. It comprises a 44 KByte instruction memory and 16 KByte dual-port data memory. The average power consumption of the deblocking filter for decoding a 1080i H.264 encoded baseline video is 86 mW.

E. Network on Chip

Both Networks-on-Chip are master-slave point-to-point networks with 32 bit bus-width. Burst transfers of up to 63 data words and static priority arbitration per slave are supported. For latency improvement, the NoCs operate on negative clock transition while all other modules operate on positive clock edge. Nevertheless, the NoCs work at the full system clock frequency. A sustained throughput of 5.47 GBit/s is achieved for each master-slave connection. The crossbar-like architecture allows each master to communicate with one slave in parallel. The chip area are consumed by the NoCs is 0.4 mm^2.

F. Overall MPSoC

Considering that both DC212GP, all vector and scalar DSPs, the CoreManager and LDPC decoder are fully loaded and simultaneously running, the overall dynamic power consumption of these components is 1260 mW. However, full utilization is not very likely to appear. If we consider a more realistic utilization of 80% for each component, a dynamic power of about 950 mW would be observed. If we now add the static power consumption of 130 mW and the clock tree power

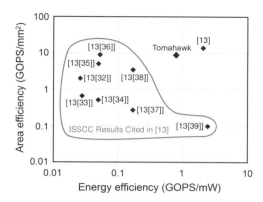

Fig. 5. Tomahawk added to graph from [13]: Area efficiency versus energy efficiency normalized to a 1V 90nm process and 12 bit adder equivalents

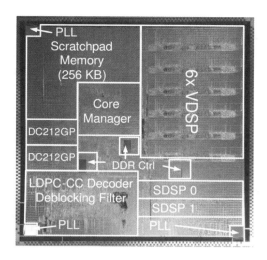

Fig. 6. Chip Micrograph

consumption of 445 mW (for all inactive components) we end up with 1525 mW core power consumption for a realistic application scenario. However, this has to be proved by a real application which was not yet tested on the Tomahawk. The huge clock tree power of 445 mW is due to missing clock gating at all peripheral components.

In order to compare the performance values of the complete Tomahawk MPSoC with [13], we scaled the dynamic power consumption of the fully loaded chip by $0.69 \cdot 0.5$, where the first scaling factor comes from the voltage difference of 1.3 V and 1.0 V (i.e. $(1.0V)^2/(1.3V)^2 = 0.69$) and the second factor is due to the process gain when going from 130 nm to 90 nm (frequency remains the same) [14]. From Fig. 5 it can be observed, that the Tomahawk outperforms existing designs by an order of magnitude, nearly achieving the ASIC results of [13].

V. CONCLUSION

We presented Tomahawk, a low power, heterogeneous MP-SoC for signal processing applications. A major component of the Tomahawk is a dedicated scheduling unit called Core-Manager. This unit is able to automatically schedule signal processing tasks onto the cores, taking data and control dependencies into account. Therefore, the Tomahawk represents a new architectural approach for MPSoCs in which the software developer is released from the complicated task scheduling and synchronization burdens. Furthermore, the Tomahawk chip offers compute power for LTE/WiMAX baseband processing while approaching the power efficiency of ASIC solutions.

Our further research efforts comprehend the enhancement of the CoreManager towards real-time task scheduling as well as dynamic power scaling of the computing cores.

ACKNOWLEDGMENTS

We would like to acknowledge Prof. René Schüffny and his team consisting of Holger Eisenreich, Georg Ellguth and Jens-Uwe Schlüssler from the Parallel VLSI-Systems and Neural Circuits Chair at our University for doing a great job at the backend. Furthermore, we would like to thank Frank Siebler, Markus Ullmann, Johannes Lange, Arne Lehmann, Boris Boesler and Patrick Herhold as well as the ZMD AG Dresden and the Institute of Semiconductors and Microsystems of our University. Finally we would like to thank Synopsys, Tensilica and Altera for sponsoring Software, IP and Hardware. The major part of this work has been done within the scope of the WIGWAM project, funded by the German Federal Ministry of Education and Research. A minor part was funded by the European Union within the scope of the E2R project.

REFERENCES

[1] U. Ramacher, "Software-defined radio prospects for multistandard mobile phones," *Computer*, vol. 40, no. 10, pp. 62–69, 2007.
[2] J. Glossner, D. Iancu, M. Moudgill, G. Nacer, S. Jinturkar, S. Stanley, and M. Schulte, "The sandbridge sb3011 platform," *EURASIP J. Embedded Syst.*, vol. 2007, no. 1, pp. 16–16, 2007.
[3] M. Horowitz and W. Dally, "How scaling will change processor architecture," in *Proceedings of the IEEE Solid-State Circuits Conference, 2004, Digest of Technical Papers ISSCC*, February 2004, pp. 132 – 133.
[4] K. Asanovic, R. Bodik, B.C. Catanzaro, J. J. Gebis, P. Husbands, K. Keutzer, D.A. Patterson, W.L. Plishker, J. Shalf, S. W. Williams, and K. A. Yelick, "The landscape of parallel computing research: A view from berkeley," Tech. Rep. UCB/EECS-2006-183, EECS Department, University of California, Berkeley, Dec 2006.
[5] Olli Silven and Kari Jyrkkä, "Observations on power-efficiency trends in mobile communication devices," *EURASIP J. Embedded Syst.*, vol. 2007, no. 1, pp. 17–17, 2007.
[6] E. A. Lee and D. G. Messerschmitt, "Synchronous data flow," *Proceedings of the IEEE*, vol. 75, no. 9, pp. 1235–1245, 1987.
[7] M. Winter and G. Fettweis, "Interconnection generation for system-on-chip design," in *Proceedings of International Symposium on System-on-Chip 2006*, Tampere, Finland, November 2006, pp. 91–94.
[8] G. Cichon, P. Robelly, H. Seidel, E. Matus, M. Bronzel, and G. Fettweis, "Synchronous transfer architecture (sta)," in *Proceedings of the 4th International Workshop on Systems, Architectures, Modeling, and Simulation (SAMOS'04)*, Samos, Greece, July 2004, pp. 126–130.
[9] P. Bellens, J. M. Perez, R. M. Badia, and J. Labarta, "CellSS: a programming model for the cell be architecture," in *Proceedings of the ACM/IEEE Supercomputing 2006 Conference*, November 2006.
[10] D. Pham, S. Asano, M. Bolliger, M.N. Day, H.P. Hofstee, C. Johns, J. Kahle, A. Kameyama, J. Keaty, Y. Masubuchi, M. Riley, D. Shippy, D. Stasiak, M. Suzuoki, M. Wang, J. Warnock, S. Weitzel, D. Wendel, T. Yamazaki, and K. Yazawa, "The design and implementation of a first-generation cell processor," in *Solid-State Circuits Conference, 2005. Digest of Technical Papers. ISSCC. 2005 IEEE International*, February 2005, vol. 1, pp. 184–592.
[11] H. Seidel, *A Task-level Programmable Processor*, WiKu, Duisburg, October 2006.
[12] M. Bimberg, M.B.S. Tavares, E. Matus, and G. Fettweis, "A high-throughput programmable decoder for ldpc convolutional codes," in *Proceedings of the 18th IEEE International Conference on Application-specific Systems, Architectures and Processors (ASAP'07)*, Montreal, Canada, July 2007.
[13] D. Markovic, B. Nikolic, and R.W. Brodersen, "Power and area minimization for multidimensional signal processing," *IEEE J. Solid-State Circuits*, vol. 42, no. 4, pp. 922–934, April 2007.
[14] K. Flautner, "The wall ahead is made of rubber," in *4th HiPEAC Industrial Workshop on Compilers and Architectures*, Cambridge, UK, November 2007.

2.6 Gb/s Over a Four-Drop Bus Using an Adaptive 12-Tap DFE

Henrik Fredriksson and Christer Svensson
Electronic Devices, Dept. of EE, Linköping University
SE-581 83 Linköping, Tel. +46 13 28 {22 54, 12 23}, {henfr, christer}@isy.liu.se

Abstract—**For PC DRAM buses, the number of slots per channel has decreased as data rates have increased. This limits the maximum memory capacity per channel. Signal equalization can be used to increase bit-rates for channels with a large number of slots and offer a cost effective method to solve the memory capacity problem. This paper presents a blind adaptive decision feedback equalizer (DFE) that enables high data-rates with a large number of slots per channel. Measurements at 2.6 Gb/s over a four-drop bus are presented.**

I. INTRODUCTION

Multi-drop buses have traditionally been used for DRAM memory access in PCs. As the data-rates on these buses have increased, the maximum number of slots per channel have been reduced in order to keep signal integrity intact. Though the capacity per module has increased, the reduction of slots per channel limits the memory capacity per channel [1]. Techniques such as parallel channels and fully-buffered DIMM [2] are used to fulfill memory capacity demands but they are expensive in terms of package pins, PCB area and extra circuits.

The number of slots per channel have been reduced due to intersymbol interference (ISI) caused by signal reflections at impedance mismatches in multi-drop junctions and terminations. The use of high speed equalizer circuits to mitigate ISI in point-to-point channels are reported frequently. The circuit presented here uses a DFE to mitigate extensive ISI at a multi-drop memory bus, thereby enabling high data-rates *and* a large number of slots per channel.

II. EQUALIZER FOR MULTI-DROP BUSES

Circuits for high-speed equalization of point-to-point channels have been published frequently in recent years [3], [4], etc. High speed equalizer implementations for multi-drop buses have also been presented [5], [6]. These implementations have only used one or two tap equalizers. The severe ISI on bus structures with a large number of endpoints can benefit from significantly longer equalizer filters. With this paper we present an equalizer with 12 taps operating at similar data-rates as the one tap structures previously presented for multi-drop buses. The main effects that have forced the reduction of memory slots per bus are destructive interference caused by reflections and termination impedance mismatch. Both cause complex frequency response with severe attenuation at relatively low frequencies. To compensate for the channel, a high-speed equalizer requires high flexibility. The difference

in channel response to the individual memory endpoints together with requirements on low latency means that the filter coefficients in an equalizer has to be changed accurately and quickly.

III. IMPLEMENTED DFE STRUCTURE

A test-chip that fulfills the requirements from the previous section have been designed. The test-chip comprises a mixed signal DFE, memory emulating pattern generator circuitry and bit error-counting logic. The DFE is implemented using a digital feedback filter, DACs, and analog subtraction of the ISI through current summation (fig. 1). The digital feedback filter and DAC structure adds a fixed parasitic load to the analog summation nodes. The analog signal path is then independent of the filter length which enables the use of a long and flexible filter. The ability to add an offset to the DAC output eliminates the need for any analog offset compensation circuitry and enables efficient implementation of blind equalizer adaptation as described in section III-D.

A. Analog Input Stage

The analog part of the equalizer circuit is shown in fig. 2. The received analog input signal (v_{in}) is connected to a voltage to differential current converter (VC) block. The input stages of this block consist of two current mirrors with resistors at the input nodes. The resistors sets the common mode current out from the stage, linearizes the output current, and together with two additional resistors set the input impedance of the receiver. The differential output current signal of the VC block occur at the nodes $a+$ and $a-$. The output of a differential current steering DAC is also connected to these nodes to perform the DFE ISI subtraction. The loads of these nodes are the diode-connected P-MOS transistors of the differential comparator current mirror input.

The cross-coupled-inverter based comparator acts as a diode load during reset. The consistent diode load configuration gives low impedance nodes which ensure a high bandwidth even as the DAC structure adds substantial parasitic capacitance to the summation nodes ($a+,a-$). The signal path from the input signal to the comparator nodes show a simulated 3dB bandwidth exceeding 4.3 GHz in the 0.13 μm CMOS technology used.

B. Receiving Dual Data Rate Signaling

Two comparators are used to retrieve received data. The two comparators are clocked with opposite clock phase which

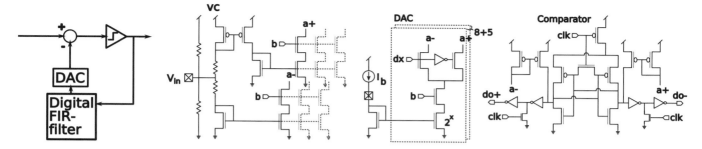

Fig. 1. Mixed signal DFE structure

Fig. 2. Analog receiver circuitry

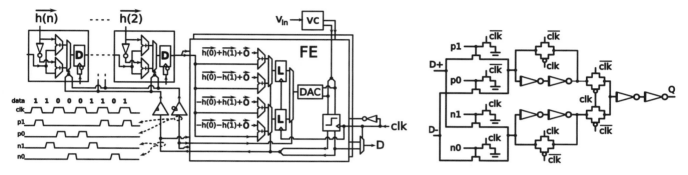

Fig. 3. DFE implementation

Fig. 4. MUX-DE-DFF

enables efficient DDR functionality. DFE subtraction and filtering of the two last filter taps are done individually for each comparator in front-end blocks (FE in fig. 3). Calculation of the last two filter taps are unfolded in each FE block. Hereby, a larger fraction of the clock phase can be reserved for DAC settling in the critical timing loop. Furthermore, a digitally controlled offset value ($\vec{o}$ in fig. 3) can be added individually for each comparator to individually compensate for offsets in input stage, DAC and comparator.

The active reset differential comparator is shown in fig. 2. The comparator output signals form a native self-timed output data representation as illustrated in the time diagram of fig. 3. The signals form the input signals to the digital FIR filter described in section III-C. Unfolding of each filter tap in this filter creates a structure where the comparator output signal drives a multiplexer followed by a DFF. The self timed data representation enables this multiplexer to be implemented as a part of the DFF input (fig. 4). This enables reduction of the filter data path delay and enables significant load reduction of the comparator output nodes.

C. Carry-Save Digital Filter

The computation pace of the implemented digital filter equals the receiving data-rate. The feedback loop of the DFE structure sets tight latency constraints for the filter. The self timed data representation in combination with unfolding enables close to the entire clock phase time for filter tap calculation. Still the desired data rates prevent the use of normal carry propagation or carry merge adder structures. The filter have therefore been implemented using carry-save data

representation which eliminates the need for carry merge or carry propagation. The redundant data representation of carry-save arithmetics increase the number of D-flip-flops in the filter and will also make the unfolding result select multiplexers (seen in fig. 3) wider which will increase the fan-out of the time critical comparator output signals. Only every second carry is saved to give a good trade-off between the gate depths in the adder and carry-save-DFF overhead and comparator output load. The structure of one filter tap is shown in fig. 5. The critical carry propagation path is here reduced to two full adders (FA) at the expense of four extra flip flops. The logic function of each two bit add and subtract block (the dotted squares in fig. 5) have been analyzed and the function have been implemented using nand-gates, xor-cells and multiplexers with a total logic depth of four cells.

Subtraction of two complement numbers rely on the discard of the MSB carry signal. Normal carry-save representation does therefore not form a binary weighted number and can therefore not be used in a DAC. Carry overflow correction [7] have been implemented in the MSB full adders which enables the sum and carry bits to be interpreted as a (redundant) binary weighted number. The DACs are designed for that representation which eliminates the need for final carry summation.

D. Blind Adaptation

The use of blind adaptation to set equalizer filter coefficients enables extraction of the channel characteristics and adaptation to slow changes of the channel characteristics during data transmissions. The sign-sign-least-mean-square (SS-LMS) algorithm [8] has been implemented on chip to

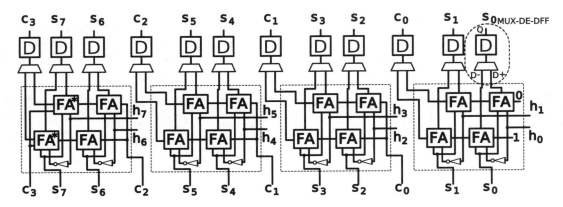

Fig. 5. One carry-save arithmetics filter tap

enable blind adaptation. The algorithm requires last detected data and the sign of the error signal. The error signal is defined as the difference between the nominal value for a detected bit and the actual value detected. The implemented DFE structure enables the required sign error detection to be added with minimum extra hardware.

The added hardware is a third FE block to the two that are shown in fig. 3. By adding an offset corresponding to half of the eye opening to the DAC in this block, the trig-point of that comparator is shifted from the center of the eye to one of the edges. A PRBS sequence controls whether the upper or lower eye-edge is selected. If the recovered data bit corresponds to the selected edge, the third comparator output corresponds to the sign-of-the-error and the DFE coefficients are updated according to the SS-LMS algorithm. If the recovered data bits show that the wrong eye-edge was selected, no coefficients are updated. The third FE block is clocked with a clock frequency that is $1/N$ of the data recovery clock. N is selected to be 20 or 21 using a PRBS generator, in order to de-correlate the updating phase with any received data pattern.

The adaptation algorithm where implemented in Verilog and layout where generated by standard synthesize and place-and-route software. In a simple form, the adaptation logic consist of one up/down counter for each filter coefficient and a few logic gates. The length of the counter sets the convergence speed and residue coefficient noise. To test different efficient counter lengths, the test-chip implements the adaptation as add/subtract summation blocks with programmable adder coefficients. The size of the adaptation block in the test-chip is therefore significantly larger then for the case when the counter length is fixed. The maximum efficient counter length where 32 bits in the test-chip.

Channel characteristics will differ with module configuration (as illustrated in section IV) and with addressed module endpoint. The digital filter and adaption ensure fast switching between coefficient sets. The adaptation logic could easily be expanded with one set of up/down counters per module slot or functionality to swap equalization coefficient sets between a register file and the counters.

E. BER Measurement Logic

Circuits to detect transmission errors are implemented on the test-chip. The test-chip includes a block that can generate a fixed periodic pattern or a PRBS signal at two times the clock rate. The pattern can be programmed using a low speed serial interface. The signal can be transmitted off-chip using a high speed inverter based driver. The signal can also be compared to the output signal from the DFE. Two identical physical test-chips are used to measure the equalizer performance. One chip is transmitting a pattern at one end of a test channel. The DFE of a second test-chip receives the signal. The pattern generator blocks are programmed to generate the same pattern and the signal from the DFE is compared to the pattern generated in the receiver test-chip. A programmable delay is used to compensate for signal propagation delay and the difference between the two signals are counted.

IV. MEASUREMENT RESULTS

The test circuit was manufactured in a 0.13 μm 5M standard CMOS process. The circuit utilizes single ended transmitters, an adaptive 12 tap 8 bit single ended DFE receiver, and a BER measurement circuit. The chip operates at 1.2 V supply with a current consumption of 93 mA for the receiver equalizer and the coefficient updating logic when receiving at 2.6 Gb/s. A micro-graph of the circuit is shown in fig. 6. The equalizer circuit occupies 0.047 mm^2 and the coefficient updating logic 0.14 mm^2.

Chips have been bonded in a receiver configuration on a low cost standard FR4 PCB with a 10 cm long signal strip-line and four DRAM slot connectors. Chips have also been bonded in a transmit configuration onto a PCB emulating a DDR memory module. Inactive modules are emulated by a PCB with 200 Ω, 4.7 pF termination. To illustrate the severe ISI conditions of a four drop bus, eye opening measurements at the receiver chip, using a 4 GHz probe, at 2.6 Gb/s for three different module configurations are shown in fig. 7. The presented equalizer have been used to receive these signals. The on-chip bit-error counter have been used and the bit-error-rates verses receiver clock phase have been measured. Measured BER bathtubs (for a PRBS-64 signal) and equalizer coefficients settings for the three different configurations are shown in fig. 8.

Fig. 6. Chip micro-graph

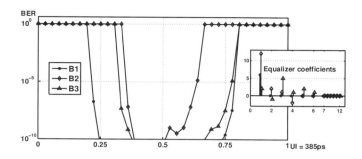

Fig. 8. Bathtub traces for three different module configurations and corresponding equalizer coefficients

Overflow compensated carry-save arithmetics and self-timed input data representation are used in the filter to enable high clock rates and low latency. Blind adaptation is performed with minimum added analog hardware. The digital signal processing and minimalistic analog implementation form a structure that will benefit greatly from technology scaling. The results show that multiple module single ended memory buses can be used at data rates of several Gb/s, indicating that the memory capacity per bus problem can be solved with existing bus structures even for future data-rates.

VI. ACKNOWLEDGEMENTS

The authors thank Dr. Chang-Hyun Kim at Samsung Electronics, Dr. Georg Braun at Qimonda and Randy Mooney at Intel for their financial and technical support of this project.

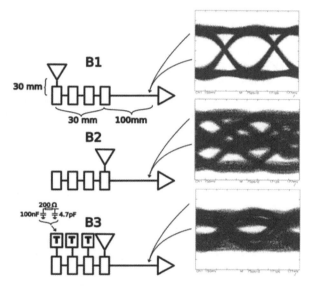

Fig. 7. Eye diagram before equalization for three different module configurations

A. Timing Recovery

For a DFE, the equalized eye will appear at the input of the comparators. Any normally used timing recovery circuitry can be added to this node for timing recovery. The use of a blind DFE can even relax the timing recovery constraints. It have been shown that the same blind adaptation algorithm that have been used in this paper can to a certain extent open the eye at arbitrary phase difference between transmitter and receiver clocks [9].

V. CONCLUSIONS

Measurements on a DFE-receiver test-chip shows data-rates of up to 2.6 Gb/s over a four drop bus structure with electrical characteristics similar to a DDR memory bus. BER $< 10^{-9}$ at $> 20\%$ of the symbol time has been demonstrated. The implemented DFE features a 12 tap digital FIR filter with less than one clock phase time latency and fast reconfigurability which enables efficient multi-drop-bus communication.

REFERENCES

[1] J. Haas and P. Vogt, "Fully-buffered DIMM technology moves enterprise platforms to the next level," *Technology@Intel Magazine*, March 2005.
[2] JEDEC STANDARD, "FBDIMM: Architecture and Protocol," January 2007, jESD206.
[3] B. S. Leibowitz, J. Kizer, H. Lee, F. Chen, A. Ho, M. Jeeradit, A. Bansal, T. Greer, S. Li, R. Farjad-Rad, W. Stonecypher, Y. Frans, B. Daly, F. Heaton, B. W. Garlepp, C. W. Werner, N. Nguyen, V. Stojanovic, and J. L. Zerbe, "A 7.5 Gb/s 10-Tap DFE Receiver with First Tap Partial Response, Spectrally Gated Adaptation, and 2nd-Order Data-Filtered CDR," in *IEEE International Solid-State Circuits Conference, 2007 Digest of Technical Papers.*, 2007, pp. 228–229.
[4] C.-F. Liao and S.-I. Liu, "A 40Gb/s CMOS Serial-Link Receiver with Adaptive Equalization and CDR," in *IEEE International Solid-State Circuits Conference, Digest of Technical Papers*, vol. 1, 2008, pp. 100–101.
[5] S.-J. Bae, H.-J. Chi, H.-R. Kim, and H.-J. Park, "A 3Gb/s 8b single-ended transceiver for 4-drop DRAM interface with digital calibration of equalization skew and offset coefficients," in *IEEE International Solid-State Circuits Conference, Digest of Technical Papers*, vol. 1, 2005, pp. 520–521.
[6] H.-J. Chi, J.-S. Lee, S.-H. Jeon, S.-J. Bae, J.-Y. Sim, and H.-J. Park, "A 3.2Gb/s 8b Single-Ended Integrating DFE RX for 2-Drop DRAM Interface with Internal Reference Voltage and Digital Calibration", a 3gb/s 8b single-ended transceiver for 4-drop dram interface with digital calibration of equalization skew and offset coefficients booktitle =."
[7] T. G. Noll, "Carry-Save Architectures for High-Speed Digital Signal Processing," *Journal of VLSI Signal Processing*, pp. 121–140, 1991.
[8] J. G. Proakis, *Digital Communications.* McGray-Hill, 2001.
[9] H. Fredriksson and C. Svensson, "Mixed-Signal DFE for Multi-Drop, Gb/s, Memory Buses — a Feasibility Study," in *IEEE International Symposium on VLSI Design, Automation and Test 2006. Proceedings*, April 2006.

An 8Gbps 2.5mW On-Chip Pulsed-Current-Mode Transmission Line Interconnect with a Stacked-Switch Tx

Tomoaki Maekawa[1], Hiroyuki Ito[2] and Kazuya Masu[1]

[1] Integrated Research Institute, Tokyo Institute of Technology

[2]Precision and Intelligence Laboratory, Tokyo Institute of Technology

4259-R2-17 Nagatsuta, Midori-ku, Yokohama 226-8503 Japan

Tel.: +81-45-924-5031, Fax: +81-45-924-5166

Email: paper@lsi.pi.titech.ac.jp

Abstract—**This paper proposes a high energy-efficient pulsed-current-mode transmission line interconnect (PTLI) for on-chip networks. The stacked-switch transmitter (Tx) is introduced for saving a static power of Tx. Point-to-point and multi-drop PTLIs are demonstrated, and simulation results show that the 5-mm-long PTLI with six Txs and six receivers (Rxs) can achieve multi-drop signaling. The point-to-point PTLI with a 5-mm-long transmission line is fabricated by using 90 nm Si CMOS process and can transmit 8 Gbps signals with power consumption of 2.5 mW and a delay of 164 ps.**

I. Introduction

A network on chip (NoC) has been investigated with the increase of the number of circuit blocks [1]. On-chip networks are applied for communicating among these blocks in NoCs, and performances of NoCs are strongly affected by on-chip networks which require wide bandwidths, low latency, low powers and small areas. Especially, power saving is important; Green IT has been becoming one of the most significant technology-directions recently. A lot of powers in on-chip networks are dissipated at interconnects due to increase of wiring resistance and capacitance. A big issue is that power consumption of conventional on-chip interconnects, i.e. so-called RC lines, is proportional to signal frequency; it is very hard to improve energy dissipation per a bit. The use of copper lines and low-k dielectric has been widely applied and saves powers for transmitting signals, however long interconnects still consume large powers.

Another solution is an introduction of circuit techniques such as on-chip transmission line interconnects (TLIs). TLIs have been proposed for improving latency, bandwidth and power consumption of high-speed long interconnects [2]–[9]. It is reported that TLIs have better power efficiencies than conventional on-chip lines as a line length and a signal frequency increase [3]–[6], [8]. Because current-mode differential-amplifiers are used for a transmitter (Tx) and a receiver (Rx) in TLIs, and power consumption of TLIs is almost determined by static power consumption of Tx and Rx and does not depend on signal frequency. However, that means TLIs waste powers if TLIs are applied to paths with a low activity factor or for transmitting lower bit-rate signals. Another design difficulty is large attenuation of on-chip transmission lines which have loss of over 10 dB at 10 GHz. Tx has to output large amplitude signals for compensating loss of the transmission line and usually consumes larger powers than

Rx. Thus, improvement of Tx power-efficiency is crucial for further power saving of on-chip TLIs and is also an important challenge for applying transmission line technologies to on-chip networks.

This work proposes an on-chip pulsed-current-mode transmission line interconnect (PTLI) with a stacked-switch Tx which does not consume static powers and generates return-to-zero (RZ) codes. PTLIs using RZ signals have been proposed in [7], and features of our interconnect are as follows:

1) Our interconnect mainly consists of transistors and does not have capacitors which usually consume a large area.
2) Pulse widths, which should be optimized by considering spectral efficiency and power consumption, are adjustable.

Our Tx outputs pulse-shaped RZ signals and only consumes powers at signal transitions. Tx has high output impedance at standby states, and our Tx and Rx can be applied to bidirectional and multi-drop signaling which save an area of TLIs and would improve extensibility of on-chip networks [9].

The organization of this paper is as follows. Circuit operations of Tx are explained, and it will be shown that a multi-drop signal transmission can be achieved by using proposed Txs in Section II. A fabricated point-to-point PTLI and its measurement results are introduced in Section III. The paper is concluded in Section IV.

II. The Proposed PTLI.

A schematic of the proposed PTLI is shown in Fig. 1. PTLI consists of pre-buffers for generating differential signals, stacked-switch Txs, an on-chip differential transmission line (DTL) and Rx as shown in Fig. 1 (a). Rail-to-rail signals are input into the PTLI, and Txs convert rail-to-rail signals to pulse-shaped differential RZ-signals. RZ signals propagate in the DTL at electromagnetic-wave speed. Rx amplifies pulse signals and converts RZ signals to non-return-to-zero (NRZ) signals. A buffer is used for measurements. Details of Tx and Rx are explained as follows.

A. The stacked-switch Tx.

Tx consists of four switches and delay circuits as shown in Fig. 1 (b). Delay circuits output τ-lagged signals, and a delay time τ can be changed by controlling bias voltages V_{cntp} and V_{cntn}. τ determines pulse widths of signals. Pulse width, i.e. the delay time τ, should be designed considering a trade-off

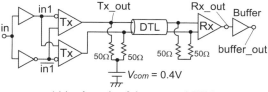

(a) A schematic of the proposed PTLI.

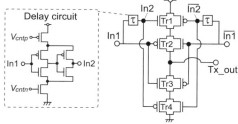

(b) A schematic of Tx.

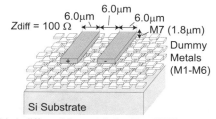

(c) A differential transmission line (DTL) structure.

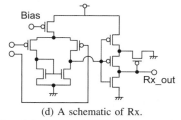

(d) A schematic of Rx.

Fig. 1.   Schematics of the proposed PTLI and a transmission line structure.

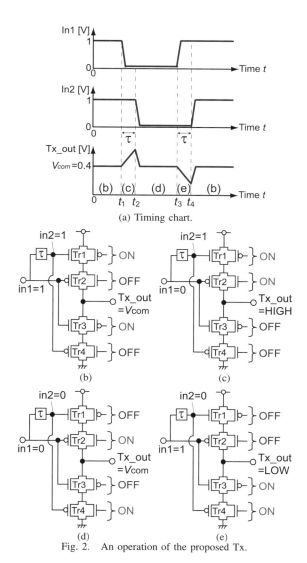

(a) Timing chart.

(b)   (c)   (d)   (e)

Fig. 2.   An operation of the proposed Tx.

between power consumption and spectra of signals. Currents flow only when signals transit, thus narrow pulse-signals are preferred for saving powers. Frequency components of pulse signals become higher as pulse-width reduces, and sharp pulse-signals have larger attenuation than thick pulse-signals. The proposed PTLI is designed to achieve the smallest power with 100-ps-pulse-width signaling. 100 ps is a minimum pulse-width of RZ signals at 10 Gbps. V_{com} stabilizes common-mode voltages of Tx outputs.

A circuit operation of the proposed stacked-switch Tx is as follows. Fig. 2 is used to explain operations.

1) $0 \leq t < t_1$ (Fig. 2 (b))

An input voltage of Tx (in1) is assumed to be 1 (high level) as shown in Fig. 2 (b), and Tx is in a steady state. Tr1 and Tr3 are on, and Tr2 and Tr4 are off. There are no current paths among a power supply, Tx_out and a ground. Thus, Tx does not consume a power. Output impedance is very high, and Tx_out is V_{com}.

2) $t_1 \leq t < t_2$ (Fig. 2 (c))

After the in1 becomes 0 (low level), Tr2 and Tr3 turn on and off, respectively. An output of the delay circuit (in2) is still 1, and states of Tr1 and Tr4 do not change.

A current flows into DTL from the power supply, and Tx_out becomes high.

3) $t_2 \leq t < t_3$ (Fig. 2 (d))

After τ passed, in2 changes to 1. Then, Tr1 and Tr4 turn off and on, respectively. The current from the power supply is blocked, and Tx_out drops to V_{com}.

4) $t_3 \leq t < t_4$ (Fig. 2 (e))

The input in1 becomes 1, and Tr2 and Tr3 change to off and on, respectively. States of Tr1 and Tr4 are not changed because of the delay circuit. The current flow into the ground from the DTL, and a voltage level of Tx_out goes down.

5) $t_4 \leq t$ (Fig. 2 (b))

The output voltage of the delay circuit (in2) becomes 1 at t_4, i.e. after τ of t_3. The current to the ground is blocked after Tr4 becomes off. Then, the voltage of Tx_out increases to V_{com}, and Tx repeats above operations.

Currents do not flow among the power supply, Tx_out and the ground at steady states. Thus, the proposed Tx can save powers at low bit-rate transmissions and signalings with a low activity

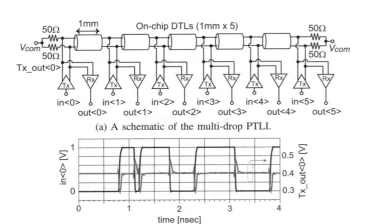

(a) A schematic of the multi-drop PTLI.

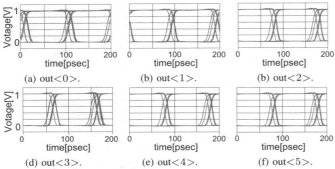

(b) Simulated time-domain waveforms at 10 Gbps.

Fig. 3. A schematic and simulated waveforms of a multi-drop PTLI.

(a) out<0>.   (b) out<1>.   (b) out<2>.

(d) out<3>.   (e) out<4>.   (f) out<5>.

Fig. 4. Simulated eye-patterns at Rx outputs. PRBS of $2^9 - 1$ is input into in<0>.

factor. Output impedance of Tx is high at steady states, which enables multi-drop and bidirectional signal transmissions without degradation of signal integrity [9].

B. DTL and Rx.

Fig. 2 (c) shows a transmission line structure. Metal and dielectric are aluminum and silicon dioxide. A line width and a space between lines are 6.0 μm. Differential impedance at high frequencies is 100 Ω.

Rx consists of a differential amplifier and a p-schmitt trigger circuit. The differential amplifier outputs difference of Rx-input signals, and the schmitt trigger circuit converts RZ signals to NRZ signals.

C. Simulations of the proposed PTLI.

Performances of the proposed PTLI are simulated, and a feasibility of multi-drop transmissions using proposed Txs is discussed. Fig. 3 (a) is a schematic of the multi-drop PTLI with six IOs. A line length is 5 mm, and pseudo random bit sequence (PRBS) of $2^9 - 1$ is input into in<0>. Txs and Rxs are connected every 1 mm and share one DTL. 90 nm Si CMOS process and measured S-parameter of the 1-mm-long DTL are used for simulations. Simulation results show that Tx outputs pulse-shaped RZ-signals as shown in Fig. 3 (b).

Fig. 4 shows simulated eye-patterns at 10 Gbps, and simulated performances are summarized in Table I. 10 Gbps

TABLE I

PERFORMANCE SUMMARY OF THE MULTI-DROP PTLI IN SIMULATIONS.

Process	90 nm Standard Si CMOS process
Signal frequency	10 Gbps
Power consumption supply voltage = 1.0 V, @10 Gbps	7.6 mW (Total of a Tx and 5 Rxs)
Energy per Bit	0.76 pJ/bit
Delay	140 ps (between in<0> and out<5>)

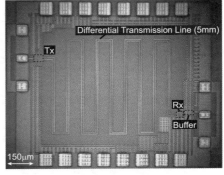

Fig. 5. A chip micrograph of the test circuit.

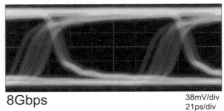

(a) A measured eye-pattern.

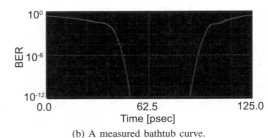

(b) A measured bathtub curve.

Fig. 6. Measurement results of the point-to-point PTLI at 8 Gbps.

multi-drop signaling can be achieved by applying proposed Txs although deterministic jitters due to bandwidth-limitation of Rx are observed. There is a trade-off between power consumption and a bandwidth, and this paper focuses on a low power operation of Rx.

III. MEASUREMENTS AND DISCUSSIONS

A 5-mm-long point-to-point PTLI is fabricated by using 90 nm Si CMOS process, and Fig. 5 is a chip micrograph. $2^9 - 1$ PRBS is input into Tx through a RF probe, and an output signal from the buffer is measured. A measured eye-pattern and a bathtub curve at 8 Gbps are shown in Fig. 6. The maximum bit-rate in measurements is lower than that in simulations because of a deterministic jitter shown in Fig. 6 (a). A main reason is a bandwidth of the buffer; the buffer itself operates up to around 10 Gbps in measurements.

TABLE II

PERFORMANCE SUMMARY OF THE POINT-TO-POINT PTLI IN
MEASUREMENT.

Process	90 nm Standard Si CMOS process
Maximum bit rate	8.5 Gbps
Power consumption power supply = 1.0 V, @8 Gbps	Tx: 1.2 mW
	Rx: 1.3 mW
	Total: 2.5 mW
Energy per Bit	0.31 pJ/bit
Delay (w/o buffer)	164 ps
Area	Tx: $48 \times 78 \, \mu m^2$
	Rx: $22 \times 32 \, \mu m^2$

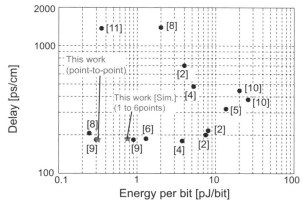

Fig. 7. Performance comparisons. Smaller delay and smaller energy per bit mean better performance.

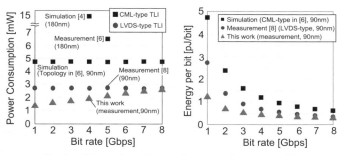

Fig. 8. Bit-rate dependences of power and energy per bit.

Performances of the point-to-point PTLI are summarized in Table II. Maximum bit rate is determined by eye-width and is 8 Gbps. Eye-width margin is assumed to be over 20 % of period at bit error rate of 10^{-12}. Power consumption without the buffer is 2.5 mW, and energy per bit is 0.31 pJ/bit. Delay time between "in" and "Rx_out" shown in Fig. 1 (a) is 164 ps, which is calculated by subtracting simulated buffer delay from measured delay between "in" and "Rx_out" in Fig. 1 (a).

Delay and energy per bit are compared in Fig. 7. The proposed PTLI has the same delay time as other TLIs. Energy per bit of our interconnect is almost the same as that of [9] and is bigger than that of [8]. Because operating frequency of the interconnect of [8] is higher than the proposed PTLI: As compared to power consumption at 8 Gbps, PTLI has smaller power consumption than [8] as shown in Fig. 8. Power consumption of conventional TLIs does not depend on bit-rate as described in Section I, and energy per bit increases as bit-rate reduces as shown in Fig. 8. Power of PTLI reduces as

bit-rate reduces. Thus, increase of energy per bit by reducing bit rate is gradual as compared to conventional TLIs.

The number of signal transition decreases as bit rate reduces, which is the same situation as the activity factor decreases. Thus, it is expected that the proposed PTLI has better energy per bit than conventional TLIs as the activity factor becomes low. The proposed PTLI would be useful for improving a bandwidth and a power efficiency of on-chip networks that frequently change their activity factors and bit rates.

IV. CONCLUSION

This paper proposed a high energy-efficient on-chip PTLI with the stacked-switch Txs for on-chip networks. The 5-mm-long multi-drop PTLI with six IOs in 90 nm Si CMOS process can transmit 10 Gbps signals with power consumption of 7.6 mW in simulations. The point-to-point PTLI was fabricated by using 90 nm Si CMOS process and achieved 8 Gbps signaling with 2.5 mW and delay of 164 ps through a 5-mm-long transmission line. Our interconnect has a superior power efficiency as compared to conventional on-chip high-speed interconnects not only at high bit-rate signaling but at signaling with low bit-rate and a low activity factor.

ACKNOWLEDGEMENTS

This work was partially supported by MEXT.KAKENHI, JSPS.KAKENHI, NEDO, and VDEC in collaboration with STARC, Fujitsu Limited, Matsushita Electric Industrial Company Limited, NEC Electronics Corporation, Renesas Technology Corporation, Toshiba Corporation, Cadence Design Systems, Inc., and Agilent Technologies Japan, Ltd.

REFERENCES

[1] K. Lee, et al., "Low-Power Network-on-Chip for High-Performance SoC Design", IEEE Transactions on Very Large Scale Integration Systems, Vol. 14, No. 2, pp. 148–160, 2006.
[2] R. T. Chang, et al., "Near Speed-of-Light Signaling Over On-Chip Electrical Interconnects" IEEE Journal of Solid-State Circuits, Vol. 38, No. 5, pp. 834–838, May, 2003.
[3] H. Ito, et al., "On-Chip Transmission Line for Long Global Interconnects", IEEE International Electron Devices Meeting, pp. 677–680, Dec., 2004.
[4] S. Gomi, et al., "Differential Transmission Line Interconnect for High Speed and Low Power Global Wiring," IEEE Custom Integrated Circuits Conference, pp. 325-328, Oct., 2004.
[5] H. Ito, et al., "4 Gbps On-Chip Interconnection using Differential Transmission Line," IEEE Asian Solid-State Circuits Conference, pp. 417–420, Nov., 2005.
[6] T. Ishii, et al., "A 6.5-mW 5-Gbps On-Chip Differential Transmission Line Interconnect with a Low-Latency Asymmetric Tx in a 180nm CMOS Technology," IEEE Asian Solid-State Circuits Conference, pp. 131–134, Nov., 2006.
[7] A. P. Jose, et al., "Pulsed Current-Mode Signaling for Nearly Speed-of-Light Intrachip Communication," IEEE Journal of Solid-State Circuits, Vol. 41, No. 4, pp. 772-780, 2006.
[8] H. Ito, et al., "A Low-Latency and High-Power-Efficient On-Chip LVDS Transmission Line Interconnect for an RC Interconnect Alternative," IEEE International Interconnect Technology Conference, pp. 193-195, June, 2007.
[9] H. Ito, et al., "A Bidirectional- and Multi-Drop-Transmission-Line Interconnect for Multipoint-to-Multipoint On-Chip Communications," IEEE Journal of Solid-State Circuits, Vol. 43, No. 4. pp.1020-1029, April, 2008.
[10] E. D. Kyriakis-Bitzaros, et al.,"Realistic End-to-End Simulation of the Optoelectronic Links and Comparison with the Electrical Interconnections for System-on-Chip Applications," Journal of Lightwave Technology, vol. 19, no. 10, pp. 1532-1542, Oct. 2001.
[11] K. Lee, et al., "A 51mW 1.6GHz On-Chip Network for Low-Power Heterogeneous SoC Platform," in IEEE Int. Solid-State Circuits Conference Dig. Tech. Papers, pp.152-153 2004.

Implementation of a Phase-encoding Signalling Prototype Chip

Crescenzo D'Alessandro[1], Alex Bystrov[2], Alex Yakovlev[2]

[1]picoChip Designs Ltd., Riverside Buildings, 108 Walcot Street, Bath, BA1 5BG, UK

[2]Microelectronics Design Group, School of EECE, Merz Court, Newcastle University, NE1 7RU, UK

Abstract—We report the results of the first prototype chip containing a silicon implementation of dual-rail phase-encoded links, where information is transmitted using the order of events on a pair of wires. The results show successful communication at bitrates exceeding 2 GB/s using standard-cell implementations on a 0.13μm technology.

I. INTRODUCTION

The design of high-speed, reliable interconnects has been for a long time a crucial part of the design of integrated circuits. Since the inception of the System-on-Chip (SoC) paradigm, which allow designers to incorporate a number of heterogeneous functional units on a single chip, issues such as bandwidth requirements, operating speed, bus width for the individual units deployed requires careful planning and design to ensure correct operation. Schemes like the Network-on-Chip (NoC) propose methods to simplify the design of the interconnect fabric by using a well-defined structure which is predictable and scalable.

However, the physical layer of a NoC can still pose problems to the designer. The expected bandwidth on a branch of the network can be high, and both synchronous and asynchronous implementations of the link can suffer from power, bandwidth and reliability limitations. Examples of work on the physical implementation of links for NoC applications (and more generally for on-chip signalling, typically across long distances) can be found in [1], [12], [8], [9], [10], [11].

Phase-encoding signalling was proposed initially in [6] as a method to address the problem of reliable links with respect to single-event upsets. The link is composed of two wires which transmit a clock signal modulated by the data differently on the two lines, so that the order of events indicates the data item being transmitted. The idea is that once an item is sent, any interference on either wire which happens away from the actual transmission of a data item (i.e. away from the two edges indicating the signal) is then filtered out as the other wire is not switching. Figure 1 shows an example of this behaviour. In the figure, t_1 and t_0 are the communicating lines; the reference signal could be a local (wrt the sender) clock and only modulates t_1 and t_0, but is not sent across. The reader is referred to [7] for a more detailed description of the scheme.

We report the results obtained with a prototype chip with a number of phase-encoded links. Dual-rail (in different forms, as described in the following sections) and multiple-rail implementations are present on the chip, fabricated in 0.13μm

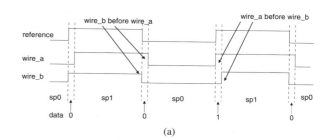

Figure 1. Example of waveforms for dual-rail phase encoding

technology: 2.254Gb/s signalling was achieved using dual-rail signalling across the chip with no repeaters.

II. CHIP IMPLEMENTATION

A. Top-level

The chip was packaged in a 48-pin DIL package, limiting the number of pins available for interfacing with external devices. The test plan involved using an FPGA board to drive the chip to minimize the amount of circuitry required to operate the chip. Of the 48 pins, 32 were used to write and read data from the chip, two for handshaking with the producer[1], two for handshaking with the consumer, four for selecting the type of signalling, one for reset and one for monitoring operation (BUSY signal, described in the following text). The rest of the pins were used for power and ground connections.

A controller was synthesized to multiplex/demultiplex the input/outputs to and from the pads. The same input/output pins are used for internal and external signalling, and also for dual- and multiple-rail signalling.

The chip measured 1.5×1.5 mm; the sender and receiver implementations were placed at opposite corners of the chip to maximize the distance between them, achieving a distance of around 2.5 mm. Figure 2 shows the place-and-routed chip as seen from the P&R tool. The senders can be seen at the bottom-left corner, while the receivers are at the top-right corner. In the top-left corner are the external sender/receivers, while in the bottom-right corner are the multiple-rail senders; the receivers are in the top-left corner just right of the external circuitry. The light congestion was deliberate to mimic realistic placement of the sender/receiver structures. Similarly when

---

[1]We indicate with "producer" and "consumer" the communicating sides before and after the phase-encoded link, while with "sender" and "receiver" we denote the circuitry pair which performs the communication.

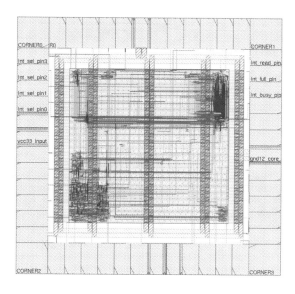

Figure 2. Place-and-Routed chip

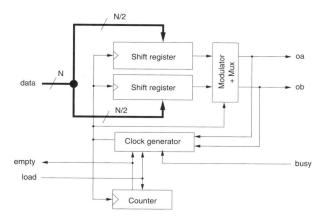

Figure 3. Sender block diagram

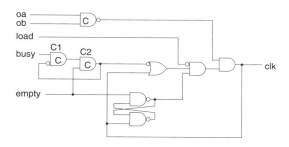

Figure 4. Clock generation circuitry

one sender/receiver pair is selected, the unused structures continue to run to cause deliberate interference, although the magnitude of the latter could not be measured.

The selector is a 4-bit switch which allows the input/output pins to be multiplexed for various link functions.

B. Link modules top-level

The link is self-timed, in the sense that the reference signal for signalling is locally generated rather than using an external clock. The generation of the reference signal is data-driven in a Globally-Asynchronous, Locally Synchronous (GALS) fashion [14] and uses handshaking to interact with the producer/consumer pair, and also to indicate that the receiver side is ready to receive data. The handshaking between the sender and receiver sides is performed using a BUSY signal generated at the receiver: when this signal is low, the sender can transmit (i.e. the sender's reference can be started). Once the first item is received the signal is asserted indicating that the link is being used. The signal is finally de-asserted once the consumer reads the data after completion of transaction; the sender's reference can then be re-started once a new item of data has been loaded. The handshaking is therefore performed per-word rather than per-byte, saving significant amount of signalling time (another example can be found in [8]). The "request" side of the handshaking is redundant as the signal transmitted contains embedded the sender's reference.

The handshaking between the sender and the producer is performed using an EMPTY signal which is asserted when the sender has no data to transmit and a LOAD signal which is asserted when data is made available by the producer (this signal is used to sample the input data pins). Synchronization is performed outside the chip. Similarly, the receiver interacts with the consumer asserting a FULL signal when a packet has been received, and receiving a READ signal which is asserted

by the consumer to indicate that the data has been sampled and a new item can be transmitted. The next sections will describe in more details the reference generation circuitry and the relationship between this and the handshaking mechanism.

C. Senders

The sender structures were designed to provide self-timed transmission, using a locally-generated data-driven "clock" [14]. Figure 3 shows the block diagram of the sender, while Figure 4 depicts the clock generation circuitry. The producer loads the data into two parallel shift registers: they are used to provide data for the rising and the falling edge of the local clock. Notice the two C-Elements C1 and C2: these two cells are used to implement a decoupled pipeline stage pair based on the traditional Muller pipeline, using BUSY and EMPTY as the handshaking signals (EMPTY is not inverted as it is semantically inverted to BUSY). The cross-coupled NAND gate pair is used to prevent the clock from starting when not required: the clock is started when EMPTY, BUSY and LOAD are low, and is stopped when EMPTY is high. It is then prevented from restarting until BUSY is high.

The modulator was implemented using a standard-cell implementation (a modification of the repeater proposed in [4] synthesized using PETRIFY) in some receivers and as a full-custom implementation in others. The latter is also a modification of one of the repeater designs described in the mentioned work. Figure 5 shows the implementation of the full-custom sender.

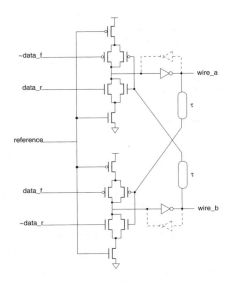

Figure 5. Custom cell pair for dual-rail phase-encoding

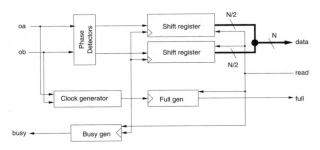

Figure 6. Receiver block diagram

D. Receivers

The block diagram for the receiver is shown in Figure 6. The two shift registers load the values produced by the phase detectors; each phase detector recovers the data on either the rising and falling edge of the input signals; the shift-registers are arranged so that the data recovered is sampled at the opposite edge, to allow some time for resolution in case of metastability. The phase detectors were implemented using either a flip-flop or cross-coupled NAND and NOR gates, as described in [7].

Figure 7 shows the implementation of the receiver, iden-

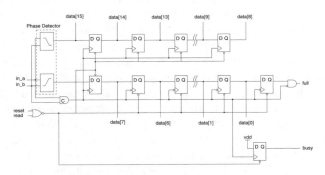

Figure 7. Receiver implementation

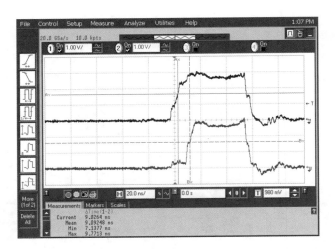

Figure 8. Example of observed waveforms for BUSY (top) and FULL (bottom) signals

tical for all link implementations apart from the phase-detectors. The phase-detectors implemented using cross-coupled NAND/NOR gates presented the problem of maintaining the output valid until the next relevant edge was recovered. To ensure correct recovery a memory element was introduced after the cross-coupled gates to sample and hold the result until the next transmission on the same edge.

E. Other structures

The chip also contains a differential phase-encoding signalling scheme [3], where the lines switch in different directions when a data item is sent. This allows the filtering of errors if spurious transitions occur on both wires at the same time when the link is idle. Multiple-rail implementations are also present: a 3-wire signalling scheme and a 4-wire signalling. These will be described in forthcoming work.

The chip also implements external versions of senders and receivers, to test chip-to-chip phase-encoding signalling.

III. RESULTS

The chip was characterized using an FPGA board which performed the operations of producer and consumer. The BUSY and FULL signals were used as indication of speed, as the first indicates that the first item has been received, while the second indicates the reception of the last item. Of course mismatches in propagation delay between the generation of the two signals and their propagation to the outside of the chip will introduce some errors; however, as 8 pulses have been sent by the time the FULL signal has been generated, the error is limited.

Figure 8 shows an example of the waveforms observed. The results show data rates of around 1.25 Gb/s across all implementations; however, the best implementations reach speeds of around 2 Gb/s: the absolute maximum observed was 2.254 Gb/s using the differential phase-encoding setting [3].

The external sender/receiver pair did not work as expected, as the bandwidth of the pads was insufficient. Figure 9 shows the waveforms of the two lines seen by the oscilloscope: the levels are not sufficient to trigger the receiver chip, thus

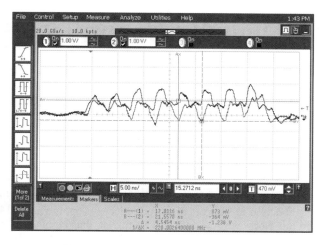

Figure 9. Dual-rail external link waveforms

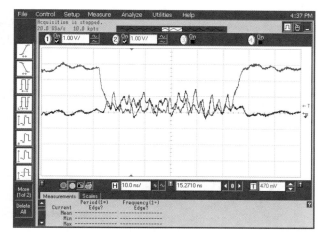

Figure 10. External waveforms for differential dual-rail phase-encoding

preventing successful communication. Figure 10 also shows the waveforms for external signalling using differential dual-rail phase-encoding signalling. The two external waveforms also show the property of the link that the clock is generated once the signals seen at the sender's side reach the threshold voltage to trigger the next transition. In phase-encoding this is sufficient to ensure that the item of data has been transmitted, and if the link is correctly buffered (using repeaters as described in [5]) it can be inferred that the receiver has obtained an item of data, although it does not ensure that the phase-detector for the transition has resolved. The resolution is expected to complete before the next rising/falling transition, but in the meantime the opposite phase-detector is ready to accept additional data. The mechanism described indicates that a baseline shift (observed on the external links) is acceptable if the link is capacitively-dominated such that the voltage levels are at all times comparable at the sender's and receiver's side.

IV. CONCLUSIONS

The prototype is encouraging and shows that phase-encoding can be successfully implemented on-chip. More

characterization is required to obtain a more accurate distribution of the speed of the link at different voltage/temperature conditions, and also in noisy conditions, to model the interference patterns found in large SoC. Additionally, newer prototype chips with longer links would allow observations of the behaviour of the link in extreme conditions. Also, a more accurate design of the external interface (different, higher-bandwidth IO cells) will allow characterization of the behaviour of the link in off-chip conditions. Finally, methods to observe on-chip waveforms (such as [13]) or to perform time measurement [2] could be deployed in future implementations to improve the characterization of the scheme.

ACKNOWLEDGEMENTS

This work was undertaken while Crescenzo D'Alessandro was at Newcastle University. The authors would like to acknowledge EPSRC support through grant EP/C512812/1.

REFERENCES

[1] W.J. Bainbridge. *Asynhcronous System-on-Chip Interconnect.* PhD thesis, University of Manchester, UK, March 2000.
[2] A. Bystrov, D. J. Kinniment, G. Russell, O. V. Maevsky, and A. V. Yakovlev. On-chip structures for timing measurement and test. *Microprocessors and Microsystems*, 27(9):473–483, October 2003.
[3] C. D'Alessandro, A. Bystrov, and A. Yakovlev. Improved phase-encoding signalling. *Electronics Letters*, 43(4):216–217, February 2007.
[4] C. D'Alessandro, N. Minas, K. Heron, D. Kinniment, and A. Yakovlev. Noc communication strategies using time-to-digital conversion. In *Proceedings of the First International Symposium on Networks-on-Chips, NOCS 2007*, pages 65–74, 2007.
[5] C. D'Alessandro, A. Mokhov, A. Bystrov, and A. Yakovlev. Delay/phase regeneration circuits. In *Proceedings. 13th International Symposium on Asynchronous Circuits and Systems. ASYNC 2007*, 2007.
[6] C. D'Alessandro, D. Shang, A. Bystrov, and A. Yakovlev. PSK Signalling on SoC Buses. In *Integrated Circuit and System Design. Power and Timing Modeling, Optimization and Simulation. Proceedings of PATMOS 2005*, volume 3728 of *Lecture Notes in Computer Science*. Springer, 2005.
[7] C. S. D'Alessandro, D. Shang, A. Bystrov, A.V. Yakovlev, and O. Maevsky. Phase-encoding for on-chip signalling. *IEEE Transactions on Circuits and Systems-I: Regular Papers*, 55(2):535–545, March 2008.
[8] R. Dobkin, R. Ginosar, and A. Kolodny. Fast asynchronous shift register for bit-serial communication. In *Proc. 12th ASYNC*, pages 117–126, March 2006.
[9] R. R. Dobkin, Y. Perelman, T. Liran, R. Ginosar, and A. Kolodny. High rate wave-pipelined asynchronous on-chip bit-serial data link. In *ASYNC '07: Proceedings of the 13th IEEE International Symposium on Asynchronous Circuits and Systems*, pages 3–14, Washington, DC, USA, 2007. IEEE Computer Society.
[10] R. Ho, K. Mai, and M. Horowitz. Efficient on-chip global interconnects. In *2003 Symposium on VLSI Circuits, 2003. Digest of Technical Papers.*, pages 271–274, June 2003.
[11] R. Ho, I. Ono, F. Liu, R. Hopkins, A. Chow, J. Schauer, and R. Drost. High-speed and low-energy capacitively-driven on-chip wires. In *IEEE International Solid-State Circuits Conference, 2007. ISSCC 2007. Digest of Technical Papers.*, pages 412–612, 2007.
[12] Se-Joong Lee, Kwanho Kim, Hyejung Kim, Namjun Cho, and Hoi-Jun Yoo. Adaptive network-on-chip with wave-front train serialization scheme. In *2005 Symposium on VLSI Circuits Digest of Technical Papers*, pages 104–107, June 2005.
[13] F. Liu, R. Ho, R. Drost, and S. Fairbanks. On-chip samplers for test and debug of asynchronous circuits. In *ASYNC '07: Proceedings of the 13th IEEE International Symposium on Asynchronous Circuits and Systems*, pages 153–162, Washington, DC, USA, 2007. IEEE Computer Society.
[14] R. Mullins, G. Taylor, P. Robinson, and S. Moore. Point to point gals interconnect. In *ASYNC '02: Proceedings of the 8th International Symposium on Asynchronus Circuits and Systems*, pages 69–75, Washington, DC, USA, 2002. IEEE Computer Society.

A High-Resolution 24-dBm Digitally-Controlled CMOS PA for Multi-Standard RF Polar Transmitters

Calogero D. Presti, Francesco Carrara,
and Giuseppe Palmisano
University of Catania, Faculty of Engineering, DIEES,
Catania, Italy (cpresti@diees.unict.it)

Antonino Scuderi
STMicroelectronics
Catania, Italy

Abstract□ A Digitally-Controlled Power Amplifier (DPA) in 0.13- m 1.2-V SOI-CMOS is demonstrated, to be used as a building block in a multi-standard radio transmitter. The circuit performs direct amplitude modulation of an input RF carrier, by digitally controlling a large array of RF gain cells. It exhibits a 24.5-dBm peak output power at 1.9 GHz, and an effective resolution better than 7 bits. A novel two-stage topology for the gain cell is described, which allows the DPA to seamlessly operate from 800 MHz through 2 GHz, with a full-power efficiency larger than 40% and a small-signal gain of 14.5 dB. A new strategy is also proposed to provide a wide-range transmit power control.

I. INTRODUCTION

The demand for ubiquitous wireless connectivity has driven the interest in multi-standard transmitters (TX), which will hopefully consolidate next-generation and legacy modulation formats into a single radio. Of course, a multi-radio should comply with the most stringent performance of the worst-case modulation standard [1]. Moreover, efficient operation over a wide bandwidth from the same chip is certainly desirable. Ideally, the whole system, from the baseband digital circuitry through the power amplifier (PA), should be integrated onto a single chip, thus indicating CMOS as the technology of choice.

Recently, several CMOS multi-mode RF TX systems were reported [1]-[3]. In these implementations, however, one external PA is still required for each frequency band. The PA is indeed one of the most difficult blocks to be integrated, due to the stricter trade-offs (linearity, efficiency, etc.) found in a CMOS platform. Polar modulation is a system-level approach able to alleviate these technological deficiencies, since in a polar TX all the RF circuits operate in a constant-envelope mode, whilst linearity is delegated to some sort of feedback [4].

In this paper we present a Digitally-Controlled CMOS PA (DPA), to be used as the main building block of a multi-mode CMOS polar TX. This circuit amplifies a RF phase-modulated (PM) carrier, and simultaneously performs amplitude modulation (AM). This is achieved by properly turning on and off a set of elementary RF gain cells. In this way, the output RF amplitude is essentially proportional to a digital Amplitude Control Word (*ACW*) [2][3][5]. A novel two stage topology is introduced for the design of the gain cells, which enables efficient operation over a very wide bandwidth.

II. DIGITAL-AMPLITUDE RF POLAR TRANSMITTER

In a polar TX architecture, phase modulation is preferably performed through a PLL [3][4]. On the other hand, there are several ways to perform amplitude modulation [3]-[5]. For

example, when the PA is included in the modulator, a regulator can be used to vary the drain (or collector) supply voltage [4]. In this work, the AM path is fully digital, thus eliminating the need for digital-to-analog converters (DAC) in the TX chain.

A. AM Resolution Requirements

The resolution of the AM signal is, of course, a critical parameter. Indeed, finite resolution causes a white spectral re-growth in the proximity of the carrier. Fig. 1 shows the results of a system-level simulation, performed on an idealized polar modulator. It is interesting to note that spectral purity improves by approximately 6 dB/bit, as predicted by elementary DAC theory. The legacy EDGE modulation is more demanding than WCDMA, since the relative power at a 600-kHz offset must not exceed –60 dB. This can be achieved by using a 7-bit AM resolution, with a 10-dB margin.[1]

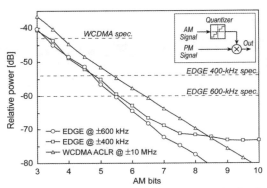

Figure 1. Simulated spectral purity for WCDMA and EDGE signals at the output of an idealized digital-amplitude polar modulator (in the inset).

B. Proposed Polar Transmitter Architecture

The block diagram of the proposed polar TX is depicted in Fig. 2. The DPA itself is driven by the PM signal and by a 10-bit *ACW*. The DPA architecture is similar to that of a segmented DAC [6]. First, the 7 most significant bits are decoded, and then they control 127 identical gain cells, whilst the 3 least significant bits control as many binary-weighted cells. In spite of the discussed 7-bit requirement, 3 extra bits must be implemented, since AM distortion will degrade effective resolution, as discussed in Section IV.

Modern wireless standards also require the *average* output power level to be set across several orders of magnitude (e.g.

---

[1] The –40 dB limit of OFDM WLAN signals would be easily met as well [5].

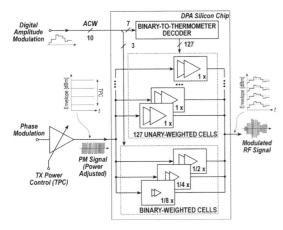

Figure 2. Proposed polar transmitter architecture, including the block diagram of the Digitally-Controlled Power Amplifier.

74 dB in WCDMA). This feature cannot be implemented in the digital-amplitude domain, since an extremely high number of bits would be required. In the proposed architecture, the DPA gain cells are appropriately biased, so that the output power will *also* be proportional to the PM signal envelope, even when this signal is very small. The PM envelope can be set straightforwardly, by exploiting a simple VGA, according to an external Transmit Power Control (TPC) signal. Since AM is not present in the input PM carrier, the DPA linearity with respect to the RF input is not of concern, nor the VGA should be linear, thus reducing the overall TX power consumption.

III. CIRCUIT DESCRIPTION

A schematic of the DPA chip is shown in Fig. 3. Only one elementary cell is depicted, the others being identical or binary-scaled replicas of it. Cells are laid out in a rectangular array. The commutation sequence is a custom 2-dimensional version of the hierarchical scheme [6]. All cells are connected in parallel, by two H-tree input and output interconnect networks. This solution reduces the RF path mismatch to less than 100 μm, thus avoiding phase jumps when the *ACW* varies.

The elementary cell is a two-stage differential amplifier. It is controlled by an enable (*EN*) signal, which is synchronized through a register. An extra inverter (connected to V_{DD1}) rejects the noise from the digital supply rail $V_{DD,dig}$. When *EN* is high, transistor *M7* is in triode region, and *M8-M10* are off. The first gain stage (*M1-M4*) is a complementary common-emitter amplifier, in which the nFETs are ac-coupled through C_1 to the RF input. The first stage is dc-coupled to the second stage (*M5-M6*). Most importantly, this topology avoids any narrowband inter-stage matching network, thus making the circuit inherently wideband. In this respect, a complementary driver stage is the optimal choice, in terms of power efficiency.

A bias gate voltage is generated on the chip from a reference current I_B. Transistor *M12* forms a mirror with *M1-M2* (*M11* is added to match *M7*). *M3* and *M4* are then self-biased through the large resistors R_1, and form a mirror structure with *M5-M6*. Hence, by simply turning off *M7*, both stages are switched off. The off-state gain of the cell is further reduced by *M8*, *M9*, and *M10*. No disconnection from the input terminals occurs in the off state, thus strongly limiting the

variations of the total input capacitance, which remains, to the first order, equal to $127 \cdot (C_{gs1,2} + C_{gs3,4})$. In this way, the input impedance shift with *ACW* is small and distortion is reduced.

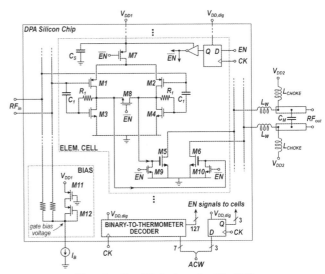

Figure 3. Simplified schematic of the DPA.

The mechanism through which digital amplitude modulation is actually accomplished depends on the amplitude of the input RF signal.

When the input signal is small, the two stages operate in the linear region. Therefore the cell acts as a current source, and the total RF output current will be linearly proportional to *ACW*. As a result, the output RF envelope, which is the product between RF current and load impedance, will be proportional to *ACW* as well, as desired. Under these circumstances, the only source of AM distortion is the finite impedance at the DPA output, which decreases non-linearly as the *ACW* is increased (i.e., as soon as new *M5-M6* pairs are turned on).

On the other hand, when the input signal is large, the first stage will work as a pair of inverters, and *M5-M6* will be hard-switched. Of course, a large bypass capacitor C_S is needed to provide the charge flowing to the gate of *M5-M6*. The output matching network (composed by bond wires L_W, a differential transmission line, and C_M) is designed to bring the amplifier in a class-E-like mode, and to optimize saturated efficiency. In this hard-switching regime, the AM modulation is heavily non-linear. Predistortion of the *ACW* and PM signals will be needed to achieve the desired modulation accuracy [3].

IV. EXPERIMENTAL RESULTS

The DPA was fabricated in a 0.13-μm 1.2-V SOI-CMOS technology by STMicroelectronics. The chip, shown in Fig. 4, measures 0.9 x 1.2 mm. Layout is pad limited, due to the large *ACW* bus width. Of course, the *ACW* pad interface is not needed in a fully-integrated TX system. The choice of a SOI process is useful for the future integration of the DPA with other blocks needed in a multi-mode architecture, such as the RF power switches described in [7]. The DPA was mounted on a differential FR4 printed circuit board. Measurements are referred to the board connectors.

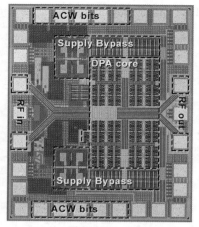

Figure 4.   DPA chip micrograph.

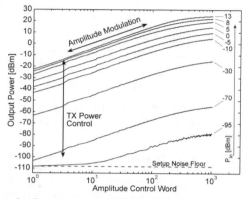

Figure 5.   Output power vs. *ACW* at increasing P_{in} (f_{RF} = 1.9 GHz).

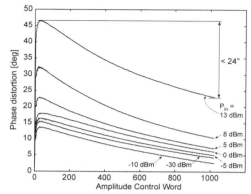

Figure 6.   Phase distortion at various P_{in} (f_{RF} = 1.9 GHz).

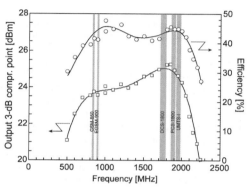

Figure 7.   Measured output power and efficiency at the 3-dB gain compression point, vs. carrier frequency. Lines are guides to the eye.

The channel length of all transistors is 0.13 μm, except for *M5-M6*, which are 0.28-μm 2.5-V FETs. However, no process option is used, since such feature is customarily needed for standard digital I/O interfaces. The supply voltages are set to $V_{DD,dig}$ = V_{DD1} = 1.2 V and V_{DD2} = 2.1 V. The final stage supply voltage is chosen to reliably operate *M5-M6*, according to a recent study on FET degradation under RF stress in CMOS power amplifiers [8]. Concerning this, no significant power drop was recorded after several hours of full-power testing, despite the <0.01-dB resolution of the measurement setup.

A.   Output transfer characteristic

The DPA output power is shown in Fig. 5, at P_{in} ranging from 13 dBm down to –95 dBm, and f_{RF} = 1.9 GHz. For each input level, the output power monotonically increases with *ACW*. Typical maximum power at P_{in} = 13 dBm is 24.5 dBm. Small-signal gain at *ACW* = 1023 (full scale) is 14.5 dB. The data reported in Fig. 5 were also utilized to characterize the AM distortion and the resolution of the DPA.

On the other hand, PM distortion was measured by means of a network analyzer, at 1.9 GHz. As shown in Fig. 6, the maximum PM distortion occurs at P_{in} = 13 dBm, being lower than 24°. No significant phase jumps are observed, demonstrating the effectiveness of the H-tree RF interconnects.

As expected, both AM and PM distortion at low input power are smaller, due to the more linear operation of the cells.

B.   Bandwidth and Efficiency

The output matching network is the only frequency-selective part of the circuit. Hence, it was designed to maximally exploit the inherent wide bandwidth of the DPA chip. In this respect, it is known that class-E amplifiers can demonstrate a highly efficient saturated operation over a very wide bandwidth, when loaded by a low-Q matching network [9]. In this circuit, the Q is small both because of the limited impedance transformation ratio and because of some loss through the H-tree on-chip drain connection.

Fig. 7 reports the output power and the overall efficiency (P_{out} / total DC power) at the 3-dB compression point vs. input frequency. An output power larger than 23.5 dBm, with an efficiency better than 40%, is maintained from 800 MHz up to 2 GHz, thus covering all cellular bands. This is achieved without any matching reconfiguration, and it is a direct consequence of the novel wideband cell topology.

Furthermore, the AM step response risetime is as small as 2 ns. This is limited by an *RC* filter, inserted in each cell at the inverter's output, in order to slightly smooth the $\overline{EN}$ signal.

The modulation approach here implemented has also an important impact on the DPA *average* efficiency, i.e. on the power consumption when the output envelope is lower than the maximum achievable, as occurs in high-data-rate RF links. In Fig. 8, the efficiency obtained by sweeping the *ACW* (at various P_{in} levels) is compared to the efficiency obtained by sweeping P_{in}, at *ACW* = 1023 (i.e. by actually exploiting the

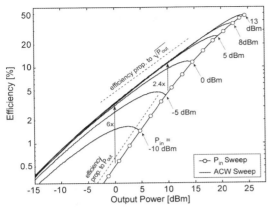

Figure 8. Measured efficiency vs. output power (f_{RF} = 1.9 GHz). Comparison between classic P_{in} sweep and ACW sweep.

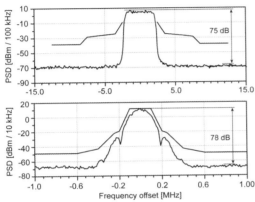

Figure 9. WCDMA (top) and EDGE (bottom) calculated spectra at the DPA output, after amplitude and phase predistortion (P_{in} = 13 dBm, f_{RF} = 1.9 GHz).

DPA as a traditional PA). When P_{in} is swept, efficiency is basically proportional to the output power. On the contrary, when ACW is swept, the DC current is proportional to the output *envelope*, since unused cells are turned off, and efficiency becomes proportional to the square root of P_{out} [5]. This effectively reduces the average power consumption, especially because the TX system will be rarely used at its full power [7]. For example, 2.4x and 6x efficiency improvements are measured at P_{out} = 10 dBm and 0 dBm, respectively.

C. AM Effective Resolution

As in most polar TX systems, the DPA requires feedback to correct its non-linear AM and PM transfer characteristics. Due to the digital nature of the AM signal, adaptive digital predistortion (DPD) is certainly an attractive method.

In order to correctly assess the effective DPA resolution and the achievable modulation accuracy, a DPD system, based on a look-up table, was implemented in a DSP simulation environment, similarly to what is described in [10], by using the measured AM and PM transfer characteristics. As expected, the implemented 10-bit DPA resolution is not maintained after DPD, because the AM transfer characteristic is *compressed*, as seen in Fig 5. In other words, after DPD, the lowest DPA output levels are associated to a much wider ACW range, thus causing a resolution loss. This is the reason why 3

extra bits had to be added to the 7-bit requirement. However, the linearized effective resolution is largely sufficient, since, with respect to the targeted 7 bits, the differential non-linearity is as low as DNL_{RMS} = 0.17 LSB, and DNL_{MAX} = 0.45 LSB.

The simulated WCDMA and EDGE spectra, after DPD, are reproduced in Fig. 9. As expected, a white noise floor appears, whose relative amplitude is within the specifications, with a large margin, thus further validating the design choices.

V. CONCLUSIONS

A Digitally-Controlled Power Amplifier has been implemented in a 0.13-µm 1.2-V SOI-CMOS process. The circuit digitally performs amplitude modulation of an RF carrier, with an effective resolution better than 7 bits. Thanks to a novel two-stage circuit topology, an output power larger than 24 dBm is reliably delivered over an extremely wide bandwidth of one octave, with an overall efficiency better than 40%. A novel methodology is also proposed to accommodate a wide-range TX power control, as required, for example, by the WCDMA standard.

These results, together with a 2-ns step-response risetime, demonstrate that the proposed DPA constitutes a promising building block in the design of next-generation multi-mode and multi-band RF polar transmitters.

ACKNOWLEDGMENT

The authors gratefully acknowledge Prof. P. M. Asbeck, UCSD, for numerous discussions, S. Pornpromlikit, UCSD, for valuable help with measurements, and B. Rauber, STMicroelectronics, for technology support.

REFERENCES

[1] P. Eloranta *et al.*, "A multimode transmitter in 0.13 µm CMOS using direct-digital RF Modulator," *IEEE J. Solid-State Circuits*, vol. 42, pp. 2774–2784, 2007.

[2] P. T. M. van Zeijl and M. Collados, "A digital envelope modulator for a WLAN OFDM polar transmitter in 90-nm CMOS," *IEEE J. Solid-State Circuits*, vol. 42, pp. 2204–2211, 2007.

[3] R. B. Staszewski *et al.*, "All-digital PLL and transmitter for mobile phones," *IEEE J. Solid-State Circuits*, vol. 40, pp. 2469–2482, 2005.

[4] A Hadjichristos *et al.*, "A highly integrated quad band low EVM polar modulation transmitter for GSM/EDGE applications," in *Proc. IEEE 2004 Custom Integrated Circ. Conf.*, pp. 565-568, 2004.

[5] A. Kavousian, D. K. Su, and B. A. Wooley, "A digitally modulated polar CMOS PA with 20MHz signal BW", in *Proc. IEEE 2007 Int. Solid-State Circ. Conf.*, pp. 78-79, Feb. 2007.

[6] Y. Nakamura et al., "A 10-bit 70MS/s CMOS D/A converter," in *Proc. 1990 Symposium on VLSI Circuits*, pp. 57-58, 1990.

[7] A. Scuderi, C. D. Presti, F. Carrara, B. Rauber, and G. Palmisano, "A Stage-Bypass SOI-CMOS Switch for Multi-Mode Multi-Band Applications", in *Proc. IEEE 2008 RF Integrated Circ. Conf.*, in press.

[8] C. D. Presti, F. Carrara, A. Scuderi, S. Lombardo, and G. Palmisano, "Degradation mechanisms in CMOS power amplifiers subject to radiofrequency stress and comparison to the DC case," in *Proc. IEEE International Reliability Physics Symposium*, pp. 86–92, April 2007.

[9] F. H. Raab, "Effects of circuit variations on the class-E tuned power amplifier," *IEEE J. Solid-State Circuits*, vol. 13, pp. 239–247, 1978.

[10] M. Faulkner and Mats Johansson, "Adaptive Linearization Using Predistortion–Experimental Results," *IEEE Trans. Vehicular Technology*, vol. 43, pp. 323-332, 1994.

A 1.2V, 17dBm Digital Polar CMOS PA with Transformer-based Power Interpolating

Xin He, Manel Collados, Nenad Pavlovic, and Jan van Sinderen

NXP Semiconductors, High Tech Campus 37, 5656AE, Eindhoven, The Netherlands

xin.he@nxp.com

Abstract Targeting for WLAN applications, this paper presents a digital polar power amplifier in a 65nm digital CMOS process, with 17dBm maximum RMS output power at 1.2V supply voltage. To reduce the out-of-band alias caused in the direct digital-to-RF power conversion, a transformer-based power interpolating technique is implemented. This also improves the average efficiency by adaptively configuring the interpolation stages. The measured power added efficiency remains between 8.9% and 12.7% over power range from 12dBm to 17dBm. The achieved power level allows for eliminating the commonly used external PA stage.

I. INTRODUCTION

To reduce the PCB area and lower the total cost, there is an increasing demand to integrate the power amplifier (PA) with the transceiver on the same die for Bluetooth and WLAN applications. This requires a PA architecture that is suitable for integrating all the blocks in the same advanced CMOS technology, and can deliver an RMS output power up to 17dBm (for WLAN) with high average power efficiency. In comparison with conventional IQ transmitter with linear PA, the recently proposed digital polar transmitter is very attractive since it combines the DAC, the up-conversion mixer and the PA in a single block with relatively high efficiency [1-4]. The first digital polar transmitters for WLAN applications have been published in [3] and [4], achieving a maximum RMS power level 13.6dBm and 9.4dBm respectively, while the peak drain efficiency is below 10%.

II. DIGITAL POLAR ARCHITECTURE

As show in Fig. 1, in a digital polar transmitter the IQ signals are first converted to amplitude and phase signals, which is similar to the analog polar transmitter. The difference is that in the digital polar transmitter, the output envelope is generated by switching on/off unit currents inside the envelope modulator, instead of varying the bias voltage or supply voltage in the analog polar transmitter. Using the same sampling clock to drive the AM and the PM path allows for the synchronization of the AM and the PM path in wide-band applications, avoiding significant spectral re-growth. Essentially the digital envelope-modulated polar transmitter is a digital-to-RF power converter. The discrete-time to continuous-time conversion introduces spectral replicas at the offset of the sampling clock frequency and its higher order harmonics with respect to the carrier, which may violate the out-of-band spectrum emissions mask. Although the digital-to-RF power conversion offers an inherent *sinc* attenuation, those unwanted out-of-band spurs have to be further suppressed by interpolating the input at high sampling frequency [5], or filtering the output of the amplifier by an additional RF filter. The use of an additional RF filter is not desired because it not only increases the size and BOM, but also attenuates the wanted output. Therefore N-fold linear interpolation combined with high sampling rate is preferred. In [3] and [4], the output stage is split into four parallel unit matrixes that are sequentially switched by four quadrature-phased sampling clocks. By summing the interpolated output currents, the frequency aliases at the offset of the fundamental, 2x, and 3x sampling clock frequencies are suppressed to a lower level that complies with the out-of-band emission mask.

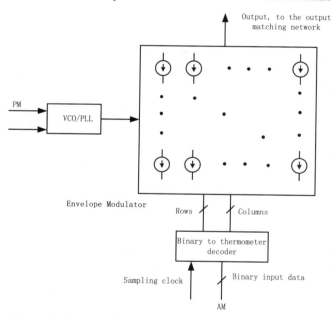

Fig. 1. The diagram of the digital envelope-modulated polar transmitter.

In this paper multiple transformers are employed to interpolate output power in the digital polar transmitter. In literature the applications of transformer-based power combing have been reported to achieve high output power at low supply voltage, and enable the use of thin-oxide transistors in deep sub-micron CMOS processes [6-8]. In addition to the benefits obtained in the transformer-based power combining, the proposed transformer-based power interpolating has the extra function to suppress out-of-band aliases in the digital polar transmitter. By adapting the interpolating stages, the average efficiency can be also improved.

III. CIRCUIT ARCHITECTURE AND IMPLEMENTATION

As shown in Fig. 2, multiple transformers can be employed to combine multiple equivalent output stages, in order to achieve higher output power with lower supply voltage. In each stage the voltage swing is also lowered. Therefore it is very attractive for digital CMOS processes to implement such PA because the breakdown voltage of CMOS processes is much lower than that of GaAs processes.

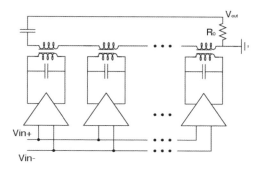

Fig. 2. PA with transformer-based power combining.

A simple diagram of the digital polar PA with the proposed transformer-based power interpolating is presented in Fig. 3. The output stage is split into four sections. Each section consists of a unit matrix, while the input data are latched by one of the four phased clocks (90 degrees phase shift between each other). Instead of summing output currents, the output voltage is stacked from the secondary stages of the four transformers. Due to the four phase clocking, the original one large envelope step is split into four smaller steps, thus achieving the desired power interpolation at the output. Moreover, the output voltage swing is evenly distributed in four sections by the transformers, resulting in a lower voltage swing in one section. Therefore it is possible to use thin-oxide transistors to achieve high power efficiency at high output power, thus eliminating an external PA stage.

Another advantage of using transformer-based power interpolating is that the maximum operating frequency can be improved. There is only one unit matrix in one section, and the size is relatively small, yielding less parasitic inductance with respect to the transformer inductance.

A. Switchable output transformers

As indicated in [5], the spectrum image rejection can be improved by increasing the number of interpolation stages. On the other hand, the image spurs may only violate the spectrum mask at high output power. Therefore it is possible to configure the number of the interpolation stages, adapting to the output power level. The benefit of configuring different number of interpolation stages at different power levels is that the average power efficiency can be improved, since the PA can still operate at high efficiency when some sections (stages) shown in Fig.3 are turned off. It acts as a dynamic output matching network: at high power level each section sees a low load impedance; at low power level those sections which are switched on see a higher impedance, given by

$$R_L = 50/N$$

where N is the number of active interpolation stages.

In the circuit the on/off control of each section is realized

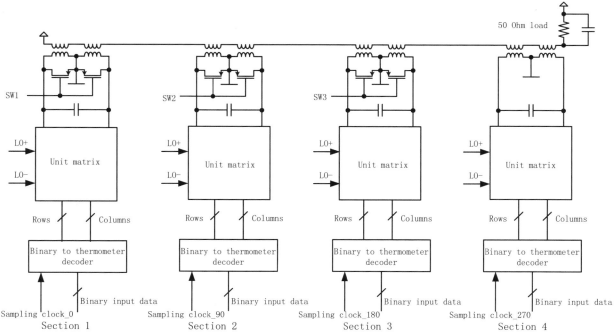

Fig. 3. The simplified diagram of the digital polar PA with transformer-based power interpolating.

by switching on/off the PMOS transistors parallel to the primary stage of the transformer. When the control signal is "1", the two PMOS transistors are turned off, and the section is turned on. When the control signal is "0", the PMOS transistors are turned on, yielding low impedance (ideally zero) at the primary stage of the transformer. Now the section is turned off when the thermometer output is set zero, and the secondary stages in nearby sections just see a "short" node. In practice, the four-fold interpolation PA turns into a two-fold interpolation PA if two sections are turned off. Particularly there is no interpolation if three sections are turned off. By properly sizing the PMOS transistors, it only slightly degrades the power efficiency in simulation.

B. Unit cell configuration

The schematic of the unit cell implemented in the circuit is shown in Fig. 4. The differential unit cell outputs are connected to the primary stage of the transformer in each section. To improve the reliability of the thin-oxide transistors, a cascode structure is employed in the output stage. By changing the bias voltage at the gates of the cascode transistors the output gain can be also controlled.

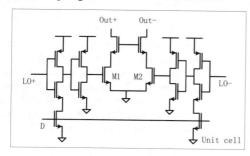

Fig. 4.   The schematic of the unit cell.

To improve the power efficiency, the on/off control of the unit cell is moved from the output stage to the LO path in the unit cell implementation. When D is 1, the LO signal can be passed to the output stage. When D is 0, the gate voltage of the output transistors M1 and M2 is zero, therefore there is no current flowing to the output. Additional benefit is that the LO is isolated from the output when D is zero, thus alleviating the LO leakage problem.

C. Distributed LO buffer

In high power applications, the power consumed by driving the LO signals is also high. Moreover, the LO leakage caused by parasitic coupling can be strong, thus significantly degrading the EVM at low power level. To address these problems, a column-buffered LO driving strategy is used. Instead of driving the N x N unit cells directly, the LO signals first pass N column buffers which are controlled by column selection signals generated in the thermo-meter decoder. The diagram of the column buffer is shown in Fig. 5.   The output of the column buffer feeds the N unit cells in the corresponding column. With such configuration, there is no LO presented in the column when the column is turned off, further alleviating the LO leakage.

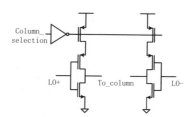

Fig. 5.   The schematic of the column LO buffer.

IV.   LAYOUT

The digital polar PA described above is implemented in a 65nm digital CMOS process with two thick metal layers together with the Alucap layer. A photograph of the chip is shown in Fig. 6. The die area is approximately 2 mm^2. In the layout the primary stage of the transformer is single turn and formed by M4, M5, and M6, while the secondary stage is also single turn and formed by M7 together with Alucap. The secondary stage is just stacked on top of the primary stage for higher coupling factor, and hence higher power efficiency. Furthermore "8" shape technique is employed to layout the four transformers, which minimizes the effects of internal flux cancellation caused by adjacent stages, and hence improves power efficiency [8].

The size of one unit matrix containing 256 unit cells (8 binary bits) is 170um x 90um, while the size of one transformer is 350um x 350um. One advantage of using transformer-based power interpolating is that the size of the unit cell matrix is much smaller than the transformer in one section, thus enhancing the maximum operating frequency capability.

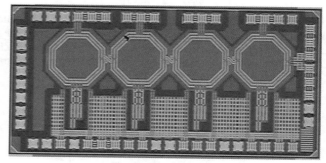

Fig. 6.   Die photograph.

V.   MEASUREMENT RESULTS

To measure EVM of the transmitted WLAN OFDM signals without PLL on chip, MATLAB is used to generate the envelope and phase signals for a data-rate of 54Mb/s using 64QAM. During the measurement, the data bus from a HP80000 data generator feeds the eight binary envelope bits of the digital polar PA at a clock-rate of 240MHz. Simultaneously, the arbitrary waveform generator which is also clocked at 240MHz modulates the RF signal generator, generating the phase-modulated carrier.

Since the measurement is performed after packaging in HVQFN32, the large inductance introduced by the long bonding wire shifts the center frequency of the digital polar PA from 2.4GHz to 1.5GHz. Fig. 7 demonstrates the output spectrum over a larger frequency span. The in-band IEEE mask is fulfilled with sufficient margin. The envelope replicas at +/-240MHz offset from the carrier are roughly 10 dB lower than the out-of-band emission mask, thus avoiding the use of an additional RF filter.

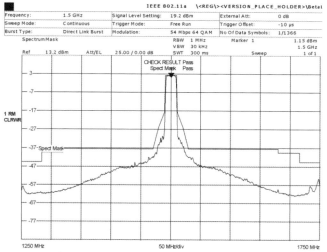

Fig. 7.   The measured wide-band OFDM spectrum.

The measured maximum RMS power is 15.8dBm (17 dBm including 1.2dB loss from the PCB and the cable), with a mean EVM of -29.1dB. Under the maximum output power, the output stage in four sections totally consumes 297mA currents at 1.2V supply voltage, yielding a drain efficiency (DE) of 14%. Including 30mA currents consumed in the LO driver, the resulting power added efficiency (PAE) is 12.7%. Compared to [3], the difference between DE and PAE in this work is smaller, due to the distributed LO buffers.

When two output sections are switched off, the measured maximum RMS power is 12.5dBm, while DE and PAE are 9.8% and 8.9%, respectively. Fig. 8 plots the curves of output power and DE over the number of active interpolation stages. When all the sections are turned off, the measured LO leakage is about -45dBm, which is mainly caused by the coupling between the bonding wires of the LO input and the RF output.

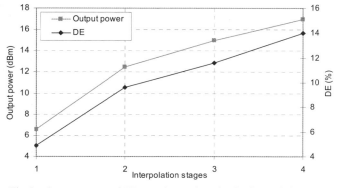

Fig. 8.   Output power and DE over the number of active interpolation stages.

The comparison between this design and other designs is presented in Table 1.

TABLE I.   COMPARISION OF DIGITAL POLAR PA FOR OFDM WLAN

Ref	Center frequency (GHz)	EVM (dB)	Output power (dBm)	DE	PAE	Supply voltage
[3]	1.56	-26.8	13.6	9.2%	7.2%	1.7V
[4]	2.45	-27.2	9.4	8.1%	NA	3V
This work	1.5	-29.1	17	14%	12.7%	1.2V

VI.   CONCLUSION

The prototype design described in this paper implements a high power digital polar CMOS PA using the proposed transformer-based power interpolating. It achieves a maximum RMS power of 17dBm under a 54Mb/s 64QAM WLAN signal, with a DE of 14% and a PAE of 12.7% at 1.2V supply voltage. The measured spectrum fulfills both the in-band IEEE mask and the out-of-band emission mask with sufficient margin. The average power efficiency is also improved by switching on/off each section at low power level. The achieved power level is high enough to eliminate an external PA stage for WLAN applications.

REFERENCES

[1] R. B. Staszewski, et. al., "All-Digital PLL and Transmitter for Mobile Phones," *IEEE J. Solid-State Circuits*, vol. 40, no. 12, pp. 2469-2482, Dec.,2005.

[2] A. Shameli, A. Safarian1, A. Rofougaran, M. Rofougaran, F. De Flaviis, "A Novel DAC Based Switching Power Amplifier for Polar Transmitter," *IEEE Custom Integrated Circuits Conference*, 2006.

[3] A. Kavousian, D.K. Su, B. A. Wooley, "A Digitally Modulated Polar CMOS PA with 20MHz Signal BW," *ISSCC Digest of Technical Papers*, 2007.

[4] P.T.M. van Zeijl, M. Collados "A Multi-Standard Digital Envelope Modulator for Polar Transmitters in 90nm CMOS," *IEEE Radio Frequency Integrated Circuits Symposium*, 2007.

[5] Y. Zhou and J. Yuan, "A 10-Bit Wide-Band CMOS Direct Digital RF Amplitude Modulator," *IEEE J. Solid-State Circuits*, vol. 38, no. 7, pp.1182-1188, July, 2003.

[6] I. Aoki, S. D. Kee, D. Rutledge, and A. Hajimiri, "Distributed active transformer: A new power combining and impedance transformation technique," *IEEE Trans. Microwave Theory Tech.*, vol. 50, no. 1, Jan. 2002.

[7] G. Liu, T.K. Liu, A. M. Niknejad, "A 1.2V, 2.4GHz Fully Integrated Linear CMOS Power Amplifier with Efficiency Enhancement," *IEEE Custom Integrated Circuits Conference*, 2006.

[8] P. Haldi, D. Chowdhury, G. Liu, and A.M. Niknejad, "A 5.8 GHz Linear Power Amplifier in a Standard 90nm CMOS Process Using a 1V Power Supply," *IEEE Radio Frequency Integrated Circuits Symposium*, pp. 431-434, 2007.

A 2.4-GHz +25dBm P-$_{1dB}$ linear Power Amplifier with Dynamic Bias Control in a 65-nm CMOS Process

Po-Chih Wang, Kai-Yi Huang, Yu-Fu Kuo, Ming-Chong Huang, Chao-Hua Lu, Tzung-Ming Chen, Chia-Jun Chang, Ka-Un Chan, Ta-Hsun Yeh, Wen-Shan Wang, Ying-Hsi Lin and Chao-Cheng Lee

Realtek Semiconductor Corp.

Hsinchu, Taiwan

phking@realtek.com.tw

Abstract—**A 2.4GHz linear CMOS power amplifier (PA) for OFDM WLAN application in 65nm CMOS technology is presented. The cascode PA operating from 3.3V employs the proposed asymmetric lightly doped drain MOSFET (A-LDD) structure as common-gate stage to sustain large signal stress and 1.2V core device as common source stage to provide high frequency operation. Beside, dynamic bias technique is used not only to increase efficiency but also improve the linearity. In the measurement, the breakdown voltage of the A-LDD MOSFET can achieve 6.2V compared to standard I/O device of 5V. A PA EVM of □29dB is achieved at output power of 17dBm with DC current of 173mA from 3.3V supply. Also, it reveals the output P1dB of PA is 25.3dBm.**

I. INTRODUCTION

With the development of RF technology, CMOS process becomes a promising choice because of the advantages for low cost and high integration with digital circuit. A large number of CMOS RF building blocks has been demonstrated and can keep pace with the advanced technology ones, such as SiGe and GaAs. But the advantage is mainly restricted in the small signal circuit. For the linear power amplifier design, the efficiency-linearity tradeoff and reliability becomes the most challenge in the CMOS technology. To keep high fidelity OFDM signal through power amplification is the most important business in WLAN system, due to the modulation format has a high peak to average power ratio (PAPR) of 8~10dB. Conventional RF linear CMOS PA's are usually biased as Class A [1] to minimize nonlinear distortion. However, it gives the maximum power added efficiency (PAE) near maximum output power level, and drop sharply as the power level decrease. Therefore, linear CMOS PA's face the linearity-efficiency tradeoff, and efficiency boosting at average power level is required. Three techniques to boost efficiency of linear PA have been investigated for many years. Doherty PA [2], based on modulating load impedance according to instantaneous power level, is the first one. However, the load impedance becomes hard to control when considering the parasitic in package and process variation, and the linearity will suffer. The second one is the most popular strategy of envelope tracking (ET)[3], which adapt the power supply voltage dynamically, and efficiency enhancement result. Nevertheless, the modulator inherently suffers from trade off between bandwidth and efficiency. Besides, the

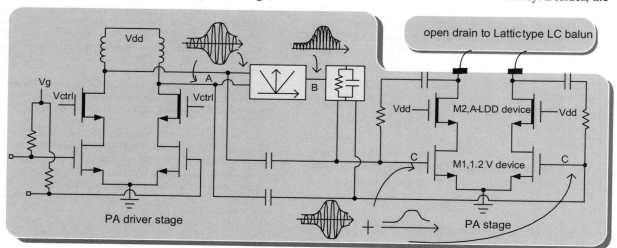

Figure 1. Simplified schematic of 65nm linear CMOS PA.

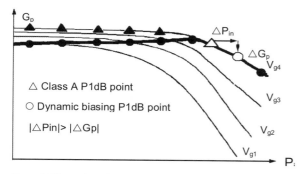

Figure 2. Illustration of PA gian curve with dynamic biasing technique.

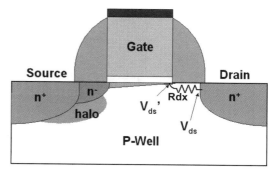

Figure 3. Structure of A-LDD MOSFET .

cascode architecture is often used to guarantee the reliability, and the knee voltage is much higher than common source architecture. Therefore, the efficiency improvement may be inferior. Rather than modulating supply voltage, the last one is dynamic biasing which control the bias current through gate node according to the input signal level. This technique has faster tracking speed to accommodate the wideband OFDM signal of 20MHz and will be insensitive to the parasitic at output node of PA. Also, the linearity (P1dB) will be somewhat improved due to the trans-conductance curve of CMOS PA, which will be discussed later.

As the CMOS process scaling, the limitation of low operation voltage will reduce the maximum output power, even though the conventional I/O device is used. The drain breakdown, including drain to source punch-through, drain to gate oxide breakdown, and hot carrier effect is the main reliability issue. Recently, lots of studies deal with power device for PA design such as LDMOS [4]. However, the extra mask is necessary for a stable LDMOS and it is not usually provided in advance technology by IC foundry. Besides, the long drift region is necessary for the high voltage drop. It will increase the device size. Low cost, small size and short time to market are always to be the important considerations for IC industry. Therefore, we employ a special MOS device as the common gate stage of the PA called A-LDD MOSFET that having an asymmetric LDD structure based on 65nm technology. It is modified from standard I/O device and no extra mask is required.

The outline of this paper is as follows. In Section II, the circuit architecture of the 65nm CMOS PA is presented and the dynamic biasing technique is discussed. Section III describes the device implementation of A-LDD MOSFET using 65nm CMOS technology. The measurement result is presented in section IV, followed by conclusion in section V.

II. CMOS PA WITH DYNAMIC BIAS CONTROL

A. 65nm CMOS PA Circuit topology

Figure 1. shows the simplified circuit of 65nm differential PA. Cascode configuration with standard driving transistor M1 and A-LDD common-gate transistor M2 is used for compromise between high frequency performance and reliability. Resistor shunt feedback method is used to stabilize the PA circuit. The Lattice-type LC-balun is implemented on board to minimize power loss and provide optimal impedance for power combining from PA to antenna. In order to control

the output power level, changing the gain of the PA driver by switching the cascode transistor is used [4]. In our design, 30dB control range with 6dB step is implemented. Also, the envelope detector is implemented to provide dynamic control of the PA.

B. Dynamic Biasing technique

The stringent requirement of PA linearity can be accomplished by class-A PA. Unfortunately, such biasing technique would lead to waste of DC current when the power of incoming signal is small, hence degrading power added efficiency (PAE). Dynamic bias technique, which control gate "dc" bias voltage with varying envelop of RF input signal to adapt the drain current dynamically has been implemented in [5]. The technique ensures that the amplifier always has sufficient bias current to amplify incoming signal linearly without drawing an excessive supply current at low amplitude signal. This will greatly reduce the average current from supply for OFDM system to transmit large peak to average power ratio signal. In our design, as shown in Figure 1., the envelope tracking circuit detects the output differential signal of PA driver (differential node A), and provides gate "dc" bias voltage to the PA. The gate "dc" bias will recombine with the RF signal at the differential node C of PA input. The envelope tracking circuit includes rectifier that commutates the RF signal at node B and low pass filter to eliminate the unwanted harmonic signal. The 3-dB bandwidth of the filter should be chosen carefully to compromise the tracking speed of OFDM signal and suppression of the unwanted harmonics.

C. Comparison Between Dynamic Biasing and Class A PA

To compare the power saving ability from Class-A PA to dynamic biasing ones, let's consider the following case. Generally, the peak to average power ratio of an OFDM signal is roughly 9dB, this means:

$$\frac{P_{av}}{P_{peak}} = \frac{V_o^2 / (2R_L)}{V_{dd}^2 / (2R_L)} \approx \frac{1}{8} \quad (1)$$

in which V_o and V_{dd} is the output voltage of PA and supply voltage, respectively, and R_L is the optimal load for Class-A

PA. For the same output level transmission, the DC power consumption of Class-A PA is

$$P_{classA} = \frac{V_{dc}}{R_L} * V_{dc} \qquad (2)$$

If an optimal bias level is provided dynamically, the DC power consumption of the dynamic bias PA will be

$$P_{dy} = \frac{V_o}{R_L} * V_{dc} \qquad (3)$$

From (1), (2) and (3), the resulting relationship of DC power consumption between Class-A PA and dynamic bias ones in an OFDM system is

$$P_{dy} \approx 0.35 \cdot P_{classA} \qquad (4)$$

This means 65 % power saving is achieved from class-A PA to dynamic biasing ones.

The 1-dB compression point of power gain (G_p) with dynamic biasing is often higher than one obtained at Class A bias (V_{g4}), as shown in Figure 2. This is attributed to the nonlinear characteristic of CMOS trans-conductance (G_m), in which the Gm is smaller at low gate bias (V_{g1}) compared to high gate bias (V_{g4}). Therefore, the PA with dynamic biasing has a higher linear range. In the measurement result, the P1dB point of PA with dynamic biasing is 1.7dB higher than Class A ones.

III. A-LDD MOS DEVICE IN 65NM TECHNOLOGY

Due to the highest voltage drop of the cascode topology lies in the drain-source voltage of the common-gate transistor in the RF frequency operation, an A-LDD MOSFET structure as shown in figure 3. is implemented to sustain large signal operation. The devices were manufactured by standard mixed signal 65nm technology provided by IC foundry. Both baseband and RF GSG testkey were measured for device characterization and modeling. In order to create a large voltage drop region at drain side, the drain LDD is removed by blocking the LDD and Halo implant. Only one logic operation layer is necessary to form LDD/Halo implant region by mask tooling so there is no extra process step required. Due to the LDD block, the drain edge does not overlap the gate edge. It strengthens the drain to gate oxide breakdown voltage. In addition, the maximum lateral electric field is far away the gate edge due to drain spacer region. The hot carrier effect is weakened so that the short channel length can be used to have higher cutoff frequency compared with conventional I/O device. The A-LDD MOSFET structure has been used as common gate in the 65nm CMOS PA design. Although the A-LDD MOSFET presents significant nonlinear parasitic resistor Rdx at drain node, the simulation result shows no significant different performance compared to conventional device. This is because large multi-finger devices are in parallel to form the common gate stage, and the Rdx is negligible compared to the impedance of output matching.

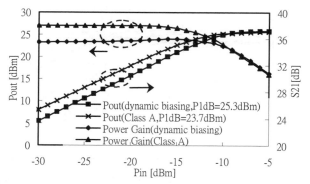

Figure 4. Measured PA Performance (S_{21}, output power).

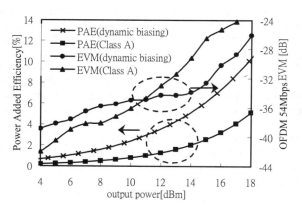

Figure 5. Measured PA efficiency versus EVM

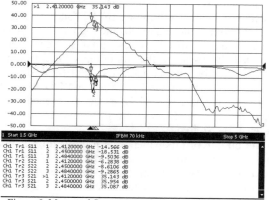

Figure 6. Measured S-parameter performance of PA

IV. INTEGRATION MEASUREMENT RESULT

Figure 4. shows the measured PA performance, it reveals output P_{1dB} of 25.3dBm and S_{21} of 33.9dB in dynamic biasing PA compared to Class A ones, in which P_{1dB} of 23.7dBm and S_{21} of 36dB. This result shows the dynamic biasing has 1.6dB higher linear range. To confirm dynamic bias function, a comparison of fixed (Class A) and dynamic bias in terms of EVM and PAE is shown in Figure 5. At 17dBm OFDM (64QAM, 54Mbps) signal power, the PA with dynamic bias achieves PAE of 8.9% with EVM of −28.5 dB compared to constant bias ones which shows PAE of 3.3% with EVM of

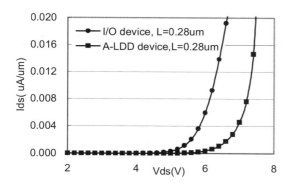

Figure 7. Measured drain off breakdown BVdss at Vg=0V

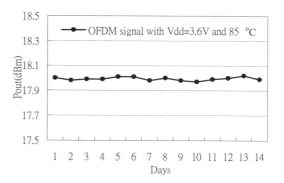

Figure 8. Measured PA output power with stress conditions

−25.3dB. This figure also shows the PA with dynamic bias can deliver 2dB more output power than that using Class A bias while meeting the more stringent EVM of −28dB. Figure6. shows the S-parameter measurement with S_{21} of 36dB, S_{11}<-9.5dB and S_{22} <-6.2dB, respectively. The measured result of drain off breakdown voltage of the A-LDD MOSFET and its counterpart, 2.5V I/O device, are shown in Figure 7.. The drain off breakdown voltage of A-LDD MOSFET can achieve about 6.2V compared to the standard device of 5V breakdown voltage.

To test the reliability of the CMOS PA, extreme environment conditions were imposed on the circuit. The PA is operated under 3.6V Vdd and elevated temperature of 85 °C, while providing 18dBm (OFDM signal) output power for two weeks. Figure 8. shows the result with no power degradation, which confirms the robustness of the PA design for the WLAN application. The chip is fabricated in 65 nm CMOS technology. The die size of 1.5mm×1.5mm is housed in a 32-pin QFN package, and the size of core circuit including PA driver and PA is 0.3mm×0.75mm. The PA performance is summarized in TABLE I, and the chip layout is shown in Figure 9.

V. CONCULSION

A 2.4GHz linear CMOS power amplifier (PA) for OFDM WLAN application in 65nm CMOS technology is presented. The cascode PA employs the proposed asymmetric lightly dope drain MOSFET (A-LDD) structure as common-gate stage to sustain large signal stress and 1.2V core device as common source stage to provide high frequency operation. Beside, dynamic bias technique is used not only to increase efficiency but also improve the linearity. The measured result

TABLE I.   Summary of Power Amplifier Performance

Parameter	Results for 2.4GHz band
Power Consumption @P_{out}	571mW/331mW @ 17dBm/DC
Output P_{1dB}	25.3 dBm
EVM @P_{out} (54Mb/s)	-29dB@17dBm
PAE @P_{out}	8.9%@17dBm
Power Gain	35 dB
Technology	65 nm 1P7M1U CMOS

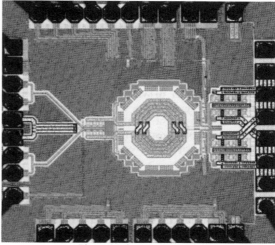

Figure 9.Micrograph of the chip

shows the PA EVM of -29dB is achieved at output power of 17dBm with PAE of 8.9% for a 54Mbps OFDM signal. Also, the reliability testing result show the PA is robust for the WLAN system under unrealistic stress condition. The high linearity, adequate efficiency and robustness make the PA suitable for WLAN application.

Reference

[1] R. Chang, D. Weber, M.L. Lee et al., "A Fully integrated RF Front-End with Independent RX/TX Matching and +20dBm Output Power for WLAN Applications," *ISSCC Dig.Tech. Paper, pp. 564-565, Feb. 2007*

[2] S. Cripps, *RF Power Amplifiers for Wireless Communications, 1st ed. Norwood, MA: Artech House.*

[3] Feipeng Wang, Donald F. Kimball et al., "A Monolithic High-Efficiency 2.4-GHz 20-dBm SiGe BiCMOS Envelope-Tracking OFDM Power Amplifier," *IEEE J. Solid-State Circuits,vol. 42,no. 6, pp.1271-1281, June. 2007*

[4] J. Ramos and M. Steyaert, "STI/LOCOS compatible LDMOS structure in Standard CMOS," *Electron. Lett., vol.39, no. 19, pp. 1417-1419, Sep. 2003.*

[5] Po-Chih Wang, Chia-Jun Chang et al "A 2.4GHz Fully Integrated Transmitter Front End with +26.5-dBm On-Chip CMOS Power Amplifier," *IEEE Radio Frequency IC Symp. Dig.,2007, pp. 263-266.*

The work reported here is the subject of patent applications by the authors. Licenses and further technical information are available to interested parties

0.13-□m SiGe BiCMOS Radio Front-End Circuits for 24-GHz Automotive Short-Range Radar Sensors

Angelo Scuderi

Automotive Product Group, RF Competence Center
STMicroelectronics
Stradale Primosole 50, 95121, Catania, Italy
Email: angelo-apg.scuderi@st.com

Egidio Ragonese, Giuseppe Palmisano

DIEES
Università di Catania, Facoltà di Ingegneria
Viale A. Doria 6, 95125 Catania, Italy
Email: eragone@diees.unict.it, gpalmisano@diees.unict.it

Abstract□ **This paper presents the key blocks of a 24-GHz front-end for vehicular short-range radar sensors implemented in a 0.13-□m SiGe BiCMOS process. In particular, a three-stage low-noise amplifier with transformer-based loads, a frequency synthesizer, consisting of 24-GHz voltage-controlled oscillator in closed loop with an N-integer PLL, and an ultra-wideband transmitter based on a RF current steering switch are detailed. The low-noise amplifier provides an outstanding power gain of 35 dB and a noise figure as low as 3.4 dB, guarantying an input 1-dB compression point of □12 dBm. The transmitter is able to deliver 0-dBm output power at 24 GHz, complying with 1-ns pulse transmission requirements.**

I. INTRODUCTION

Advanced driver assistance systems (ADAS) are becoming the most attractive solution to reduce the vehicular accident probability. ADAS systems face both comfort functionalities (i.e. ACC, stop&go, night vision, etc.) and safety functions (i.e. ESP, collision warning, collision mitigation, etc.), preparing the car for an inevitable accident (belt tensioner, emergency break, etc.) up to reduce the crash severity acting on restraint system (airbags) or post-crash devices (telematics, emergency call, etc.). In this scenario, radar sensors are considered the eligible technology to interact with both safety and comfort devices providing data on obstacle positions. To achieve a complete inspection around the car, a radar system takes advantage of two classes of sensors. Long-range radar (LRR) sensors cover a limited angle (±10°) ahead of the car at distances of few meters to about 150 m and are typically used for autonomous cruise control (ACC) applications. Short-range radar (SRR) sensors cover a significant part of the azimuth angle and finally look around the car (100° to 360°) at distances up to 20 m.

Although the growing importance of radar systems a global standardization is not yet achieved. Regulation institutes, such as the Federal Communication Commission (FCC) and the European Telecommunications Standards Institute (ETSI), recently allocate unlicensed bands for ultra-wideband (UWB) SRR in USA and EU, respectively. In

2002, the FCC regulation indicates a band as large as 7 GHz between 22 to 29 GHz allowed for SRR devices [1]. In order to support the development of UWB SRR systems in commercial silicon-based technology, the EU permits the temporary use of a band between 22 to 26.625 GHz until June 2013 [2]. From 2013 new cars should be equipped with radar sensors operating only in the frequency range 76-81 GHz.

Unfortunately, at present the high operating frequency of such systems limits the large diffusion posing serious problems concerning cost, yield, manufacturing and testing on high-volume productions in commercial silicon-based technologies. In particular, the radio front-end still represents the bottleneck for the development of a silicon-integrated radar system.

In this paper several crucial blocks, such as low-noise amplifier (LNA), phase locked loop (PLL), and UWB transmitter, for 24-GHz automotive SRR sensor application are presented.

II. CIRCUIT DESIGN

A. Low-Noise Amplifier

The simplified schematic of the LNA is shown in Fig. 1.

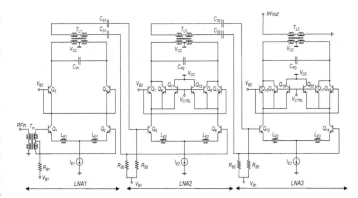

Figure 1. Simplified schematic of the 3-stage LNA.

The circuit consists of three gain stages, which exploit a fully differential topology to avoid detrimental effects of parasitic ground inductance and to provide high rejection of common-mode spurious signals and substrate noise. Each amplifier stage adopts a transformer-loaded cascode topology, which allows first-rate reverse isolation, excellent power gain, and high linearity to be achieved. The first stage, *LNA1*, was designed to achieve simultaneous noise/input impedance matching by using optimum transistor sizing and emitter inductors (L_{E1}). On the contrary, in both *LNA2* and *LNA3* inductive emitter degeneration (L_{E2}, L_{E3}) was employed to trade-off power gain and linearity performance. Transformer resonant loads (T_{L1}, T_{L2}, and T_{L3}) were accurately designed to optimize the overall power gain performance by maximizing the transformer characteristic resistance (TCR) [3]. The design of an integrated transformer is an issue of great concern at *mm*-wave frequencies since the adopted inductance values fall in the sub-nH range [4]. Moreover, the TCR optimization procedure requires iterative steps and time consuming electromagnetic (EM) simulations. For these reasons, scalable lumped model was first exploited to define the spiral geometrical parameters, and then a 2D EM simulator (Agilent Momentum) was used to validate the transformer layout structure and refine its EM behavior, taking into account the connection paths. Finally, to guarantee the required gain bandwidth flatness, which is an issue of great concern in multi stage amplifiers with resonant load, the inter-matching LC networks were properly designed.

A variable-gain approach is also adopted to relax linearity requirements of the *I-Q* mixers and subsequent blocks in the receiver chain. As shown in Fig. 1, a single-bit gain control is achieved by means of the control voltage, V_{CTRL}. In particular, at low-gain setting ($V_{CTRL} = 2.5$ V) the current delivered to the resonant load depends on the emitter area ratio of transistors $Q_{8,9}$, $Q_{11,12}$ ($Q_{16,17}$, $Q_{19,20}$), while at high-gain setting ($V_{CTRL} = 0$ V) the stages work as traditional cascode amplifiers. This technique significantly increases the receiver linearity, still maintaining excellent noise figure performance. At the output, differential-to-single-ended conversion is inherently provided by the transformer T_{L3}, while at the input an integrated balun (T_{in}) was included for testing purpose.

The layout drawing of *mm*-wave Si-based blocks is a crucial phase in the overall design flow. Indeed, geometrical asymmetries, interconnection path parasites, and EM coupling produce considerable degradation of the expected results. Moreover, a poor on-chip ground reference, due to the stringent metal density rules of modern processes further deteriorates both circuit reliability and performance. For these reasons, much attention was paid to the design of differential signal paths in terms of symmetry and length. This was also accomplished by adopting a symmetric interleaved structure for the transformer loads T_L and differential folded microstrips to implement degeneration inductors L_E. Furthermore, a low-resistance/low-inductance ground plane was adopted, which makes use of an appropriate metal 2/metal 3 pattern to meet density requirements still implementing a well-defined on-chip ground reference for the LNA. Finally, extensive EM post-layout simulations were carried out to take into account *RLC* parasitics and coupling effects.

B. 24-GHz Synthesizer

The design of a frequency synthesizer working at operating frequency higher than 5 GHz is an issue of great concern. The design of both low-noise oscillator and high-frequency prescaler represents the bottleneck to demonstrate the feasibility of Si-based chips for high-frequency applications. This work uses a 24-GHz PLL, adopting a well-established architecture composed of phase/frequency detector (PFD), charge pump, external loop filter, voltage-controlled oscillator (VCO), and *N*-integer divider. Using a division ratio *N* of 2048 a 24.125-GHz carrier is achieved with a PLL reference frequency f_{REF} of 11.78 MHz. A second order loop filter is used to set PLL bandwidth at 200 kHz.

The VCO, whose simplified schematic is depicted Fig. 2, uses a bipolar core with high-*Q LC* resonator. An issue of great concern is the design of both capacitors and inductor in the *LC* tank. This resonator exploits accumulation MOS (A-MOS) variable capacitors and a single-turn inductor whose value at 24 GHz is as low as 230 pH. As reported in [4], both measurements and modeling of such sub-nH spirals are quite critical. To overcome these problems and take into account all connection paths, EM simulators are extensively adopted during the resonator design.

Finally, the *N*-integer divider is designed using a chain of 11 divider-by-two stages. Each stage uses flip-flop in closed-loop master-slave configuration. High-speed flip-flops are designed using current-mode-logic *D*-latches. Each divider drives the subsequent one using an emitter follower stage. The design of high-speed D-latches requires accurate *RLC* extraction and evaluation of connection paths during layout drawing. To this aim, in addition to conventional post layout flows, commercial EM simulator was largely exploited to guarantee working capabilities beyond 30 GHz.

C. UWB Transmitter

The modulated pulses are generated by using a sub-ns switch, whose simplified schematic is shown in Fig. 3. A current steering approach is adopted. The 24-GHz signal drives the RF port, while the pulse signal coming from the pulse generator (PG) steers the RF signal into the output port to generate the 24-GHz modulated pulse. The switch is properly designed to deliver a 0-dBm output power complying with 1-ns pulse transmission requirements, thus avoiding the need of an additional amplifier. A resonant load composed of MIM capacitor, C_L, and stacked transformer, T_{LOAD}, is adopted. The design of the output transformer T_{LOAD} is an issue of great concern. First a simplified lumped model [5] was exploited to define the transformer geometrical parameters and then a commercial 3D EM simulator, Ansoft HFSS, was used to simulate the layout structure, taking into account all the connection paths. The monolithic transformer provides both differential-to-single-ended conversion of the output signal and ESD protection, as well. Thanks to the secondary inductor of T_{LOAD}, the current generated by electrostatic discharge is shorted to the ground without any ESD protection diode loading the RF stage.

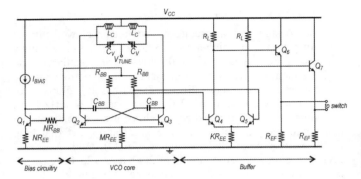

Figure 2.   Simplified schematic of the VCO and buffer.

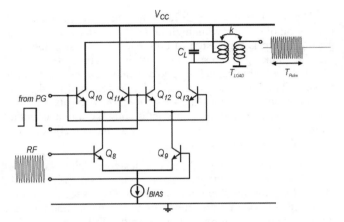

Figure 3.   Simplified schematic of TX output switch.

III.   EXPERIMENTAL RESULTS

A 0.13-□m SiGe:C BiCMOS technology featuring high-speed npn transistors with f_T/f_{max} of 166/175 GHz, dual V_T dual gate oxide CMOS devices, high-quality passives and 6-level metal copper back-end was used [6]. For testing purpose, the chips were mounted on a 400-□m thick FR4 substrate adopting chip-on-board assembly technique.

The die photograph of the LNA is shown in Fig. 4. The LNA measurement setup consists of a two-port HP8510 vector network analyzer, a Summit 12000 Cascade Microtech prober, and an Agilent N8975A noise figure analyzer. Testing was carried out at 2.5-V supply voltage. Raw data were de-embedded only for the input stacked balun loss. The power gain and noise figure at high-gain setting are reported in Fig. 5. The amplifier achieves a maximum gain of 35 dB and a 3.4-dB noise figure. At low-gain setting the LNA provides a 14.5-dB power gain, while exhibiting a noise figure of 4.5 dB. Thanks to the gain-control functionality, the circuit achieves a 1-dB compression point (P_{1dB}) of –12 dBm. Both input and output return losses are shown in Fig. 6. The LNA exhibits a S_{12} better than –53 dB in the whole operative frequency range, thus demonstrating the effectiveness of the adopted isolation techniques.

The die photograph of the overall UWB transmitter is shown in Fig. 7. The PLL was characterized using Agilent 4440A spectrum analyzer, which features an operating bandwidth as large as 26.5 GHz. The output spectrum centered at 24.125 GHz carrier is shown in Fig. 8. The carrier presents two tones at a frequency offset of ±11.78 MHz (PLL reference frequency f_{REF}), whose levels are 50 dBc lower. The measured output power is about –4.65 dBm, which corresponds to a delivered power of –0.8 dBm considering a cable loss of 3.8 dB at 24 GHz. The maximum power is 1.5 dBm measured at 24.9 GHz.

Figure 4.   Die photograph of the 3-stage LNA.

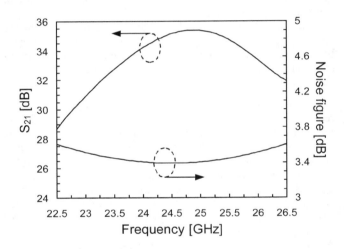

Figure 5.   Power gain (S_{21}) and noise figure at high-gain setting ($V_{CTRL} = 0$ V, $P_{IN} = -30$ dBm).

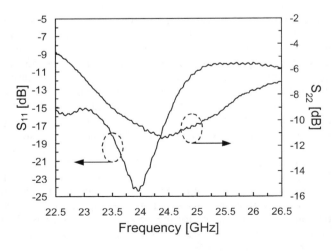

Figure 6.   Input (S_{11}) and output (S_{22}) return losses.

The VCO exhibits a tuning range of 4.7 GHz from 20.4 to 25.1 GHz, when the f_{REF} sweeps between 9.78 to 12.2 MHz. The measured phase noise is −104.3 dBc/Hz at 1-MHz offset from the carrier at 24.125 GHz, as shown in Fig. 9. The VCO core consumes 5.8 mA from a 2.5-V power supply.

Fig. 10 shows the measured spectrum of the UWB transceiver with a pulse repetition frequency (PRF) fixed to 10 MHz. The spectrum presents a main lobe centered at 24.125 GHz with two nulls at 23.25 and 25.08 GHz respectively, which indicate a pulse transmission with T_{Pulse} of 1.1 ns. The spectrum presents two secondary lobes, whose power spectral density is 10 dBc lower than the main lobe. The carrier at 24.125 GHz is visible as a single tone due to the continuous leakage, as well. Basically, TX leakage is limited by the isolation of transistors Q_{10}, Q_{11}, Q_{12}, Q_{13} in off state (see at Fig. 3).

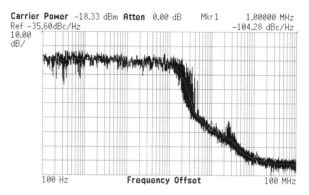

Figure 9. Phase-noise at 1-MHz offset from the 24.125-GHz carrier.

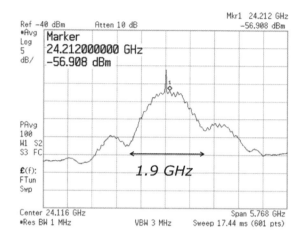

Figure 10. Output spectrum for 1-ns trasmitted pulse (PRF = 10 MHz, RBW = 1 MHz).

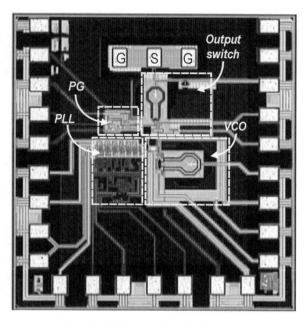

Figure 7. UWB transmitter die photograph.

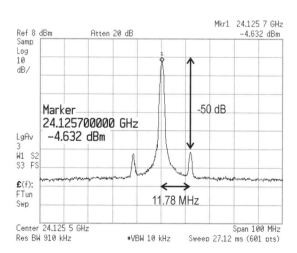

Figure 8. Frequency synthesizer output spectrum.

ACKNOWLEDGMENT

The authors would like to thank Alessandro Castorina, STMicroelectronics, Catania, Italy, for his valuable assistance with measurements.

REFERENCES

[1] "First report and order, revision of part 15 of the commission's rules regarding ultra wideband transmission systems," FCC, Washington, DC, ET Docket 98 153, 2002.

[2] ETSI EN 302 288-1: "Electromagnetic compatibility and Radio spectrum Matters (ERM); Short Range Devices; Road Transport and Traffic Telematics (RTTT); Short range radar equipment operating in the 24 GHz range; Part 1: Technical requirements and methods of measurement".

[3] F. Carrara, A. Italia, E. Ragonese, and G. Palmisano, "Design methodology for the optimization of transformer-loaded RF circuits, *IEEE Trans. Circuits Syst. I*, vol. 53, pp. 761 768, Apr. 2006.

[4] T. Biondi, A. Scuderi, E. Ragonese, and G. Palmisano, "Sub-nH inductor modeling for RF IC design," *IEEE Microwave Wireless Comp. Lett*, vol. 15, pp. 922-924, Dec. 2005.

[5] T. Biondi, A. Scuderi, E. Ragonese, and G. Palmisano, "Analysis and modeling of layout scaling in silicon integrated stacked transformers," *IEEE Trans. Microwave Theory Tech.*, pp. 2203-2210, Apr. 2006.

[6] M. Laurens *et al.*, "A 150 GHz f_T/f_{max} 0.13 □m SiGe:C BiCMOS technology," in *Proc. IEEE Bipolar/BiCMOS Circuits Technol. Meeting*, Oct. 2003, pp. 199-202.

A 24GHz FMCW Radar Transmitter in 0.13 µm CMOS

Yiqun Cao*, M. Tiebout†, Vadim Issakov ‡

*Infineon Technologies, Munich, Germany,
Email yiqun.cao@infineon.com
† Infineon Technologies Austria, Villach, Austria,
Email marc.tiebout@infineon.com
‡ University of Paderborn, Paderborn, Germany,
Email VIssakov@mail.uni-paderborn.de

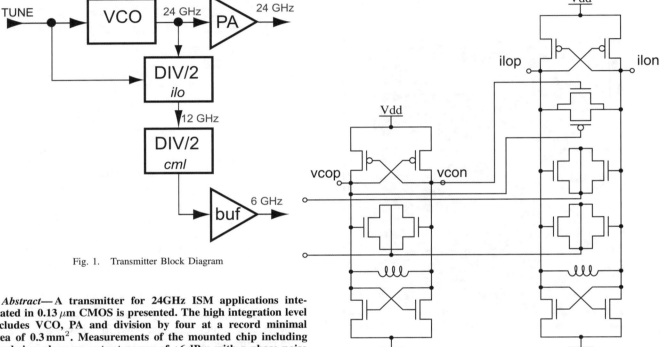

Fig. 1.   Transmitter Block Diagram

Fig. 2.   VCO and ILO schematic

Abstract— **A transmitter for 24GHz ISM applications integrated in 0.13 µm CMOS is presented. The high integration level includes VCO, PA and division by four at a record minimal area of 0.3 mm². Measurements of the mounted chip including bondwires show an output power of +6 dBm with a phase noise of -102 dBc/Hz@1 MHz offset at a power consumption of 64 mW from a single 1.5 V supply.**

I. INTRODUCTION

This work concentrates on the world-wide usable frequency spectrum in the 200 MHz ISM-band at 24 GHz as the wideband frequency ranges between 22 and 26 GHz are condition to regional and time restrictions. Whereas previous CMOS work concentrated just on building blocks or complex large area phased array transmitters and receivers [1–4] aiming at wireless communications, this work presents a minimal area RF FMCW radar transmitter aiming at industrial and consumer applications as e.g. door openers. Due to the small available bandwidth of 200 MHz the realization of a pulse radar is virtually impossible and an FMCW implementation is preferred, relaxing the design requirements as only the phase needs to be modulated and the power amplifier can

be operated in saturation. As the maximal allowed radiated power in the ISM band is 11dBm and the gain of directive antennas at 24 GHz attains easily 6dBi, design target is an output power around 5 dBm (including the bondwires), which seems feasible in a cheap standard 0.13µm CMOS process and opens applications today covered by infrared based devices.

II. DESIGN

Fig. 1 shows the block diagram of the proposed CMOS highly integrated solution. It contains all critical RF-functions. As the transmitter output frequency is divided down to 6GHz, this work can easily be extended to a complete PLL imple-

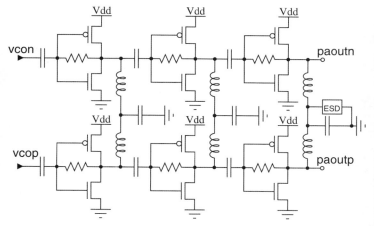

Fig. 3. PA Schematic

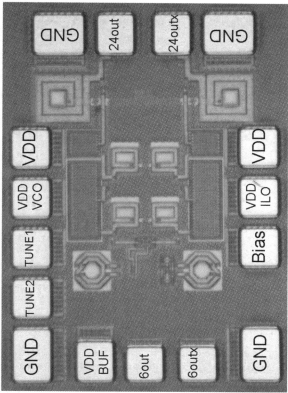

Fig. 4. Chip Photograph

TABLE I

MEASUREMENT SUMMARY

Spec	measured
Pout	6 dBm (board)
Freq. Min.	23.8 GHz
Freq. Max.	25.2 GHz
Chip Area	0.29 mm²
Active Area	0.23 mm²
Phasenoise	-102 dBc/Hz @ 1 MHz
Supply	1.5 V
Current	64 mW

menting a direct phase modulator. As shown in Fig. 1 no buffers were inserted between VCO and PA and between VCO and divider. This is trivially beneficial for the power consumption, but also for the functionality of the transmitter as it allows to benefit from the high voltage swing of the VCO. The design challenge however gets tough, as a simultaneous co-design of VCO, PA and divider is necessary since performances and frequencies of operation are now closely coupled, not to forget layout parasitics from the on-chip 24 GHz connections. The VCO was implemented with a current re-using nmos/pmos VCO topology as described in [5]. The LC-tank design includes the loads from the PA and divider by two, nevertheless aims at a tuning range of at least 1 GHz. The first division by two was implemented as a differential direct injection locked oscillator (ILO) described in [6] as it offers the smallest possible input load to the VCO leaving more headroom to the PA input devices. The schematic of the VCO and ILO combination is shown in Fig. 2. To track the locking range of the ILO to the VCO, it shares the tuning input with the VCO and another varactor for coarse tuning was added. The LC-tank of the ILO and of to the VCO match well as they use an identical inductor and are laid out using the same varactor and MOS cells. The output signal is further divided to a more easy to handle output frequency of 6 GHz by a CML-divider [7].

The three-stage PA is based on a high frequency use of a CMOS inverter-like circuit topology similar as the LNA in [8] and shown in Fig. 3. The VCO output is fed to the PA through an AC-coupling capacitor, which was realized as a MIMcap because of its low parasitic capacitance. For small signals, the nmos-pmos inverter like topology can be seen as an efficient current reusing transconductance stage, for large signals it acts like a switching digital inverter. In any case the feedback resistor guarantees an optimal biasing point. The inductors between the outputs tune out the drain capacitances and wiring at the output nodes and input capacitance of the next PA stage. At low frequencies the common-mode stability is provided by the AC-coupling input capacitance, at high frequencies

common mode stability is provided by the capacitive load to the middle node of the drain to drain coil set.

The output impedance match is provided by the parallel LC-tank consisting of the output inductors and all MOS, parasitic and pad capacitances at the output nodes of the PA. All RF relevant parts including coil-sets, pads and interconnects were simulated using the 2.5D EM-simulator SONNET and added to the circuit as nport s-parameter elements. Simulation results match well to the measurements in terms of output power and frequencies. The simulations show that at the output of the last PA stage, a rail to rail full swing signal is generated, which unfortunately is about halfed after the bondwires leading to a measured and simulated output power of around 6 dBm.

499

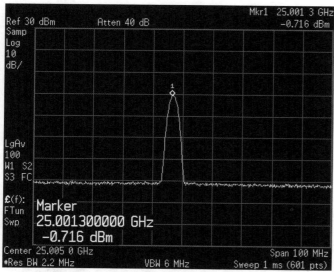

Fig. 5. Transmitter Output Spectrum @ Vtune = 1 V. Losses in board, connectors and cables account for 6.6 dB

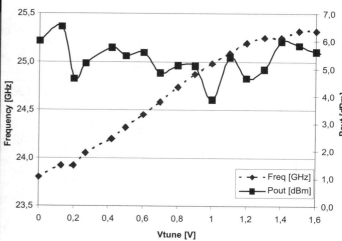

Fig. 6. Measured Frequency and Output Power versus Tuning Voltage

III. MEASUREMENTS

Fig. 4 shows the chip photograph of the 24 GHz transmitter testchip. Die area including pads is only 0.47 mm by 0.63 mm. The chip was processed in INFINEON's standard 0.13m CMOS with 6 Cu layers and one Al pad top level [9]. Only the analog MIMcap option was used and no RFCMOS options like a thick top metal or a high-resistivity substrate. For measurements, the chips were mounted directly on a PCB (chip-on-board). The chip was thinned to 185 μm as necessary for the targeted low-cost VQFN package, also reducing the bond-wire lengths. To convert the differential output signal to single ended, a rat-race balun was realized on the PCB. Figure 5 shows the output spectrum including the losses in the balun, PCB-striplines, SMA-connectors and cabling which total to 6.6 dB. The output frequency and de-embedded output power versus tuning voltage is shown in Fig. 6. The resulting de-embedded measured output power of 5 dBm matches well to the target application. All circuit supplies were connected to a single 1.5 V supply voltage. The power consumption of the PA, VCO, ILO and CML-divider is respectively 23 mA, 4.3 mA, 7.5 mA, and 7.9 mA, totaling to 64 mW. An additional 24 mA is consumed by the divider output buffer. The performance of this work is summarized in Table II (Pdc without divider output buffer). Fig. 7 shows the free-running phase noise measurement of the output signal.

IV. COMPARISON

Table II shows a comparison of this work with recently published work in SiGe and CMOS technologies. The output power is difficult to compare as most work provides only on-wafer measurements without the losses in the bond-wire. It is nevertheless clear that this work excels in terms of lowest power consumption, high integration level, widest tuning range, low phase noise and small area.

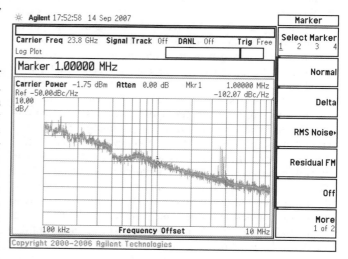

Fig. 7. Measured Phasenoise

V. CONCLUSIONS

An integrated transmitter for 24 GHz ISM applications is realized in 0.13 μm CMOS. The high integration level includes VCO, PA and division by four at a record minimal area of 0.3 mm^2. Measured output power of the mounted chip including bondwires is +6 dBm. The phase noise is -102 dBc/Hz@1 MHz offset at an output frequency of 23.8GHz. The power consumption is only 64 mW from a single 1.5 V supply. The inclusion of bondwire effects as in a cheap mass-market VQFN package and the small area integration into CMOS with further high-integration perspectives open up consumer markets for 24GHz ISM radar applications.

VI. ACKNOWLEDGMENTS

This work was supported under the German BMBF funded project EMCpack / FASMZS 16SV3295.

TABLE II

PERFORMANCE OF RECENTLY PUBLISHED 24GHz WORK, VCO = VOLTAGE CONTROLLED OSCILLATOR, ILO = INJECTION LOCKED OSCILLATOR, LO = LOCAL OSCILLATOR, DIV = DIVIDER, PA = POWER AMPLIFIER, PS = PHASE SHIFTER, IQ = IN- AND QUADRATURE-PHASE

	Architecture	Technology	Freq. [GHz]	Freq. Range [MHz]	Pout [dBm]	PNoise [dBc/Hz]	Area [mm^2]	Pdc [mW]	Vdc V
[10]	LO,PS,PA	0.18 μm CMOS	8	NA	22	NA	3	395	1
[11]	VCO,Div,PA	0.35 μm SiGe BiCMOS	21.5	1250	12.5	NA	3.04	NA	5
[2]	VCO,IQ,4xPA	0.18 μm CMOS	24	NA	14.5 on-wafer	NA	14.28	788	2.5
[12]	VCO,IQ,3xPA	0.13 μm CMOS	24	NA	8	-80 @50kHz	1.8	100	1.2
[13]	Pulser,PA,Bandgap	0.25 μm SiGe BiCMOS	24	NA	12.5 on-wafer	NA	1.04	360	4.5
[14]	2xVCO,PA	0.15 μm GaAs mHEMT	24	1400	10	-98 @1MHz	7.6	260	2.2
this	**VCO,ILO,Div,PA**	**0.13 μm CMOS**	**24**	**1400**	**6 board**	**-102 @1MHz**	**0.29**	**64**	**1.5**

REFERENCES

[1] A. Komijani, A. Hajimiri, " A 24GHz 14.5dBm Fully-Integrated Power Amplifier in 0.18m CMOS," in *CICC Proceedings*, Sep. 2005.

[2] A. Natarajan, A. Komijani, A. Hajimiri, "A Fully Integrated 24-GHz Phased-Array Transmitter in CMOS," *IEEE JOURNAL OF SOLID-STATE CIRCUITS*, vol. 40, no. 12, Dec. 2005.

[3] X. Guan, A. Hajimiri, "A 24-GHz CMOS Front-End," *IEEE JOURNAL OF SOLID-STATE CIRCUITS*, vol. 39, no. 2, Feb. 2004.

[4] S. Shin, M. Tsai, R. Liu, K. Lin, H. Wang, "A 24-GHz 3.9 dB NF Low-Noise Amplifier Using 0.18m CMOS Technology," *IEEE MICROWAVE AND WIRELESS COMPONENTS LETTERS*, vol. 15, no. 7, July 2005.

[5] M. Tiebout, "Low power, low phase noise, differentially tuned quadrature VCO-Design in standard CMOS," *IEEE Journal Solid-State Circuits*, vol. 36, July 2001.

[6] M. Tiebout, "A CMOS Direct Injection-Locked Oscillator Topology as High-Frequency Low-Power Frequency Divider," *IEEE Journal Solid-State Circuits*, vol. 39, pp. 1170–1174, July 2004.

[7] H.-D. Wohlmuth, D. Kehrer, and W. Simbürger, "A High Sensitivity Static 2:1 Frequency Divider up to 19 GHz in 120 nm CMOS," in *Radio Frequency Integrated Circuits Symposium*, Seattle, June 2002, IEEE, pp. 231–234.

[8] Y. Cao, V. Issakov and M. Tiebout, " A 2kV ESD protected 18GHz LNA with 4dB NF in 0.13μm CMOS ," in *ISSCC Proceedings*, Feb. 2008.

[9] T. Schiml, S. Biesemans, G. Brase, et al, "A 0.13 μm CMOS Platform with Cu/ Low-k Interconnects for System On Chip Applications," in *VLSI Digest of Technical Papers*. IEEE, 2001, pp. 101–102.

[10] S Hamedi-Hagh, and C.A.T. Salama, "CMOS wireless phase-shifted transmitter," *IEEE JOURNAL OF SOLID-STATE CIRCUITS*, vol. 39, no. 8, pp. 1241–1252, Aug. 2005.

[11] A. Ghazinour, P. Wennekers, J. Schmidt, Y. Yin, R. Reuter, and J. Teplik, "A fully-monolithic SiGe-BiCMOS transceiver chip for 24 GHz applications," in *BTCM Proceedings*. IEEE, Sep. 2003, pp. 181–184.

[12] C. Cao, Y. Ding, X. Yang, J.-J. Lin, A.K. Verma, J. Lin, F. Martin, and K.K. O, "A 24-GHz Transmitter with an On-Chip Antenna in 130-nm CMOS," in *VLSI Circuits Symp. Dig*. IEEE, June 2006, pp. 148–149.

[13] P. Zhao, H. Veenstra, J.R. Long, " A 24GHz Pulse-Mode Transmitter for Short-Range Car Radar ," in *RFIC Proceedings*. IEEE, June 2007, pp. 379 – 382.

[14] R. Kozhuharov, A. Jirskog, N. Penndal, and H. Zirath, "Single-Chip 24-GHz Synthesizer for a Radar Application," in *CSIC Symp. Dig*. IEEE, Nov. 2006, pp. 205–208.

ESSCIRC Author Index

Evaluation of Intrinsic Parameter Fluctuations on 45, 32 and 22nm Technology Node LP N-MOSFETs

B. Cheng, S. Roy, A. R. Brown, C. Millar, A. Asenov

Dept. of Electronics & Electrical Engineering
University of Glasgow
Glasgow, U.K.
B.Cheng@elec.gla.ac.uk

Abstract—The quantitative evaluation of the impact of key sources of statistical variability (SV) are presented for LP nMOSFETs corresponding to 45nm, 32nm and 22nm technology generation transistors with bulk, thin body (TB) SOI and double gate (DG) device architectures respectively. The simulation results indicate that TBSOI and DG are not only resistant to random dopant induced variability, but also are more tolerant to line edge roughness induced variability. Even two technology generations ahead from their bulk counterparts, DG MOSFETs will still have 4 times less variability than bulk devices.

I.   INTRODUCTION

Statistical variability (SV), which arises from the discrete nature of charge and the granularity of matter, is one of the fundamental limitations of device scaling [1]. According to ITRS 2007 [2], bulk MOSFET scaling is rapidly approaching an end and random discrete dopants (RDD) are one of the important limiting factors on bulk scalability. New device architectures, such as ultra thin body (UTB) and double gate (DG) SOI will be required in the near future in order to keep the benefits of scaling on track. For example, the ITRS predicts that UTB SOI will be introduced in 2010 for HP applications. In concept, these new architectures are more RDD resistant. However, from a yield perspective, the early quantitative evaluation of the magnitude of SV in new device architectures is still extremely important since SV has to be contained by design margins due to its purely random nature. For instance, although UTB SOI devices tolerate very low channel doping and hence have reduced RDD SV, the impact of RDD in the source/drain regions still needs to be taken into account. At the same time, studies of the impact of line edge roughness (LER), which is notoriously difficult to scale due to the molecular structure of photoresist, show that in bulk MOSFETs beyond gate lengths of 20nm it can overtake RDD in becoming the dominant IPF source [3]. This implies that the impact of LER on UTB SOI and DG device SV cannot be ignored and has to be studied in detail. Finally, some concerns were raised in the past that SV associated with statistical body thickness variations introduced by atomic scale interface roughness may play important role in UTB and DG device architectures [4] [5].

In this paper using 3D statistical device simulations, we study the impact of the above three sources of statistical variability on 45nm, 32nm and 22nm technology generation transistors with bulk, thin body (TB) SOI and double gate (DG) device architectures respectively

II.   DEVICE STRUCTURE AND CALIBRATION

The simulated devices are 32nm UTB SOI and 22nm DG template device architectures, corresponding to LP devices at the 32nm and 22 nm technology generations respectively, developed by the PULLNANO consortium. Bulk LP nMOSFETs from the STMicroelectronics 45nm technology platform were also simulated as reference devices in this variability study [6] and the results are compared with experimentally measured variability.

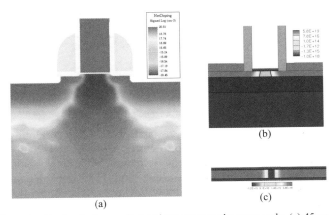

Figure 1   Device doping profiles and structures at the same scale. (a) 45nm node bulk device, (b) 32nm node TBSOI device, (c) 22nm node DG device

The device structures and doping profiles are shown in Fig.1. For 45nm node bulk devices, the physical poly-gate length is 42nm, and effective oxide thickness (EOT) is 1.7nm.

Both 32 and 22 nm technology generation devices feature TiN metal gate and high-k dielectric. The physical gate lengths are 32 and 22nm, EOT are 1.2 and 1.1nm, and silicon body thicknesses are 7 and 10nm respectively with a low p-type doping concentration of $1.2 \times 15 cm^{-3}$ in the channel region. The simulations were carried out with the Glasgow statistical 3D device simulator, which solves the carrier transport equations in the drift-diffusion approximation with Density Gradient (DG) quantum corrections for both electrons and holes [7]. The simulator has been calibrated against the I_d-V_g characteristics of the 32 and 22 nm devices obtained from a commercial TCAD simulator, by adjusting the effective mass parameters involved in DG formalism, and the mobility model parameters. The simulations were carried at a low drain bias of 50mV, and high drain bias of 1.1V for 45nm technology generation devices. The high drain bias was reduced to 1V for 32 and 22nm technology generation devices. The calibration results are shown in Fig. 2. Good agreement has been achieved between the commercial TCAD and the Glasgow atomistic simulator.

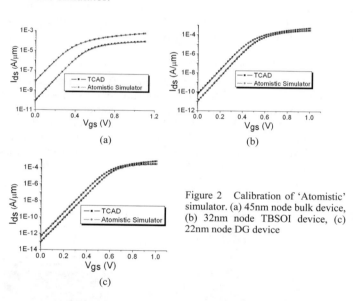

(a)

(b)

(c)

Figure 2 Calibration of 'Atomistic' simulator. (a) 45nm node bulk device, (b) 32nm node TBSOI device, (c) 22nm node DG device

III. IPF SIMULATION METHODOLOGY

Both RDD and LER are studied for 45nm, 32nm and 22nm technology generation devices. Poly Gate Granularity (PGG) is investigated as an important additional variation source for bulk MOSFET, while Body Thickness Variation (BTV) and its associated Oxide thickness fluctuations (OTF) are studied as additional sources of UTB SOI and DG device variability. In the simulations, the RDD are generated from a continuous doping profile by placing doping atoms on silicon lattice sites within the device with a probability determined by the local ratio between dopant and silicon atom concentration [8]. The LER is introduced through 1D Fourier synthesis. Random gate edges are generated from a power spectrum corresponding to a Gaussian autocorrelation function [9]. For all devices, RMS amplitude Δ is 1.3 nm, which is the value achievable with present state-of-the-art lithography systems [10]. Correlation length Λ is 30nm for the 45nm technology generation, and 25nm for the 32nm and 22nm technology generations respectively. The PGG is introduced by the

random generation of poly-grains for the whole gate region from a large AFM image of polysilicon grains [11], while the average grain size is 65nm. BTV (OTF) is introduced through 2D Fourier synthesis, and both top and bottom random interface roughness are generated from a power spectrum corresponding to an Exponential autocorrelation function. The digitalized roughness step is 0.3nm, with a correlation length Λ of 1.8nm [12].

IV. RESULTS AND DISCUSSION

For each individual source of variability, 3D simulations of 200 statistically different MOSFETs were carried out in order to extract the threshold voltage variation. The typical potential distributions introduced by RDD for the 45nm, 32nm and 22nm technology generation devices are shown in Fig. 3. The much smoother potential distribution in the channel regions of the UTB SOI and DG device clearly demonstrates the improved RDD variability associated with the very low channel doping concentration.

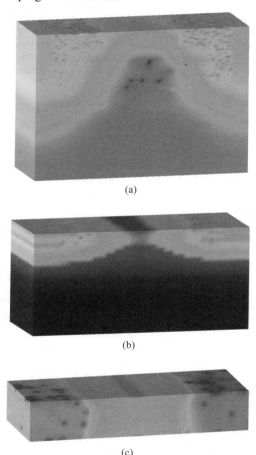

(a)

(b)

(c)

Figure 3 Typical potential distributions corresponding to RDD, plots are not to the same scale. (a) 45nm node bulk device, (b) 32nm node TBSOI device, (c) 22nm node DG device

The histogram of threshold voltage distribution introduced by RDD is shown in Fig.4. From a σV_T point of view, 32nm node UTB SOI devices have almost one order of magnitude improvement comparing to their 45nm node bulk counterpart. Although 22nm node DG devices have a slightly large RDD related threshold voltage variability (compared to 32nm node UTBSOI device), they still show 7-8 times improvement compared to bulk devices which have almost double the gate length.

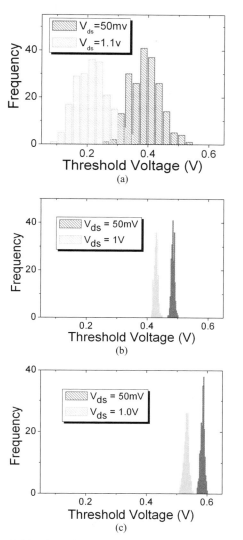

Figure 4 Threshold voltage distributions due to RDD. (a) 45nm node bulk device, (b) 32nm node TBSOI device, (c) 22nm node DG device

Fig.5 shows the histogram of threshold voltage distribution introduced by LER. Although all three technology nodes have similar LER parameters, the variation results are quite different from these which might be anticipated. Despite both UTB SOI and DG devices having much shorter channel lengths compared to their bulk counterparts, at low drain bias the LER induced SV in UTB SOI is 6 times better than that of bulk devices, while DG has more than 3 times improvement over bulk devices. At high drain bias conditions, although the improvements are not as great as in the low drain bias case, UTB SOI and DG still show improvements of almost 4 times and 2.5 times respectively. Results in LER simulation indicates UTB SOI and DG devices have much better electrostatic integrity comparing to their bulk counterparts, and are much less sensitive to channel length variation. The relatively large increase in the threshold variation at high drain

bias indicates that for UTB SOI and DG devices, DIBL is dominant short channel effect, although its absolute value is much smaller than in the bulk MOSFETs. Due to the much improved RDD performance in UTB SOI and DG devices, the dominant SV source under high drain bias conditions is LER.

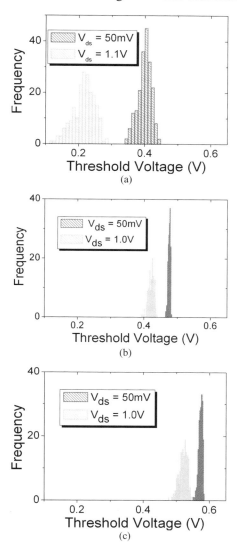

Figure 5 Threshold voltage distributions due to LER. (a) 45nm node bulk device, (b) 32nm node TBSOI device, (c) 22nm node DG device

It has been demonstrated that for thin body SOI with silicon body thickness of 4nm and beyond, a single change of atomic layer will have a dramatic impact on device characteristics [4]. However in our UTB SOI and DG devices with silicon body thickness of 7 and 10nm respectively, the single atomic layer thickness variation has only a weak impact on the position of the electron ground state, and as a result, threshold voltage variation is negligible. Furthermore, the associated OTF induced gate capacitance variation also has a limited impact on threshold voltage variation since V_T is mainly determined by the metal gate work function. The overall BTV/OTF results for the UTB SOI and DG transistors are shown in Fig.6.

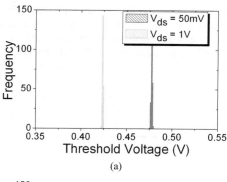

(a)

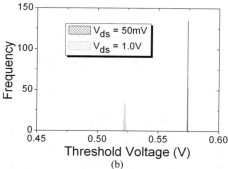

(b)

Figure 6 Threshold voltage distributions due to BTF/OTF. (a) 32nm node TBSOI device, (b) 22nm node DG device

The main results from the simulation are summarized in Table 1. The statistical summation of simulated individual contributions on 45nm node LP nMOSFETs gives $\sigma V_T \approx$ 62mV at V_{ds} of 50mV, and $\sigma V_T \approx$ 67mV at V_{ds} of 1.1V. While the measurement of matching test structures gives $\sigma V_T \approx$ 62mV at V_{ds} of 50mV, and $\sigma V_T \approx$ 69mV at V_{ds} of 1.1V. This demonstrates the good agreement between simulation and experiment. Due to lack of information on metal gate local work function variation, the impact of metal gate on TBSOI and DG device threshold voltage variation is not included in this study. From the simulation, the overall variation for 32nm node TBSOI device is $\sigma V_T \approx$ 6.2mV at V_{ds} of 50mV, and $\sigma V_T \approx$ 11mV at V_{ds} of 1.0V, and increases to $\sigma V_T \approx$ 8.6mV at V_{ds} of 50mV, and $\sigma V_T \approx$ 15mV at V_{ds} of 1.0V for 22nm node DG device.

TABLE 1	Summary of simulation results of IPF sources					
	45nm σV_T (mV)		32nm σV_T (mV)		22nm σV_T (mV)	
	V_{ds}(50mV)	V_{ds}(1.1V)	V_{ds}(50mV)	V_{ds}(1.0V)	V_{ds}(50mV)	V_{ds}(1.0V)
RDD	50	52	5.3	6.1	6.4	8.1
LER	20	33	3.3	8.6	5.8	13
PPG	30	26	N/A	N/A	N/A	N/A
Combined	62	67	6.2	11	8.6	15
Measured	62	69	N/A	N/A	N/A	N/A

V. Conclusion

The impact of key SV sources, such as RDD, LER PPG and BTV, on 45nm, 32nm and 22nm technology technology generation LP nMOSFETs have been investigated in detail. This study covers three generations of device architectures: bulk, UTB SOI and DG. For 45nm node bulk technology,

simulation results agree well with measurement, although measurement for 32nm node TBSOI and 22nm node DG device are not currently possible. Simulation results indicate that compared to their bulk counterparts, UTB SOI and DG MOSFETs not only have much lower RDD variability, but also have significantly improved LER variability due to much better electrostatic integrity. The overall variation introduced by the key SV sources can be more than 4 times less in the DG transistors, two generations in advance of their bulk counterparts, which indicates that the scaling window of silicon CMOS is still open from an SV perspective, but will require the introduction of UTB device concepts.

ACKNOWLEDGMENT

This work has been funded by the European Commission under the PULLNANO project.

REFERENCES

[1] A. Asenov, Simulation of statistical variability in Nano MOSFETs, 2007 Symposium on VLSI Technology, 2007, pp 86-87

[2] http://www.itrs.net.

[3] G. Roy, A. Brown, F. Adamu-Lema, S. Roy, A. Asenov, "Simulation study of individual and combined sources of intrinsic parameter fluctuations in conventional nano-MOSFETs", *IEEE Trans on Electron Devices*, vol. 53, pp.3063-3070, 2006.

[4] K. Uchida, H. Watanabe, A. Kinoshita, J. Koga, T. Numata, S. Takagi, "Experimental study on carrier transport mechanism in ultrathin-body SOI n- and p-MOSFETs with SOI thickness less than 5nm", *IEDM Tec. Dig.* pp. 47-50, 2002

[5] A. R. Brown, F. Adamu-Lema, A. Asenov, "Intrinsic parameter fluctuations in Nanometer scale thin-body SOI devices introduced by interface roughness", *Superlattices and Microstructures*, Vol.34, pp. 283-291, 2003

[6] A. Cathignol, B. Cheng, D. Chanemougame, A. Brown, K. Rochereau, G. Ghibaudo, A. Asenov, "Quantitative evaluation of statistical variability sources in a 45nm technological node LP N-MOSFET", *IEEE Electron Devices.letter*, in press.

[7] G. Roy, A. R. Brown, A. Asenov and S. Roy, "Bipolar Quantum Corrections in Resolving Individual Dopants in 'Atomistic' Device Simulation", *Superlattices and Microstructures*, Vol.34 pp.327-334 (2003).

[8] A. Asenov, G. Slavcheva, A. Brown, J. Davies, S. Saini, "Increase in the random dopant induced threshold fluctuations and lowering in sub-100nm MOSFETs due to quantum effects: A 3-D Density-Gradient simulation study", *IEEE Trans on Electron Devices*, vol. 48, pp.722-729, 2001

[9] A. Asenov, S. Kaya, A. Brown, "Intrinsic parameter fluctuations in decananometer MOSFETs introduced by gate line edge roughness", *IEEE Trans on Electron Devices*, vol. 50, pp.1254-1260, 2003

[10] J. Taiault, J. Foucher, J.H. Tortai, O. Jubert, S. Landis and S. Pauliac, "Line edge roughness characterization with three-dimensional atomic force microscope: Transfer during gate patterning process", J. Vac. Sci. Technol. B. Vol. 23, pp. 3070-3079 (2005).

[11] A. Brown, G. Roy, A, Asenov, "Poly-Si gate related variability in decananometer MOSFETs with conventional architecture", *IEEE Trans on Electron Devices*, vol. 54, pp.3056-3063, 2007

[12] A. Asenov, A. Brown, J. Davies, S. Kaya, G. Slavcheva, "Simulation of intrinsic parameter fluctuation in decananometer and nanometer-scale MOSFETs", *IEEE Trans on Electron Devices*, vol. 50, pp.1837-1852, 2003

Impact of Strain on LER Variability in bulk MOSFETs

Xingsheng Wang*, Scott Roy, Asen Asenov
Device Modelling Group, Department of Electronics and Electrical Engineering
University of Glasgow
Glasgow G12 8LT, United Kingdom
*E-mail: xswang@elec.gla.ac.uk

Abstract—**This paper presents the first comprehensive three-dimensional (3D) simulation results of modern strained nMOSFETs under the influence of statistical variability, induced by gate line edge roughness (LER). The focus is the impact of strain on the LER induced variability. Stress engineering is introduced and its effects are explored. New detailed results concerning strain variability induced by LER in the channel are demonstrated, and further strain enhanced variability is captured statistically. Finally, the effects of different LER magnitude on strained devices are investigated.**

I. INTRODUCTION

With the progressive scaling of CMOS devices, typical gate lengths are now in the deep deca-nanometer regime, and intrinsic parameter fluctuations have become more important in determining device variability. Random discrete dopants, line edge roughness and poly-silicon granularity in bulk MOSFETs are the main sources of intrinsic parameter fluctuations [1]-[3]. Statistical variability of device electrical parameters is also transferred to higher circuit levels, influencing the functionality and yield of corresponding systems [4][5].

In modern devices, the process induced stress engineering has been used to enhance device performance since its first introduction at the 90 nm technology generation [6]-[9]. Deterministic studies and simulations of the impact of strain on devices subject to realistic layouts [10], and OPC lithography correction [11] have shown that geometry induced strain variations play an important role in determining functionality. We have previously shown that intentional strain enhances drive current, but also enhances the variability caused by LER in almost the same proportion [12].

However, the details of how LER influences the channel strain distribution and how strain variability statistically influences device electrical characteristics – and introduces additional variability – are still unclear. In addition, there has been no study of the effect of LER magnitudes on strained devices. This paper aims to develop an advanced 3D simulation methodology to capture the effects of LER on statistical variability in strained devices, and quantitatively explore their effects. The simulation strategy and device calibration will be covered in section II, following the principles laid out in [12]. Channel strain and enhanced mobility variability due to strain variation will be investigated in section III. In section IV deterministic results are laid out and analysed. Statistical simulations have been done to investigate how strain variability gives rise to an increased variation in both drive current and leakage current, while indeed increasing the average on-current. Strain induced enhancement variation has been investigated to illustrate the additional variation due to strain variability. Different magnitudes of LER have a strong effect on the variability of device electrical characteristics both with and without the inclusion of strain. Conclusions in section V have been drawn.

II. SIMULATION METHODOLOGY AND CALIBRATIONS

Using an advanced TCAD simulation suite [13], our simulation is based on 3D device structures and 3D process simulation. It is necessary to simulate 3D devices to accurately model the effects of LER, whose variation extends into the third dimension. In addition, narrow devices are more dependent on lateral effects such as shallow trench isolation (STI), which makes 3D device structures produced from process simulation vital for accuracy. LER is introduced in the gate mask pattern at the process simulation stage, and its traces are modelled based on real LER captured from different examples of 193 nm lithography. The spacer deposition following gate patterning almost mirrors the roughness of the gate edges, which guarantees effective transfer of strain from the cap layer. A 30 nm thick tensile contact etch stop layer was deposited on the device, which is the main stressor acting on the n-channel MOSFET. Device simulations adopt drift/diffusion models which include quantum corrections. A stress-dependent mobility model [14] is employed to take into account the strain mobility enhancement.

Our simulations are based on a real Toshiba device [15]. Doping concentration calibration is carried out for arsenic in the source/drain extensions and indium in the channel for process simulation. Id-Vd curves at different linearly increasing gate voltages are also calibrated at the device simulation level. This well matched benchmarking guarantees the accuracy of our simulations [12].

This work is carried out under the EPSRC project, "Meeting the design challenges of nano-CMOS electronics" (EP/E003125/1).

III. LER AND STRAIN EFFECTS

As minimal LER is typically in the 5 nm range [16], it causes the significant problems when gate lengths scale to the deca-nanometer regime. Minimal LER is non tool related and unavoidable in 193 nm lithography due to resist granularity and other inherent physical limitations. Our modelled LER traces are based on a Fourier synthesis approach [16]. LER clearly causes a fluctuation in the p-n junction definition, locally altering the effective gate length, and therefore the electrical properties of the transistor. Due to the gate acting as a mask to source/drain extension ion implantation, the gate LER is definitely duplicated to some degree in the roughness of the doping profile, causing the p-n junction line to fluctuate (Fig. 1). This situation is especially evident just below the gate. However, it has to be noticed that even here, thermal annealing smoothes in part the junction roughness, and suppresses its highest frequencies.

A normal stress of 1.8 GPa is set in the intrinsic tensile cap layer. This leads to a uniaxial tensile strain along the channel (Fig. 1) with a compressive strain normal to the channel plane. As an observation of stress components in the channel 1 nm below the oxide/silicon interface: stress yy is on average 1.267×10^8 Pa, stress xx is -5×10^6 Pa, stress zz is -1.445×10^8 Pa while shear stress components are comparatively small: less than 10^6 Pa. According to [13][14] a rough calculation based on above stress levels shows the yy value of the mobility enhancement tensor to be 1.21, which means that strained devices should exhibit an additional ~21% drain current at low voltage.

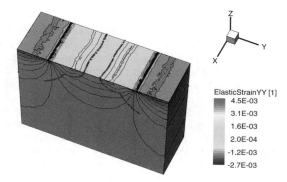

Figure 1. 3D distribution of the elastic strain tensor yy value in the silicon substrate. Tensile strain in the channel is clearly shown, with strain variability due to a sample LER.

Due to gate LER, delivery of the strain to the channel also reflects the rough boundary of gate line, giving rise to an irregularity of strain across the width of the channel direction. This local strain variability further induces local variability in the carrier velocity/mobility enhancement, and hence overall current variability, in addition to that due to local channel length variability in unstrained devices. As a sample, the top trace in Fig. 2 shows that the local shortening of the channel has higher local channel-direction normal strain, and the bottom figure shows that the average electron velocity in this strained device has increased by about 21.5% compared with a corresponding unstrained device (extracted when $Vgs = Vds = Vdd$), with local fluctuations which follow the induced strain.

LER in an unstrained device can induce local current variations, but local strain fluctuations induce additional mobility variability with a highly consistent fluctuation trend, overlaid on an average mobility increase due to the average tensile strain. The mobility of strained devices in the channel shortening regions of Figs. 1 and 2 increases more due to higher strain, and this in turn strengthens the 'hotspot' effect, introducing additional variability.

Notice that the strain variation across the channel is smaller than might otherwise be expected, because the gate boundary (subject to LER) is remote from the highest stress areas by the spacer thickness, and because substrate tensile stress provides a measure of stress compensation in the channel. Decreasing the spacer thickness between gate and source or drain from 52nm to 32nm can significantly enhance the tensile strain in the channel, and it also enhances the strain variation (Fig. 3). For the 52nm spacer, the mean value of strain component yy in Figure 2 is 1.0883×10^{-3}, and *Max-Min*$=3.868 \times 10^{-5}$, therefore the fluctuation ratio *(Max-Min)/Average* is of the order of 3.6%. However for a thin 32 nm spacer (Fig. 3), the average is 1.5156×10^{-3}, and *Max-Min*$=6.2 \times 10^{-5}$, so the fluctuation ratio is approximately 4.1%. This indeed illustrates enhancement of the impact of LER on strain variability when the distance between gate and source or drain gets smaller.

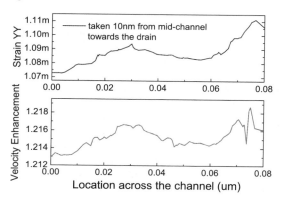

Figure 2. The upper trace is the 1D elastic strain yy value 10nm from the middle of the channel across the device width, 1nm under the gate dielectric. The bottom trace is the corresponding electron velocity enhancement due to the strain, indicating the strain induced mobility variability in the nMOSFET.

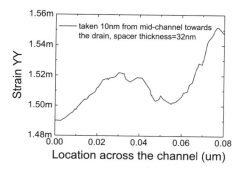

Figure 3. A thinner spacer guarantees increased strain, but also increases the strain variability due to LER.

IV. STRAIN ENHANCED VARIABILITY

A. Deterministic strain performance enhancement

The original intrinsic cap layer stress and cap layer thickness determine the overall strain, while gate length and spacer thickness are important factors affecting channel strain distribution. 2D simulations have been performed to explore how these factors determine the transistor drive current. The magnitude of the cap stress directly determines on-current enhancement; the more stress originated by the cap layer, the more drive current from the device. A linear relationship between drive current and intrinsic cap layer stress is shown in Fig. 4. The cap layer thickness is also a direct factor influencing on-current. Thicker cap layers can gain more strain and more performance enhancement. Obviously unlimited intrinsic stress is impossible, and only a finitely thick effective cap layer can be deposited due to transistor size.

However, device scaling provides additional advantage in stress engineering. Fig. 4 (right graph) shows that drive current will increase as gate length gets smaller. This wins back some benefits from the limitations of small devices.

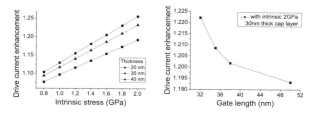

Figure 4. The left graph shows on-current enhancement dependence on intrinsic stress and tensile cap thickness. The right graph shows the relationship of drive current to gate length, with fixed spacer size.

B. Strain enhanced statistical variability

Intentional stress aimed at improving device performance can significantly increase mobility and therefore drive current. However, mobility changes due to LER and varying strain may also enhance statistical variability caused by LER. Based on our calibrated device, 50 nominally identical devices patterned with different LER have been simulated (Fig. 5). The LER has typical parameters of root mean square (rms) Δ = 2.0 nm and correlation length 20 nm [16].

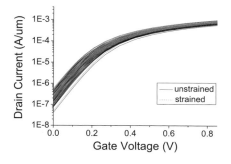

Figure 5. 50 simulated high drain Id-Vg curves of nominal identical devices with/without stress, influenced by LER Δ=2 nm.

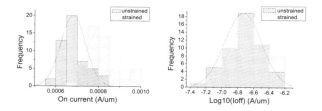

Figure 6. The left graph shows statistics of on-current variation. Strained devices have larger current on average, but also bigger variation. The right graph shows off-current distribution of devices with/without strain.

On-current distribution with and without the effects of strain is shown in Fig. 6. Strained devices (simulated using the basic piezoresistance model) gain more drive current in each device. LER leads to variation of drive current, no matter if the device is strained or not. A statistical analysis for LER Δ =2 nm shows that devices without strain have a standard deviation 58 μA/μm, with the mean value 681 μA/μm. The device without LER has on-current 666 μA/μm. Strained devices have a standard deviation 69 μA/μm with a higher mean 813 μA/μm (Fig. 6). Both the mean and standard deviation of the strained devices increase by 19.4%. It seems that the mobility enhancement indeed increases current, and makes both the mean and standard deviation proportionally bigger. Fig. 7 emphasizes this point by showing its linear correlation between individual drive currents of unstrained and strained devices.

As illustrated in the distribution of logarithmic plot of leakage current in Fig. 6, the off-currents of unstrained devices are fitted with a log-normal distribution. Strained devices are also enhanced, but with a bigger variation than for the on-current.

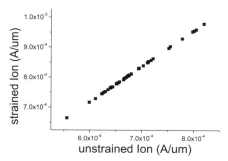

Figure 7. The correlation of strained device on-currents to unstrained device on-currents.

Further analysis in Figure 8 shows that the on-current enhancement also has some variation, i.e. the mobility for every device does not increase by the same factor, and this comes from the difference of each device entire specific electric characteristics with specific local strain variability in the channel due to corresponding LER. Namely each device with specific LER has a specific local strain enhancement. The figure shows that drive current or mobility enhancement of single device derived from particular local strain distribution has some distribution. Statistical results show that they have an averaged enhancement 19.44% with a standard deviation

0.13%. As shown in section III the effect of gate spacers on delivery of strain to the channel is one reason for this small variation. This variability shows the different entire-enhancement of strain, while each device averaged mobility enhancement definitely increases the variation singly caused by LER. From this viewpoint, LER has a number of effects on devices' electrical characteristics, one of which is an indirect effect through strain variability. For leakage current, the enhanced variability of off-current has a larger standard deviation than that of the on-current (Fig. 8). The off-current increase has the average increase 20.94% with standard deviation 0.31%. This means that strain indeed has additional variability contributed to off-current, which contributes to the overall LER induced variability.

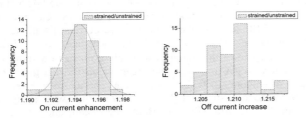

Figure 8. The left graph shows the statistics of on-current enhancement. The right graph shows the statistical distribution of off-current due to strain, which is wider compared with the drive current enhancement distribution. Strained devices show additional variation due to local fluctuations in mobility enhancement.

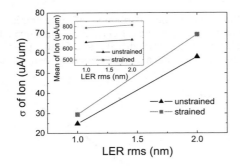

Figure 9. Statistical results of drive current for LER Δ=1nm and 2nm.

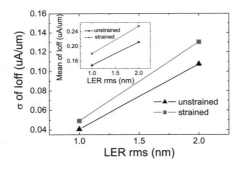

Figure 10. Statistical results of leakage current for LER Δ=1nm and 2nm.

Simulations for devices with LER rms Δ =1 nm have also been carried out. Results, comparing the two magnitudes of LER are shown in Figs. 9 and 10. Different LER magnitude

has a strong effect on both drive current and leakage current whether devices are strained or not. No matter devices are strained or not, bigger LER increases the variation of Ion and $Ioff$, while it also significantly increases the mean value of $Ioff$ in contrast with a small increase in Ion. From Figs. 9 and 10, strained devices indeed obtain a drive current enhancement, but also increase leakage current for nMOSFETs. No matter the value of the LER, strained devices have more variation in Ion and $Ioff$ compared with unstrained devices.

V. CONCLUSIONS

3D nMOSFET simulations which capture the strain variability due to LER, and the resultant effects on transistor mobility, on- and off-currents, have been presented. Tensile strain in the channel does not only increase mobility and drive current, but also enhances the current variability in devices subject to LER. At the same time local strain variation of each device causes specific local additional mobility enhancement variability which strengthens that caused by first order LER effects. Our results – the first ensemble device simulations to investigate the statistics of strain and LER induced intrinsic parameter fluctuations – show that for on-current this increased variability is, to first order, in proportion to the increase in overall average drive current. Variability in off-current is greater, proportionately, than the increase in off-current due to the strain source. However enhancements also have second order effects. Larger LER rms greatly increases the variation of drain current, and strained devices enhance this effect.

REFERENCES

[1] A. Asenov, A.R. Brown, J.H. Davis, S. Kaya, and G. Slavcheva, IEEE Trans. Electron Devices, 50(9), 2003, pp.1837-1852. Invited paper.

[2] G. Roy, A.R. Brown, F. Adamu-Lema, S. Roy and A. Asenov, IEEE Trans. on Electron Devices, 53(12), 2006, pp.3063-3070.

[3] A.R. Brown, G. Roy, and A. Asenov, IEEE Trans. on Electron Devices, 54(11), 2007.

[4] B. Cheng, S. Roy, G. Roy, F. Adamu-Lema and A. Asenov, Solid-State Electronics, 49(5), 2005, pp.740.

[5] M. Miyamura, et al., Symp. on VLSI Tech., Dig. Tech. papers, 2007, pp.22-23.

[6] S. Takagi, et al., IEDM Tech. Digs., 2003, pp.57-60.

[7] T. Ghani, et al., IEDM Tech. Digs., 2003, pp.978-980.

[8] Z. Luo, et al., Symp. on VLSI Tech., Dig. Tech. papers, 2007, pp.16-17.

[9] K. Mistry, et al.,IEDM Tech. Digs., 2007, pp.247-250.

[10] V. Moroz, L. Smith, X-W. Lin, D. Pramanik, and C. Rollins, Proc. of ISQED, 2006.

[11] L. Sponton, L. Bomholt, D. Pramanik W. Fichtner, Proc. of SISPAD, 2006.

[12] X. Wang, B. Cheng, S. Roy, A. Asenov, Proc. of ULIS 2008, pp.89-92.

[13] Sentaurus Manual, 2007.03.

[14] Charles S. Smith, Phys. Rev., Vol. 94 number 1, 1954.

[15] S. Inaba, et al., IEEE Trans. Electron Devices, 49(12), 2002, pp.2263-2270.

[16] A. Asenov, S. Kaya, and A. Brown, IEEE Trans. Electron Devices, 50(5), 2003, pp.1254-1260.

On the Stability of Fully Depleted SOI MOSFETs Under Lithography Process Variations

Christian Kampen, Tim Führner, Alexander Burenkov, Andreas Erdmann, Jürgen Lorenz and Heiner Ryssel
Fraunhofer Institute of Integrated Systems and Device Technology
Schottkystrasse 10, 91058 Erlangen, Germany
Telephone: +49(0)9131761-224
Fax: +49(0)9131761-212
Email: chirstian.kampen@iisb.fraunhofer.de

Abstract— In this paper, a TCAD-based simulation study on lithography process-induced gate length variations has been performed. This study aims at evaluating fully depleted silicon on insulator (FD SOI) MOSFETs for next generation CMOS devices. Critical dimensions (CDs) have been obtained using rigorous lithography simulations. The impact of the resulting gate length variations on the electrical behavior of MOSFET devices has been evaluated by process and device simulations. FD SOI MOSFETs have been compared to bulk MOSFETs.

I. INTRODUCTION

Fully depleted silicon on insulator (FD SOI) CMOS devices are the most promising transistors for future integrated circuit technologies. Due to lightly doped channels and isolated silicon bodies, they offer big advantages in their I_{on}/I_{off} behavior and short channel effect immunity over comparable bulk MOSFETs. Furthermore, the light doping concentrations in the channels should reduce the impact of process variations on the electrical behavior since channel doping fluctuations are eliminated. However, the impact of process variations was so far mainly studied and understood for conventional bulk MOSFET devices.

Numerical simulations are well suited for fundamental, yet time and cost efficient, studies on the impact of process variations on MOSFETs devices [1]. As valid compact models for the new SOI MOSFET architectures are still not fully available [2], numerical TCAD simulations provide a promising way for efficient variability studies.

In this work, a concept for a fully TCAD-based variability investigation is presented. For that, we have coupled rigorous lithography simulations to numerical process and device simulations in order to study the impact of lithography-induced gate length variations on modern FD SOI devices and conventional bulk MOSFETs with a physical gate length of 32 nm.

II. SIMULATION SETUP

This work is based on a simulation framework which can be used to include and combine different simulation tools. The framework is based on the scripting language Python and makes use of the Python network toolkit Twisted. By employing this architecture, independent simulations can be performed concurrently, for example, on different nodes on a high performance computing cluster. This leads to a significant reduction of the overall computation time. A detailed discussion can be found elsewhere [3]. In this work, we have used the framework to couple the rigorous Fraunhofer IISB lithography simulation tool *Dr.LiTHO* [4] to the Sentaurus TCAD suite of Synopsys [5] for a fully TCAD-based process variation simulation study.

A. Process and device simulation setup

Three types of CMOS devices have been investigated in this work. At first, we have modeled a fully depleted silicon on insulator (FD SOI) nMOSFET and pMOSFET with a very lightly doped (1×10^{15} cm^{-3}) channel and substrate below the buried oxide. The physical gate length has been set to 32 nm, the body thickness to 10 nm, the gate oxide to 1.2 nm, and the buried oxide to 20 nm. For the second type of CMOS devices, we have used the former FD SOI setup but with an increased substrate doping concentration of 1×10^{20} cm^{-3} for the nMOS and of 5×10^{19} cm^{-3} for the pMOS, to achieve a better DIBL control [6] and therefore a better stability versus process variability.

Additionally, bulk nMOS and pMOS transistors have been modeled for comparison, in order to investigate possible advantages of FD SOI MOSFETs concerning process variability. For the bulk MOSFETs, we have assumed a relatively lightly doped substrate of 1×10^{17} cm^{-3} combined with heavily doped pockets around the active source/drain regions and the same gate oxide thickness as used for the FD SOI MOSFETs.

As the electrical behavior is strongly dependent on the threshold voltage level, junction and gate work function engineering has been applied to level the threshold voltages of all investigated MOSFET device architectures. For the FD SOI MOSFETs without ground plane doping, the gate work function has been set to midgap. Due to the highly doped substrate of the second SOI MOSFET types, the gate work function has to be shifted by ± 0.11 eV to reach the threshold voltage of ~ 320 mV for nMOS and pMOS. Metal gates with comparable work functions as highly doped polysilicon have been assumed for the bulk MOSFETs to achieve $V_{th} \sim 320$ mV.

After the process simulation and a re-meshing step, numerical device simulations have been performed for extracting the

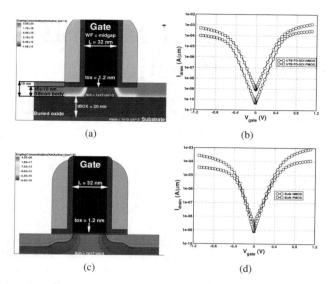

Fig. 1. Default MOSFET setups; (a) FD SOI geometrical shape, (b) FD SOI transfer characteristics NMOS & PMOS, (c) Bulk MOSFET geometrical shape, (d) Bulk MOSFET transfer characteristic NMOS & PMOS

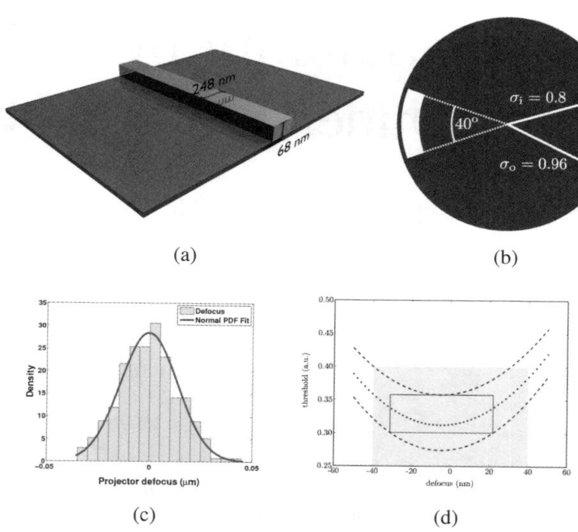

Fig. 2. Lithography process setup; (a) Mask geometry, (b) Illumination source, (c) Normally distributed projector defocus, (d) Calculated process window

default behavior of the different CMOS devices at the default physical gate length of 32 nm. For the device simulation, the conventional drift-diffusion model has been employed by using several standard simulation models [5] and the adjustment of the saturation velocity for nano-scaled CMOS devices [7]. Quantum mechanical depletion at the silicon-oxide interface has been taken into account by using the modified local density approximation model (MLDA) [8]. Then, the transfer characteristics at low drain voltages of 0.05 V and high drain voltages ($V_{drain} = V_{gate} = 1.1$ V) have been calculated (Fig. 1(b)&1(d)) to achieve electrical parameters like the threshold voltage, on-current and off-current.

B. Lithography simulation

A 193 nm water immersion lithography process has been examined in this work. Thus, a numerical aperture NA of 1.2 is assumed. We have used an attenuated phase shifting mask (AttPSM) with a MoSi absorber (n: 2.442, k: -0.586) on a glas substrate (Fig. 2(a)). The absorber dimensions of 62 nm (wafer scale) width and 68 nm thickness have been obtained by a coarse pre-optimization. Due to the sub-wavelength dimension of 45 nm aspired for the final CD, electromagnetic field (EMF) effects have been taken into account, and mask nearfield computations have been performed, using the Waveguide Method [9] of *Dr.LiTHO* [4], without Hopkins approximation.

A dipole quasar setup with an inner radius (σ_i) of 0.8 and an outer radius (σ_o) of 0.96 (normalized to the NA) has been used as illumination source for the lithography simulation (Fig. 2(b)). The opening angle of the poles is set to 40 °, while y-polarized light with an intensity of preferred state (IPS) of 1 has been considered. Furthermore, no full resist development model is used. Instead a threshold model is employed to indirectly render the exposure dose.

The lithography process window analysis (allowing up to

10 % CD variations) yielded a depth of focus of 52 nm and a "threshold latitude" of 8.5 %. In order to study the impact of lithography variations not only under feasible conditions, the variation range has been dilated to ±40 nm around the best focus and to a threshold range of 0.25 - 0.4 (Fig. 2(d)).

After the CD has been calculated, a fixed etch bias of 13 nm is assumed.

III. SIMULATION RESULTS

Nearly 8600 variations of the physical gate length have been simulated for each device architecture. This dataset is created by random, normally distributed variations of the defocus (Fig.2(c)) and a linear walk through the lithography threshold range.

First of all, an appropriate probability density distribution function (PDF) of the CD has been determined. For a fixed threshold of 0.32, the best fit of the PDF has been found for the generalized extreme value (GEV) distribution, which is in contrast to the gaussian distribution, strongly asymmetric. Fig. 3(a) displays the PDF of the CD at a fixed threshold of 0.32 and the PDF fit by the GEV. At each fixed threshold value, a GEV function has been identified for the critical dimension. On the other hand, the PDF of the CD over the whole experiment seems to be more complicated, as it could not be represented by any of the standard probability density distribution functions.

The threshold voltage of the FD SOI MOSFETs, however, seems to be GEV distributed over the whole experiment (Fig. 3(b)) as well. This result leads to the conclusion, that standard 6σ approximations for the allowed threshold voltage variability are not valid anymore for FD SOI devices if photolithographic related fluctuations are considered. On the other hand, due to the fact that the FD SOI devices seem to have the same type of probability distribution function as the

TABLE I

RELATIVE STANDARD DEVIATION OF THE THRESHOLD VOLTAGE AND THE
CRITICAL DIMENSION; INITIAL RSD(CD) = 15.5 %

Device	RSD(V_{th})	RSD$_{Opt}$(V_{th})	RSD$_{Opt}$(CD)
FD SOI NMOS	16.4 %	6.8 %	7.9 %
FD SOI PMOS	18.9 %	6.3 %	6.5 %
FD SOI NMOS GP	13.6%	6.0 %	8.7 %
FD SOI PMOS GP	16.5 %	6.1 %	6.7 %
Bulk NMOS	8.6 %	5.9 %	14.8 %
Bulk PMOS	4.3 %	1.5 %	7.12 %

critical dimension of the lithography process, threshold voltage variations of the FD SOI MOSFETs can be easily established if CD variations are known. In a first approximation, the relative standard deviation (RSD) values for V_{th} of the FD SOI MOSFETs are nearly equal to the RSD of the CD (RSD(CD) = 15.5 %).

The threshold voltage of the bulk MOSFET architecture still shows a normal distribution under gate length variations (Fig. 3(c)). This results from the changing channel doping concentrations, caused by the converging pockets at smaller gate lengths. This assumption is supported by Fig. 4, where the threshold voltage is plotted over the critical dimension. Due to the highly doped pockets, short channel effects are largely suppressed, as it is shown by the diamonds and right oriented triangles in Fig. 4.

Although the silicon body is isolated by the buried oxide in the FD SOI MOSFETs, a strong short channel effect can be observed (Fig. 4), which leads to a $V_{th} = 0$ state of the MOSFETs, already at gate lengths below ∼17 nm. Even the heavily ground plane doping leads only to a negligible small shift to smaller gate lengths. This short channel effect results in a strong variability of the leakage current, which can be observed in Fig. 5, where $I_{off}(I_{on})$ is plotted. Although the FD SOI devices exhibit a much higher I_{on}/I_{off} relation at a fixed off-current than the bulk MOSFETs, the leakage current of the bulk MOSFETs seems to be less sensitive to gate length fluctuations, due to the pocket implants.

Table I summarizes the values of the relative standard deviations (RSD) of the threshold voltages of each MOSFET architecture, discussed in this paper. The highest standard deviation of ∼19 % has been found for the FD SOI PMOS transistor without ground plane doping. Furthermore, by using the ground plane doping, threshold voltage variability is only suppressed by nearly 2.5 %. The lowest RSD(V_{th}) has been found for the bulk PMOS.

One option to reduce process induced variations would be to adjust the lithography process window by using MOSFET specific parameter criteria, as it has already been reported [3]. For example, a gate overdrive criterion can be used to define a new optimized lithography process window. So, by using a gate overdrive criterion that allows only a ±5 % variation of the gate overdrive around the nominal value (∼780 mV in this case) [3], the variations of the threshold voltages can

be reduced by a factor of about two. Table I displays the resulting relative standard deviations of the threshold voltage (RSD$_{opt}$(V_{th})) and the appropriate allowed fluctuations of the critical dimension (RSD$_{opt}$(CD)) for each device architecture. For that, the bulk NMOS allows the greatest fluctuation of the physical gate length (14.8 %) at a threshold voltage fluctuation of about 6 %. But, as in a CMOS process the gates of NMOS and PMOS devices are produced in the same lithography step, the CD variations should not exceed the smallest of both allowed CD standard deviations, defined by the gate overdrive criterion.

In Fig. 6, the recalculated lithography process windows are displayed, which have been obtained by using the gate overdrive criterion. Applying the gate overdrive criterion on the FD SOI nMOS architecture leads to a shrinkage of the initial process window. That results in very tough lithography process conditions, as the depth of focus has to be reduced from 52 nm to 43 nm at a threshold latitude of nearly 7 %. The resized process window of the bulk nMOSFET on the one hand allows only a depth of focus of 40 nm, but at a threshold latitude above the initial process window, which defuses the lithography process conditions.

IV. CONCLUSION

In this paper, we have demonstrated efficient variability studies by using a traditional TCAD approach combined with rigorous lithography simulations. Fully depleted silicon on insulator MOSFETs and conventional bulk MOSFETs are studied concerning their threshold voltage stability under lithography process variations. Due to the heavily doped pocket implants, the electrical behavior of the bulk MOSFET appeared to be more stable than the FD SOI. On the other hand, the SOI MOSFETs exhibit a better I_{on}/I_{off} relation than bulk MOSFETs but has, for the process that has been considered in this work, a wider range of leakage current variability.

Asymmetric probability density distribution functions have been found for the CD at fixed lithography threshold values and for the threshold voltages of the FD SOI MOSFETs over the whole simulation experiment. Therefore, 6σ approximations of the threshold voltage cannot be used in case of FD SOI MOSFETs under photolithography variations.

Furthermore, it could be shown that the optimization of the lithography process window by MOSFET parameter-specific stability criteria, leads to an efficient decrease of the electrical parameter fluctuations of each CMOS device architecture by a factor of nearly two.

Finally, it could be demonstrated that the combination of rigorous lithography and numerical process and device simulations is well suited to investigate the impact of variability on next generation CMOS devices.

V. ACKNOWLEDGMENT

This research is in part supported by the European Commission's Information Society Technologies Programme, under PULLNANO project contract No. IST-026828.

REFERENCES

[1] A. Asenov, A. R. Brown, J. H. Davies, S. Kaya, and G. Slavcheva, "Simulation of intrinsic parameter fluctuations in decananometer and nanometer-scale mosfets," *Electron Devices, IEEE Transactions on*, 2003.

[2] A. Burenkov, C. Kampen, J. Lorenz, and H. Ryssel, "Pre-silicon spice modeling of nano-scaled soi mosfets," in *ULIS Conference*, 2008, pp. 215–218.

[3] T. Führer, C. Kampen, I. Kodrasi, A. Burenkov, and A. Erdmann, "A simulation study on the impact of lithographic process variations on cmos device preformance," in *to be published in Proc. SPIE*, 2008.

[4] T. Führer, T. Schnattinger, G. Ardelean, and A. Erdmann, "Dr.LiTHO: a development and research lithography simulator," in *Proc. SPIE*, vol. 6520, 2007, p. 65203F.

[5] *Sentaurus TCAD*, Release z-2007.03 ed., Synopsys, Mountain View, CA, USA, 2007.

[6] T. Ernst and S. Cristoloveanu, "Buried oxide fringing capacitance: a new physical model and its implication on soi device scaling and architecture," in *SOI Conference*, 1999, pp. 38–39.

[7] J. Bude, "Mosfet modeling into the ballistic regime," in *SISPAD*, Seattle, WA, September 2000, pp. 23–26.

[8] G. Paasch and H. Übensee, "A modified local density approximation: Electron density in inversion layers," *Physica Status Solidi (b)*, vol. 113, no. 1, pp. 165–178, 1982.

[9] P. Evanschitzky and A. Erdmann, "The impact of euv mask defects on lithographic process performance," *SPIE*, vol. 5504, p. 111, 2005.

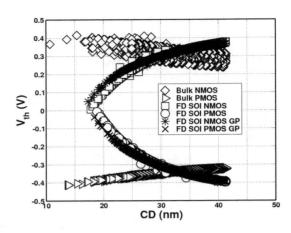

Fig. 4. Threshold voltage behavior of FD SOI MOSFETs (lightly doped and heavily doped substrate) and bulk MOSFETs under lithography process variations

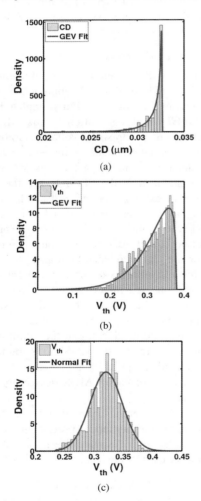

Fig. 3. Probability density distribution functions: (a) CD at a threshold value of 0.32, type of PDF: GEV; (b) V_{th} of the SG FD SOI, type of PDF: GEV; (c) V_{th} of the bulk MOSFET, type of PDF: Normal

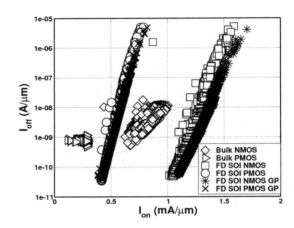

Fig. 5. On - Off current behavior of FD SOI MOSFETs (lightly doped and heavily doped substrate) and bulk MOSFETs under lithography process variations

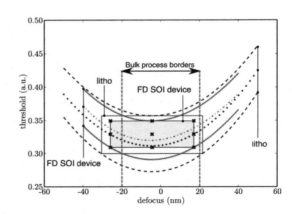

Fig. 6. MOSFET parameter specific resized lithography process windows; initial, FD SOI NMOS process specific and bulk NMOS process specific